Kinematics, Dynamics, and Design of Machinery

Second Edition

Abridged

Kenneth J. Waldron / Gary L. Kinzel

CD Included

WILEY
CUSTOM SERVICES

To order books or for customer service, please call 1(800)-CALL-WILEY (225-5945).

Printed in the United States of America.

ISBN 978-0-471-69919-4

10 9 8 7 6 5

SECOND EDITION

KINEMATICS, DYNAMICS, AND DESIGN OF MACHINERY

K. J. WALDRON
Stanford University

G. L. KINZEL
The Ohio State University

WILEY

JOHN WILEY & SONS, INC.

Acquisitions Editor *Joseph Hayton*
Associate Director of Marketing *Ilse Wolfe*
Senior Production Editor *Valerie A. Vargas*
Senior Designer *Madelyn Lesure*
This book was set in 10/12 Times Roman by Argosy and printed and bound by Hamilton Printing. The cover was printed by Lehigh Press.

This book is printed on acid-free paper. ∞

Library of Congress Cataloging-in-Publication Data
Waldron, Kenneth J.
Kinematics, dynamics, and design of machinery / by K.J. Waldron and G.L. Kinzel.—2nd ed.
p. cm.
Includes bibliographical references.
ISBN 0-471-24417-1 (cloth)
1. Machinery, Kinematics of. 2. Machinery, Dynamics of. 3. Machine design. I. Kinzel, Gary L., 1944– II. Title.

TJ175.W35 2003

621.8'1—dc21 2003050053

ISBN 0-471-24417-1
ISBN 0-471-42917-1 (WIE)

Printed in the United States of America

10 9 8 7 6 5 4 3 2 1

CONTENTS

CHAPTER 1 *INTRODUCTION* **1**

1.1 Historic Perspective **1**
1.2 Kinematics **2**
1.3 Design: Analysis and Synthesis **2**
1.4 Mechanisms **3**
1.5 Planar Linkages **7**
1.6 Visualization **9**
1.7 Constraint Analysis **11**
1.8 Constraint Analysis of Spatial Linkages **18**
1.9 Idle Degrees of Freedom **23**
1.10 Overconstrained Linkages **25**
1.11 Uses of the Mobility Criterion **29**
1.12 Inversion **30**
1.13 Reference Frames **31**
1.14 Motion Limits **31**
1.15 Actuation **32**
1.16 Coupler-Driven Linkages **37**
1.17 Motion Limits for Slider-Crank Mechanism **38**
1.18 Interference **40**
1.19 Practical Design Considerations **44**
  1.19.1 Revolute Joints **44**
  1.19.2 Prismatic Joints **46**
  1.19.3 Higher Pairs **47**
  1.19.4 Cams vs. Linkages **47**
  1.19.5 Actuation **48**
Problems **54**

CHAPTER 2 *GRAPHICAL POSITION, VELOCITY, AND ACCELERATION ANALYSIS FOR MECHANISMS WITH REVOLUTE JOINTS OR FIXED SLIDES* **60**

2.1 Introduction **60**
2.2 Graphical Position Analysis **61**
2.3 Planar Velocity Polygons **62**
2.4 Graphical Acceleration Analysis **65**
2.5 Graphical Analysis of a Four-Bar Mechanism **67**
2.6 Graphical Analysis of a Slider-Crank Mechanism **74**
2.7 The Velocity Image Theorem **76**
2.8 The Acceleration Image Theorem **79**
2.9 Solution by Inversion **84**
Problems **89**

CHAPTER 3 *LINKAGES WITH ROLLING AND SLIDING CONTACTS AND JOINTS ON MOVING SLIDERS* **96**

3.1 Introduction **96**
3.2 Reference Frames **96**
3.3 General Velocity and Acceleration Equations **98**
  3.3.1 Velocity Equations **98**
  3.3.2 Acceleration Equations **101**
  3.3.3 Chain Rule for Positions, Velocities, and Accelerations **101**
3.4 Special Cases for the Velocity and Acceleration Equations **104**
  3.4.1 Points *P* and *Q* Fixed to *B* **104**
  3.4.2 *P* and *Q* Are Coincident **105**
  3.4.3 *P* and *Q* Are Coincident and in Rolling Contact **105**
3.5 Linkages with Rotating Sliding Joints **106**
3.6 Rolling Contact **111**
  3.6.1 Basic Kinematic Relationships for Rolling Contact **112**
  3.6.2 Modeling Rolling Contact Using a Virtual Linkage **118**
3.7 Cam Contact **121**
  3.7.1 Direct Approach to the Analysis of Cam Contact **121**
  3.7.2 Analysis of Cam Contact Using Equivalent Linkages **124**
3.8 General Coincident Points **128**
  3.8.1 Velocity Analyses Involving General Coincident Points **130**
  3.8.2 Acceleration Analyses Involving General Coincident Points **130**
Problems **136**

CHAPTER 4 *INSTANT CENTERS OF VELOCITY* **145**

4.1 Introduction **145**
4.2 Definition **145**
4.3 Existence Proof **146**
4.4 Location of an Instant Center from the Directions of Two Velocities **147**
4.5 Instant Center at a Revolute Joint **148**
4.6 Instant Center of a Curved Slider **148**
4.7 Instant Center of a Prismatic Joint **148**
4.8 Instant Center of a Rolling Contact Pair **149**
4.9 Instant Center of a General Cam-Pair Contact **149**
4.10 Centrodes **150**
4.11 The Kennedy–Aronholdt Theorem **153**
4.12 Circle Diagram as a Strategy for Finding Instant Centers **155**
4.13 Using Instant Centers: The Rotating-Radius Method **156**
4.14 Finding Instant Centers Using Drafting Programs **164**
Problems **165**

CHAPTER 5 *ANALYTICAL LINKAGE ANALYSIS* **171**

5.1 Introduction **171**
5.2 Position, Velocity, and Acceleration Representations **172**
5.2.1 Position Representation **172**
5.2.2 Velocity Representation **172**
5.2.3 Acceleration Representation **174**
5.2.4 Special Cases **175**
5.2.5 Mechanisms to Be Considered **175**
5.3 Analytical Closure Equations for Four-Bar Linkages **175**
5.3.1 Solution of Closure Equations for Four-Bar Linkages When Link 2 Is the Driver **176**
5.3.2 Analysis When the Coupler (Link 3) Is the Driving Link **179**
5.3.3 Velocity Equations for Four-Bar Linkages **179**
5.3.4 Acceleration Equations for Four-Bar Linkages **180**
5.4 Analytical Equations for a Rigid Body after the Kinematic Properties of Two Points Are Known **184**
5.5 Analytical Equations for Slider-Crank Mechanisms **187**
5.5.1 Solution to Position Equations When θ_2 Is Input **190**
5.5.2 Solution to Position Equations When r_1 Is Input **192**
5.5.3 Solution to Position Equations When θ_3 Is Input **193**
5.5.4 Velocity Equations for Slider-Crank Mechanism **194**
5.5.5 Acceleration Equations for Slider-Crank Mechanism **195**
5.6 Analytical Equations for the Slider-Crank Inversion **200**
5.6.1 Solution to Position Equations When θ_2 Is Input **202**
5.6.2 Solution to Position Equations When θ_3 Is Input **204**
5.6.3 Solution to Position Equations When r_3 Is Input **204**
5.6.4 Velocity Equations for the Slider-Crank Inversion **205**
5.6.5 Acceleration Equations for the Slider-Crank Inversion **207**
5.7 Analytical Equations for an RPRP Mechanism **211**
5.7.1 Solution of Closure Equations When θ_2 Is Known **212**
5.7.2 Solution of Closure Equations When r_4 Is Known **213**
5.7.3 Solution of Closure Equations When r_3 Is Known **215**
5.7.4 Velocity and Acceleration Equations for an RPRP Mechanism **216**
5.8 Analytical Equations for an RRPP Mechanism **218**
5.8.1 Solution When θ_2 Is Known **219**
5.8.2 Solution When r_1 Is Known **220**
5.8.3 Solution When r_3 Is Known **221**
5.9 Analytical Equations for Elliptic Trammel **223**
5.9.1 Analysis When θ_3 Is Known **224**
5.9.2 Analysis When r_1 Is Known **225**
5.10 Analytical Equations for the Oldham Mechanism **228**
5.10.1 Analysis When θ_2 Is Known **229**
5.10.2 Analysis When r_2 Is Known **230**
5.11 Closure or Loop-Equation Approach for Compound Mechanisms **233**
5.11.1 Handling Points Not on the Vector Loops **236**
5.11.2 Solving the Position Equations **237**
5.12 Closure Equations for Mechanisms with Higher Pairs **243**
5.13 Notational Differences: Vectors and Complex Numbers **248**
Problems **251**

CHAPTER 6 *PLANAR LINKAGE DESIGN* **257**

6.1 Introduction **257**
6.2 Two-Position Double-Rocker Design **260**
6.2.1 Graphical Solution Procedure **260**
6.2.2 Analytical Solution Procedure **261**
6.3 Motion Generation **263**
6.3.1 Introduction **263**
6.3.2 Two Positions **263**
6.3.3 Three Positions with Selected Moving Pivots **266**
6.3.4 Synthesis of a Crank with Chosen Fixed Pivots **266**
6.3.5 Design of Slider-Cranks and Elliptic Trammels **268**
6.3.6 Order Problem and Change of Branch **270**
6.3.7 Analytical Approach to Rigid-Body Guidance **276**
6.4 Function Generation **283**
6.4.1 Function Generation Using a Four-Bar Linkage **285**
6.4.2 Design Procedure When $y = y(x)$ Is to Be Generated **287**
6.4.3 Selection of Design Positions **288**
6.4.4 Summary of Solution Procedure for Four-Bar Linkage and Three Precision Points **289**
6.4.5 Graphical Approach to Function Generation **293**
6.5 Synthesis of Crank-Rocker Linkages for Specified Rocker Amplitude **294**
6.5.1 Extreme Rocker Positions and Simple Analytical Solution **294**
6.5.2 The Rocker Amplitude Problem: Graphical Approach **295**
6.5.3 Transmission Angle **300**
6.5.4 Alternative Graphical Design Procedure Based on Specification of O_2–O_4 **301**
6.5.5 Analytical Design Procedure Based on Specification of O_2–O_4 **304**
6.5.6 Use of Analytical Design Procedure for Optimization **307**
6.6 Path Synthesis **308**
6.6.1 Design of Six-Bar Linkages Using Coupler Curves **309**
6.6.2 Motion Generation for Parallel Motion Using Coupler Curves **315**
6.6.3 Four-Bar Cognate Linkages **318**
References **320**
Problems **321**

CHAPTER 7 *SPECIAL MECHANISMS* **329**

7.1 Special Planar Mechanisms **329**
7.1.1 Introduction **329**
7.1.2 Approximate Straight-Line Mechanisms **329**
7.1.3 Exact Straight-Line Mechanisms **332**
7.1.4 Pantographs **333**
7.2 Spherical Linkages **340**
7.2.1 Introduction **340**
7.2.2 Gimbals **343**
7.2.3 Universal Joints **343**
7.3 Constant-Velocity Couplings **347**
7.3.1 Geometric Requirements of Constant-Velocity Couplings **347**
7.3.2 Practical Constant-Velocity Couplings **347**
7.4 Automotive Steering and Suspension Mechanisms **349**
7.4.1 Introduction **349**
7.4.2 Steering Mechanisms **349**
7.4.3 Suspension Mechanisms **353**
7.5 Indexing Mechanisms **354**
7.5.1 Geneva Mechanisms **354**
References **359**
Problems **360**

CHAPTER 8 *PROFILE CAM DESIGN* **362**

8.1 Introduction **362**
8.2 Cam–Follower Systems **363**
8.3 Synthesis of Motion Programs **364**
8.4 Analysis of Different Types of Follower Displacement Functions **366**
8.5 Uniform Motion **367**
8.6 Parabolic Motion **368**
8.7 Harmonic Follower-Displacement Programs **373**
8.8 Cycloidal Follower-Displacement Programs **375**
8.9 General Polynomial Follower-Displacement Programs **376**
8.10 Determining the Cam Profile **381**
8.10.1 Graphical Cam Profile Layout **381**
8.10.2 Analytical Determination of Cam Profile **391**
References **417**
Problems **417**

INDEX **662**

CHAPTER 1

INTRODUCTION

1.1 HISTORIC PERSPECTIVE

A mechanism is a machine composed of rigid members that are jointed together. The members interact with one another by virtue of the joints. The joints are formed by portions of the surfaces of the members joined that contact one another. The geometries of the contacting surface segments determine the properties of each joint.

Mechanisms may be simple or complex. Figure 1.1 shows a walking machine that is composed of dozens of mechanisms that must be coordinated through complex control systems. Other machines may involve only a single mechanism.

The design of mechanisms is a technical area that is unique to mechanical engineering. Its history stretches back to prehistoric times. Artisans such as blacksmiths and carpenters also functioned as the designers of mechanisms. One of the original functions of engineers was the design of mechanisms both for warfare and for peaceful uses. In Renaissance times, we find Leonardo da Vinci depicting a sophisticated variety of mechanisms, mostly for military purposes. Sometime thereafter the distinction between civil engineering and military engineering appeared. The modern era in mechanism design, along with the

FIGURE 1.1 The Adaptive Suspension Vehicle. Each leg is a planar pantograph mechanism hinged to the body about an axis parallel to the longitudinal axis of the vehicle.

history of mechanical engineering as a distinct discipline, can be viewed as starting with James Watt.

That is not to say that the subject has remained static. In fact, there have been dramatic changes in the practice of mechanism design in recent years. Traditionally, machines have been designed to be powered by a single "prime mover," with all functions mechanically coordinated. That tradition certainly predates Watt. Recent developments in computer technology, coupled with improvements in electric motors and other actuators, have made it possible to use a different approach. This is an approach in which machines are powered by multiple actuators coordinated electronically. The resulting machines are simpler, less expensive, more easily maintained, and more reliable. Another major change is in the techniques used in mechanism design. The use of interactive computer graphics has had a dramatic impact on design practice. One of our motivations in producing this book, even when a number of excellent texts are already available in mechanism kinematics, is to provide a treatment that reflects these changes in practice.

1.2 KINEMATICS

Kinematics is the study of position and its time derivatives. Specifically, we are concerned with the positions, velocities, and accelerations of points and with the angular positions, angular velocities, and angular accelerations of solid bodies. Together these entities are sufficient to describe the motions of solid bodies. The position of a body can be defined by the position of a nominated point of that body combined with the angular position of the body. In some circumstances we are also interested in the higher time derivatives of position and angular position.

The subject of kinematics is a study of the geometry of motion. This is an accurate title because kinematics is geometry with the element of time added. The bulk of the subject matter of this book is often referred to as the kinematics of mechanisms. Our objective is to present techniques that can be used to design mechanisms to meet specific motion requirements. That is why the subject matter is approached from a mechanical designer's perspective.

1.3 DESIGN: ANALYSIS AND SYNTHESIS

The material in this book falls into two classifications. The first consists of techniques to determine the positions, velocities, and accelerations of points in the members of mechanisms and the angular positions, velocities, and accelerations of those members. These are kinematic analysis techniques. The second type of material comprises methods for mathematically determining the geometry of a mechanism to produce a desired set of positions and/or velocities or accelerations. These are rational synthesis techniques.

The activity that distinguishes engineering from science is design. Science is the study of what is; engineering is the creation of what is to be. This creative activity is design or, more formally, synthesis. The rational synthesis techniques developed by kinematicians offer a rather direct route to mechanism design that lends itself well to automation using computer graphics workstations. However, these techniques do not represent the only way to design mechanisms and they are relatively restrictive: Rational synthesis techniques exist only for specific types of mechanism design problems, and many practical mechanism design problems do not fit within the available class of solutions. An alternative is to use informal synthesis. This is a methodology used by engineers to solve design problems in many technical areas, not just in mechanism design. The basic procedure is to "guess" a set of dimensions and then use analysis to check the resulting performance. The dimensions are then adjusted to attempt to match more closely the performance specifications, and the mechanism is analyzed again. The process is repeated until an acceptably close match to the specifications is achieved. Thus, a primary use of the analysis material is also in mechanism design.

From an engineering point of view, it is not possible to treat mechanism design solely in terms of kinematics. The motivation for performing an acceleration analysis is often to enable inertia forces on the links to be calculated, allowing, in turn, computation of the forces transferred between links and the internal forces, or stresses, within the links. Mechanisms must usually drive loads, as well as generate motions. Of course, as soon as we introduce the concept of force, we leave the domain of pure kinematics and enter that of kinetics. Insofar as the largest forces in many mechanisms are inertia forces created by motion, it is convenient to study them within the general framework of kinematic techniques. There is also an important symmetry between the geometry of the force distribution and that of the velocity distribution that is particularly useful when working with spatial mechanisms. Thus, it is entirely appropriate to treat mechanism statics or kinetics within the general geometry of motion framework constructed to study mechanism kinematics. Such a treatment is presented in the later chapters of this book.

1.4 MECHANISMS

Mechanisms are assemblages of rigid members connected together by joints. Mechanisms transfer motion and mechanical work from one or more actuators to one or more "output" members. For the purposes of kinematic design, we idealize a mechanism to a kinematic linkage in which all the members are assumed to be perfectly rigid and are connected by kinematic joints. A kinematic joint is formed by direct contact between the surfaces of two members. One of the earliest codifications of mechanism kinematics was that of Reuleaux (1876),[1] and some of the basic terminology we use originated with him. He called a kinematic joint a "pair." He further divided joints into "lower pairs" and "higher pairs." A lower pair joint is one in which contact between two rigid members occurs at every point of one or more surface segments. A higher pair is one in which contact occurs only at isolated points or along line segments. All other things being equal, a higher pair will produce higher contact stresses than will a lower pair.

Joints are the most important aspect of a mechanism to examine during an analysis. They permit relative motion in some directions while constraining motion in others. The types of motion permitted are related to the number of degrees of freedom (dof) of the joint. The number of degrees of freedom of the joint is equal to the number of independent coordinates needed to specify uniquely the position of one link relative to the other constrained by the joint.

Lower pair joints are necessarily restricted to a relatively small number of geometric types, because the requirement that surface contact be maintained constrains the geometry of the contacting surfaces. It can be shown that there are only six fundamentally different types of lower pair joints, classified by the types of relative motion that they permit. There is, in contrast, an infinite number of possible higher pair geometries. The lower pair joint types are shown in Table 1.1. Some important examples of higher pair joints are shown in Table 1.2.

[1] Reuleaux, F., *The Kinematics of Machinery* (Translated and edited by A. B. W. Kennedy), Dover Publications, Inc., New York, 1963.

TABLE 1.1 Lower Pair Joints

Connectivity (Number of degrees of freedom)	Names	Letter symbol	Typical form	Sketch symbol
1	Revolute Hinge Turning pair	R	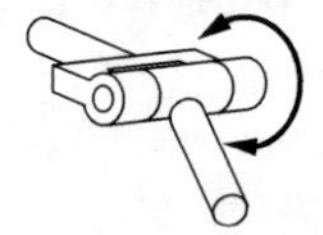	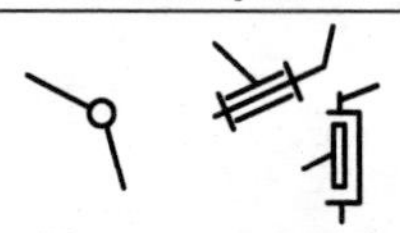
1	Prismatic joint Slider Sliding pair	P	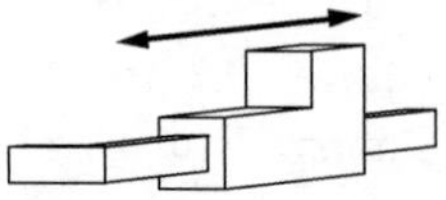	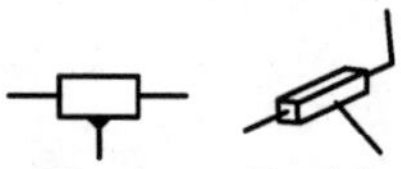
1	Screw joint Helical joint Helical pair	H	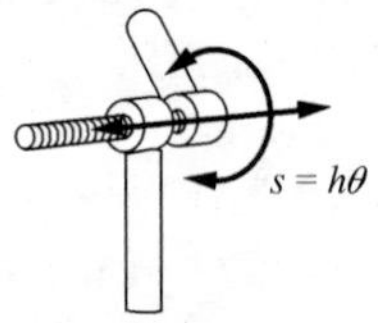	
2	Cylindrical joint Cylindrical pair	C	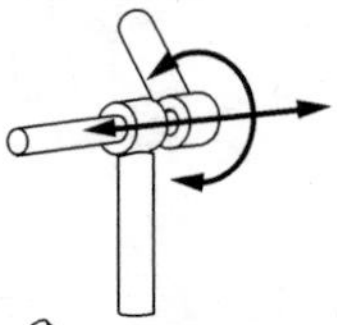	
3	Spherical joint Ball joint Spherical pair	S	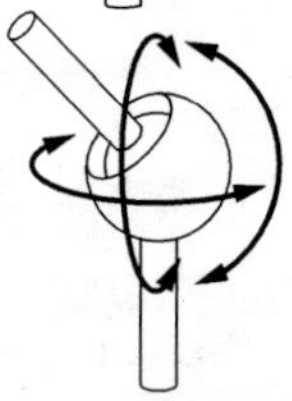	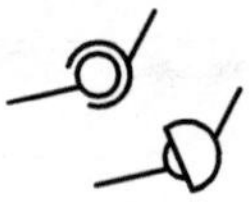
3	Planar joint Planar pair	P_L	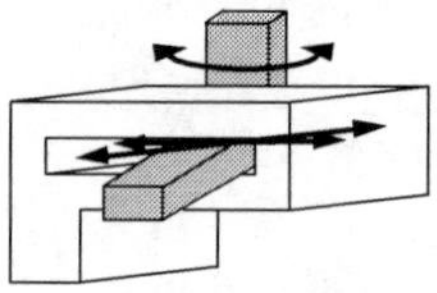	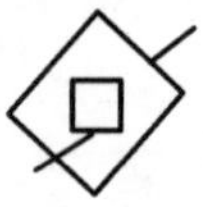

Lower pair joints are frequently used in mechanism design practice. They give good service because wear is spread out over the contact surface and because the narrow clearance between the surfaces provides good conditions for lubrication and a tight constraint on the motion. Changes in the geometric properties of the joint with wear occur slowly for a lower pair. At least as important are the simple geometries of the relative motions that these joints permit.

Higher pair joints that involve pure rolling contact, or that approximate that condition, are also used frequently. In pure rolling contact, the points in one of the two joint surfaces that are actually in contact with the other surface at any instant are at rest relative to that surface. Hence there is no relative sliding of the surfaces and joint friction and wear are minimized. Physically, the limitation of this kind of joint is the stress intensity that the material of the contacting bodies can support. Stresses are necessarily high because of the very small

TABLE 1.2 Some Higher Pair Joints

Connectivity (Number of degrees of freedom)	Names	Typical form	Comments
1	Cylindrical roller	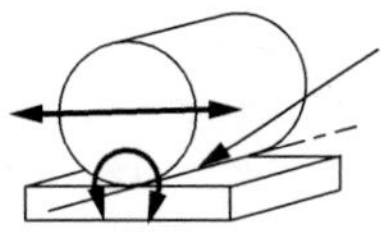	Roller rotates about this line at this instant in its motion. Roller does not slip on the surface on which it rolls.
2	Cam pair	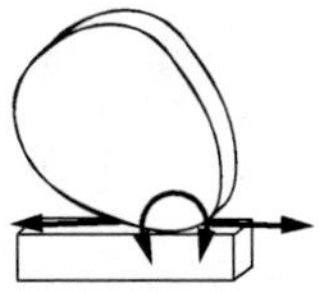	Cam rolls and slides on follower.
3	Rolling ball	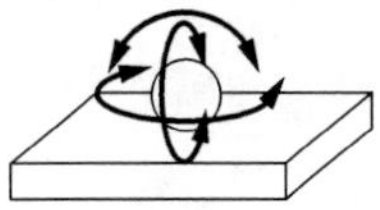	Ball rolls without slipping.
4	Ball in cylindar		Ball can rotate about any axis through its center and slide along cylinder axis.
5	Spatial point contact	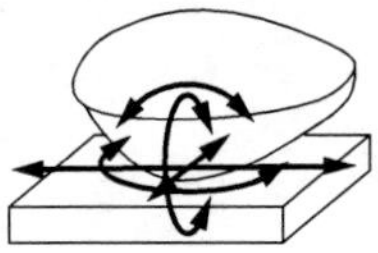	Body can rotate about any axis through the contact point and slide in any direction in the tangent plane.

contact areas. If the bodies were perfectly rigid, contact would occur only at discrete points or along a line, the contact area would be zero, and the stresses would be locally infinite!

Lower pair joints such as revolute joints and cylindrical joints are also often simulated by systems such as ball or roller bearings in which there are actually many elements acting in parallel. The actual contact joints in a ball bearing are rolling contacts, which are higher pairs. In this way, the low-friction properties of rolling contacts are exploited to obtain a joint with lower friction and higher load and relative speed capabilities than would be possible with a plain revolute joint. At the same time, the simple overall relative motion geometry of the revolute joint is retained. This is one example of a compound joint in which the joint is actually a complex mechanism but is regarded as kinematically equivalent to a simple revolute. Several examples of compound joints are shown in Table 1.3.

Conversely, higher pairs are sometimes replaced by equivalent lower pair joints (Fig. 1.2). For example, a pin-in-a-slot joint becomes a combination of a revolute joint and a prismatic joint. Note that this involves adding extra members to the mechanism. In both the case in which a lower pair is replaced by a rolling contact bearing, or compound joint, and this case, the two mechanisms are said to be *kinematically equivalent*. This means that the relative motions that are permitted between the bodies in the two cases are the same, even though the joint is physically quite different.

The number of degrees of freedom of a joint is the minimum number of independent parameters required to define the positions of all points in one of the bodies it connects relative to a reference frame fixed to the other. The term *connectivity* is used to denote this freedom of the body, even though the "joint" may be something very elaborate such as the antifriction bearing shown in Table 1.3 and Fig. 1.3. If motion is restricted to a plane, the maximum number of degrees of freedom is three. In general spatial motion, the maximum number is six. The connectivity or number of degrees of freedom for each joint is listed in Tables 1.1, 1.2, and 1.3 in the first column.

TABLE 1.3 Some Examples of Compound Joints

Connectivity	Name	Form
1	Ball bearing Antifriction bearing Rolling contact friction	
2	Universal joint Hooke joint Cardan joint	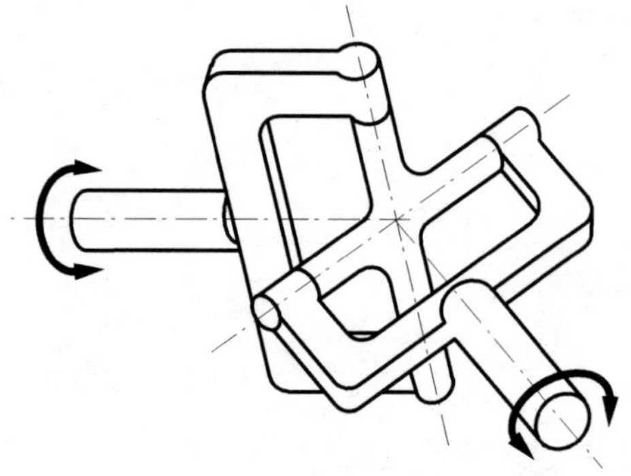
1	Roller slide Roller glide	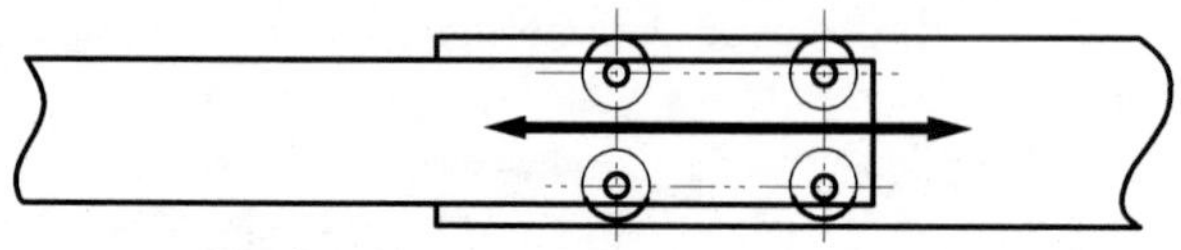

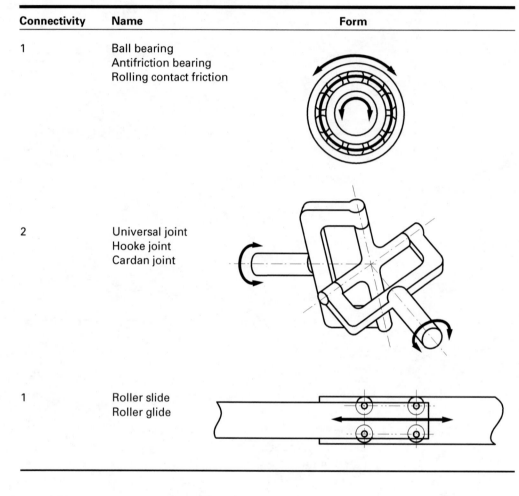

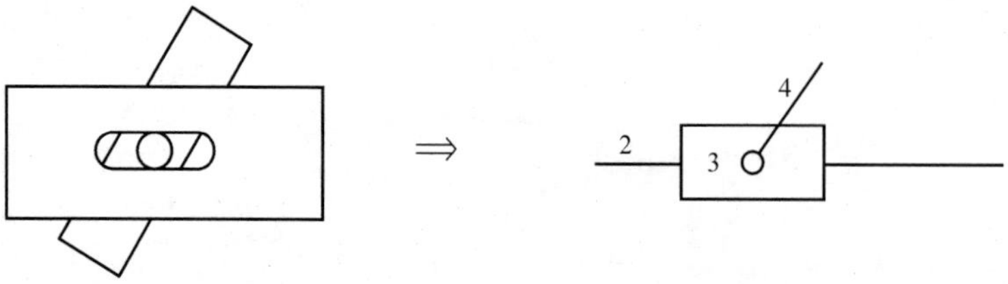

FIGURE 1.2 Replacement of a higher pair joint by a kinematically equivalent combination of lower pair joints.

FIGURE 1.3 Various rolling-element and plain bearings.

1.5 PLANAR LINKAGES

A planar linkage is one in which the velocities of all points in all members are directed parallel to a plane, called the plane of motion. The only lower pair joints that are properly compatible with planar motion are revolute and prismatic joints. The axes of rotation of all revolute joints must be normal to the plane of motion because points would not move in parallel planes otherwise. The directions of sliding of all prismatic joints must be parallel to the plane of motion, since all points in a member connected to another by a prismatic joint move on lines parallel to the sliding direction relative to the second member. Occasionally other lower pair joints will appear in what is otherwise a planar linkage; however, they then function only as revolute or prismatic joints. For example, a spherical joint may be substituted for a revolute joint, but if the linkage is functionally planar, that spherical joint will operate as a revolute joint with rotation occurring only about the axis normal to the plane of motion. This type of situation will be discussed in more detail in the context of degrees of freedom and mobility.

A common schematic method of representing planar linkages is to represent revolute joints by small circles, as shown in Table 1.1. Binary links—those that have two joints mounted on them—are represented as lines joining those joints. Ternary links—those that have three joints mounted on them—are represented as triangles with the joints at the vertices, and so on. Examples of the resulting representations are shown in Figs. 1.4–1.6. The link geometries may then be easily reproduced, giving an accurate view of the linkage in a specified position. Alternatively, the schematic may be used conceptually without accurate geometric data to indicate the topology of the linkage. Topology is the branch of geometry that deals with issues of connectedness without regard to shape. Links with three or more joints should be shaded or crosshatched. Otherwise, the schematic for a quaternary link, one with four joints, cannot be distinguished from the schematic for a four-bar linkage loop.

A kinematic chain is any assemblage of rigid links connected by kinematic joints. A closed chain is one in which the links and joints form one or more closed circuits. Each closed circuit is a loop in which each link is attached to at least two other links.

Prismatic joints are represented by means of a line in the direction of sliding, representing a slide, with a rectangular block placed on it. This produces linkage representations such as those shown in Fig. 1.6.

A *frame* or base member is a link that is fixed. That is, it has zero degrees of freedom relative to the fixed coordinate system. A *linkage* is a closed kinematic chain with one link selected as the frame.

In cases in which it is necessary to distinguish the base member of a linkage, it is customary not to show the base as a link in the normal manner but to indicate joints to base by "mounts," as shown in Figs. 1.7 and 1.8.

The term *mechanism* is somewhat interchangeable with *linkage*. In normal usage, mechanism is a somewhat more generic term encompassing systems with higher pairs, or

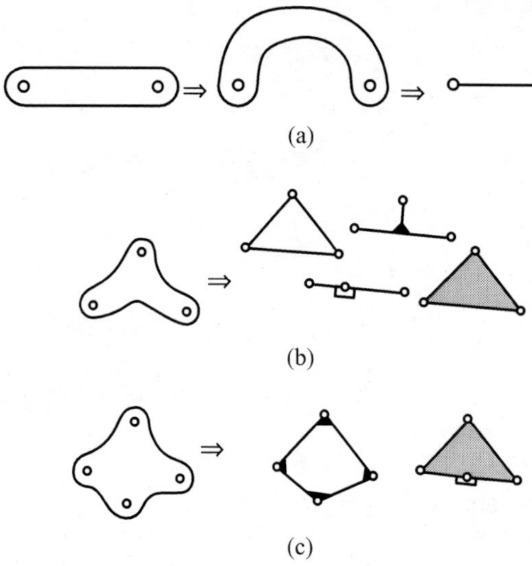

FIGURE 1.4 Representations of links. (a) Binary links: those to which two joints are mounted. (b) Ternary links and (c) Quaternary links; these have three and four joints, respectively.

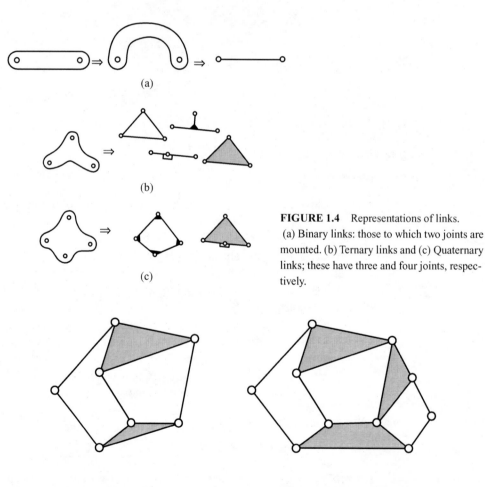

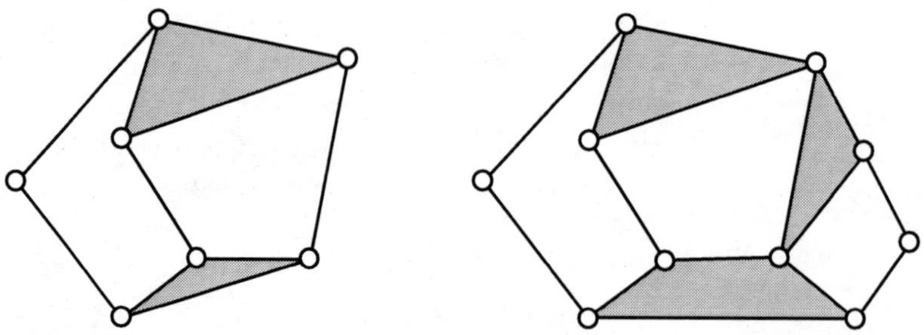

FIGURE 1.5 Conventional representations of planar linkages. Revolute joints are indicated by circles. Binary links, those with two joints mounted on them, are represented by line segments. Ternary links, with three joints, are represented by triangles, and so on.

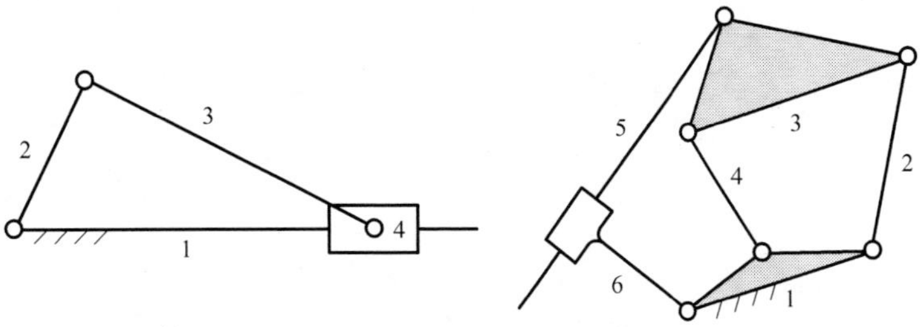

FIGURE 1.6 Representations of planar linkages with prismatic joints. (a) A four-bar slider-crank mechanism. Note that the sliding "block" is a binary member of the mechanism with a revolute joint and a prismatic joint providing the connections to adjacent members in the loop. The fillets connecting the block to a binary member represented by a line in (b) represent a rigid connection. Thus, the combination is, in this case, a binary member of the linkage.

combinations of lower and higher pair joints, whereas the term linkage tends to be restricted to systems that have only lower pair joints. Mechanisms or linkages are generally represented by their links and joints. The links are numbered with the frame link usually taken as link 1.

Simple, single-loop linkages are given a symbolic designation by a sequence of letters denoting joint types written in clockwise order beginning and ending with the joints mounted to the frame link as shown in Fig. 1.9. The letter designations for the different joints are given in Table 1.1.

The profiles of the contacting surfaces of higher pairs, such as cams and followers, are drawn in planar linkages producing representations such as that shown in Fig. 1.10. Those surfaces must be general (not necessarily circular) cylinders whose straight-line generators are normal to the plane of motion. The profile drawn is, therefore, the generating curve of the cylinder shown in Fig. 1.11. The cylinder is generated by translating that curve along a straight line in the direction normal to its plane. The familiar cylinder with a circular generating curve is called a right circular cylinder.

1.6 VISUALIZATION

Because linkage motion is inextricably intertwined with geometry, it is always important to the designer to visualize the motion. In this respect, planar linkages are relatively easy to work with because their geometry and loci representing their motion can be drawn on a two-dimensional surface. Nevertheless, it can be very difficult to visualize successive positions of the links of a planar linkage from only a drawing of that linkage in a representative position. Yet this succession of positions and the relative locations of all the links in each of the positions are very important when trying to predict effects such as interference with each other and with other machine parts. Mechanism designers have traditionally solved this problem by constructing simple physical models with the links cut from cardboard and revolute joints formed by pins or grommets. Cards cut from a manila folder with thumbtacks for revolute joints provide an acceptable material for quick visualization models. Prototyping kits (Fig. 1.12) or even children's construction toys (Fig. 1.13) provide an alternative that requires more construction time but gives a more functional model.

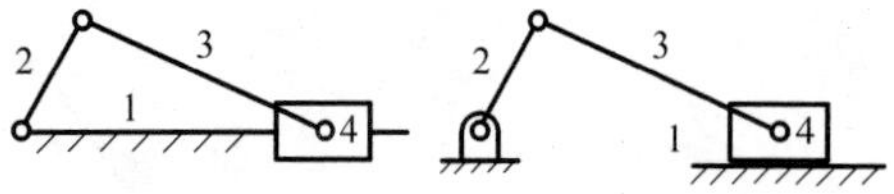

FIGURE 1.7 Selection of a frame member converts the chain of Fig. 1.6a into a linkage. This linkage is known as a slider-crank linkage.

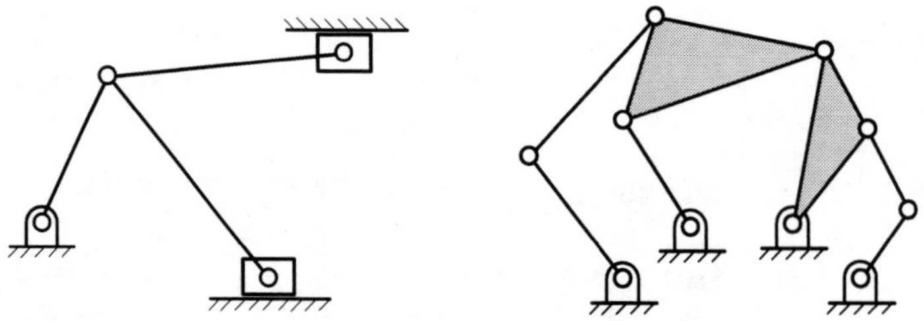

FIGURE 1.8 Representations of planar linkages with the base link not shown in the same form as the other links. The page can be thought of as representing the base link. The joints to the base link are indicated by hatched "mounts."

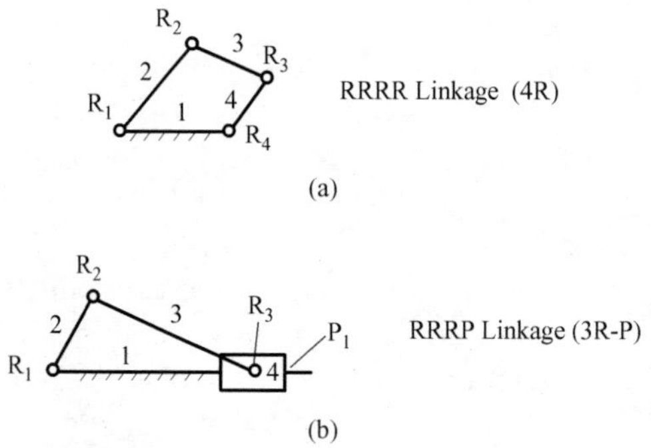

FIGURE 1.9 Designation of single-loop linkages by means of their joints. The joints are taken in clockwise order around the loop, starting and finishing with a joint to frame.

When mechanisms are designed using computer graphics systems, animation on a computer is often used to visualize the motion of the mechanism, rather than construction of a physical model. Animation should be used with caution, however. As will be seen in section 1.18 of this chapter, there are important interference effects that do not lend themselves to planar representation but which, if present, are immediately apparent in a physical model.

Furthermore, adding realistic boundary profiles to the representations of links on computer graphic systems is often time consuming and simply not worth the effort when trying a variety of different alternative linkage configurations. Instead, quick physical visualization models may be a more efficient alternative. The reader is urged to get into the habit of constructing simple models to visualize the motions of linkages that are being designed or analyzed, and to make use of computer animation when it is available.

Three-dimensional systems are much more difficult than planar systems to visualize because the depths of the positions for points on the links are no longer constant. Construction of an adequate physical model is often a major effort requiring machining to shape three-dimensional parts. In this case the most efficient solution is to use one of the solid

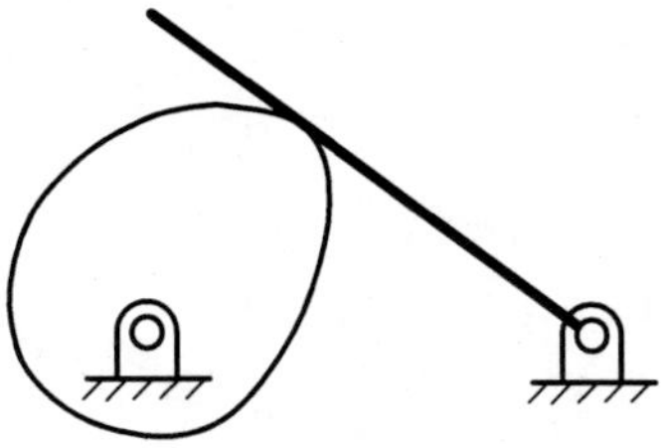

FIGURE 1.10 Representation of a plate cam with a rocker follower. The face of the follower is a plane, so it is represented by a line. The cam is represented by its profile curve.

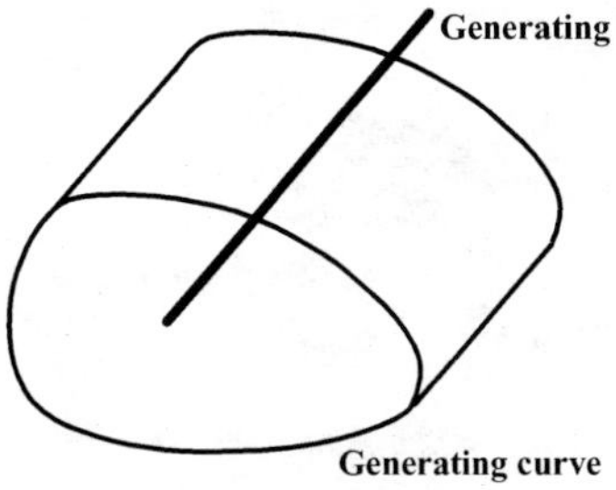

FIGURE 1.11 General cylinder. The generating curve is a plane curve. Its plane is normal to the generating line. The surface may be considered to be generated by moving the generating curve so that a point on it moves along the generating line. Alternatively, it may be generated by moving the generating line so that a point on it traverses the generating curve.

modeling software packages that support linkage joint representations and animation of the linkage. Construction of the model involves a considerable effort since each link must be described as a three-dimensional solid. Nevertheless, the effort is usually much less than would be required for the construction of a physical model. Usually it is possible to change the viewpoint from which the representation is projected. This allows the motion to be viewed from several different directions. It also allows areas of interference to be identified and corrected.

1.7 CONSTRAINT ANALYSIS

The number of degrees of freedom of a body is the number of independent coordinates needed to specify uniquely the position of that body relative to a given reference frame. Similarly, we call the minimum number of coordinates needed to specify uniquely the positions of all of the members of a system of rigid bodies the number of degrees of freedom of that system. In fact, we will use the concept of the number of degrees of freedom in three distinct but closely related ways. The first is the number of degrees of freedom of a body relative to a specified reference frame, which is the definition just given. The second is the number of degrees of freedom of a kinematic joint. The third is the number of degrees of freedom of a linkage or mechanism.

Both because "number of degrees of freedom" is such a mouthful and because we are using a distinct concept, we will refer to the number of degrees of freedom of a joint as its *connectivity*. In addition, the term will apply to the number of relative freedoms between two bodies. Likewise, we will refer to the number of degrees of freedom of a linkage as the *mobility* of that linkage. These terms may be formally defined as follows:

If a kinematic joint is formed between two rigid bodies that are not otherwise connected, the *connectivity* of that joint is the number of degrees of freedom of motion of (either) one of the two bodies joined relative to the other.

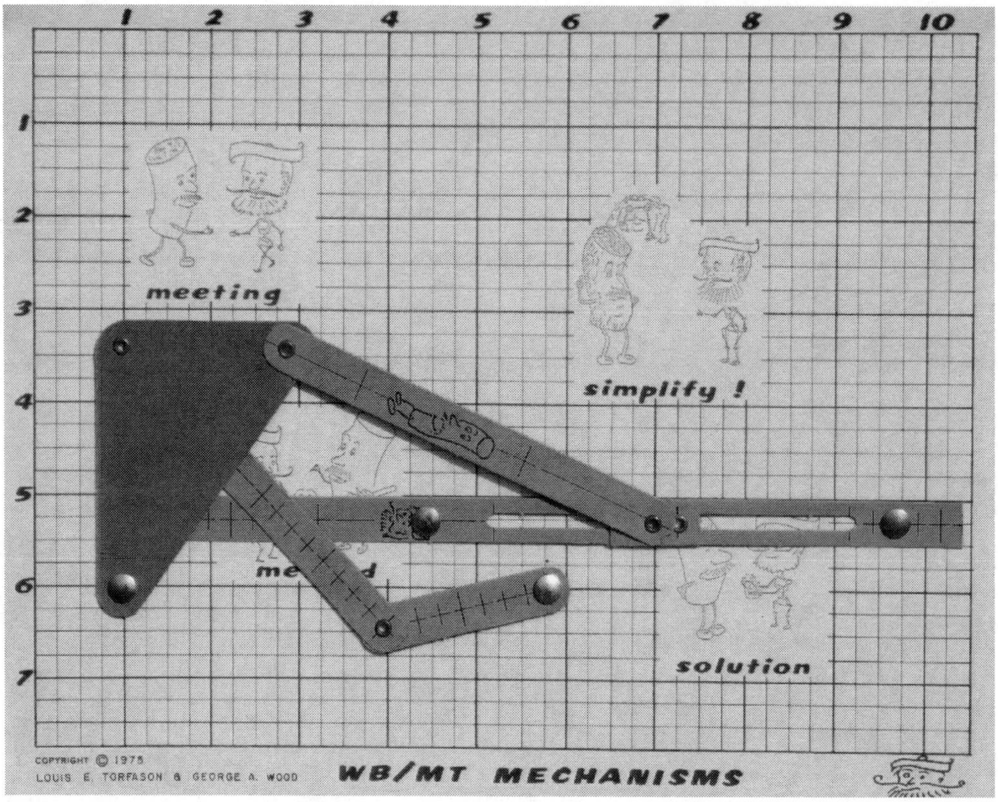

FIGURE 1.12 J. Woody Blockhead model.[2]

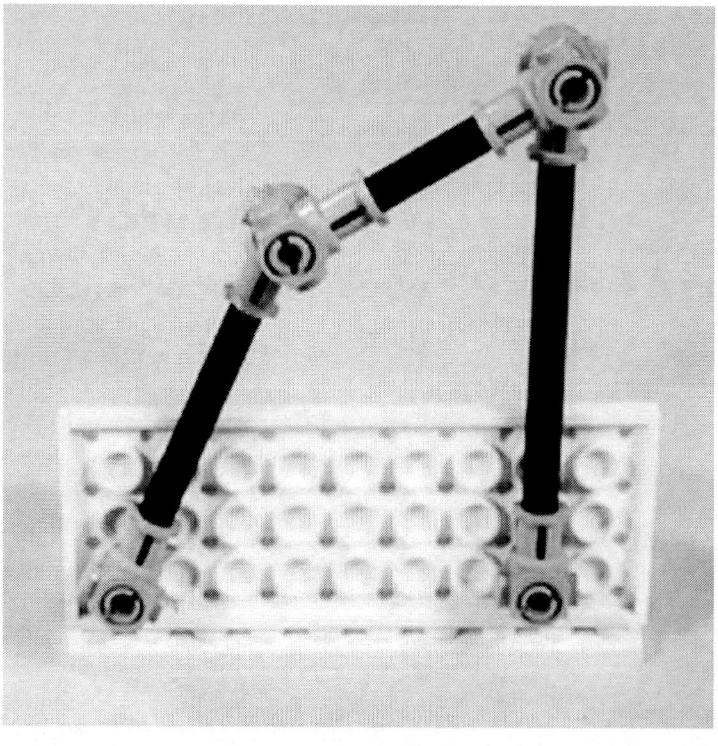

FIGURE 1.13 Model made with LEGOS Technics.[3]

[2] Wood, G. A., and Torfason, L. E., *Mechanism Modeling,* Wood & Torfason, Lincoln, MA, 1975.
[3] LEGO Systems, Inc., 555 Taylor Road, Enfield, CT.

The *mobility* of a mechanism is the minimum number of coordinates needed to specify the positions of all members of the mechanism relative to a particular member chosen as the base or frame.

The mobility, or number of degrees of freedom of a linkage, is used to determine how many pair variables must be specified before the positions of all of the points on all of the members of the linkage can be located as a function of time. A linkage has a mobility of one or more. Traditionally, almost all linkages had one degree of freedom. However, in modern design practice, linkages with two or more degrees of freedom are becoming more common. If the mobility is zero or negative, as determined by the constraint equations developed in the following, the assemblage is a structure. If the mobility is zero, the structure is statically determinate. If the mobility is negative, the structure is statically indeterminate.

To compute the mobility, let us consider the planar case first and then extend the results to the spatial case. As indicated in Fig. 1.14, in the plane, a body moving freely has three degrees of freedom. Suppose that in a given linkage there are n links. If they are all free to move independently, the system has mobility $3n$. If one link is chosen as the frame link, it is fixed to the base reference frame and loses all of its degrees of freedom. Therefore the total mobility of the system is $3(n-1)$ with no joints formed between the members.

If a joint with connectivity f_i (f_i degrees of freedom) is formed between two bodies, the mobility of the system is diminished since those two bodies originally had three degrees of freedom of motion relative to one another. After formation of the joint, they have only f_i degrees of freedom of relative motion. Hence the reduction in the system mobility is $3-f_i$. If joints continue to be formed until there are j joints, the loss of system mobility is

$$(3-f_1)+(3-f_2)+\ldots+(3-f_j)=\sum_{i=1}^{j}(3-f_i)=3j-\sum_{i=1}^{j}f_i$$

Then the total mobility of the linkage will be

$$M=3(n-1)-\left(3j-\sum_{i=1}^{j}f_i\right)=3(n-j-1)+\sum_{i=1}^{j}f_i \tag{1.1}$$

Equation (1.1) is called a constraint criterion. There are many different-appearing versions of this relationship to be found in the literature. They all, in fact, are equivalent to one another, except that some are restricted to a subset of the cases covered by Eq. (1.1).

A problem arises in some cases in which more than two members are apparently connected by the same joint. Typically, three or more members are pinned together by the same shaft and are free to rotate relative to one another about the same revolute axis. This difficulty is readily resolved if we recall that a kinematic joint is formed by contact between the surfaces of *two* rigid bodies. This is the reason for Reuleaux's name "pair" for what we here call a "joint." Considering the present case, we see that there is not one joint but several between the bodies. In fact, if p members are connected by a "common" joint, the connection is equivalent to $p-1$ joints all of the same type. Inclusion of this number in j, and using $(p-1)f_i$ in the connectivity sum of Eq. (1.1) will ensure correct results. This is illustrated in a later example (see Example 1.3).

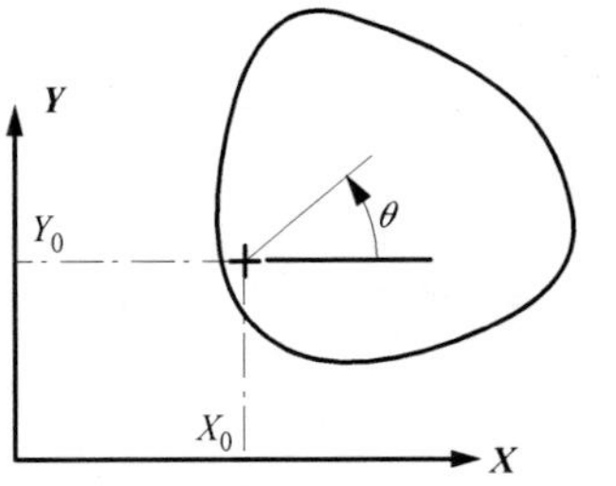

FIGURE 1.14 One set of three coordinates that can be used to describe planar motion. The number of degrees of freedom of a body is the number of independent coordinates needed to specify its position. Therefore, a body moving freely in a plane has three degrees of freedom.

EXAMPLE 1.1
Degrees of Freedom in a Simple Four-Bar Linkage

Determine the mobility of the planar four-bar linkage shown in Fig. 1.15.

Solution

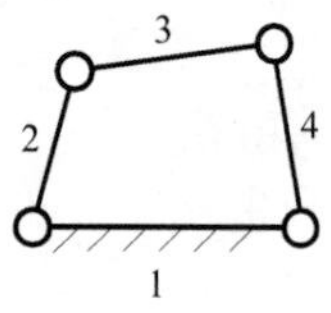

$$n = j = 4$$

$$\sum_{i=1}^{j} f_i = j \times 1 = 4$$

$$M = 3(4 - 4 - 1) + 4 = 1$$

FIGURE 1.15 Mobility analysis of a planar four-bar linkage.

EXAMPLE 1.2
Degrees of Freedom in a Complex Mechanism

Determine the mobility of the linkage shown in Fig. 1.16. The linkage is planar and all joints have connectivity one.

Solution

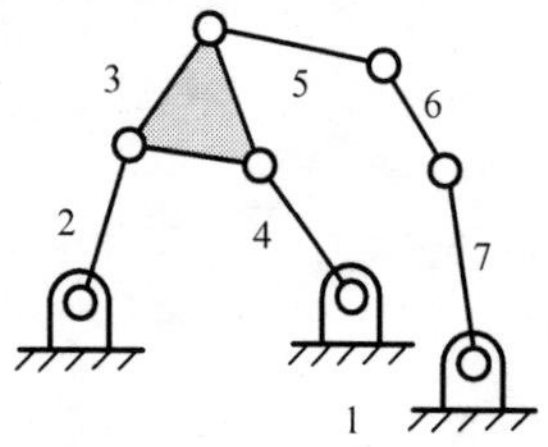

$$n = 7,\ j = 8$$

$$\sum_{i=1}^{j} f_i = j \times 1 = 8$$

$$M = 3(7 - 8 - 1) + 8 = 2$$

FIGURE 1.16 Mobility analysis of a two-loop planar linkage.

Notice that the base member must always be counted even when it is not shown in the same way as the other members but just by a set of "bearing mounts."

EXAMPLE 1.3
Degrees of Freedom When Joints Are Coincident

Determine the mobility of the linkage shown in Fig. 1.17. The linkage is planar and all joints have connectivity one. Links 3, 4, and 5 are connected at the same revolute joint axis.

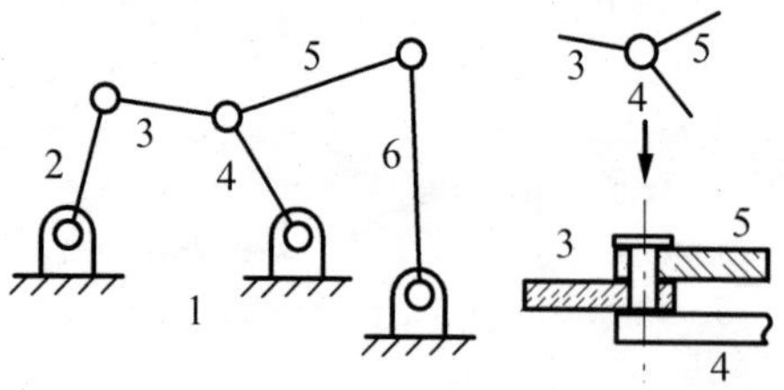

FIGURE 1.17 Mobility analysis of a linkage when more than two members come together at a single point location.

Solution

$$n = 6,\ j = 7$$

$$\sum_{i=1}^{j} f_i = j \times 1 = 7$$

$$M = 3(n - j - 1) + \sum_{i=1}^{j} f_i = 3(6 - 7 - 1) + 7 = 1$$

As indicated previously, when p members are connected at the same joint axis, then $p-1$ joints are associated with the same axis. Hence the location where links 3, 4, and 5 come together counts as two revolute joints. As indicated in the figure, members 3 and 5 can be thought of as being connected to link 4 by two separate revolute joints that have the same axis of rotation.

EXAMPLE 1.4 *Degrees of Freedom for a Mechanism Containing a Higher Pair*

Determine the mobility of the linkage shown in Fig. 1.18. The linkage is planar and not all of the joints have connectivity one.

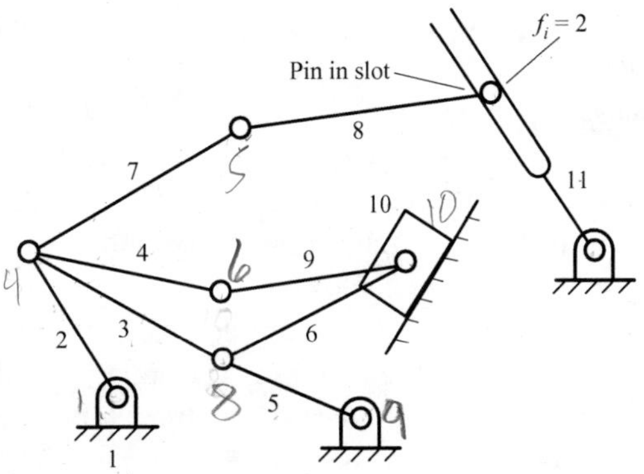

FIGURE 1.18 Mobility analysis of a linkage with various types of joints.

Solution

In this mechanism, there are three places where more than two links come together at the same revolute joint location. In addition, there is a pin-in-a-slot joint that permits two degrees of freedom (connectivity equals two). Therefore, the joints must be counted carefully. When this is done, we find n and j to be

$$n = 11,\ j = 14$$

and

$$\sum_{i=1}^{j} f_i = 13 \times 1 + 1 \times 2 = 15$$

Then,

$$M = 3(n - j - 1) + \sum_{i=1}^{j} f_i = 3(11 - 14 - 1) + 15 = 3$$

A special case that deserves attention occurs when the mobility in Eq. (1.1) is set to one and all joints have connectivity one ($f_i = 1$). Then, Eq. (1.1) gives

$$1 = 3(n - j - 1) + j$$

or

$$4 = 3n - 2j \tag{1.2}$$

Because n and j are integers, n must be even because 4 and $2j$ are both even numbers. This is an example of a Diophantine equation. That is one that admits only integral solutions. Written as an expression for j in terms of n, the equation becomes

$$j = 3n/2 - 2$$

Some of the possible solutions are listed in Table 1.4. In each case, the joints may be either revolute or prismatic joints, since they are the only lower pair joints that can properly be included in planar linkages.

Solution 1 gives the rather trivial case of two bodies connected by a single revolute or slider joint. This is shown in Fig. 1.19a. Actually, this mechanism is very common. For example, a door, its hinges, and the door frame form an open kinematic chain and a mechanism of this type.

Solution 2 gives a single, closed loop of four members with four joints. Two forms are shown in Figs. 1.19b and 1.19c. The one in Fig. 1.19b is the planar four-bar linkage that forms a major element in planar linkage theory. The one in Fig. 1.19c is the slider-crank linkage, which is also extensively studied.

Solution 3 presents two new features. First members with more than two joints mounted on them appear. Second, even when only revolute joints are included, there are two possible, topologically distinct, configurations of six members with seven joints. These are respectively named the Watt and Stephenson six-bar chains and are shown in Fig. 1.20.

Solution 4 gives 16 possible different topological configurations, shown in Fig. 1.21, and solution 5 gives 230. The number increases very rapidly with larger numbers of members. For example, solution 6 gives 6856 configurations (Hunt, 1978).[4]

From this discussion, it should be apparent why we spend so much effort on the design of four-link mechanisms. The four-link arrangement is the simplest possible nontrivial linkage. It turns out that most design requirements can be met by four- or six-link mechanisms.

Note that, in this discussion, the type of the joints was not specified. All that was specified was that the joints have connectivity one and that the linkage is planar and has mobility one. Although the joints pictured in Figs. 1.19–1.21 are all revolute, rolling contact joints could be substituted for any of the joints, and prismatic joints could be substituted

TABLE 1.4 Different Integer Solutions to Eq. (1.2) for Mobility of One

Solution number	n	j	Number of configurations
1	2	1	1
2	4	4	1
3	6	7	2
4	8	10	16
5	10	13	230
6	12	16	6856

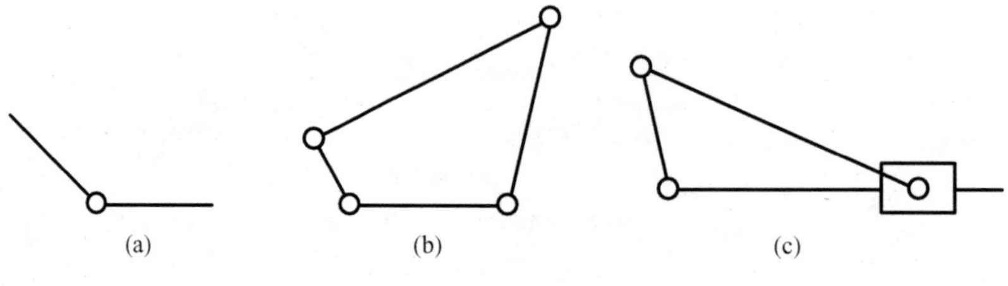

FIGURE 1.19 Solutions of the planar mobility equation for $M = 1$ when $n = 2$ and $n = 4$.

[4] Hunt, K. H., *Kinematic Geometry of Mechanisms*, Oxford University Press, Oxford, UK, p. 40, 1978.

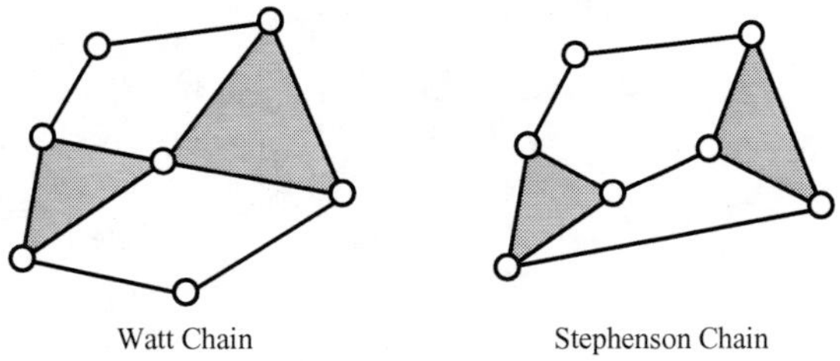

FIGURE 1.20 The two solutions of the planar mobility equation for seven revolute joints. $M = 1$ and each kinematic chain has six members.

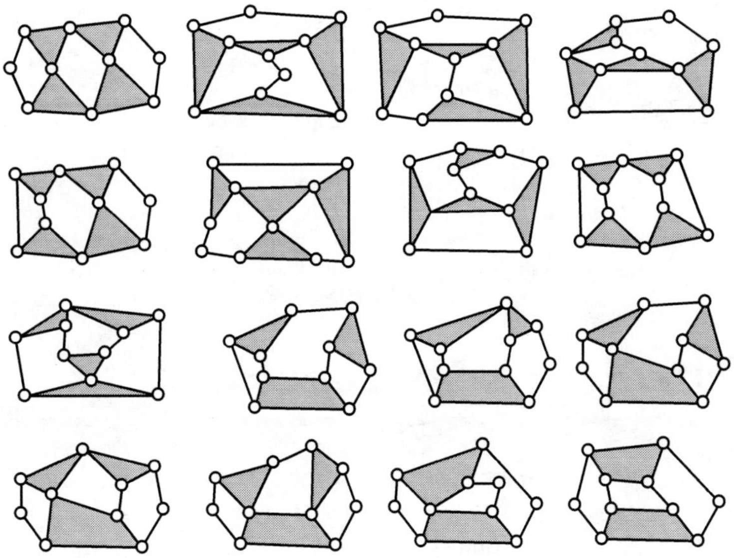

FIGURE 1.21 The 16 solutions of the planar mobility equation for 10 revolute joints. $M = 1$ and each kinematic chain has eight members.

for some of them. Thus, even if the joints are confined to lower pairs, the four-link, four-joint solution represents the four different chains shown in Fig. 1.22. The Scotch yoke, based on the 2R-2P chain, is shown in Fig. 1.23.

Further, as discussed later in this chapter, the important concept of inversion generates several different linkages from any mechanism based on the 3R-P and 2R-2P chains. An inversion is a different mechanism derived from a given mechanism or linkage by changing the base member. "Different" means that the motion relative to the frame that can be produced by the inversion is different from that provided in the original mechanism, that is, the inversion produces a different general form for the paths of points on the different links or a different input–output function.

A different inversion is produced for each choice of frame link. As a result, the 3R-P chain produces four different mechanisms. In the basic slider-crank mechanism, the frame member has one revolute and one prismatic joint mounted on it. We can also make the slider the frame. The other two inversions are turning block linkages in which the base has two revolutes mounted on it. The 2R-2P chain can produce three different mechanisms: The Scotch yoke has one revolute and one prismatic joint mounted on the frame, the double slider has two prismatic joints on the frame, and the third mechanism, the Oldham coupling, has both revolutes mounted on the frame.

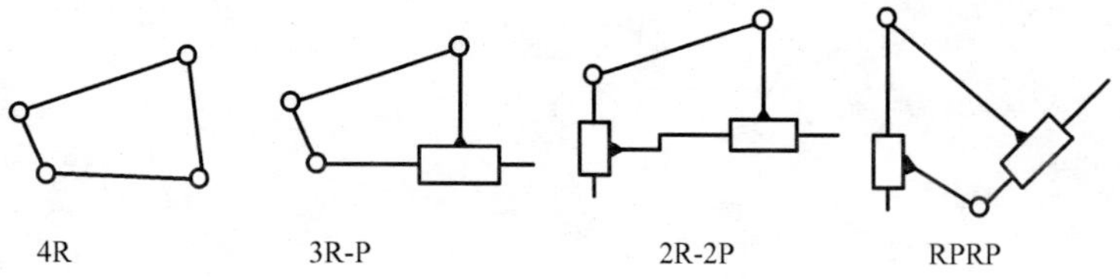

FIGURE 1.22 Four different forms of four-bar chains with combinations of revolute and prismatic joints.

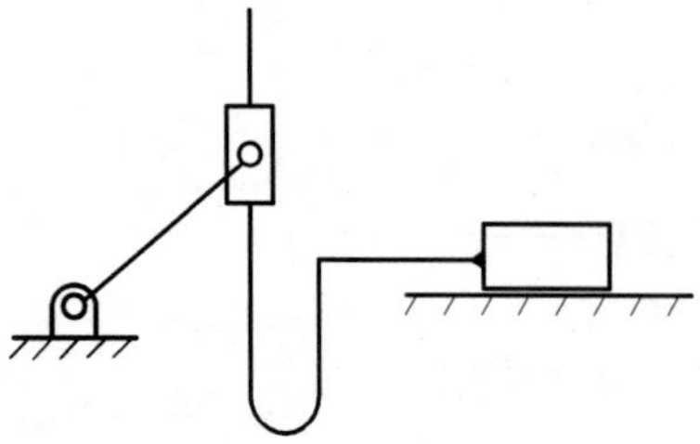

FIGURE 1.23 The 2R-2P chain as a Scotch yoke mechanism.

1.8 CONSTRAINT ANALYSIS OF SPATIAL LINKAGES

In spatial motion, each body that moves freely has six degrees of freedom rather than three. Using exactly the same reasoning as was used in the planar case, the constraint criterion equation becomes

$$M = 6(n - j - 1) + \sum_{i=1}^{j} f_i \tag{1.3}$$

This is called the Kutzbach criterion. If only lower pair joints are involved, each with connectivity one, the equations become

$$M = 6(n - j - 1) + j = 6n - 5j - 6$$

If the linkage is required to have mobility one, this gives

$$6n = 7 + 5j \tag{1.4}$$

Equation (1.4) corresponds to Eq. (1.2) derived in the case of planar motion. Like that equation, it is a Diophantine equation that admits only integral values of the variables. Evidently, j must be odd because $5j$ must be odd to combine with the odd number 7 to produce the even number $6n$. The sum $7 + 5j$ must also be divisible by 3. Solutions to Eq. (1.4) are a little harder to generate than those of Eq. (1.2). The simplest solution is given by $j = 1$ and $n = 2$. This is exactly the same as the simplest solution in the planar case depicted in Fig. 1.19a. The next allowable solution is $j = 7$ and $n = 7$. This is a single, closed loop with seven members and seven joints. It bears the same relationship to general spatial linkage topologies that the planar four-bar linkage does to planar ones. The next order solution is $j = 13$, $n = 12$. There are three distinct topological forms in this case. For spatial mechanisms, the complexity increases with the number of members and joints even more rapidly than it does for planar joints.

EXAMPLE 1.5
Degrees of Freedom in a Spatial Mechanism

Determine the mobility of the linkage shown in Fig. 1.24. The linkage is spatial. The joints are lower pairs of the types labeled.

Note how the three-dimensional joints are drawn. There is no formalism that is more or less universally recognized for representing spatial mechanisms as there is for planar linkages; however, we will follow the symbols shown in Table 1.1.

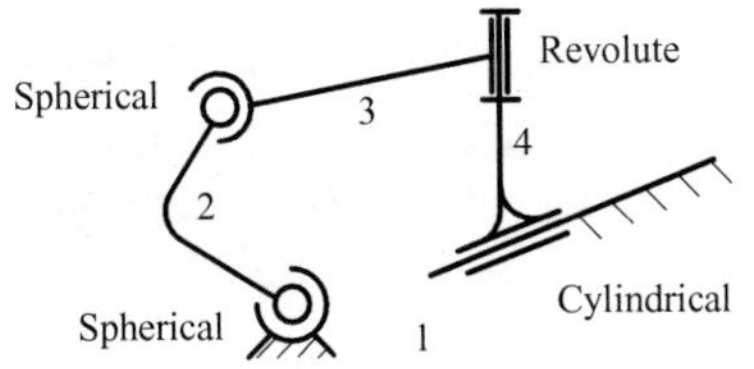

FIGURE 1.24 A four-member, single-loop, spatial linkage.

Solution

$$n = j = 4$$

$$\sum_{i=1}^{j} f_i = 2 \times 3 + 1 \times 1 + 1 \times 2 = 9$$

$$M = 6(n - j - 1) + \sum_{i=1}^{j} f_i = 6(4 - 4 - 1) + 9 = 3$$

Another way of looking at the constraint criterion is in terms of closures. Imagine building up the linkage by starting with the base link and successively adding members and joints. If a joint connects an additional member to the system, the number of degrees of freedom is increased by f_i, if f_i is the connectivity of that joint, and the numbers of members and joints are both increased by one. If a joint is made between two members that are already part of the linkage, the total number of degrees of freedom is decreased by the number of constraints imposed by that joint. The number of constraints imposed by a joint is the number of degrees of freedom lost by the system when that joint is formed. For a spatial mechanism, it is $6 - f_i$ since two bodies have six degrees of freedom of motion relative to one another when they are free of each other and only f_i degrees of freedom of relative motion after the joint is formed. Also, in this case, the formation of the joint results in the formation of a closed loop of members and joints within the linkage. This is called a closure. Proceeding in this manner, we can express the mobility of the linkage as

$$M = \sum_{i=1}^{j} f_i - 6c$$

where c is the number of closures. Now, when a closure is formed, the number of members does not increase, whereas the number of joints increases by one. If there are no closures (open kinematic chains), the number of link members is given by

$$n = j + 1$$

the additional member being the base member. Therefore, if there are c closures in the linkage

$$c = j + 1 - n$$

Thus, substitution for c in the expression for the mobility leads to Eq. (1.4). The relationship among c, j, and n is illustrated in Fig. 1.25.

The reason for looking at the constraint criterion from this viewpoint is that it relates to the position analysis of a spatial linkage. When a closure is formed, a set of six algebraic equations called closure equations can be written. The formulation of these equations will be briefly treated in Chapter 9, although their study lies largely beyond the scope of this book. The quantity $6c = 6(j + 1 - n)$ is therefore the number of equations available for position analysis of the mechanism. The variables in those equations are the joint parameters, the variables needed to fix the relative positions of the bodies connected by each joint. There are f_i of these joint parameters for joint i. Therefore the total number of variables in the linkage is

$$c = \sum_{i=1}^{j} f_i$$

In this way, it may be seen that Eq. (1.4) expresses the mobility of the linkage as the number of variables less the number of equations for the system.

Yet another viewpoint on the constraint criterion that it is productive to pursue is that of static force analysis. Free body diagrams can be drawn for all members except the base. Six static equilibrium equations can be written for each free body. Hence there are $6(n - 1)$ equations describing the system. At each joint there is a number of reaction force and torque components that is equal to the number of constraints of that joint. These force components are the variables in a static force analysis. Since the number of constraints at joint i is $6 - f_i$, the number of variables is

$$\sum_{i=1}^{j}\left(6 - f_i\right) = 6j - \sum_{i=1}^{j} f_i$$

Therefore, the difference between the number of variables and the number of equations is

$$6j - \sum_{i=1}^{j} f_i - 6\left(n - 1\right) = -M$$

Thus, the mobility is meaningful from the point of view of static force analysis also. If M = 0, the linkage is not movable and is a structure. The position problem can be solved to obtain the joint positions that cannot vary. The static equilibrium problem can be solved for all of the reaction force and torque components. The structure is statically determinate since there is a unique solution to the static equilibrium problem.

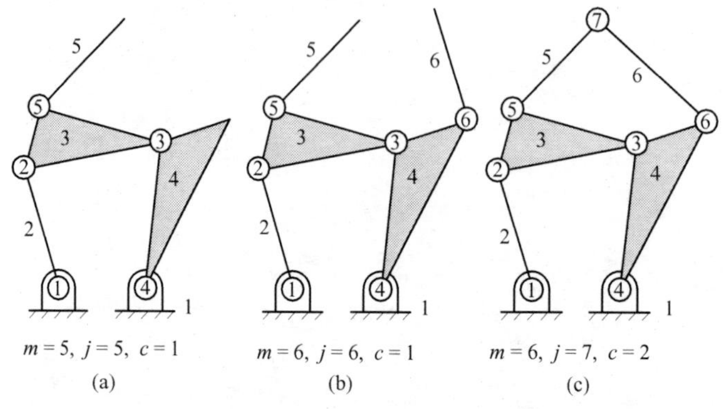

FIGURE 1.25 The effect of adding a member to a linkage together with a joint (b) and of adding a joint without an additional member (c). Adding a joint without a member always closes a loop within the linkage.

If the mobility is –1, the number of equations for the position problem exceeds the number of variables. Therefore, in general there is no solution to the position problem. For a solution to exist it is necessary for the equations to be dependent. This means that the geometry of the mechanism must satisfy the conditions needed for the equations to be dependent. Physically, this means that, in general, it is not possible to assemble the linkage. One or more of the closures cannot be made. However, if the link geometry is changed to bring the surfaces for the closing joint into alignment, the linkage may be assembled.

From the viewpoint of force analysis, the mobility is the number of static equilibrium equations less the number of force variables: the converse of the situation for position analysis. Thus, if $M = -1$ there is one more force variable than the number of force equations. Therefore, in this case solutions of the system exist, but there is no unique solution. The force problem cannot be solved without additional information relating the forces in the system. The linkage is a statically indeterminate structure. If the links are modeled as elastic rather than rigid solids, compatibility of their deflections under load provides the necessary additional relationship.

Conversely, if the mobility is one or more, the number of position variables is greater than the number of position equations. Solutions to the system exist, but there is no unique solution. The number of force equations is greater than the number of force variables, so, in general, no solution to the static force problem exists. In practice, application of an arbitrary set of loads to the linkage would lead to rapid, uncontrolled acceleration, and the system behavior could not be described without writing dynamic equations. However, this invalidates the assumption of a static model.

Specification of the value of a joint parameter is equivalent to fixing that joint. Physically, it might be done by putting an actuator on that joint that would hold it in position. The joint can now support a force, or torque. The effect is to increase the number of unknown force variables by one. If a linkage has mobility one, fixing the position of a joint with connectivity one converts it into a structure. It also converts the static force problem from one in which there is one more equation than there are variables to one in which the number of variables is the same as the number of equations. That is, it is statically determinate.

Fixing the torque applied about a revolute joint, or the force applied by an actuator at a prismatic joint, has a quite different effect. It does not change the number of variables or the number of equations in either the position or the force problem. This is because having a passive joint is already equivalent to fixing the force or torque variable about that joint. The torque applied at a passive revolute joint is fixed to zero. Changing it to any other value does not affect the number of unknown variables. Of course, it does affect the values of the unknown force variables.

This effect is quite important in practical applications of multiply actuated mechanisms. Consider the manipulator arm shown in Fig. 1.26. It has seven members (italic numbers) and six joints. The heavy dashed lines with bold numbers indicate the joint axes. Joints 1, 2, 4, 5, and 6 are revolute joints. Joint 3 is a prismatic joint. The axes of joints 3 and 4 are the same. Member 1 is the base member.

Applying the constraint criterion to this mechanism, we have $n = 7$, $j = 6$, and $\Sigma f_i = 6$, so

$$M = 6(n - j - 1) + \sum_{i=1}^{j} f_i = 6(7 - 6 - 1) + 6 = 6$$

If we actuate all of the joints so that we can specify their positions, the position of the mechanism is uniquely specified.

Consider now what happens if the manipulator grips an object that is fixed relative to the base member, as is shown in Fig. 1.27. It is assumed that the gripper grasps the object

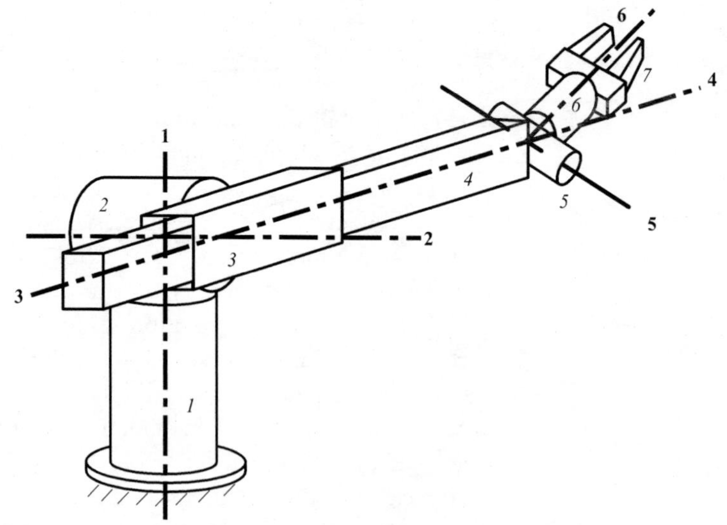

FIGURE 1.26 A robotic manipulator that is used to produce general spatial motions of its gripper. The mechanism has seven members, indicated by the italic numbers, and six joints. Joints 1, 2, 4, 5, and 6 are revolutes. Joint 3 is a prismatic joint. The heavy dashed lines indicate the joint axes. The axes of joints 3 and 4 are coincident.

tightly so that no relative motion is possible. The effect is to make link 7 a part of link 1. Therefore, application of the constraint criterion gives $n = 6, j = 6$, and $\Sigma f_i = 6$, so

$$M = 6(n - j - 1) + \sum_{i=1}^{j} f_i = 6(6 - 6 - 1) + 6 = 0$$

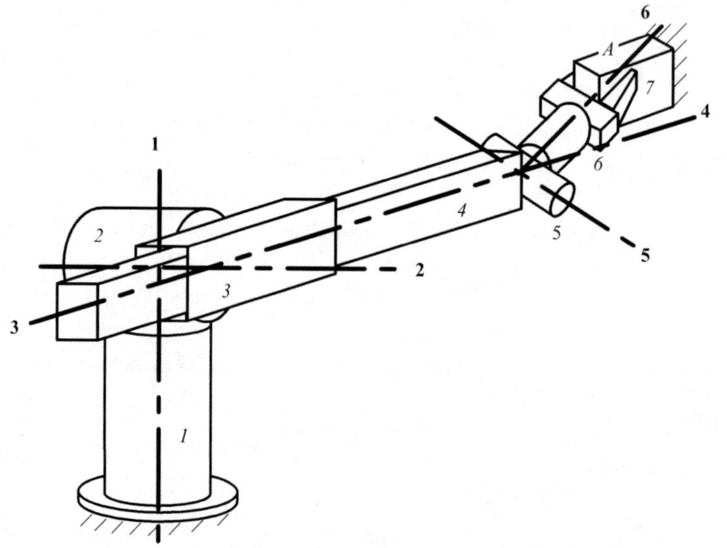

FIGURE 1.27 The robotic manipulator of Fig. 1.26 gripping a fixed object. If the gripper grasps the object so that no relative motion is possible, the gripper becomes fixed to member one. This reduces the number of members in the system to six and closes a loop.

The mechanism is now a structure, and we do not have the liberty of setting the joint variables to any value we wish. Attempting to control the mechanism by commanding joint positions, as is done when the manipulator is moving freely, is not effective in this case. Since most manipulator structures are very stiff, a small position error results in very large forces on the actuators. The usual result is that the actuator controllers become unstable, producing violent vibratory behavior. However, commanding the actuators to produce specified forces or torques eliminates the problem. The actuator torques and forces can be set to any desired set of values. In this way it is possible to apply a specified force system to the fixed object A by means of the manipulator. Notice that commanding forces and torques all the time is not a solution. If actuator forces are commanded when the manipulator is moving freely, the number of static equilibrium equations exceeds the number of variables by six and the manipulator will perform rapid uncontrolled movements, violating the assumption of static stability.

1.9 IDLE DEGREES OF FREEDOM

Equation (1.4) sometimes gives misleading results. There are several reasons for this. One is the phenomenon of idle degrees of freedom. Consider the linkage shown in Fig. 1.28. This linkage has four members and four joints. Two of the joints are revolutes. The other two are spherical joints. This mechanism is quite often used in situations such as the steering mechanisms of automobiles. Applying the constraint criterion, we have $n = 4$, $j = 4$, and $\Sigma f_i = 2 \times 1 + 2 \times 3 = 8$. Therefore

$$M = 6(n - j - 1) + \sum_{i=1}^{j} f_i = 6(4 - 4 - 1) + 8 = 2$$

Nevertheless, practical experience with this mechanism shows that there is a unique value of the output joint angle, ϕ, for any given value of the input angle, θ. How can this be explained?

Examination of the mechanism reveals that the coupler member is free to spin about the line through the centers of the two spherical joints. This motion—termed an idle degree of freedom—can take place in any position of the linkage without affecting the values of the input and output joint angles. That is, an idle degree of freedom is one that does not affect the input–output relationship of the linkage.

The real problem here is that usually we are not really interested in the mobility of the entire linkage, that is, of all of its links. Rather, we are interested in the connectivity that the linkage provides as a joint between two of its members. This is a new use of the term connectivity. Previously we applied it only to simple joints at which the members contact each other directly. However, a mechanism constrains the number of degrees of freedom of relative motion of any two of its members. Therefore it can be regarded as forming a kinematic joint between any two of its members. We can define its connectivity as a joint between those members and as the number of degrees of freedom of relative motion that it permits between the members.

In the example of Fig. 1.28, the connectivity of the linkage as a joint between the input and output members is one, even though the mobility of the linkage is two, and the connectivity between links 3 and 1 is two. The mobility places an upper bound on the connectivity of the mechanism as a joint between any two of its members. There is no simple method of directly determining connectivity, so the mobility equation is used. If the mobility is one and

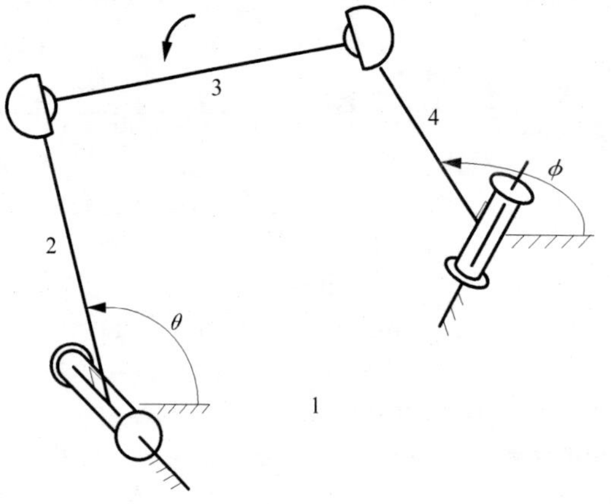

FIGURE 1.28 A spatial four-member, four-joint linkage. Two of the joints are revolutes. The other two are spherical joints. θ is the input-joint angle, and ϕ is the output-joint angle. The linkage has an idle degree of freedom since member 3 can spin about the line joining the centers of the spherical joints without affecting the relationship between θ and ϕ.

the linkage is not overconstrained in some local region, there is no problem. The connectivity of the linkage as a joint between any two of its members is also one. If the mobility is greater than one, strictly speaking, all that can be said is that the connectivity between any given pair of members may be equal to the mobility or may be less than that number. Fortunately, idle degrees of freedom usually can be identified by inspection.

Another example is shown in Fig. 1.29. This is one form of the so-called Stewart platform mechanism. This mechanism is commonly used to produce general spatial motions in aircraft simulators for training pilots. The output member is connected to the base by six "limbs," each of which has an actuated prismatic joint in the middle and two spherical joints at either end. There are 14 members: 2 in each of the limbs plus the base and output members. There are 18 joints: 6 prismatic joints and 12 spherical joints. Hence $\Sigma f_i = 6 \times 1 + 12 \times 3 = 42$. Therefore

$$M = 6(n - j - 1) + \sum_{i=1}^{j} f_i = 6(14 - 18 - 1) + 42 = 12$$

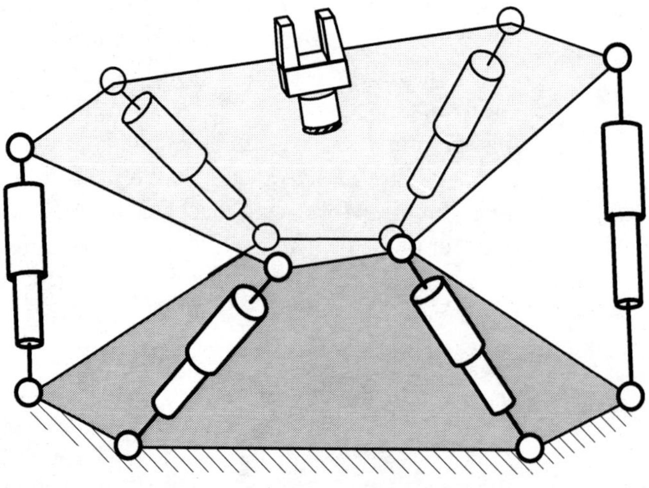

FIGURE 1.29 Stewart platform.

However, it is easily seen that each limb is free to spin about the line joining the centers of its spherical joints without affecting the position of the output member relative to the base. Therefore, the mechanism has six idle degrees of freedom, and its connectivity as a joint between base and output member is

$$C = M - 6 = 6$$

Therefore, by appropriately positioning the actuated prismatic joints, the output member can be placed in any position within its working volume.

Although idle degrees of freedom are most common in spatial linkages, they can also occur in planar linkages. Typically, this occurs when cam roller followers are involved. For example, if the mobility of the linkage in Fig. 1.30 is computed, it will be found to be one if there is rolling contact between the roller (link 5) and the cam (link 6) at point *C*. However, if there is cam contact at *C*, the mobility will be two. The extra degree of freedom is associated with the free rotation of link 5 relative to the frame. Usually, this rotation will be of no interest because the motion of all of the other links in the mechanism will be unaffected by this rotation.

To locate the idle degrees of freedom, it is first necessary to identify the input link and output link. Then one must check to determine if a single link or a combination of connected links can move without altering the relative position of the input and output links. Idle degrees of freedom are dependent both on geometry and on the choice of the input and output. In some cases, idle degrees of freedom can exist for one choice of input and output but not for a different choice.

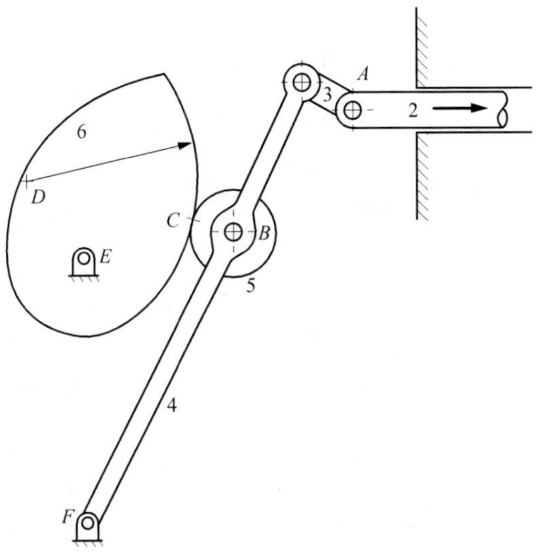

FIGURE 1.30 Planar mechanism with an idle degree of freedom.

1.10 OVERCONSTRAINED LINKAGES

A second reason why the constraint criteria [Eqs. (1.1) and (1.4)] sometimes give misleading results is the phenomenon of overconstraint. A mechanism can be overconstrained either locally or generally. If the mechanism is overconstrained locally, a portion of the system may be a structure, but the entire mechanism can move. When this happens, we must replace that portion of the linkage with a single rigid body and recompute the mobility of the mechanism. An example is shown in the planar system of Fig. 1.31a.

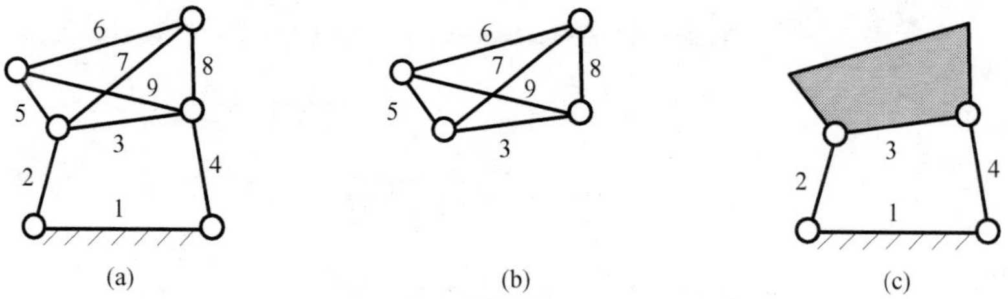

FIGURE 1.31 (a) A planar mechanism in which part of the mechanism is a structure, leading to a misleading value of mobility. All joints are revolutes. (b) The part of the mechanism that is a statically indeterminate structure. (c) A modified model of the linkage that gives the correct mobility value.

Here $n = 9, j = 2 \times 1 + 2 \times 2 + 2 \times 3 = 12$. Note that there are two joints at which three members are connected and two at which four members are connected. $\Sigma f_i = j - 12$. Hence

$$M = 3(n - j - 1) + \sum_{i=1}^{j} f_i = 3(9 - 12 - 1) + 12 = 0$$

However, it can be observed that the portion of the linkage consisting of members 3, 5, 6, 7, 8, and 9 is a statically indeterminate structure. This portion is shown in Fig. 1.31b. Here $n = 6$, and because three members are connected at each joint location, $j = 4 \times 2 = 8$. Also, $\Sigma f_i = j = 8$. Therefore,

$$M = 3(n - j - 1) + \sum_{i=1}^{j} f_i = 3(6 - 8 - 1) + 8 = -1$$

revealing the statically indeterminate nature of the structure and the source of the error in the mobility value. A portion of the linkage that is a statically determinate structure does not cause an error in calculating mobility.

To compute a correct value of mobility, the linkage is remodeled as shown in Fig. 1.31c with the portion that is a structure replaced by a single, rigid member. The linkage is now revealed to be a planar four-bar linkage for which the mobility is one.

Mechanisms, especially spatial mechanisms, can also be generally overconstrained. Figure 1.32 shows a spatial linkage with four members and four revolute joints. It has a special geometry. The opposite members are identical, and the normals to the pairs of axes in the links intersect at the joint axes. The lengths of those normals (a and b) are related to the angles between successive axes (α and β) by the relationship

$$a \sin \beta = b \sin \alpha$$

As was demonstrated approximately one hundred years ago by Bennett, this linkage has mobility one. However, if we apply the constraint criterion with $n = j = 4$ and $\Sigma f_i = 4$, the result is

$$M = 6(n - j - 1) + \sum_{i=1}^{j} f_i = 6(4 - 4 - 1) + 4 = -2$$

In this case, because of the special geometry, the position equations of the linkage turn out to be dependent in all positions. For this reason, the effective number of equations is only three, rather than the six that would be expected for a single closed loop. Because the constraint criterion calculates the difference between the number of position variables and the number of available equations, it miscounts the mobility by three degrees of freedom. It

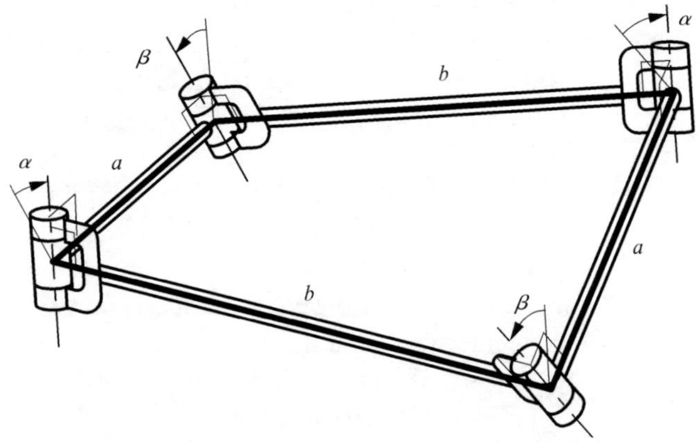

FIGURE 1.32 The Bennett mechanism. The side lengths and twist angles obey the relationship $a \sin \beta = b \sin \alpha$.

turns out that rather a large number of linkages have anomalous mobility like the Bennett mechanism. They are called overconstrained linkages. Many of these are largely curiosities. However, there are several very important families of overconstrained linkages that are exceedingly common in engineering practice.

The most common example of overconstraint is the family of planar linkages. There is no *a priori* reason why planar linkages should not obey the general spatial mobility criterion. Nevertheless, they do not. Equation (1.3) gives a value for M that is always $3c$ less than the correct value, where c is the number of independent closure equations for the linkage. The fact that planar linkages obey Eq. (1.1), which has the same form as Eq. (1.3) but with the coefficient 6 replaced by 3, indicates that only three of the six equations produced by any closure are independent for a planar linkage.

Another common family of overconstrained linkages is the family of spherical linkages. These are linkages whose joints are all revolutes. The axes of those joints all pass through a single point. Figure 1.33 shows a spherical four-bar linkage.

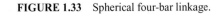

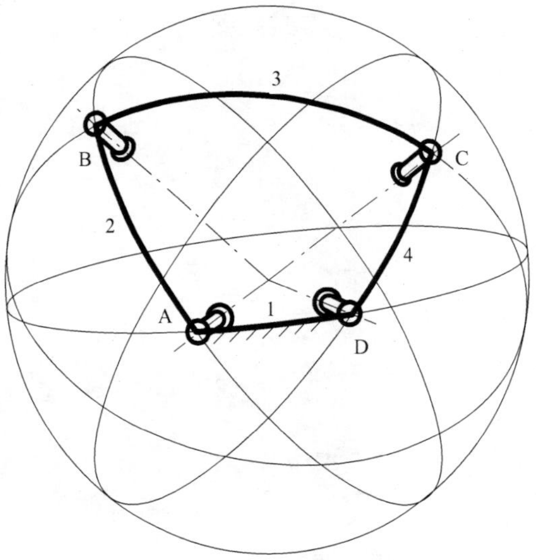

FIGURE 1.33 Spherical four-bar linkage.

Spherical linkages obey the same form of constraint criterion as planar linkages and the Bennett linkage. Thus, three of the equations resulting from each closure in a spherical linkage are always dependent.

Compared with properly constrained linkages [those that obey Eq. (1.3)], overconstrained linkages have properties that are different in important and practical ways. They tend to be much stiffer and stronger in supporting loads, particularly those orthogonal to the direction of motion at the point of application. However, they are sensitive to dimensional accuracy in their members. This requires manufacture to relatively tight tolerances, which can increase cost. Conversely, properly constrained linkages are completely insensitive to link geometry, as far as mobility is concerned. This means that, in lightly loaded situations, they can absorb abuse that deforms links and still function, at least after a fashion. This is an important property in situations such as the control linkages of agricultural machinery. In heavily loaded situations, the design engineer will often deliberately increase the degree of overconstraint to improve stiffness and strength. An example is the bucket support linkage of a front-end loader. A photograph of the loader is shown in Fig. 1.34, and one of the bucket support linkages is identified in Fig. 1.35.

In principle, only one of the two planar inverted, slider-crank linkages is needed to lift or support the bucket. In this case, we would have $n = j = \Sigma f_i = 4$ and

$$M = 6(n - j - 1) + \sum_{i=1}^{j} f_i = 6(4 - 4 - 1) + 4 = -2$$

Since the true mobility is 1, the degree of overconstraint is $1 - (-2) = 3$. However, the linkage is doubled up with identical linkages supporting each end of the bucket. This gives $n = 6$ and $j = \Sigma f_i = 8$. Thus

$$M = 6(n - j - 1) + \sum_{i=1}^{j} f_i = 6(6 - 8 - 1) + 8 = -10$$

Therefore, for the doubled linkage the degree of overconstraint is $1 - (-10) = 11$. The result is a much stronger mechanism since the individual planar loops do not have to support the

FIGURE 1.34 Front-end loader. If analyzed using the planar mobility equations, the mechanism will be found to have fewer than one degree of freedom. Parallel actuators are used on both sides of the machine to balance the load and increase stiffness. The loader part of the machine has two degrees of freedom. (Courtesy of Deere & Company, Moline, Illinois.)

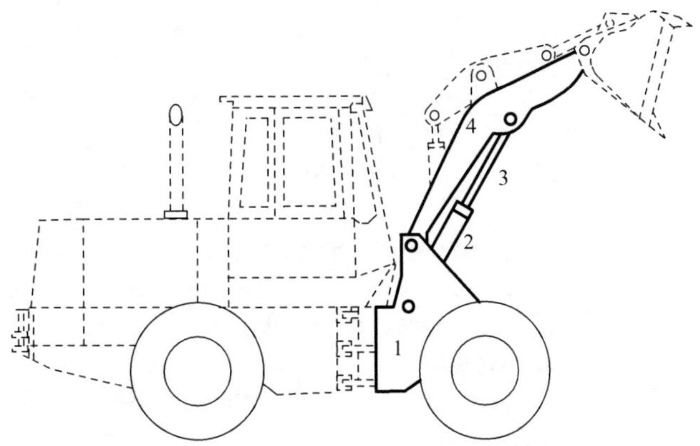

FIGURE 1.35 Schematic of the right-side bucket support linkage for the front-end loader in Fig. 1.34.

large out-of-plane moments that a single linkage would have to support. The cost is that the axes of the corresponding joints on either side must be collinear to a high degree of accuracy, requiring careful manufacturing.

1.11 USES OF THE MOBILITY CRITERION

The mobility criterion is most useful to the engineer when an unfamiliar mechanical system is examined. It allows a quick check to determine whether the links, joints, and actuators identified are consistent with system function. Inconsistency may indicate that some elements have been misidentified or that passive degrees of freedom are present. Of course, as already discussed, overconstraint may also need to be considered. In particular, if the linkage is planar or spherical, the appropriate form of the constraint equation should be used in place of the general form.

It is possible to formulate expressions for the mobility that accommodate overconstrained closures of arbitrary type. These expressions are equivalent to the form

$$M = \sum_{k=1}^{c} b_k + \sum_{i=1}^{j} f_i \tag{1.5}$$

where $c = n - j - 1$ is the number of closures of the linkage, and b_k is the loop closure rank. That is, it is the number of independent closure equations for that loop.

Unfortunately, unless the values of b_k associated with the different closures can be identified by inspection, such expressions have no value because the mobility equation gives a quick check of the number of position variables and independent equations without the need to develop those equations. However, the only way to verify an overconstrained closure of a type not identifiable by inspection is to develop the closure equations and analyze them for dependency. Therefore the quick-check advantage of the mobility equation disappears, and there is no way to derive information about the linkage without performing a complete position analysis.

1.12 INVERSION

A commonly used tactic in studying mechanism kinematics is inversion. This is a change of the fixed reference frame from one link to another that causes different characteristics of the motion relative to the frame. For example, Fig. 1.36 shows the different inversions of a slider-crank linkage, and Fig. 1.37 shows the inversions of a pin-in-a-slot mechanism. The pin-in-a-slot inversions are often used as inexpensive substitutes for the slider-crank inversions. The motion characteristics of the coupler links for each of the mechanisms are all very different. Nevertheless, the linkage topology and the relative angular relationships among the links are the same in all cases. Therefore, useful information obtained from the study of the linkage in one inversion can be transferred to the study of other inversions. Note that in Fig. 1.36, the relative positions of all of the joints are the same for the position chosen. It is only when the mechanisms move that the different motion characteristics are revealed.

To determine the inversions of a mechanism, it is convenient to start with the chain from which the mechanism is formed. A different linkage results whenever a different link is selected as the frame.

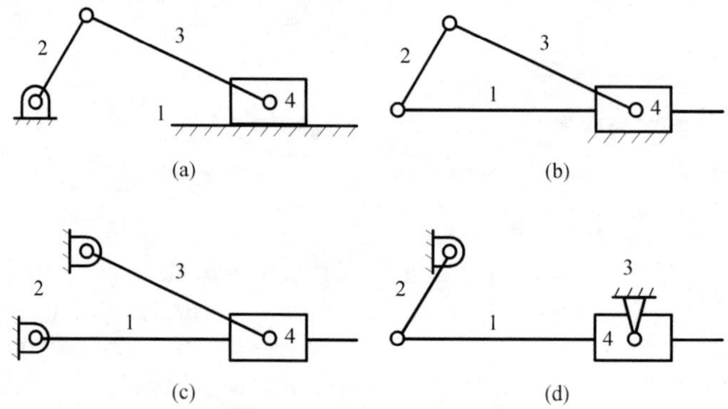

FIGURE 1.36 Inversions of the slider-crank linkage. The linkage in (a) is the original linkage and those in (b), (c), and (d) are the inversions.

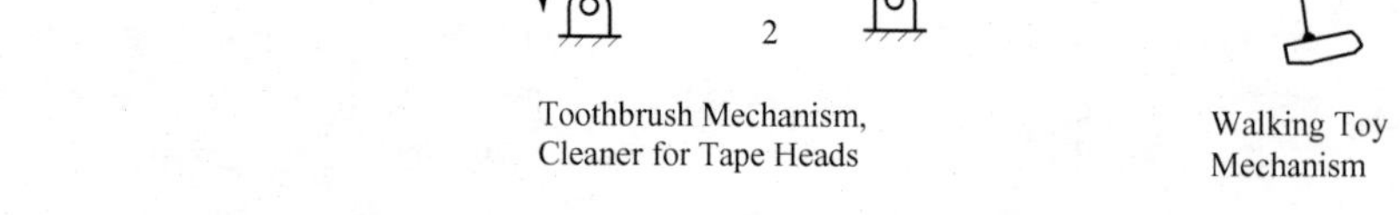

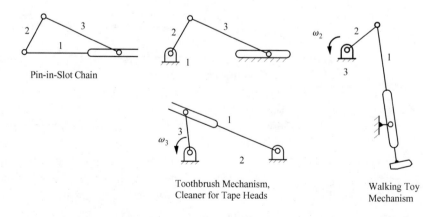

FIGURE 1.37 Uses of inversions of a pin-in-a-slot linkage.

1.13 REFERENCE FRAMES

It is necessary to be careful about reference frames when working with systems of many bodies. A reference frame can be attached to each body, and we can express positions, velocities, and accelerations relative to any or all of them.

As far as kinematics is concerned, there is no restriction on the use of reference frames. All frames are equally viable. We can invert from one frame to another without restriction.

It is only when we introduce forces and enter the realm of kinetics that a restriction appears. It is then that Newton's first and second laws, which relate motion properties to force, are true only if all motion properties are referred to a common reference frame. This common reference frame must be of a special type, called an inertial reference frame. For the purposes of mechanism design the inertial reference frame is almost always fixed to the earth. There are engineering problems, such as the design of mechanisms to be carried on spacecraft, for which the primary inertial reference frame must be used. The primary inertial reference frame is fixed relative to the "fixed" stars. A more complete discussion of inertial reference frames can be found in most texts on rigid-body dynamics. Einstein showed that in a space–time framework all reference frames are equally valid, thereby removing the Newtonian distinction between inertial reference frames and others. However, in the domain in which mechanical engineers usually operate, Newtonian mechanics provides a very accurate simplification of relativistic mechanics that is of great practical utility.

It is important to remember that position and motion properties can be expressed only relative to a reference frame. The habit of referring to a velocity or acceleration of a point relative to another point has been commonplace in this subject. This will be found to be convenient in some types of problems, particularly in graphical analysis, and there is no harm in using it provided that it is clearly understood that it is a shorthand expression for the velocity or acceleration of the first point relative to a reference frame in which the second point is fixed. The identity of that reference frame should always be kept in mind.

In many discussions in the following, it will be convenient to have a notation that explicitly states the reference frame in which a particular vector is expressed. A method that is often used is to indicate the reference frame by means of a superscript placed in front of the symbol for the vector. For example, ${}^1\boldsymbol{v}_A$ indicates the velocity of point A relative to reference frame 1, and ${}^2\boldsymbol{\omega}_3$ indicates the angular velocity of member 3 relative to reference frame 2.

Usually, we will associate one reference frame with each member of a linkage and will number it to agree with the number of the linkage. Reference frame 1 will usually refer to the fixed link. Unfortunately, the use of superscripts to indicate reference frames complicates expressions and makes them more difficult to read. For this reason, the superscripts will usually be dropped when all vectors are referred to reference frame 1.

1.14 MOTION LIMITS

A member of a linkage that is connected to the base by a revolute joint and that rotates completely as the linkage moves through its motion cycle is called a *crank*. Usually, there will also be members in the linkage that look exactly like cranks because they are connected to the base by a revolute, but these cannot rotate completely.

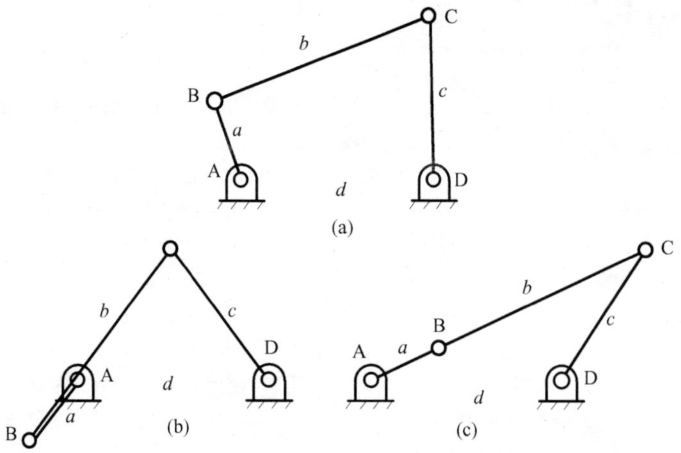

FIGURE 1.38 Limiting positions of joint C of a four-bar linkage.

Consider the four-bar linkage shown in Fig. 1.38a in which the link AB is a crank rotating fully about the revolute joint A. It will be assumed to rotate continuously in the counterclockwise direction. Complete revolution of this link requires that it pass through the positions shown in Figs. 1.38b and 1.38c. Now consider the motion of the revolute joint D. Prior to reaching the position of Fig. 1.38b link CD was rotating counterclockwise about joint D. In the position of Fig. 1.38b further rotation of CD about D in the counterclockwise direction is not possible. CD comes to rest and reverses its direction of motion. Similarly, before entering the position of Fig. 1.38c, the link CD is rotating clockwise about the joint D. In this position, further rotation in this direction is not possible and the link comes to rest and then reverses direction. The positions shown in Figs. 1.38b and 1.38c are called motion limit positions for the joint D. The link CD does not perform a full rotation but simply oscillates between these positions. That is, it is not a crank but a rocker.

1.15 ACTUATION

At this point it is necessary to introduce some terminology to describe the different members of a four-bar linkage. The fixed link, that is, the member to which the frame of reference is attached, is called the base or frame. The two members that are connected to the base by revolute joints are called turning links. The link that is jointed to both turning links and has no direct connection to the base is called the coupler. The turning links may be further distinguished by the terms crank, for a link capable of complete revolution relative to the base, and rocker, for a link that is only capable of oscillating between motion limits.

A linkage is actuated, or driven, by applying a force to one of its moving links or a torque to one of the axes. This may be done in a variety of ways, as is evident from the number of different types of commercial actuators (Fig. 1.39). It is frequently convenient for that powered link to be connected to the base by a revolute joint. The linkage may then be actuated by applying a torque to that link. In this case it is usually also preferable that the link be continuously rotatable since it may then be actuated by means of a continuously rotating motor. For this reason it is important to be able to identify four-bar linkages that have continuously rotatable joints and to locate those joints. This may be done by means of a simple set of rules called Grashof's rules.

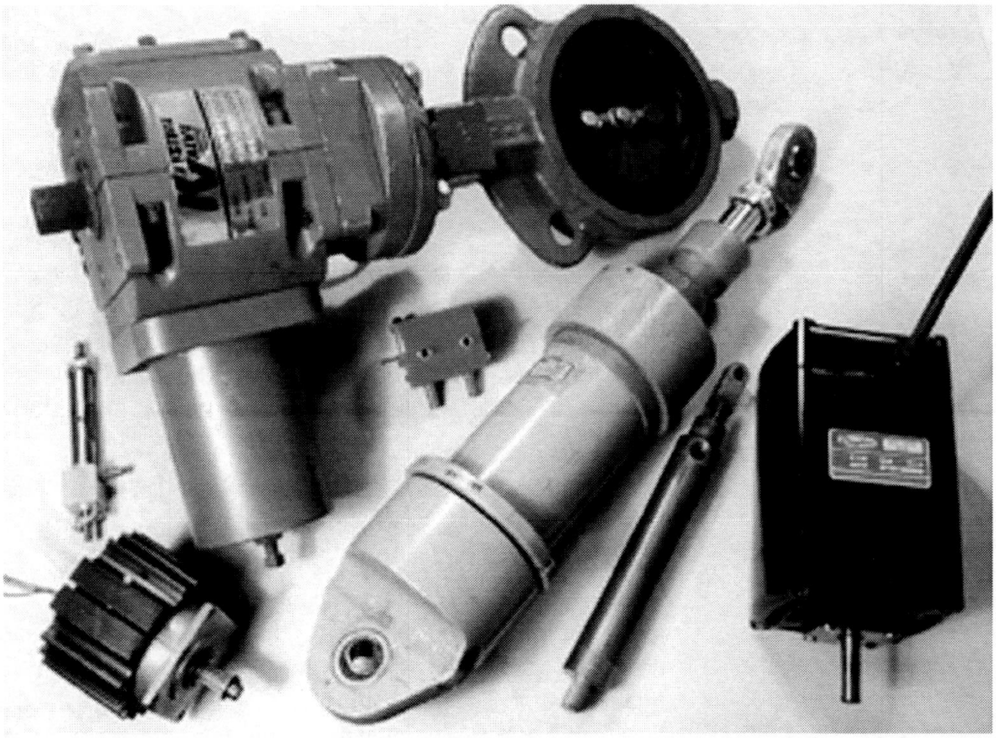

FIGURE 1.39 Photograph of a variety of actuators.

Grashof distinguished two fundamentally different types of four-bar linkage by means of the inequality

$$s + \ell < p + q \tag{1.6}$$

where, as shown in Fig. 1.40, s is the length of the shortest side, ℓ is the length of the longest side, and p and q are the lengths of the other two sides. Linkages that obey this inequality (Grashof type 1 linkages) have two joints that perform complete rotations and two that oscillate between motion limits. The two fully rotatable joints are those on either end of the shortest link. Linkages that do not obey the inequality (Grashof type 2 linkages) have no fully rotatable joints. All four joints then oscillate between motion limits.

The behavior of a linkage that obeys the Grashof inequality is strongly dependent on the locations of the fully rotatable joints relative to the base link. That is, it is dependent on the inversion of the linkage. The following additional rules distinguish three subtypes that have different behaviors:

1. If the shortest link is jointed to the base, the linkage is a crank–rocker (Fig. 1.41). The joint between the shortest link and the base is fully rotatable. Hence that link is a crank.

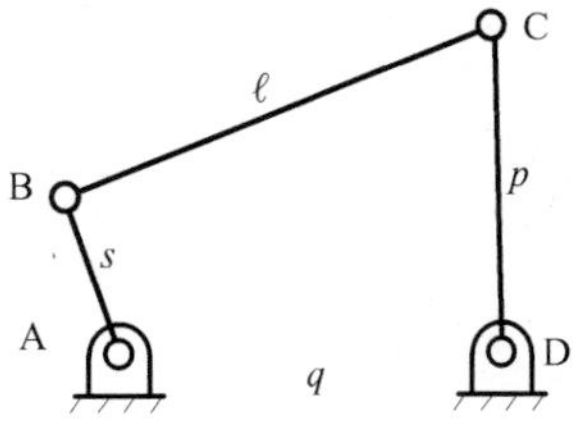

FIGURE 1.40 Nomenclature for Grashof's inequality.

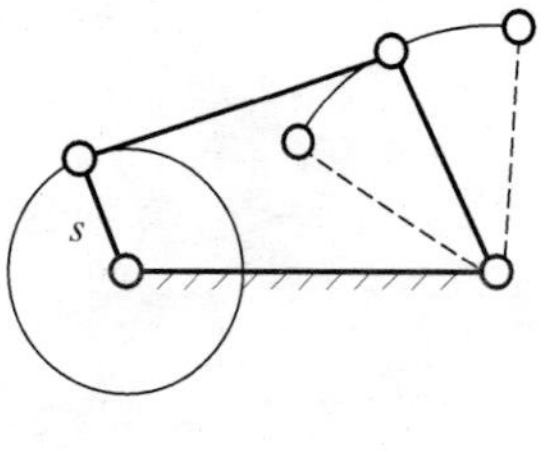

FIGURE 1.41 Crank–rocker subtype of Grashof type 1 linkage. This linkage type occurs when the shortest link is jointed to the base of the linkage.

The other fully rotatable joint connects that crank to the coupler. Hence the other joint connected to the base is not fully rotatable, and the link it connects to base oscillates. It is the rocker. A crank–rocker can be conveniently driven by the joint connecting the crank to the base (or the joint connecting the crank to the coupler).

2. If the shortest link is the base, both joints at the base are fully rotatable, and so both links connected to the base are cranks (Fig. 1.42). The linkage is a double-crank, also known as a drag-link. It may be conveniently actuated at either of the base joints.
3. If the shortest link is the coupler, neither base joint is fully rotatable (Fig. 1.43). The linkage is a type 1 double-rocker. Its behavior is different from that of type 2 double-rockers, those that do not satisfy the inequality, because in the type 1 linkage the two floating joints can rotate completely. The result is that the coupler tumbles, performing a complete rotation relative to the base. Either joint attached to the coupler can be driven by a continuous rotation motor. This mechanism is often used in oscillating fans. The angular motion of the coupler of a type 2 double-rocker is an oscillation relative to the base.

The Grashof inequality may be proved as follows:

Consider the linkage shown in Fig. 1.44a. To perform a complete rotation it must pass through the positions shown in Figs. 1.44b and 1.44c. Let a be the length AB, b the length BC, c the length CD, and d the length DA. It is assumed that

$$a < d$$

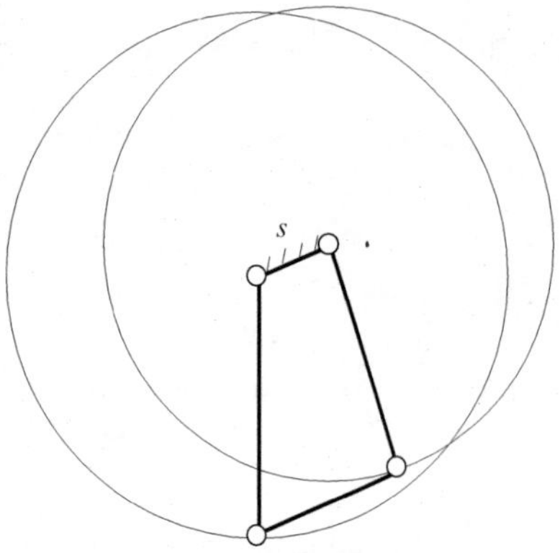

FIGURE 1.42 Double-crank subtype of Grashof type 1 linkage. This linkage type is also called a drag-link. It occurs when the shortest link is the base.

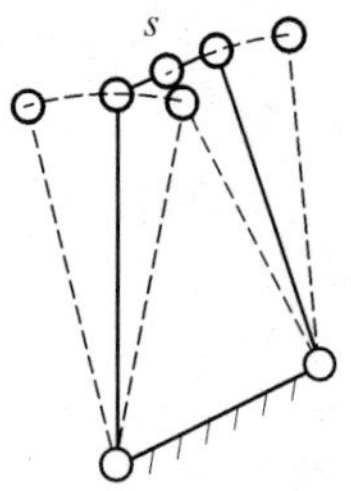

FIGURE 1.43 Type 1 double-rocker. This subtype occurs when the shortest link is the coupler.

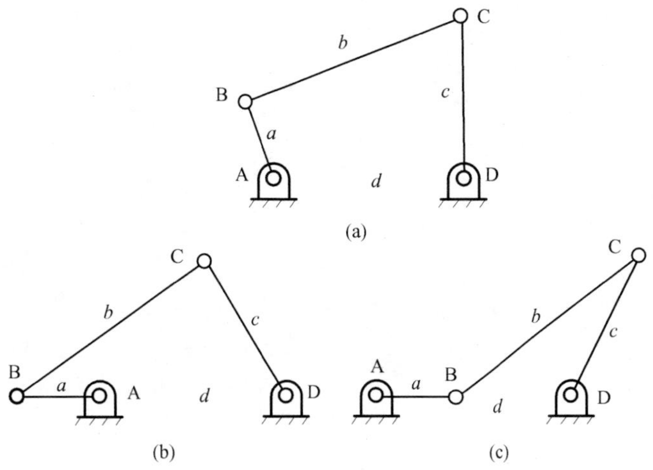

FIGURE 1.44 Extreme positions for a four-bar linkage.

The triangle inequality states that the sum of the lengths of any two sides of a triangle is greater than that of the third. This inequality may be applied three times to Fig. 1.44b to give

$$a + d < b + c \tag{a}$$

$$b < c + a + d \tag{b}$$

$$c < b + a + d \tag{c}$$

It may also be applied three times to Fig. 1.44c to give

$$d - a < b + c \tag{d}$$

$$b < c + d - a \tag{e}$$

$$c < b + d - a \tag{f}$$

Examination of these inequalities reveals that if (e) is true then (b) is certainly true, because the right-hand side of (b) is that of (e) plus $2a$. We say that Inequality (e) is stronger than Inequality (b). Hence Inequality (b) can be eliminated. Inequality (e) can be written in the form

$$a + b < c + d \tag{e$'$}$$

by adding a to both sides of the inequality.

Similarly, Inequality (c) is certainly true if Inequality (f) is true. Once again, the right-hand side of Inequality (c) is larger by $2a$. Inequality (f) assumes the form

$$a + c < b + d \tag{f$'$}$$

if a is added to both sides.

Inequality (d) is certainly true if Inequality (a) is true, since its left-hand side is less than that of Inequality (a) by $2a$. Hence, the six inequalities are reduced to three: (a), (e′), and (f′). Addition of both sides of Inequalities (a) and (e′) gives

$$2a + b + d < 2c + b + d$$

so that

$$a < c$$

Likewise, addition of both sides of Inequalities (a) and (f′) gives

$$2a + c + d < 2b + c + d$$

so that

$$a < b$$

Since a has also been assumed to be less than d, it follows that a is the shortest link length. Now, whichever of the inequalities (a), (e′), and (f′) has the longest link length on the left added to a will be the strongest. That is, the left-hand side is largest and the right-hand side is smallest. Whichever one this is assumes the form

$$s + \ell < p + q$$

where $s = a$ is the shortest link length, ℓ is the longest link length, and p and q are the two remaining link lengths.

It must be remembered that we assumed that a was less than d. It is also necessary to deal with the case in which a is larger than d. This can be handled by inverting the linkage so that AB becomes the base link and DB becomes the link jointed to it by the continuously rotatable joint. Pursuing the application of the triangle inequality then results in d being the shortest link length, and the Grashof inequality again results.

What we have shown so far is that the Grashof inequality is a necessary condition for the presence of a fully rotatable joint, and that joint is always at one end of the shortest link. Now, there can never be just one fully rotatable joint in a four-bar linkage. There must always be at least two. If there were just one fully rotatable joint, a topological contradiction would result when the rotations of AB relative to the other links after one cycle were to be considered. If that link were to perform a complete rotation about joint A, and joints B, C, and D were to oscillate back to their initial positions, AB would have performed a complete rotation relative to each of the other links. That is, it would have performed a complete revolution relative to BC. However, joint B has not performed a complete revolution but, rather, has performed zero net rotation. Hence there cannot be just one completely rotatable joint. Since we have shown that any completely rotatable joint must be at one end of the shortest link, it follows that there are two completely rotatable joints, and they are at either end of the shortest link. This completes the proof of Grashof's rules.

The shortest link of a type 1 linkage performs a complete revolution in each motion cycle relative to the other members. The net rotations of the fully rotatable joints on either end of that link cancel one another so that the net rotations of the remaining links relative to one another are zero for a complete motion cycle.

Of course, sometimes it is not necessary for the mechanism to perform a complete motion cycle. A restricted range of driving joint motion may be adequate. In that case linear actuators, such as hydraulic or pneumatic cylinders acting across the driving joint, may be used. However, it is still necessary that the driving joint not pass through a motion limit within the necessary range of motion. Grashof's rules are often useful in ensuring that this does not happen.

Occasionally it is necessary to drive a crank–rocker linkage by oscillating the rocker through a part of its motion range. In this case the linkage is usually referred to as a rocker–crank.

The reasons associated with the use of type 2 double-rocker linkages, or with the use of type 1 linkages driven by rockers rather than cranks, will be better understood after a discussion of linkage synthesis. Often, a linkage that is synthesized to produce a specific motion cannot be driven through that motion without the driving joint passing through a motion limit position. In that case, a solution might be to drive the other base joint.

A special case arises when

$$s + \ell = p + q$$

This is called a transition linkage or Grashof neutral linkage. In this case the linkage can assume a "flattened" configuration as shown in Fig. 1.45. When passing through this position, it can change from one to the other of the two configurations in which the linkage can be assembled with a given driving crank angle. In practice, this is often undesirable because it leads to unpredictable behavior and possibly large loads on the members and joints.

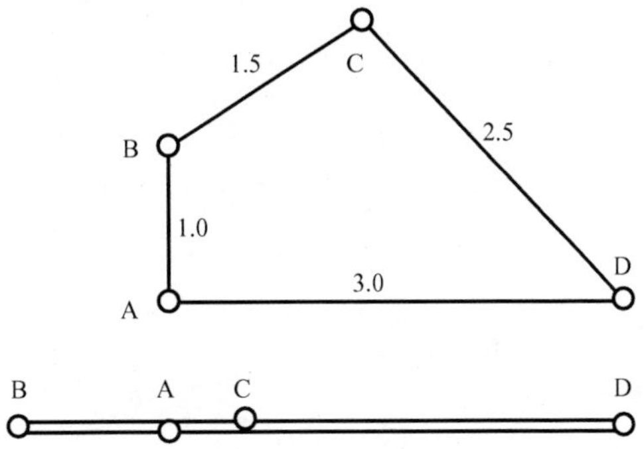

FIGURE 1.45 Grashof neutral linkage.

1.16 COUPLER-DRIVEN LINKAGES

In some applications linkages are actuated not by applying a force or torque to one of the links jointed to the base but rather by applying a force or torque to the coupler, the member that has no direct connection to the base. Everyday examples are not uncommon. Polycentric hinges for heavy doors or for automotive hood and trunk lids come to mind.

It is still important for a coupler-driven mechanism not to pass through a motion limit within the desired motion range. The motion limit positions for a coupler drive are quite different from those for a crank drive. They are the positions in which the two rotating links become parallel, as shown in Fig. 1.46. In these positions the angular motion of the coupler ceases and must reverse if motion is to continue. Elimination of these motion limits produces a linkage whose coupler performs a complete revolution relative to the base link. Because in a type 1 linkage the shortest link rotates completely relative to the remaining links, that link must be either the coupler or the base. It follows that the Grashof subtypes for which complete rotation of the coupler relative to the base is possible are the type 1 double-rocker and drag-link subtypes.

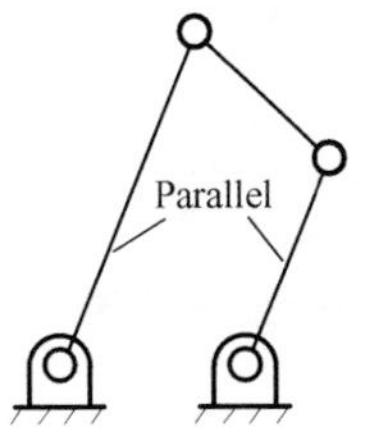

FIGURE 1.46 Motion limit for the coupler.

1.17 MOTION LIMITS FOR SLIDER-CRANK MECHANISM

The limits for a slider-crank mechanism can be determined by considering the combinations of link lengths that will cause the linkage to lock up. A typical slider-crank is shown in Fig. 1.47.

The limit positions of the rotating link a (Fig. 1.47) are determined when the coupler link is perpendicular to the direction of slider travel. The limiting assembly position occurs for one of the four geometries shown in Fig. 1.48.

From the four limit positions shown in Fig. 1.48, it is apparent that the following relationships must be maintained to allow the slider-crank to be driven through a full 360° rotation of the crank:

$$b > a$$

and

$$b - a > c$$

where

a = length of the crank

b = length of the coupler

c = offset distance from crank-ground pivot to slider pin (measured positive upward)

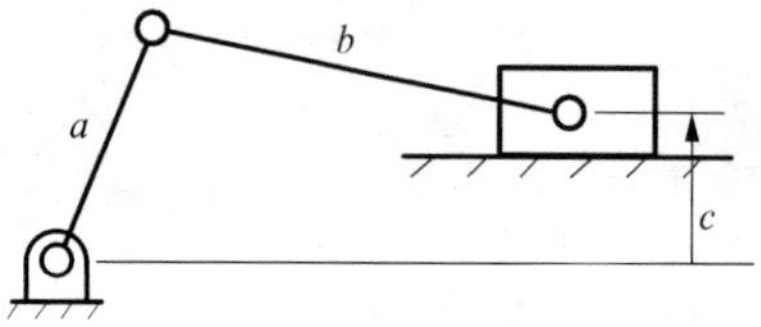

FIGURE 1.47 General slider-crank mechanism with offset dimension c.

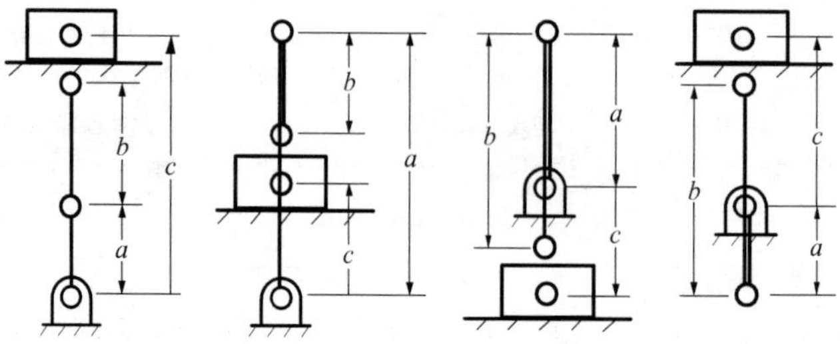

FIGURE 1.48 Positions for which the slider-crank mechanism cannot be assembled.

EXAMPLE 1.6
Using Grashof's Equation

In the Watt six-bar linkage shown in Fig. 1.49, the joint between links 5 and 6 must be placed on the arc indicated. Using Grashof's rule, determine the region for joint E that will allow full rotation of link 6. The critical dimensions are

$$AB = 1.14 \text{ in}, \; BC = 2.26 \text{ in}, \; AD = 1.74 \text{ in}$$

$$AF = 2.00 \text{ in}, \; DE = 2.68 \text{ in}, \; c = 1.09 \text{ in}$$

Solution

Consider first the slider–crank mechanism (ABC) even though the crank AB does not rotate 360°. Clearly, if the crank AB can rotate for 360°, it will not lock up in any intermediate position. Based on the dimensions given,

$$BC > AB$$

and $BC - AB = 1.12$. Therefore,

$$BC - AB > c$$

and the crank of the slider-crank mechanism can rotate a full 360°.

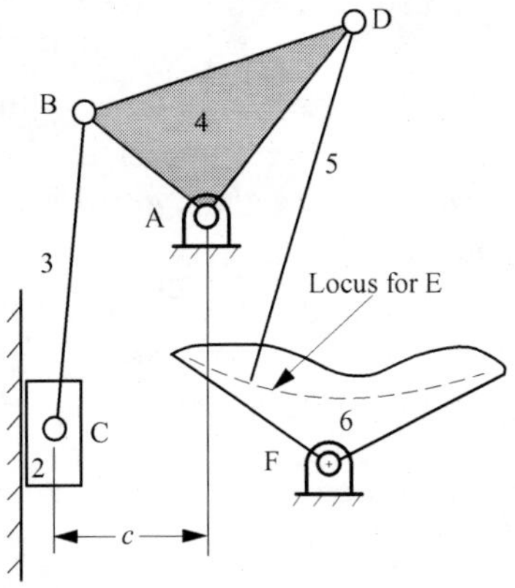

FIGURE 1.49 Mechanism for which point E is to be determined.

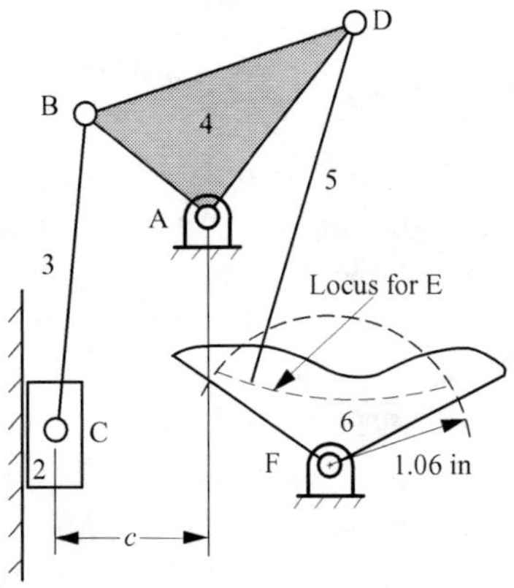

FIGURE 1.50 Allowable range for point E.

Next consider the crank–rocker mechanism ($ADEF$). For a crank–rocker, link 6 must be the crank, which means that EF must be the shortest link. The longest link is DE. Therefore, based on Eq. (1.6), for $ADEF$ to be a crank–rocker mechanism,

$$EF + DE < AF + AD$$

or

$$EF + 2.68 < 2.00 + 1.74$$

or

$$EF < 1.06 \text{ in}$$

The allowable range for E is shown in the Fig. 1.50.

1.18 INTERFERENCE

This is a topic that is often ignored in courses and texts on mechanism design. That is unfortunate since a full-cycle-motion capability can be prevented by topological interference even when Grashof's rules indicate that it is possible. An understanding of topological interference is particularly important at the present time, when linkages are often designed using CAD systems and their functioning checked by animation rather than by construction of physical models. It is very difficult to represent topological interference adequately on a planar display. For this reason, the reader is urged to construct models using cardboard and thumbtacks, or whatever other appropriate materials are available, when reading this section. That is the best way to gain an understanding of the nature of topological interference. There is also a tendency to regard interference as a result of the physical shape of the links and as something that can be avoided if enough care is given to the design of the physical link geometry. That is not what we are talking about here. Topological interference is a fundamental property of a linkage configuration in the same way that Grashof type is. It cannot be avoided by simply reshaping the links.

Topological interference really affects only the capability of executing a complete motion cycle using a rotary input. If oscillatory motion over a partial cycle is all that is required, topological interference can usually be circumvented.

The topological and physical limitation that the links cannot pass through each other creates difficulties in arranging for input and output motion transfer to and from type 1 linkages. When a simple, type 1 four-bar linkage is viewed as a three-dimensional structure with revolute joint axes of finite length, there is only one way in which it can be assembled to avoid any of the links or joint axes having to pass through each other. This is shown in Fig. 1.51. The problem is the fully rotatable joints.

The oscillatory joints of a type 1 linkage never pass through positions in which their joint angles ϕ and ψ, shown in Fig. 1.51, become either zero or π. If either one did so, the joint diagonally opposite it would be at a motion limit, preventing it from making a complete rotation. Consequently, the axes of these joints never cross the lines of the links BC and DA, so there is no interference. However, when joint A is fully rotated, the axis of joint B must cross the line DA and, since AB is the shortest link, it must cross between D and A. Likewise, when joint B is fully rotated, the axis of joint A will cross the line BC between B and C. Viewing the linkage from a direction normal to the joint axes, it can be seen that, if joint B is on one side of the link AB, the link DA must be on the other side, otherwise the link will cut the joint axis. Similarly, joint A must be on the opposite side of AB to link BC. It follows that, in the direction along the link axes, BC and DA are on either side of AB and

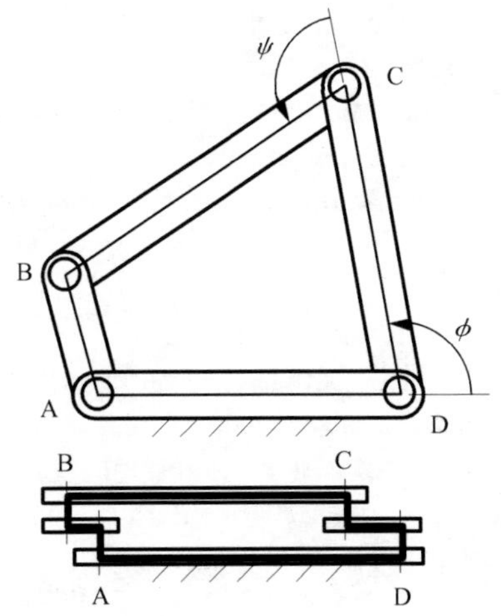

FIGURE 1.51 Assembly of type 1 linkage needed to avoid interference.

CD. This may seem to be dependent on the physical realization of the links, but it is, in fact, a fundamental topological property of the loop.

The simplest situation for motion transfer is when both input and output motions are rotary. Motion can then be transferred into and out of the linkage by means of shafts attached to the turning links. Interference constrains the arrangement of the input and output shafts, as shown in Fig. 1.52. If the linkage is a *crank-rocker,* both shafts must enter from the same side to avoid interference between the shafts and the coupler link. Notice that the shafts must pass through the base link to get to the turning links, which are on the inside of the linkage in this inversion. Physically, the shafts are supported in bearings mounted in the base link.

If the linkage is a *drag-link*, the shafts may be attached directly to the turning links, one on either side, since those links are on the outside of the linkage in this inversion. However, if this is done, the fixed bearings may be moved to the outside, essentially turning the

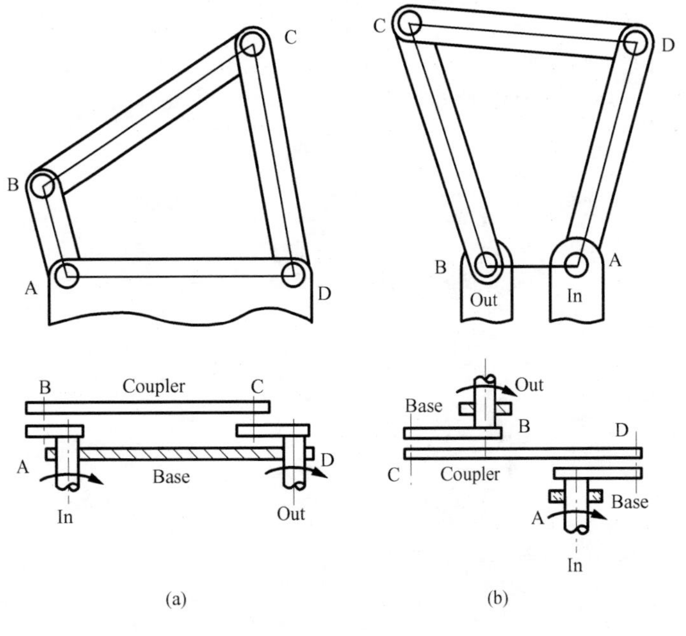

FIGURE 1.52 Shaft drive of (a) crank-rocker and (b) drag-link linkages.

base link inside out. The base link becomes a pair of fixed bearing mounts on either side of the linkage, as shown in Fig. 1.52b. A drag-link linkage must always be mounted in this manner to achieve full-cycle motion, regardless of the means of input or output, since otherwise the coupler must pass through the base.

The discussion of rotary input and output to *type 1 double-rocker* linkage will be left until later since it is not possible to achieve full-cycle motion with a crank drive in this type of linkage.

A more complex case is that in which the input is rotary and motion must be transferred from a point on the coupler link. This is easy enough to arrange in the crank-rocker case, as shown in Fig. 1.53, since the base and coupler are on the outside of the linkage.

Much more difficult is the case in which motion must be transferred from a point on a crank or on the coupler of a drag-link. Because the coupler moves between the cranks there is no way to avoid interference of a shaft coming off the coupler with those cranks in full-cycle motion. Furthermore, because the two parts of the base are outside the cranks, there is also a problem of interference with the base. This latter problem also affects the transfer of motion to or from points on the cranks.

It is possible to circumvent the interference problem for motion transfer from points on a crank by "doubling" the crank. This is shown in Fig. 1.54. The crank is essentially duplicated on the outside of the base bearing. A shaft rigidly fixed to both the crank and the duplicate passes through the bearing forming the base joint and ensures that both move together. This effectively makes points on the crank available outside the base, where additional links can be attached at motion transfer joints. In this way, multiloop linkages such as that shown in Fig. 1.55 can be built up and driven by the driving crank of the master drag-link loop.

If the transfer point is reasonably close to the base joint of the crank, the result in Fig. 1.54a can be achieved by using a bearing of sufficiently large diameter to encompass the transfer point. This is shown in Fig. 1.54b.

There is no simple way to transfer motion from a point on the coupler of the drag-link without preventing full-cycle mobility. It can be done by splitting one of the joints between the crank and coupler, allowing the linkage loop to pass through itself. This requires the addition of at least one auxiliary link, so the mechanism, strictly speaking, is no longer a four-bar one. The yoke shown in Fig. 1.55 carries the two bearings that replace the simple joint of the original linkage. It is undesirable to leave this link unconstrained, so it is usual to add a second link connecting it to base, as shown in the figure. This allows the coupler to

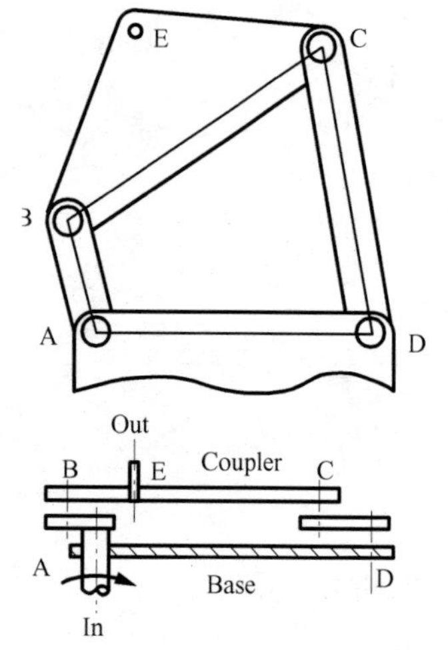

FIGURE 1.53 Transfer of motion from a point on the coupler of crank-rocker mechanism.

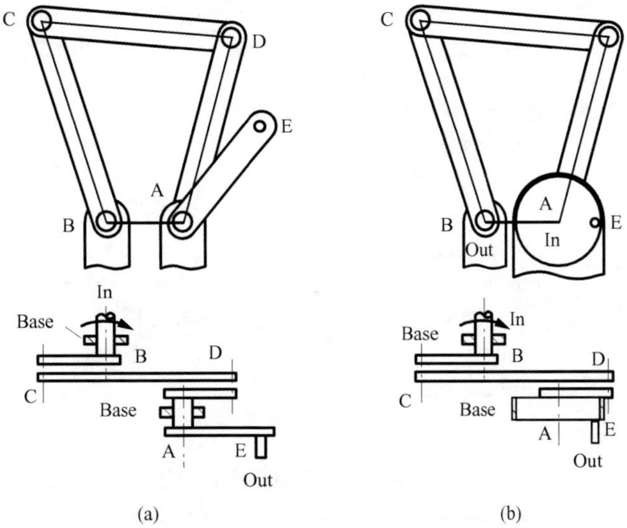

FIGURE 1.54 Motion transfer from a point on the crank of a drag-link.

be moved outside the crank. However, it is still not possible to transfer motion directly from a point on the coupler because of interference with the yoke. For this reason, the coupler is doubled in the same way that the crank was in Fig. 1.54, producing the six-bar arrangement shown. As can be seen, this is quite an extensive modification!

The situation for a coupler drive, in which the driving torque is applied to the coupler link and the output motion is taken off that same link, is quite similar. The two linkage types that can, in principle, perform complete motion cycles in the coupler drive mode are the *type 1 double-rocker* and *drag-link* types. Both present a problem because the base and coupler are inside the cranks in the basic loop. The type 1 double-rocker can be made to allow full-cycle motion, without interference, by doubling the coupler.

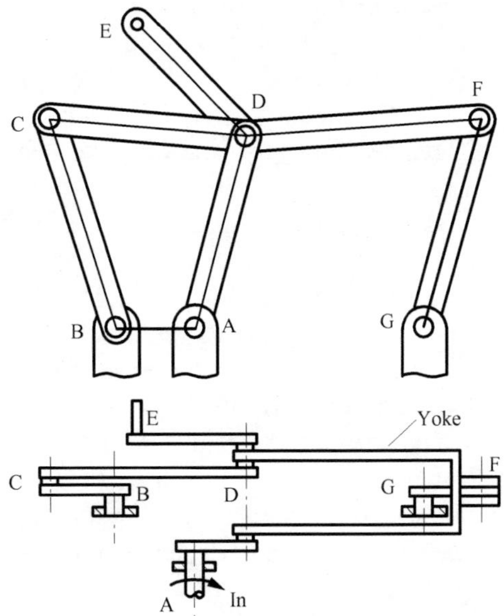

FIGURE 1.55 Six-bar modification to achieve motion transfer from the coupler of a drag-link linkage.

Once again, the drag-link presents additional problems because of the necessity of splitting the base resulting in the base being outside the cranks. Coupler-driven full-cycle motion of a simple drag-link is not possible because of interference. The six-bar arrangement of Fig. 1.55 can be used for full-cycle motion that is identical to that of the drag-link with coupler drive.

All of the foregoing discussion relates only to full-cycle motion, that is, to motion in which the driving link performs a complete rotation. If oscillation through a partial motion cycle is adequate for the application, interference can always be avoided by modifying the physical shapes of the links. This is true even for the drag-link type. Type 2 linkages can also be used in this mode. One only has to ensure that it is not necessary for such linkages to pass through motion limit positions of the driving link when traversing the desired segment of the motion cycle.

1.19 PRACTICAL DESIGN CONSIDERATIONS

1.19.1 Revolute Joints

A rubbing contact between two members, here called a kinematic joint, is also known as a bearing. Design of bearings to perform satisfactorily for long periods under load is the focus of the subject of tribology. Although an in-depth treatment of tribology is beyond the scope of this book, it is necessary for the mechanism designer to be aware of the limitations that may be placed on a design by the necessity of having bearings.

Revolute joints perform well under many conditions. As with all the lower pairs, the distribution of contact ideally over a surface distributes and normally slows wear. The closed geometry of the joint provides good conditions for trapping lubricant between the joint surfaces.

A revolute joint that is in continuous, unidirectional rotation at relatively high speeds can enter a regime called hydrodynamic lubrication in which the relative movement of the bearing elements acts to entrain lubricant and maintain a separation between the solid journal elements. The entrainment action creates an area of elevated pressure in the lubricant that supports the load on the bearing. The establishment of hydrodynamic action is often assisted by pumping lubricant into the bearing. In principal, once hydrodynamic action is established, there is no contact between the solid bearing elements, and hence there is no wear. The effective friction is solely due to viscous resistance in the lubricant and is, therefore, low. Typically wear occurs only when the machine is started up and shut down. The crankshaft support bearings and the bearings between the crankshaft and the connecting rods of an automotive engine are typical examples of hydrodynamic bearings.

Another type of bearing that has some of the characteristics of a hydrodynamic bearing, but is free of some of its limitations, is a hydrostatic bearing. Here the objective remains the same, to carry the bearing load by a pressure differential in the lubricant and to maintain separation between solid bearing journals at all times. However, in this case, the pressure to support the bearing load is provided by pumping the lubricant into the bearing on the loaded side at an elevated pressure. Hydrostatic bearings do not rely on continuous rotation to maintain bearing action. Therefore, they can be used when the rotation speeds are low, or when the direction of rotation reverses. They do tend to be expensive, because close tolerances are needed to minimize lubricant leakage out of the bearing and because of the need for a relatively high-capacity lubricant pump. Hydrostatic bearings are usually used for the main rotor bearings on large turbogenerator sets.

When the speed of rotation is slow, or reverses, a greased bushing or a solid contact bearing may be used. These bearing types are geometrically similar and differ only in the use of a liquid lubricant. Usually that lubricant will be a viscous grease. The high viscosity both promotes some hydrodynamic action and diminishes leakage out the sides of the bearing. Frequent lubrication is, nevertheless, necessary for this type of bearing. The materials should also be chosen to provide adequate performance and wear resistance even in the absence of lubricant.

Solid contact bearings rely on the choice of contacting materials to provide both low friction and wear resistance. Teflon has a low coefficient of friction with most metals. It is also relatively hard and highly temperature resistant for a plastic material. Consequently, it is frequently chosen for one element of a bearing pair. Other plastic materials such as nylon and delrin are also used. Note that the same material should never be used for both journal members of a solid bearing pair because journals with similar materials can weld together at small asperities when driven under load, resulting in high friction and rapid wear. This is why bronze bushings are frequently partnered with steel journals for greased bearings. Generally harder materials wear better than softer ones. Hence steel is preferred to aluminum for bearing journals. One final caution is that some materials should never be lubricated with petroleum-based lubricants. Nylon tends to absorb oil and swell and fail. Solid lubricants such as graphite or molybdenum disulphide can be used when petroleum-based lubricants are not an option because of material or other constraints.

Yet another alternative for the support of rotary motion is provided by rolling element bearings. Here the load is transferred between the journals by hardened steel balls or rollers trapped between the journals. The contact between one of these rolling elements and the journal is, of course, a higher pair joint. However, the combined effect of all the balls or rollers rolling on the journals is kinematically equivalent to a revolute joint. Lubricants are used, but the way in which they work is somewhat different from that of lubricants in other types of joints. This kind of action is called boundary lubrication. The lubricant is squeezed to very high pressures between the rolling element and journal and plays a role in distributing the load over both elements. The contact between a ball and journal is a point, if both are perfectly rigid, and that between a roller and journal is a line. In either case the load is ideally locally infinite. Of course, elastic deformation of the elements acts to distribute the load over a local area. The boundary lubrication mechanism assists in this load distribution.

Because pure rolling contact does not involve sliding of one member over another, wear, of the type found in other bearings, is not an issue for rolling contact bearings. Also, the effective friction can be very low, and rolling element bearings work well with motion cycles that stop or reverse. However, the very high contact stresses in the elements require very hard, and very accurately manufactured, rolling elements and journals. Consequently, rolling element bearings can be relatively expensive. They are also relatively bulky and are not well suited to situations where space is limited. The principal failure mode of a rolling element bearing is fatigue owing to the high contact, or Hertzian, stresses in the rolling elements and journals. This leads to subsurface cracking and eventual spalling, or breaking out of pieces from the surface of a rolling element. Once this process starts, the bearing tends to fail quite rapidly. The nature of the failure mode is such that all rolling elements have finite life. Unfortunately that life is statistically distributed over a significant range, making it relatively difficult to predict failure and apply preventive maintenance procedures to change bearings before failure occurs.

1.19.2 Prismatic Joints

Compared to revolute joints, prismatic joints are much more problematic in their application. As will be shown, they are sensitive to the direction and manner of load application. Also, a prismatic joint cannot be infinite in length so all prismatic joints experience motion reversals, which precludes the use of fully established hydrodynamic lubrication.

If a sliding joint is loaded by a connecting rod, as in a slider-crank mechanism, the loading force is applied along the line through the bearing center, as shown in Fig. 1.56a. The friction force along the joint direction is proportional to the normal force. If the friction force exceeds the component of the applied force along the slide direction the joint will jam. That is, if the angle between the axis of the connecting rod and the normal to the joint direction is less than the friction angle

$$\phi = \tan^{-1} \mu$$

where μ is the coefficient of friction, the joint will jam.

Figure 1.56b shows another effect that may lead to jamming of the slider. Applying a load offset from the slider surfaces results in an applied moment that must be resisted by a couple composed of normal forces, as shown in the figure. In a real prismatic joint, there must be a small clearance between the members. The application of the offset force, $\boldsymbol{F}$, causes the block to angulate slightly relative to the shaft so that contact actually occurs only at the ends of the joint. Thus, the block is subject to normal and friction forces at the locations shown in the figure. The joint will jam if

$$F < \mu N$$

However, for horizontal force and moment equilibrium

$$2\mu N = F \text{ and } aF = bN$$

Therefore, the joint will jam if

$$b < 2\mu a$$

Offset loads and loading directions at large angles to the joint direction also combine to produce jamming.

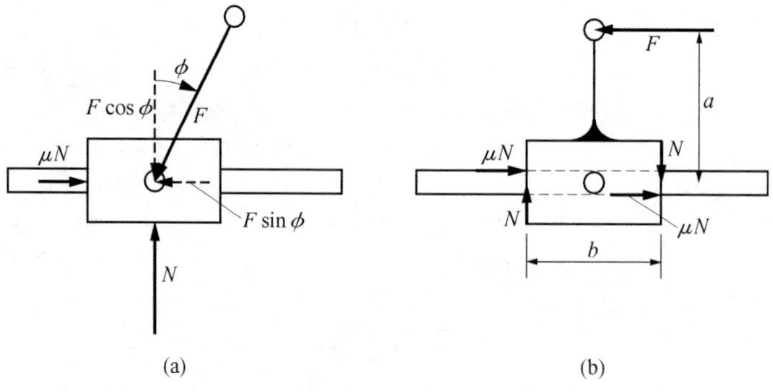

FIGURE 1.56 Jamming in sliding joints. In (a), the slide will jam if the angle between the applied force F and the direction of sliding becomes too great. The slider will jam when the angle ϕ is less than $\tan^{-1}\mu$. In (b), the slider will jam because of the offset force if $2\mu a < b$.

Jamming is best avoided by shunning designs that have sliding joints with poor loading geometries. If such a geometry cannot be avoided, jamming caused by offset loading may be alleviated by increasing the length of the prismatic joint, if space allows. Increasing b until it is greater than any expected value of $2\mu a$ should avoid the problem. Of course, reducing the effective coefficient of friction is effective in either case. That might be done by lubrication, or by choice of a low-friction material combination. Lubrication as a solution may be problematic if jamming is a catastrophic failure mode. Sooner or later, the joint is likely to have too little lubricant.

The best solution, in many cases, is to use a rolling contact joint to minimize the effective coefficient of friction. Roller on rail configurations that are kinematically equivalent to a prismatic joint are available. A ball bushing is a relatively inexpensive and compact device. It must roll on a smooth, hardened steel shaft. A ball bushing does not provide any restraint on twisting about the shaft axis. For this reason, when ball bushings are used, the bushings and shafts are usually configured in parallel pairs.

1.19.3 Higher Pairs

Pure rolling contact may not require any lubrication, or special attention, as is the case of the contact between a vehicle tire and the ground. Sliding contacts, however, can result in very rapid wear, jamming, and failure unless they are carefully designed and lubricated. Combined rolling and sliding, as in a gear mesh, also requires careful attention to lubrication at any but the lowest loads and speeds. Gears that carry significant loads and power flows are normally enclosed in gearboxes to allow lubricant to be actively splashed or pumped over them. The gearbox allows lubricant to run off the gears and collect in the bottom of the box, or sump, for recycling.

Cam and follower pairs are particularly demanding with respect to lubrication, especially if flat-faced followers are used. The valve timing cams in an automotive engine are housed in a sealed chamber so they can be bathed in lubricant. Oil is often pumped through the rocker shaft to ports in the faces of the followers to ensure lubrication and some hydrodynamic action over the rubbing surfaces.

1.19.4 Cams vs. Linkages

As will be seen, both cams and linkages are used to generate irregular motions. As solutions to design problems requiring irregular motions, they each have their strengths and weaknesses. Cams are usually easier to design geometrically but much harder to make work satisfactorily. The lubrication issues involved in rubbing contact have already been referred to. In low volumes, cams are expensive to manufacture. However, if the volume of parts needed is high enough to justify manufacture of a die and production of the cams by near net shape methods such as injection molding, die casting, forging, or powder metallurgy, cam mechanisms can be very economical. Cams are particularly convenient for timing mechanisms, such as valve lifters. They are easily designed to dwell in a set position for a set portion of the motion cycle.

Linkages are robust and inexpensive, particularly if only revolute joints are needed. They are economical to manufacture in either large or small volumes. Lubrication is, relatively speaking, very easy. However, linkages do not allow as much freedom to the designer as cams. It is quite difficult to design a high-quality dwell mechanism using only linkages. Also, linkages often consume more space than cam mechanisms.

Given an irregular motion generation problem, most experienced machine designers will seek a linkage solution first, unless the problem is clearly better suited to a cam.

1.19.5 Actuation

Introduction Linkages and mechanisms are used to transfer mechanical work from a generating site to a site at which it produces a useful effect. An actuator is a motor or other device that generates mechanical work in a controlled manner. Traditionally, machines for complex operations involving many subfunctions, like printing or packaging, were powered by a single motor, referred to as the *prime mover*, with all of the subfunctions being performed by linkages of various types. The prime mover was sometimes a large electric motor, but it could equally be an internal combustion engine, a steam engine, or a water turbine. Once the system was tuned, timing was not an issue since everything was powered in lockstep off the same power train. This type of machine can achieve rapid cycle rates and hence high productivity. It is an appropriate design when motors are expensive and inflexible in their operation. It is still the best configuration for very high production rates such as when producing beverage cans or loading tissues into a package.

Improvements in actuator technologies have resulted in relatively compact and inexpensive devices that can be controlled with precision. Combining these with digital control technology has made it possible to replace mechanical coordination via linkages with digital coordination. This has several potential advantages. Production and other machines can be much more flexible in their operation. It is no longer necessary to design and build a machine especially to fill, cap, and label bottles of a particular shape. Rather, the same machine can be reprogrammed to fill a different type of bottle. The only mechanical changes needed are relatively minor tooling articles. Likewise, a production line can accommodate several different models of automobile, and many options on each, by use of digital reconfiguration for each model and option.

There is a large number of different actuator types available. We will review only the three most commonly used types: electric actuators, hydraulic actuators, and pneumatic actuators. In-depth discussion of these technologies is beyond the scope of this book.

Operational Stability A useful way of characterizing the behavior of an actuator is to plot force, for a linear actuator, or torque, for a rotary actuator, against speed. The shape of this characteristic curve and its relationship to the corresponding characteristic of the load have important implications for the behavior of the actuator under load. Consider the torque–speed curve shown on Fig. 1.57. The torque–speed demand curve of a typical load is also shown. In many applications, but not all, load increases with speed. Since the actuator torque is equal to the load at point A, the system will tend to settle into that operating point. If the speed increases above ω_A, the load torque will exceed the actuator torque and the system will tend to decelerate back to speed ω_A. Conversely, if the speed decreases below ω_A, the actuator torque will exceed the load torque and the system will tend to accelerate back to point A. This is an example of stable operation. Note also that this actuator has

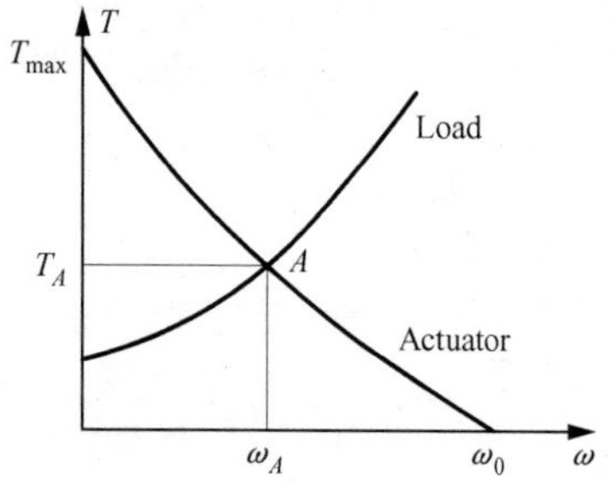

FIGURE 1.57 Torque–speed characteristics of actuator and load for stable operation.

a finite maximum speed, which is the speed ω_0 at which the actuator torque drops to zero. ω_0 is called the *no-load speed.*

Consider now the situation depicted on Fig. 1.58. Here the actuator torque–speed characteristic increases in torque with increasing speed. The load torque does not increase as rapidly with speed. The operating point at which the actuator torque is equal to the load is point B. If the system is operating at point B, and the speed fluctuates even slightly higher than ω_B, the actuator torque will exceed the load torque and the system will accelerate to even higher speed. Obviously the speed will continue to increase without bound and the system will *run away*, possibly resulting in catastrophic failure. Conversely, if the speed fluctuates even slightly below ω_B, the load torque will exceed the actuator torque and the system will decelerate further. Very quickly the speed will drop to zero and the system will *stall*. It is not possible for the system to operate at point B. This is an example of an unstable operating point.

Many actuators display torque–speed curves that climb to a peak and then decline to zero with increasing speed. With a given load they may display both stable and unstable operating points. An internal combustion engine is a good example. A change gearbox is necessary in an automobile to keep the operating point on the declining side of the torque–speed curve. If the operating point shifts to the opposite side of the peak of the characteristic, the engine will stall. The torque T_S that the actuator produces at zero speed is called the *stall torque*.

Electric Actuation There are a truly bewildering variety of electrical actuators on the market today. The use of new technologies, such as solid-state power switching technologies, has allowed the introduction of new architectures and new uses for traditional architectures. New permanent magnet technologies have resulted in greatly improved performance for some classes of electrical actuator.

Electric motors work by virtue of the force experienced by a conductor carrying a current in the presence of a magnetic field. The magnetic field may be generated by a winding or by permanent magnets. The field interacts with the conductors in a second winding to produce torque. The mechanically fixed structure is called the *stator.* The rotating structure is called the *rotor*. If the rotor carries windings it is also called an *armature.* To produce a continuous torque, the electric field must typically rotate relative to the structure that generates it so that it maintains a fixed relationship to the magnetic field.

Electric machines actually produce a very modest torque or force in proportion to their weight. However, an electric motor may operate at very high speeds. These characteristics mean that, if reduction of weight or bulk is important, the output of the electric motor must be reduced in speed, and proportionately increased in torque, by means of a mechanical transmission. Alternatively, if motor size and weight are not a problem, a motor with a very large frame size and a large number of poles may be used. The speed of an electric

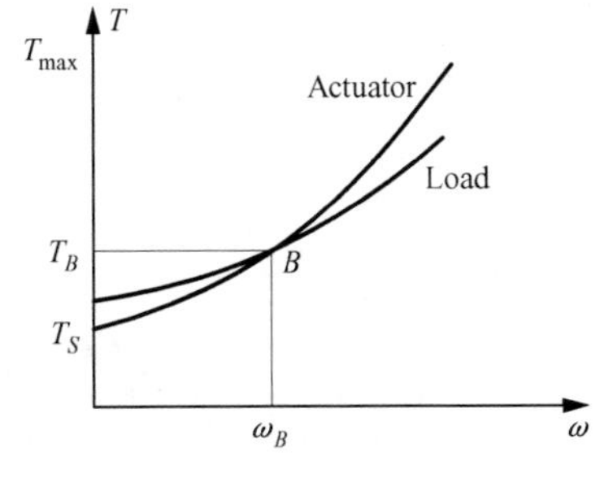

FIGURE 1.58 Torque–speed characteristics of actuator and load resulting in unstable operation.

motor is inversely proportional to the number of poles used in the field winding. It is easier to accommodate a large number of poles in a larger frame size. Consequently, smaller motors tend to have higher operating speeds.

Commutated Motors A commutator is a mechanical switch that is used to switch the current-carrying coils in the motor armature so that the torque produced is always in the same direction. The armature is the switched winding of the motor. Traditionally it was the winding on the rotor: the part of the motor mounted on the rotating shaft. In some modern motors the armature winding is in the stator: the part of the motor mounted to the fixed housing. A mechanical commutator is formed of a number of conducting segments mounted to form a cylindrical surface on the rotor, against which two or more "brushes" bear. The current is passed between the brush and whatever segment with which it is in contact. At one time the brushes consisted of bundles of fine brass wires (hence the name). Now they are solid blocks of conducting material, usually carbon.

Brushes eventually wear out and must be replaced. There may also be arcing between the brushes and the commutator segments producing radio interference and other problems. Commutation may also be done by solid-state electronic switching. Hall effect sensors are used to trigger the switches at the appropriate times. At the same time, the rotor and stator are reversed, with the field being on the rotor. Use of permanent magnets rather than field windings means that there is no need for any electrical connections to the rotor. The rotor magnets are commonly made from rare-earth materials that can maintain higher field strengths than traditional ferrous magnets. The result is a brushless direct current (DC) motor that works like a commutated motor, but it is mechanically simpler and more rugged and reliable.

All electric motors that run off direct current are commutated, whether by mechanical commutators or solid-state switches. Synchronous motors are an important class of motors that run off alternating current and are also commutated. The speed of a synchronous motor is locked to the frequency of the alternating current supply. This is useful in applications in which it is desired that the motor run at constant speed. Such applications range from electric clocks all the way up to large mill motors.

There are differences in the performance characteristics of mechanically commutated DC motors depending on the connectivity relationship between the field and armature windings. The field may be excited by an external source, in which case the motor is called externally excited. More often the field is excited by the same source as the current in the armature. If the field and armature windings are connected in parallel, the motor is called a *shunt wound* motor. If the torque produced by the motor is plotted against rotation speed, a shunt wound motor will have a characteristic performance curve like that shown in Fig. 1.59. It will have relatively constant torque over its typical operating range. The torque will eventually decline with speed, and there will be a finite maximum speed at which the torque becomes zero.

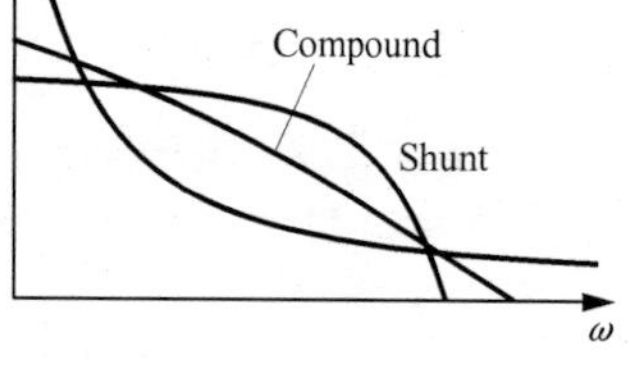

FIGURE 1.59 Torque–speed characteristics typical of DC motors of the shunt wound, series wound, and compound types.

If the field windings are connected in series with the armature windings, the machine is called a *series wound* motor. This results in somewhat different performance characteristics, as shown in Fig. 1.59. The torque at stall or low speed is very high, with a sharp initial drop-off with increasing speed. Ideally the torque never drops to zero. The motor continues to produce some torque even at very high speed. Consequently, operation is unstable at no load. This can be very dangerous in practice if a series wound DC machine is allowed to run with no load. What then happens is the motor "runs away," continuing to accelerate until the stresses produced by centrifugal forces reach the mechanical strength limits of the rotor components. At that point the rotor explodes, with very destructive consequences. Despite this risk, the characteristics of series wound motors are attractive for use as traction motors in electrically powered vehicles, with the motor being directly coupled mechanically to the load. In principle, a traction motor is never operated at no load.

What is often done, either to achieve series-machine-like behavior, but with a finite maximum speed, or to otherwise optimize the performance characteristics for a given application, is to use a hybrid configuration in which some of the field windings are in series with the armature and some are in parallel. The result is called a *compound wound* motor.

At this point it should also be pointed out that most electric motors cannot be run continuously at *stall*, which is zero speed, or at very low speed. This is because in those circumstances the motor is producing little, if any, mechanical power, and the current through the windings is limited only by their resistance. The power generated by passage of current through the windings is converted entirely into heat. The current is high, because there is no back emf to oppose its flow. The high current at stall is the reason for the high starting torque, since torque is proportional to armature current in these machines. However, the heat generated is the product of the square of the current and the winding resistance. If the motor is held at, or near, stall for an appreciable length of time, heat will typically build up until it damages the motor. This may happen by burning insulation, melting windings, or by heating permanent magnets beyond their Curie point. If heated beyond the Curie temperature, a permanent magnet loses its magnetism, and the motor ceases to function.

The ability of the motor to operate near stall may be seen to be a matter of heat transfer. If the motor is sufficiently well cooled to be able to dissipate the heat generated at stall without a damaging rise in temperature, it may be operated in that regime. That is important for some classes of machine, including industrial robots. Motors that can be operated at or near stall are called *torque motors*.

Noncommutated Motors There are also several types of electric motor that do not use commutators. The most commonly used type is the induction motor. In this type of alternating current (AC) motor, the armature has a simple "squirrel cage" configuration. The armature current necessary to produce torque is induced by the alternating current in the stator winding. Induction motors have torque–speed characteristics like that shown in Fig. 1.60. For stable operation it is necessary to operate the motor on the high-speed side of the

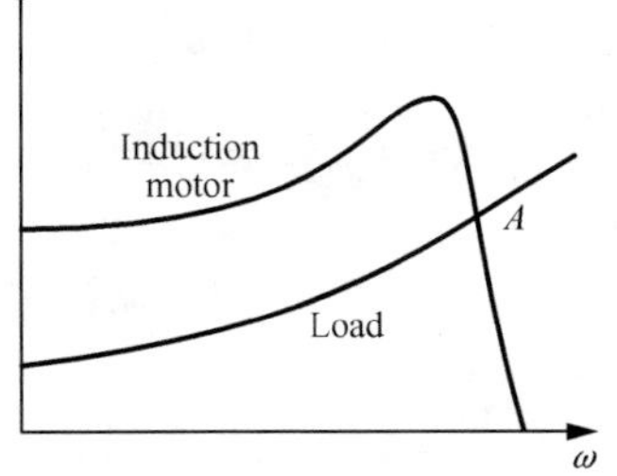

FIGURE 1.60 Torque–speed characteristic of induction motors. With the load characteristic shown, the motor will be self-starting and will operate stably at point A.

hump in the torque–speed curve so that a decrease in speed produces an increase in torque. In contrast to the other types of electric motor we have discussed, the torque is typically not at its highest at stall. In some applications this may mean that the motor cannot be started under load but must be started with reduced load and brought up to a speed above that at which peak torque occurs before the load is applied. This may require use of a clutch to unload the motor. More typically the load torque is also low at start-up, as shown in Fig. 1.60, and the motor will start under load and reach a stable operating point. Induction motors are very popular in industrial applications because they are simple, rugged, and relatively inexpensive. They are best suited to situations in which constant speed need only be approximated. The steep slope of the torque–speed curve on the high-speed side of the hump means that speed will not change much, regardless of load fluctuations.

Another type of motor that does not use a commutator is commonly referred to as a stepping motor. In this type of motor, the torque is generated magnetically, rather than electromagnetically, as in other types of motor. The motor has a number of discrete, equally spaced stable positions. Feeding a voltage pulse to it causes it to rotate to the next stable position. Consequently, stepping motors are very useful for indexing. It is not necessary to provide a means of keeping track of position since the position of the motor is known simply by counting the number of pulses supplied to it.

Solenoids A solenoid is a simple, cylindrical winding that when energized by a direct current draws a ferromagnetic core into itself. Solenoids are used as simple, two-state, linear actuators.

Solenoids are not suited to providing variable force or stroke. Electric linear actuators for long or controllable stroke are compound devices using rotary motors in combination with power screws, racks and pinions, or similar mechanisms.

Speed Control The advent of solid-state power-switching devices has revolutionized electric actuator control. Pulse-width modulators and phase-controlled rectifiers make it possible to control DC motors without the energy losses inherent in earlier methods, which basically used potentiometer configurations. Variable frequency inverters that convert DC into AC, or AC into AC with different frequencies, allow synchronous and induction machines to be run as variable-speed devices.

DC devices typically respond to the *average* supply voltage. Pulse-width modulation controls that average by chopping a constant-voltage DC input into a train of pulses with controlled widths, thereby controlling the *average* voltage going to the motor. Phase-controlled rectifiers work similarly with an AC supply by switching off the supply at a designated phase on each transmitted half-cycle. This kind of device rectifies AC into DC with a controlled average voltage.

Inverters are devices that produce alternating current from direct current. Again, modern, solid-state power electronics has permitted the design of rugged, efficient, compact inverters that produce alternating current at variable, controlled frequencies. This allows AC motors to be used as servomotors. Induction motors powered by variable-frequency inverter drives are now used as traction drives in heavy mining machinery.

These developments have allowed controlled actuators, or servomotors, to be made much simpler, more compact, and more rugged than in the past. However, the cost and complexity have shifted to the control electronics from which the motor is supplied. When selecting electric actuators it is important to remember that the power control unit may cost as much, or more, than the motor.

Hydraulic Actuation An alternative to electric actuation is the use of a fluid power system. This term encompasses both hydraulic and pneumatic actuation systems.

In a hydraulic system energy is transmitted via a flowing liquid. Liquid at high pressure is provided by a pump, which might be driven by an electric motor, as is the case in the hydraulic actuation systems used on some industrial robots, or directly by the engine in the case of the hydraulic systems used in construction machinery.

Hydraulic actuators provide much higher force or torque per unit weight than electric actuators. For this reason they seldom require speed-reducing transmissions. Hydraulic actuation is often the system type of choice in heavy-duty applications, particularly when light weight and/or compactness are desired.

Hydraulic cylinders are widely used as linear actuators, particularly when loads are large and strokes are long. Just as the construction types of many electric motors are similar, if not identical to those of electric generators, hydraulic motors are very similar in construction to hydraulic pumps. That said, there is a considerable variety of different configurations available.

There are actually several different types of hydraulic power transmission systems in use. One common type uses a pressure-regulated supply pump to provide a near-constant supply pressure drop. The pressure to each of several actuators in the system is then tailored to that needed to support the load by means of a control valve.

Another type of hydraulic transmission is a hydrostatic system in which the flow of fluid to the actuator is controlled by means of a variable-displacement pump. This configuration requires use of a separate, variable-displacement pump for each actuator. It is a much more efficient type of system than the valve-controlled configuration, but it tends to be less compact. However, a hydrostatic system does not require a large reservoir for heat rejection like a valved system does.

Pneumatic Actuation The most common type of pneumatic actuator is a cylinder that is very similar in construction to a hydraulic cylinder. A pneumatic system is supplied by a compressor, rather than a pump. Some compressors are similar in construction to types of hydraulic pump, but others are quite different. Control valves for pneumatic systems also usually closely resemble their hydraulic counterparts.

Pneumatic actuation has been very popular for fixed automation equipment when high power levels are not required, for example in "light automation." The attraction is relatively low cost and easy maintenance. However, pneumatic systems do not lend themselves well to proportional control. The compressibility of air as a working fluid makes accurate control very problematic. Traditional pneumatic actuator arrangements required only two or a few discrete positions. This is acceptable for fixed automation in which the whole system is designed around a single product but does not work well for flexible automation in which the same machine or line may be reprogrammed to produce several different models or products.

Pneumatic systems share some of the shortcomings of electrical systems in the form of low force-to-weight ratios. This is because they are usually operated at supply pressures an order of magnitude lower than those of hydraulic systems. The low supply pressure is needed because the low viscosity of air compared to hydraulic oil makes it much harder to design seals to contain it at high pressure. Air motors perform much the same function in a pneumatic system that electric motors do in an electric system, providing a means of generating relatively high mechanical power by running a rotary device at high speed. As with electric motors, air motors usually have to be geared down to provide useful torque–speed characteristics. An air motor is basically a compressor running in reverse, so it is a much more complex device than a simple pneumatic cylinder.

PROBLEMS

EXERCISE PROBLEMS ON LINKAGE STRUCTURE

1.1 Find a mechanism as an isolated device or in a machine and make a realistic sketch of the mechanism. Then make a freehand sketch of the kinematic schematics for the mechanism chosen.

1.2 Cabinet hinges use various types of linkages for the guiding mechanism. Identify three types of cabinet hinges employing more than a simple revolute joint and make a freehand sketch of the kinematic mechanism used.

1.3 The drawings shown are pictorial representations of real mechanisms that are commonly encountered. Make a freehand sketch of the kinematic schematic representation of each mechanism.

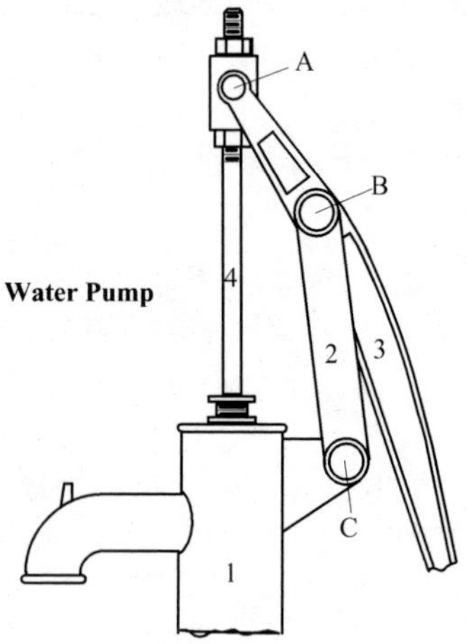

Water Pump

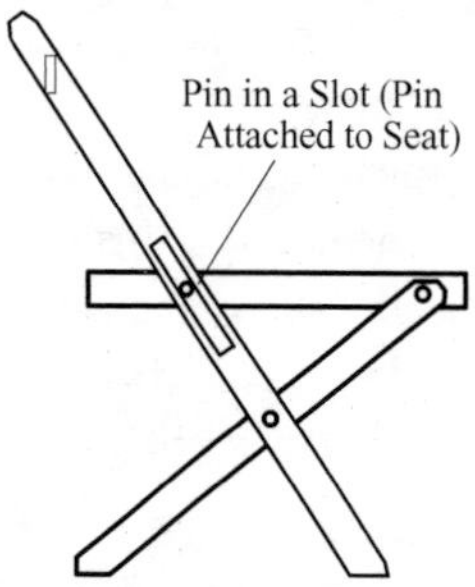

Folding Chair

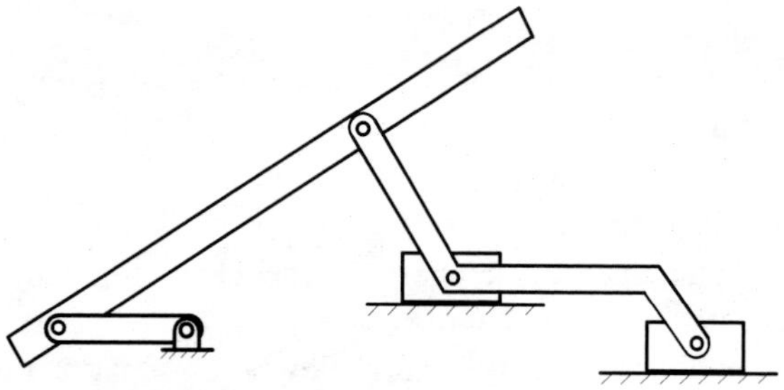
Casement Window Mechanism

1.4 Linkages are often used to guide devices such as computer keyboards in and out of cabinets. Find three such devices, and make a freehand sketch of the kinematic mechanisms used for the devices.

1.5 Four-bar linkages are used in common devices found around the home and at businesses. Locate six such devices and make a freehand sketch of each device and describe its function.

EXERCISE PROBLEMS ON MECHANISM MOBILITY FOR PLANAR MECHANISMS

1.6 Calculate the mobility, or number of degrees of freedom, of each of the mechanisms in Problem 1.3.

1.7 Determine the number of members, number of joints, and mobility of each of the planar linkages shown.

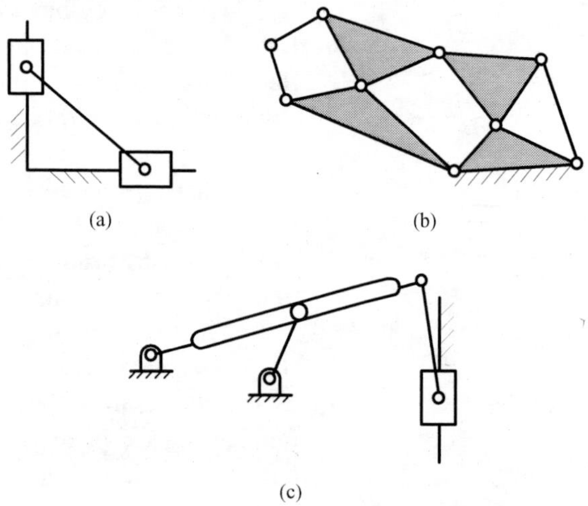

1.8 Determine the number of members, number of joints, and mobility of each of the planar linkages shown.

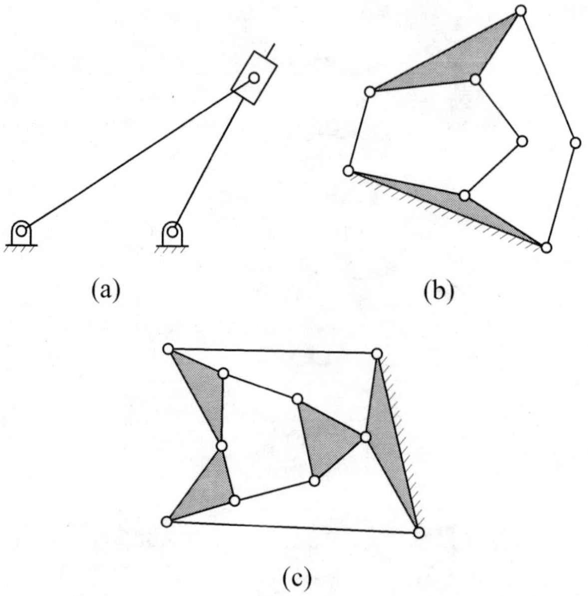

1.9 Determine the mobility and the number of idle degrees of freedom of each of the planar linkages shown. Show the equations used and identify the input and output links assumed when determining your answers.

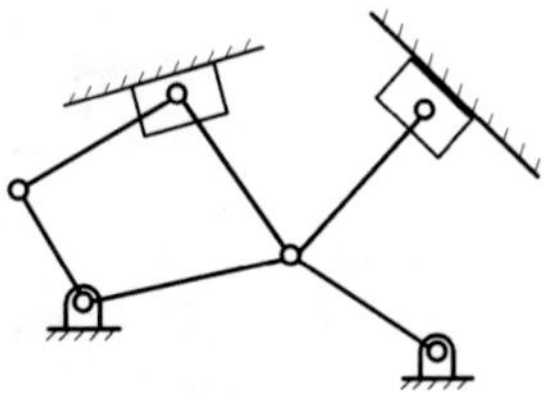

(a)

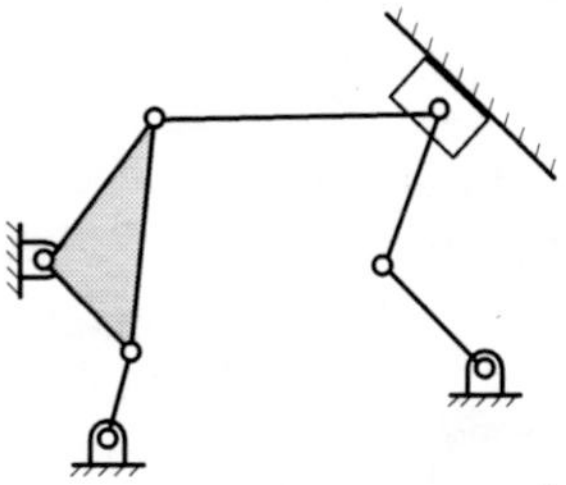

(b)

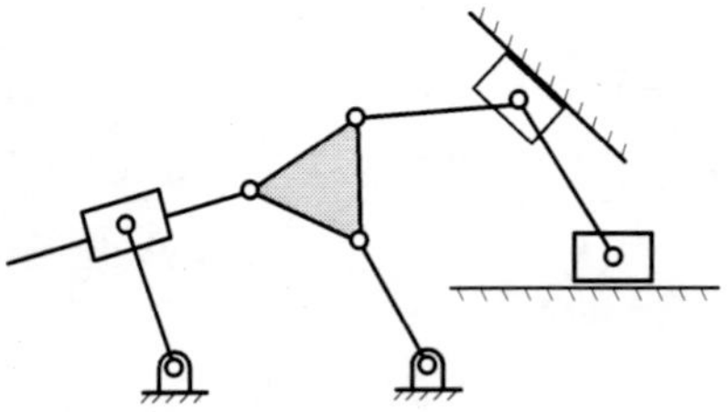

(c)

1.10 Determine the mobility and the number of idle degrees of freedom of the linkages shown. Show the equations used and identify any assumptions made when determining your answers.

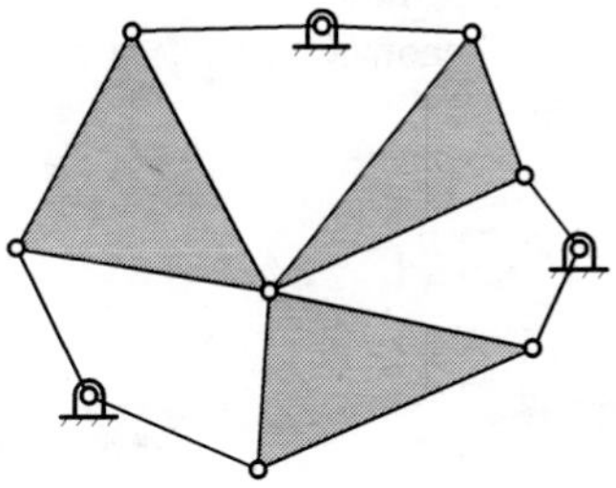

(a)

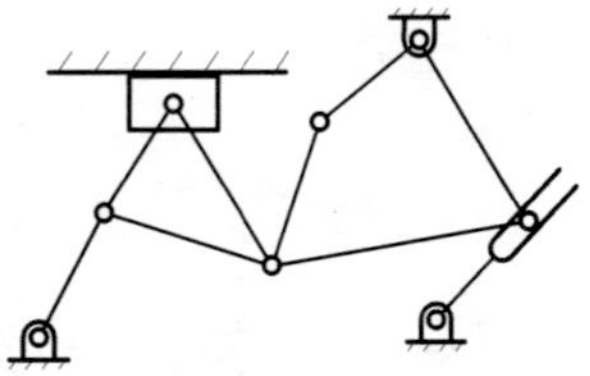

(b)

1.11 Determine the mobility and the number of idle degrees of freedom associated with the mechanism shown. Show the equations used and identify any assumptions made when determining your answers.

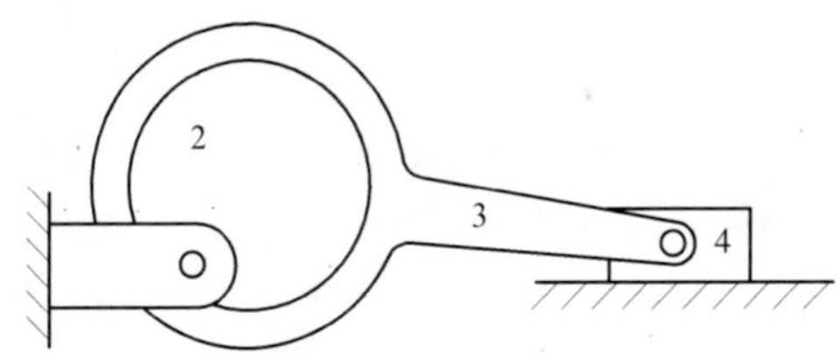

1.12 Determine the mobility of each of the planar linkages shown. Show the equations used to determine your answers.

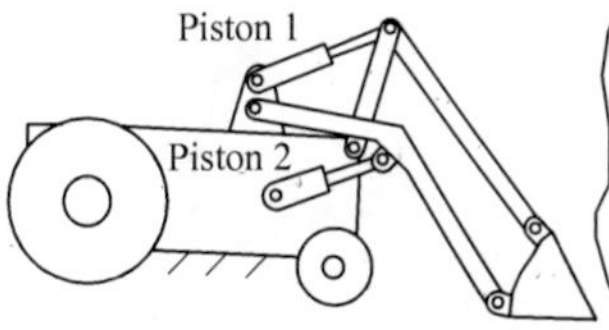

(a)

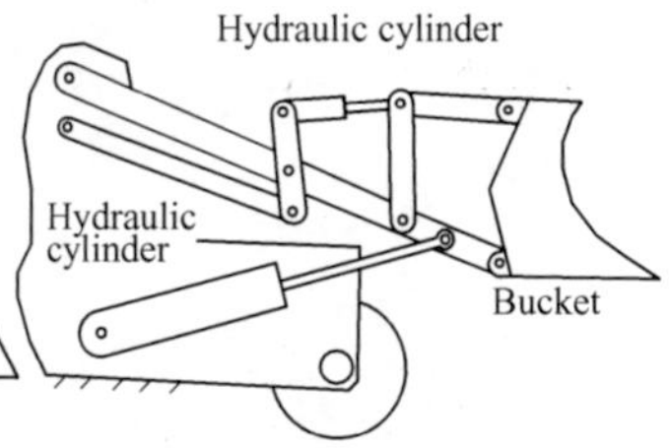

(b)

1.13 Determine the mobility and the number of idle degrees of freedom of each of the planar linkages shown. Show the equations used and identify any assumptions made when determining your answers.

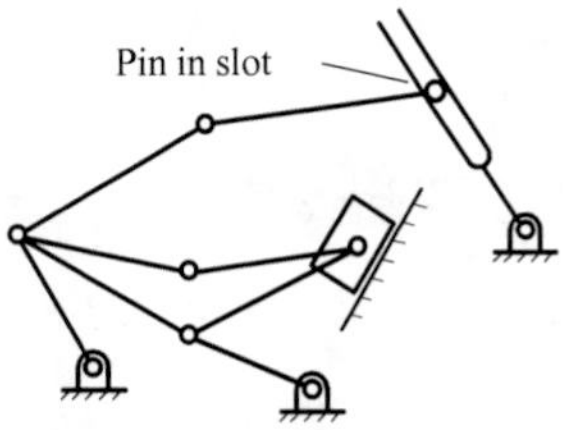

(a)

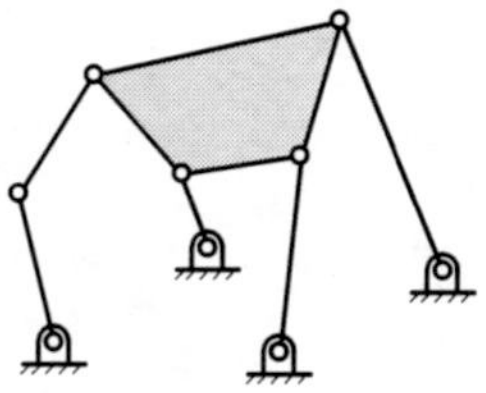

(b)

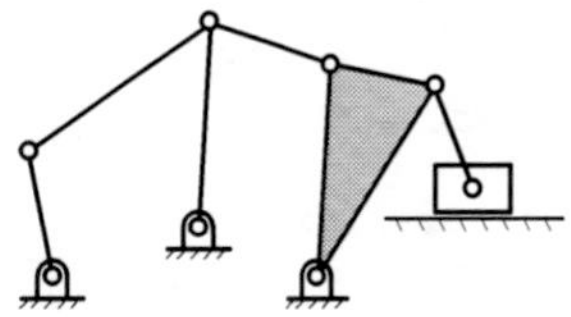

(c)

1.14 Determine the mobility and the number of idle degrees of freedom of each of the planar linkages shown. Show the equations used to determine your answers.

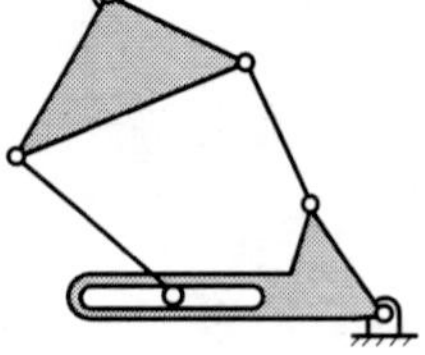

(a)

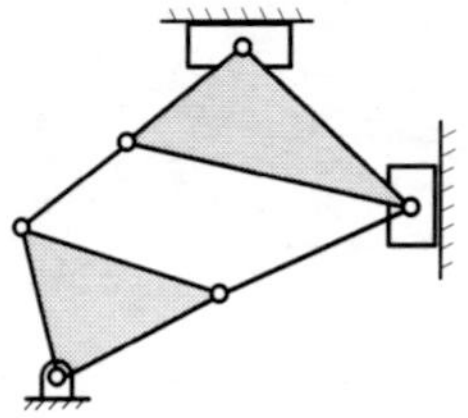

(b)

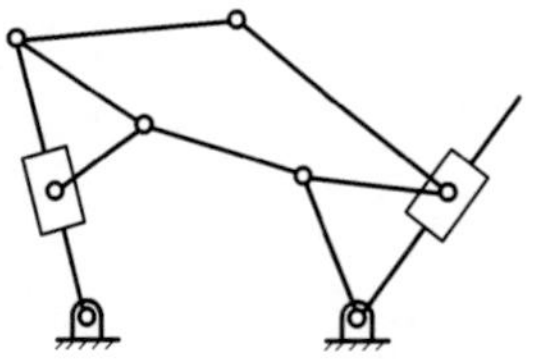

(c)

1.15 Determine the mobility and the number of idle degrees of freedom of each of the planar linkages shown. Show the equations used and identify any assumptions made when determining your answers.

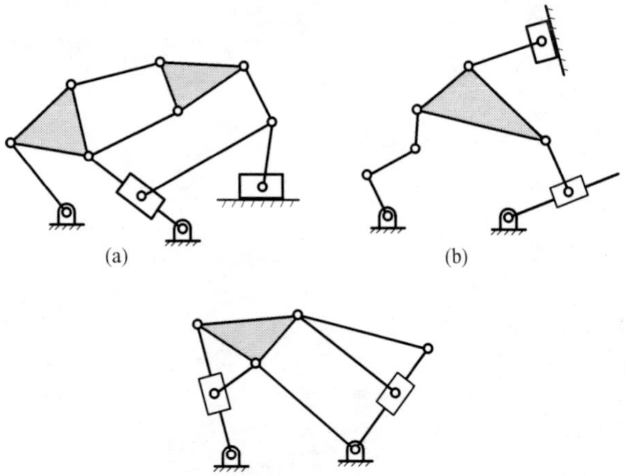

1.16 If position information is available for all points in the planar linkage shown, can all of the velocities be determined uniquely if the value of ω is given? Explain your answer.

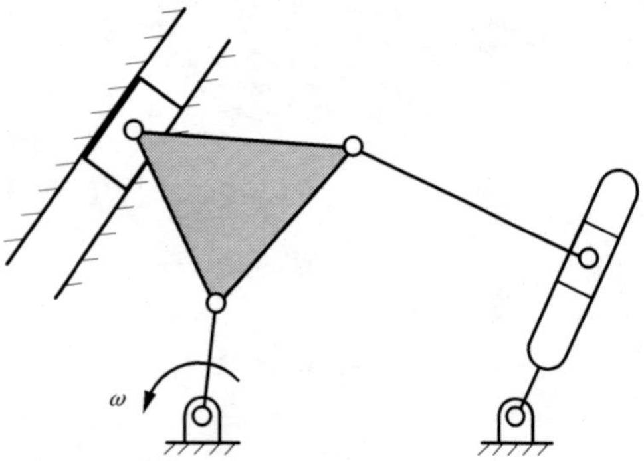

1.17 Determine the mobility and the number of idle degrees of freedom associated with each mechanism. Show the equations used and identify any assumptions made when determining your answers.

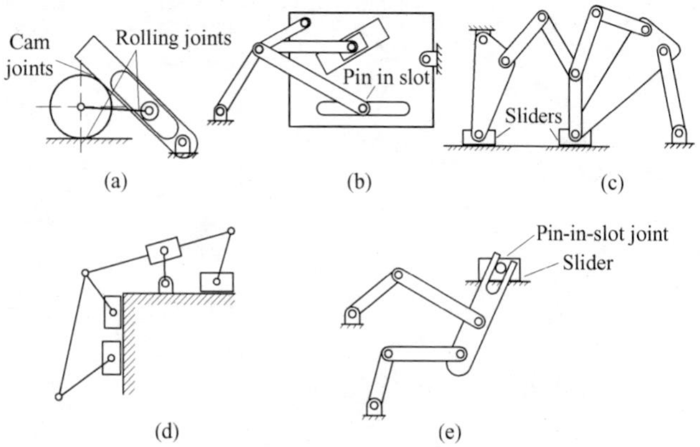

[5] Problem courtesy of Joseph Davidson, Arizona State University.

1.18[5] Determine the mobility and the number of idle degrees of freedom associated with the mechanism shown. The mechanism is a side-dumping car that consists of body 2 and truck 3 connected together by two six-bar linkages, *ABCDEF* and *AGHKLMN*. Link *NM* is designed as a latch on its free end (see left drawing). When jack 1 is operated, body 3 is lifted to the dumping position shown in the right-hand drawing. Simultaneously, the six-bar linkage *AGHKLMN* opens the latch on link *NM* and raises link *GH*. Linkage *ABCDEF* swings open side *BC* and the load can be dumped at some distance from the car (see right-hand drawing). Show the equations used to determine your answers.

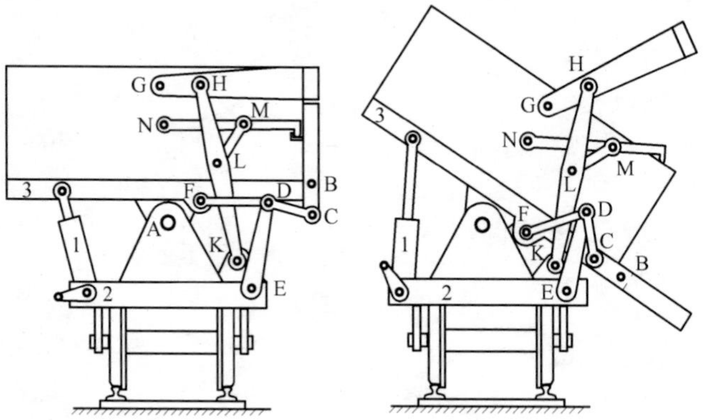

1.19 Determine the mobility and the number of idle degrees of freedom associated with the mechanism shown. The round part rolls without slipping on the pieces in contact with it that slide on the fixed surfaces.

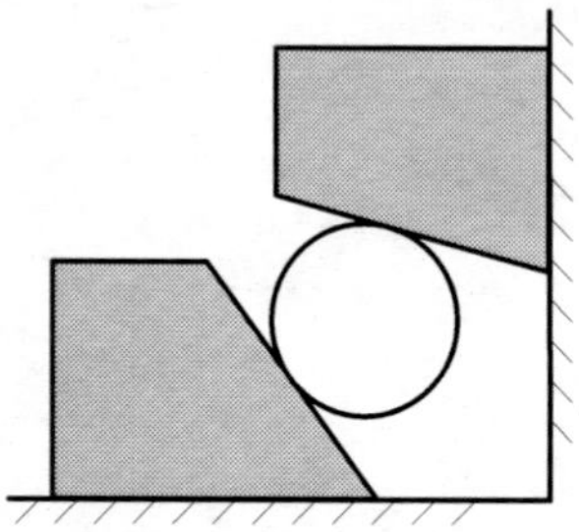

1.20 Determine the mobility and the number of idle degrees of freedom for each of the mechanisms shown. Show the equations used and identify any assumptions made when determining your answers.

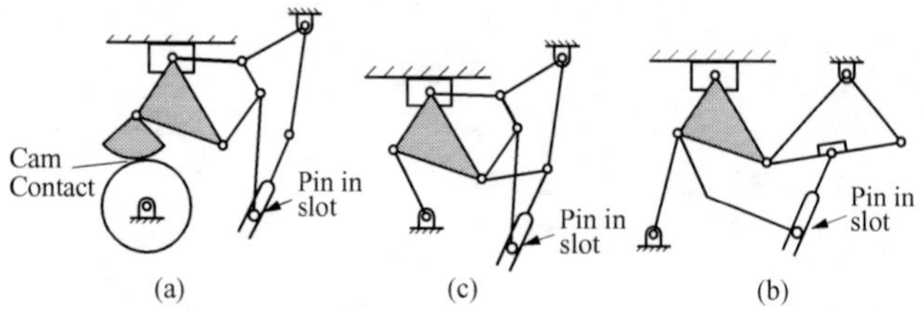

1.21 Determine the mobility and the number of idle degrees of freedom for each of the mechanisms shown. Show the equations used and identify any assumptions made when determining your answers.

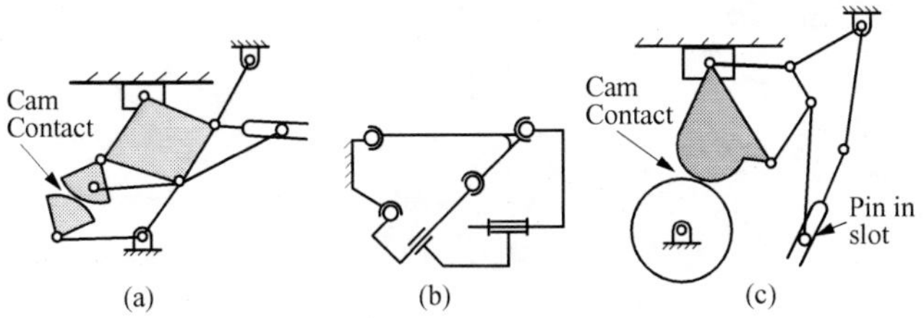

1.22[6] Determine the mobility and the number of idle degrees of freedom associated with the mechanism shown. The figure is a schematic of the entire linkage for a large power shovel used in strip mining. It can cut into a bank 20-m high and can dump to a height of 14.5 m. Link 7 is connected to link 8 with a revolute joint. Show the equations used and identify any assumptions made when determining your answers.

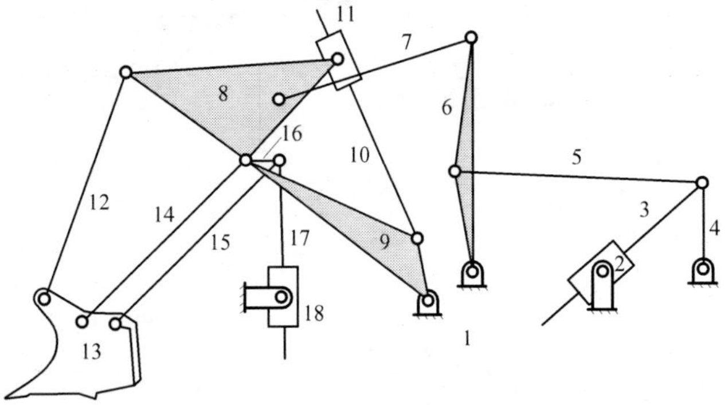

1.23 In the figure is a portion of the support mechanism for the dipper on a large earth-moving machine used in removing overburden in strip-mining operations. The fixed centers for the portion of the mechanism really move, but useful information can be obtained by observing the dipper motion relative to the "frame" as shown in the sketch. Both links 4 and 5 are mounted at O_4. Links 4 and 6 are parallel and of equal length. The dipper is moved by a hydraulic cylinder driving crank 5 about its O_4. Determine the mobility of the mechanism.

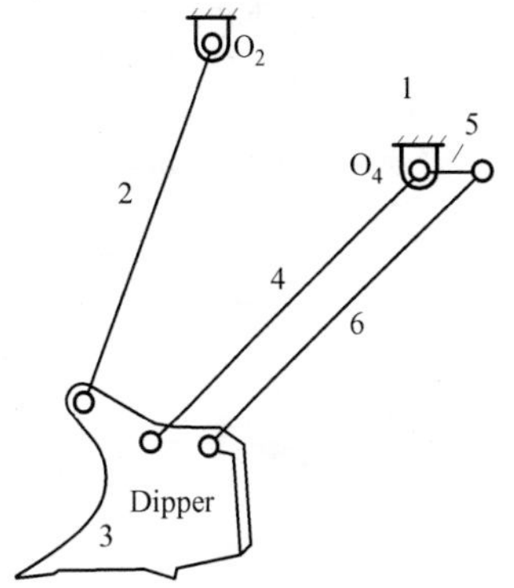

EXERCISE PROBLEMS ON MECHANISM MOBILITY FOR SPATIAL MECHANISMS

1.24 Determine the number of members, number of joints, mobility, and the number of idle degrees of freedom of each of the spatial linkages shown. For the idle degrees of freedom, identify the input and output links assumed.

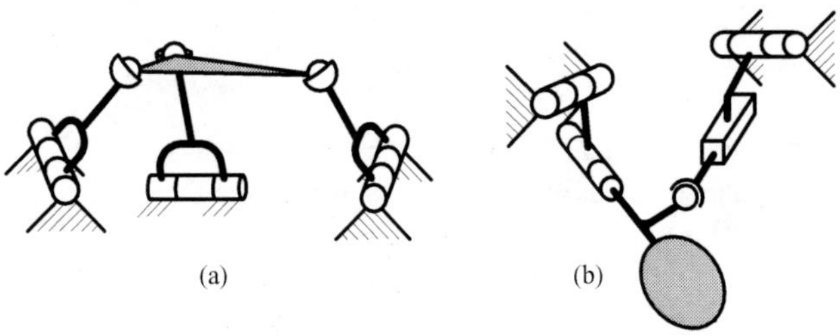

1.25 Determine the mobility and the number of idle degrees of freedom of the spatial linkages shown. Show the equations used to determine your answers. For the idle degrees of freedom, identify the input and output links assumed.

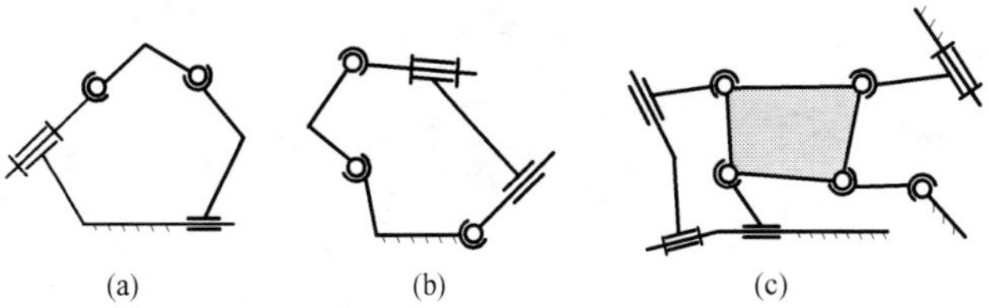

[6] Problem courtesy of Joseph Davidson, Arizona State University.

1.26 Determine the mobility and the number of idle degrees of freedom of the spatial linkages shown. Show the equations used to determine your answers. For the idle degrees of freedom, identify the input and output links assumed.

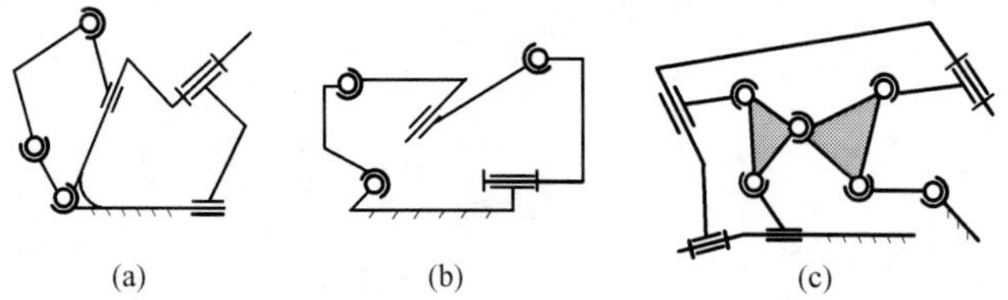

(a) (b) (c)

1.27 Determine the mobility and the number of idle degrees of freedom for each of the mechanisms shown. Show the equations used to determine your answers. For the idle degrees of freedom, identify the input and output links assumed.

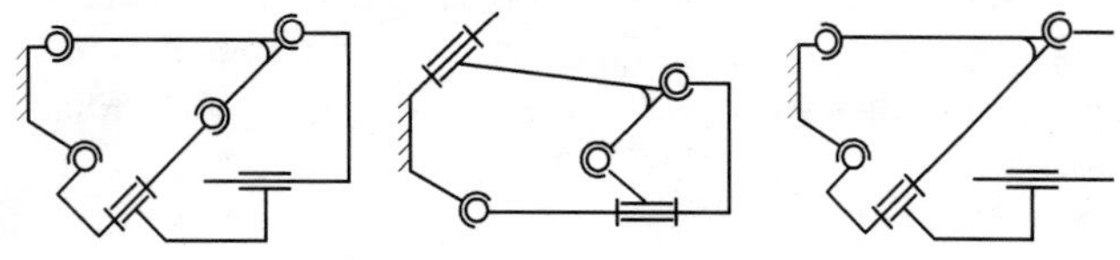

(a) (b) (c)

1.28 Determine the mobility and the number of idle degrees of freedom associated with each mechanism.[7] Show the equations used to determine your answers.

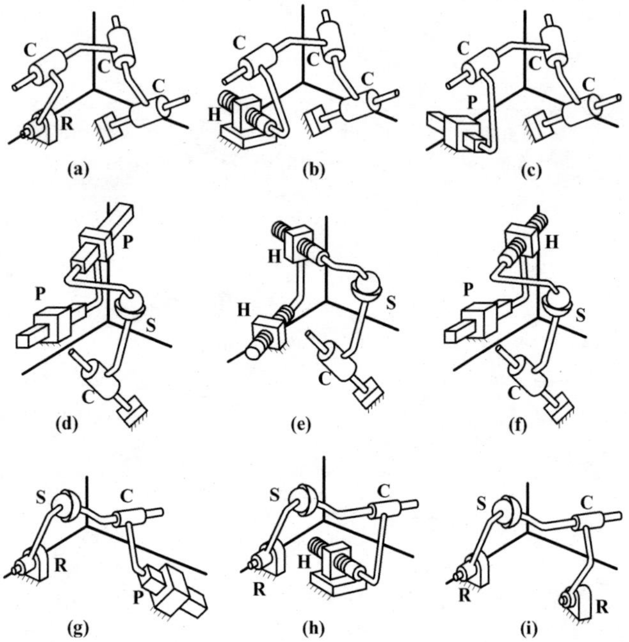

1.29 Determine the mobility and the number of idle degrees of freedom for each of the mechanisms shown. Show the equations used to determine your answers. For the idle degrees of freedom, identify the input and output links assumed.

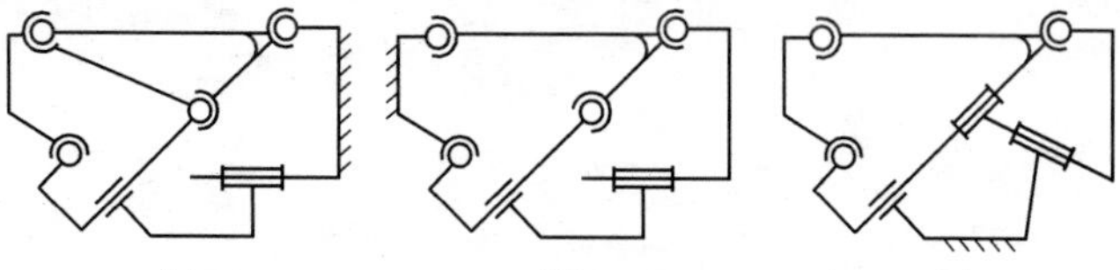

(a) (b) (c)

EXERCISE PROBLEMS ON FOUR-BAR LINKAGE TYPE (GRASHOF'S EQUATION)

1.30 Determine which (if either) of the following linkages can be driven by a constant-velocity motor. For the linkage(s) that can be driven by the motor, indicate the driver link.

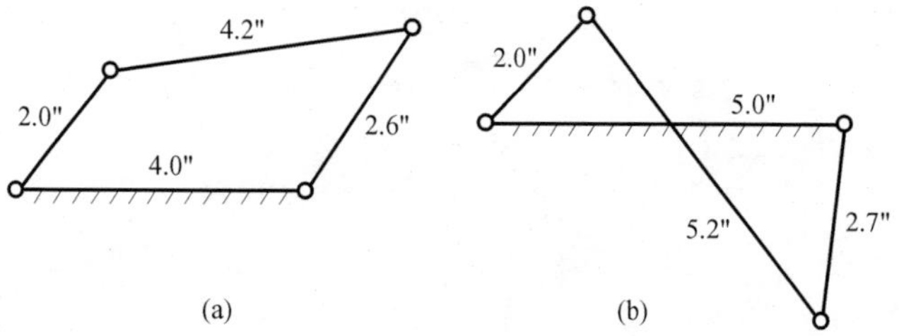

(a) (b)

1.31 Assume that you have a set of links of the following lengths: 2 in, 4 in, 5 in, 6 in, and 9 in. Design a four-bar linkage that can be driven with a continuous-rotation electric motor. Justify your answer with appropriate equations, and make a scaled drawing of the linkage. Label the crank, frame, coupler, and rocker (follower).

1.32 Assume that you have a set of links of the following lengths: 20 mm, 30 mm, 45 mm, 56 mm, and 73 mm. Design a four-bar linkage that can be driven with a continuous-rotation electric motor. Justify your answer with appropriate equations, and make a freehand sketch (labeled) of the resulting linkage. Label the crank, frame, coupler, and rocker (follower).

1.33 For the four-bar linkages shown, indicate whether they are Grashof type 1 or 2 and whether they are crank–rocker, double-crank, or double-rocker mechanisms.

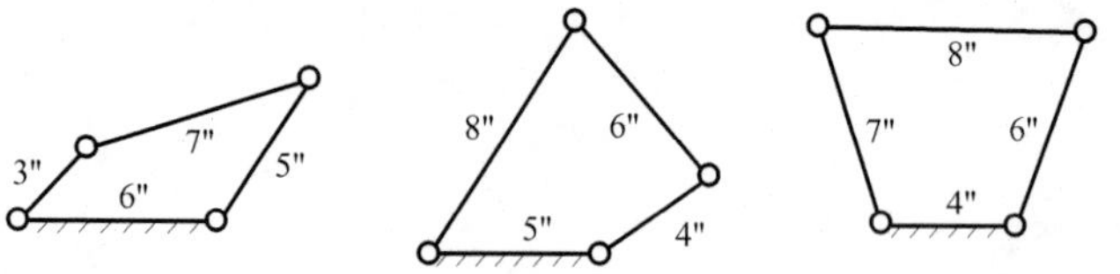

(a) (b) (c)

[7] Problem based on paper entitled "A Number Synthesis Survey of Three-Dimensional Mechanisms" by L. Harrisberger, *Trans. ASME, J. Eng. Ind.*, pp. 213–220, May 1965.

1.34 You are given a set of three links with lengths 2.4 in, 7.2 in, and 3.4 in. Select the length of a fourth link and assemble a linkage that can be driven by a continuous-rotation motor. Is your linkage a Grashof type 1 or Grashof type 2 linkage? (Show your work.) Is it a crank-rocker, double-rocker, or double-crank linkage? Why?

1.35 You have available a set of eight links from which you are to design a four-bar linkage. Choose the links such that the linkage can be driven by a continuous-rotation motor. Sketch the linkage and identify the type of four-bar mechanism resulting.

$L_1 = 2''$, $L_2 = 3''$, $L_3 = 4''$, $L_4 = 6''$, $L_5 = 7''$, $L_6 = 9.5''$, $L_7 = 13''$, and $L_8 = 9''$

1.36 Determine the number of fully rotating cranks in the planar mechanisms shown. Show your calculations.

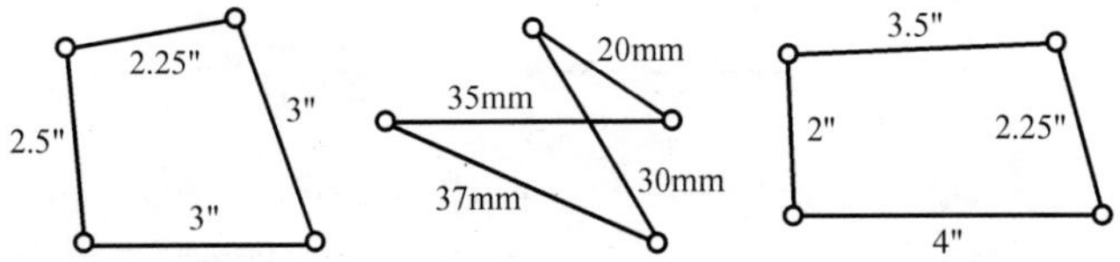

(a) (b) (c)

1.37 If the link lengths of a four-bar linkage are $L_1 = 1$ mm, $L_2 = 3$ mm, $L_3 = 4$ mm, and $L_4 = 5$ mm and link 1 is fixed, what type of four-bar linkage is it? Also, is the linkage a Grashof type 1 or 2 linkage? Answer the same questions if $L_1 = 2$ mm.

1.38 You are given two sets of links. Select four links from each set such that the coupler can rotate fully with respect to the others. Sketch the linkage and identify the type of four-bar mechanism in each case.

(a) $L_1 = 5''$, $L_2 = 8''$, $L_3 = 15''$, $L_4 = 19''$, and $L_5 = 28''$.

(b) $L_1 = 5''$, $L_2 = 2''$, $L_3 = 4''$, $L_4 = 3.5''$, and $L_5 = 2.5''$.

1.39 The mechanisms shown are drawn to scale.

(a) Sketch kinematic schematics showing the relationships between the members and joints.

(b) Determine the Grashof type of the four-bar linkage in each mechanism.

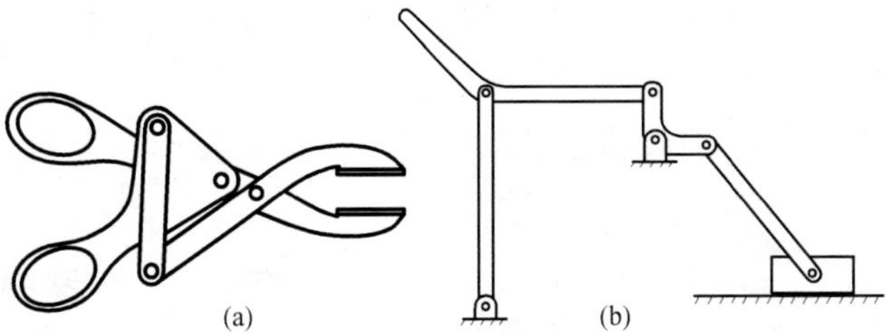
(a) (b)

CHAPTER 2

GRAPHICAL POSITION, VELOCITY, AND ACCELERATION ANALYSIS FOR MECHANISMS WITH REVOLUTE JOINTS OR FIXED SLIDES

2.1 INTRODUCTION

Historically, planar linkage analysis problems were solved graphically using drafting equipment. In recent years computer techniques have offered a viable and attractive alternative. Some teachers of the subject now prefer to concentrate their time on analytical approaches. Nevertheless, there are still many situations in which graphical techniques offer the most efficient solution, and the insight into the problem obtained by an understanding of the graphical approach is, we feel, essential. For this reason we have chosen to present both approaches. In Chapters 2–4, we present the graphical approach, and in Chapter 5, we present the analytical approach.

We have separated the presentation of graphical analyses into three chapters. In this chapter, we present the analysis of mechanisms with only revolute joints or sliders on fixed slides. Such mechanisms constitute the majority of mechanisms found in the real world. These mechanisms can also be analyzed using relatively simple equations derived from basic physics. In Chapter 3, mechanisms involving higher pairs and moving slides will be addressed. The approach to analyzing these mechanisms is more involved than that required in Chapter 2 because moving coordinate systems must be considered directly.

In Chapter 4, we present a special graphical procedure based on instant centers of velocity. When two laminae are moving relative to one another there exists, at every instant, a point in one lamina that is at rest relative to the other, and vice versa. This is the instant center of relative motion of those laminae. The technique of velocity analysis based on instant centers presents advantages when solving certain types of problems. Therefore, it is advantageous for the engineer to be familiar with this technique, as well as the vector polygon technique. This is a very powerful procedure if only velocities are important, and the graphical approach gives considerable insight into the design of planar mechanisms.

A purely analytical approach to kinematic analysis based on vector loop equations is presented in Chapter 5. This procedure can be easily programmed, but, unless a program is readily available, it is typically much more time consuming than a graphical analysis when only one position of the mechanism is of interest.

There is a tendency to discard traditional graphical techniques in favor of numerical solutions based on the analytical formulations presented in Chapter 5. However, there are many situations in which graphical techniques are useful. For example, it is necessary to check and debug computer programs. This is done most effectively by comparing the numerical solutions of sample problems with solutions to the same problems obtained using completely different techniques. Graphical techniques are ideal for providing these alternative solutions. At other times, a quick answer to a problem is needed, and no suitable program is available. Rather than writing and debugging a program specifically to solve the problem, one often finds it to be more efficient to use the graphical approach. Most important, insight into the kinematic geometry that governs all mechanism behavior is obtained by an understanding of the graphical approach.

2.2 GRAPHICAL POSITION ANALYSIS

Regardless of what procedure is used for a linkage analysis, it is *always* necessary to determine the angular positions of the links before a velocity analysis can be performed. Likewise, it is necessary to know the link angular velocities before an acceleration analysis can be performed. That is, the kinematic analysis of a linkage must *always* proceed in this sequence: position analysis, then velocity analysis, then acceleration analysis. If the linkage has one degree of freedom and the driver is a crank, the angular position, angular velocity, and angular acceleration of a driving link must all be specified for a solution to be possible. If the driving member is connected to the base by a prismatic joint, the linear position, velocity, and acceleration of any point in that link must be specified.

When working graphically, the position analysis consists of simply drawing the linkage to scale. Usually this is so straightforward that it tends to be forgotten as an important step in the solution process. The representation used is a geometric skeleton of the linkage: links with revolute joints are represented by the line, or lines, joining the joint axes. Prismatic joints are represented by lines in the direction of sliding. Revolute joints are usually represented only by the points that are the intersections of their axes with the plane of motion. The way the method works in the analysis of a simple linkage is illustrated in the examples. (See, for example, Fig. 2.8.) Note that this is different from the linkage skeleton representation used in Chapter 1. However, it is sometimes useful to indicate revolute joints by small circles centered on the joint axes and prismatic joints by sliding blocks. If this is done, the present representation becomes a geometrically accurate equivalent of the linkage skeleton.

As will be shown in Chapter 5, the position equations for mechanisms are inherently nonlinear. In many cases, the mechanism can be assembled (or drawn) in two possible configurations. It is necessary to know before the analysis is conducted which solution is desired. This will be illustrated in the examples that will be discussed after the equations for velocity and acceleration are developed.

We will begin the analysis of velocities and accelerations with a relatively simple case involving two points fixed to the same rigid link. The equations for this case are commonly developed in courses in mechanics using the procedure we shall use here. The equations developed will be directly applicable to mechanisms with revolute joints and/or sliders on fixed lines. We will illustrate the use of the procedure with several examples.

For more complex joints, a more rigorous and general approach will be used to develop the velocity and acceleration equations. This will entail identifying the coordinate systems relative to which each of the vectors is described and relative to that for which the time derivatives are desired. It will be shown that the velocity and acceleration equations developed for the case of two points on a rigid link are special cases of the more general equations. This procedure will be given in Chapter 3.

2.3 PLANAR VELOCITY POLYGONS

Velocity analysis is the determination of the angular velocities of different links in a mechanism and of the velocities of points on the links, given either the angular velocity of some member or the velocity of some point on the link designated as the input. The vector polygon technique will be used here to solve the velocity and acceleration equations. The method facilitates the solution of a large variety of velocity and acceleration problems and also has the advantage that the acceleration polygon solution has a strong similarity to that of the velocity polygon, which makes it relatively straightforward to learn and remember. Almost all practical problems can be solved by this approach.

In theory, however, the technique is not general. It is possible to formulate problems that cannot be solved by the methods presented here. Special techniques have been developed that allow treatment of some of the simpler cases that are not amenable to the vector polygon method; nonetheless, it is possible to formulate problems that cannot be solved by even these embellished techniques. The reader is referred to books by Hirschhorn,[1] Hall,[2] and Holowenko[3] for the auxiliary-point technique and other methods of handling more general mechanisms. It should be emphasized, however, that problems that cannot be solved by the methods presented in this chapter are rarely encountered in practice.

The key to the graphical velocity analysis of most linkages is the relationship between the velocities of any two points embedded in a rigid body. This relationship is

$$\boldsymbol{v}_B = \boldsymbol{v}_A + \boldsymbol{\omega} \times \boldsymbol{r}_{B/A} \tag{2.1}$$

where A and B are points fixed in a moving lamina (rigid body) as shown in Fig. 2.1, $\boldsymbol{v}_A$ and $\boldsymbol{v}_B$ are the respective velocities relative to the frame of those points, $\boldsymbol{r}$ is the vector $\overrightarrow{AB}$, and $\boldsymbol{\omega}$ is the angular velocity of the lamina relative to the frame. Basically, if we draw a line on the lamina, $\boldsymbol{\omega}$ is the time rate of change of the angular orientation of that line with respect to time.

For Eq. (2.1) to be valid, it is important that points A and B be fixed to the same rigid link. If one of the points is attached to a different link, the equation is incomplete. This case is covered in Chapter 3. In the examples, we will use subscripts on the point letters (e.g., A_2) to identify the link to which each point is attached to ensure that the proper points are being considered when using the equation. When developing the equations here, however, subscripts will not be used because only one link is being considered.

To prove this relationship, consider the two points A and B fixed in the lamina shown in Fig. 2.1. The lamina is moving with general planar motion. Let the position of point A relative to a fixed reference frame be $\boldsymbol{r}_A$, and let that of point B be $\boldsymbol{r}_B$. The vector $\overrightarrow{AB}$ is $\boldsymbol{r}_{B/A}$ and is pointed from A to B. Therefore

$$\boldsymbol{r}_B = \boldsymbol{r}_A + \boldsymbol{r}_{B/A} \tag{2.2}$$

Differentiating Eq. (2.2) with respect to time gives

$$\boldsymbol{v}_B = \boldsymbol{v}_A + d\boldsymbol{r}_{B/A} / dt$$

Now, since points A and B are fixed in the moving lamina, vector $\boldsymbol{r}_{B/A}$ is fixed in that lamina and moves with it. It has constant length, so only its direction changes. Let the change in

[1] Hirschhorn, J., *Kinematics and Dynamics of Plane Mechanisms,* McGraw-Hill Book Co., New York, 1962.
[2] Hall, A., *Kinematics and Linkage Design,* Balt Publishers, West Lafayette, IN, 1966.
[3] Holowenko, A. R., *Dynamics of Machinery,* John Wiley & Sons, Inc., New York, 1955.

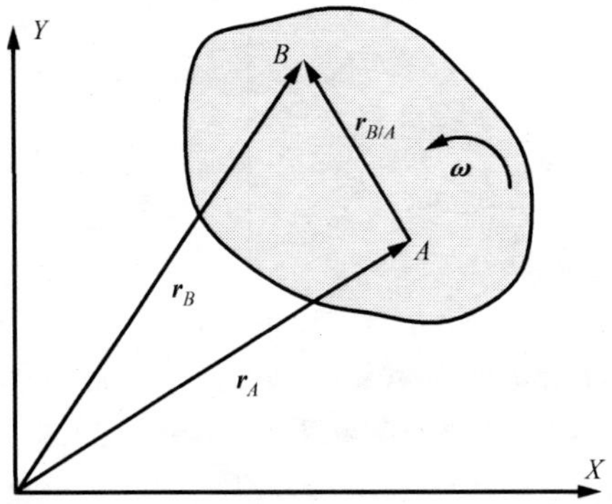

FIGURE 2.1 Position relationships of two points embedded in a moving lamina.

direction in a small time interval δt be $\delta\theta$, as shown in Fig. 2.2. The magnitude of the change in $\boldsymbol{r}_{B/A}$ is

$$\delta r = r_{\boldsymbol{B}/A}\,\delta\theta$$

As δt and hence $\delta\theta$ approach zero, the angle between the vectors $\delta\boldsymbol{r}_{B/A}$ and $\boldsymbol{r}_{B/A}$ approaches 90°. If ω is the magnitude of the angular velocity of the lamina,

$$\delta\theta = \omega\delta t$$

Therefore

$$\delta r/\delta t = r_{B/A}\,\omega$$

so, in the limit as δt approaches zero,

$$\left|d\boldsymbol{r}_{B/A}/dt\right| = r_{B/A}\,\omega$$

If $\boldsymbol{\omega}$ is considered to be a vector normal to the plane of motion, clockwise (CW) if directed away from the observer and counterclockwise (CCW) if directed toward the observer, the direction of $d\boldsymbol{r}_{B/A}/dt$ is normal to $\boldsymbol{\omega}$ and to $\boldsymbol{r}_{B/A}$ and obeys the right-hand screw rule with respect to those vectors. Therefore $d\boldsymbol{r}_{B/A}/dt$ can be represented by the expression

$$d\boldsymbol{r}_{B/A}/dt = \boldsymbol{\omega}\times\boldsymbol{r}_{B/A} \tag{2.3}$$

What we have actually derived here is a general expression for the derivative of a vector of constant magnitude ($\boldsymbol{r}_{B/A}$) embedded in a lamina in planar motion, for which $\boldsymbol{\omega}$ is the angular velocity relative to a fixed reference frame. We will make use of this expression in Chapter 3 and elsewhere.

Thus

$$\boldsymbol{v}_B = \boldsymbol{v}_A + \boldsymbol{\omega}\times\boldsymbol{r}_{B/A} \tag{2.1}$$

As will be shown in Chapter 3, this expression is actually valid for general spatial motion, although the derivation here applies only to planar motion.

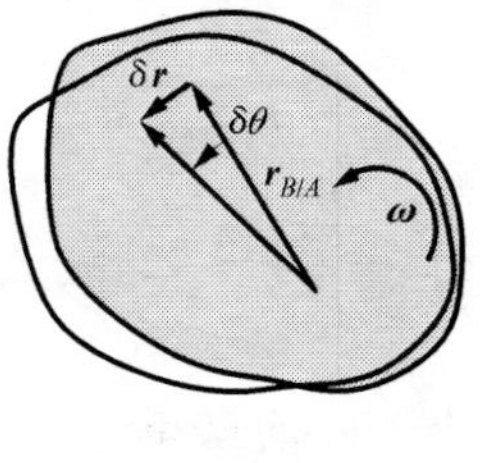

FIGURE 2.2 Successive positions of the lamina separated by a small time interval, δt.

It is convenient to write Eq. (2.1) in the form

$$\boldsymbol{v}_B = \boldsymbol{v}_A + \boldsymbol{v}_{B/A} \tag{2.4}$$

where

$$\boldsymbol{v}_{B/A} = \boldsymbol{\omega} \times \boldsymbol{r}_{B/A} \tag{2.5}$$

The vector $\boldsymbol{v}_{B/A}$ is usually called the velocity of B relative to A, although, strictly speaking, it is meaningless to talk of a velocity relative to a point. Velocities are vectors and are measured relative to reference frames. Therefore, $\boldsymbol{v}_{B/A}$ would be the velocity of point B relative to a reference frame that has its origin at point A and that moves so as to be always parallel to the fixed frame.

If only one letter is used as a subscript (e.g., $\boldsymbol{v}_B$), the resulting velocity is called an absolute velocity. This means that it is the derivative of a position vector that has its tail fixed to a point that has zero velocity. From Eq (2.4) it is clear that $\boldsymbol{v}_B = \boldsymbol{v}_{B/A}$ if $\boldsymbol{v}_A = 0$. Note that point A need not be absolutely fixed; it might have a velocity that is only momentarily zero.

The basic technique used in a graphical linkage analysis is to work from one or more points with known velocity to one of unknown velocity using the relationship in Eq. (2.1) between the velocities of two points fixed in the same lamina. The intersections of the axes of revolute joints with the plane of motion form transfer points because they are actually coincident points fixed in two different links. Thus, the velocity of a revolute joint can be obtained by considering it to be a point in one of the links it connects. That information can then be used by considering the point to be fixed in the other link.

Equation 2.4 can be represented graphically as the vector triangle shown in Fig. 2.3. This triangle can always be solved given the direction and magnitude of one of the three vectors and the directions of the remaining two. This is the normal situation in planar velocity analysis. Again, the way in which this works will be illustrated in several examples after all of the necessary equations have been developed.

Based on Eq. (2.5), to find the angular velocity $\boldsymbol{\omega}$ for a given link, we must compute the relative velocity between two points on the link, and the velocity must be given relative to the desired reference frame. For example, the relative velocity relationship for points B and A can be written as

$$\boldsymbol{v}_{B/A} = \boldsymbol{\omega} \times \boldsymbol{r}_{B/A} \tag{2.6}$$

The vectors in Eq. (2.6) will be mutually orthogonal, as indicated schematically in Fig. 2.4. Because we will know the lines along which each of the vectors must lie, the main problem is to determine the directions along the lines and the magnitudes of each of the vectors. Given any two of the vector directions, we can find the direction of the third by observing the directions given by the right-hand screw rule. Two examples are shown in Fig. 2.4.

Notice that $\boldsymbol{v}_{B/A}$ and $\boldsymbol{r}_{B/A}$ are always perpendicular to each other. Also, visually, we can determine the direction of $\boldsymbol{v}_{B/A}$ by rotating $\boldsymbol{r}_{B/A}$ 90° in the direction of $\boldsymbol{\omega}$. Similarly, if we

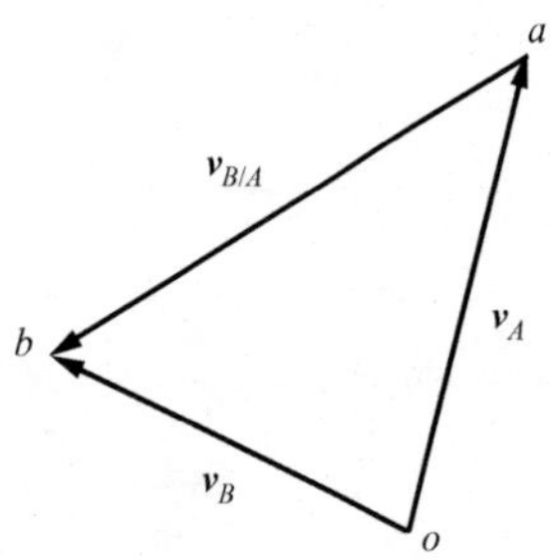

FIGURE 2.3 Velocities of two points embedded in a lamina.

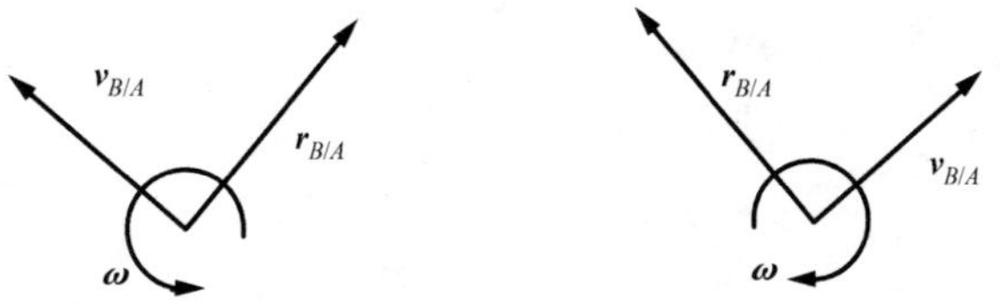

FIGURE 2.4 The direction relationship among the vectors $\boldsymbol{v}_{B/A}$, $\boldsymbol{\omega}$, and $\boldsymbol{r}_{B/A}$ for planar motion.

know the directions of $\boldsymbol{r}_{B/A}$ and $\boldsymbol{v}_{B/A}$, we can determine the direction of $\boldsymbol{\omega}$ by visualizing the direction in which we must rotate $\boldsymbol{r}_{B/A}$ to obtain the direction of $\boldsymbol{v}_{B/A}$.

Because the three vectors in Eq. (2.5) are orthogonal, their magnitudes are related by

$$\left|\boldsymbol{v}_{B/A}\right| = \left|\boldsymbol{\omega}\right|\left|\boldsymbol{r}_{B/A}\right| \tag{2.7}$$

Given any two of the three magnitudes in Eq. (2.7), we can easily solve for the third magnitude.

2.4 GRAPHICAL ACCELERATION ANALYSIS

Just as was the case for velocity analysis, the key to most graphical acceleration analyses is the relationship between the accelerations of two points fixed in the same rigid lamina or link. This relationship can be derived by differentiating the velocity relationship with respect to time. Rewriting Eq. (2.1) we obtain

$$\boldsymbol{v}_B = \boldsymbol{v}_A + \boldsymbol{\omega} \times \boldsymbol{r}_{B/A} \tag{2.1}$$

Differentiating gives

$$\boldsymbol{a}_B = \boldsymbol{a}_A + (d\boldsymbol{\omega}/dt) \times \boldsymbol{r}_{B/A} + \boldsymbol{\omega} \times (d\boldsymbol{r}_{B/A}/dt)$$

As was shown in Section 2.3,

$$d\boldsymbol{r}_{B/A}/dt = \boldsymbol{\omega} \times \boldsymbol{r}_{B/A}$$

Also, angular acceleration $\boldsymbol{\alpha}$ is defined to be $d\boldsymbol{\omega}/dt$. Hence

$$\boldsymbol{a}_B = \boldsymbol{a}_A + \boldsymbol{\alpha} \times \boldsymbol{r}_{B/A} + \boldsymbol{\omega} \times \left(\boldsymbol{\omega} \times \boldsymbol{r}_{B/A}\right) \tag{2.8}$$

As will be demonstrated in Chapter 3, this expression is generally valid for three-dimensional motion, although it has been derived here only in the planar motion context. For planar motion, it is possible to simplify the expression by noting that, in this case, $\boldsymbol{\omega}$ and $\boldsymbol{r}_{B/A}$ are orthogonal, as shown in Fig. 2.5. Also, $\boldsymbol{\omega} \times \boldsymbol{r}_{B/A}$ has the magnitude $\omega\, r_{B/A}$ and is normal to both $\boldsymbol{\omega}$ and $\boldsymbol{r}_{B/A}$ in the sense given by the right-hand screw rule. Then, $\boldsymbol{\omega} \times (\boldsymbol{\omega} \times \boldsymbol{r}_{B/A})$ has the magnitude $\omega^2 r_{B/A}$ and is orthogonal to both $\boldsymbol{\omega}$ and $\boldsymbol{\omega} \times \boldsymbol{r}_{B/A}$. Applying the right-hand screw rule, it can be seen that this vector $\boldsymbol{\omega} \times (\boldsymbol{\omega} \times \boldsymbol{r}_{B/A})$ is always in the negative $\boldsymbol{r}_{B/A}$ direction. Therefore it can be written as $-\omega^2 \boldsymbol{r}_{B/A}$, and the relationship between the accelerations of points A and B is

$$\boldsymbol{a}_B = \boldsymbol{a}_A + \boldsymbol{\alpha} \times \boldsymbol{r}_{B/A} - \omega^2 \boldsymbol{r}_{B/A} \tag{2.9}$$

It is usual to write

$$\boldsymbol{a}^{\mathrm{r}}_{B/A} = -\omega^2 \boldsymbol{r}_{B/A} \text{ and } \boldsymbol{a}^{\mathrm{t}}_{B/A} = \boldsymbol{\alpha} \times \boldsymbol{r}_{B/A} \tag{2.10}$$

with $\boldsymbol{a}^{\mathrm{r}}_{B/A}$ called the radial component of the acceleration of B relative to A and $\boldsymbol{a}^{\mathrm{t}}_{B/A}$ called the tangential component of the acceleration of B relative to A. As was noted in the case of

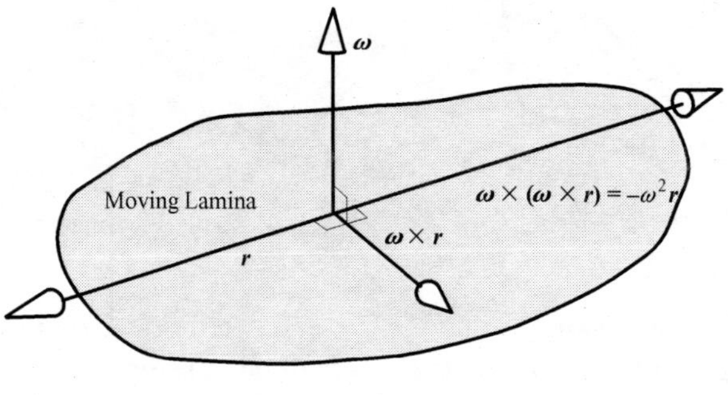

FIGURE 2.5 The derivation of the relationship $\omega \times (\omega \times \boldsymbol{r}) = -\omega^2\boldsymbol{r}$, which is valid for planar motion.

velocities, it is not really proper to talk about the velocity or acceleration of one point relative to another point. The vector $\boldsymbol{a}_{B/A}$ is really the acceleration of point B relative to a reference frame with origin at A and moves so that it is always parallel to the fixed frame.

The vector polygon corresponding to Eq. (2.8) is shown schematically in Fig. 2.6. If a velocity analysis of the linkage has been performed, the angular velocities of all the links are known, and so the radial component $\boldsymbol{a}^r_{B/A} = -\omega^2\boldsymbol{r}_{B/A}$ can always be calculated and plotted. Hence, if one of the other vectors is also known, and the directions of the remaining two are also known, the polygon can be solved in very much the same way as the vector triangle was used in the velocity analysis. This is the normal procedure for a graphical acceleration analysis.

The angular acceleration for a given link is obtained in the same manner as the angular velocity except that the *tangential* component of relative acceleration is used instead of the linear velocity. To find a value of $\boldsymbol{\alpha}$, we must know the tangential component of the relative acceleration between any two points on the link. For example, the relative tangential acceleration relationship for points B and A can be written as

$$\boldsymbol{a}^t_{B/A} = \boldsymbol{\alpha} \times \boldsymbol{r}_{B/A} \tag{2.11}$$

Because we will know the lines along which the vectors must lie, the main problem again is to determine the directions along the lines and the magnitude of each of the vectors. Given any two of the vector directions, we can find the direction of the third by observing the directions given by the right-hand screw rule. Two examples are shown schematically in Fig. 2.7.

Notice that these relationships are exactly the same as for the velocity expressions if $\boldsymbol{\omega}$ is replaced by $\boldsymbol{\alpha}$ and $\boldsymbol{v}_{B/A}$ is replaced by $\boldsymbol{a}^t_{B/A}$. In particular, notice that $\boldsymbol{a}^t_{B/A}$ and $\boldsymbol{r}_{B/A}$ are always perpendicular to each other. Also, we can determine the direction of $\boldsymbol{a}^t_{B/A}$ by visually rotating $\boldsymbol{r}_{B/A}$ 90° in the direction of $\boldsymbol{\alpha}$. Similarly, if we know the directions of $\boldsymbol{r}_{B/A}$ and $\boldsymbol{a}^t_{B/A}$, we can determine the direction of $\boldsymbol{\alpha}$ by visualizing the direction in which we must rotate $\boldsymbol{r}_{B/A}$

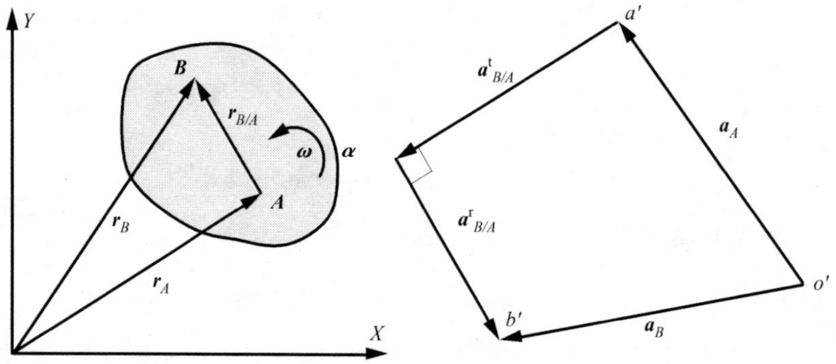

FIGURE 2.6 Accelerations of two points embedded in a moving lamina.

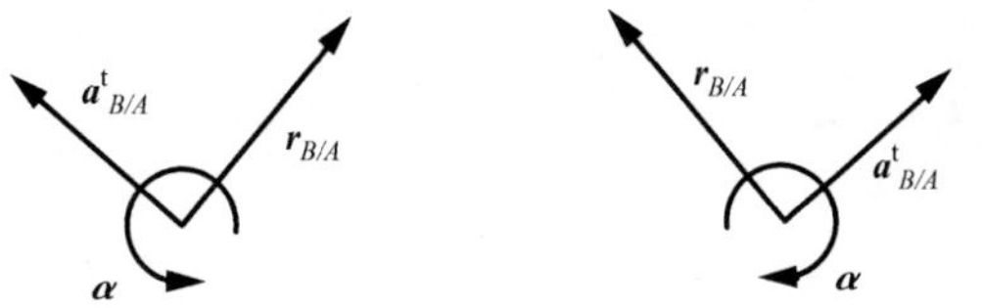

FIGURE 2.7 The direction relationship among the vectors $\boldsymbol{a}^t_{B/A}$, $\boldsymbol{\alpha}$, and $\boldsymbol{r}_{B/A}$ for planar motion.

to obtain the direction of $\boldsymbol{a}^t_{B/A}$.

Because the three vectors in Eq. (2.10) are orthogonal, their magnitudes are related by

$$\left|\boldsymbol{a}^t_{B/A}\right| = |\boldsymbol{\alpha}||\boldsymbol{r}_{B/A}| \tag{2.12}$$

Given any two of the three magnitudes in Eq. (2.12), we can easily solve for the third magnitude.

2.5 GRAPHICAL ANALYSIS OF A FOUR-BAR MECHANISM

Having derived the basic equations for relative velocities and accelerations between two points on a rigid link, we will illustrate the use of the equations for the graphical analysis of several mechanisms. The first example involves the position, velocity, and acceleration analysis of the four-bar mechanism given in Fig. 2.8. The analysis for this example will be conducted in detail, but in subsequent examples, less detail will be given. In all of the examples, subscripts will be used to identify the links to which the points are attached. This is necessary because *the equations derived in Sections 2.3 and 2.4 apply only when the points (A and B) are fixed to the same link or lamina.*

EXAMPLE 2.1 *Graphical Analysis of a Four-Bar Mechanism*

Determine the angular positions, angular velocities, and angular accelerations of all members of the linkage shown in Fig. 2.8 when link AB is at 60° to the horizontal. Also find the position, velocity, and acceleration of point E in the coupler member of the linkage. Link AB is driven at a constant angular velocity of 10 rad/s CCW.

Solution

(a) Position Analysis

We will first address the graphical determination of the link positions. The first step is to choose a scale. The larger the scale, the more accurate the results. Therefore, it is best to use a drawing table with a drafting machine and B- or C-sized drawing paper if accurate results are desired. A CAD system that supports the construction of lines and arcs and locates intersections of lines and arcs may also be used. In the present case, we want to fit the figure onto a regular book page, so the construction will be described when it is drawn at half-scale (1 in on the drawing corresponds to 2 in on the actual mechanism). The reader is encouraged to draw the figures in this, and following examples, at full scale when working through them.

The construction is shown in the position diagram in Fig. 2.9. A horizontal line representing the base link is drawn first, and the two points bounding an interval of 2 in (half-scale) are marked to represent A and D. Next locate point B, which is where the driver link (link 2) is joined to the coupler (link 3). A line through point A at an angle of 120° to AD is drawn, and a point on that line at a distance of 1.25 in is marked to represent point B. Next locate point C, which is where the coupler is joined to the rocker (link 4).

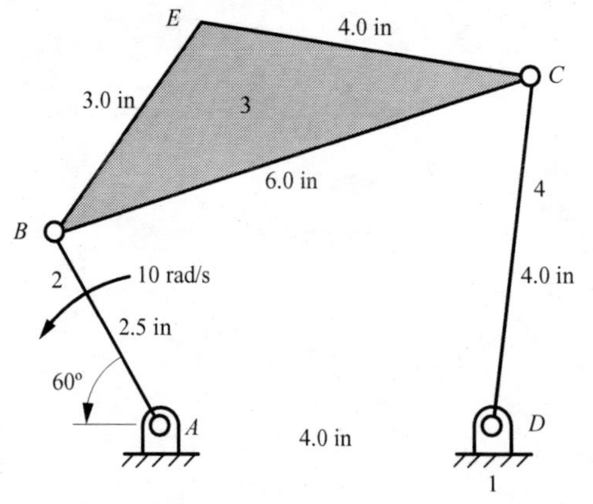

FIGURE 2.8 The four-bar linkage of Example 2.1. (Note that the figure has been reduced in size for printing.)

To locate point C, a compass is set to a radius of 3.0 in, and an arc is drawn with center point B. The compass is then reset to a 2.0-in radius, and a second arc is drawn with center D. C is at the intersection of the two arcs. Actually, there are two possible intersection points corresponding to the two assembly modes of the mechanism. This is a common situation with many mechanisms, and it is necessary for the designer to know which assembly mode is desired. In the present case, the correct one is easily located by referring to Fig. 2.8.

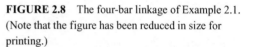

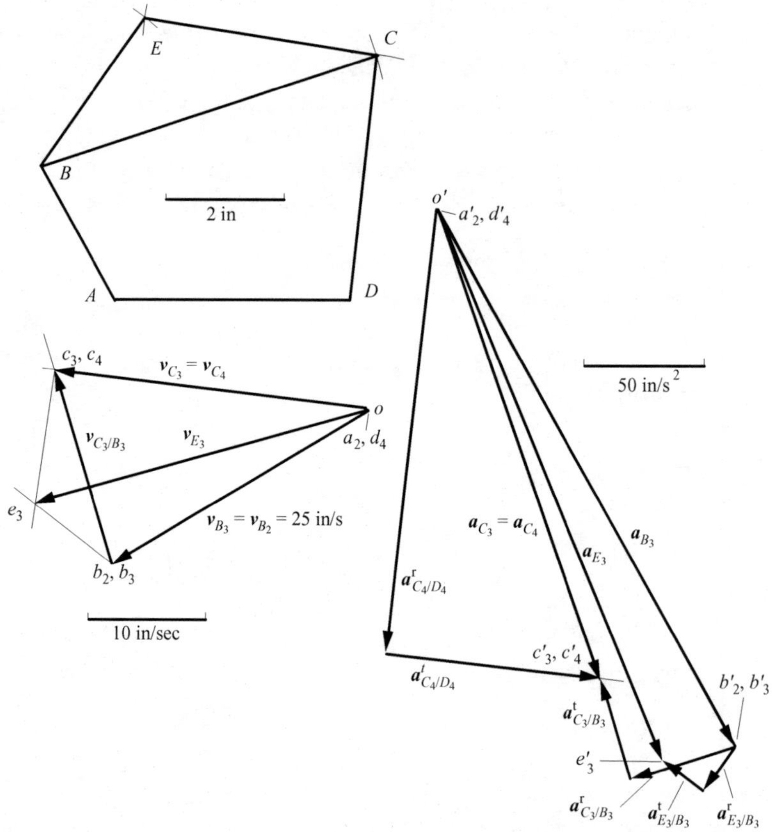

FIGURE 2.9 Position, velocity, and acceleration polygons for the four-bar linkage of Fig. 2.8. Note that the position solution is necessary to draw the velocity polygon, and the velocity polygon is needed to draw the acceleration polygon. (Note also that the size of the figure has been reduced in the printing process.)

Point E can now be located in a similar manner to that used for C because we know the distance from point E to point B and to point C. The compass is set to a radius of 1.5 in (the scaled distance from E to B), and an arc is drawn with center B. The compass is reset to a radius of 2.0 in (the scaled distance from E to C), and an arc is drawn with center C. E is at an intersection of the two arcs. Once again two intersections are possible (one below BC and one above BC), and the correct intersection can be identified by referring to Fig. 2.8.

This completes the construction of the scale drawing of the linkage and hence completes the solution of the position analysis problem. The resulting construction is shown in Fig. 2.9. The angular positions of the links may be measured from the drawing. Likewise, the position of point E can be measured and the coordinates can be multiplied by the scale factor of 2. In practice, if the position analysis is being performed solely as a preliminary step to a velocity analysis, the angular positions of the links and the position of point C would not need to be measured directly. Rather, the angular information would be directly transferred to the velocity diagram using a drawing machine or drafting triangles to construct normal or parallel lines. For the acceleration analysis, however, the linear distances would be required.

(b) Velocity Analysis

In the velocity analysis, we will typically use the same points in the same order that we used for the position analysis. We will first compute the velocity of point B, then the velocity of C, and finally the velocity of E. Location B is the location of two points, B_2 and B_3, and to be rigorous, we need to identify which of the points we are considering. Start with B_2, which is the point on driver link 2. We want to compute $\boldsymbol{v}_{B_2}$, which is the absolute velocity of point B_2.

This absolute velocity can be expressed as the relative velocity between B_2 and any point that has zero velocity. The point we shall use is A_2. It has zero velocity because it is always coincident with A_1, which is fixed to frame 1. All points in frame 1 have zero velocity. Then the velocity expression in Eq. (2.1) can be written as

$$\boldsymbol{v}_{B_2} = \boldsymbol{v}_{A_2} + \boldsymbol{v}_{B_2/A_2} = \boldsymbol{\omega}_2 \times \boldsymbol{r}_{B/A}$$

because points A_2 and B_2 are both on the same link or lamina (link 2). Note that we do not need to identify the link associated with A and B in $\boldsymbol{r}_{B/A}$ because all of the A's have the same coordinates, and all of the B's also have the same coordinates.

Note also that we know the directions and magnitudes for both $\boldsymbol{\omega}_2$ and $\boldsymbol{r}_{B/A}$, and we know that the two vectors are orthogonal to each other. Therefore, by the cross product, the velocity $\boldsymbol{v}_{B_2/A_2}$ will be orthogonal to $\boldsymbol{\omega}_2$ and $\boldsymbol{r}_{B/A}$, and the direction will be given by the right-hand screw rule. The relationship among the three vectors is represented by a diagram similar to that shown in Fig. 2.5. We can compute the magnitude of the velocity of B_2 from an equation similar to Eq. (2.6). The magnitude is given by

$$\left|\boldsymbol{v}_{B_2/A_2}\right| = \left|\boldsymbol{\omega}_2\right|\left|\boldsymbol{r}_{B/A}\right| = (10 \text{ rad/s})(2.5 \text{ in}) = 25 \text{ in/s}$$

The direction for $\boldsymbol{v}_{B_2/A_2}$ is given by using the right-hand rule or by rotating $\boldsymbol{r}_{B/A}$ 90° in the direction of $\boldsymbol{\omega}_2$.

It is now necessary to select a scale to plot $\boldsymbol{v}_{B_2/A_2}$. We used a scale of 10 in/s to 1 in in the velocity diagram shown in Fig. 2.9. This scale is based on the input velocity. We are assuming that all of the vectors will be of about the same order of magnitude. If the polygon began to move off of the page, we would need to select a new scale and redraw the vectors.

We must also select a starting point for drawing the velocity polygon. This starting point is labeled with a lower case *o* for origin. It is also called the velocity pole. Obviously, this starting point will also influence whether or not the velocity polygon will fit on the page. Therefore, the velocity pole and scale are selected together.

The direction of $\boldsymbol{v}_{B_2/A_2}$ may be obtained by placing one of the orthogonal edges of a triangle along $\overrightarrow{AB}$. and drawing a line along the other edge, since $\boldsymbol{v}_{B_2/A_2}$ is normal to $\boldsymbol{r}_{B/A}$ or $\overrightarrow{AB}$. Two points, o and b_2, separated by an interval of 2.5 in are marked as shown in Fig. 2.9. On the polygon, $\overrightarrow{ob_2}$ may be labeled as the vector $\boldsymbol{v}_{B_2/A_2}$. Here we are using the convention of labeling points on the velocity polygon with *lower case* letters and the corresponding points on the position polygon with *upper case* letters. Thus, the absolute velocity of point B_2 given here by $\boldsymbol{v}_{B_2/A_2}$ would be represented on the velocity polygon by $\overrightarrow{ob_2}$ or $\overrightarrow{a_2b_2}$.

Next we want to compute the velocity of point C. We know that B_2 and B_3 are permanently pinned together so that

$$\boldsymbol{v}_{B_3} = \boldsymbol{v}_{B_2} = 25 \text{ in/s}$$

in the direction shown in Fig. 2.9. Similarly, C_3 and C_4 are permanently pinned together. Therefore,

$$\boldsymbol{v}_{C_3} = \boldsymbol{v}_{C_4}$$

Because B_3 and C_3 are both fixed to link 3, we can write a relative velocity equation similar to Eq. (2.1). That is,

$$\boldsymbol{v}_{C_3} = \boldsymbol{v}_{B_3} + \boldsymbol{v}_{C_3/B_3} \tag{2.13}$$

In Eq. (2.13), the vector $\boldsymbol{v}_{B_3}$ is entirely known. Also, because B_3 and C_3 are on the same rigid link, we know that $\boldsymbol{v}_{C_3/B_3}$ is given by

$$\boldsymbol{v}_{C_3/B_3} = \boldsymbol{\omega}_3 \times \boldsymbol{r}_{C/B}$$

Therefore, we know that the vector $\boldsymbol{v}_{C_3/B_3}$ is perpendicular to $\boldsymbol{r}_{C/B}$ or $\overrightarrow{BC}$. We can construct a line through point b_3 on the velocity polygon in a direction perpendicular to $\overrightarrow{BC}$ on the position diagram. This is easily done with the help of drafting triangles. This defines one locus of c_3. To find another locus for c_3, we need to find the direction of the vector $\boldsymbol{v}_{C_3}$. We know that $\boldsymbol{v}_{C_3} = \boldsymbol{v}_{C_4}$, and we can identify the direction of the velocity of C_4 by inspection (C can only move on a circle about point D, and therefore, $\boldsymbol{v}_{C_4}$ must be perpendicular to the line $\overrightarrow{DC}$) or we can write a relative velocity equation for $\boldsymbol{v}_{C_4}$. Again, the velocity $\boldsymbol{v}_{C_4}$ is an absolute velocity, and it can be expressed as the relative velocity between C_4 and any point that has zero velocity. If we choose D_4 as that point, the velocity equation becomes

$$\boldsymbol{v}_{C_4} = \boldsymbol{v}_{D_4} + \boldsymbol{v}_{C_4/D_4} = \boldsymbol{v}_{C_4/D_4} = \boldsymbol{\omega}_4 \times \boldsymbol{r}_{C/D} \tag{2.14}$$

Because of the cross product, it is clear that $\boldsymbol{v}_{C_4}$ must be perpendicular to $\boldsymbol{r}_{C/D}$ or the line $\overrightarrow{DC}$. To locate c_4 on the velocity polygon, draw a line through the origin point o in a direction perpendicular to $\overrightarrow{DC}$ on the position diagram. Once again, this is most easily done with drafting triangles. Because c_3 and c_4 are located at the same point, this gives a second locus for c_3 that can be determined as shown in Fig. 2.9. The vectors $\boldsymbol{v}_{B_3}$, $\boldsymbol{v}_{C_4}$, and $\boldsymbol{v}_{C_3/B_3}$ are as shown. The magnitude of $\boldsymbol{\omega}_3$ may be found from the expression for the relative velocity $\boldsymbol{v}_{C_3/B_3}$. Then,

$$\left|\boldsymbol{v}_{C_3/B_3}\right| = \left|\boldsymbol{\omega}_3\right|\left|\boldsymbol{r}_{C/B}\right|$$

or

$$\left|\boldsymbol{\omega}_3\right| = \left|\boldsymbol{v}_{C_3/B_3}\right| / \left|\boldsymbol{r}_{C/B}\right|$$

To get $\boldsymbol{v}_{C_3/B_3}$, measure the length of $\overrightarrow{b_3c_3}$ on the velocity polygon and multiply by the scale factor. In the present case,[4] $\overrightarrow{b_3c_3} = 1.65$ in, so $\boldsymbol{v}_{C_3/B_3} = 1.65 \times 10 = 16.5$ in/s. Then

$$\left|\boldsymbol{\omega}_3\right| = \left|\boldsymbol{v}_{C_3/B_3}\right| / \left|\boldsymbol{r}_{C/B}\right| = 16.5/6.0 = 2.75 \text{ rad/s}$$

To get the direction, visualize the direction in which we would have to rotate $\boldsymbol{r}_{C/D}$ to obtain the direction of $\boldsymbol{v}_{C_3/B_3}$. This is the CCW direction.

Next compute the angular velocity $\boldsymbol{\omega}_4$ from Eq. (2.14). The magnitude can be found from an expression for the relative velocity $\boldsymbol{v}_{C_4/D_4}$. Then,

$$\left|\boldsymbol{v}_{C_4/D_4}\right| = \left|\boldsymbol{\omega}_4\right|\left|\boldsymbol{r}_{C/D}\right|$$

[4] The distances identified refer to the original drawings developed for this book. Because the drawings were reduced when the book was printed, the distances reported here cannot be measured directly from the book pages. However, the results can be verified by making measurements from the drawings and using the small scales included with each of the drawings.

or

$$|\boldsymbol{\omega}_4| = |\boldsymbol{v}_{C_4/D_4}|/|\boldsymbol{r}_{C/D}|$$

To obtain the velocity $\boldsymbol{v}_{C_4/D_4}$, measure the distance $\overrightarrow{c_4d_4}$ on the velocity polygon and multiply by the scale factor. In the present case, $\overrightarrow{c_4d_4} = 2.69$ in, so $\boldsymbol{v}_{C_4/D_4} = 2.69 \times 10 = 26.9$ in/s. Then

$$|\boldsymbol{\omega}_4| = |\boldsymbol{v}_{C_4/D_4}|/|\boldsymbol{r}_{C/D}| = 26.9/4.0 = 6.73 \text{ rad/s}$$

To get the direction, visualize the direction in which we would have to rotate $\boldsymbol{r}_{C/D}$ to obtain the direction of $\boldsymbol{v}_{C_4/D_4}$. The direction is CCW.

The velocity of point E_3 may be obtained by considering first the point pair E_3 and B_3 and then the pair E_3 and C_3. Both pairs are fixed to member 3. The relative velocity expressions are

$$\boldsymbol{v}_{E_3} = \boldsymbol{v}_{B_3} + \boldsymbol{v}_{E_3/B_3} = \boldsymbol{v}_{B_3} + \boldsymbol{\omega}_3 \times \boldsymbol{r}_{E/B} \tag{2.15}$$

and

$$\boldsymbol{v}_{E_3} = \boldsymbol{v}_{C_3} + \boldsymbol{v}_{E_3/C_3} = \boldsymbol{v}_{C_3} + \boldsymbol{\omega}_3 \times \boldsymbol{r}_{E/C} \tag{2.16}$$

The velocities $\boldsymbol{v}_{C_3}$ and $\boldsymbol{v}_{B_3}$ are known and have been plotted as $\overrightarrow{ob_3}$ and $\overrightarrow{oc_3}$ on the velocity polygon. We can compute $|\boldsymbol{v}_{E_3}|$ two different ways as implied by Eqs. (2.15) and (2.16). One way is to compute the cross product in Eq. (2.15) and add the resulting vector to $|\boldsymbol{v}_{E_3}|$. We could make similar calculations using Eq. (2.16). A second way is to solve both equations simultaneously. Using Eq. (2.15), we know that $|\boldsymbol{v}_{E_3}|$ lies on a line through b_3 on the velocity diagram and is perpendicular to $\overrightarrow{EB}$ on the position diagram. Similarly, $|\boldsymbol{v}_{E_3}|$ lies on a line through c_3 on the velocity diagram and is perpendicular to $\overrightarrow{EC}$ on the position diagram. The point e_3 lies on the intersection of the two lines, and $|\boldsymbol{v}_{E_3}|$ is the vector from o to the point e_3.

The magnitude of $|\boldsymbol{v}_{E_3}|$ can be obtained by measuring $\overrightarrow{oe_3}$ and multiplying by the scale factor. The distance $\overrightarrow{oe_3} = 2.93$ in, so $|\boldsymbol{v}_{E_3}| = 29.3$ in/s. Its direction may be measured from the diagram with a protractor. The direction is $-164.9°$ with the zero angle reference being horizontal and positive to the right. This completes the velocity analysis of the linkage.

(c) Acceleration Analysis

The acceleration analysis can be conducted using the points that were used in the velocity analysis. In fact, usually the acceleration analysis can be conducted simply by differentiating the velocity equations. We will first compute the acceleration of point B_2 (and B_3), then the acceleration of C_3 (and C_4), and finally the acceleration of E_3. The acceleration of B_2 can be expressed as the absolute acceleration between B_2 and A_2. Because two points on the same rigid link are involved, an acceleration expression similar to Eq. (2.8) can be written as

$$\boldsymbol{a}_{B_2} = \boldsymbol{a}_{A_2} + \boldsymbol{a}_{B_2/A_2} = \boldsymbol{\alpha}_2 \times \boldsymbol{r}_{B/A} + \boldsymbol{\omega}_2 \times (\boldsymbol{\omega}_2 \times \boldsymbol{r}_{B/A}) = \boldsymbol{a}^{t}_{B_2/A_2} + \boldsymbol{a}^{r}_{B_2/A_2}$$

Note that we know the directions and magnitudes for $\boldsymbol{\omega}_2$, $\boldsymbol{\alpha}_2$, and $\boldsymbol{r}_{B/A}$, and therefore we can compute each of the vectors in the equation. Because of the cross product, the acceleration $\mathbf{a}^{t}_{B_2/A_2}$ will be orthogonal to $\boldsymbol{\alpha}_2$ and $\boldsymbol{r}_{B/A}$, and the direction will be given by the right-hand screw rule. The direction of $\mathbf{a}^{r}_{B_2/A_2}$ will be opposite to the direction of $\boldsymbol{r}_{B/A}$. We can compute the magnitude of $\mathbf{a}^{t}_{B_2/A_2}$ from an equation similar to Eq. (2.10). The magnitude is given by

$$|\boldsymbol{a}^{t}_{B_2/A_2}| = |\boldsymbol{\alpha}_2||\boldsymbol{r}_{B/A}| = (0)(2.5 \text{ in}) = 0$$

The magnitude of the radial component can be computed by using Eq. (2.8). Then,

$$\boldsymbol{a}^{r}_{B_2/A_2} = \boldsymbol{\omega}_2 \times (\boldsymbol{\omega}_2 \times \boldsymbol{r}_{B/A}) = |\boldsymbol{\omega}_2|^2 |\boldsymbol{r}_{B/A}| = 10^2(2.5) = 250 \text{ in/s}^2$$

and the direction is opposite to that of $\boldsymbol{r}_{B/A}$. The direction of $\mathbf{a}^{r}_{B_2/A_2}$ is therefore 60° below the horizontal (down and to the right). It is now necessary to choose a scale and starting point (acceleration pole) and plot the acceleration of point B_2. We will use a scale of 50 in/s^2 to 1 in to ensure that the diagram will fit on a quarto-sized page. The acceleration $\boldsymbol{a}_{B_2/A_2} = \boldsymbol{a}^{r}_{B_2/A_2}$ is plotted in Fig. 2.9 as $\overrightarrow{o'b'_2}$. Here we are using the convention that a lower case letter with a prime (′) indicates the acceleration of the corresponding point on the position diagram. The most convenient way to plot a line parallel to $\overrightarrow{AB}$ is to place a drafting triangle with one of the two orthogonal sides along $\overrightarrow{ob_2}$ on the velocity diagram, and draw a line through o' along the other side of the triangle. Since $\overrightarrow{ob_2}$ is normal to $\overrightarrow{AB}$, this results in a line parallel to $\overrightarrow{AB}$. Once again, $\overrightarrow{o'b_2'}$ is directed down and to the right because it is in the minus $\overrightarrow{AB}$ direction.

Next we want to compute the acceleration of point C. Recall that B_2 and B_3 are permanently pinned together. Therefore,

$$\boldsymbol{a}_{B_2} = \boldsymbol{a}_{B_3} = 250 \text{ in/s}^2$$

in the direction shown in Fig. 2.9. Similarly, C_3 and C_4 are permanently pinned together. Therefore,

$$\boldsymbol{a}_{C_3} = \boldsymbol{a}_{C_4}$$

Because B_3 and C_4 are both fixed to link 3, we can write the following relative acceleration equation:

$$\boldsymbol{a}_{C_3} = \boldsymbol{a}_{B_3} + \boldsymbol{a}_{C_3/B_3} = \boldsymbol{a}_{B_3} + \boldsymbol{a}^{\mathrm{r}}_{C_3/B_3} + \boldsymbol{a}^{\mathrm{t}}_{C_3/B_3} \tag{2.17}$$

In Eq. (2.17), the vector $\boldsymbol{a}_{B_3}$ is entirely known. Also, the radial component of the acceleration that is a function of position and velocity only can be computed directly from the following:

$$\boldsymbol{a}^{\mathrm{r}}_{C_3/B_3} = \boldsymbol{\omega}_3 \times \left(\boldsymbol{\omega}_3 \times \boldsymbol{r}_{C/B}\right)$$

From the velocity analysis, we computed the magnitude of the angular velocity to be $|\boldsymbol{\omega}_3| = 2.75$ rad/s. The radial acceleration is a vector from C to B on the position diagram (opposite $\boldsymbol{r}_{C/B}$), and the magnitude is given by

$$\left|\boldsymbol{a}^{\mathrm{r}}_{C_3/B_3}\right| = \left|\boldsymbol{\omega}_3\right|^2 \left|\boldsymbol{r}_{C/B}\right| = 2.75^2(6) = 45.4 \text{ in/s}^2$$

A convenient way to draw a line parallel to $\overrightarrow{BC}$ is, again, to place a triangle with one of the orthogonal sides along $\overrightarrow{b_3c_3}$ on the velocity polygon and draw a line along the other orthogonal side through point b'_3. The direction is down and to the left because this component is in the minus $\boldsymbol{r}_{C/B}$ direction.

The tangential component $\boldsymbol{a}^{\mathrm{t}}_{C_3/B_3}$ is given by

$$\boldsymbol{a}^{\mathrm{t}}_{C_3/B_3} = \boldsymbol{\alpha}_3 \times \boldsymbol{r}_{C/B}$$

The magnitude of $\mathbf{a}^{\mathrm{t}}_{C_3/B_3}$ is unknown because $\boldsymbol{\alpha}_3$ is unknown. However, this vector will be normal to $\overrightarrow{BC}$. Hence a line is drawn through the tip of the $\mathbf{a}^{\mathrm{r}}_{C_3/B_3}$ vector to represent this direction. This defines one locus of c'_3. To find another locus for c'_3, we need to find another equation for the vector $\boldsymbol{a}_{C_3}$. We know that $\boldsymbol{a}_{C_3} = \boldsymbol{a}_{C_4}$, and we can write an equation for the acceleration of C_4. Again, the acceleration $\boldsymbol{a}_{C_4}$ is an absolute acceleration, and it can be expressed as the relative acceleration between C_4 and any point that has zero acceleration. If we choose D_4 as that point, the acceleration equation becomes

$$\boldsymbol{a}_{C_4} = \boldsymbol{a}_{C_4/D_4} = \boldsymbol{a}^{\mathrm{r}}_{C_4/D_4} + \boldsymbol{a}^{\mathrm{t}}_{C_4/D_4}$$

The radial component of the acceleration is a function of position and velocity only and can be computed directly from the following:

$$\boldsymbol{a}^{\mathrm{r}}_{C_4/D_4} = \boldsymbol{\omega}_4 \times \left(\boldsymbol{\omega}_4 \times \boldsymbol{r}_{C/D}\right)$$

From the velocity analysis, we computed the magnitude of the angular velocity to be $|\boldsymbol{\omega}_4| = 6.73$ rad/s. The radial acceleration is a vector from C to D on the position diagram (opposite $\boldsymbol{r}_{C/D}$), and the magnitude is given by

$$\left|\boldsymbol{a}^{\mathrm{r}}_{C_4/D_4}\right| = \left|\boldsymbol{\omega}_4\right|^2 \left|\boldsymbol{r}_{C/D}\right| = 6.73^2(4) = 181.2 \text{ in/s}^2$$

This vector is plotted from o' in Fig. 2.9.

The tangential component $\mathbf{a}^{\mathrm{t}}_{C_4/D_4}$ is given by

$$\boldsymbol{a}^{\mathrm{t}}_{C_4/D_4} = \boldsymbol{\alpha}_4 \times \boldsymbol{r}_{C/D}$$

The magnitude of $\boldsymbol{a}^{t}_{C_4/D_4}$ is unknown because $\boldsymbol{\alpha}_4$ is unknown. However, this vector will be normal to $\overrightarrow{BD}$. Hence a line is drawn through the tip of the $\boldsymbol{a}^{r}_{C_4/D_4}$ vector to represent this direction. This defines a second locus for c'_3 and c'_4. The points c'_3 and c'_4 are located where the two loci intersect as shown in Fig. 2.9. The vectors $\boldsymbol{a}^{t}_{C_3/D_3}$, $\boldsymbol{a}^{t}_{C_4/D_4}$, and $\boldsymbol{a}^{r}_{C_4/D_4}$ are as shown. The magnitude of $\boldsymbol{\alpha}_3$ may be found from the expression for the tangential component of the relative acceleration between C_3 and B_3. Then,

$$\left|\boldsymbol{a}^{t}_{C_3/B_3}\right| = |\boldsymbol{\alpha}_3||\boldsymbol{r}_{C/B}|$$

or

$$|\boldsymbol{\alpha}_3| = \left|\boldsymbol{a}^{t}_{C_3/B_3}\right| / |\boldsymbol{r}_{C/B}|$$

To get $|\boldsymbol{a}^{t}_{C_3/B_3}|$, measure the length of the vector on the acceleration polygon and multiply by the scale factor. On the acceleration polygon, the length of the line corresponding to $|\boldsymbol{a}^{t}_{C_3/B_3}|$ is 0.847 in. Therefore, $|\boldsymbol{a}^{t}_{C_3/B_3}| = 0.847 \times 50 = 42.2$ in/s^2. Then

$$|\boldsymbol{\alpha}_3| = \left|\boldsymbol{a}^{t}_{C_3/B_3}\right| / |\boldsymbol{r}_{C/B}| = 42.2/6.0 = 7.06 \text{ rad/s}^2$$

To get the direction, visualize the direction in which we would have to rotate $\boldsymbol{r}_{C/B}$ to obtain the direction of $|\boldsymbol{a}^{t}_{C_3/B_3}|$. The direction is CCW.

Next compute the angular acceleration $\boldsymbol{\alpha}_4$. The magnitude can be found from an expression for the tangential component of the relative acceleration $\boldsymbol{a}^{t}_{C_4/D_4}$. Then,

$$\left|\boldsymbol{a}^{t}_{C_4/D_4}\right| = |\boldsymbol{\alpha}_4||\boldsymbol{r}_{C/D}|$$

or

$$|\boldsymbol{\alpha}_4| = \left|\boldsymbol{a}^{t}_{C_4/D_4}\right| / |\boldsymbol{r}_{C/D}|$$

To obtain the magnitude of the tangential component of acceleration, measure $|\boldsymbol{a}^{t}_{C_4/D_4}|$ on the acceleration diagram and multiply by the scale factor. From Fig. 2.9, $|\boldsymbol{a}^{t}_{C_4/D_4}| = 1.816 \times 50 = 90.8$ in/s^2. Then

$$|\boldsymbol{\alpha}_4| = \left|\boldsymbol{a}^{t}_{C_4/D_4}\right| / |\boldsymbol{r}_{C/D}| = 90.8/4.0 = 22.7 \text{ rad/s}^2$$

To get the direction, visualize the direction that we would have to rotate $\boldsymbol{r}_{C/D}$ to obtain the direction of $|\boldsymbol{a}^{t}_{C_4/D_4}|$. The direction is CW.

The acceleration of point E_3 may be obtained by considering first the point pair E_3 and B_3 and then the pair E_3 and C_3. Both pairs are fixed to member 3. The relative acceleration expressions are

$$\boldsymbol{a}_{E_3} = \boldsymbol{a}_{B_3} + \boldsymbol{a}_{E_3/B_3} = \boldsymbol{a}_{B_3} + \boldsymbol{a}^{r}_{E_3/B_3} + \boldsymbol{a}^{t}_{E_3/B_3} = \boldsymbol{a}_{B_3} + \boldsymbol{\omega}_3 \times (\boldsymbol{\omega}_3 \times \boldsymbol{r}_{E/B}) + \boldsymbol{\alpha}_3 \times \boldsymbol{r}_{E/B} \tag{2.18}$$

and

$$\boldsymbol{a}_{E_3} = \boldsymbol{a}_{C_3} + \boldsymbol{a}_{E_3/C_3} = \boldsymbol{a}_{C_3} + \boldsymbol{a}^{r}_{E_3/C_3} + \boldsymbol{a}^{t}_{E_3/C_3} = \boldsymbol{a}_{C_3} + \boldsymbol{\omega}_3 \times (\boldsymbol{\omega}_3 \times \boldsymbol{r}_{E/C}) + \boldsymbol{\alpha}_4 \times \boldsymbol{r}_{E/C} \tag{2.19}$$

The accelerations $\boldsymbol{a}_{B_3}$ and $\boldsymbol{a}_{C_3}$ are known and have been plotted as $\overrightarrow{o'b'_3}$ and $\overrightarrow{o'c'_3}$ on the acceleration polygon. As in the corresponding case of velocities, we can compute $\boldsymbol{a}_{E_3}$ two different ways as implied by Eqs. (2.18) and (2.19). One way is to compute the cross products in Eq. (2.18) and add the resulting vectors to $\boldsymbol{a}_{B_3}$. We could also make similar calculations using Eq. (2.19). A second way is to solve both equations simultaneously as was done in the velocity analysis. We will use the first procedure here. To determine $\boldsymbol{a}_{E_3}$ using Eq. (2.18), we must compute $\boldsymbol{a}^{r}_{E_3/B_3}$ and $\boldsymbol{a}^{t}_{E_3/B_3}$. The direction of the radial component is opposite to that of $\boldsymbol{r}_{E/B}$, and the magnitude is given by

$$\left|\boldsymbol{a}^{r}_{E_3/B_3}\right| = |\boldsymbol{\omega}_3|^2 |\boldsymbol{r}_{E/B}| = 2.75^2(3) = 22.7 \text{ in/s}^2$$

This vector is added to $\boldsymbol{a}_{B_3}$ in Fig. 2.9.

The direction of $\boldsymbol{a}^{t}_{E_3/B_3}$ is found using the right-hand screw rule or by turning $\boldsymbol{r}_{E/B}$ 90° in the direction of $\boldsymbol{\alpha}_3$. Recall that $\boldsymbol{\alpha}_3$ is CCW. The magnitude of $\mathbf{a}^{t}_{E_3/B_3}$ is given by

$$\left|\boldsymbol{a}^{t}_{E_3/B_3}\right| = |\boldsymbol{\alpha}_3||\boldsymbol{r}_{E/B}| = 7.06(3) = 21.2 \text{ in/s}^2$$

This vector is plotted in Fig. 2.9. The point e'_3 is located at the tip of $\boldsymbol{a}^t_{E_3/B_3}$. The acceleration of E_3 is located by the vector from o' to e'_3 on the acceleration diagram. To determine the magnitude, measure $\overrightarrow{o'e'_3}$ and multiply by the scale factor. The result is

$$\left|\boldsymbol{a}_{E_3}\right| = 4.85 \times 50 = 2421.5 \text{ in/s}^2$$

The vector is pointed in a direction that is 67° below the horizontal and to the right. A much more efficient way to locate point e'_3 will be presented later in this chapter.

2.6 GRAPHICAL ANALYSIS OF A SLIDER–CRANK MECHANISM

The analysis of a slider-crank mechanism depends on whether the crank or the slider is the driver. If the crank is the driver, we need to know the angular position, velocity, and acceleration of the crank. If the slider is the driver, we need to know the position, velocity, and acceleration of some point on the slider. Note that each point on the slider will have a unique position, but all points will have the same velocity and the same acceleration.

We will analyze the slider-crank mechanism shown in Fig. 2.10, where the crank is the driver. As was the case for the four-bar linkage, the key to the acceleration analysis of this mechanism is the relationship between the velocities and accelerations of two points on the same rigid body.

EXAMPLE 2.2
Graphical Analysis of a Slider–Crank Mechanism

Find $\boldsymbol{a}_C$ and $\boldsymbol{\omega}_3$ for the slider–crank linkage in the position shown in Fig. 2.10. The crank *AB* (link 2) is driven at a constant angular velocity of 10 rad/s CCW. *C* is the axis of the revolute joint connecting the connecting rod, link 3, to the slider, link 4. In the position shown, *AB* is at 45° to *AC*, and the link lengths are shown on the drawing.

Solution

(a) Position Analysis

The linkage is first drawn to scale to establish the direction of member *BC*. To do this, first locate the horizontal line through *A* and on which *C* lies. Next, draw member *AB* to scale. Then draw an arc scaled to represent 8 in and centered at *B*. The arc intersects the horizontal line through *A* at two locations. The desired location is to the right of *A* as indicated in Fig. 2.10. The scaled drawing is shown in Fig. 2.11.

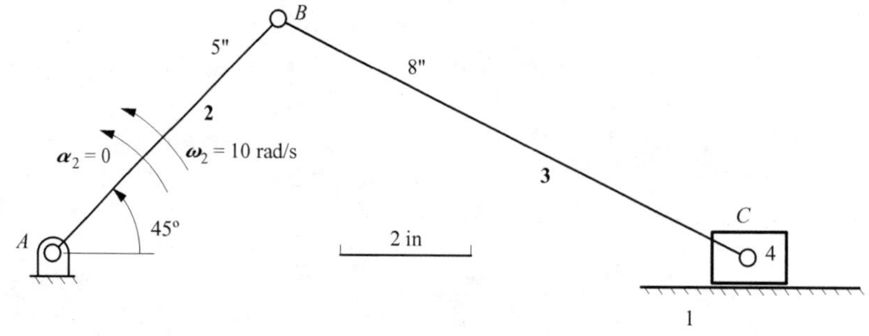

FIGURE 2.10 The slider–crank linkage to be analyzed in Example 2.2.

(b) Velocity Polygon

The basic equation to be solved is

$$\boldsymbol{v}_{C_3} = \boldsymbol{v}_{B_3} + \boldsymbol{v}_{C_3/B_3} = \boldsymbol{v}_{B_2} + \boldsymbol{v}_{C_3/B_3} = \boldsymbol{v}_{B_2/A_2} + \boldsymbol{v}_{C_3/B_3}$$

From the given data, we have

$$\boldsymbol{v}_{B_2} = \boldsymbol{v}_{B_2/A_2} = \boldsymbol{\omega}_2 \times \boldsymbol{r}_{B/A} = 10 \times 5 = 50 \text{ in/s (normal to } \boldsymbol{r}_{B/A})$$

The direction for the velocity of C_3 must be horizontal. This lets us solve the basic velocity equation as shown in Fig. 2.11. By measurement in Fig. 2.11, we obtain

$$\left|\boldsymbol{v}_{C_3/B_3}\right| = 1.98 \times 20 = 39.6 \text{ in/s}$$

Then

$$\left|\boldsymbol{\omega}_3\right| = \left|\boldsymbol{v}_{C_3/B_3}\right| / \left|\boldsymbol{r}_{C/B}\right| = 39.6 / 8 = 4.95 \text{ rad/s}$$

in the CW direction.

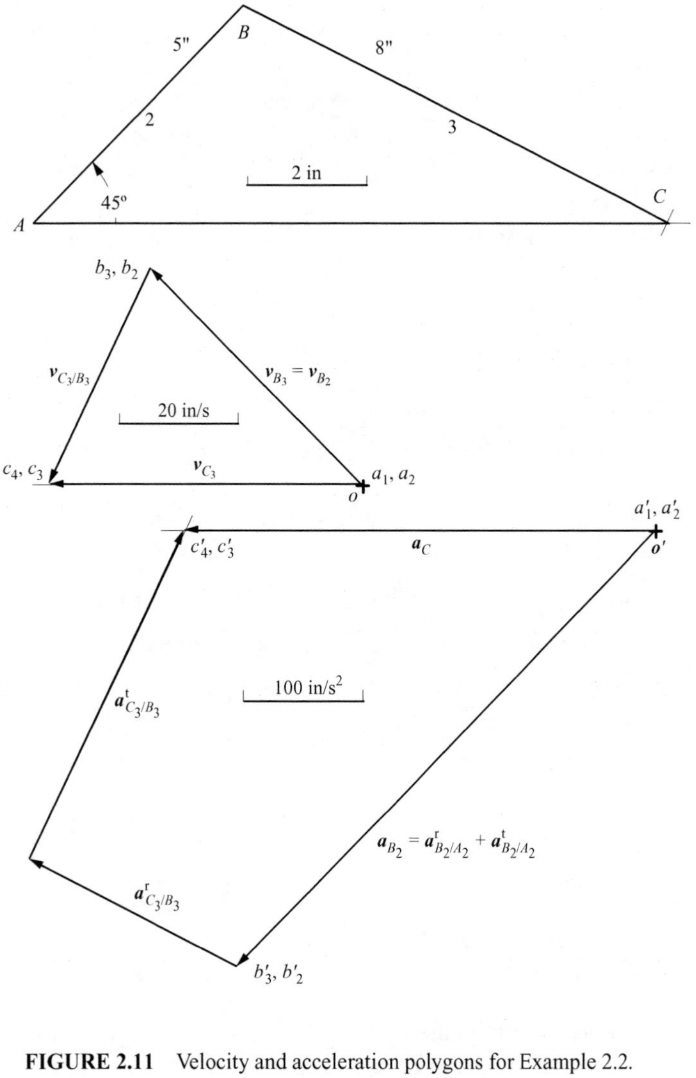

FIGURE 2.11 Velocity and acceleration polygons for Example 2.2.

(c) Acceleration Polygon

The basic acceleration equation to be solved is

$$\boldsymbol{a}_{C_3} = \boldsymbol{a}_{B_2/A_2} + \boldsymbol{a}_{C_3/B_3} = \boldsymbol{a}^{\text{r}}_{B_2/A_2} + \boldsymbol{a}^{\text{t}}_{B_2/A_2} + \boldsymbol{a}^{\text{r}}_{C_3/B_3} + \boldsymbol{a}^{\text{t}}_{C_3/B_3}$$

From the given data, we have

$$\left|\boldsymbol{a}^{\text{r}}_{B_2/A_2}\right| = |\boldsymbol{\omega}_2|^2 |\boldsymbol{r}_{B/A}| = 10^2(5) = 500 \text{ in/s}^2$$

$$\left|\boldsymbol{a}^{\text{t}}_{B_2/A_2}\right| = |\boldsymbol{\alpha}_2||\boldsymbol{r}_{B/A}| = 0(5) = 0$$

Using information from the velocity analysis, we obtain

$$\left|\boldsymbol{a}^{\text{r}}_{C_3/B_3}\right| = |\boldsymbol{\omega}_3|^2 |\boldsymbol{r}_{C/B}| = 4.95^2(8) = 196 \text{ in/s}^2$$

The direction for the acceleration of C_3 must be horizontal, and the basic acceleration equation can now be solved for the acceleration of C_3, as shown in Fig. 2.11. By measurement in Fig. 2.11, we get

$$\left|\boldsymbol{a}_{C_3}\right| = 3.98(100) = 398 \text{ in/s}^2$$

and

$$\left|\boldsymbol{a}^{\text{t}}_{C_3/B_3}\right| = 2.98 \times 100 = 298 \text{ in/s}^2$$

Then

$$|\boldsymbol{\alpha}_3| = \left|\boldsymbol{a}^{\text{t}}_{C_3/B_3}\right| / |\boldsymbol{r}_{C/B}| = \frac{298}{8} = 37.3 \text{ rad/s}^2$$

in the CCW direction.

The steps for the total analysis are summarized in the following, and the results are shown in Fig. 2.11.

1. Draw the linkage to scale.
2. Construct the velocity polygon and compute $\boldsymbol{\omega}_3$.
3. Compute the magnitudes of $\boldsymbol{a}^{\text{r}}_{B_2/A_2}$, $\boldsymbol{a}^{\text{t}}_{B_2/A_2}$, and $\boldsymbol{a}^{\text{r}}_{C_3/B_3}$ and identify their directions.
4. Choose a suitable scale and plot $\boldsymbol{a}^{\text{r}}_{B_2/A_2}$ opposite to $\boldsymbol{r}_{B/A}$. Put the tail of the vector at the acceleration pole, o'.
5. Plot $\boldsymbol{a}^{\text{t}}_{B_2/A_2}$ (zero in this case) normal to $\boldsymbol{r}_{B/A}$ and through the tip of $\boldsymbol{a}^{\text{r}}_{B_2/A_2}$. The tip of $\boldsymbol{a}^{\text{t}}_{B_2/A_2}$ gives the point b'_2. Here, the direction for $\boldsymbol{a}_{B_2/A_2}$ is in the direction of $-\boldsymbol{r}_{B/A}$.
6. Plot vector $\boldsymbol{a}^{\text{r}}_{C_3/B_3}$ opposite to $\boldsymbol{r}_{C/B}$ with its tail at point b'_2.
7. Draw a line through the tip of vector $\boldsymbol{a}^{\text{r}}_{C_3/B_3}$ normal to line $\overrightarrow{BC}$.
8. Draw a line through o' parallel to line $\overrightarrow{AC}$. The intersection of the lines drawn in steps 7 and 8 gives point c'_3.
9. Measure the magnitude $\boldsymbol{a}_C$ as $\overrightarrow{o'c'_3}$ and note its direction.
10. Measure $\boldsymbol{a}^{\text{t}}_{C_3/B_3}$ and compute $\boldsymbol{\alpha}_3 = |\boldsymbol{a}^{\text{t}}_{C_3/B_3}|/|\boldsymbol{r}_{C/B}|$. Note that the sense of $\boldsymbol{\alpha}_3$ is found by visualizing C rotating about B so that C moves in the $\boldsymbol{a}^{\text{t}}_{C_3/B_3}$ direction.

2.7 THE VELOCITY IMAGE THEOREM

To conduct a graphical analysis of a linkage with more than one loop, it is necessary to obtain the velocities of additional points on a rigid link once the kinematic properties of the first two points are known. After the velocity and acceleration of two points are known, the angular velocity of the body can be determined. Knowing the velocity of a point and the angular velocity of the body, the velocity of any other point on the rigid body can be computed using Eqs. (2.4) and (2.5). Similarly, if the velocity analysis has been conducted, and the acceleration of a point and the angular acceleration of the body are known, the acceleration of any other point on the body can be found using Eq. (2.9). An alternative method for determining the velocity and acceleration of a third point on a rigid body is to use the concept of velocity and acceleration image. The velocity image theorem will be discussed first.

Notation As indicated previously, a convenient means of labeling the velocity polygon is to use a lower case letter to identify the absolute velocity of each point on the position diagram. A vector from the velocity pole to the point will then represent the absolute velocity of the point. A vector between any two points will correspond to the relative velocity between the points. For example, in Fig. 2.12, $\boldsymbol{v}_{C/B} = \overrightarrow{bc}$.

Consider the triangle *PQR* formed by three points (*P*, *Q*, and *R*) all fixed to the same rigid body. The velocity image theorem states that given the triangle *PQR* in a rigid body, the triangle *pqr* in the velocity diagram will be similar to triangle *PQR*, rotated from *PQR* by 90° in the positive $\boldsymbol{\omega}$ direction, and magnified by the factor ω. This theorem, stated here for triangles, can be extended to apply to any polygon, because any polygon can be broken down into triangles, or indeed to any shape, since any shape can be approximated by a polygon to any desired degree of accuracy. Thus, the velocity image of any geometric shape is similar to that geometric shape, rotated relative to that shape through 90° in the positive $\boldsymbol{\omega}$ direction, and is magnified by a factor ω.

The proof of the theorem can be developed using Fig. 2.13. In that figure, the position diagram for the rigid link is *PQR* and the velocity diagram is *pqr*. Using $\boldsymbol{v}_{Q/P}$ as an example, we get

$$\boldsymbol{v}_{P/Q} = \boldsymbol{\omega} \times \boldsymbol{r}_{P/Q}$$

Therefore, $\boldsymbol{v}_{Q/P}$ is normal to $\overrightarrow{PQ}$ and has the magnitude ωPQ. Hence $\overrightarrow{pq}$ has magnitude ωPQ and is rotated 90° in the $\boldsymbol{\omega}$ direction. Similarly $\overrightarrow{qr} = \omega RP$ and is rotated 90° in the $\boldsymbol{\omega}$ direction. Hence, triangle *pqr* is similar to triangle *PQR,* is rotated from triangle *PQR* through 90° in the $\boldsymbol{\omega}$ direction, and is magnified over triangle *PQR* by a factor ω.

Note that the velocity image can be used to determine directly the velocity of any point in the rigid body given the position of the point and the velocity diagram. Conversely, the location of a point with a given velocity can be found by mapping points in the velocity diagram to points in the position diagram.

The manner in which the velocity image is used to analyze multiloop linkages is illustrated in Example 2.3 involving a six-bar linkage.

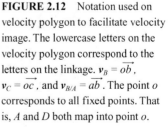

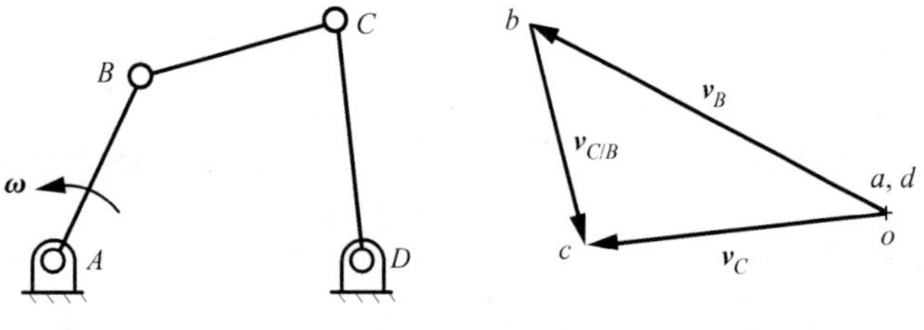

FIGURE 2.12 Notation used on velocity polygon to facilitate velocity image. The lowercase letters on the velocity polygon correspond to the letters on the linkage. $\boldsymbol{v}_B = \overrightarrow{ob}$, $\boldsymbol{v}_C = \overrightarrow{oc}$, and $\boldsymbol{v}_{B/A} = \overrightarrow{ab}$. The point *o* corresponds to all fixed points. That is, *A* and *D* both map into point *o*.

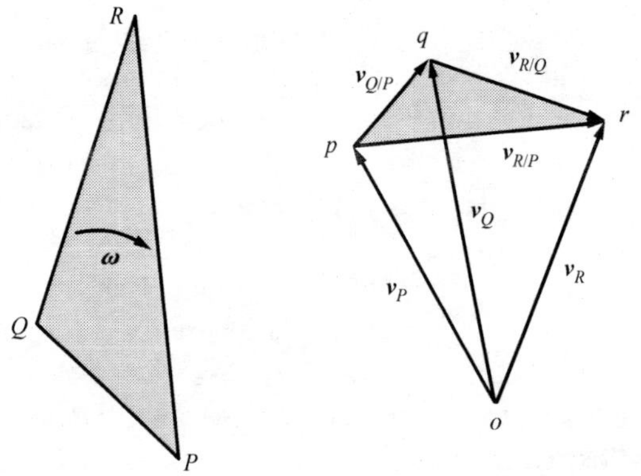

FIGURE 2.13 Link *PQR* and its velocity image in the velocity polygon. Triangle *pqr* is similar to triangle *PQR* and is rotated from it by 90° in the $\boldsymbol{\omega}$ direction.

EXAMPLE 2.3 *Graphical Velocity Analysis of Six-Bar Linkage*

Develop a procedure for finding the angular velocities of links 3, 5, and 6 and the velocity of point *B* of the linkage shown in Fig. 2.14.

Solution

The polygons for the analysis are shown in Fig. 2.14. The velocity analysis starts with the slider–crank part of the mechanism. The equations involved and the order in which they are solved are given in the following:

$$\boldsymbol{v}_{B_3} = \boldsymbol{v}_{B_2} = \boldsymbol{v}_{B_2/A_2} = \boldsymbol{\omega}_2 \times \boldsymbol{r}_{A/B}$$

and

$$\boldsymbol{v}_{C_3} = \boldsymbol{v}_{B_3} + \boldsymbol{v}_{C_3/B_3}$$

Next we will find the velocity of point D_3 by image. Then the dyad (links 5 and 6) can be analyzed using

$$\boldsymbol{v}_{E_5} = \boldsymbol{v}_{E_6}$$

$$\boldsymbol{v}_{E_5} = \boldsymbol{v}_{D_5} + \boldsymbol{v}_{E_5/D_5} = \boldsymbol{v}_{D_5} + \boldsymbol{\omega}_5 \times \boldsymbol{r}_{E/D}$$

$$\boldsymbol{v}_{E_6} = \boldsymbol{v}_{F_6} + \boldsymbol{v}_{E_6/F_6} = \boldsymbol{\omega}_6 \times \boldsymbol{r}_{E/F}$$

Steps

1. Draw the linkage to scale in the position given.
2. Select a suitable scale and plot $\boldsymbol{v}_{B_3} = \boldsymbol{v}_{B_2/A_2} = \overrightarrow{ob}$ normal to line $\overrightarrow{AB}$. Point *o* represents the points on the fixed frame and all other points with zero velocity. That is, *all* points with zero velocity in the linkage map into point *o*, and all points at *o* map to the linkage as points with zero velocity.
3. Draw a line through point *o* parallel to line $\overrightarrow{AC}$. The velocity of C_3 must lie on this line.
4. Draw a line through point b_3 normal to line $\overrightarrow{BC}$. The intersection of the lines drawn in steps 3 and 4 gives point c_3.
5. Now find the velocity image of D_3. Start by drawing a line through point b$_3$ normal to line $\overrightarrow{BD}$.
6. Draw a line through point c_3 normal to line $\overrightarrow{CD}$. The intersection of the lines drawn in steps 5 and 6 is point d_3.
7. Next locate e_5 (and e_6). Start by drawing a line through point d_3 normal to line $\overrightarrow{DE}$.
8. Draw a line through point *o* normal to line $\overrightarrow{EF}$. The intersection of the lines drawn in steps 7 and 8 is point e_5.
9. Compute ω_3 from $|\boldsymbol{\omega}_3| = |\boldsymbol{v}_{C_3/B_3}|/|\boldsymbol{r}_{C/B}|$. Note that the sense is CCW. This is inferred by noting that C_3 must rotate CCW about B_3 to move in the direction of $\boldsymbol{v}_{C_3/B_3}$.

10. Compute ω_5 from $|\boldsymbol{\omega}_5| = |\boldsymbol{v}_{D_5/E_5}|/|\boldsymbol{r}_{D/E}|$. The sense is CCW, since D_5 must rotate CCW about E_5 to move in the direction of $\boldsymbol{v}_{D_5/E_5}$.
11. Compute ω_6 from $|\boldsymbol{\omega}_6| = |\boldsymbol{v}_{E_6/F_6}|/|\boldsymbol{r}_{E/F}|$. The sense is CW, since E_6 must move CW about D_6 to move in the direction of $\boldsymbol{v}_{E_6/F_6}$.

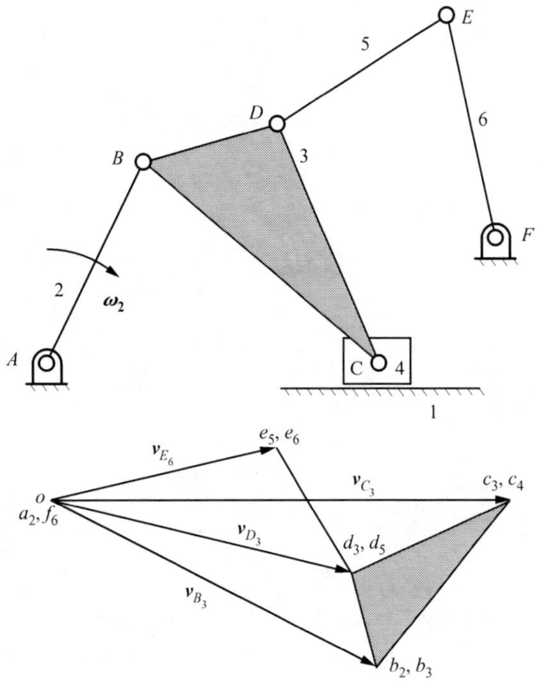

FIGURE 2.14 The linkage and velocity polygon of Example 2.3. The velocity image theorem is used to locate point d_3.

The velocity image theorem is very useful for finding the velocity of a point on the coupler of a linkage at which an additional joint is placed. It is important to notice that the *shape* of any velocity polygon (i.e., all angles within it) is determined only by the dimensions of the linkage. See, for instance, Fig. 2.14. Further, the speed at which the linkage is operated can affect only the *size*, or scale, of the polygon and not the shape. This property will play a pivotal role in later sections (e.g., Section 2.9).

2.8 THE ACCELERATION IMAGE THEOREM

As was the case in the velocity analysis, an acceleration image theorem provides an easy way to obtain accelerations of additional points on a rigid body when the accelerations of two points are already known. This is useful when multiple loops are involved in the linkage. In the acceleration diagram we will use primed lower case letters to indicate the absolute accelerations of various points. Thus $\boldsymbol{a}_{Q/P} = \overrightarrow{p'q'}$, $\boldsymbol{a}_{B/A} = \overrightarrow{a'b'}$, etc. Once again, o' on the acceleration diagram corresponds to the pole where all points with zero acceleration map.

The acceleration image theorem states that, if PQR is a triangle fixed in a rigid link in motion relative to the fixed frame, then triangle $p'q'r'$ is similar to triangle PQR.

Triangle $p'q'r'$ is magnified by a factor that is a function of α and ω and is rotated from triangle PQR by an angle that is also a function of $\boldsymbol{\alpha}$ and $\boldsymbol{\omega}$.

Proof To prove the acceleration image theorem, we will use Fig. 2.15. Then

$$\boldsymbol{a}_{Q/P} = \overrightarrow{p'q'} = -\omega^2 \boldsymbol{r}_{Q/P} + \alpha \left|\boldsymbol{r}_{Q/P}\right| \boldsymbol{n}'$$

where $\boldsymbol{n}'$ is normal to $\boldsymbol{r}_{Q/P}$. Therefore the magnitude of the relative acceleration vector is given by

$$\left|\overrightarrow{p'q'}\right| = PQ\sqrt{\omega^4 + \alpha^2}$$

Similarly

$$\left|\overrightarrow{q'r'}\right| = QR\sqrt{\omega^4 + \alpha^2}$$

and

$$\left|\overrightarrow{r'p'}\right| = RP\sqrt{\omega^4 + \alpha^2}$$

Hence triangle $p'q'r'$ is similar to triangle PQR. The magnification factor is $\left|\overrightarrow{r'p'}\right|/RP = \left|\overrightarrow{q'r'}\right|/QR = \left|\overrightarrow{p'q'}\right|/PQ = \sqrt{\omega^4 + \alpha^2}$. Referring to Fig. 2.15, we see that the angle of rotation is

$$\theta = \pi - \tan^{-1}\left(a^{\mathrm{t}}_{Q/P} / a^{\mathrm{r}}_{Q/P}\right)$$

or

$$\theta = \pi - \tan^{-1}\left(\alpha/\omega^2\right)$$

Once again, this result can be extended to cover members of any shape by noting that any polygon may be broken down into triangles, and any area bounded by a plane curve may be approximated by a polygon as closely as desired.

Because the angle of rotation in the acceleration image is not usually 90º, similar triangles must be constructed by making corresponding angles equal.

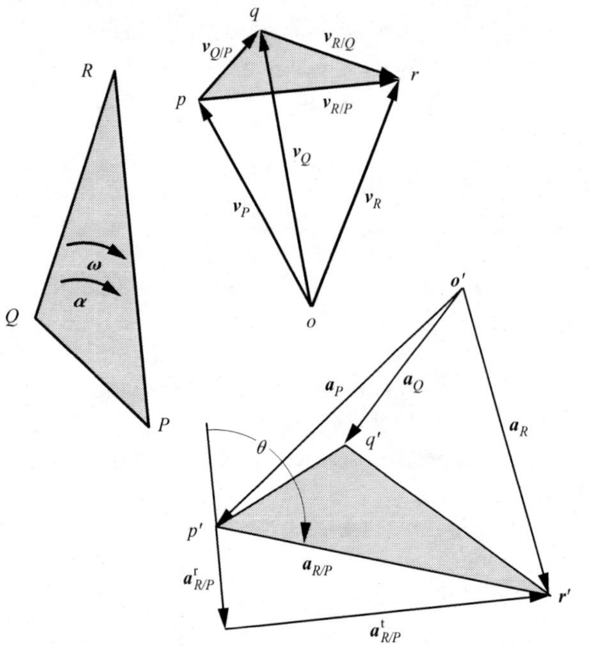

FIGURE 2.15 The acceleration image theorem. The example used is the same as for the velocity image in Fig. 2.13. Triangle $p'q'r'$ is similar to triangle PQR in the original lamina. Hence it is also similar to triangle pqr, which is the velocity image of PQR. If $\boldsymbol{a}_P$ is plotted, together with the radial and transverse components of the acceleration of R relative to P ($\boldsymbol{a}_{R/P}$) to locate points p' and r', q' can be located from the image to give $\boldsymbol{a}_Q$.

EXAMPLE 2.4 ***Graphical Acceleration Analysis of a Six-Bar Linkage***

Given the dimensions of the linkage shown in Fig. 2.16, find $\boldsymbol{a}_C$ and $\boldsymbol{\alpha}_6$ if $\boldsymbol{\omega}_2$ = 60 rpm CW and $\boldsymbol{\alpha}_2 = 0$.

Solution

The results of the analysis are shown in Fig. 2.17. The scales for position, velocity, and acceleration are shown with the polygons. The velocity analysis follows the procedure developed in Example 2.3. The initial equation to be solved is for the slider-crank mechanism. That is,

$$\boldsymbol{v}_{C_3} = \boldsymbol{v}_{B_3} + \boldsymbol{v}_{C_3/B_3}$$

where

$$\boldsymbol{v}_{B_3} = \boldsymbol{v}_{B_2} = \boldsymbol{v}_{B_2/A_2} = \boldsymbol{\omega}_2 \times \boldsymbol{r}_{B_2/A_2}$$

Next we will find the velocity of point D_3 by image. Then the dyad (links 5 and 6) can be analyzed using

$$\boldsymbol{v}_{E_5} = \boldsymbol{v}_{D_5} + \boldsymbol{v}_{E_5/D_5} = \boldsymbol{v}_{E_6} = \boldsymbol{v}_{F_6} + \boldsymbol{v}_{E_6/F_6}$$

Steps

1. Draw the linkage to scale.
2. Compute the magnitude of $\boldsymbol{v}_B = \boldsymbol{v}_{B_2/A_2}$ and identify its direction. Plot it as the vector $\overrightarrow{ob}$.

$$\omega_2 = 60 \times 2\pi/60 = 6.283 \text{ rad/s}$$

$$v_B = 6.283 \times 1.5 = 9.42 \text{ in/s normal to } \overrightarrow{AB}$$

3. Draw a line through point b normal to line $\overrightarrow{BC}$.
4. Draw a line through o parallel to $\overrightarrow{AC}$. The intersection of this line with that plotted in step 3 gives point c_3 (and c_4).
5. Construct triangle bcd similar to triangle BCD, thereby locating point d_3. This step is a use of the velocity image theorem.
6. Draw a line through point d normal to line $\overrightarrow{DE}$.
7. Draw a line through point o normal to $\overrightarrow{EF}$. The intersection of this line with that drawn in step 6 gives point e_5 (and e_6).

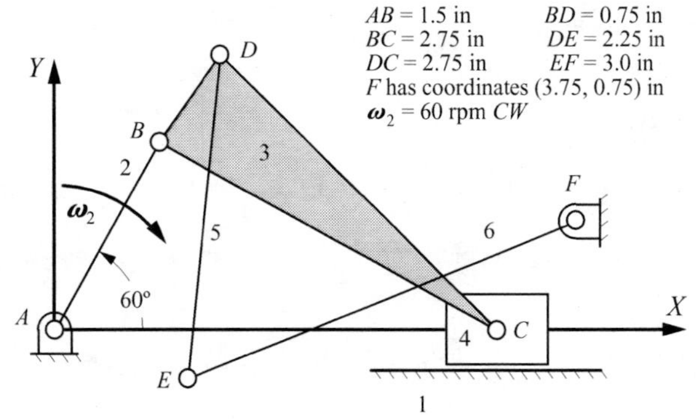

FIGURE 2.16 Problem statement for Example 2.4.

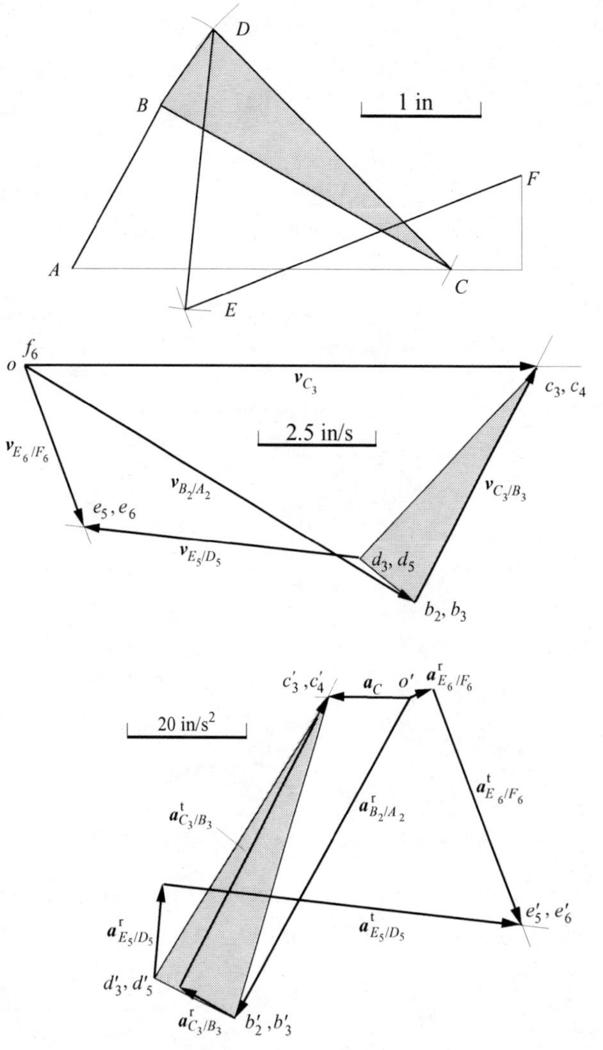

FIGURE 2.17 Position, velocity, and acceleration polygons for Example 2.4.

8. Measure the magnitudes of $\boldsymbol{v}_{C_3/B_3} = \overrightarrow{c_3b_3}$, $\boldsymbol{v}_{E_5/D_5} = \overrightarrow{e_5d_5}$, and $\boldsymbol{v}_{E_6} = \overrightarrow{f_6e_6}$:

$$v_{C_3/B_3} = 5.34 \text{ in/s}, \quad v_{E_5/D_5} = 5.82 \text{ in/s}, \quad v_{E_6} = 3.41 \text{ in/s}$$

9. Compute $|\boldsymbol{\omega}_3| = |\boldsymbol{v}_{C_3/B_3}|/|\boldsymbol{r}_{C/B}|$, $|\boldsymbol{\omega}_5| = |\boldsymbol{v}_{D_5/E_5}|/|\boldsymbol{r}_{D/E}|$, and $|\boldsymbol{\omega}_6| = |\boldsymbol{v}_{E_6/F_6}|/|\boldsymbol{r}_{E/F}|$:

$\boldsymbol{\omega}_3 = 5.34/2.75 = 1.94$ rad/s in the CCW direction, $\boldsymbol{\omega}_5 = 5.82/2.25 = 2.59$ rad/s in the CW directior
$\boldsymbol{\omega}_6 = 3.41/3.0 = 1.137$ rad/s in the CCW direction

This completes the velocity analysis of the linkage.

10. For the acceleration analysis, we must solve the equation

$$\boldsymbol{a}_{C_3} = \boldsymbol{a}^{\text{r}}_{B_2/A_2} + \boldsymbol{a}^{\text{t}}_{B_2/A_2} + \boldsymbol{a}^{\text{r}}_{C_3/B_3} + \boldsymbol{a}^{\text{t}}_{C_3/B_3}$$

Next we will find the acceleration of point D_3 (and D_5) by image. Then the dyad can be analyzed using

$$\boldsymbol{a}_{E_5} = \boldsymbol{a}_{D_5} + \boldsymbol{a}^{\text{r}}_{E_5/D_5} + \boldsymbol{a}^{\text{t}}_{E_5/D_5} = \boldsymbol{a}_{E_6} = \boldsymbol{a}_{F_6} + \boldsymbol{a}^{\text{r}}_{E_6/F_6} + \boldsymbol{a}^{\text{t}}_{E_6/F_6}$$

First compute $\boldsymbol{a}_{B_2} = \boldsymbol{a}^r_{B_2/A_2}$ and plot as the vector $\overrightarrow{o'b_2'}$:

$\boldsymbol{a}_{B_2} = 1.5 \times 6.283^2 = 59.2$ in/s² in the $\overrightarrow{BA}$ direction

11. Compute the magnitudes of vectors $\boldsymbol{a}^r_{C_3/B_3}$, $\boldsymbol{a}^r_{E_5/D_5}$, $\boldsymbol{a}^r_{E_6/F_6}$, and identify their directions:

$\boldsymbol{a}^r_{C_3/B_3} = 2.75 \times 1.94^2 = 10.35$ in/s² in the $\overrightarrow{BC}$ direction

$\boldsymbol{a}^r_{E_5/D_5} = 2.25 \times 2.59^2 = 15.09$ in/s² in the $\overrightarrow{ED}$ direction

$\boldsymbol{a}^r_{E_6/F_6} = 3.0 \times 1.137^2 = 3.87$ in/s² in the $\overrightarrow{EF}$ direction

12. Plot vector $\boldsymbol{a}^r_{C_3/B_3}$ in the $\overrightarrow{CB}$ direction with its tail at b'.

13. Draw a line normal to line $\overrightarrow{CB}$ through the tip of vector $\boldsymbol{a}^r_{C_3/B_3}$.

14. Draw a line through o' parallel to line $\overrightarrow{AC}$. The intersection of this line with that drawn in step 13 gives point c'_3.

15. Construct triangle $b'c'd'$ similar to triangle BCD to locate point d'_3. This step is a use of the acceleration image theorem.

16. Plot $\boldsymbol{a}^r_{E_5/D_5}$ in the $\overrightarrow{ED}$ direction with its tail at point d'.

17. Draw a line normal to $\overrightarrow{ED}$ through the tip of vector $\boldsymbol{a}^r_{E_5/D_5}$.

18. Plot $\boldsymbol{a}^r_{E_6/F_6}$ in the $\overrightarrow{EF}$ direction with its tail at o'.

19. Draw a line normal to $\overrightarrow{EF}$ through the tip of vector $\boldsymbol{a}^r_{E_6/F_6}$. The intersection of this line with that drawn in step 17 gives the point e'_5 (and e'_6).

20. Measure the magnitudes of $\boldsymbol{a}_{C_4}$ and $\boldsymbol{a}^r_{E_6/F_6}$:

$$\left|\boldsymbol{a}_{C_4}\right| = 13.9 \text{ in/s}^2, \ \left|\boldsymbol{a}^t_{E_6/F_6}\right| = 40 \text{ in/s}^2$$

21. Compute $\boldsymbol{\alpha}_6 = |\boldsymbol{a}^t_{E_6/F_6}|/|\boldsymbol{r}_{E/F}|$:

$$\boldsymbol{\alpha}_6 = 40/3.0 = 13.3 \text{ rad/s}^2 \text{ in the CCW direction}$$

22. The sense of $\boldsymbol{\alpha}_6$ is obtained by visualizing E rotating about F so as to move in the $\boldsymbol{a}^t_{E_6/F_6}$ direction.

EXAMPLE 2.5
Using Velocity and Acceleration Images

The mechanism in Fig. 2.18 is drawn to scale. Also given is the velocity polygon for the slider–crank linkage, and the acceleration of point B on the round link is shown on the acceleration polygon. Use the image technique to determine the velocity and acceleration of point D_4. Then determine the velocity and acceleration images of link 4.

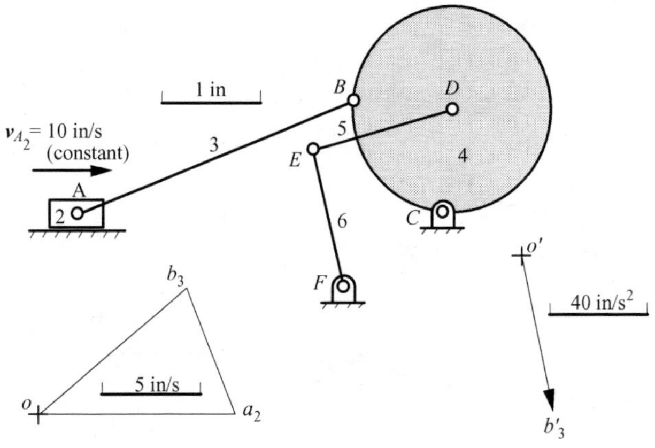

FIGURE 2.18 Figure for Example 2.5.

Solution

To solve the problem, we need only find the image of point D_4 on both the velocity and acceleration diagrams. The images of link 4 will both be circles with centers at d and d', respectively, and with radii of bd and $b'd'$, respectively. We find the velocity image of D_4 by constructing triangle bdc similar to BDC to locate d and drawing the circle centered at d and with radius bd. Similarly, the acceleration image is found by constructing the triangle $b'd'c'$ similar to BDC and drawing the circle centered at d' and with radius $b'd'$. The solution is shown in Fig. 2.19.

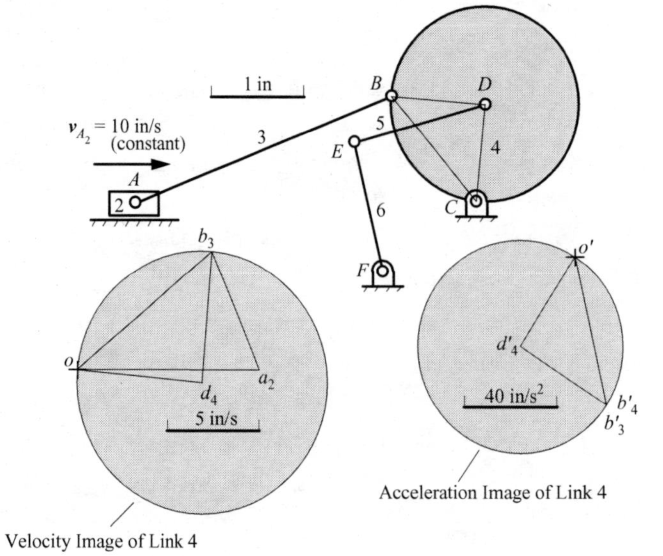

FIGURE 2.19 Solution to Example 2.5.

2.9 SOLUTION BY INVERSION

In general, if we have a linkage where the driver link is not part of a four-bar loop that contains the frame as one of the members, it is not possible to analyze the linkage directly using the vector polygon approach. The Stephenson six-bar linkage shown in Fig. 2.20 can be solved using the techniques in the previous sections *provided* the driving crank is O_AA or O_BB. However, if the linkage is driven by crank O_CC, the linkage cannot be analyzed using the techniques developed so far. This is because O_CC does not form a part of any four-bar loop in the linkage. Consequently, plotting the velocity, or acceleration, of point C does not provide enough information to close a velocity or acceleration polygon.

If the position of the linkage is known, however, a velocity solution can be achieved recognizing that all of the velocities in the linkage are linearly related to the velocity of the input member. Therefore, we can solve the velocity problem indirectly by first assuming the linkage to be driven by O_AA, rotating at 1 rad/s in a specified direction. The velocity polygon is completed and the angular velocity of O_CC is found. A scaling factor is then computed. It is the ratio of the actual angular velocity of O_CC to that calculated. It also carries a sign that is positive if both angular velocities are in the same direction and negative if they are opposed. All velocities and angular velocities are then multiplied by that scaling factor to complete the solution.

This solution technique is an example of *inversion*. The driving and driven cranks are interchanged to perform the solution. That is, the linkage is inverted by having the driver

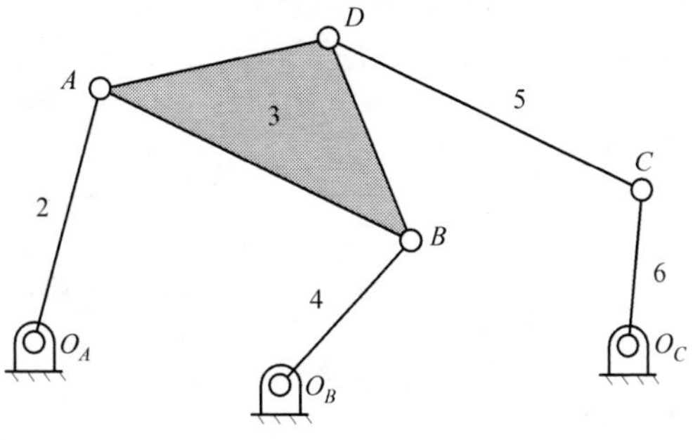

FIGURE 2.20 A simple linkage that can be analyzed using the techniques of the preceding sections if it is driven by crank O_AA, or by crank O_BB, but not by crank O_CC.

moved to a different location. This may seem different from inversion as described in Chapter 1, in which the base link is changed. However, it is closely related, as will be seen later when we deal with the case in which the mechanism is driven via a floating link. A detailed discussion of the issues involved in inversion is also given by Goodman.[5]

A serious situation arises in most problems requiring inversion. It was assumed earlier that the position of the linkage was known. Normally, that is not the case, and it is first necessary to determine the angular positions of all links by drawing the linkage to scale. Consideration of Fig. 2.20 reveals, however, that this is not straightforward when the position of crank O_CC is given. Again, the problem is that this crank does not form part of a four-bar loop but appears only in loops with five members. Therefore it is not possible to complete the loop when only the position of that crank is given.

One approach to the solution of this problem is to note that when the angular position of crank O_CC is specified, point D can lie anywhere on a circle with center point C and radius length CD. The position of point D is also constrained by the four-bar linkage O_AABO_B to lie on a unique curve, called a coupler curve. If the coupler curve is plotted, its intersection with the circle gives the location of point D. Unfortunately, the coupler curve is a complicated planar curve of degree six. The only reasonably efficient way to plot it is to construct successive positions of the linkage O_AABO_B as the angular position of the crank O_AA is incremented. Also, there may be as many as six intersections between the coupler curve and the circle, giving up to six different possible positions of the linkage with crank O_CC in the specified position. Each gives an acceptable assembly configuration for the linkage, so the designer must choose the proper one for a given application.

Another approach to the problem is to iterate for the location of the dyad made up of links D and C; this technique works well when the linkage is drawn using a computer graphics package. For this approach, assume a position for link O_AA, draw the rest of the linkage, and note the position of link O_CC. If the position of link O_CC is not correct, select a different position for link O_AA and reconstruct the linkage again. Measure the position of link O_CC and continue changing O_AA and measuring the position of O_CC until O_CC is in the desired orientation. This may take a number of iterations; however, once the proper position for O_AA is bounded, the procedure will converge fairly rapidly.

If the entire range of motion for the linkage is of interest, then accurately locating the position of O_CC in specific positions is not necessarily an issue. Link O_AA can be located in

[5] Goodman, T.P., "An Indirect Method for Determining Accelerations in Complex Mechanisms." *Trans. ASME*, Nov., 1958, pp. 1676–1682.

representative positions in its range of motion and the analysis can be conducted for each position. Smooth curves can then be drawn through the results.

A procedure for the solution of problems that can be approached by inversion is detailed in Example 2.6.

EXAMPLE 2.6
Velocity Analysis by Inversion

The linkage shown in Fig. 2.21 is driven by crank O_CC. Find the angular velocities of all members of the linkage for the position in which θ_C is 135°. The angular velocity of O_CC is 10 rad/s CCW. O_AA = 2 in, AB = 3.5 in, O_BB = 3.25 in, CD = 2.5 in, O_CC = 2.75 in, and AD = BD = 2.0 in. With origin at O_A, O_B is the point (3.0, 0) and O_C is the point (4.5, –0.5).

Solution

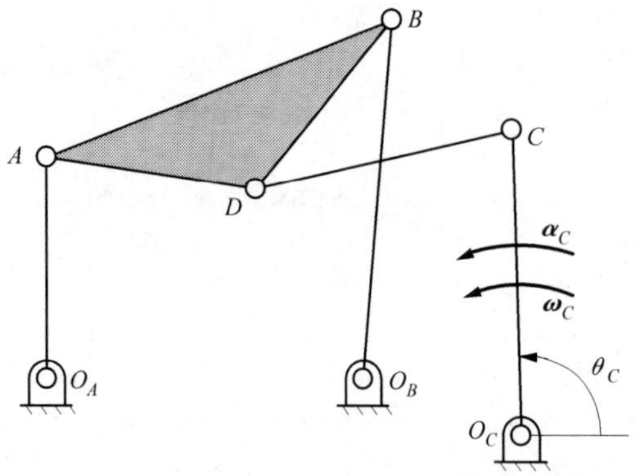

FIGURE 2.21 The linkage of Example 2.6. This is an example of a linkage that cannot be solved graphically without the use of inversion techniques.

We must conduct the analysis by starting with the position analysis.

(a) Position

It is first necessary to construct the linkage in the specified position. The intersection of the coupler curve generated by point D with the circular locus of D centered on C is shown in Fig. 2.22. The coupler curve is plotted by constructing the four-bar O_AABO_B in successive positions with equal increments of the angle of the crank O_AA and plotting the corresponding positions of point D. This process is not shown on the figure, but the basic steps are as follows:

1. Plot O_A, O_B, and O_C
2. Select the angle O_BO_AA and plot O_AA .
3. With center A and radius AB, draw an arc.
4. With center O_B and radius O_BB draw an arc. Its intersection with the arc from step 3 is point B.
5. Construct the triangle ABD on line AB to locate point D.
6. Increment angle O_BO_AA and repeat steps 1–5.
7. Plot the coupler curve, that is, the locus of the successive positions of point D. The comma-shaped curve shown in Fig. 2.22 is the resulting coupler curve.

The configuration of the linkage can now be constructed as follows:

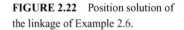

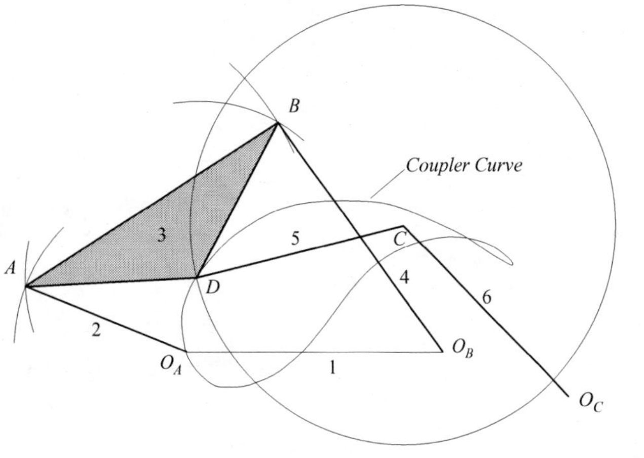

FIGURE 2.22 Position solution of the linkage of Example 2.6.

8. O_CC is drawn at the specified angle and a circle is drawn with center C and radius CD. Its intersections with the coupler curve give possible positions of point D for the specified value of θ_C. Notice that there are two possible positions for D in this case. (There may be as many as six.) We choose the position of D that gives the linkage configuration closest to that shown in Fig. 2.21.

   Once D is located, point A is located as follows:

9. Set radius O_AA and strike an arc centered on O_A.
10. Set radius $\overrightarrow{DA}$ and strike an arc centered on D. The intersection with the arc of step 9 is point A.
11. Construct triangle ABD on $\overrightarrow{DA}$ to locate point B. The linkage can now be drawn in the specified position.

(b) Velocities

The procedure for solving for the velocities is to draw the velocity polygon with the angular velocity of link 2 assumed to be $\Omega_2 = 1$ rad/s. The value of the angular velocity of link 6, Ω_6, is found for this assumption and a scaling factor is calculated to scale Ω_6 to the specified value of $\omega_6 = 10$ rad/s. The same scaling factor is then applied to all other velocities and angular velocities to give their correct values when $\omega_6 = 10$ rad/s. This is a solution by *inversion* because it is necessary first to solve the problem with link 2 assumed to be the driving crank rather than working directly with the actual driving crank, which is link 6. The solution with the assumed value of ω_2 is inverted to that with the required value of ω_6 by scaling it.

For the velocity analysis, the basic equations that we will solve are

$$\boldsymbol{v}_A = \boldsymbol{v}_{A/O_A} = \boldsymbol{\omega}_2 \times \boldsymbol{r}_{A/O_A}$$

$$\boldsymbol{v}_B = \boldsymbol{v}_A + \boldsymbol{v}_{B/A}$$

$$\boldsymbol{v}_D = \boldsymbol{v}_A + \boldsymbol{v}_{D/A} = \boldsymbol{v}_B + \boldsymbol{v}_{D/B}$$

$$\boldsymbol{v}_C = \boldsymbol{v}_D + \boldsymbol{v}_{C/D} = \boldsymbol{v}_{C/O_C}$$

The steps are as follows:

1. Compute the value of $\boldsymbol{v}_A$ with the assumption that $\Omega_2 = 1$ rad/s CCW, and plot $\boldsymbol{v}_A$ (as $\overrightarrow{oa}$) normal to $\overrightarrow{O_AA}$ as shown in Fig. 2.23:

$$v_A = 2.0 \times 1 = 2 \text{ rad/s}$$

2. Draw a line through a normal to $\overrightarrow{AB}$.

3. Draw a line through o normal to $\overrightarrow{O_BA}$. The intersection of this line with that of step 2 gives point b.
4. Draw a line through a normal to $\overrightarrow{AD}$.
5. Draw a line through b normal to $\overrightarrow{BD}$. The intersection of this line with that from step 4 gives point d (velocity image).
6. Draw a line through d normal to $\overrightarrow{CD}$.
7. Draw a line through o normal to $\overrightarrow{O_CC}$. The intersection of this line with that from step 6 gives point c.
8. Measure $v_C = \overrightarrow{oc}$ and compute Ω_6:

$$v_C = 1.214 \text{ in/s}$$

$$\Omega_6 = v_C / O_CC = 1.214 / 2.75 = 0.441 \text{ rad/s}$$

9. Compute the scaling factor $\sigma = \omega_6 / \Omega_6$, where ω_6 is the specified angular velocity of link 6:

$$\sigma = 10/0.441 = 22.7$$

Since both the calculated and specified values of $\boldsymbol{\omega}_6$ are CCW, σ is positive. If they had been in opposite directions, σ would be negative.

10. Compute the angular velocities $\boldsymbol{\Omega}_2$, $\boldsymbol{\Omega}_3$, $\boldsymbol{\Omega}_4$, and $\boldsymbol{\Omega}_5$ and scale the results:

$$\boldsymbol{\omega}_2 = \sigma \times \boldsymbol{\Omega}_2 = 1 \times 22.7 = 22.7 \text{ rad/s in the CCW direction}$$

$$\boldsymbol{\omega}_3 = \sigma \times \boldsymbol{\Omega}_3 = \sigma \times v_{BA} / AB = 22.7 \times 1.09 / 3.5 = 7.05 \text{ rad/s CCW}$$

$$\boldsymbol{\omega}_4 = \sigma \times \boldsymbol{\Omega}_4 = \sigma \times v_B / O_BB = 22.7 \times 1.62 / 3.25 = 11.32 \text{ rad/s CCW}$$

$$\boldsymbol{\omega}_5 = \sigma \times \boldsymbol{\Omega}_5 = \sigma \times v_{CD} / CD = 22.7 \times 0.42 / 2.5 = 3.73 \text{ rad/s CCW}$$

This completes the velocity analysis.

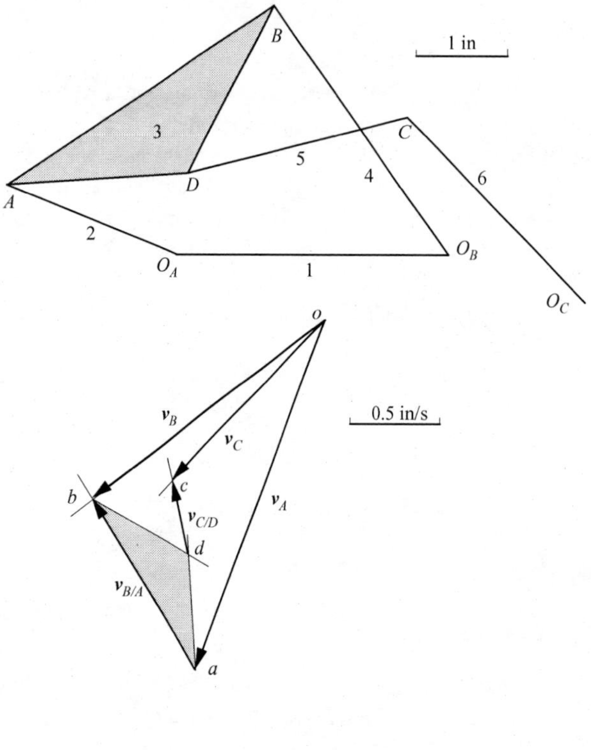

FIGURE 2.23 Velocity solution for Example 2.6.

PROBLEMS

EXERCISE PROBLEMS INVOLVING THE VELOCITY AND ACCELERATION ANALYSIS OF SINGLE-LOOP MECHANISMS

2.1 In the mechanism shown, link 2 is rotating CCW at the constant rate of 2 rad/s. In the position shown, link 2 is horizontal and link 4 is vertical. Write the appropriate vector equations, solve them using vector polygons, and

(a) determine $\mathbf{v}_{C_4}$, $\boldsymbol{\omega}_3$, and $\boldsymbol{\omega}_4$;

(b) determine $\mathbf{a}_{C_4}$, $\boldsymbol{\alpha}_3$, and $\boldsymbol{\alpha}_4$.

Link lengths: $AB = 75$ mm, $CD = 100$ mm.

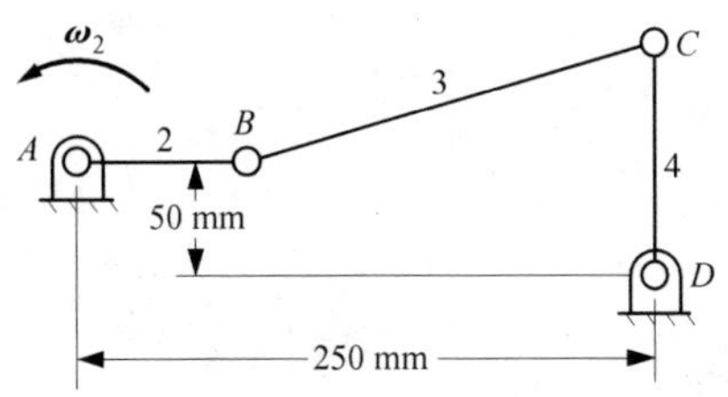

2.2 In the mechanism shown, link 2 is rotating CCW at the constant rate of 500 rad/s. In the position shown, link 2 is vertical. Write the appropriate vector equations, solve them using vector polygons, and

(a) determine $\mathbf{v}_{C_4}$, $\boldsymbol{\omega}_3$, and $\boldsymbol{\omega}_4$;

(b) determine $\mathbf{a}_{C_4}$, $\boldsymbol{\alpha}_3$, and $\boldsymbol{\alpha}_4$.

Link lengths: $AB = 1.2$ in, $BC = 2.42$ in, $CD = 2$ in.

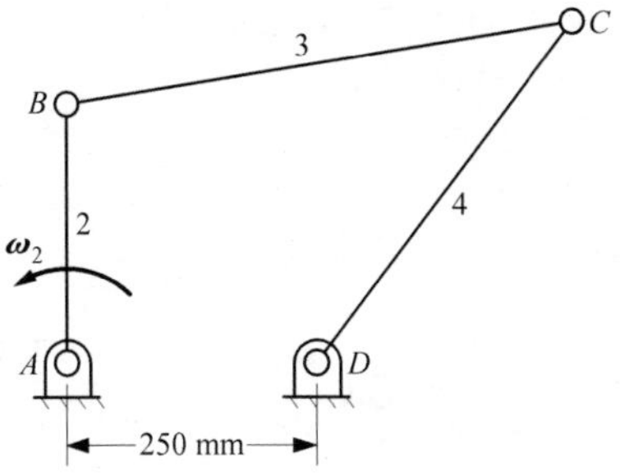

2.3 In the mechanism shown, link 2 is rotating CW at the constant rate of 10 rad/s. In the position shown, link 4 is vertical. Write the appropriate vector equations, solve them using vector polygons, and

(a) determine $\mathbf{v}_{C_4}$, $\boldsymbol{\omega}_3$, and $\boldsymbol{\omega}_4$;

(b) determine $\mathbf{a}_{C_4}$, $\boldsymbol{\alpha}_3$, and $\boldsymbol{\alpha}_4$.

Link lengths: $AB = 100$ mm, $BC = 260$ mm, $CD = 180$ mm.

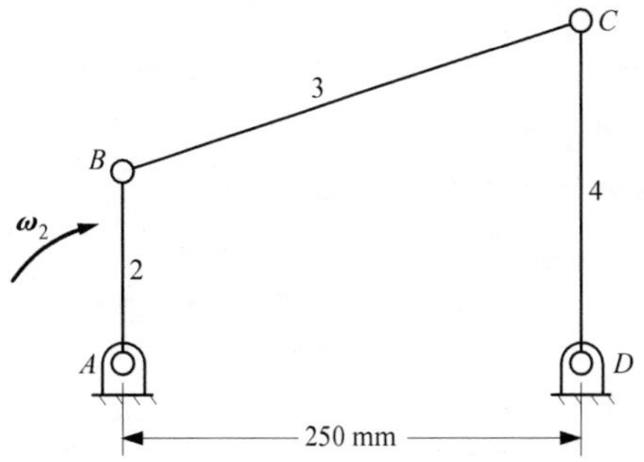

2.4 In the mechanism shown, link 2 is rotating CW at the constant rate of 4 rad/s. In the position shown, θ is 53°. Write the appropriate vector equations, solve them using vector polygons, and

(a) determine $\mathbf{v}_{C_4}$, $\boldsymbol{\omega}_3$, and $\boldsymbol{\omega}_4$;

(b) determine $\mathbf{a}_{C_4}$, $\boldsymbol{\alpha}_3$, and $\boldsymbol{\alpha}_4$.

Link lengths: $AB = 100$ mm, $BC = 160$ mm, $CD = 200$ mm.

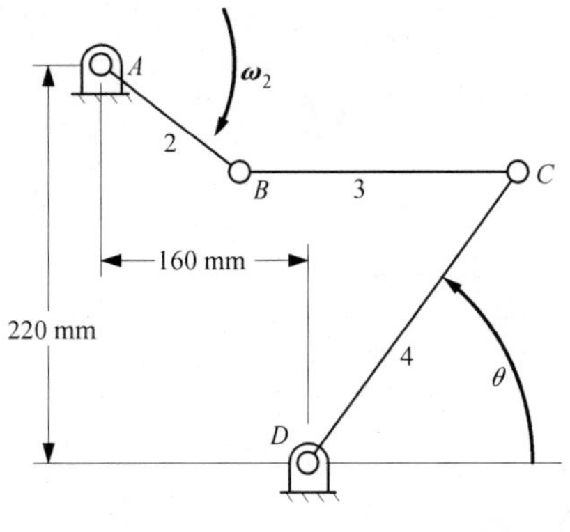

2.5 In the mechanism shown, link 2 is rotating CCW at the constant rate of 4 rad/s. In the position shown, link 2 is horizontal. Write the appropriate vector equations, solve them using vector polygons, and

(a) determine $\mathbf{v}_{C_4}$, $\boldsymbol{\omega}_3$, and $\boldsymbol{\omega}_4$;

(b) determine $\mathbf{a}_{C_4}$, $\boldsymbol{\alpha}_3$, and $\boldsymbol{\alpha}_4$.

Link lengths: $AB = 1.25$ in, $BC = 2.5$ in, $CD = 2.5$ in.

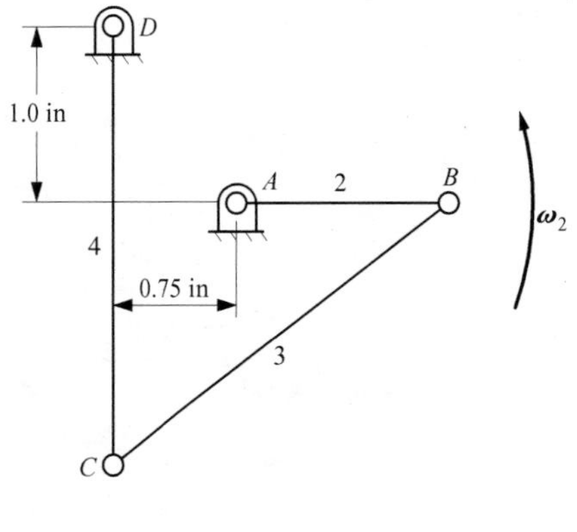

2.6 In the mechanism shown, link 2 is rotating CW at the constant rate of 100 rad/s. In the position shown, link 2 is horizontal. Write the appropriate vector equations, solve them using vector polygons, and

(a) determine $\boldsymbol{v}_{C_4}$, $\boldsymbol{\omega}_3$;

(b) determine $\boldsymbol{a}_{C_4}$, $\boldsymbol{\alpha}_3$.

<u>Link lengths:</u> $AB = 60$ mm, $BC = 200$ mm.

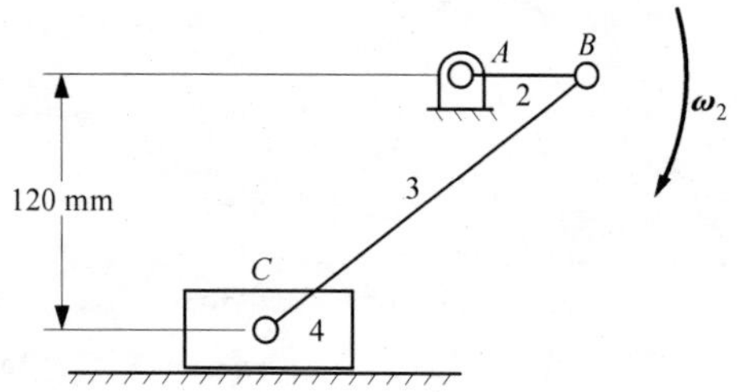

2.7 In the mechanism shown, link 4 is moving to the left at the constant rate of 4 ft/s. Write the appropriate vector equations, solve them using vector polygons, and

(a) determine $\boldsymbol{\omega}_3$ and $\boldsymbol{\omega}_4$;

(b) determine $\boldsymbol{\alpha}_3$ and $\boldsymbol{\alpha}_4$.

<u>Link lengths:</u> $AB = 10$ ft, $BC = 20$ ft.

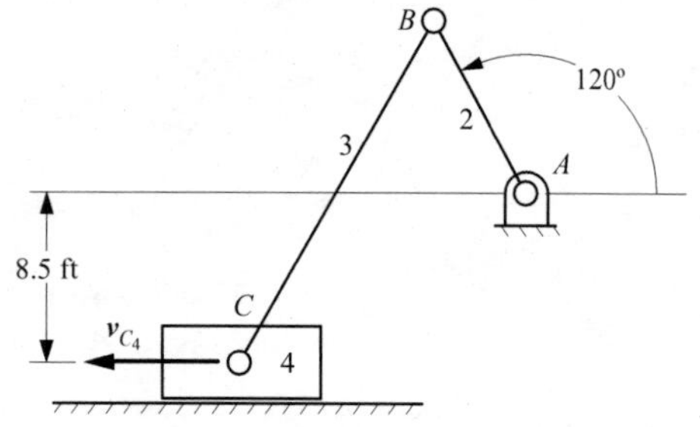

2.8 In the mechanism shown, link 4 is moving to the right at the constant rate of 20 in/s. Write the appropriate vector equations, solve them using vector polygons, and

(a) determine $\boldsymbol{\omega}_3$ and $\boldsymbol{\omega}_4$;

(b) determine $\boldsymbol{\alpha}_3$ and $\boldsymbol{\alpha}_4$.

<u>Link lengths:</u> $AB = 5$ in, $BC = 5$ in.

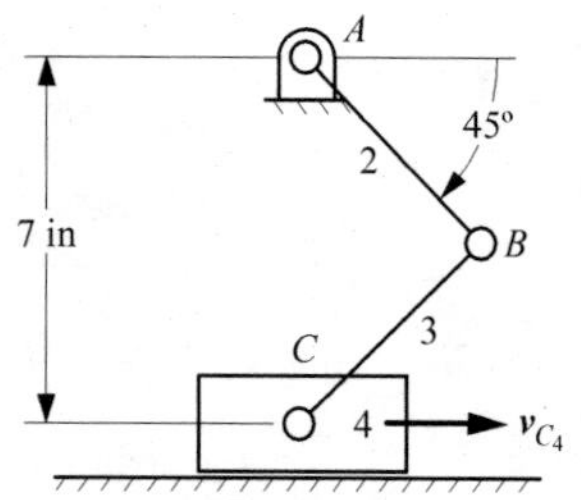

2.9 In the mechanism shown, link 4 is moving to the left at the constant rate of 0.6 ft/s. Write the appropriate vector equations, solve them using vector polygons, and determine the velocity and acceleration of point A_3.

<u>Link lengths:</u> $AB = 5$ in, $BC = 5$ in.

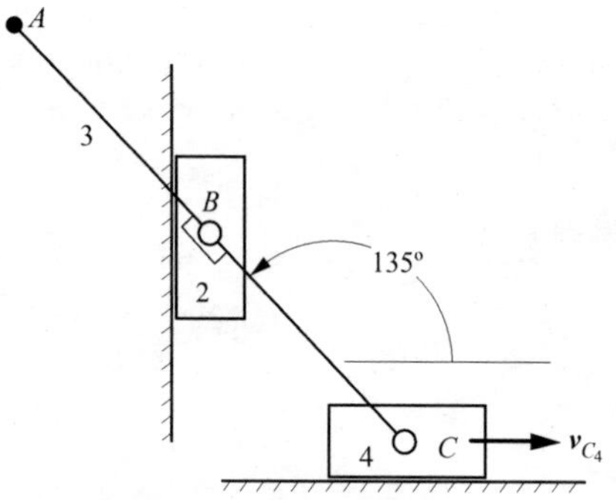

2.10 In the mechanism shown, link 4 moves to the right with a constant velocity of 75 ft/s. Write the appropriate vector equations, solve them using vector polygons, and

(a) determine $\boldsymbol{v}_{B_2}$, $\boldsymbol{v}_{G_3}$, $\boldsymbol{\omega}_2$, $\boldsymbol{\omega}_3$;

(b) determine $\boldsymbol{a}_{B_2}$ $\boldsymbol{a}_{G_3}$, $\boldsymbol{\alpha}_2$, and $\boldsymbol{\alpha}_3$..

<u>Link lengths:</u> $AB = 4.8$ in, $BC = 16.0$ in, $BG = 6.0$ in.

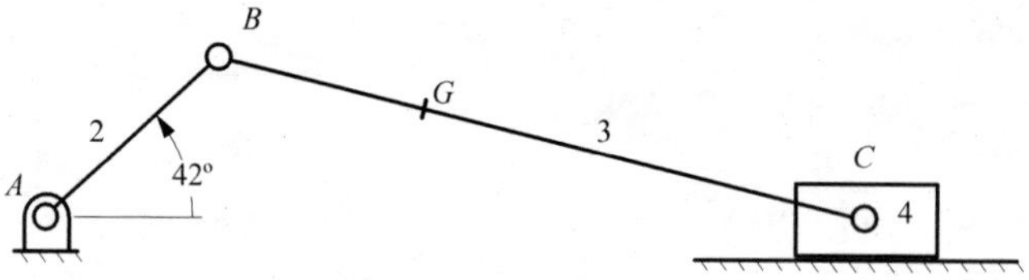

2.11 For the four-bar linkage, assume that $\boldsymbol{\omega}_2 = 50$ rad/s CW and $\boldsymbol{\alpha}_2 = 1600$ rad/s^2 CW. Write the appropriate vector equations, solve them using vector polygons, and

(a) determine $\boldsymbol{v}_{B_2}$, $\boldsymbol{v}_{C_3}$, $\boldsymbol{v}_{E_3}$, $\boldsymbol{\omega}_3$, and $\boldsymbol{\omega}_4$;

(b) determine $\boldsymbol{a}_{B_2}$, $\boldsymbol{a}_{C_3}$, $\boldsymbol{a}_{E_3}$, $\boldsymbol{\alpha}_3$, and $\boldsymbol{\alpha}_4$.

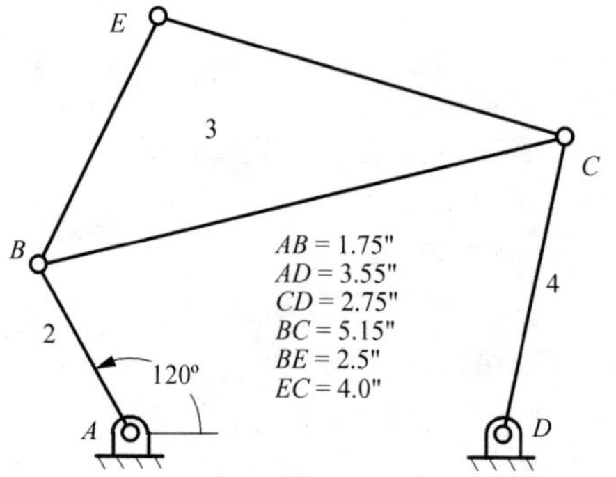

2.12 Re-solve Problem 2.11 if $\boldsymbol{\omega}_2 = 50$ rad/s CCW and $\boldsymbol{\alpha}_2 = 0$.

2.13 In the mechanism shown, link 2 is rotating CW at the rate of 180 rad/s. Write the appropriate vector equations, solve them using vector polygons, and

(a) determine $\boldsymbol{v}_{B_2}$, $\boldsymbol{v}_{C_3}$, $\boldsymbol{v}_{E_3}$, $\boldsymbol{\omega}_3$, and $\boldsymbol{\omega}_4$;

(b) determine $\boldsymbol{a}_{B_2}$, $\boldsymbol{a}_{C_3}$, $\boldsymbol{a}_{E_3}$, $\boldsymbol{\alpha}_3$, and $\boldsymbol{\alpha}_4$.

Link lengths: $AB = 4.6$ in, $BC = 12.0$ in, $AD = 15.2$ in, $CD = 9.2$ in, $EB = 8.0$ in, $CE = 5.48$ in.

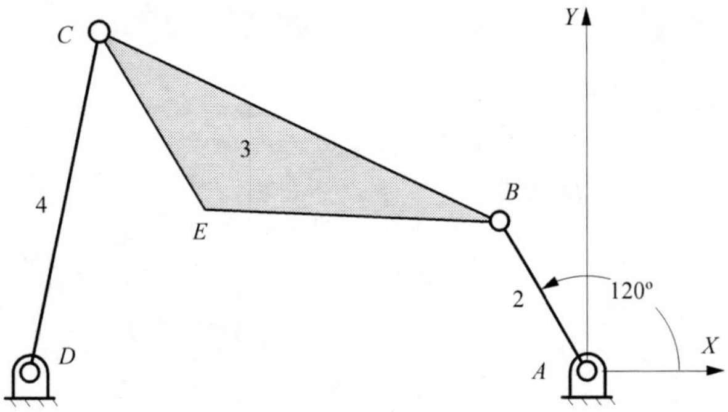

2.14 The accelerations of points A and B in the coupler shown are as given. Determine the acceleration of the center of mass G and the angular acceleration of the body. Draw the vector representing $\boldsymbol{a}_G$ from G.

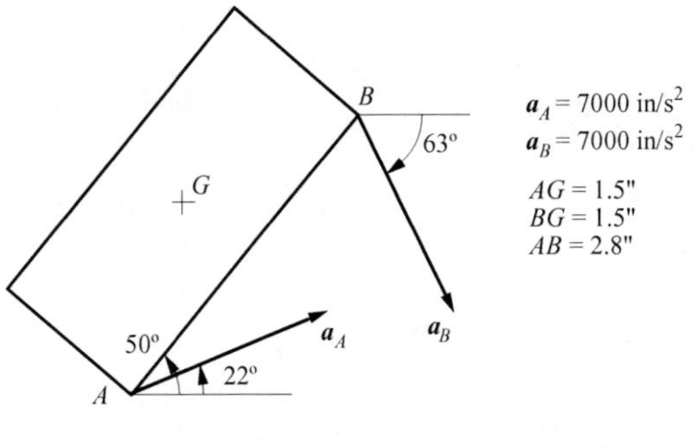

2.15 Crank 2 of the push-link mechanism shown in the figure is driven at a constant angular velocity $\boldsymbol{\omega}_2 = 60$ rad/s (CW). Find the velocity and acceleration of point F and the angular velocity and acceleration of links 3 and 4.

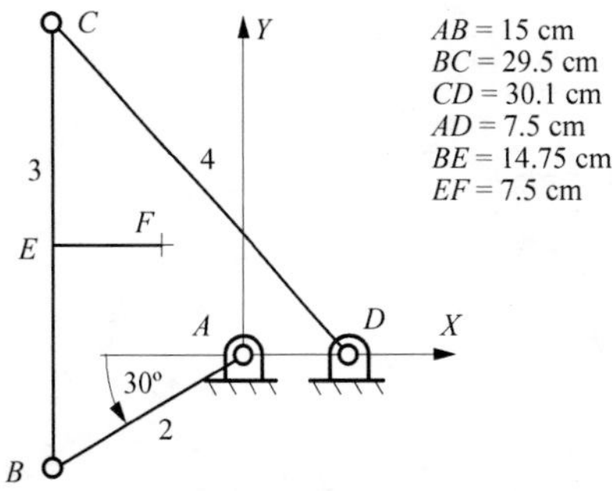

2.16 For the straight-line mechanism shown in the figure, $\boldsymbol{\omega}_2 =$ 20 rad/s (CW) and $\boldsymbol{\alpha}_2 = 140$ rad/s^2 (CW). Determine the velocity and acceleration of point B and the angular acceleration of link 3.

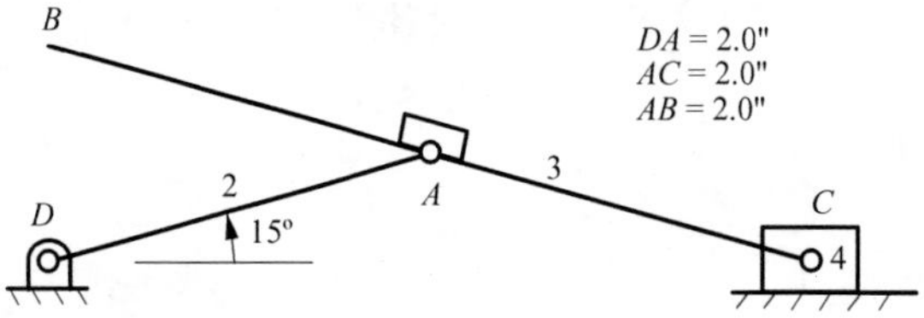

2.17 For the data given in the figure below, find the velocity and acceleration of points B and C. Assume $\boldsymbol{v}_A = 20$ ft/s and $\boldsymbol{a}_A =$ 400 ft/s^2 in the directions specified in the drawing. $\boldsymbol{\omega}_2 = 24$ rad/s (CW) and $\boldsymbol{\alpha}_2 = 160$ rad/s^2 (CCW).

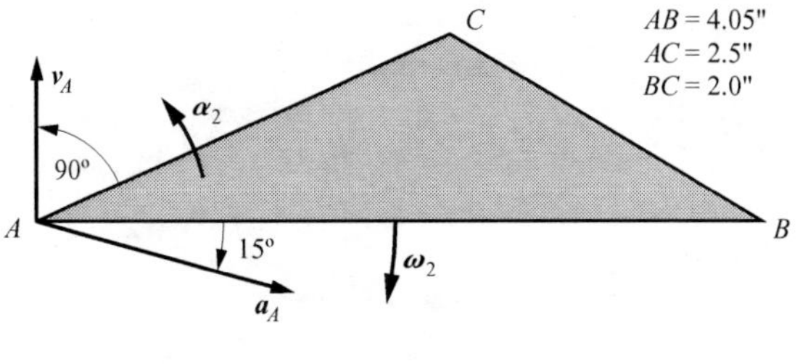

2.18 In the mechanism shown, link 2 is turning CCW at the constant rate of 10 rad/s. Draw the velocity and acceleration polygons for the mechanism, and determine $\boldsymbol{a}_{G_3}$ and $\boldsymbol{\alpha}_4$.

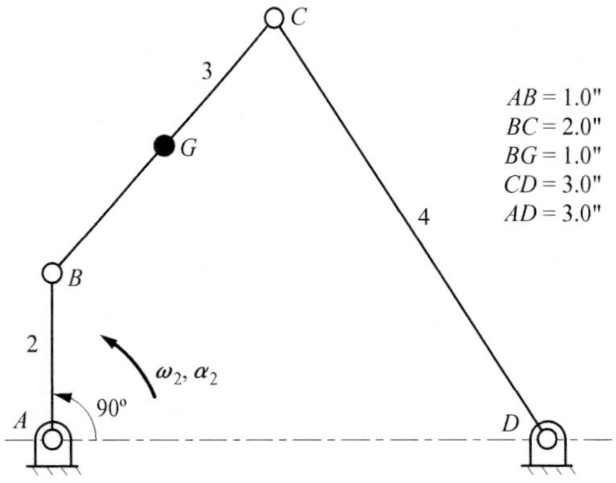

2.19 If $\omega_2 = 100$ rad/s CCW (constant) find the velocity and acceleration of point E.

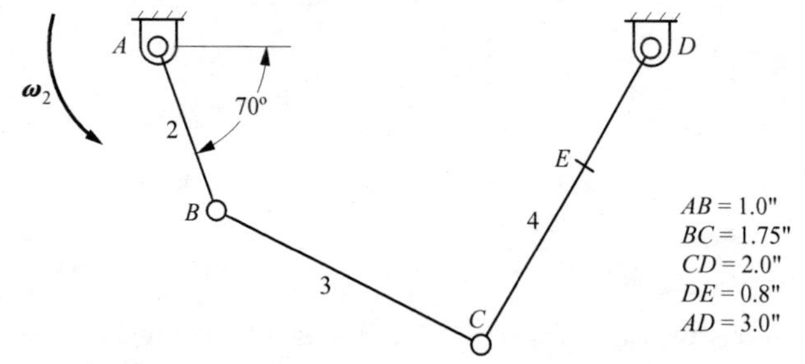

EXERCISE PROBLEMS INVOLVING THE VELOCITY AND ACCELERATION ANALYSIS OF MULTILOOP MECHANISMS

2.20 Draw the velocity polygon to determine the velocity of link 6. Points A, C, and E have the same vertical coordinate.

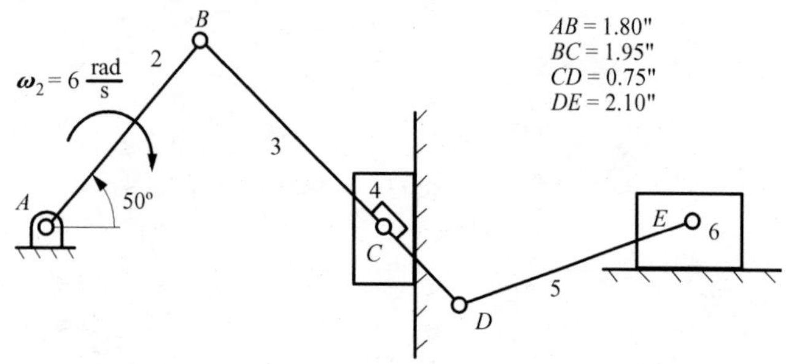

2.21 Link 2 of the linkage shown in the figure has an angular velocity of 10 rad/s CCW. Find the angular velocity of link 6 and the velocities of points B, C, and D.

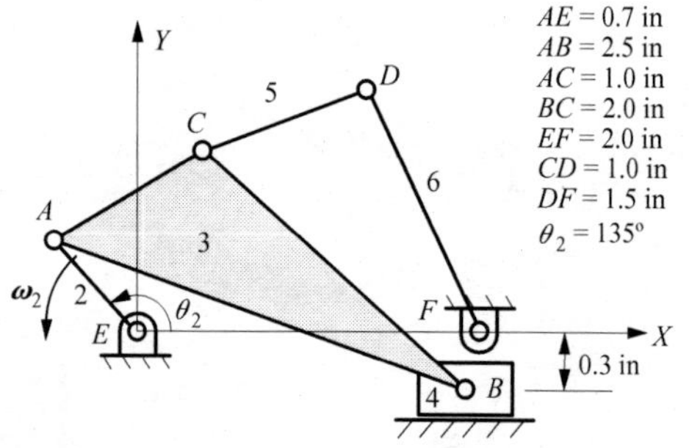

2.22 The linkage shown is used to raise the fabric roof on convertible automobiles. The dimensions are given as shown. Link 2 is driven by a DC motor through a gear reduction. If the angular velocity $\omega_2 = 2$ rad/s CCW, determine the linear velocity of point J, which is the point where the linkage connects to the automobile near the windshield.

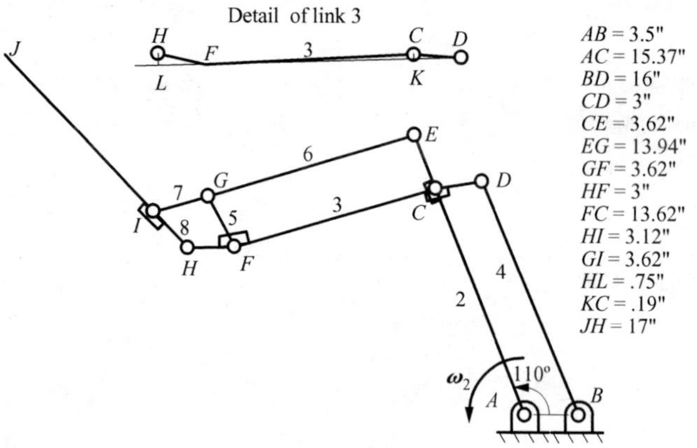

2.23 In the mechanism shown, determine the sliding velocity of link 6 and the angular velocities of links 3 and 5.

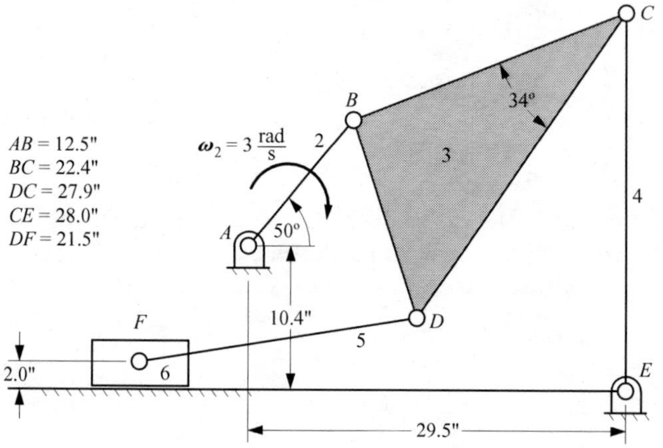

2.24 In the mechanism shown, $v_{A_2} = 15$ m/s with direction downward. Draw the velocity polygon, and determine the velocity of point D on link 6 and the angular velocity of link 5.

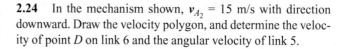

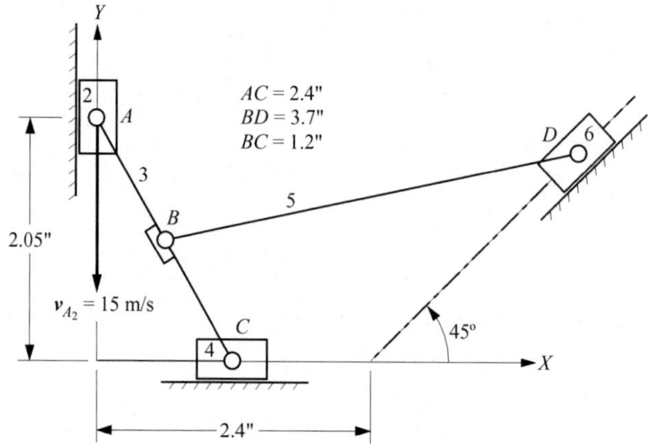

2.25 In the mechanism shown, points E and B have the same vertical coordinate. Find the velocities of points B, C, and D of the double-slider mechanism shown in the figure if crank 2 rotates at 42 rad/s CCW.

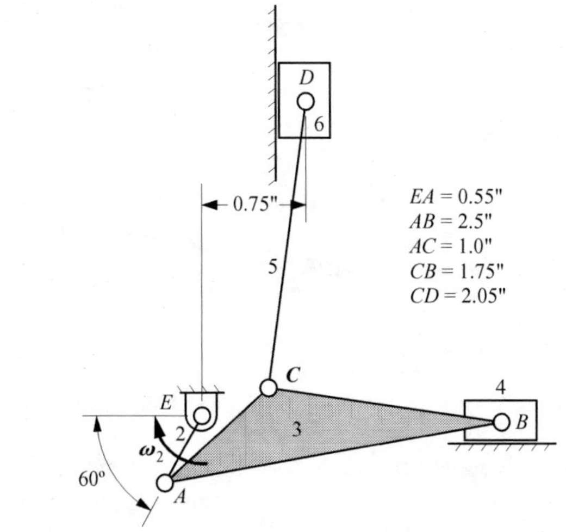

2.26 Given v_{A_4} = 1.0 ft/s to the left, find v_{B_6}.

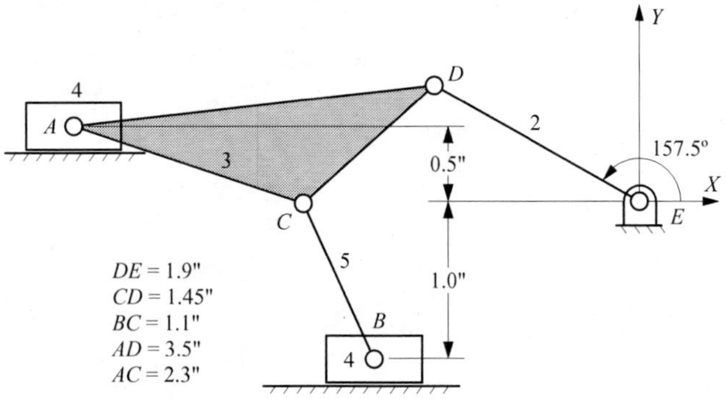

2.27 If v_{A_2} = 10 cm/s as shown, find v_{C_5}.

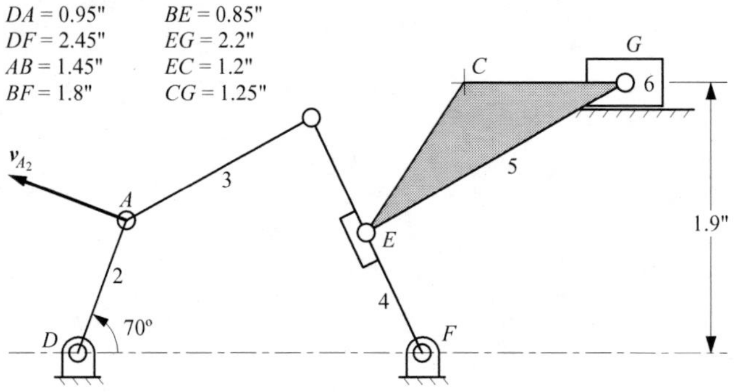

2.28 If v_{A_2} = 10 in/s as shown, find the angular velocity of link 6.

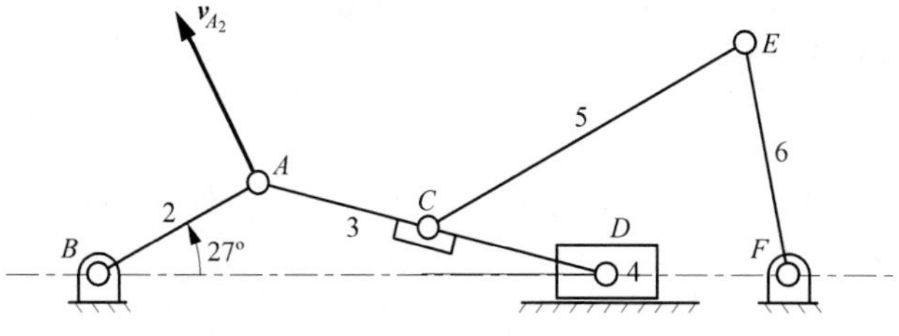

2.29 The angular velocity of link 2 of the mechanism shown is 20 rad/s, and the angular acceleration is 100 rad/s² at the instant being considered. Determine the linear velocity and acceleration of point F_6.

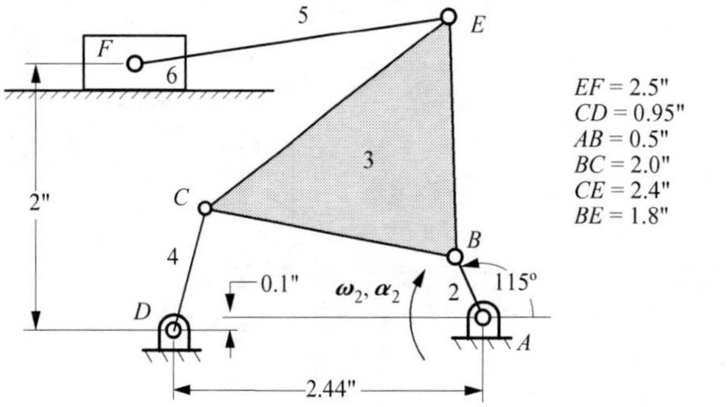

2.30 In the drag-link mechanism shown, link 2 is turning CW at the rate of 130 rpm. Construct the velocity and acceleration polygons and compute the following: a_{E_5}, a_{F_6}, and the angular acceleration of link 5.

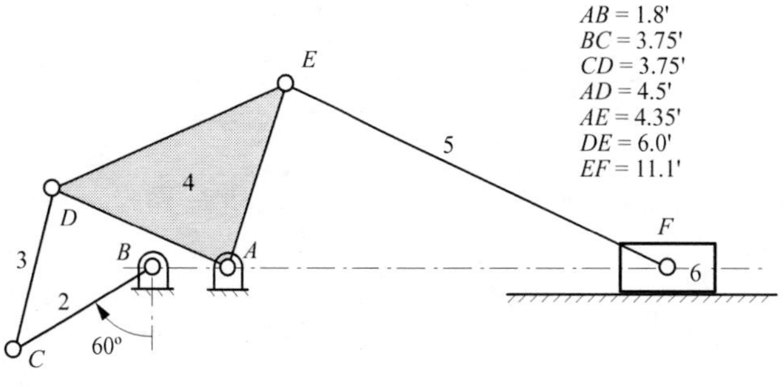

2.31 The figure shows the mechanism used in a two-cylinder 60-degree V-engine consisting, in part, of an articulated connecting rod. Crank 2 rotates at 2000 rpm CW. Find the velocities and acceleration of points *B*, *C*, and *D* and the angular acceleration of links 3 and 5.

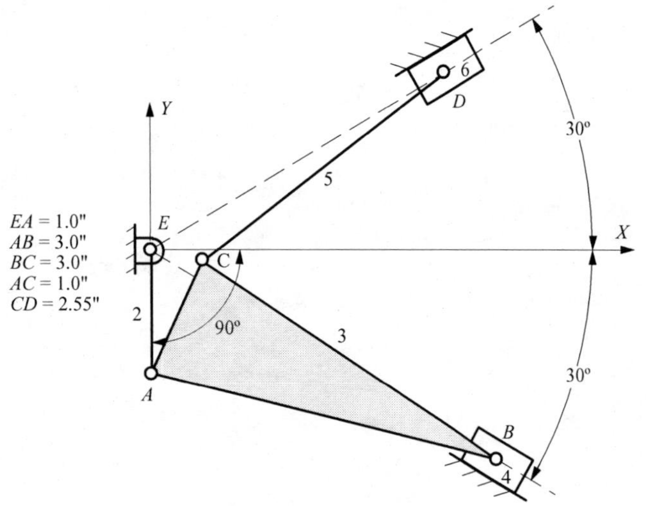

EXERCISE PROBLEMS INVOLVING THE VELOCITY AND ACCELERATION IMAGE

2.32 In the mechanism shown, $\omega_2 = 4$ rad/s CCW (constant). Write the appropriate vector equations, solve them using vector polygons, and

(a) determine v_{E_3}, v_{E_4}, ω_3;

(b) determine a_{E_2}, a_{E_4}, α_3.

Also find the point in link 3 that has zero acceleration for the position given.

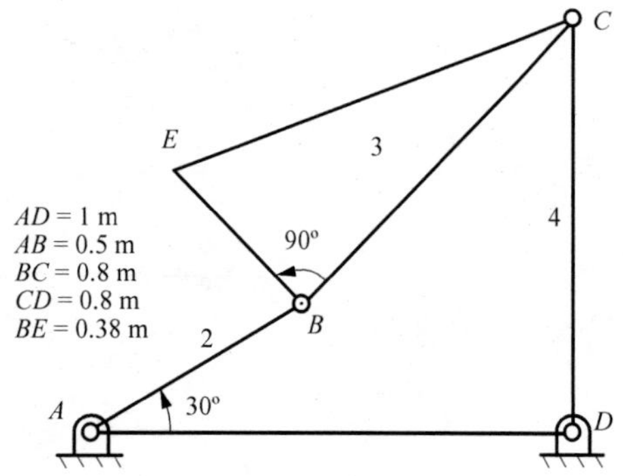

2.33 In the mechanism shown, point *A* lies on the *X* axis. Draw the basic velocity and acceleration polygons and use the image technique to determine the velocity and acceleration of point D_4. Then determine the velocity and acceleration images of link 4. Draw the images on the velocity and acceleration polygons.

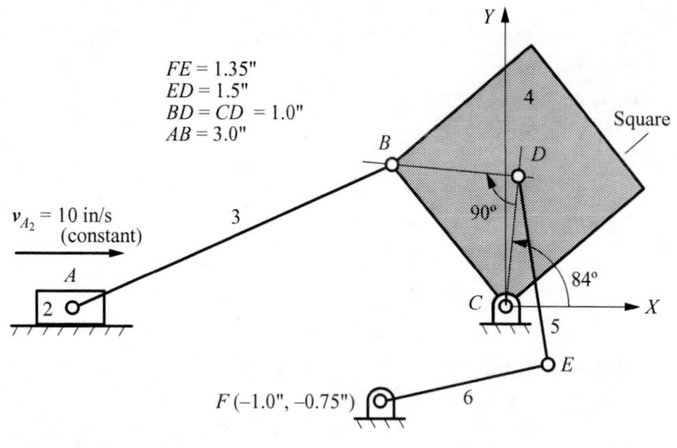

2.34 In the mechanism shown, the velocity of A_2 is 10 in/s to the right and is constant. Draw the velocity and acceleration polygons for the mechanism, and record values for angular velocity and acceleration of link 6. Use the image technique to determine the velocity of points D_3 and E_3, and locate the point in link 3 that has zero velocity.

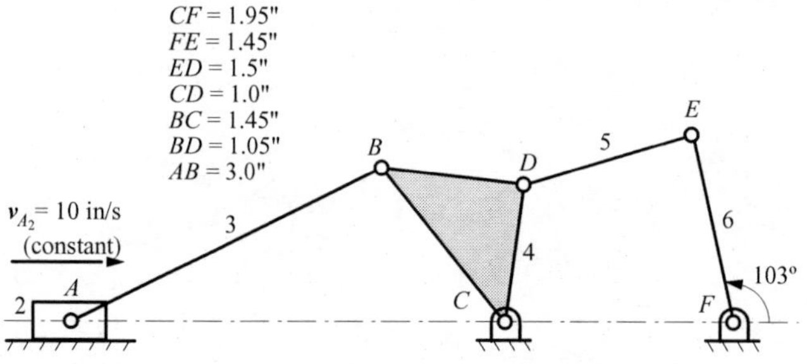

2.35 The instant center of acceleration of a link can be defined as that point in the link that has zero acceleration. If the accelerations of points *A* and *B* are as given in the rigid body shown, find the point *C* in that link at which the acceleration is zero.

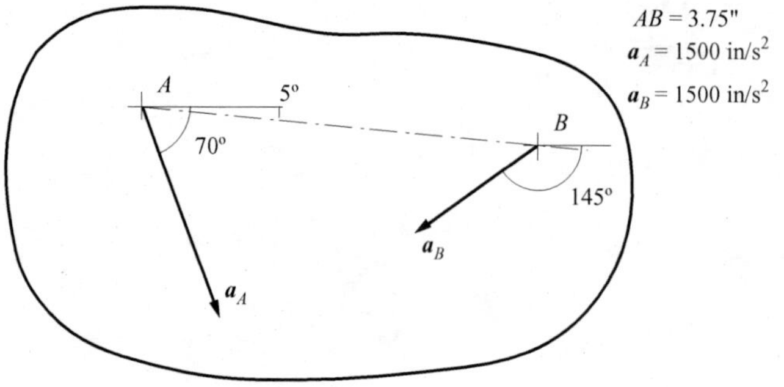

2.36 The following are given for the mechanism shown in the figure:

$$\omega_2 = 6.5 \text{ rad/s } (\text{CCW}),\ \alpha_2 = 40 \text{ rad/s}^2 \ (\text{CCW})$$

Draw the velocity polygon, and locate the velocity of point E using the image technique.

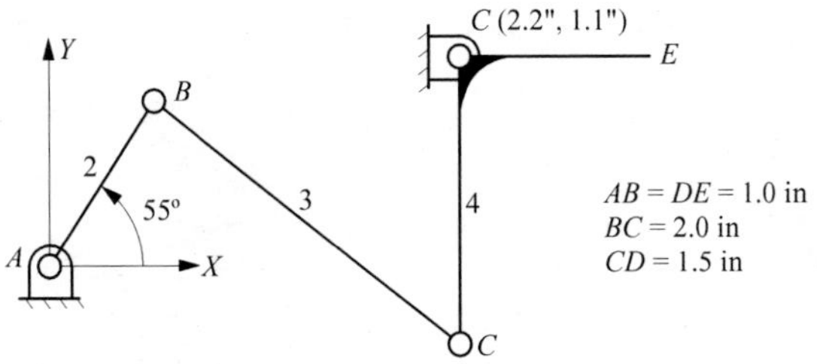

2.37 In the mechanism shown, find ω_6 and α_3. Also, determine the acceleration of D_3 by image.

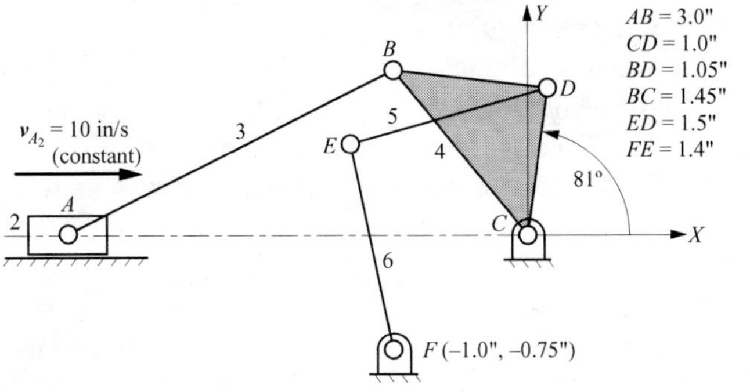

2.38 In the mechanism shown, $\omega_2 = 1$ rad/s (CCW) and $\alpha_2 = 0$ rad/s². Find ω_5, α_5, v_{E_6}, and a_{E_6} for the position given. Also find the point in link 5 that has zero acceleration for the position given.

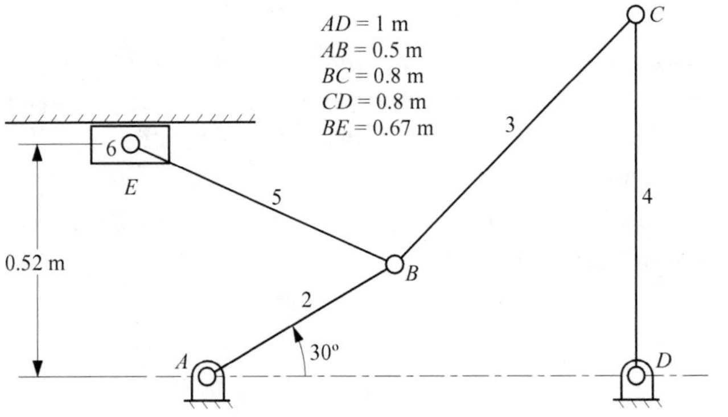

2.39 Part of an eight-link mechanism is shown in the figure. The velocity and acceleration of point D_7 are given. Find ω_7 and α_7 for the position given. Also find the velocity of G_7 by image.

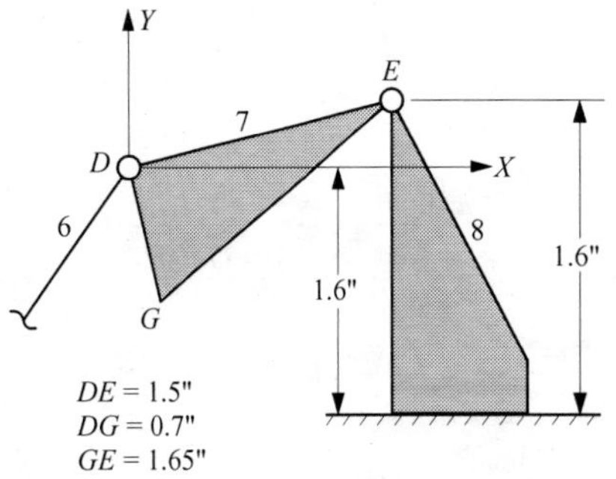

$v_{D_7} = 5.0 \angle 320^\circ$ in/s $\qquad a_{D_7} = 40 \angle 260^\circ$ in/s²

2.40 In the mechanism shown, link 2 is rotating CW at the constant rate of 3 rad/s. In the position shown, link 2 is horizontal. Write the appropriate vector equations, solve them using vector polygons, and

(a) determine v_{C_4}, v_{E_4}, ω_3, and ω_4;

(b) determine a_{C_4}, a_{E_4}, α_3, and α_4.

<u>Link lengths:</u> $AB = 3$ in, $BC = BE = CE = 5$ in, $CD = 3$ in.

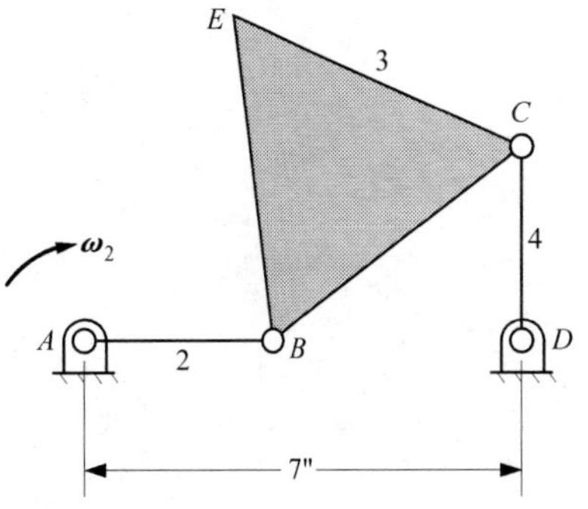

2.41 Part of a 10-link mechanism is shown in the figure. The velocity and acceleration of points D_7 and F_8 are given. Find ω_8 and α_7 for the position given. Also find the velocity of G_7 by image.

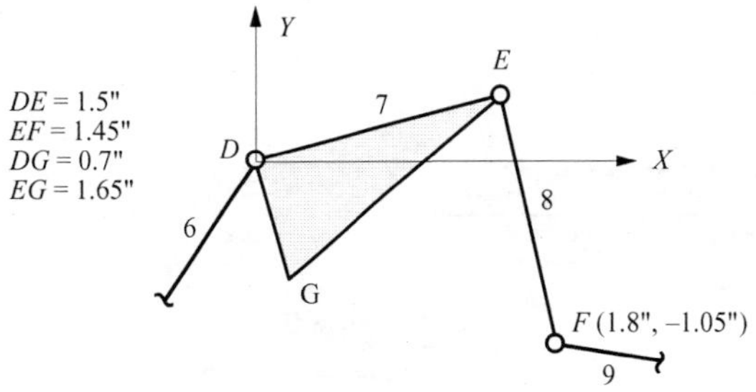

$v_{D_7} = 6.0 \angle 353^\circ$ in/s $\qquad a_{D_7} = 40 \angle 235^\circ$ in/s²

$v_{F_8} = 7.5 \angle 54^\circ$ in/s $\qquad a_{F_8} = 30 \angle 305^\circ$ in/s²

CHAPTER 3

LINKAGES WITH ROLLING AND SLIDING CONTACTS AND JOINTS ON MOVING SLIDERS

3.1 INTRODUCTION

The methods introduced in Chapter 2 are straightforward and are perfectly adequate for analysis of linkages that have only revolute joints or sliding joints on fixed slides. However, to analyze linkages with other types of joints, including those with moving sliding joints, it is necessary to base the analysis on a more complex theory. The problem arises from differentiation of vector quantities that are referred to moving reference frames.

As was discussed in Chapter 1, a kinematic joint is formed by any contact between two bodies. The methods discussed in Chapter 2 apply only to linkages in which all the joints have the very specialized, surface-of-revolution geometry of revolute joints, or, in relatively few cases, the equally special generalized cylindrical surface geometry of prismatic joints. There are many other possible types of kinematic joints, a number of which are of great practical importance. In this chapter we provide the basic analysis tools needed to deal with linkages that include these more general joint types.

Many mechanisms include rolling contacts and contacts with irregularly shaped bodies. A cam mechanism will often include a cylindrical follower rolling on the irregularly shaped cam. Any wheeled vehicle makes use of rolling contact with the terrain over which it travels. When two bodies are in rolling contact the point in one body that contacts the other body is instantaneously at rest relative to that body. That is, its velocity relative to that body is zero. However, after an infinitesimally small time interval, that point will have separated from the body and will no longer be at rest relative to it. Thus, although the velocity of the contacting point relative to the body contacted is zero, its acceleration is not zero and is, in fact, directed along the contact normal away from the contacted body.

Other commonly used mechanisms have sliding joints that are not fixed relative to the base, but rotate. The Coriolis component of acceleration, which governs the direction of rotation of cyclonic weather systems, can also lead to significant internal loads in mechanisms. This is particularly relevant to mechanisms that have rotating sliding joints.

To address problems involving linkages of these types it is necessary first to think about what we mean by a reference frame and the implications of relative motion of two reference frames for velocity and acceleration analysis.

3.2 REFERENCE FRAMES

If a linkage involves only revolute joints or sliders on fixed lines, the equations developed in Sections 2.3 and 2.4 are sufficient for conducting the kinematic analysis. However, for other types of joints, the equations become more complex, and it is necessary to use more than one reference frame for the velocities and accelerations. In general, each link must be assumed to have a reference frame attached to it. In fact, when each link is manufactured, the machine tool that is used to form the link geometry will be guided relative to the local coordinate system or reference frame fixed to the link.

As is shown in Fig. 3.1, the position of a given point (Q) can be quite different when it is measured relative to a different reference frame. Further, as will be demonstrated in the following, the velocity of a point relative to the fixed frame R depends not only on its velocity relative to a moving reference frame, such as frame M, but also on the velocity and angular velocity of frame M relative to frame R.

When it is important to distinguish the reference frames to which positions, velocities, and accelerations are referred, we will use a superscript before the vector symbol to identify the relevant reference frame. Typically, we will use the link number or letter as the reference frame for that link. That is the notation used on Fig. 3.1. Thus, ${}^{M}O$ is the origin of the reference frame fixed to lamina M, and ${}^{M}\mathbf{r}_Q$ is the position of point Q relative to frame M.

Typically, we will use the link number or letter as the reference frame for that link. Thus, if B is a general link that is moving relative to another link R, ${}^{R}\boldsymbol{\omega}_B$ is the angular velocity of the moving body B, relative to frame R. Then ${}^{B}\boldsymbol{\omega}_R = -{}^{R}\boldsymbol{\omega}_B$ is the angular velocity of frame R relative to body B. ${}^{R}\mathbf{v}_Q$ is the absolute velocity of point Q relative to frame R, and ${}^{B}\mathbf{r}_Q$ is the position of point Q relative to the reference frame fixed to body B. ${}^{2}\boldsymbol{\alpha}_3$ is the angular acceleration of member 3 relative to the reference frame fixed in member 2.

The vector ${}^{R}\mathbf{v}_{B/A}$ is usually called the velocity of B relative to A in reference frame R. However, as discussed earlier, this terminology is technically incorrect. Vectors must be measured relative to reference frames. Therefore, ${}^{R}\mathbf{v}_{B/A}$ would be the velocity of point B relative to a reference frame R that has its origin at point A and moves so as always to be parallel to the fixed frame. Similarly, one would call ${}^{R}\mathbf{r}_{Q/P}$ the position of Q relative to a reference frame, with origin at P, that remains at all times parallel to the frame R. The complexity of this statement explains the widespread use of the term "position of Q relative to P" for ${}^{R}\mathbf{r}_{Q/P}$.

Often, *when all vectors are referred to the same reference frame R*, we will drop the superscript R to simplify the notation. That is, $\boldsymbol{\omega}_B = {}^{R}\boldsymbol{\omega}_B$. This was the case in Chapter 2 when the fixed frame (link 1) was understood to be the reference frame for all vectors.

The basis of the velocity analysis of planar linkages is the relationship between the velocities of two different points when something about the motion of the two points is known relative to a moving coordinate system. To derive this relationship in a form suitable for the formulation of a velocity polygon, let us consider the points P and Q shown in

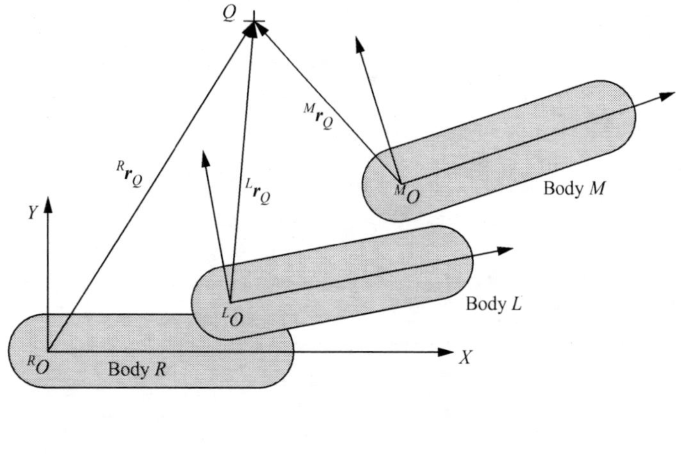

FIGURE 3.1 Position of a point relative to three different reference frames. The position of point Q relative to frame M is ${}^{M}\mathbf{r}_Q$. This vector is quite different from that of the position of point Q relative to the reference frame fixed to lamina L: ${}^{L}\mathbf{r}_Q$ or from that to the position of the same point relative to lamina R: ${}^{R}\mathbf{r}_Q$.

Fig. 3.2. If ${}^R\mathbf{r}_P$ is the absolute position of point P relative to reference frame R, ${}^R\mathbf{r}_Q$ is the absolute position of Q relative to reference frame R, and ${}^B\mathbf{r}_{Q/P}$ is the vector from point P to point Q defined relative to the moving reference system B, then we can write

$$ {}^R\mathbf{r}_Q = {}^R\mathbf{r}_P + {}^B\mathbf{r}_{Q/P} \tag{3.1} $$

Note that Eq. (3.1) is the same as Eq. (2.2) with superscripts added to aid in keeping track of the reference frames. As indicated before, the vector ${}^B\mathbf{r}_{Q/P}$ is called the position of Q relative to P when the observer is fixed relative to reference system B.

Although P and Q may be fixed to body B, Eq. (3.1) is valid regardless of the link to which points P and Q are fixed (i.e., P and Q may be fixed to link B or some other link). To obtain the velocities, we must differentiate Eq. (3.1) when the observer is in reference frame R.

Note that, in the position considered, the coordinate axes for systems B and R must be parallel. This condition will be assumed in all future developments requiring multiple coordinate systems. Otherwise we cannot add vector components as implied in Eq. (3.1). If the nominal coordinate systems attached to the two links are not parallel, we must use another set of coordinate systems that are momentarily parallel. The two coordinate systems fixed to a given link would be related by a simple coordinate transformation.

3.3 GENERAL VELOCITY AND ACCELERATION EQUATIONS

3.3.1 Velocity Equations

When we differentiate Eq. (3.1) with the observer in the reference system R, we get

$$ \frac{{}^R d}{dt}\left({}^R\mathbf{r}_Q\right) = \frac{{}^R d}{dt}\left({}^R\mathbf{r}_P\right) + \frac{{}^R d}{dt}\left({}^B\mathbf{r}_{Q/P}\right) \tag{3.2} $$

The derivatives of the position vectors defined relative to reference system R can be represented in a straightforward manner as velocities relative to reference system R because the reference axes relative to which the vectors are defined are fixed to R and do not move with time. Therefore, Eq. (3.1) becomes

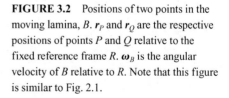

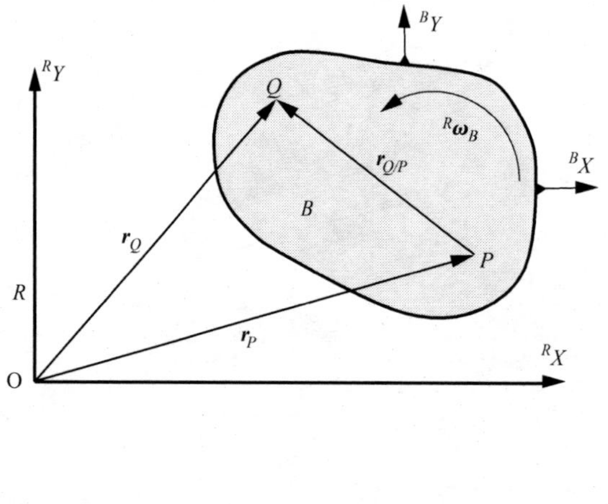

FIGURE 3.2 Positions of two points in the moving lamina, B. $\mathbf{r}_P$ and $\mathbf{r}_Q$ are the respective positions of points P and Q relative to the fixed reference frame R. $\boldsymbol{\omega}_B$ is the angular velocity of B relative to R. Note that this figure is similar to Fig. 2.1.

$$ {}^R\boldsymbol{v}_Q = {}^R\boldsymbol{v}_P + \frac{{}^R d}{dt}\left({}^B\boldsymbol{r}_{Q/P}\right) \tag{3.3} $$

However, note that ${}^B\boldsymbol{r}_{Q/P}$ is a vector defined relative to the coordinate system fixed to body B, and the reference axes of body B rotate relative to those of reference system R with an angular velocity ${}^R\boldsymbol{\omega}_B$. Therefore the derivative $\frac{{}^R d}{dt}({}^B\boldsymbol{r}_{Q/P})$ must account for this rotation. In particular, the derivative involves two terms, one associated with the change in magnitude of the vector and one associated with the change in direction. This is apparent if we represent the vector ${}^B\boldsymbol{r}_{Q/P}$ as a general three-dimensional vector in terms of its components and unit vectors. Then,

$$ {}^B\boldsymbol{r}_{Q/P} = x\,{}^B\boldsymbol{i} + y\,{}^B\boldsymbol{j} + z\,{}^B\boldsymbol{k} $$

and

$$ \begin{aligned} \frac{{}^R d}{dt}\left({}^B\boldsymbol{r}_{Q/P}\right) &= \frac{{}^R d}{dt}\left(x\,{}^B\boldsymbol{i} + y\,{}^B\boldsymbol{j} + z\,{}^B\boldsymbol{k}\right) \\ &= \left(\frac{{}^R dx}{dt}{}^B\boldsymbol{i} + \frac{{}^R dy}{dt}{}^B\boldsymbol{j} + \frac{{}^R dz}{dt}{}^B\boldsymbol{k}\right) + \left(x\frac{{}^R d\,{}^B\boldsymbol{i}}{dt} + y\frac{{}^R d\,{}^B\boldsymbol{j}}{dt} + z\frac{{}^R d\,{}^B\boldsymbol{k}}{dt}\right) \end{aligned} \tag{3.4} $$

In the first term, the derivatives of the components correspond to the change in the length of the vector, and this is defined relative to the coordinate system fixed to body B. Therefore, this is just the velocity defined relative to body B. The second term accounts for the rotation of the coordinate axes of B relative to the reference frame R.

Because ${}^B\boldsymbol{i}$, ${}^B\boldsymbol{j}$, and ${}^B\boldsymbol{k}$ are unit vectors, only their directions can change with time. We can determine how to evaluate the derivatives if we look at an infinitesimal angular displacement $\delta\theta$ of body B relative to R during an infinitesimal time increment δt.

Because infinitesimal angular rotations are involved, we can treat $\delta\theta$ as a vector with x, y, z components (i.e., $\delta\theta = \delta\theta_x{}^R\boldsymbol{i} = \delta\theta_y{}^R\boldsymbol{j} = \delta\theta_z{}^R\boldsymbol{k}$) and determine how each component changes the directions of the unit vectors. The angular velocity will be the change in the angular position during the infinitesimal time increment δt. That is,

$$ \omega_x = \frac{{}^R\delta\theta_x}{\delta t}, \quad \omega_y = \frac{{}^R\delta\theta_y}{\delta t}, \quad \omega_z = \frac{{}^R\delta\theta_z}{\delta t} $$

and

$$ {}^R\boldsymbol{\omega}_B = \omega_x\,{}^R\boldsymbol{i} + \omega_y\,{}^R\boldsymbol{j} + \omega_z\,{}^R\boldsymbol{k} \tag{3.5} $$

To identify the trend, consider the effect of the angular components about the X axis. For the x direction (unit vector ${}^B\boldsymbol{i}$), the change in the unit vector is represented in Fig. 3.3. From the figure,

$$ {}^R d\left({}^B\boldsymbol{i}\right) = 1\,{}^R\boldsymbol{j}\,d\theta_z - 1\,{}^R\boldsymbol{k}\,d\theta_y \tag{3.6} $$

The change takes place during the time increment δt. Therefore, dividing Eq. (3.6) by δt we get

$$ \frac{{}^R d}{dt}\left({}^B\boldsymbol{i}\right) = {}^R\boldsymbol{j}\omega_z - {}^R\boldsymbol{k}\omega_y = {}^R\boldsymbol{\omega}_B \times {}^B\boldsymbol{i} = \begin{vmatrix} {}^R\boldsymbol{i} & {}^R\boldsymbol{j} & {}^R\boldsymbol{k} \\ \omega_x & \omega_y & \omega_z \\ 1 & 0 & 0 \end{vmatrix} $$

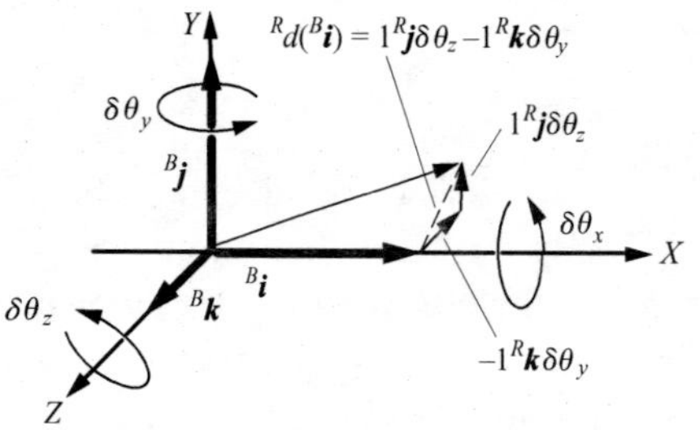

FIGURE 3.3 Change in $\boldsymbol{i}$ owing to a rotation about the X, Y, and Z axes fixed to R.

Similarly,

$$\frac{{}^{R}d}{dt}\left({}^{B}\mathbf{j}\right) = {}^{R}\boldsymbol{\omega}_B \times {}^{B}\mathbf{j}$$

$$\frac{{}^{R}d}{dt}\left({}^{B}\mathbf{k}\right) = {}^{R}\boldsymbol{\omega}_B \times {}^{B}\mathbf{k}$$

Therefore,

$$x\frac{{}^{R}d\,{}^{B}\mathbf{i}}{dt} + y\frac{{}^{R}d\,{}^{B}\mathbf{j}}{dt} + z\frac{{}^{R}d\,{}^{B}\mathbf{k}}{dt} = x\,{}^{R}\boldsymbol{\omega}_B \times {}^{B}\mathbf{i} + y\,{}^{R}\boldsymbol{\omega}_B \times {}^{B}\mathbf{j} + z\,{}^{R}\boldsymbol{\omega}_B \times {}^{B}\mathbf{k}$$
$$= {}^{R}\boldsymbol{\omega}_B \times \left(x\,{}^{B}\mathbf{i} + y\,{}^{B}\mathbf{j} + z\,{}^{B}\mathbf{k}\right) = {}^{R}\boldsymbol{\omega}_B \times {}^{B}\mathbf{r}_{Q/P}$$

Then,

$$\frac{{}^{R}d}{dt}\left({}^{B}\mathbf{r}_{Q/P}\right) = \left(\frac{{}^{R}dx}{dt}{}^{B}\mathbf{i} + \frac{{}^{R}dy}{dt}{}^{B}\mathbf{j} + \frac{{}^{R}dz}{dt}{}^{B}\mathbf{k}\right) + \left(x\frac{{}^{R}d\,{}^{B}\mathbf{i}}{dt} + y\frac{{}^{R}d\,{}^{B}\mathbf{j}}{dt} + z\frac{{}^{R}d\,{}^{B}\mathbf{k}}{dt}\right)$$
$$= {}^{B}\mathbf{v}_{Q/P} + {}^{R}\boldsymbol{\omega}_B \times {}^{B}\mathbf{r}_{Q/P} \tag{3.7}$$

Now, Eq. (3.3) can be written as

$${}^{R}\mathbf{v}_Q = {}^{R}\mathbf{v}_P + {}^{B}\mathbf{v}_{Q/P} + {}^{R}\boldsymbol{\omega}_B \times {}^{B}\mathbf{r}_{Q/P} \tag{3.8}$$

Before proceeding to the development of the acceleration equations, it is interesting to note that Eq. (3.7) is quite general. We could have derived a similar expression for the derivative of *any* vector that is defined relative to a moving coordinate system. For example, if $\boldsymbol{s}$ is any vector (e.g., position, velocity, or acceleration) and if U and W are any two different coordinate systems,

$$\frac{{}^{U}d}{dt}\left({}^{W}\mathbf{s}\right) = \frac{{}^{W}d}{dt}\left({}^{W}\mathbf{s}\right) + {}^{U}\boldsymbol{\omega}_W \times {}^{W}\mathbf{s} \tag{3.9}$$

Note that angular velocity is a property of a body and linear velocity is a property of a point. In both cases, it is necessary to specify, or at least understand, which reference frame is used to define the quantity. Also note that if the vector is defined in the coordinate system in which the observer stands, the term involving the angular velocity will be zero. That is,

$${}^{U}\boldsymbol{\omega}_U = 0$$

3.3.2 Acceleration Equations

The acceleration equations will involve the derivative of each angular velocity. In general, angular acceleration can be written as

$$^{R}\boldsymbol{\alpha}_{B}=\frac{^{R}d}{dt}\left(^{R}\boldsymbol{\omega}_{B}\right)$$

where again B is the moving body and R is the reference system. As in the case of the angular velocity, the angular acceleration is a property of the entire body. It is a vector and has a magnitude and direction.

If a velocity vector is defined in the coordinate system in which the observer is located, the corresponding acceleration can be expressed simply. For example, if the velocity vector is given by $^{R}\mathbf{v}_{Q}$, then the acceleration is given by

$$^{R}\boldsymbol{a}_{Q}=\frac{^{R}d}{dt}\left(^{R}\mathbf{v}_{Q}\right)$$

To obtain the linear acceleration relationship for the points P and Q in Fig. 3.2, we can differentiate Eq. (3.8). Differentiating term by term with the observer in reference system R gives

$$^{R}\boldsymbol{a}_{Q}=\frac{^{R}d}{dt}\left(^{R}\mathbf{v}_{Q}\right)=\frac{^{R}d}{dt}\left(^{R}\mathbf{v}_{P}\right)+\frac{^{R}d}{dt}\left(^{B}\mathbf{v}_{Q/P}\right)+\frac{^{R}d}{dt}\left(^{R}\boldsymbol{\omega}_{B}\times{}^{B}\mathbf{r}_{Q/P}\right)$$

Considering each term and recognizing that vectors $^{B}\mathbf{v}_{Q/P}$ amd $^{B}\mathbf{r}_{Q/P}$ are both defined relative to the moving coordinate system (B), we get, after differentiation,

$$^{R}\boldsymbol{a}_{Q}={}^{R}\boldsymbol{a}_{P}+\frac{^{B}d}{dt}\left(^{B}\mathbf{v}_{Q/P}\right)+{}^{R}\boldsymbol{\omega}_{B}\times{}^{B}\mathbf{v}_{Q/P}+{}^{R}\boldsymbol{\alpha}_{B}\times{}^{B}\mathbf{r}_{Q/P}+{}^{R}\boldsymbol{\omega}_{B}\times\left(^{B}\mathbf{v}_{Q/P}+{}^{R}\boldsymbol{\omega}_{B}\times{}^{B}\mathbf{r}_{Q/P}\right)$$

and collecting terms gives

$$^{R}\boldsymbol{a}_{Q}={}^{R}\boldsymbol{a}_{P}+{}^{B}\boldsymbol{a}_{Q/P}+2\,{}^{R}\boldsymbol{\omega}_{B}\times{}^{B}\mathbf{v}_{Q/P}+{}^{R}\boldsymbol{\alpha}_{B}\times{}^{B}\mathbf{r}_{Q/P}+{}^{R}\boldsymbol{\omega}_{B}\times\left(^{R}\boldsymbol{\omega}_{B}\times{}^{B}\mathbf{r}_{Q/P}\right) \tag{3.10}$$

Note that in the last term, the operation ($^{R}\boldsymbol{\omega}_{B}\times{}^{B}\mathbf{r}_{Q/P}$) must be carried out before the operation $^{R}\boldsymbol{\omega}_{B}\times(^{R}\boldsymbol{\omega}_{B}\times{}^{B}\mathbf{r}_{Q/P})$. Obviously, $(\boldsymbol{\omega}\times\boldsymbol{\omega})\times\boldsymbol{r}\neq\boldsymbol{\omega}\times(\boldsymbol{\omega}\times\boldsymbol{r})$.

The term $2^{R}\boldsymbol{\omega}_{B}\times{}^{B}\mathbf{v}_{Q/P}$ is called the Coriolis term and is a function of velocities only. The term $^{R}\boldsymbol{\alpha}_{B}\times{}^{B}\mathbf{r}_{Q/P}$ is the transverse or tangential component of acceleration identified before. This component of acceleration is perpendicular to the radius vector. The term $^{R}\boldsymbol{\omega}_{B}\times(^{R}\boldsymbol{\omega}_{B}\times{}^{B}\mathbf{r}_{Q/P})$ is the radial component of acceleration. In planar motion, but not in general, it points in the direction *opposite* to the radius vector. The term $^{B}\boldsymbol{a}_{Q/P}$ is the acceleration of Q relative to P when the observer is in the moving body B.

3.3.3 Chain Rule for Positions, Velocities, and Accelerations

When dealing with mechanisms with a relatively large number of members, it is helpful to have relationships between the relative velocities and accelerations of several points and between the relative angular velocities and angular accelerations of several members. These relationships are particularly relevant to the spatial chain mechanisms discussed in Chapter 9.

Positions, Velocities, and Accelerations of Points Let *A, B, C, D*, and *E* be any arbitrary points moving with respect to the reference frame *R* as shown in Fig. 3.4. Then a position equation can be written as

$$^R\boldsymbol{r}_{E/D}+{}^R\boldsymbol{r}_{D/C}+{}^R\boldsymbol{r}_{C/B}+{}^R\boldsymbol{r}_{B/A}={}^R\boldsymbol{r}_{E/A} \tag{3.11}$$

This type of equation is just a simple expression of vector addition, and it applies regardless of the number of points involved. For velocities, we can differentiate Eq. (3.11) with the observer in system *R*. Then,

$$^R\boldsymbol{v}_{E/D}+{}^R\boldsymbol{v}_{D/C}+{}^R\boldsymbol{v}_{C/B}+{}^R\boldsymbol{v}_{B/A}={}^R\boldsymbol{v}_{E/A} \tag{3.12}$$

and the acceleration equation becomes

$$^R\boldsymbol{a}_{E/D}+{}^R\boldsymbol{a}_{D/C}+{}^R\boldsymbol{a}_{C/B}+{}^R\boldsymbol{a}_{B/A}={}^R\boldsymbol{a}_{E/A} \tag{3.13}$$

Equations (3.11) through (3.13) are applicable to any set of points, and they are especially useful when determining the kinematic information for points on mechanisms after the basic kinematic information associated with each link is known. They are also useful when analyzing manipulators and robots.

The relationship among three *arbitrary* points (*A, B, C*) is

$$^R\boldsymbol{r}_{C/A}={}^R\boldsymbol{r}_{C/B}+{}^R\boldsymbol{r}_{B/A}$$

Then,

$$^R\boldsymbol{r}_{C/B}={}^R\boldsymbol{r}_{C/A}-{}^R\boldsymbol{r}_{B/A} \tag{3.14}$$

Because *A* is arbitrary, Eq. (3.14) indicates that we can find the relative position between two points by subtracting the relative position vectors between the two points and the same third point. Similarly, for velocities and accelerations,

$$^R\boldsymbol{v}_{C/B}={}^R\boldsymbol{v}_{C/A}-{}^R\boldsymbol{v}_{B/A} \tag{3.15}$$

and

$$^R\boldsymbol{a}_{C/B}={}^R\boldsymbol{a}_{C/A}-{}^R\boldsymbol{a}_{B/A} \tag{3.16}$$

Note the positions of *A, B*, and *C* in each of the expressions.

Relative Angular Velocities A chain rule for angular velocities works the same way as for linear velocities except that now reference systems are involved instead of points, as shown in Fig. 3.5. Consider three coordinate systems (1, 2, and 3) that are *momentarily parallel*. Then,

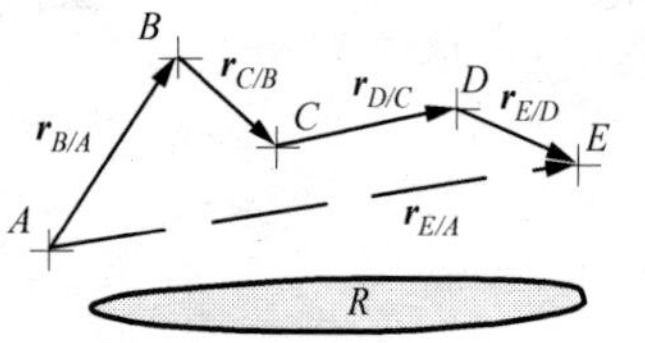

FIGURE 3.4 Relationship among the positions of a series of points.

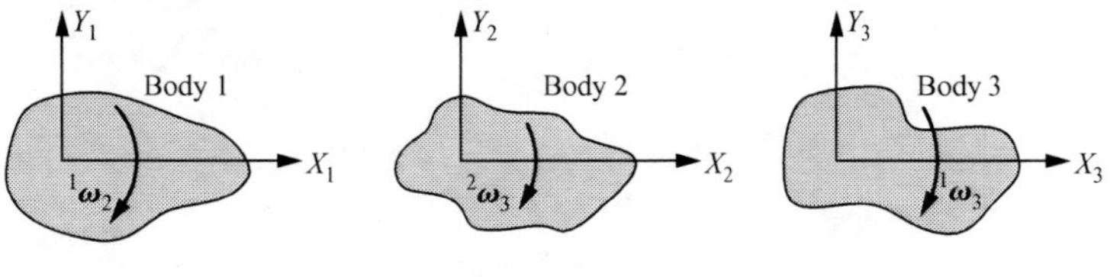

FIGURE 3.5 Relationship among the angular velocities for three links.

$$^1\boldsymbol{\omega}_3 = {^1\boldsymbol{\omega}_2} + {^2\boldsymbol{\omega}_3} \tag{3.17}$$

and

$$^2\boldsymbol{\omega}_3 = {^1\boldsymbol{\omega}_3} - {^1\boldsymbol{\omega}_2} = {^1\boldsymbol{\omega}_3} + {^2\boldsymbol{\omega}_1} \tag{3.18}$$

This means we can find the relative angular velocity between any two bodies by computing the angular velocity difference between each of the bodies and the same third body (in this case body 1).

For n bodies, the relative angular velocities are related by

$$^n\boldsymbol{\omega}_1 = {^2\boldsymbol{\omega}_1} + {^3\boldsymbol{\omega}_2} + {^4\boldsymbol{\omega}_3} + \cdots + {^{n-1}\boldsymbol{\omega}_{n-2}} + {^n\boldsymbol{\omega}_{n-1}}$$

Relative Angular Accelerations For relative accelerations, we can differentiate the relative velocity equation, Eq. (3.17):

$$\frac{^1d}{dt}\left({^1\boldsymbol{\omega}_3}\right) = \frac{^1d}{dt}\left({^1\boldsymbol{\omega}_2}\right) + \frac{^1d}{dt}\left({^2\boldsymbol{\omega}_3}\right) \tag{3.19}$$

The first two terms are straightforward because the derivatives are both taken with respect to the reference system in which each vector is defined. That is,

$$\frac{^1d}{dt}\left({^1\boldsymbol{\omega}_3}\right) = {^1\boldsymbol{\alpha}_3}, \qquad \frac{^1d}{dt}\left({^1\boldsymbol{\omega}_2}\right) = {^1\boldsymbol{\alpha}_2}$$

The third term is a vector described in the second coordinate system (superscript 2). Therefore using Eq. (3.9), this term can be written as

$$\frac{^1d}{dt}\left({^2\boldsymbol{\omega}_3}\right) = \frac{^2d}{dt}\left({^2\boldsymbol{\omega}_3}\right) + {^1\boldsymbol{\omega}_2} \times {^2\boldsymbol{\omega}_3} = {^2\boldsymbol{\alpha}_3} + {^1\boldsymbol{\omega}_2} \times {^2\boldsymbol{\omega}_3}$$

The relative angular acceleration expression in Eq. (3.19) can then be written as

$$^1\boldsymbol{\alpha}_3 = {^1\boldsymbol{\alpha}_2} + {^2\boldsymbol{\alpha}_3} + {^1\boldsymbol{\omega}_2} \times {^2\boldsymbol{\omega}_3}$$

This expression can be extended to n bodies using

$$^1\boldsymbol{\alpha}_n = {^1\boldsymbol{\alpha}_{n-1}} + {^{n-1}\boldsymbol{\alpha}_n} + {^1\boldsymbol{\omega}_{n-1}} \times {^{n-1}\boldsymbol{\omega}_n}$$

Then,

$$^1\boldsymbol{\alpha}_n = {^1\boldsymbol{\alpha}_2} + {^2\boldsymbol{\alpha}_3} + {^3\boldsymbol{\alpha}_4} + \cdots + {^{n-1}\boldsymbol{\alpha}_n} + {^1\boldsymbol{\omega}_2} \times {^2\boldsymbol{\omega}_3} + {^1\boldsymbol{\omega}_3} \times {^3\boldsymbol{\omega}_4} + {^1\boldsymbol{\omega}_4} \times {^4\boldsymbol{\omega}_5} + \cdots + {^1\boldsymbol{\omega}_{n-1}} \times {^{n-1}\boldsymbol{\omega}_n}$$

Note that, in the plane, all of the $\boldsymbol{\omega}$'s will be parallel, making the cross products all zero. Thus in *planar* problems, the chain rule for angular accelerations reduces to:

$$^1\boldsymbol{\alpha}_n = {}^1\boldsymbol{\alpha}_2 + {}^2\boldsymbol{\alpha}_3 + {}^3\boldsymbol{\alpha}_4 + \cdots + {}^{n-1}\boldsymbol{\alpha}_n \quad \text{(planar problems)}$$

Note that this equation could be treated as a scalar equation if signs are applied to the magnitudes of the angular accelerations according to some rule (say + for CCW and – for CW).

3.4 SPECIAL CASES FOR THE VELOCITY AND ACCELERATION EQUATIONS

Equations (3.8) and (3.10) are the most general forms for the relative velocity and acceleration equations for points that we will encounter in the kinematic analysis of linkages. In most practical problems, some of the terms in the expressions are zero. Three special cases often occur, and these will be discussed separately in the following.

3.4.1 Points *P* and *Q* fixed to *B*

This is the most common situation that exists in the analysis of mechanisms. If *P* and *Q* are both fixed to *B*, as shown in Fig. 3.6, we have

$$^B\boldsymbol{v}_{Q_B/P_B} = {}^B\boldsymbol{a}_{Q_B/P_B} = 0 \tag{3.20}$$

because *P* and *Q* do not have any motion relative to an observer in the moving body *B*. When Eq. (3.20) is used to simplify Eqs. (3.8) and (3.10), the results are

$$^R\boldsymbol{v}_Q = {}^R\boldsymbol{v}_P + {}^R\boldsymbol{\omega}_B \times \boldsymbol{r}_{Q/P} \tag{3.21}$$

which can be recognized as being the same as Eq. (2.1), and

$$^R\boldsymbol{a}_Q = {}^R\boldsymbol{a}_P + {}^R\boldsymbol{\alpha}_B \times \boldsymbol{r}_{Q/P} + {}^R\boldsymbol{\omega}_B \times \left({}^R\boldsymbol{\omega}_B \times \boldsymbol{r}_{Q/P} \right) \tag{3.22}$$

which is the same as Eq. (2.8).

Here we have dropped the superscript on $\boldsymbol{r}_{Q/P}$ because all coordinate systems are assumed to be parallel, and $\boldsymbol{r}_{Q/P}$ will have the same coordinates in all coordinate systems. Note also that we could have rewritten Eqs. (3.8) and (3.10) relative to any other link; however, only the choice of the link (*B*) to which *Q* and *P* are attached simplifies the equation. Using the radial and tangential notation, we can also rewrite Eq. (3.22) as

$$^R\boldsymbol{a}_Q = {}^R\boldsymbol{a}_P + {}^R\boldsymbol{a}^{\mathrm{r}}_{Q/P} + {}^R\boldsymbol{a}^{\mathrm{t}}_{Q/P}$$

where

$$^R\boldsymbol{a}^{\mathrm{t}}_{Q/P} = {}^R\boldsymbol{\alpha}_B \times \boldsymbol{r}_{Q/P} \tag{3.23}$$

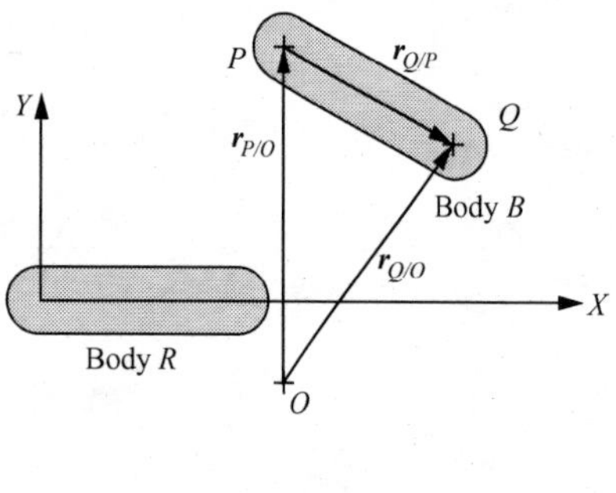

FIGURE 3.6 Two points fixed to the same link.

and

$$ {}^{R}\boldsymbol{a}^{\mathrm{r}}_{Q/P} = {}^{R}\boldsymbol{\omega}_B \times \left({}^{R}\boldsymbol{\omega}_B \times \boldsymbol{r}_{Q/P} \right) \tag{3.24} $$

We will use the radial and tangential notation extensively in mechanism analyses. For planar mechanisms, ${}^{R}\boldsymbol{a}^{\mathrm{t}}_{Q/P}$ and ${}^{R}\boldsymbol{a}^{\mathrm{r}}_{Q/P}$ will be orthogonal to each other because ${}^{R}\boldsymbol{\omega}_B$ and ${}^{R}\boldsymbol{\alpha}_B$ are both orthogonal to $\boldsymbol{r}_{Q/P}$. In spatial mechanisms, however, this will not always be the case.

3.4.2 *P* and *Q* Are Coincident

A second special case in kinematics is that in which P and Q belong to different bodies but are momentarily coincident. This case is shown in Fig. 3.7. Then, $\boldsymbol{r}_{P/Q}$ is momentarily zero, and Eqs. (3.8) and (3.10) reduce to

$$ {}^{R}\boldsymbol{v}_Q = {}^{R}\boldsymbol{v}_P + {}^{B}\boldsymbol{v}_{Q/P} \tag{3.25} $$

If Eqs. (3.25) and (3.8) are considered carefully, it is apparent that the equation for the relative velocity remains the same regardless of the body chosen as the moving body. This means that the relative velocity term ${}^{B}\boldsymbol{v}_{Q/P}$ is independent of the coordinate system chosen for the "moving" body. Therefore,

$$ {}^{i}\boldsymbol{v}_{Q/P} = {}^{B}\boldsymbol{v}_{Q/P} = {}^{R}\boldsymbol{v}_{Q/P} $$

where i and B are *any* systems.

The acceleration equation, Eq. (3.10), simplifies to

$$ {}^{R}\boldsymbol{a}_Q = {}^{R}\boldsymbol{a}_P + {}^{B}\boldsymbol{a}_{Q/P} + 2\,{}^{R}\boldsymbol{\omega}_B \times {}^{B}\boldsymbol{v}_{Q/P} \tag{3.26} $$

Here, the Coriolis term is a function of velocities, so it can be computed as soon as the velocity analysis is completed. Only ${}^{B}\boldsymbol{a}_{Q/P}$ involves new information not available from the velocity analysis.

3.4.3 *P* and *Q* Are Coincident and in Rolling Contact

If points P and Q are not only momentarily coincident but also in rolling contact, Eqs. (3.25) and (3.26) can be simplified still further. This condition is shown in Fig. 3.8. If two points are in rolling contact, they have the same velocity and their relative velocity must be zero. This means that

$$ {}^{B}\boldsymbol{v}_{Q/P} = 0 $$

$$ {}^{R}\boldsymbol{v}_Q = {}^{R}\boldsymbol{v}_P $$

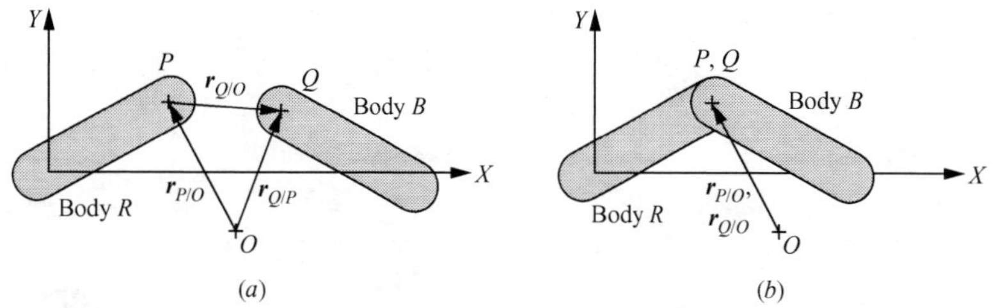

FIGURE 3.7 Condition when two separate points (a) become momentarily coincident (b).

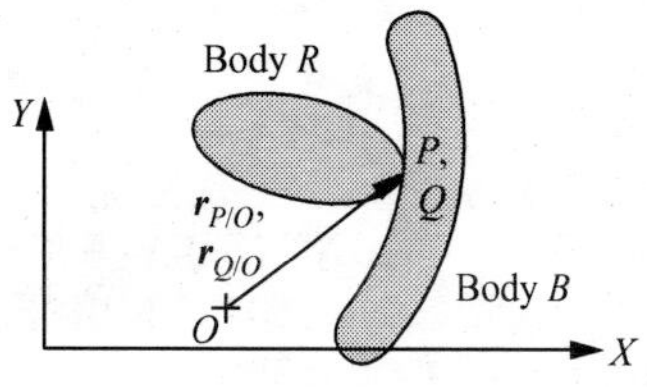

FIGURE 3.8 Condition for rolling contact.

and

$$^{R}\boldsymbol{a}_Q = {}^{R}\boldsymbol{a}_P + {}^{B}\boldsymbol{a}_{Q/P}$$

Using logic similar to that used with Eq. (3.25), it is apparent that although the relative acceleration ${}^{B}\boldsymbol{a}_{Q/P}$ is not usually zero, it is independent of whatever coordinate system is used for reference. This means that the relative acceleration will be the same when observed from any of the links in the mechanism.

We will examine examples of the special cases in the following. To simplify the equations and the nomenclature, we will use a superscript to identify the coordinate system only when the coordinate system is different from 1. Therefore, if no superscript is indicated as was done in Chapter 2, the frame coordinate system is automatically implied.

3.5 LINKAGES WITH ROTATING SLIDING JOINTS

Mechanisms in this class can have either a slider that slides on a line that is rotating or a pin-in-a-slot joint where the slot is straight and rotating. These cases are shown in Fig. 3.9, where the link numbers have been chosen arbitrarily.

Mechanisms with sliders that rotate are common in practice. Typical examples are door closers, the hydraulic cylinders on power shovels, and the power cylinders on some robots. The pin-in-slot joints, often with a free-spinning roller centered on the pin, are typically used as inexpensive substitutes for slider joints. They function where the transmitted loads are low. Examples where they appear are electric toothbrush mechanisms, audiotape cleaners, and walking-toy mechanisms.

The analysis of these mechanisms can be approached using the special case in section 3.4.2 for relative velocities and accelerations of coincident points. The resulting velocity and acceleration equations for two coincident points P and Q are given by Eqs. (3.25) and (3.26). Dropping the superscript R for the frame, we get

$$\boldsymbol{v}_Q = \boldsymbol{v}_P + {}^{B}\boldsymbol{v}_{Q/P}$$

$$\boldsymbol{a}_Q = \boldsymbol{a}_P + {}^{B}\boldsymbol{a}_{Q/P} + 2\boldsymbol{\omega}_B \times {}^{B}\boldsymbol{v}_{Q/P}$$

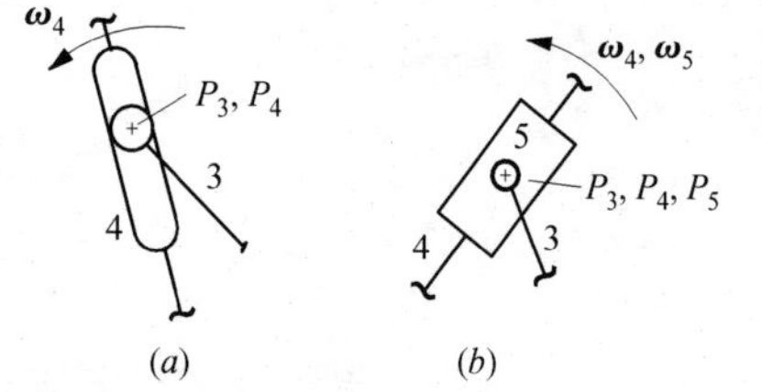

FIGURE 3.9 Joints that can be analyzed as rotating sliding joints. (a) Pin in straight slot, (b) rotating slider. The link numbers have been chosen arbitrarily.

When the points are coincident, P and Q will share the same coordinates, and they will usually be designated by the same letter with a subscript identifying the link to which they are attached. For example, if 3 and 4 are the links to which the coincident points are attached, if body B corresponds to link 5, and if the frame is 1, the velocity and acceleration equations can be written as

$$\boldsymbol{v}_{P_3} = \boldsymbol{v}_{P_4} + {}^5\boldsymbol{v}_{P_3/P_4} \tag{3.27}$$

and

$$\boldsymbol{a}_{P_3} = \boldsymbol{a}_{P_4} + {}^5\boldsymbol{a}_{P_3/P_4} + 2\boldsymbol{\omega}_5 \times {}^5\boldsymbol{v}_{P_3/P_4} \tag{3.28}$$

Once again, ${}^5\boldsymbol{a}_{P_3/P_4}$ is called the acceleration of P_3 relative to P_4 when the observer is in system 5. The term $2\boldsymbol{\omega}_5 \times {}^5\boldsymbol{v}_{P_3/P_4}$ is the Coriolis component of acceleration, and it can be written as $\boldsymbol{a}^{C}_{P_3/P_4}$. Eq. (3.28) can then be written as

$$\boldsymbol{a}_{P_3} = \boldsymbol{a}_{P_4} + {}^5\boldsymbol{a}_{P_3/P_4} + \boldsymbol{a}^{C}_{P_3/P_4}$$

for graphical analyses.

In planar motion, the Coriolis component is normal to ${}^5\boldsymbol{v}_{P_3/P_4}$ and has the magnitude $2(\omega_5)|{}^5\boldsymbol{v}_{P_3/P_4}|$. Its sense is obtained by imagining ${}^5\boldsymbol{v}_{P_3/P_4}$ to be rotating about its tail in the $\boldsymbol{\omega}_5$ direction. The direction of movement of the head of ${}^5\boldsymbol{v}_{P_3/P_4}$ gives the sense. To illustrate the manner in which Eqs. (3.27) and (3.28) are used in graphical linkage analysis, consider the following example.

EXAMPLE 3.1 *Velocity and Acceleration Analysis of a Quick-Return Mechanism*

Find the sliding velocities of the slide, the angular accelerations of links 3 and 4, and the acceleration of slide 5 for the quick-return mechanism of Fig. 3.10. The dimensions are as shown. Link 2 is driven with a constant angular velocity of 10 rpm CCW.

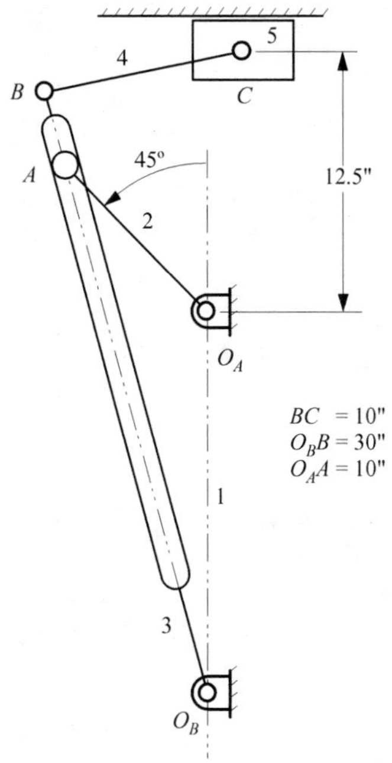

FIGURE 3.10 The quick return linkage to be analyzed in Example 3.1.

Solution Link 2 is the driver, so we will begin the analysis with point A_2. We must conduct the velocity analysis first. If that analysis is done carefully, we can proceed with the same points for the acceleration analysis. As in the previous examples, we will develop the basic equations first and then give the graphical procedure for solving them. The velocity of point A_2 is given by

$$\boldsymbol{v}_{A_2} = \boldsymbol{v}_{A_2/O_A} = \boldsymbol{\omega}_2 \times \boldsymbol{r}_{A_2/O_A}$$

In the analysis of mechanisms of this type, it is important to identify the link in which the observer is located. Therefore, the left superscripts will be maintained when the coordinate system is different from 1. We must now use the coincident point A_3 to be able to develop an equation relating a point on link 2 to a point on link 3. We can write the relative velocity equation in one of two ways:

$$\boldsymbol{v}_{A_2} = \boldsymbol{v}_{A_3} + \boldsymbol{v}_{A_2/A_3} = \boldsymbol{v}_{A_3} + {}^3\boldsymbol{v}_{A_2/A_3} \tag{3.29}$$

or

$$\boldsymbol{v}_{A_3} = \boldsymbol{v}_{A_2} + \boldsymbol{v}_{A_3/A_2} = \boldsymbol{v}_{A_2} + {}^2\boldsymbol{v}_{A_3/A_2} \tag{3.30}$$

To solve the problem, we must be able to recognize the direction of the relative velocity defined in the moving coordinate system. Referring to the mechanism in Fig. 3.10, we see that if the observer is fixed to link 2, it is not possible to identify directly the direction of the velocity ${}^2\boldsymbol{v}_{A_3/A_2}$; however, if the observer is in link 3, it is possible to identify the direction of the velocity ${}^3\boldsymbol{v}_{A_2/A_3}$ because the pin at A is constrained to move along the straight slot in link 3. Therefore, the direction of the velocity ${}^3\boldsymbol{v}_{A_2/A_3}$ must be along the slot. Because we can determine the direction of ${}^3\boldsymbol{v}_{A_2/A_3}$ by inspection, Eq. (3.29) is more useful than Eq. (3.30).

In problems such as this, it is important to identify clearly the links relative to which the velocity directions can be identified. The same links can be used for the subsequent acceleration analysis, and it is usually much easier to visualize velocities than it is to visualize accelerations.

After Eq. (3.29) is solved for the unknowns, $\boldsymbol{v}_{A_3}$ will be known. Then $\boldsymbol{v}_{B_3}$ can be found from the velocity image of link 3 using O_B, A_3, and B_3. Knowing $\boldsymbol{v}_{B_3}$, which is the same as $\boldsymbol{v}_{B_4}$ we can write the following equation for the velocity of C_4:

$$\boldsymbol{v}_{C_4} = \boldsymbol{v}_{B_4} + \boldsymbol{v}_{C_4/B_4} \tag{3.31}$$

Because the directions of $\boldsymbol{v}_{C_4}$ and $\boldsymbol{v}_{C_4/B_4}$ are known, we can solve Eq. (3.31) for the unknowns. After Eqs. (3.29) and (3.31) are solved, we can compute the angular velocities of links 3 and 4 from

$$\boldsymbol{v}_{B_3/O_B} = \boldsymbol{\omega}_3 \times \boldsymbol{r}_{B_3/O_B}$$

and

$$\boldsymbol{v}_{C_4/B_4} = \boldsymbol{\omega}_4 \times \boldsymbol{r}_{C_4/B_4}$$

For the acceleration analysis, we need only differentiate Eqs. (3.29) and (3.31). The results are

$$\boldsymbol{a}_{A_2} = \boldsymbol{a}_{A_3} + \boldsymbol{a}_{A_2/A_3}$$

and

$$\boldsymbol{a}_{C_4} = \boldsymbol{a}_{B_4} + \boldsymbol{a}_{C_4/B_4}$$

Expanding the equations in terms of vectors relative to moving coordinate systems, we obtain

$$\boldsymbol{a}^{\mathrm{r}}_{A_2/O_A} + \boldsymbol{a}^{\mathrm{t}}_{A_2/O_A} = \boldsymbol{a}^{\mathrm{r}}_{A_3/O_B} + \boldsymbol{a}^{\mathrm{t}}_{A_3/O_B} + {}^3\boldsymbol{a}_{A_2/A_3} + 2\left(\boldsymbol{\omega}_3 \times {}^3\boldsymbol{v}_{A_2/A_3}\right) \tag{3.32}$$

and

$$a_{C_4} = a_{B_3/O_B} + a^{r}_{C_4/B_4} + a^{t}_{C_4/B_4} \tag{3.33}$$

where

$a^{r}_{A_2/O_A} = r_{A_2/O_A}\omega_2^2$ from A to O_A

$a^{t}_{A_2/O_A} = \alpha_2 \times r_{A_2/O_A}$ perpendicular to $\overrightarrow{AO_A}$

$a^{r}_{A_3/O_B} = r_{A_3/O_B}\omega_2^2$ from A to O_B

$a^{t}_{A_3/O_B} = \alpha_3 \times r_{A_3/O_B}$ (α_3 is unknown but the result is perpendicular to $\overrightarrow{AO_B}$)

${}^3a_{A_2/A_3}$ has a magnitude that is unknown but its direction is along the slot in link 3

$2(\omega_3 \times {}^3v_{A_2/A_3})$ is the Coriolis acceleration perpendicular to ${}^3v_{A_2/A_3}$

a_{C_4} is along the slider path of link 5

a_{B_3/O_B} is found by acceleration image of link 3

$a^{r}_{C_4/B_4} = r_{C_4/B_4}\omega_4^2$ from C to B

$a^{t}_{C_4/B_4} = \alpha_4 \times r_{C_4/B_4}$ has a magnitude that is unknown but a direction that is perpendicular to $\overrightarrow{CB}$.

Based on the position and velocity analyses, there will be only two unknown magnitudes in Eqs. (3.31) and (3.33). All of the directions will be known. Therefore, the equations can be solved.

Steps

1. Draw linkage to scale as shown in Fig. 3.11.
2. Compute v_{A_2}, and plot v_{A_2} normal to $\overrightarrow{O_AA}$ as $\overrightarrow{oa_2}$.

   $\omega_2 = 10 \times 2\pi/60 = 1.0472$ rad/s CCW

   $v_{A_2} = \omega_2 \times \mathbf{r}_{A_2/O_A} \times 10 = 10.472$ in/s perpendicular to AO_A in the direction shown in Fig. 3.11.
3. Draw a line through a_2 parallel to $\overrightarrow{O_BB}$.
4. Draw a line through o normal to $\overrightarrow{O_BA_3}$. The intersection with the line from step 3 gives point a_3.
5. Locate b_3 using the velocity image $\dfrac{ob_3}{oa_3} = \dfrac{O_BB}{O_BA}$.

   $ob_3 = 7.26 \times (30/26.48) = 8.22$ in/s
6. Draw a line through b_3 normal to $\overrightarrow{BC}$.
7. Draw a line through o parallel to the slide. Its intersection with the line drawn in step 6 gives point c_4.
8. Measure $v_{C_4} = oc_4$, $v_{A_2/A_3} = \overrightarrow{a_2a_3}$ and $v_{C_4/B_4} = \overrightarrow{c_4b_4}$.

   $v_{C_4} = 11.06$ in/s, $v_{A_2/A_3} = 5.09$ in/s, $v_{C_4/B_4} = 2.823$ in/s
9. Compute $\omega_3 = v_{A_3/O_B}/r_{A_3/O_B}$ and $\omega_4 = v_{C_4/B_4}/r_{C_4/B_4}$.

   $$\omega_3 = (9.07)/(26.37) = 0.344 \text{ rad/s CCW}$$

   $$\omega_4 = 2.823/5 = 0.565 \text{ rad/s CCW}$$

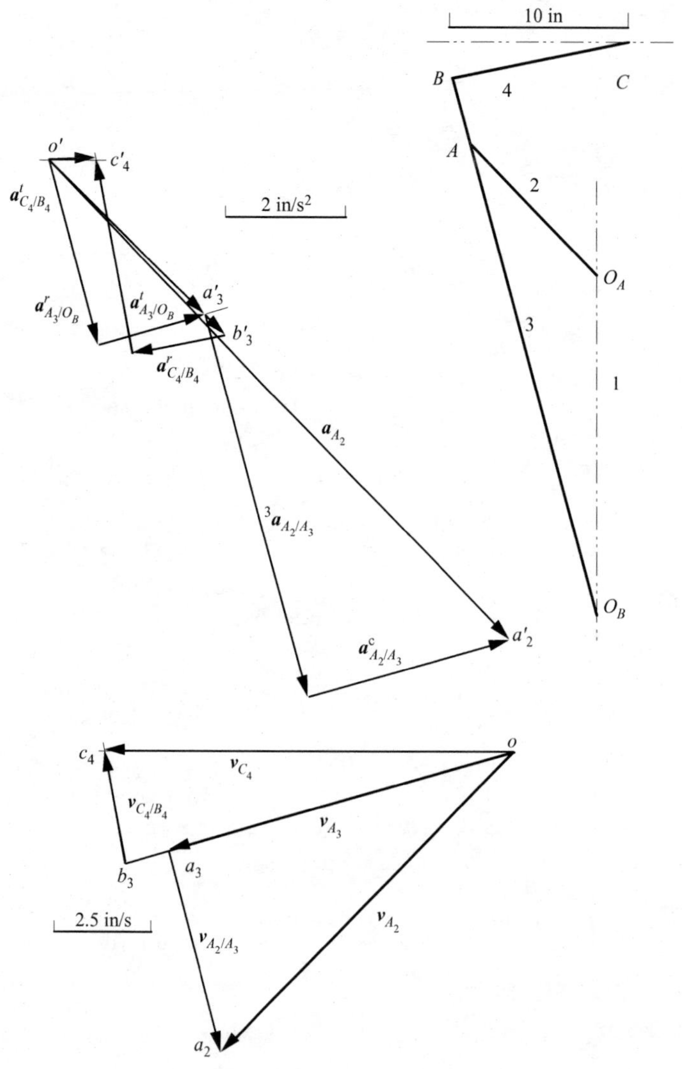

FIGURE 3.11 Solution for Example 3.1.

10. Get the senses of $\boldsymbol{\omega}_3$ and $\boldsymbol{\omega}_4$ by looking at the directions of rotation of $\boldsymbol{r}_{A_3/O_B}$ and $\boldsymbol{r}_{C_4/B_4}$ needed to get the respective relative velocity directions.
11. Compute $\boldsymbol{a}_{A_2}$ and plot it as $\overrightarrow{o'a'}$.

$$\boldsymbol{a}_{A_2} = |\boldsymbol{r}_{A_2/O_A}|\,|\boldsymbol{\omega}_2|^2 = 10 \times 1.0472^2 = 10.97 \ \text{in/s}^2$$

12. Compute $\boldsymbol{a}^{\text{C}}_{A_2/A_3} = 2(\boldsymbol{\omega}_3)(\boldsymbol{v}_{A_2/A_3})$ and get the sense of $\boldsymbol{a}^{\text{C}}_{A_2/A_3}$ by rotating $(\boldsymbol{v}_{A_2/A_3})$ 90° in the $\boldsymbol{\omega}_3$ direction. Plot it with the tip at a'_2.

$$\boldsymbol{a}^{\text{C}}_{A_2/A_3} = 2 \times 5.09 \times 0.344 = 3.50 \ \text{in/s}^2$$

13. Draw a line normal to $\boldsymbol{a}^{\text{C}}_{A_2/A_3}$ and through the tail of $\boldsymbol{a}^{\text{C}}_{A_2/A_3}$. This line corresponds to $^3\boldsymbol{a}_{A_2/A_3}$ that is along the slot.

14. Compute $\boldsymbol{a}^{\mathrm{r}}_{A_3/O_B}$ and plot it from o' in the $\overrightarrow{A_3O_B}$ direction.

$$\boldsymbol{a}^{\mathrm{r}}_{A_3/O_B} = \left|\boldsymbol{r}_{A_3/O_B}\right| \left|\boldsymbol{\omega}_3\right|^2 = 26.37 \times 0.344^2 = 3.12 \ \mathrm{in/s^2}$$

15. Draw a line through the tip of $\boldsymbol{a}^{\mathrm{r}}_{A_3/O_B}$ normal to $\overrightarrow{O_BA_3}$. This vector corresponds to $\boldsymbol{a}^{\mathrm{t}}_{A_3/O_B}$. Its intersection with the line drawn in step 13 gives point a'_3.

16. Locate point b'_3 using the acceleration image $\dfrac{o'b'_3}{o'a'_3} = \dfrac{O_BB}{O_BA}$.

$$o'b'_3 = 3.62 \times \left(30/26.37\right) = 4.12 \ \mathrm{in/s^2}$$

17. Plot $\boldsymbol{a}^{\mathrm{r}}_{C_4/B_4}$ from point b'_3 parallel to $\overrightarrow{CB}$.

$$\boldsymbol{a}^{\mathrm{r}}_{C_4/B_4} = \left|\boldsymbol{r}_{C_4/B_4}\right| \left|\boldsymbol{\omega}_4\right|^2 = 5 \times 0.608^2 = 1.85 \ \mathrm{in/s^2}$$

18. Draw a line through the tip of $\boldsymbol{a}^{\mathrm{r}}_{C_4/B_4}$ normal to $\overrightarrow{CB}$.
This vector corresponds to $\boldsymbol{a}^{\mathrm{t}}_{C_4/B_4}$.

19. Draw a line through o' parallel to the slide. Its intersection with the line generated in step 18 gives point c'_4.

20. Measure $\boldsymbol{a}^{\mathrm{t}}_{A_3/O_B}$ and $\boldsymbol{a}^{\mathrm{t}}_{C_4/B_4}$.

$$\boldsymbol{a}^{\mathrm{t}}_{A_3/O_B} = 1.870 \ \mathrm{in/s^2} \ \text{ and } \ \boldsymbol{a}^{\mathrm{t}}_{C_4/B_4} = 3.197 \ \mathrm{in/s^2}$$

21. Compute $\alpha_3 = \dfrac{\boldsymbol{a}^{\mathrm{t}}_{A_3/O_B}}{r_{A_3/O_B}}$ and $\alpha_4 = \dfrac{a^{\mathrm{t}}_{C_4/B_4}}{r_{C_4/B_4}}$ and get the senses of these angular accelerations by considering the directions of rotation needed to rotate the position vectors in the directions of $\boldsymbol{a}^{\mathrm{t}}_{A_3/O_B}$ and $\boldsymbol{a}^{\mathrm{t}}_{C_4/B_4}$, respectively.

$$\boldsymbol{\alpha}_3 = 1.870/(26.37) = 0.071 \ \mathrm{rad/s^2} \ \mathrm{CW}$$

$$\boldsymbol{\alpha}_4 = 3.197/5 = 0.640 \ \mathrm{rad/s^2} \ \mathrm{CCW}$$

22. Measure $\boldsymbol{a}_{C_4}$.

$\boldsymbol{a}_{C_4} = 0.7986$ in/s^2 directed to the right

One of the useful features of the quick-return linkage is a long range of motion with relatively uniform velocity on the forward stroke. The small value of $\boldsymbol{a}_{C_4}$ is indicative of this property.

3.6 ROLLING CONTACT

Rolling contact is quite often used in practical linkages. In addition to the obvious case of a wheel rolling on a surface or a rail, rolling contact between a cam and a roller follower is a common example. Also, the pitch cylinders of spur and helical gear pairs and the pitch cones of bevel gear pairs can be considered to be in pure rolling contact. In that case, although the actual physical contact between the gear teeth is a general combination of rolling and sliding, the gear pair can be modeled as a pair of simple elements in pure rolling contact from the point of view of investigating gross kinematic properties.

Rolling contact can be approached in two different ways, depending on the level of detail desired. If the velocities and accelerations of the rolling elements themselves are immaterial, it is possible to solve for the velocities and accelerations of the other links in a rolling-contact problem by replacing the actual linkage with a virtual linkage in which the rolling elements are replaced by a single link with length equal to the sum of their radii of curvature. If the velocities and accelerations of all the links are important, then one or more additional relative velocity (or angular velocity) relations are necessary to obtain the angular velocities of one or more rolling links. Both approaches will be discussed.

3.6.1 Basic Kinematic Relationships for Rolling Contact

Figure 3.12 shows two rigid bodies in rolling contact. The bodies are arbitrarily taken to be links 2 and 4. The contact location is B, and the centers of curvature of the two bodies corresponding to B_2 and B_4 are O_2 and O_4, respectively. At the point of contact for two bodies rolling on each other, there is no relative sliding between the two points (B_2 and B_4) at the location of contact. Because B_2 and B_4 are not only momentarily coincident but also in rolling contact, they have the same velocity, and their relative velocity must be zero. This means that

$$\boldsymbol{v}_{B_2} = \boldsymbol{v}_{B_4}$$

and

$$\boldsymbol{v}_{B_2/B_4} = {}^4\boldsymbol{v}_{B_2/B_4} = {}^4\boldsymbol{v}_{B_2} = 0$$

Note that this is exactly the same velocity condition as that for a revolute joint. Therefore, for velocities *only*, the point of rolling contact can be treated as a revolute joint. However, this is not true for accelerations.

The relative acceleration $\boldsymbol{a}_{B_2/B_4}$ is usually not zero, but it is independent of the coordinate system. Therefore,

$$\boldsymbol{a}_{B_2/B_4} = {}^4\boldsymbol{a}_{B_2/B_4} = {}^4\boldsymbol{a}_{B_2} \tag{3.34}$$

From Eq. (3.34), it is apparent that the direction of ${}^1\boldsymbol{a}_{B_2/B_4}$ is the same as the direction of ${}^4\boldsymbol{a}_{B_2}$, which is the absolute acceleration of point B_2 observed from link 4. Therefore, it is useful to determine the path that B_2 traces on 4 (or B_4 traces on 2) to determine the direction of the acceleration of ${}^4\boldsymbol{a}_{B_2}$. To do this, first imagine that link 2 is a circle and link 4 is a straight line.

From experience (for example, from looking at a bicycle tire reflector at night) we know that the path of B_2 will look as shown in Fig. 3.13. That is, the path forms a cusp at the contact location. The cusp will approach the contact point in a direction that is tangent to the normal to the contacting surfaces at the contact point, and the cusp will also leave the contact point in a direction that is tangent to the common normal. This means that the accel-

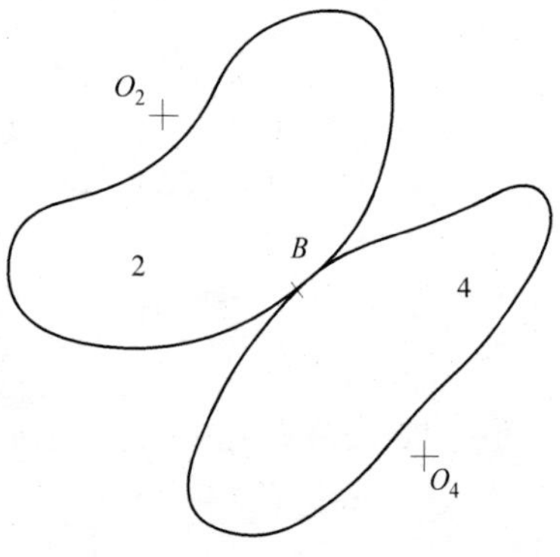

FIGURE 3.12 Two links in rolling contact.

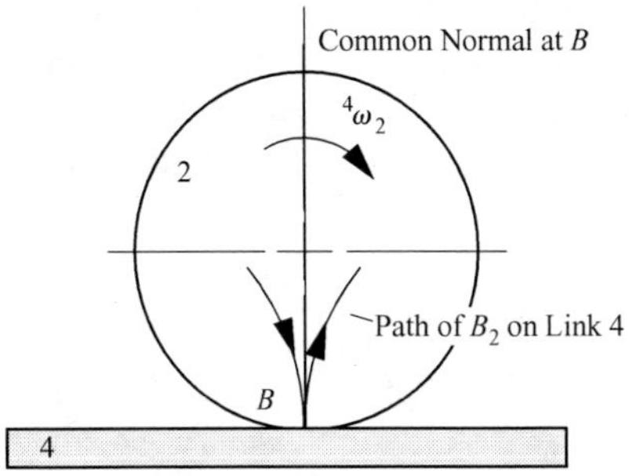

FIGURE 3.13 Path of motion of B^2 relative to link 4.

eration must be along the common normal at the point of contact. The same kind of relationship also applies for general bodies.

To conduct an acceleration analysis of mechanisms involving rolling contact, it is necessary to determine both the magnitude and direction of the relative acceleration between the two contact points. Because we know that the direction of the relative accelerations will be along the common normal at the point of contact, we need only determine the magnitude.

To do this, first consider a general rigid body R. If the contour of the rigid body is known at any given point on the contour, which must be the case for a kinematic analysis, the center of curvature, O_R, for that body can be found. If a circle of radius O_RB is drawn, that circle will be tangent to the contour at B, and it will share three points (separated by infinitesimal distances) with the curve R. This circle is called the osculating circle to the curve at point B, and the circle is a unique property of the curve for the point considered. An example is shown in Fig. 3.14.

If we consider two general links (2 and 4) in rolling contact, we can draw the osculating circle for each curve. As the two bodies roll together, the three points shared by the osculating circles will be in contact with each other. Therefore, for two differentially separated time periods, the curves could be replaced by their osculating circles. Because only two differentially separated time periods must be considered for accelerations, we can replace the original curves with their osculating circles, and the kinematic results for position, velocity, and acceleration will remain unchanged. If higher derivatives than accelerations are desired, however, we cannot replace the original surfaces with their osculating circles. Obviously, a different osculating circle may be required for each contact position if the surface of body R is general. However, for a kinematic analysis to be conducted, the geometry of the surface must be known, and therefore the osculating circle corresponding to each point on the periphery can be identified.

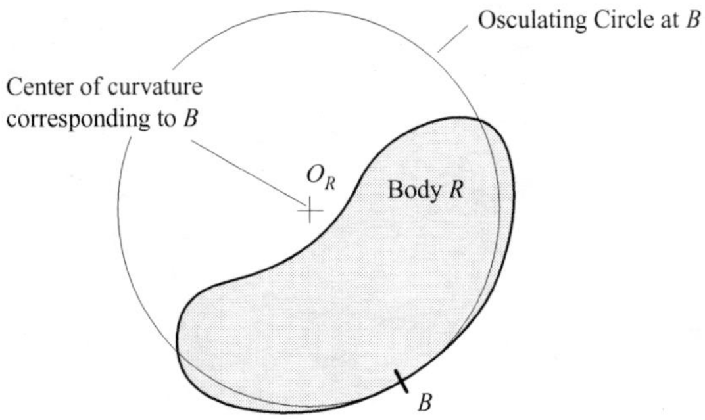

FIGURE 3.14 Osculating circle.

The replacement of the general surface with osculating circles is extremely useful in kinematics whenever higher pairs are involved. The special properties of circles make it relatively simple to analyze linkages with rolling and cam joints using this approach.

Because we can replace the two curves with their osculating circles, we can connect the two centers of curvature by a virtual link pinned to the two bodies at the centers of curvature, and the two bodies can still move relative to each other. This is precisely the condition existing when two gears in a standard transmission are meshed. For the sake of discussion, let the two bodies again be links 2 and 4 and let the virtual link be designated as *x*, as shown in Fig. 3.15. With this arrangement, we are now in a position to compute the relative acceleration ${}^4\boldsymbol{a}_{B_2/B_4}$. To do this, we will use Eq. (3.34) and compute $\boldsymbol{a}_{B_2/B_4}$, which is equal to ${}^4\boldsymbol{a}_{B_2/B_4}$.

As with any planar vector, the acceleration $\boldsymbol{a}_{B_2/B_4}$ can be resolved into two orthogonal components. It is convenient to resolve the vector into one component along the common normal to the two curves at *B* and another along the common tangent. That is,

$$\boldsymbol{a}_{B_2/B_4} = \boldsymbol{a}^{\mathrm{n}}_{B_2/B_4} + \boldsymbol{a}^{\mathrm{t}}_{B_2/B_4}$$

However, we know from our earlier discussion that the relative acceleration must lie along the common normal. Therefore, the tangential component must be zero, and the *total* relative acceleration between B_2 and B_4 can be represented as

$$\boldsymbol{a}_{B_2/B_4} = \boldsymbol{a}^{\mathrm{n}}_{B_2/B_4}$$

We can compute the normal acceleration by writing the relative accelerations among the points B_2, B_4, O_2, and O_4. That is,

$$\boldsymbol{a}_{B_2/B_4} = \boldsymbol{a}^{\mathrm{n}}_{B_2/O_2} + \boldsymbol{a}^{\mathrm{n}}_{(O_2)_x/(O_4)_x} + \boldsymbol{a}^{\mathrm{n}}_{O_4/B_4}$$

Now consider individually each term on the right-hand side of the equation. Each term will be a function of velocities and can be computed in a variety of ways. For example,

$$\boldsymbol{a}^{\mathrm{n}}_{B_2/O_2} = -\omega_2^2 \boldsymbol{r}_{B/O_2} = \left|\omega_2 v_{B/O_2}\right| \boldsymbol{n} = \frac{v^2_{B_2/O_2}}{\left|r_{B/O_2}\right|}\boldsymbol{n} \quad \left(\text{from } B \text{ towards } O_2\right)$$

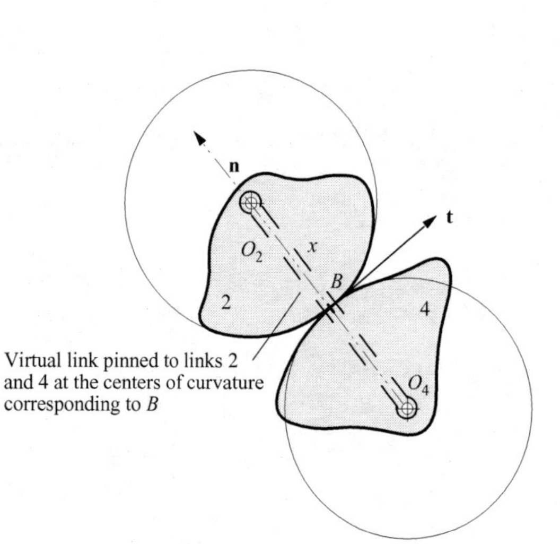

FIGURE 3.15 Virtual link pinned at the centers of curvature of the two bodies in rolling contact.

and

$$\boldsymbol{a}^{\mathrm{n}}_{O_4/B_4} = -\omega_4^2 \boldsymbol{r}_{O_4/B_4} = |\omega_4 v_{O_4/B_4}|\boldsymbol{n} = \frac{v^2_{O_4/B_4}}{|r_{O_4/B_4}|}\boldsymbol{n} \quad (\text{from } O_4 \text{ towards } B)$$

Similarly,

$$\boldsymbol{a}^{\mathrm{n}}_{(O_2)_x/(O_4)_x} = -\omega_x^2 \boldsymbol{r}_{O_2/O_4} = -|\omega_x v_{O_2/O_4}|\boldsymbol{n} = -\frac{v^2_{O_4/O_2}}{|r_{O_2/O_4}|}\boldsymbol{n} \quad (\text{from } O_2 \text{ towards } O_4) \tag{3.35}$$

To evaluate the first two expressions on the right-hand side of Eq. (3.35), we need to develop an expression for $\boldsymbol{\omega}_x$. To do this, we can derive relative velocity expressions among B_2, B_4, O_2, and O_4. Considering links 2, 4, and x, we have

$$\boldsymbol{v}_{B_2} = \boldsymbol{v}_{O_2} + \boldsymbol{v}_{B_2/O_2} = \boldsymbol{v}_{O_2} + \boldsymbol{\omega}_2 \times \boldsymbol{r}_{B/O_2}$$
$$\boldsymbol{v}_{B_4} = \boldsymbol{v}_{O_4} + \boldsymbol{v}_{B_4/O_4} = \boldsymbol{v}_{O_4} + \boldsymbol{\omega}_4 \times \boldsymbol{r}_{B/O_4}$$
$$\boldsymbol{v}_{O_2} = \boldsymbol{v}_{O_4} + \boldsymbol{v}_{O_2/O_4} = \boldsymbol{v}_{O_4} + \boldsymbol{\omega}_x \times \boldsymbol{r}_{O_2/O_4}$$

Combining these equations and recognizing that $\boldsymbol{v}_{B_2} = \boldsymbol{v}_{B_4}$, we get

$$\boldsymbol{\omega}_x \times \boldsymbol{r}_{O_2/O_4} = \boldsymbol{v}_{O_2} - \boldsymbol{v}_{O_4} = \boldsymbol{v}_{O_2/O_4} = \boldsymbol{\omega}_4 \times \boldsymbol{r}_{B/O_4} - \boldsymbol{\omega}_2 \times \boldsymbol{r}_{B/O_2} \tag{3.36}$$

Recognizing that $\boldsymbol{r}_{B/O_2} = -\boldsymbol{r}_{O_2/B}$, we can also write Eq. (3.36) as

$$\boldsymbol{\omega}_x \times \boldsymbol{r}_{O_2/O_4} = \boldsymbol{\omega}_4 \times \boldsymbol{r}_{B/O_4} + \boldsymbol{\omega}_2 \times \boldsymbol{r}_{O_2/B} \tag{3.37}$$

The magnitude of $\boldsymbol{\omega}_x$ is given by

$$\boldsymbol{\omega}_x = \frac{|\boldsymbol{\omega}_4 \times \boldsymbol{r}_{B/O_4} + \boldsymbol{\omega}_2 \times \boldsymbol{r}_{O_2/B}|}{|\boldsymbol{r}_{O_2/O_4}|} = \frac{|\boldsymbol{\omega}_2 \times \boldsymbol{r}_{O_2/B} + \boldsymbol{\omega}_4 \times \boldsymbol{r}_{B/O_4}|}{|\boldsymbol{r}_{O_2/B} + \boldsymbol{r}_{B/O_4}|}$$

If the direction is of interest, it can be determined from the vectors in Eq. (3.37).

To summarize, in rolling contact problems, we know that the two contact points (e.g., B_2 and B_4) have the same velocity. Also, given the acceleration of one of the points, say B_4, the acceleration of the other point can be computed from

$$\boldsymbol{a}_{B_2} = \boldsymbol{a}_{B_4} + \boldsymbol{a}^{\mathrm{n}}_{B_2/B_4}$$

where $\boldsymbol{a}^{\mathrm{n}}_{B_2/B_4}$ can be computed using *any* of the following:

$$\boldsymbol{a}^{\mathrm{n}}_{B_2/B_4} = \left(\frac{v^2_{B_2/O_2}}{|\boldsymbol{r}_{B_2/O_2}|} - \frac{v^2_{O_2/O_4}}{|\boldsymbol{r}_{O_2/O_4}|} + \frac{v^2_{O_4/B_4}}{|\boldsymbol{r}_{O_4/B_4}|}\right)\boldsymbol{n} \tag{3.38}$$

or

$$\boldsymbol{a}^{\mathrm{n}}_{B_2/B_4} = \left(\omega_2^2|r_{B/O_2}| - \omega_x^2|r_{O_2/O_4}| + \omega_4^2|r_{O_4/B}|\right)\boldsymbol{n} \tag{3.39}$$

or

$$\boldsymbol{a}^{\mathrm{n}}_{B_2/B_4} = \left(\left|\omega_2 v_{B/O_2}\right| - \left|\omega_x v_{O_2/O_4}\right| + \left|\omega_4 v_{O_4/B}\right|\right)\boldsymbol{n} \tag{3.40}$$

If one of the rolling surfaces is flat, the radius of curvature will approach infinity, and the corresponding acceleration term will become zero. For example, if the rolling surface for link 2 is flat, then O_2 is at infinity, and the acceleration expressions reduce to

$$\boldsymbol{a}^{\mathrm{n}}_{B_2/B_4} = \frac{v^2_{O_4/B_4}}{\left|r_{O_4/B_4}\right|}\boldsymbol{n} = \omega_4^2 \boldsymbol{r}_{O_4/B} = \left|\omega_4 v_{O_4/B_4}\right|\boldsymbol{n} \quad \left(\text{from } O_4 \text{ towards } B\right)$$

EXAMPLE 3.2
Analysis of Linkage with a Rolling-Contact Joint

In the linkage shown in Fig. 3.16, link 4 is a gear, pivoted at O_B. Link 3 is a gear meshing with 4 and has a lever fixed to it that is hinged to link 2 at A. Link 2 is driven at a constant angular velocity of 10 rad/s CCW. Find the angular acceleration of gear 4.

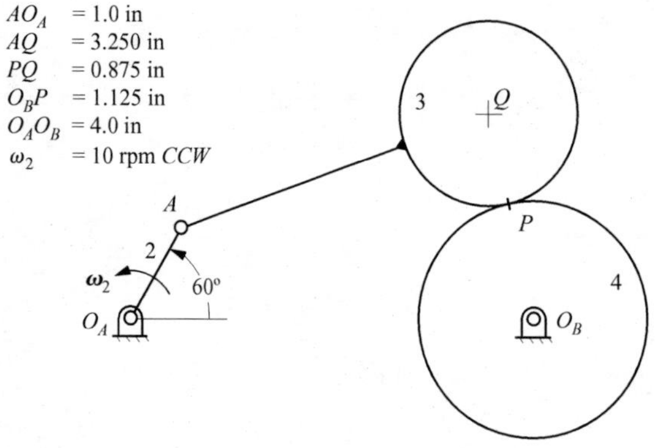

FIGURE 3.16 The linkage of Example 3.2. This is an example of a geared five-bar linkage. Geared five-bar and six-bar linkages are used quite frequently as alternatives to four-bar linkages. They allow more flexibility in synthesis than four-bar linkages because they have more dimensions that can be varied.

Solution

In this instance we cannot ignore the acceleration of either of the two contacting bodies. The angular acceleration of gear 3 is the same as that of arm AQ to which it is rigidly affixed. The angular acceleration of gear 4 is the quantity to be found.

For the velocity analysis, the equations to be solved are

$$\boldsymbol{v}_{A_2/O_A} = \boldsymbol{\omega}_2 \times \boldsymbol{r}_{A_2/O_A}$$

$$\boldsymbol{v}_{P_4/O_B} = \boldsymbol{v}_{A_3} + \boldsymbol{v}_{P_3/A_3}$$

For the acceleration analysis, the corresponding equations are

$$\boldsymbol{a}_{A_2/O_A} = \boldsymbol{a}^{\mathrm{r}}_{A_2/O_A} + \boldsymbol{a}^{\mathrm{t}}_{A_2/O_A}$$

$$\boldsymbol{a}^{\mathrm{r}}_{P_4/O_B} + \boldsymbol{a}^{\mathrm{t}}_{P_4/O_B} = \boldsymbol{a}_{A_2/O_A} + \boldsymbol{a}^{\mathrm{r}}_{P_3/A_3} + \boldsymbol{a}^{\mathrm{t}}_{P_3/A_3} + \boldsymbol{a}^{\mathrm{n}}_{P_4/P_3}$$

Here the unknowns are the magnitudes of the two transverse components, $\boldsymbol{a}^{\mathrm{t}}_{P_3/A_3}$ and $\boldsymbol{a}^{\mathrm{t}}_{P_4/O_B}$.

Steps

1. Draw the linkage to scale as shown in Fig. 3.17. To do this, first draw link 2 and locate point A. Next find the center Q, knowing that it is on a circle of radius AQ centered at A and also on a circle of radius QO_B centered at O_B. After locating Q, draw the line AQ and the circles corresponding to the pitch circles of the two gears.
2. Compute $\boldsymbol{v}_{A_2}$ and plot as $\overrightarrow{oa}$.

   $\boldsymbol{v}_{A_2} = \boldsymbol{\omega}_2 \times \boldsymbol{r}_{A_2/O_2} = 10$ in/s, $\boldsymbol{v}_{A_2}$ is normal to $\overrightarrow{O_AA}$.

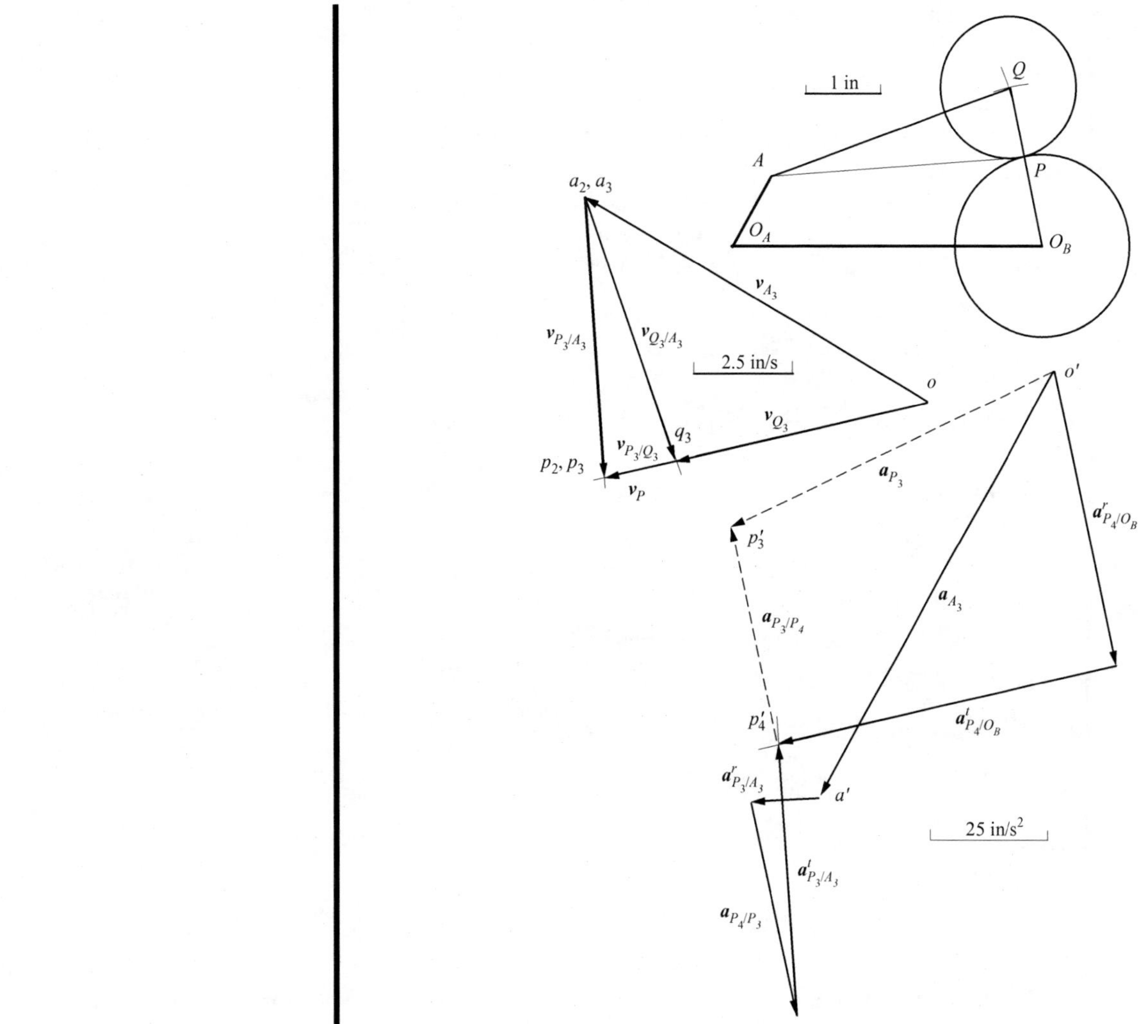

FIGURE 3.17 The graphical solution of Example 3.2.

3. Draw a line through o normal to $\overrightarrow{O_BP}$.
4. Draw line $\overrightarrow{AP}$.
5. Draw a line through a_2, a_3 normal to $\overrightarrow{AP}$. The intersection of this line with the line generated in step 3 gives the point P. Notice that since the bar $\overrightarrow{AQ}$ is rigidly fixed to gear 3, line $\overrightarrow{AP}$ is fixed in member 3. Although at any instant, the point at P_3 is fixed to member 3, a different P (and different point) is involved for each position of the linkage.
6. Draw a line through a_3 normal to $\overrightarrow{AQ}$. The intersection of this line with the line generated in step 3 gives the point q_3. Point q_3 could also have been located from points a_3 and p_3 by using the velocity image theorem.
7. Compute $\omega_3 = v_{P_3/A_3}/r_{P_3/A_3}$ and $\omega_4 = v_{P_4/O_B}/r_{O_B/P}$ and find the senses needed to give the directions of $\boldsymbol{v}_{P_3/A_3}$ and $\boldsymbol{v}_{P_4/O_B}$. Because of the pure rolling condition of the pitch circles of the gears, the velocity of point P is the same regardless of whether it is considered to be in member 3 or member 4.

   $\boldsymbol{\omega}_3 = 6.85/3.258 = 2.10$ rad/s CW

   $\boldsymbol{\omega}_4 = 38.32/1.125 = 7.39$ rad/s CCW

8. Compute $\boldsymbol{a}_{A_3} = \boldsymbol{a}^{\mathrm{r}}_{A_3/O_A}$ and plot as $\overrightarrow{o'a'}$.

$$a_{A_3} = r_{A_2/O_2} \times \omega_2^2 = 1 \times 10^2 = 100 \text{ in/s}^2$$

9. Compute and plot $\boldsymbol{a}^{\mathrm{r}}_{P_3/A_3}$ in the $\overrightarrow{PA}$ direction from point a'.

$$a^{\mathrm{r}}_{P_3/A_3} = AP \times \omega_3^2 = 3.258 \times 2.10^2 = 14.39 \text{ in/s}^2$$

10. Compute $\boldsymbol{a}_{P_4/P_3}$ using the equation form given in Eq. (3.54). Then,

$$\boldsymbol{a}^{\mathrm{n}}_{P_4/P_3} = \frac{|\boldsymbol{v}_{P_4/O_B}|^2}{r_{P_4/O_B}} + \frac{|\boldsymbol{v}_{O_B/Q_3}|^2}{r_{O_B/Q_3}} + \frac{|\boldsymbol{v}_{Q_3/P_3}|^2}{r_{Q_3/P_3}} = \frac{|8.32|^2}{1.125} + \frac{|6.54|^2}{2} + \frac{|1.92|^2}{0.875}$$
$$(P \text{ to } O_B) \quad (O_B \text{ to } Q_3) \quad (Q_3 \text{ to } P_3) \quad (P \text{ to } O_B) \quad (O_B \text{ to } Q_3) \quad (Q_3 \text{ to } P_3)$$

By arbitrarily taking direction $\overrightarrow{PO_B}$ as positive, the signs of the individual terms can be identified. Then,

$a_{P_4/P_3} = 61.53 - 21.38 = 4.21 = 44.36 \text{ in/s}^2$

Note also that $\boldsymbol{a}_{P_4/P_3} = -\boldsymbol{a}_{P_3/P_4}$ and has the direction from the center of wheel 3 toward the center of wheel 4. Plot $\boldsymbol{a}_{P_4/P_3}$ from the tip of $\boldsymbol{a}^{\mathrm{r}}_{P_3/A_3}$.

11. Draw a line through the tip of vector $\boldsymbol{a}_{P_4/P_3}$ normal to $\overrightarrow{AP}$.

12. Compute $a^{\mathrm{r}}_{P_4/O_B}$ and plot $\boldsymbol{a}^{\mathrm{r}}_{P_4/O_B}$ from o' in the $\overrightarrow{PO_B}$ direction.

$$a^{\mathrm{r}}_{P_4/O_B} = r_{P_4/O_B} \times {}^1v_4^2 = 1.125 \times 7.39^2 = 61.4 \text{ in/s}^2$$

13. Draw a line through the tip of vector $\boldsymbol{a}^{\mathrm{r}}_{P_4/O_B}$ normal to $\overrightarrow{O_BP}$. The intersection of this line with that drawn in step 11 gives p'_4.

14. Compute $\alpha_4 = a^{\mathrm{t}}_{P_4/O_B}/r_{P_4/O_B}$ and find the sense needed to give the direction of $\boldsymbol{a}^{\mathrm{t}}_{P_4/O_B}$.

$\boldsymbol{\alpha}_4 = 74.25/1.125 = 66.0 \text{ rad/s}^2$ CCW

Note that this construction, with the vectors in the order shown, gives the correct position for p'_4 but not for p'_3. This does not matter for the present purpose. However, if the correct position of p'_3 were required, either to get the absolute acceleration or to construct the acceleration image, it would be obtained by plotting $\boldsymbol{a}_{P_3/P_4}$ from p'_4 as shown in Fig. 3.17.

Although the acceleration of the contacting point in one body relative to that in the other has been worked out assuming circular contacting profiles, it can also be used if the profiles are not circular. The radius of the circular profile is simply replaced with the osculating circle of the profile at the point of contact.

3.6.2 Modeling Rolling Contact Using a Virtual Linkage

As a second example of rolling contact, we will consider the plate cam with roller follower shown in Fig. 3.18. In this mechanism, we are given the angular velocity and acceleration of link 2, and we wish only to know the angular velocity and acceleration of link 4. We are not interested in the velocity and acceleration of link 3. When this is the case, we can model the linkage with a virtual link between the centers of curvature of links 2 and 3 corresponding to the contact point P. The cam–follower mechanism can then be analyzed as the virtual four-bar linkage O_AABO_B. Line O_AA is fixed to link 2, so the angular velocity and acceleration of O_AA will be the angular velocity and acceleration for link 2.

EXAMPLE 3.3 Analysis of a Geared Linkage—Rolling Contact

Find the angular velocity and angular acceleration of the arm (link 4) of the linkage in Fig. 3.18 for $\theta = 90^\circ$ when the cam, 2, is rotated CCW with constant angular velocity 1000 rpm. The following basic dimensions are given for the mechanism:

$$O_AO_B = 4.0 \text{ in},\ O_BB = 4.25 \text{ in},\ r_2 = 0.5 \text{ in},\ r_3 = 2.5 \text{ in},\ O_AA = 1.153 \text{ in},\ AB = 0.901 \text{ in}$$

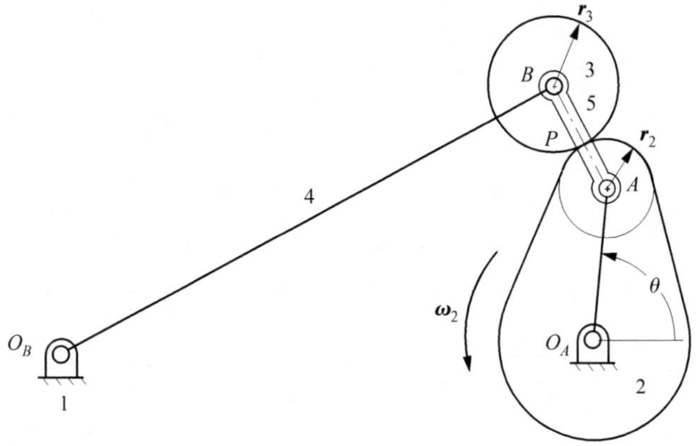

FIGURE 3.18 A plate cam with roller follower. For given angular velocity and acceleration of cam 2, the angular velocity and angular acceleration of the arm 4 can be found by replacing the linkage with the virtual four-bar linkage O_AABO_B. Here point A is the center of curvature of the cam profile at the contact point P.

Solution

The steps to analyzing this mechanism are the same as those required for the four-bar linkage in Example 2.1. The velocity equations that must be solved graphically are

$$\boldsymbol{v}_{A_2/O_2} = \boldsymbol{\omega}_2 \times \boldsymbol{r}_{A_2/O_A}$$

$$\boldsymbol{v}_{B_4/O_B} = \boldsymbol{v}_{A_2/O_A} + \boldsymbol{v}_{B_5/A_5}$$

where the virtual link is designated as link 5. The acceleration equations that must be solved are

$$\boldsymbol{a}_{A_2/O_A} = \boldsymbol{a}^{\mathrm{r}}_{A_2/O_A} + \boldsymbol{a}^{\mathrm{t}}_{A_2/O_A}$$

$$\boldsymbol{a}^{\mathrm{r}}_{B_4/O_B} + \boldsymbol{a}^{\mathrm{t}}_{B_4/O_B} = \boldsymbol{a}^{\mathrm{r}}_{A_2/O_A} + \boldsymbol{a}^{\mathrm{t}}_{A_2/O_A} + \boldsymbol{a}^{\mathrm{r}}_{B_5/A_5} + \boldsymbol{a}^{\mathrm{t}}_{B_5/A_5}$$

Steps

1. Draw the mechanism to scale as shown in Fig. 3.19. Note that, for this analysis, we need draw only the virtual mechanism.
2. Compute ω_2.

   $\omega_2 = 1000 \times 2\pi/60 = 104.75$ rad/s
3. Compute and plot $\boldsymbol{v}_{A_2/O_A}$.

   $$\boldsymbol{v}_{A_2/O_A} = \boldsymbol{\omega}_2 \times \boldsymbol{r}_{A_2/O_A} = 104.72 \times 1.153 = 120.74 \text{ in/s normal to } \overrightarrow{O_AA}$$
4. Solve the velocity equation graphically and measure v_{B_4/O_B} and v_{B_5/A_5}.

   $v_{B_5/O_B} = 38.95$ in/s; $v_{B_5/A_5} = 108.2$ in/s
5. Compute $\boldsymbol{\omega}_5$ and $\boldsymbol{\omega}_4$ and determine their senses.

   $$\boldsymbol{\omega}_5 = v_{B_5/A_5}/r_{B_5/A_5} = 108.2/0.901 = 120.1 \text{ rad/s CW}$$

   $$\boldsymbol{\omega}_4 = v_{B_4/O_B}/r_{B_4/O_B} = 38.95/4.25 = 9.16 \text{ rad/s CCW}$$

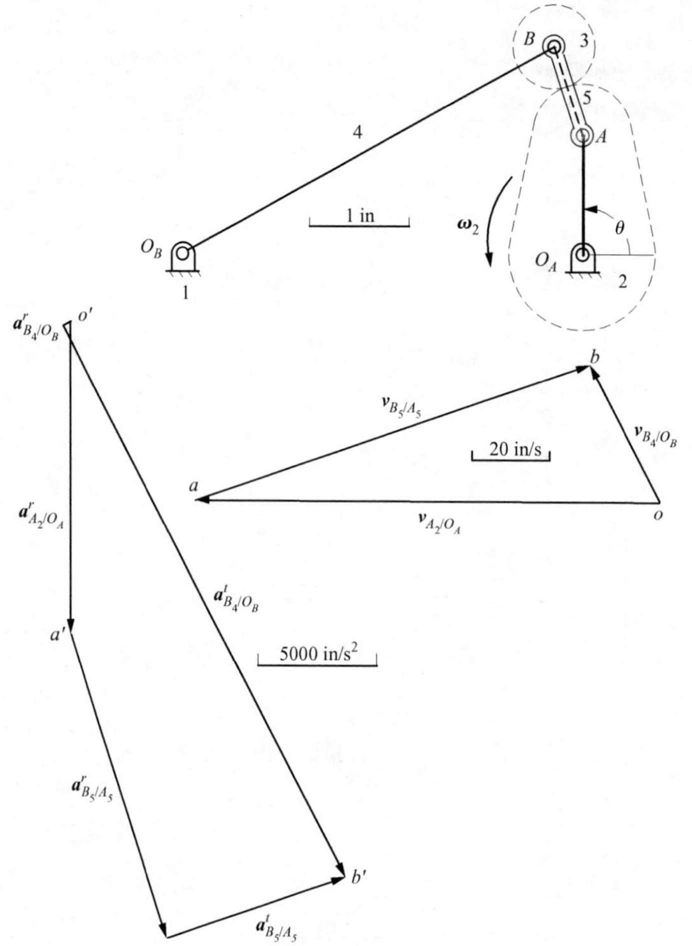

FIGURE 3.19 The velocity and acceleration polygons for Example 3.3.

Notice that $\boldsymbol{\omega}_5$ is the angular velocity of a *virtual* link containing the line AB.

6. Compute and plot $\boldsymbol{a}_{A_2/O_A} = \boldsymbol{a}^r_{A_2/O_A}$.

   $a^r_{A_2/O_A} = r_{A_2/O_A} \times \omega_2^2 = 1.153 \times 104.7^2 = 12{,}640$ in/s^2 in the $\overrightarrow{AO_A}$ direction

7. Compute and plot $\boldsymbol{a}^r_{B_4/O_B}$ from point o' and $\boldsymbol{a}^r_{B_5/A_5}$ from point a'.

   $a^r_{B_4/O_B} = r_{B_4/O_B} \times \omega_4^2 = 4.25 \times 9.16^2 = 356.6$ in/s^2 in the $\overrightarrow{BO_B}$ direction

   $a^r_{B_5/A_5} = r_{B_5/A_5} \times \omega_5^2 = 0.901 \times 120.1^2 = 13{,}000$ in/s^2 in the $\overrightarrow{BA}$ direction

8. Measure $a^t_{B_4/O_B}$.

   $a^t_{B_4/O_B} = 25{,}290$ in/s^2

9. Compute $\boldsymbol{\alpha}_4$ and determine its sense.

$$\boldsymbol{\alpha}_4 = a^t_{B_4/O_B} \Big/ r_{B/O_B} = 25{,}290 \big/ 4.25 = 4440 \text{ rad/s}^2 \text{ CW}$$

Notice that the reason this relatively simple approach can be used is that we are not interested in the angular acceleration of the roller, link 3. This is definitely not equal to the angular acceleration of the line AB, which, for convenience, was called the virtual link 5.

3.7 CAM CONTACT

The analysis of mechanisms with cam joints can be conducted either directly or through the use of equivalent linkages. We will look at the direct approach first.

3.7.1 Direct Approach to the Analysis of Cam Contact

In the general case of cam contact, there will be both rolling and sliding at the contact point, and this is probably the most typical type of higher pair contact between two bodies. If we look at two arbitrary bodies (e.g., 2 and 4 in Fig. 3.20) at the contact location B, we know B_2 and B_4 have the same coordinates:

$$\boldsymbol{r}_{B_2} = \boldsymbol{r}_{B_4}$$

However,

$$\boldsymbol{v}_{B_2} \neq \boldsymbol{v}_{B_4}$$

or

$$\boldsymbol{v}_{B_2/B_4} \neq 0$$

We can obtain some information on $\boldsymbol{v}_{B_2/B_4}$ by recognizing that coincident points are involved and

$$\boldsymbol{v}_{B_2/B_4} = {}^4\boldsymbol{v}_{B_2/B_4} = {}^4\boldsymbol{v}_{B_2}$$

Therefore, to analyze the velocity of B_2 relative to B_4 or link 4, it is convenient to represent the velocity in terms of components in the tangential (t) and normal (n) directions relative to the tangent at the contact point as shown in Fig. 3.20. Then,

$$\boldsymbol{v}_{B_2/B_4} = {}^4\boldsymbol{v}_{B_2/B_4} = {}^4\boldsymbol{v}^{\text{n}}_{B_2} + {}^4\boldsymbol{v}^{\text{t}}_{B_2}$$

If the two bodies are rigid, there can be no component of velocity in the normal direction or the bodies would either penetrate each other or separate. Therefore, the normal component of the relative velocity must be zero, and the relative velocity direction must be along the common tangent to the two bodies at the point of contact. That is,

$${}^4\boldsymbol{v}^{\text{n}}_{B_2} = 0$$

and

$$\boldsymbol{v}_{B_2/B_4} = {}^4\boldsymbol{v}^{\text{t}}_{B_2} = \boldsymbol{v}^{\text{t}}_{B_2/B_4}$$

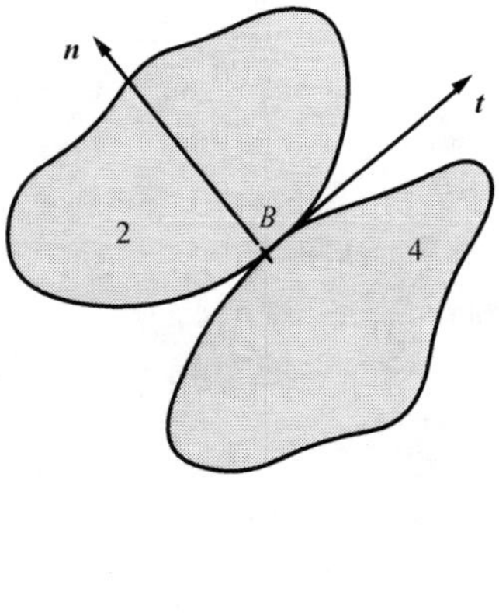

FIGURE 3.20 Cam contact.

We cannot determine anything more about ${}^4\boldsymbol{v}^{\mathrm{t}}_{B_2/B_4}$; however, knowing the direction for the relative velocity usually provides sufficient information to conduct a velocity analysis.

We cannot determine anything about $\boldsymbol{a}_{B_2/B_4}$ directly; however, if we expand $\boldsymbol{a}_{B_2/B_4}$ into normal and tangential components, we can compute additional information about it. Then,

$$\boldsymbol{a}_{B_2/B_4} = \boldsymbol{a}^{\mathrm{n}}_{B_2/B_4} + \boldsymbol{a}^{\mathrm{t}}_{B_2/B_4}$$

Note that there is no Coriolis term because the acceleration is defined in link 1 and not link 4. This is directly analogous to the case of rolling contact except that now the tangential component is not zero. However, by definition, we know the direction of the tangential component.

Using the same nomenclature as in the case of rolling contact (see Fig. 3.15), the normal component of relative acceleration is given by Eqs. (3.38), (3.39), or (3.40). For example,

$$\boldsymbol{a}^{\mathrm{n}}_{B_2/B_4} = \underset{(B\ to\ O_2)}{\frac{\left|\boldsymbol{v}_{B_2/O_2}\right|^2}{r_{B_2/O_2}}} + \underset{(O_2\ to\ O_4)}{\frac{\left|\boldsymbol{v}_{O_2/O_4}\right|^2}{r_{O_2/O_4}}} + \underset{(O_4\ to\ B)}{\frac{\left|\boldsymbol{v}_{O_4/B_4}\right|^2}{r_{O_4/B_4}}}$$

If one of the rolling surfaces is flat, the relative position vector corresponding to the center of curvature will approach infinity, and the corresponding acceleration term will become zero. For example, if the surface for link 2 is flat, then O_2 is at infinity, and the expression for the normal component of acceleration reduces to

$$\boldsymbol{a}^{\mathrm{n}}_{B_2/B_4} = \frac{\left|\boldsymbol{v}_{O_4/B_4}\right|^2}{r_{O_4/B_4}} \text{ from } O_4 \text{ to } B_4$$

EXAMPLE 3.4
Analysis of Mechanism with a Cam Joint

Find the velocity and acceleration of the cam follower (link 3) given in Fig. 3.21 if the cam is rotating at a constant angular velocity of 100 rad/s CCW.

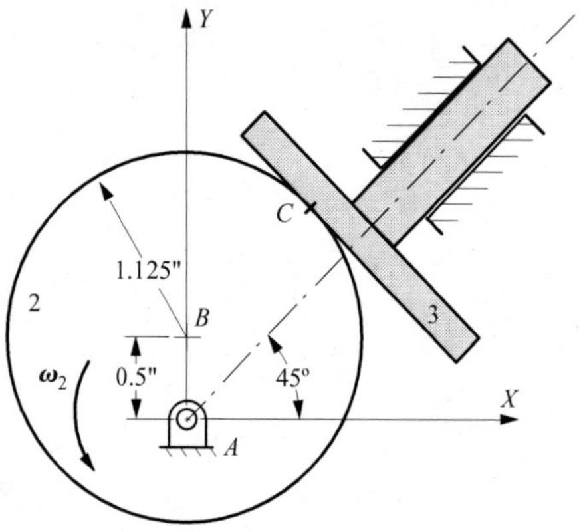

FIGURE 3.21 Cam and flat-faced follower.

Solution

To analyze the problem, we can determine the velocity and acceleration of any point on link 3 because *all* points on link 3 have the same velocity and the same acceleration. The point to choose is the contact point C_3. To solve for the velocity and acceleration of C_3, first find the velocity of point C_2. Then write the relative velocity expression between points C_2 and C_3 and solve for the velocity of C_3. The relevant equations are

$$\boldsymbol{v}_{C_2} = \boldsymbol{v}_{C_2/A_2} = \boldsymbol{\omega}_2 \times \boldsymbol{r}_{C/A}$$

and

$$\boldsymbol{v}_{C_3} = \boldsymbol{v}_{C_2} + \boldsymbol{v}_{C_3/C_2}$$

Next solve for the velocity of B_2 either directly or by image. This will be needed for the acceleration analysis. The acceleration equations that must be solved are

$$\boldsymbol{a}_{C_2} = \boldsymbol{a}_{C_2/A_2} = \boldsymbol{a}^{\text{n}}_{C_2/A_2} + \boldsymbol{a}^{\text{t}}_{C_2/A_2}$$

$$\boldsymbol{a}_{C_3} = \boldsymbol{a}_{C_2} + \boldsymbol{a}_{C_3/C_2} = \boldsymbol{a}_{C_2} + \boldsymbol{a}^{\text{t}}_{C_3/C_2} + \boldsymbol{a}^{\text{n}}_{C_3/C_2}$$

and

$$\left|\boldsymbol{a}^{\text{n}}_{C_3/C_2}\right| = \left|\boldsymbol{a}^{\text{n}}_{C_3/D_3} + \boldsymbol{a}^{\text{n}}_{D_3/B_2} + \boldsymbol{a}^{\text{n}}_{B_2/C_2}\right| = \frac{\left|\boldsymbol{v}_{C_3/D_3}\right|^2}{|\infty|} + \frac{\left|\boldsymbol{v}_{D_3/B_2}\right|^2}{|\infty|} + \frac{\left|\boldsymbol{v}_{B_2/C_2}\right|^2}{\left|\boldsymbol{r}_{B/C}\right|} = \frac{\left|\boldsymbol{v}_{B_2/C_2}\right|^2}{\left|\boldsymbol{r}_{B/C}\right|}$$

where D_3 is the center of curvature of the cam follower surface and is located at infinity. The steps in solving the equations are given in the following.

Steps

1. Draw the mechanism to scale as shown in Fig. 3.22. To do this, draw the cam circle centered at B. Next locate point A at 0.5 in below B. Then construct a line through A at an angle of 45°. This locates the direction of travel of the flat-faced follower. Finally, draw a line perpendicular to the 45° line and tangent to the cam. This locates point C.

2. Compute $\boldsymbol{v}_{C_2} = \boldsymbol{\omega}_2 \times \boldsymbol{r}_{C/A}$.

   $\boldsymbol{v}_{C_2} = 100(1.52) = 152$ in/s perpendicular to AC and in the direction shown in Fig. 3.22.

   This will locate c_2.

3. Draw a line from o at an angle of 45° with the horizontal. Point c_3 will be on this line.

4. Draw a line through the tip of c_2 and perpendicular to the line at 45°. The intersection of this line with that drawn in step 3 locates c_3.

   $\boldsymbol{v}_{C_3} = 35$ in/s in the direction shown.

5. Locate b_2 by image.

6. Compute and plot $\boldsymbol{a}_{C_2/A_2} = \boldsymbol{a}^{\text{r}}_{C_2/A_2}$.

   $\boldsymbol{a}^{\text{r}}_{C_2/A_2} = AC \times \boldsymbol{\omega}_2^2 = 1.52 \times 100^2 = 15{,}200$ in/s^2 in the CA direction

7. Draw a line from o' at an angle of 45° with the horizontal. Point c'_3 will be on this line.

8. Compute $a^{\text{n}}_{C_3/C_2}$, determine its direction, and plot the resulting vector through the tip of $\boldsymbol{a}^{\text{r}}_{C_2/A_2}$.

$$\boldsymbol{a}^{\text{n}}_{C_3/C_2} = \frac{\left|\boldsymbol{v}_{B_2/C_2}\right|^2}{\left|\boldsymbol{r}_{B/C}\right|} = \frac{|112.9|^2}{|1.11|} = 11{,}480\,\text{in/s}^2 \text{ from } B \text{ to } C$$

9. Draw a line through the tip of $\boldsymbol{a}^{\text{n}}_{C_3/C_2}$ and perpendicular to it. The intersection of this line with the line drawn in step 7 will be the point c'_3.

10. Measure a_{C_3}.

    $\boldsymbol{a}_{C_3} = 3250$ in/s^2 in the direction shown

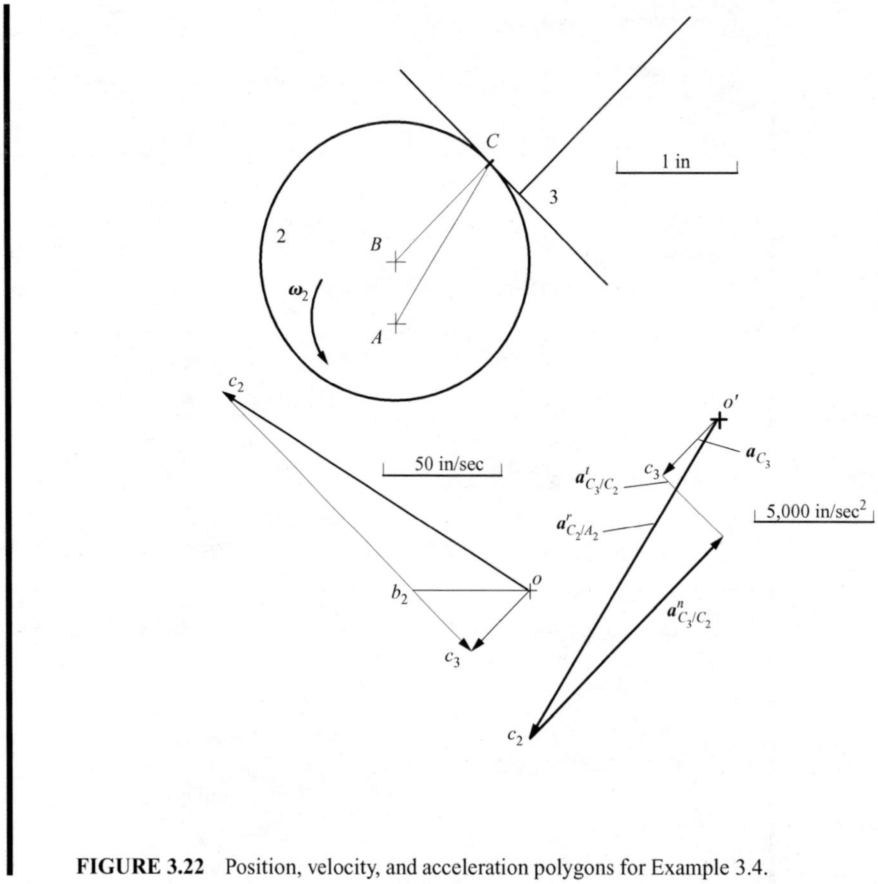

FIGURE 3.22 Position, velocity, and acceleration polygons for Example 3.4.

3.7.2 Analysis of Cam Contact Using Equivalent Linkages

Another approach to determining the velocities and accelerations is to use the concept of equivalent linkages. For this we represent the two cam surfaces by their osculating circles and attach a binary link from one center of curvature to the other using revolute joints. As in the case of rolling contact, this technique can be used for velocities and accelerations, but it will not give correct results for higher derivatives. In Fig. 3.23, link 6 is a virtual link that usually changes length with each *finite* change in position. (It is constant for differential changes in position, however.)

The use of equivalent linkages usually simplifies the velocity and acceleration analyses because the equivalent linkages are usually standard four-bar linkages or one of the inversions of the common slider-crank mechanism. For example, a simple three-link cam mechanism becomes a four-bar linkage when replaced by its equivalent linkage as shown in Fig. 3.24. In the example in Fig. 3.24, the kinematic information for link 4 (virtual link) can be computed; however, this is usually of no interest. It is important to remember that the equivalent linkage is valid for one position only. The length of the virtual link usually changes with each position of interest.

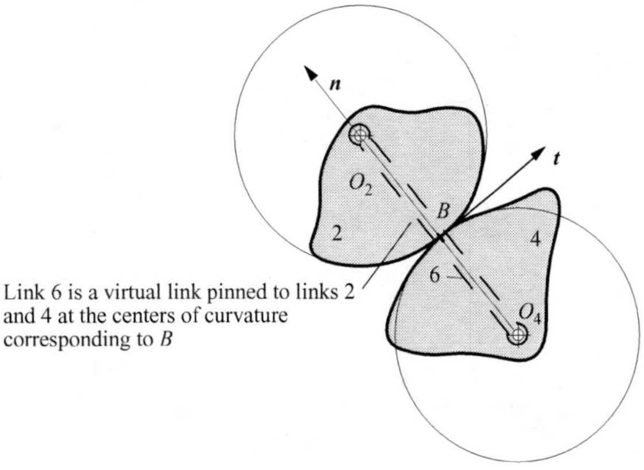

FIGURE 3.23 Virtual link pinned at the centers of curvature of the two bodies in cam contact.

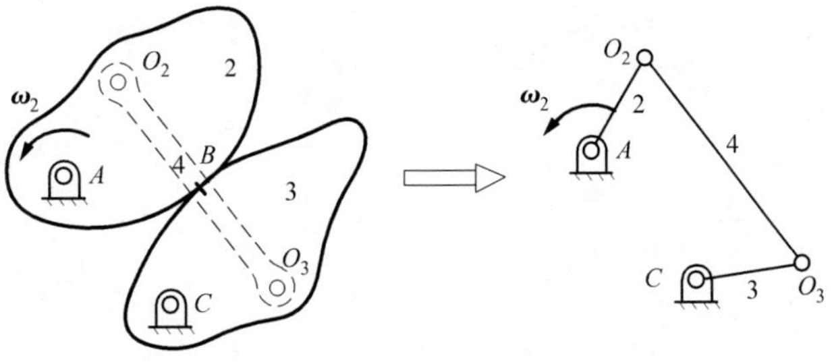

FIGURE 3.24 Equivalent linkage for cam mechanism with curved cam surfaces and revolute joints between the cams and the frame.

If one of the surfaces is flat, the virtual link becomes infinitely long, and the movement of the virtual link can be represented by a slider. An example of this is shown in Fig. 3.25. The slider need not "slide" on the face of the flat cam surface through B. The only restriction is that it slide on a line that is parallel to the cam face.

The equivalent linkage is analyzed as any other linkage with pin and slider joints would be. The kinematic properties computed for links 2 and 3 will be the same for both the equivalent linkage and the actual linkage. The equivalent linkages for the other two types of three-bar cam linkages are given in Fig. 3.26.

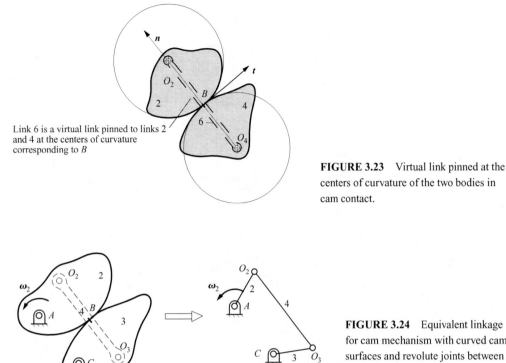

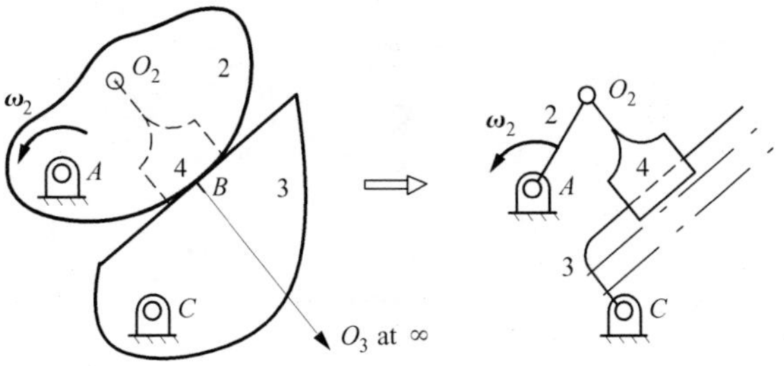

FIGURE 3.25 Equivalent linkage for cam mechanism with one flat-faced cam and revolute joints between the cams and the frame. The slider can slide on any line that is parallel to the cam face and fixed to link 3.

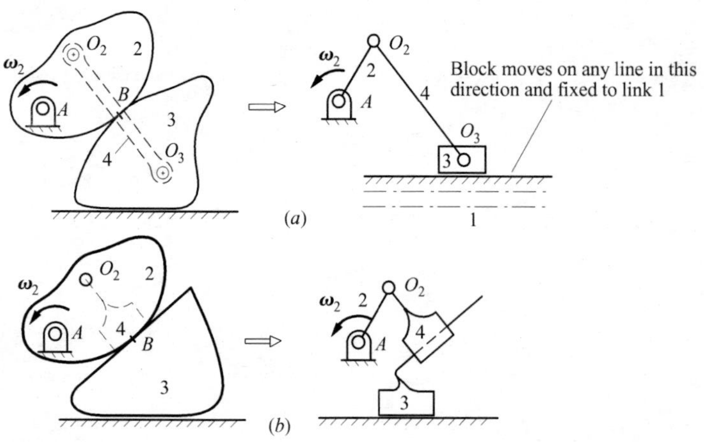

FIGURE 3.26 Equivalent linkage for cam mechanism. (a) Sliding joint between link 3 and frame. (b) Sliding between links 2 and 3 and between link 3 and frame.

EXAMPLE 3.5 *Mechanism Analysis Using an Equivalent Linkage*

Use equivalent linkages to compute the velocity and acceleration of the cam follower (link 3) in Fig. 3.21 if the cam is rotating at a constant angular velocity of 100 rad/s CCW.

Solution

The mechanism in Fig. 3.21 is of the type represented in Fig. 3.26b. Therefore, link 3, the follower, will have a sliding joint with the frame and with the virtual link (link 4). The resulting equivalent linkage is shown in Fig. 3.27. Notice that the location of the line on which link 4 must slide relative to link 3 is arbitrary as long as the line is fixed to link 3 and is parallel to the face of link 3. Therefore, the line that passes through B is chosen for simplicity. Similarly, the location of the line on which link 3 slides relative to the frame is arbitrary as long as the line is inclined at an angle of 45°.

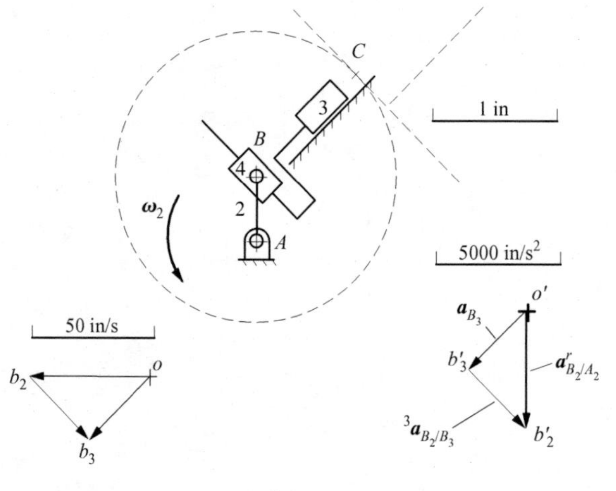

FIGURE 3.27 Position, velocity, and acceleration polygons for Example 3.5.

For the equivalent linkage, we need only find the velocity and acceleration of point B_2. The velocity and acceleration of B_3 can then be found using the procedure given in Section 3.5. The velocity equations that must be solved are

$$\boldsymbol{v}_{B_2} = \boldsymbol{v}_{B_2/A_2} = \boldsymbol{\omega}_2 \times \boldsymbol{r}_{B/A}$$

and

$$\boldsymbol{v}_{B_2} = \boldsymbol{v}_{B_3} + \boldsymbol{v}_{B_2/B_3} \tag{3.41}$$

Here we have written the velocity equation in terms of the velocity of B_2 relative to B_3 rather than vice versa because we can easily identify the direction of the velocity of B_2 relative to B_3. We also know the direction for the velocity and acceleration of B_3. The acceleration equations that must be solved are

$$\boldsymbol{a}_{B_2} = \boldsymbol{a}_{B_2/A_2} = \boldsymbol{a}^{\mathrm{r}}_{B_2/A_2} + \boldsymbol{a}^{\mathrm{t}}_{B_2/A_2}$$

$$\boldsymbol{a}_{B_2} = \boldsymbol{a}_{B_3} + \boldsymbol{a}_{B_2/B_3} = \boldsymbol{a}_{B_3} + \boldsymbol{a}^{\mathrm{c}}_{B_2/B_3} + {}^3\boldsymbol{a}_{B_2/B_3}$$

and

$$\boldsymbol{a}^{\mathrm{c}}_{B_2/B_3} = 2\boldsymbol{\omega}_3 \times {}^3\boldsymbol{v}_{B_2/B_3} = 0$$

The Coriolis term is a function of velocities only and can be computed; however, links 3 and 4 simply translate, making $\boldsymbol{\omega}_3 = 0$. Therefore, the acceleration expression becomes

$$\boldsymbol{a}_{B_2} = \boldsymbol{a}_{B_3} + {}^3\boldsymbol{a}_{B_2/B_3}$$

By geometry, ${}^3\boldsymbol{a}_{B_2/B_3}$ must move in the direction parallel to the face of the cam follower. Therefore, the equation has only two unknowns (once $\boldsymbol{a}_{B_2}$ is computed), and the equation can be solved for $\boldsymbol{a}_{B_3}$ and ${}^3\boldsymbol{a}_{B_2/B_3}$.

Steps

1. Draw the mechanism to scale using the procedure given in Example 3.4. Then draw the equivalent mechanism.

2. Compute $\boldsymbol{v}_{B_2} = \boldsymbol{\omega}_2 \times \boldsymbol{r}_{B/A}$.

   $\boldsymbol{v}_{B_2} = (\boldsymbol{\omega}_2)(\boldsymbol{r}_{B_2/A_2}) = 100(0.5) = 50$ in/s perpendicular to AB and pointed in the direction shown in Fig. 3.27.

   This will locate b_2.

3. Draw a line from o at an angle of 45° with the horizontal. Point b_3 will be on this line.

4. Draw a line through the tip of b_2 and perpendicular to the line at 45°. The intersection of this line with that drawn in step 3 locates b_3.

   $\boldsymbol{v}_{B_3} = 35$ in/s in the direction shown

5. Compute and plot $\boldsymbol{a}_{B_2/A_2} = \boldsymbol{a}^{\mathrm{r}}_{B_2/A_2}$.

   $\boldsymbol{a}^{\mathrm{r}}_{B_2/A_2} = AB \times \boldsymbol{\omega}_2^2 = 0.5 \times 100^2 = 5000$ in/s²; in the $\overrightarrow{BA}$ direction

6. Draw a line from o' at an angle of 45° with the horizontal. Point b'_3 will be on this line.

7. Draw a line through the tip of $\boldsymbol{a}^{\mathrm{r}}_{B_2/A_2}$ and parallel to the face of the cam follower (link 3). This is the direction of ${}^3\boldsymbol{a}_{B_2/B_3}$. The intersection of this line with the line drawn in step 7 will be the point b'_3.

8. Measure $\boldsymbol{a}_{B_3}$.

   $\boldsymbol{a}_{B_3} = 3250$ in/s² in the direction shown

This is the acceleration of link 3. Note that this is the same solution as obtained in Example 3.4. All points in link 3 have the same velocity and the same accelerations. Therefore, points B_3 and C_3 have the same velocity and the same acceleration. Also note that considerably less work is required to obtain the final result when equivalent linkages are used.

When equivalent linkages are used, no information is used about the relative motion at the contact point. If the relative motions between the coincident points at contact are of interest, these can be computed directly after the basic analysis is completed. This velocity might be of interest for lubrication considerations.

EXAMPLE 3.6
Analysis of Sliding Velocity in a Cam Mechanism

Find the sliding velocity at the point of contact for the mechanism in Example 3.5.

Solution

The sliding velocity at the point of contact is the relative velocity between points C_2 and C_3. This velocity can be computed from

$$\boldsymbol{v}_{C_3/C_2} = \boldsymbol{v}_{C_3} - \boldsymbol{v}_{C_2} \tag{3.42}$$

Because

$$\boldsymbol{v}_{C_3} = \boldsymbol{v}_{B_3}$$

we need only solve for $\boldsymbol{v}_{C_2}$ to determine $\boldsymbol{v}_{C_3/C_2}$ in Eq. (3.42). From Example 3.4, $\boldsymbol{v}_{C_2} = \boldsymbol{\omega}_2 \times \boldsymbol{r}_{C/A}$, and it is perpendicular to $\overrightarrow{AC}$ as shown in Fig. 3.22. The vector $\boldsymbol{v}_{C_3/C_2}$ is shown in Fig. 3.28. Measurement of the vector gives $v_{C_3/C_2} = 148$ in/s, in the direction shown in the figure.

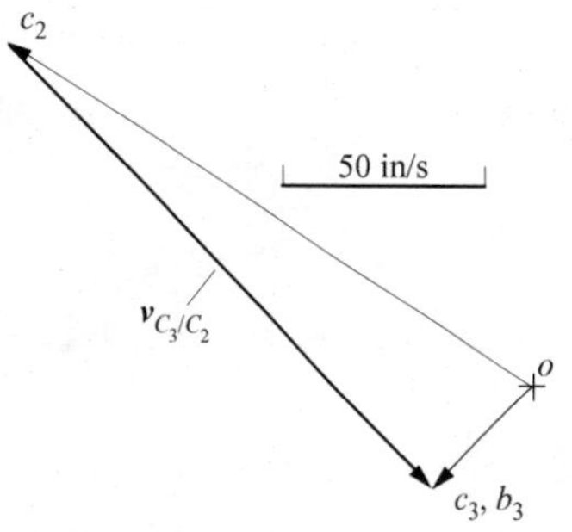

FIGURE 3.28 Calculation of the relative velocity $\boldsymbol{v}_{C_3/C_2}$.

3.8 GENERAL COINCIDENT POINTS

In mechanisms, pin-in-slot joints are common, and occasionally the slots will be curved paths. Also, occasionally, sliders will be used on circular paths that rotate. Mechanisms employing these types of joints can be analyzed using general coincident points. In general, we can use any coincident points to help in a kinematic analysis if we can recognize the path that one of the points traces on the other link. For this, we must "stand" in one link and watch the coincident point on the other link move.

For the analysis, we need the center of curvature of the path and the corresponding tangent to the path. The tangent is normal to the line from the coincident points to the center of curvature of the path. For illustration, assume that the two bodies in question are links 3 and 7, and the coincident points are located at P as shown in Fig. 3.29. Then for any coincident points,

$$\boldsymbol{v}_{P_3/P_7} = {}^7\boldsymbol{v}_{P_3/P_7} = -\boldsymbol{v}_{P_7/P_3} = -{}^3\boldsymbol{v}_{P_7/P_3}$$

Two paths will be traced, and these can be designated as path P_3/P_7 and path P_7/P_3. The paths will share a common tangent vector, and the normal to the paths will contain the two coincident points and the two centers of curvature as shown in Fig. 3.29. The path that P_3 traces on link 7 will be fixed to link 7, and the path P_7/P_3 will be fixed to link 3.

To solve problems involving general coincident points, we must be able to recognize one of the relative paths by inspection. This means that we must be able to determine the center of curvature of the path. Sometimes, we can recognize one of the relative paths but not the other. This is still useful because of the relationships

$$\boldsymbol{v}_{P_7/P_3} = -{}^7\boldsymbol{v}_{P_3/P_7}$$

and

$$\boldsymbol{v}_{P_3/P_7} = -{}^3\boldsymbol{v}_{P_7/P_3}$$

This means that if we can recognize one of the paths, we can always rewrite the kinematic equations so that the information will appear in the correct form. Some examples of paths that are obvious are given in Fig. 3.30.

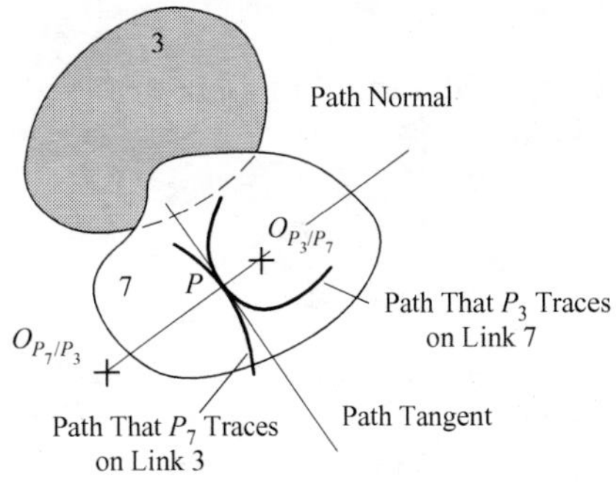

FIGURE 3.29 Geometric properties of relative paths traced by coincident points.

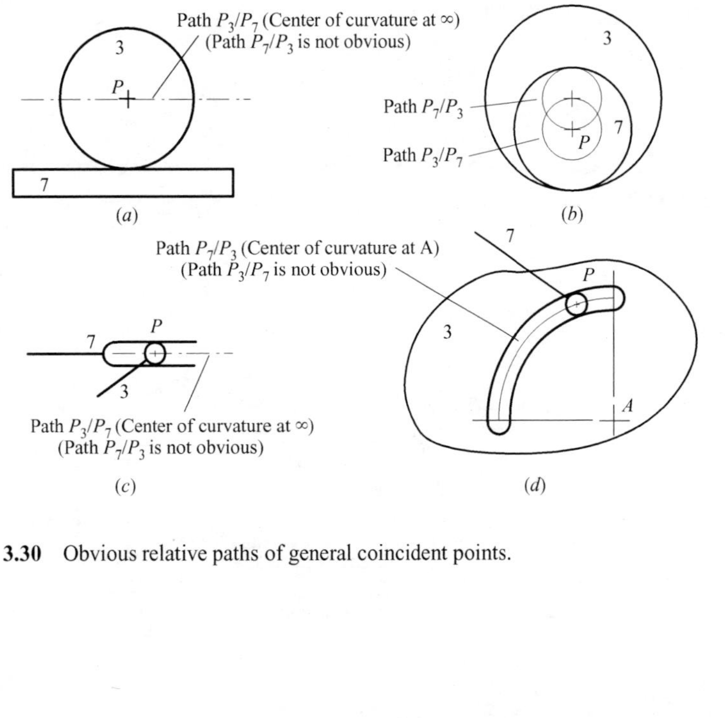

FIGURE 3.30 Obvious relative paths of general coincident points.

3.8.1 Velocity Analyses Involving General Coincident Points

The velocity analysis of mechanisms that involve general coincident points will generally require that the direction for the relative velocity vector ($\boldsymbol{v}_{P_3/P_7}$ or $\boldsymbol{v}_{P_7/P_3}$) be known. This direction can be determined by using the same technique as was used in the analyses using cam pairs. For this, we replace the path P_3/P_7 by its osculating circle at P. Recall that we can do this without compromising the accuracy of the solution as long as we are interested in only velocities and accelerations. Next connect P_3 to the center of curvature O of the path P_3/P_7 by a virtual link x. The geometry is represented schematically in Fig. 3.31.

The motion of P_3 relative to link 7 will be the same as for P_x relative to link 7 if the two points are considered to be pinned together. The relative velocity between P_3 and P_7 can then be written as

$$\boldsymbol{v}_{P_3/P_7} = {}^7\boldsymbol{v}_{P_3/P_7} = {}^7\boldsymbol{v}_{P_3/P_x} + {}^7\boldsymbol{v}_{P_x/O_x} + {}^7\boldsymbol{v}_{O_x/O_7} + {}^7\boldsymbol{v}_{O_7/P_7} \tag{3.43}$$

or because points P_3 and P_x and O_x and O_7 are considered to be pinned together, and the last term involves the motion of two points in system 7 as observed from system 7,

$$\boldsymbol{v}_{P_3/P_7} = {}^7\boldsymbol{v}_{P_3/P_7} = {}^7\boldsymbol{v}_{P_x/O_x} \tag{3.44}$$

Because two points on the same rigid link are involved, the term on the right-hand side of Eq. (3.44) can be written as

$$\boldsymbol{v}_{P_3/P_7} = {}^7\boldsymbol{v}_{P_3/P_7} = {}^7\boldsymbol{\omega}_x \times {}^x\boldsymbol{r}_{P_x/O_x}$$

This vector is perpendicular to the line from the point P to the center of curvature of the path P_3/P_7, and it is therefore along the direction of the tangent to the path. Therefore, when the direction for the relative velocity is required, we need only determine the center of curvature of the path P_3/P_7 and draw a line perpendicular to it.

The magnitude of the angular velocity term will be required for the acceleration analysis, and it can be written as

$$\left|{}^7\boldsymbol{\omega}_x\right| = \frac{\left|\boldsymbol{v}_{P_3/P_7}\right|}{\left|\boldsymbol{r}_{P_x/O_x}\right|}$$

3.8.2 Acceleration Analyses Involving General Coincident Points

The acceleration analysis is slightly more complex than the velocity analysis when general coincident points are involved. For the relative acceleration, again assume that the path that P_3 traces on link 7 is known. This means that the center of curvature of the path is also

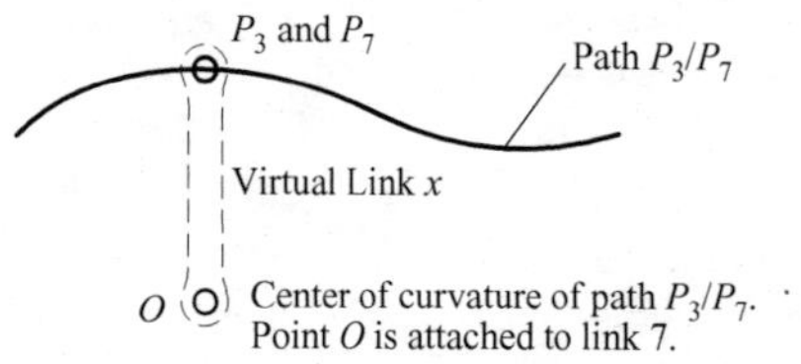

FIGURE 3.31 Connecting a virtual link from point P_3 to center of curvature of path that P_3 traces on link 7.

known. The development of the relative acceleration expression is similar to that used for the case of a rotating slider, and the relative acceleration expression can be written as

$$\boldsymbol{a}_{P_3/P_7} = {}^7\boldsymbol{a}_{P_3/P_7} + 2\boldsymbol{\omega}_7 \times {}^7\boldsymbol{v}_{P_3/P_7} + \boldsymbol{\omega}_7 \times \left(\boldsymbol{\omega}_7 \times \boldsymbol{r}_{P_3/P_7}\right) + \boldsymbol{\alpha}_7 \times \boldsymbol{r}_{P_3/P_7}$$

Because $\boldsymbol{r}_{P_3/P_7} = 0$ at the moment considered,

$$\boldsymbol{a}_{P_3/P_7} = {}^7\boldsymbol{a}_{P_3/P_7} + 2\boldsymbol{\omega}_7 \times \boldsymbol{v}_{P_3/P_7} \tag{3.45}$$

The second term in the expression is the Coriolis term, which is a function of position and velocity only. Therefore, it can be computed as soon as the velocity analysis is completed. The direction of the Coriolis term is given by the cross product. Graphically, we can get the direction by rotating ${}^7\boldsymbol{v}_{P_3/P_7}$ (which equals $\boldsymbol{v}_{P_3/P_7}$) 90º in the direction of $\boldsymbol{\omega}_7$.

The first term in Eq. (3.45) is simply the acceleration of P_3 as observed from system 7. This term can be written as

$$^7\boldsymbol{a}_{P_3/P_7} = {}^7\boldsymbol{a}_{P_3/\text{any point in system 7}} = {}^7\boldsymbol{a}_{P_3} \tag{3.46}$$

Unlike the case of the rotating slider, the direction for this acceleration component is not immediately obvious. However, by using the technique begun in the velocity analysis, we can determine a vector expression for this component that involves only one unknown.

To begin, replace the path P_3/P_7 by its osculating circle at P and rewrite the acceleration expression in Eq. (3.46) in terms of the virtual link x and the center of curvature of the path of P_3/P_7. This is similar to what was done with velocities in Eq. (3.43). The relative acceleration between P_3 and P_7 can then be written as

$$^7\boldsymbol{a}_{P_3} = {}^7\boldsymbol{a}_{P_3/P_7} = {}^7\boldsymbol{a}_{P_3/P_x} + {}^7\boldsymbol{a}_{P_x/O_x} + {}^7\boldsymbol{a}_{O_x/O_7} + {}^7\boldsymbol{a}_{O_7/P_7}$$

or because points P_3 and P_x and O_x and O_7 are pinned together, and the last term involves the motion of two points in system 7 as observed from system 7,

$$^7\boldsymbol{a}_{P_3} = {}^7\boldsymbol{a}_{P_3/P_7} = {}^7\boldsymbol{a}_{P_x/O_x} \tag{3.47}$$

Because two points on the same rigid link are involved, the term on the right-hand side of Eq. (3.63) can be written as

$$^7\boldsymbol{a}_{P_x/O_x} = {}^7\boldsymbol{a}^{\mathrm{r}}_{P_x/O_x} + {}^7\boldsymbol{a}^{\mathrm{t}}_{P_x/O_x}$$

The radial component is a function of velocities and position only and can be written as

$$^7\boldsymbol{a}^{\mathrm{r}}_{P_x/O_x} = {}^7\boldsymbol{\omega}_x \times {}^x\boldsymbol{v}_{P_x/O_x} = \frac{\left|\boldsymbol{v}_{P_x/O_x}\right|^2}{\left|\boldsymbol{r}_{P_x/O_x}\right|} = \frac{\left|\boldsymbol{v}_{P_3/P_7}\right|^2}{\left|\boldsymbol{r}_{P/O}\right|} (\text{from } P \text{ to } O)$$

The magnitude of the vector ${}^7\boldsymbol{a}^{\mathrm{t}}_{P_x/O_x}$ cannot be computed directly; however, we know that the direction is perpendicular to the line from the point P to the center of curvature of the path P_3/P_7, and it is therefore along the direction of the tangent to the path. The total acceleration can now be represented as

$$\boldsymbol{a}_{P_3/P_7} = {}^7\boldsymbol{a}^{\mathrm{t}}_{P_x/O_x} + {}^7\boldsymbol{a}^{\mathrm{r}}_{P_x/O_x} + 2\boldsymbol{\omega}_7 \times {}^7\boldsymbol{v}_{P_3/P_7}$$

or in terms of the original subscripts,

$$\boldsymbol{a}_{P_3/P_7} = {}^7\boldsymbol{a}^{\mathrm{t}}_{P_3/P_7} + {}^7\boldsymbol{a}^{\mathrm{r}}_{P_3/P_7} + 2\boldsymbol{\omega}_7 \times {}^7\boldsymbol{v}_{P_3/P_7}$$

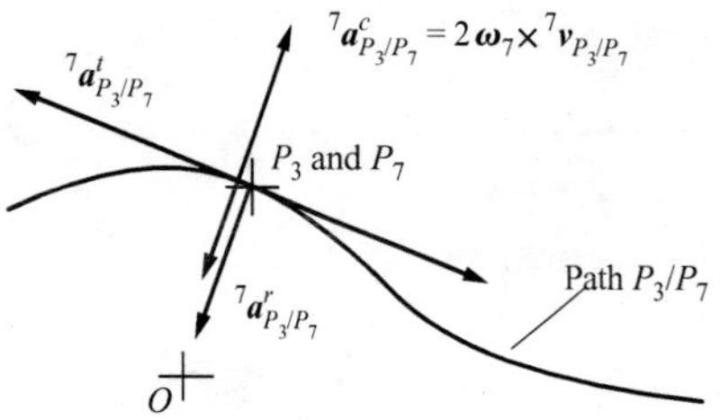

FIGURE 3.32 Acceleration components associated with the relative acceleration between P_3 and P_7.

Of the three vectors on the right-hand side of the equation, only the magnitude of $^7\boldsymbol{a}^t_{P_3/P_7}$ will be unknown after the velocity analysis. The directions for the individual terms are summarized in Fig. 3.32. Note that the radial and Coriolis terms are both normal to the tangent of the path of P_3/P_7; however, only the radial component always points from P to the center of curvature of the path of P_3/P_7. The direction of the Coriolis term will depend on the directions of both $\boldsymbol{\omega}_7$ and $^7\boldsymbol{v}_{P_3/P_7}$.

EXAMPLE 3.7 Analysis of Mechanism with a Pin-in-Slot Joint

In the mechanism shown in Fig. 3.33, point B_2 moves on a curved slot in link 3. The radius of the slot is 3 m. Points C, B, and D are collinear, and the other distances between points are as given in Fig. 3.33. Link 2 rotates with an angular velocity of 2 rad/s CCW and an angular acceleration of 3 rad/s^2 CCW. For the position shown, find the following:

1. $\boldsymbol{\omega}_3$, $\boldsymbol{\alpha}_3$, $\boldsymbol{v}_{D_3}$, and $\boldsymbol{a}_{D_3}$;
2. The center of curvature of the path that B_3 traces on link 2.

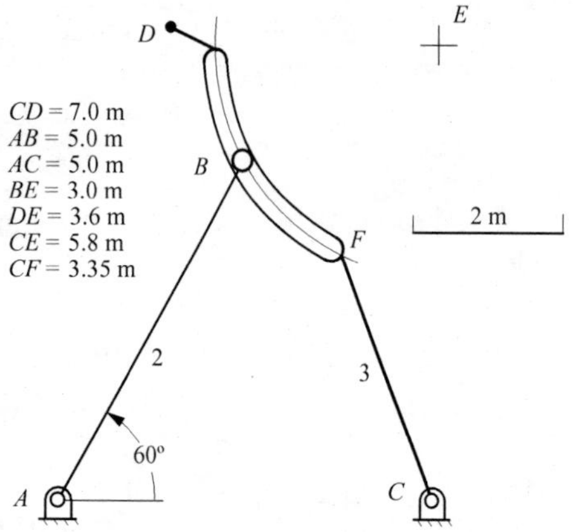

FIGURE 3.33 Mechanism for Example 3.7.

Solution

Once the position of the linkage is drawn, the following vector quantities can be measured:

$$\boldsymbol{r}_{B/A} = 5\angle 60°$$

$$\boldsymbol{r}_{B/C} = 5\angle 120°$$

$$\boldsymbol{r}_{D/C} = 7\angle 120°$$

For the velocity analysis, we can first compute the velocity of point B_2, which is

$$\boldsymbol{v}_{B_2} = \boldsymbol{v}_{B_2/A_2} = \boldsymbol{\omega}_2 \times \boldsymbol{r}_{B_2/A_2}$$

Next go to point B_3 on link 3 to get

$$\boldsymbol{v}_{B_3} = \boldsymbol{v}_{B_3/C_3} = \boldsymbol{\omega}_3 \times {}^3\boldsymbol{r}_{B/C} \perp BC$$

Because $\boldsymbol{\omega}_3$ is unknown, this term cannot be computed without another equation. Consider the two coincident points B_2 and B_3. Then,

$$\boldsymbol{v}_{B_3} = \boldsymbol{v}_{B_2} + \boldsymbol{v}_{B_3/B_2}$$

This equation is technically correct; however, we cannot recognize the path that B_3 traces on link 2. Consequently, the equation cannot be differentiated to help us in the acceleration analysis. Therefore, write the equation in terms of $\boldsymbol{v}_{B_2}$. Then,

$$\boldsymbol{v}_{B_2} = \boldsymbol{v}_{B_3} + \boldsymbol{v}_{B_2/B_3}$$

This equation is useful because we can pick out the path that B_2 traces on link 3 by inspection. This equation can be solved, although there are two unknown directions on the right-hand side. This is handled by beginning one vector at the velocity pole and ending the other vector at the end of $\boldsymbol{v}_{B_2}$.

After the velocity polygon is drawn, we can measure $\boldsymbol{v}_{B_3}$ and determine $\boldsymbol{v}_{D_3}$ by image. We can also measure $\boldsymbol{v}_{B_2/B_3}$, which will be required for the acceleration analysis.

The velocity analysis uses two basic equations:

$$\boldsymbol{v}_{B_2} = \boldsymbol{v}_{B_2/A_2}$$

and

$$\boldsymbol{v}_{B_2} = \boldsymbol{v}_{B_3/C_3} + \boldsymbol{v}_{B_2/B_3}$$

and these two equations show the solution path for the accelerations. Again start at B_2. Then,

$$\boldsymbol{a}_{B_2} = \boldsymbol{a}_{B_2/A_2} = \boldsymbol{a}^{\mathrm{t}}_{B_2/A_2} + \boldsymbol{a}^{\mathrm{r}}_{B_2/A_2} = \boldsymbol{\alpha}_2 \times {}^2\boldsymbol{r}_{B/A} + \boldsymbol{\omega}_2 \times {}^2\boldsymbol{v}_{B/A}$$

Now differentiate the velocity expression involving B_3 to get

$$\begin{aligned}\boldsymbol{a}_{B_2} &= \boldsymbol{a}_{B_3/C_3} + \boldsymbol{a}_{B_2/B_3} = \boldsymbol{a}^{\mathrm{r}}_{B_3/C_3} = \boldsymbol{a}^{\mathrm{t}}_{B_3/C_3} + {}^3\boldsymbol{a}^{\mathrm{n}}_{B_2/B_3} + {}^3\boldsymbol{a}^{\mathrm{t}}_{B_2/B_3} + 2\boldsymbol{\omega}_3 \times \boldsymbol{v}_{B_2/B_3} \\ &= \boldsymbol{\omega}_3 \times \boldsymbol{v}_{B_3/C_3} + \boldsymbol{\alpha}_3 \times {}^3\boldsymbol{r}_{B_3/C_3} + {}^3\boldsymbol{a}^{\mathrm{n}}_{B_2/B_3} + {}^3\boldsymbol{a}^{\mathrm{t}}_{B_2/B_3} + 2\boldsymbol{\omega}_3 \times \boldsymbol{v}_{B_2/B_3}\end{aligned} \tag{3.48}$$

This equation has only two unknowns and can be solved. We can compute the acceleration of D_3 using the acceleration image.

To find the center of curvature of the path that B_3 traces on link 2, we must find an expression that involves the radius of curvature of the path. This term is ${}^2\boldsymbol{a}^{\mathrm{n}}_{B_3/B_2}$, and it can be evaluated from the following:

$$\boldsymbol{a}_{B_2/B_3} = -\boldsymbol{a}_{B_3/B_2}$$

Therefore,

$$\boldsymbol{a}^{\mathrm{t}}_{B_2/B_3} = -\boldsymbol{a}^{\mathrm{t}}_{B_3/B_2}$$

and

$$\boldsymbol{a}^{\mathrm{n}}_{B_2/B_3} = -\boldsymbol{a}^{\mathrm{n}}_{B_3/B_2}$$

Also,

$${}^3\boldsymbol{a}^{\mathrm{n}}_{B_2/B_3} + 2\boldsymbol{\omega}_3 \times \boldsymbol{v}_{B_2/B_3} = -{}^2\boldsymbol{a}^{\mathrm{n}}_{B_3/B_2} - 2\boldsymbol{\omega}_2 \times \boldsymbol{v}_{B_3/B_2}$$

and

$$ {}^{2}a^{\mathrm{n}}_{B_3/B_2} = \frac{|\boldsymbol{v}_{B_3/B_2}|^2}{|\boldsymbol{r}_{B/G}|} $$

or

$$ r_{B/G} = \frac{|\boldsymbol{v}_{B_3/B_2}|^2}{|{}^{2}\boldsymbol{a}^{\mathrm{n}}_{B_3/B_2}|} $$

where G gives the location of the center of curvature of the path that B_3 traces on link 2. The location of G on the proper side of B is found by the direction of ${}^{2}\boldsymbol{a}^{\mathrm{n}}_{B_3/B_2}$, because it points from B to the center of curvature of the path.

Steps

1. Select a scale and draw link 2 at a scaled distance of 5 m at an angle of 60° to the horizontal. This will locate point B as shown in Fig. 3.34. Draw an arc of radius BE centered at B. Then draw a second arc centered at C of length CE. The intersection of this arc with the first will locate point E. Next draw the arc centered at E and of radius BE. Draw a line from point C through point B of length CD.

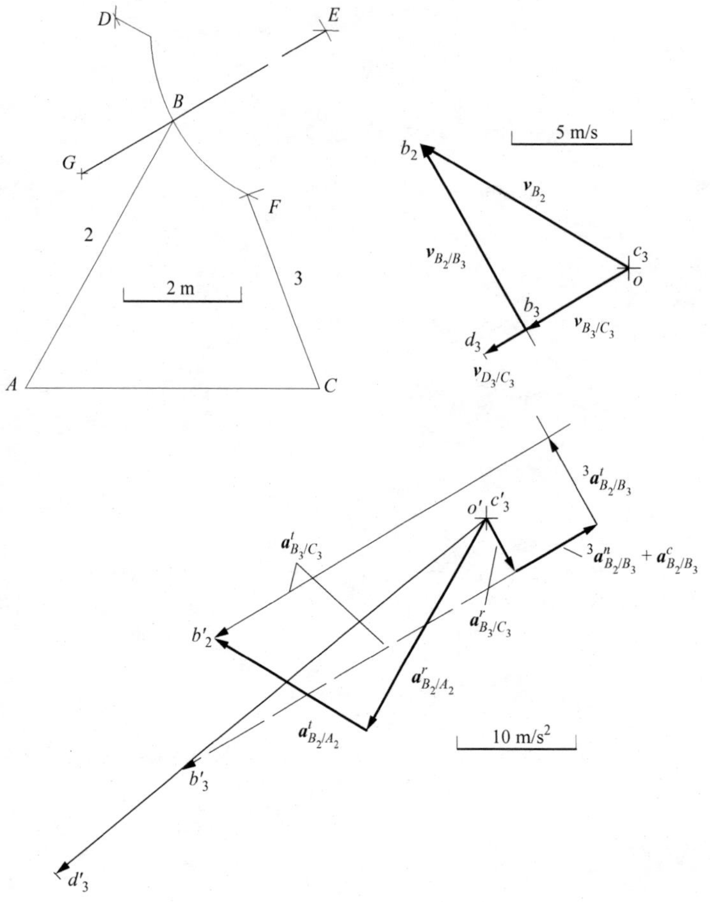

FIGURE 3.34 Solution to Example 3.7.

2. Compute $\boldsymbol{v}_{B_2} = \boldsymbol{v}_{B_2/A_2} = \boldsymbol{\omega}_2 \times \boldsymbol{r}_{B_2/A_2}$ and draw the vector from o in the direction perpendicular to BA. The sense of $\boldsymbol{v}_{B_2}$ is determined by rotation of $\boldsymbol{r}_{B_2/A_2}$ 90° in the direction of $\boldsymbol{\omega}_2$. This will locate b_2.

$$\boldsymbol{v}_{B_2/A_2} = \boldsymbol{\omega}_2 \times \boldsymbol{r}_{B_2/A_2} = (2)(5) \perp BA$$

3. Draw a line through o in the direction perpendicular to CB.
4. Draw a line through b_2 in the direction tangent to the path that B_2 traces on link 3 (perpendicular to the radius BE). The intersection of this line with that drawn in step 3 will locate point b_3. Locate the arrowheads on the velocity polygon to conform with Eq. (3.48).
5. Locate point d_3 by image.

   $od_3 = \frac{CD}{CB}$ ob$_3$. Then we get $\boldsymbol{v}_{D_3} = 7.0$ m/s at an angle of 210° to the horizontal.
6. Measure $\boldsymbol{v}_{B_2/B_3} = 8.7$ m/s at an angle of 120° to the horizontal.
7. Measure $\boldsymbol{v}_{B_3/C_3} = 5.0$ m/s at an angle of 210° to the horizontal and compute ω_3. Get the sense of $\boldsymbol{\omega}_3$ by rotating $\boldsymbol{r}_{B_3/C_3}$ 90° in the direction of $\boldsymbol{\omega}_3$ to the direction of $\boldsymbol{v}_{B_3/C_3}$.

$$\boldsymbol{\omega}_3 = \frac{\left|\boldsymbol{v}_{B_3/C_3}\right|}{\left|\boldsymbol{r}_{B_3/C_3}\right|} = \frac{5}{5} = 1\ \text{rad/s},\ \boldsymbol{\omega}_3 \text{ is CCW}$$

8. Compute $\boldsymbol{a}^{t}_{B_2/A_2}$ and $\boldsymbol{a}^{r}_{B_2/A_2}$ and, starting from o', draw the resulting vectors after scaling.

   $\boldsymbol{a}^{r}_{B_2/A_2} = \boldsymbol{\omega}_2 \times \boldsymbol{v}_{B/A} = 2(10) = 20\ \text{m/s}^2$ opposite $\boldsymbol{r}_{B/A}$

   $\boldsymbol{a}^{t}_{B_2/A_2} = \boldsymbol{\alpha}_2 \times \boldsymbol{r}_{B/A} = 3(5) = 15\ \text{m/s}^2$ perpendicular to $\boldsymbol{r}_{B/A}$ in the direction given by rotating $\boldsymbol{r}_{B/A}$ 90° in the direction of $\boldsymbol{\alpha}_2$.

   This vector is added to $\boldsymbol{a}^{r}_{B_2/A_2}$ as shown in Fig. 3.34.
9. Compute $\boldsymbol{a}^{r}_{B_3/C_3}$, ${}^3\boldsymbol{a}^{n}_{B_2/B_3}$, and $\boldsymbol{a}^{c}_{B_2/B_3}$. All of these accelerations are functions of the velocity and position data.

   $\boldsymbol{a}^{r}_{B_3/C_3} = \boldsymbol{\omega}_3 \times \boldsymbol{v}_{B_3/C_3} = 1(5) = 5\ \text{m/s}^2$ from B to C

   $${}^3\boldsymbol{a}^{n}_{B_2/B_3} = \frac{\left|\boldsymbol{v}_{B_2/B_3}\right|^2}{\left|\boldsymbol{v}_{B_3/E_3}\right|} = \frac{(8.7)^2}{3} = 25.23\ \text{m/s}^2,\ {}^3\boldsymbol{a}^{n}_{B_2/B_3} \text{ from } B \text{ to } E$$

   $\boldsymbol{a}^{c}_{B_2/B_3} = 2\boldsymbol{\omega}_3 \times \boldsymbol{v}_{B_2/B_3} = 2(1)(8.7) = 17.4\ \text{m/s}^2$ from E to B
10. Note that ${}^3\boldsymbol{a}^{n}_{B_2/B_3}$ and $\boldsymbol{a}^{c}_{B_2/B_3}$ are in opposite directions. Therefore, determine the resultant before plotting.

$${}^3\boldsymbol{a}^{n}_{B_2/B_3} + \boldsymbol{a}^{c}_{B_2/B_3} = 25.23 - 17.4 = 7.83\ \text{m/s}^2 \text{ from } B \text{ to } E$$

11. Starting from o', add the vectors $\boldsymbol{a}^{r}_{B_3/C_3}$ and ${}^3\boldsymbol{a}^{n}_{B_2/B_3} + \boldsymbol{a}^{c}_{B_2/B_3}$ as shown in Fig. 3.34.
12. Draw a line through the tip of ${}^3\boldsymbol{a}^{n}_{B_2/B_3} + \boldsymbol{a}^{c}_{B_2/B_3}$ in the direction perpendicular to ${}^3\boldsymbol{a}^{n}_{B_2/B_3} + \boldsymbol{a}^{c}_{B_2/B_3}$ and to $\boldsymbol{r}_{B/E}$ (i.e., perpendicular to the tangent to the path that B_2 traces on link 3).
13. Draw a line through the tip of $\boldsymbol{a}^{t}_{B_2/A_2}$ in the direction perpendicular to $\boldsymbol{r}_{C/B}$. The intersection of this line with that from step 12 will give ${}^3\boldsymbol{a}^{t}_{B_2/B_3}$ and $\boldsymbol{a}^{t}_{B_3/C_3}$. The locations of the arrowheads (directions) are given by Eq. (3.48).
14. Measure $\boldsymbol{a}^{t}_{B_3/C_3}$ and compute the magnitude of the angular acceleration, $\boldsymbol{\alpha}_3$.

$$\boldsymbol{\alpha}_3 = \frac{\left|\boldsymbol{a}^{t}_{B_3/C_3}\right|}{\left|\boldsymbol{r}_{B_3/C_3}\right|} = \frac{32.2}{5} = 11.2\ \text{rad/s}^2$$

The sense is given by $a^t_{B_3/C_3}$ and r_{B_3/C_3}. Namely, we rotate r_{B_3/C_3} 90° in the direction of α_3 to get the direction of $a^t_{B_3/C_3}$. The direction is CCW.

15. Locate the acceleration of D_3 by acceleration image. To do this, determine the absolute acceleration of B_3. This is done by adding $a^t_{B_3/C_3}$ to $a^r_{B_3/C_3}$ to locate b'_3. Then find d'_3 using

$$o'd'_3 = \frac{CD}{CB} o'b'_3$$

This gives $a_{D_3} = 45.9 \text{ m/s}^2$ in the direction shown in Fig. 3.34.

16. Compute ${}^2a^n_{B_3/B_2} = -({}^3a^n_{B_2/B_3} + 2\omega_3 \times v_{B_3/B_2} + 2\omega_2 \times v_{B_3/B_2})$. Arbitrarily select the direction $r_{E/B}$ as positive. Then,

$${}^2a^n_{B_3/B_2} = -(25.23 - 17.4 + 34.8) = -42.63 \text{ m/s}^2$$

The minus sign means that the direction of the center of curvature of the path is opposite $r_{E/B}$ or in the $r_{B/E}$ direction.

17. Compute the radius of curvature by locating G_2 using

$$r_{B/G} = \frac{|v_{B_3/B_2}|^2}{|{}^2a^n_{B_3/B_2}|} = \frac{(8.7)^2}{42.63} = 1.78\text{m}$$

The center of curvature is shown in Fig. 3.34.

PROBLEMS

EXERCISE PROBLEMS INVOLVING ROTATING SLIDERS

3.1 In the figure, points A and C have the same horizontal coordinate, and $\omega_3 = 30$ rad/s in the direction shown. Draw and dimension the velocity polygon. Identify the sliding velocity between the block and the slide, and find the angular velocity of link 2.

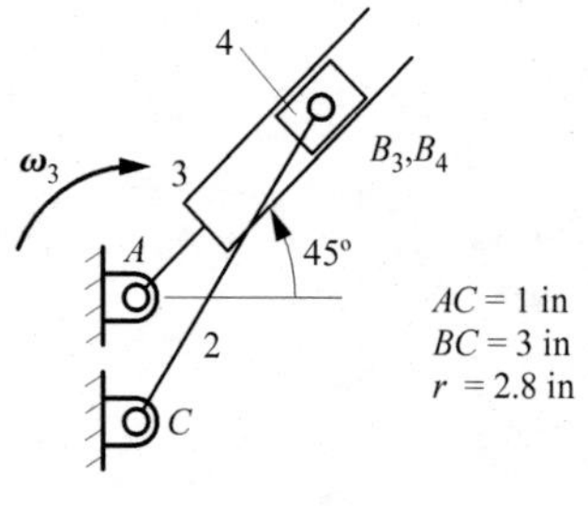

3.2 If $\omega_2 = 10$ rad/s CCW, find the velocity of point B_3.

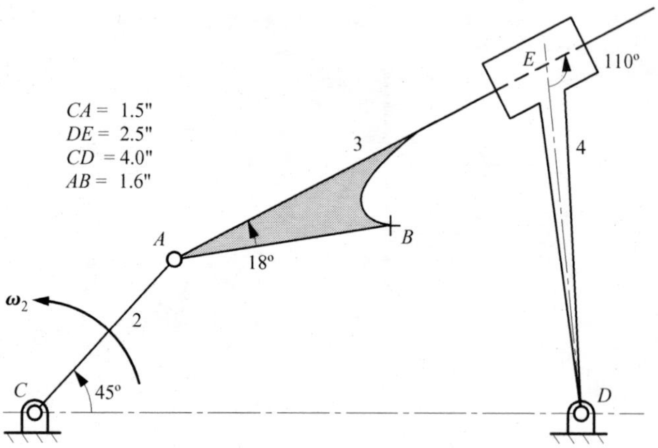

3.3 If ω_2 = 100 rad/s CCW, find v_{B_4}.

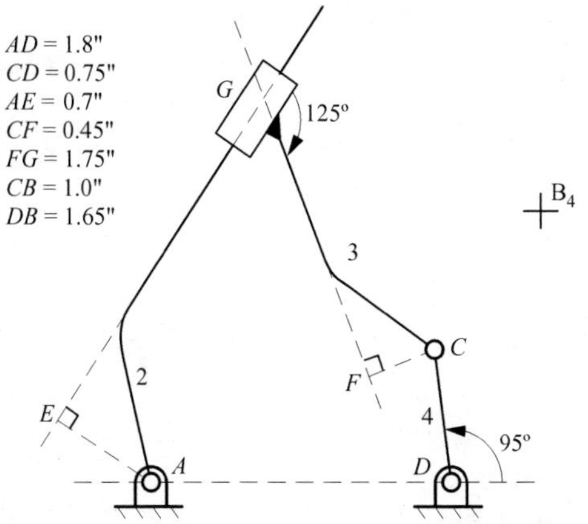

3.4 If ω_2 = 50 rad/s CCW, find v_{D_4}.

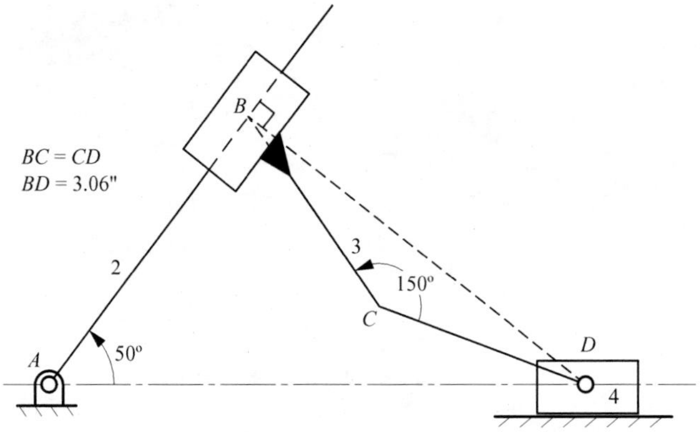

3.5 Determine the velocity and acceleration of point B on link 2.

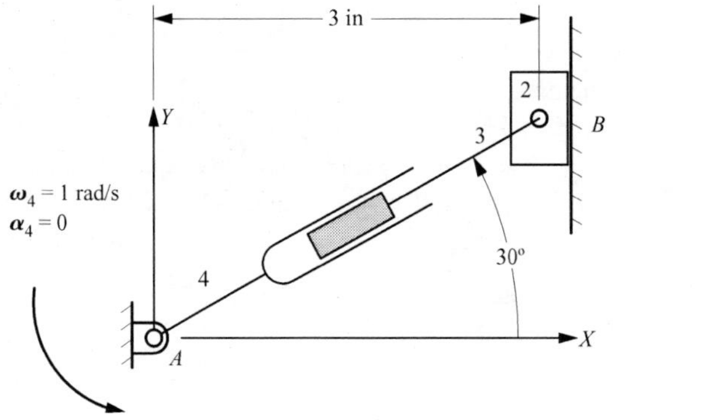

3.6 If ω_2 = 100 rad/s CCW, find ω_6.

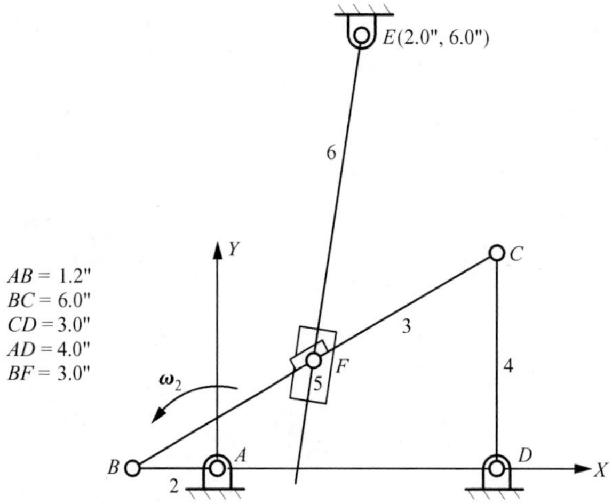

3.7 If ω_2 = 50 rad/s CCW, find the velocity of point G_5.

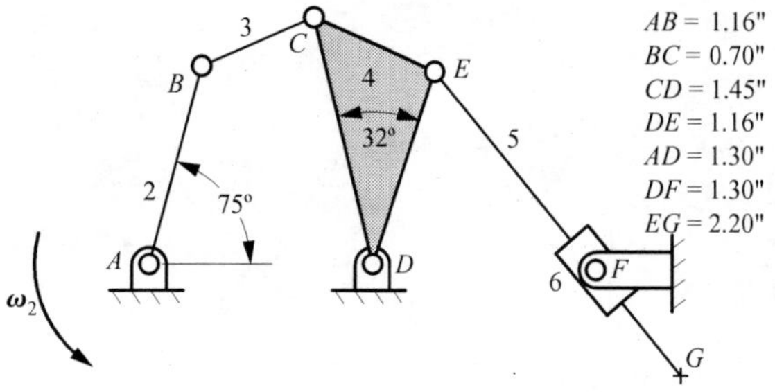

3.8 If ω_2 = 5 rad/s CCW, find ω_6.

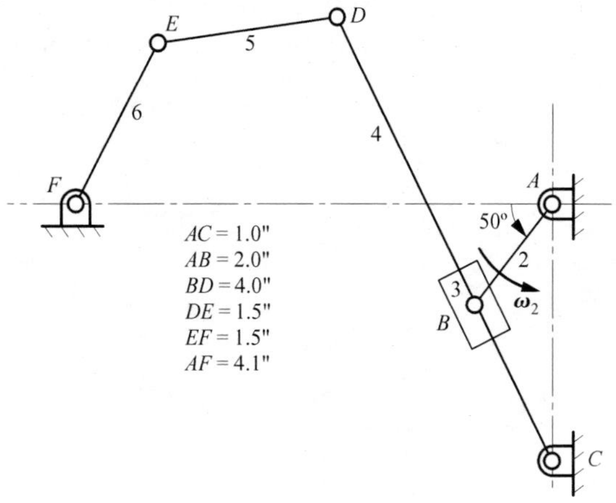

3.9 In the mechanism below, $\omega_2 = 10$ rad/s CCW. Write the velocity equations and determine the following: v_{D_4}, ω_4, v_{F_6}, and ω_6.

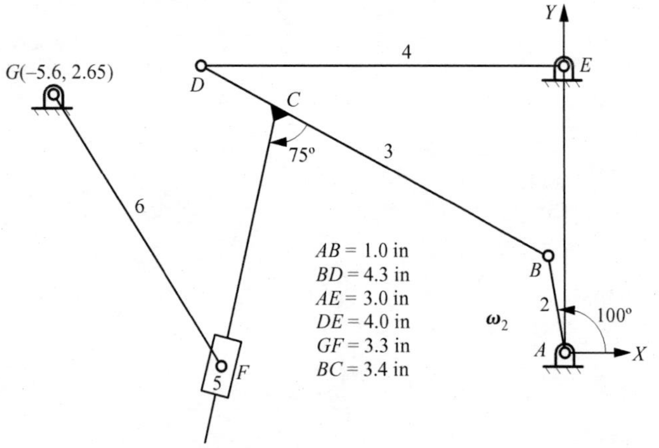

3.10 If the velocity of point A on link 2 is 10 in/s as shown, find the velocity of point C on link 5.

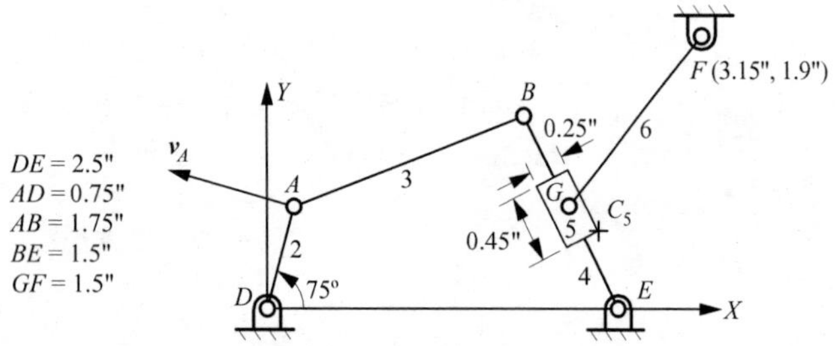

3.11 In the clamping device shown, links 3 and 4 are an air cylinder. If the opening rate of the air cylinder is 5 cm/s and the opening acceleration of the cylinder is 2 cm/s², find the angular velocity and acceleration of link 2 and the linear velocity and acceleration of point D on link 2.

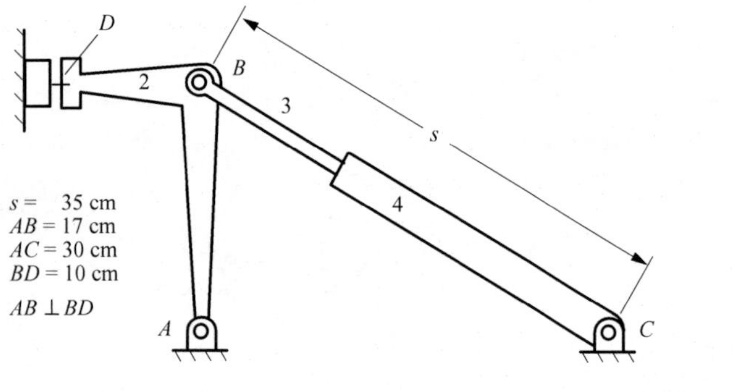

3.12 In the mechanism shown, link 4 moves to the left with a velocity of 8 in/s and the acceleration is 80 in/s² to the left. Draw the velocity and acceleration polygons and solve for the angular velocity and acceleration of link 2.

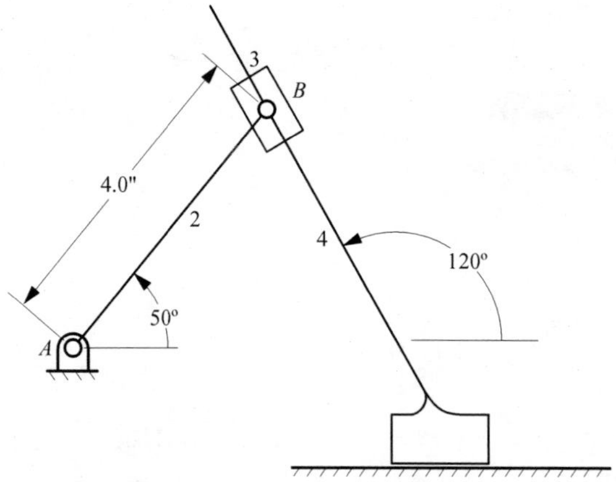

3.13 In the mechanism shown, the angular velocity of link 2 is 2 rad/s CCW and the angular acceleration is 5 rad/s² CW. Determine the following: v_{B_4}, v_{D_4}, ω_4, a_{B_4}, a_{D_4}, and α_4.

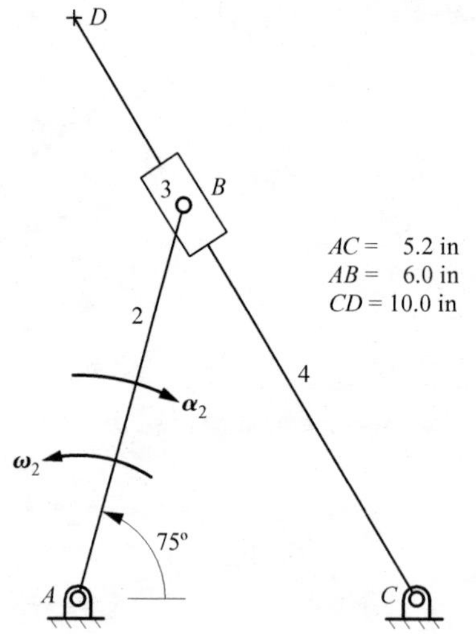

3.14 Re-solve Problem 3.13 if $\omega_2 = 2$ rad/s CCW (constant).

3.15 In the mechanism shown, the velocity and acceleration of point B are given. Determine the angular velocity and acceleration of links 3 and 4. On the velocity and acceleration diagrams, locate the velocity and acceleration of point E on link 3.

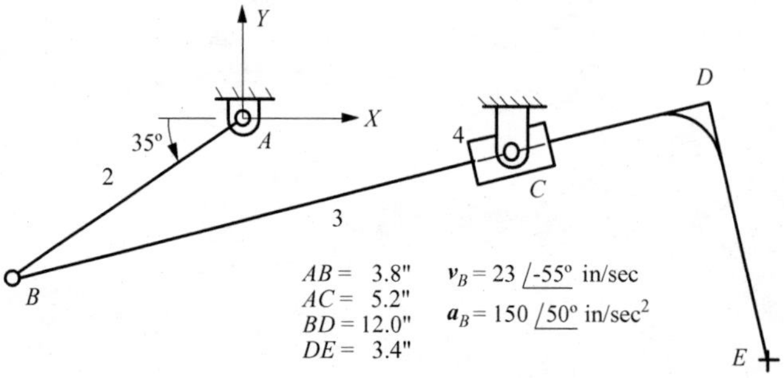

3.16 In the figure, $\boldsymbol{\omega}_2 = 500$ rad/s CCW (constant). Find $\boldsymbol{\omega}_4$, ${}^2\boldsymbol{\omega}_4$, $\boldsymbol{\omega}_3$, ${}^6\boldsymbol{\omega}_5$, ${}^3\boldsymbol{\omega}_5$, $\boldsymbol{v}_D$, $\boldsymbol{\alpha}_4$, ${}^2\boldsymbol{\alpha}_4$, $\boldsymbol{\alpha}_3$, ${}^6\boldsymbol{\alpha}_5$, and $\boldsymbol{a}_D$.

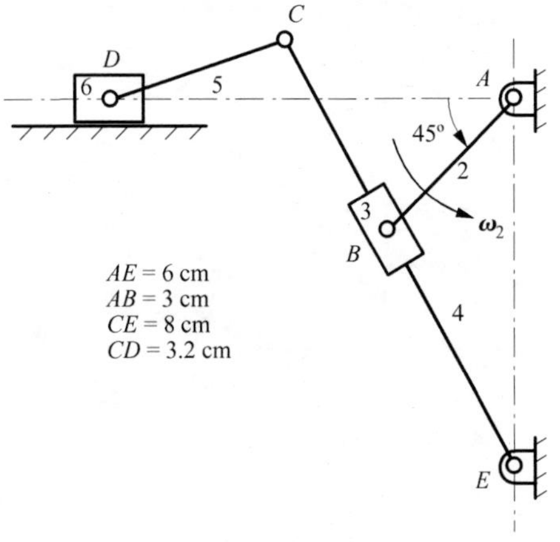

3.17 In the mechanism shown, the angular velocity of link 2 is 60 rpm CCW (constant). Determine the acceleration of point C_6 and the angular velocity of link 6.

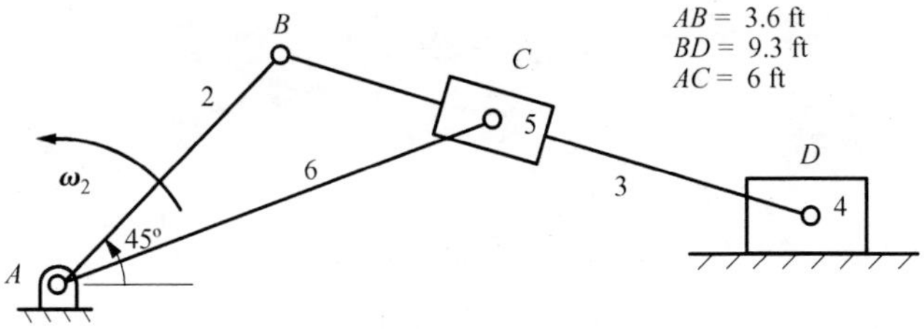

3.18 In the position shown *AB* is horizontal. Draw the velocity diagram to determine the sliding velocity of link 6. Determine a new position for point *C* (between *B* and *D*) so that the velocity of link 6 would be equal and opposite to the one calculated for the original position of point *C*.

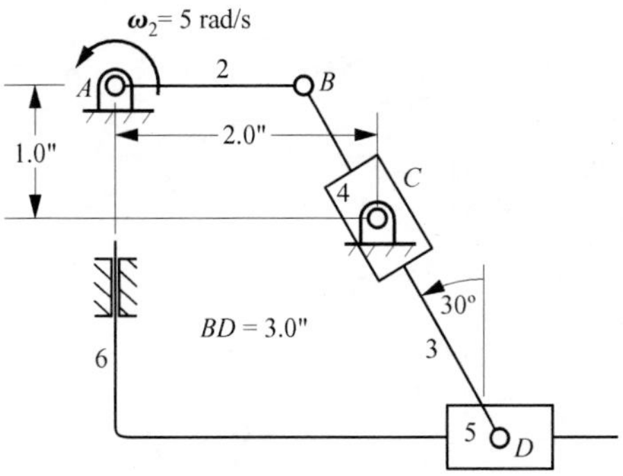

3.19 The scotch-yoke mechanism is driven by crank 2 at $\omega_2 = 36$ rad/s (CCW). Link 4 slides horizontally. Find the velocity of point *B* on link 4.

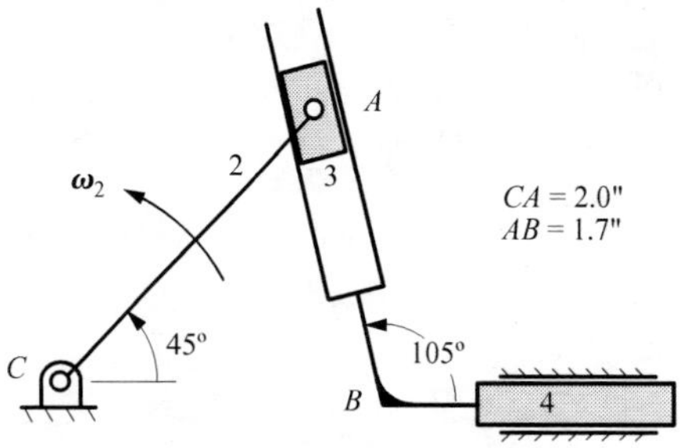

EXERCISE PROBLEMS INVOLVING ROLLING CONTACT

3.20 The circular cam shown is driven at an angular velocity $\boldsymbol{\omega}_2 = 15$ rad/s (CW) and $\boldsymbol{\alpha}_2 = 100$ rad/s$_2$ (CW). There is rolling contact between the cam and the roller, link 3. Find the angular velocity and angular acceleration of the oscillating follower, link 4.

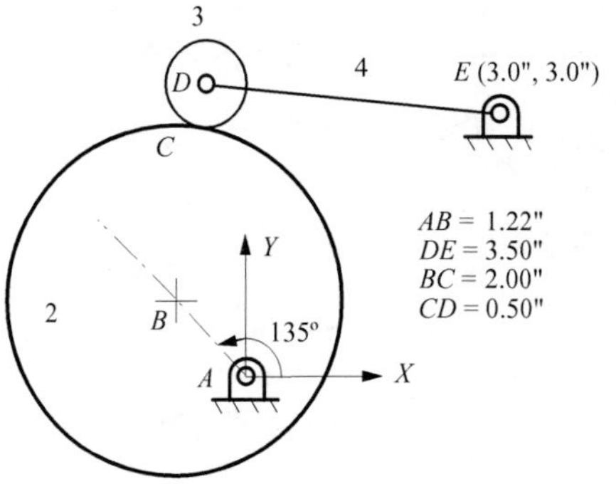

3.21 For the mechanism shown, assume that link 2 rolls on the frame (link 1) and link 4 rolls on Link 3. Assume that link 2 is rotating CW with a constant angular velocity of 100 rad/s. Determine the angular acceleration of link 3 and link 4.

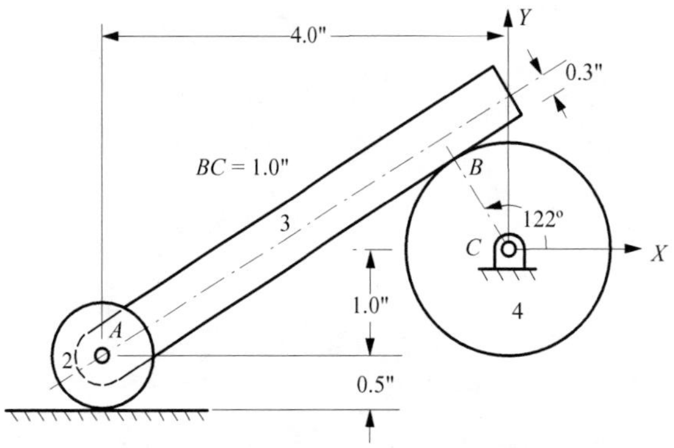

3.22 For the mechanism shown, assume that link 4 rolls on the frame (link 1). If link 2 is rotating CW with a constant angular velocity of 10 rad/s, determine the angular accelerations of links 3 and 4 and the acceleration of point E on link 3.

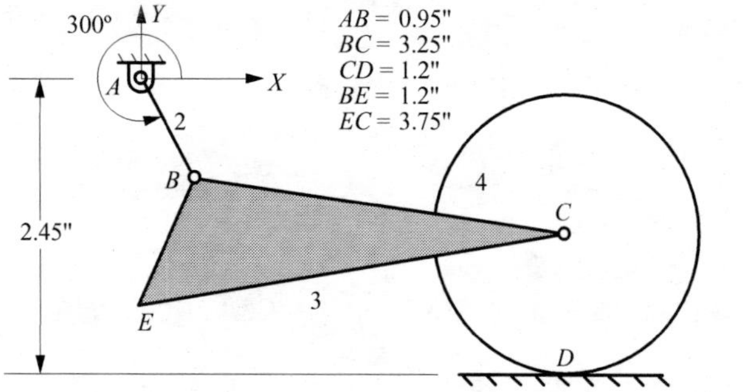

3.23 If v_{A_2} = 10 in/s (constant) downward, find ω_3, α_3, v_{C_3}, and a_{C_3}.

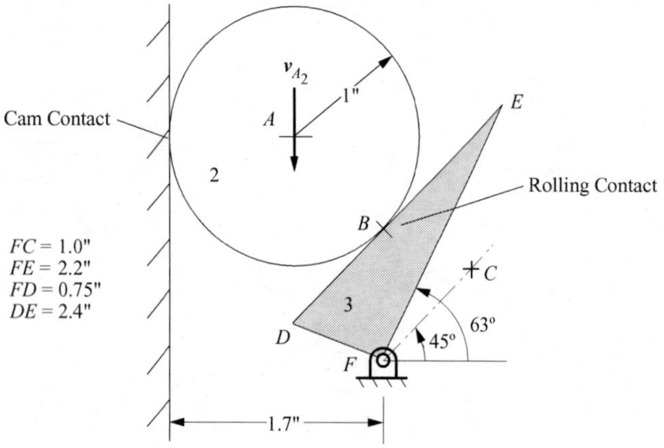

3.24 In the figure shown, points A, B, and C are collinear. If v_{A_2} = 10 in/s (constant) downward, find v_{C_3} and a_{C_3}.

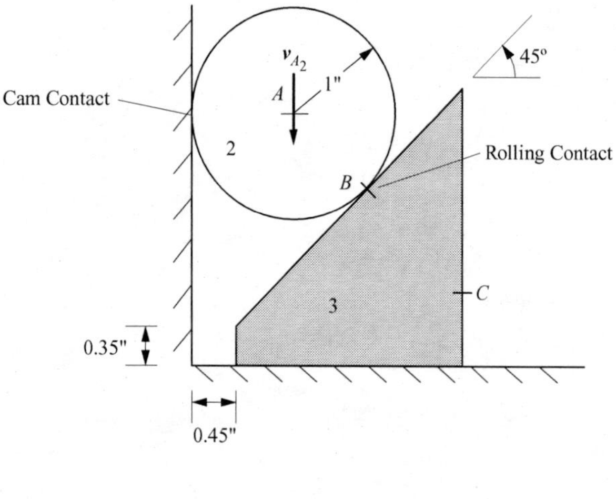

3.25 Part of an eight-link mechanism is shown in the figure. There is rolling contact at location B and the velocity and acceleration of points A_6 and C_5 are as shown. Find ω_8 and α_7 for the position given. Also find the velocity of E_7 by image.

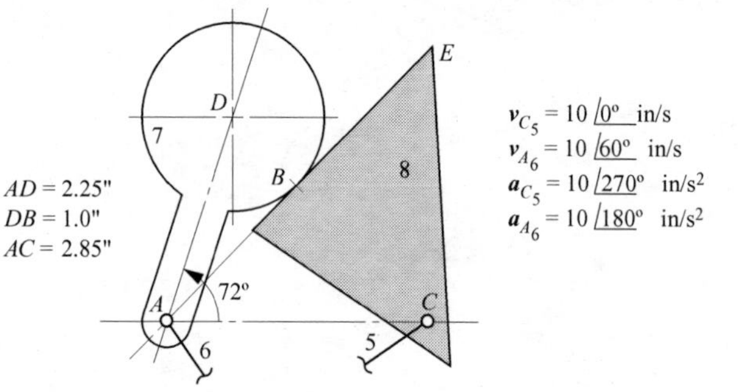

3.26 In the mechanism shown, link 2 is turning CW at the rate of 20 rad/s, and link 3 rolls on link 2. Draw the velocity and acceleration polygons for the mechanism, and determine a_{C_3} and α_3.

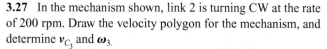

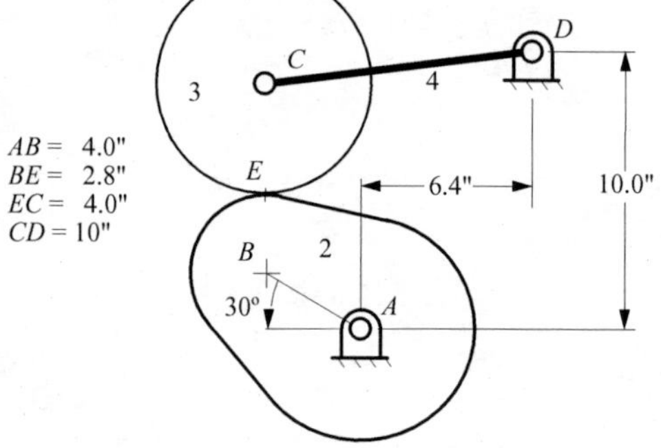

3.27 In the mechanism shown, link 2 is turning CW at the rate of 200 rpm. Draw the velocity polygon for the mechanism, and determine v_{C_3} and ω_3.

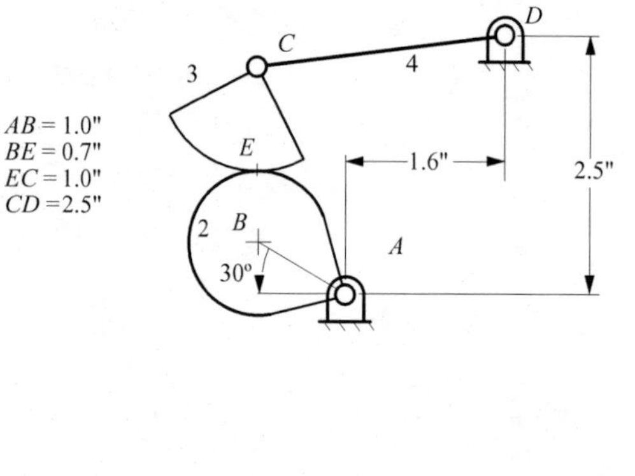

3.28 Assume that link 7 rolls on link 3 without slipping and find $\boldsymbol{\omega}_7$.

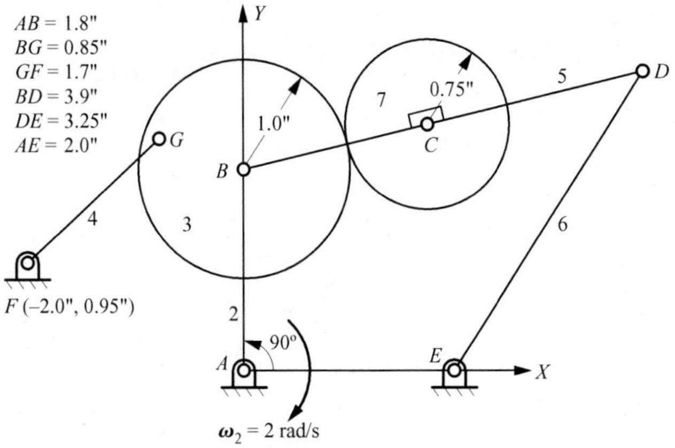

3.29 In the two-degree-of-freedom mechanism shown, $\boldsymbol{\omega}_2$ is given as 10 rad/s CCW. What should the linear velocity of link 6 be so that $\boldsymbol{\omega}_4 = 5$ rad/s CCW?

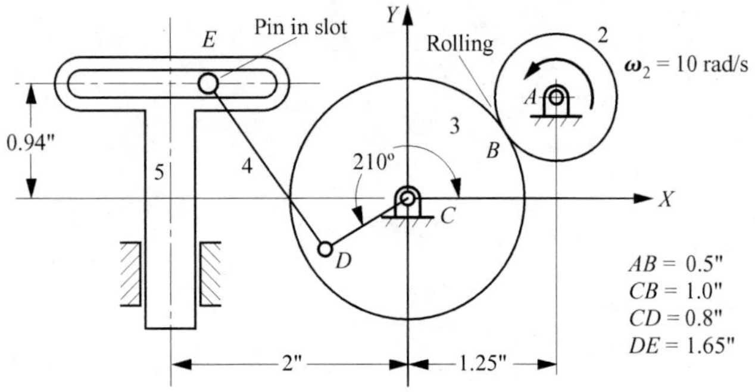

EXERCISE PROBLEMS INVOLVING CAM CONTACT

3.30 In the mechanism shown, $\boldsymbol{\omega}_2 = 10$ rad/s CW. Determine $\boldsymbol{v}_{C_3/C_2}$ and $\boldsymbol{v}_{C_3}$ using two approaches: (a) equivalent linkages and (b) coincident points at C.

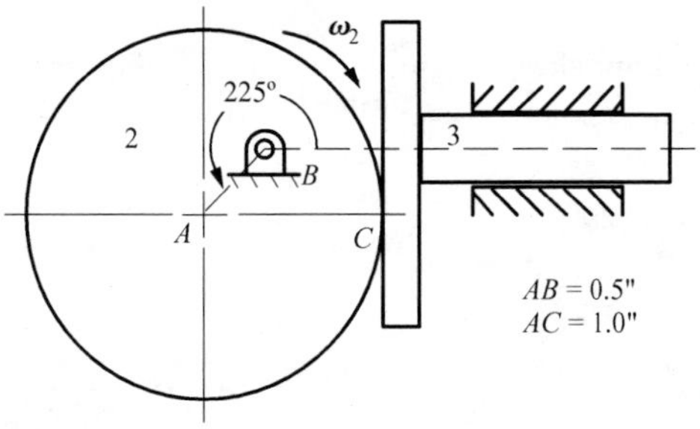

3.31 In the mechanism shown, $\boldsymbol{\omega}_2 = 20$ rad/s CCW. At the instant shown, point *D*, the center of curvature of link 3, lies directly above point *E*, and point *B* lies directly above point *A*. Determine $\boldsymbol{v}_{C_3/C_2}$ and $\boldsymbol{\omega}_3$ using: (a) equivalent linkages and (b) coincident points at *C*.

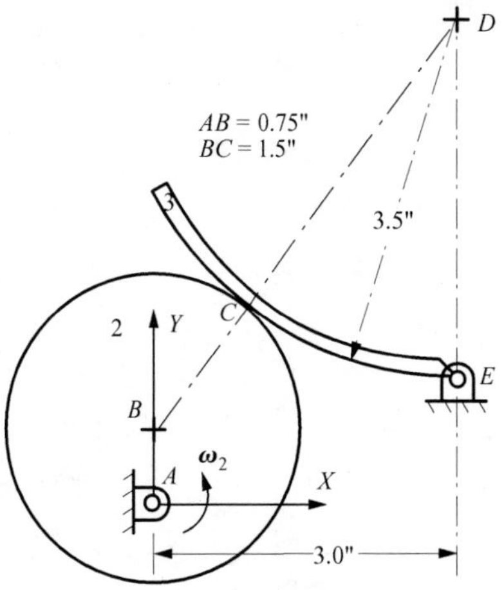

3.32 In the mechanism shown, $\boldsymbol{\omega}_2 = 100$ rad/s CCW and $\boldsymbol{\alpha}_2 = 20{,}000$ rad/s^2 CCW. In the position shown, find the velocity and acceleration of link 3 using: (a) equivalent linkages and (b) coincident points at *C*.

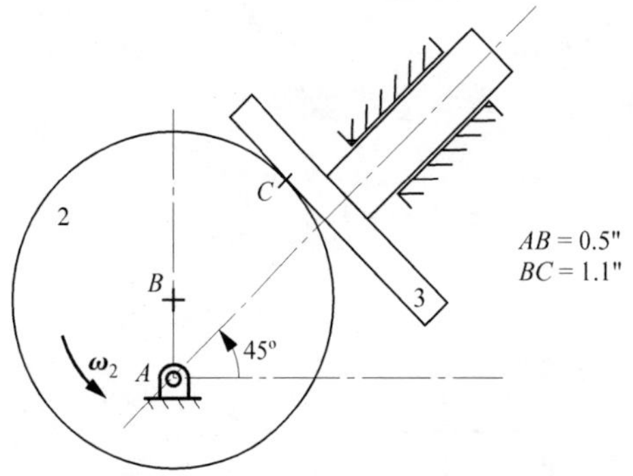

3.33 Locate all of the instant centers in the mechanism shown. If the cam (link 2) is turning CW at the rate of 900 rpm, determine the linear velocity of the follower.

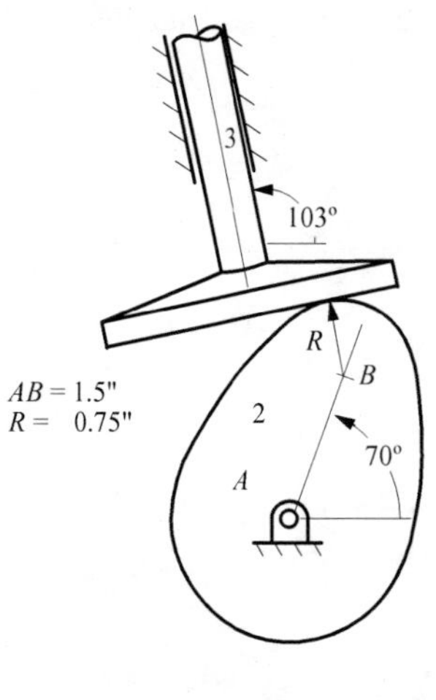

3.34 In the mechanism shown, $\boldsymbol{v}_{A_2} = 20$ in/s upward. Find $\boldsymbol{\omega}_5$ and ${}^3\boldsymbol{\omega}_4$. Indicate on link 4 the point that has zero velocity. In the drawing, H and G are the centers of curvature of links 4 and 5, respectively, corresponding to location D. F is the center of curvature of link 3 corresponding to C. Also, point G lies exactly above point E.

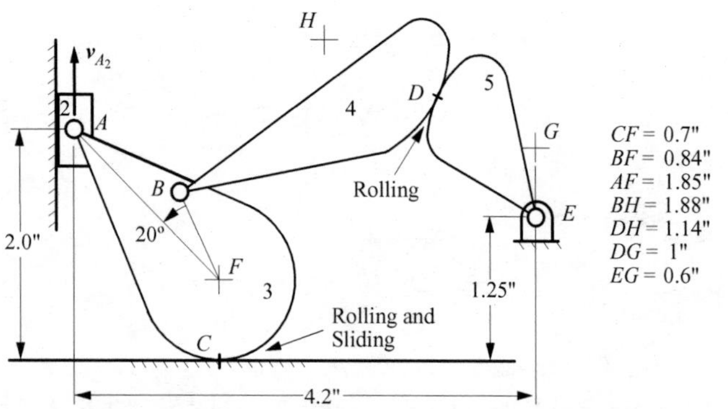

EXERCISE PROBLEMS INVOLVING GENERAL COINCIDENT POINTS

3.35 On the mechanism shown, link 4 slides on link 1, and link 3 slides on link 4 around the circle arc. Link 2 is pinned to links 1 and 3 as shown. Determine the location of the center of curvature of the path that point P_4 traces on link 2. Assume $\boldsymbol{\omega}_2 = 10$ rad/s CW and $\boldsymbol{\alpha}_2 = 100$ rad/s^2 CW.

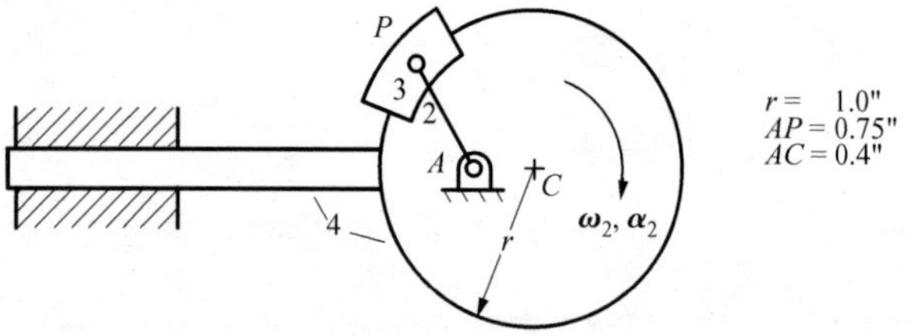

3.36 For the mechanism shown, find $\boldsymbol{\omega}_2$, $\boldsymbol{\alpha}_2$, $\boldsymbol{v}_{B_2}$, $\boldsymbol{a}_{B_2}$, $\boldsymbol{v}_{D_3}$, $\boldsymbol{a}_{D_3}$, and the location of the center of curvature of the path that point B_3 traces on link 2. Assume $AB = AC = 10$ cm, $CD = 14$ cm, $\boldsymbol{\omega}_3 = 1$ rad/s CCW, and $\boldsymbol{\alpha}_3 = 1$ rad/s^2 CW.

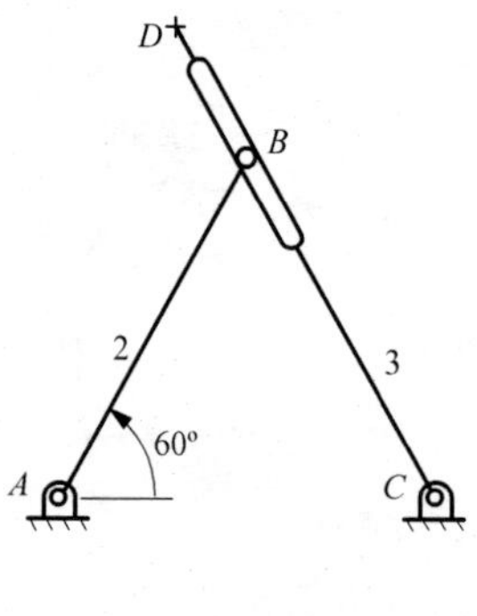

3.37 If $\boldsymbol{\omega}_2 = 10$ rad/s CCW (constant), find $\boldsymbol{v}_{B_2}$, $\boldsymbol{v}_{B_3}$, $\boldsymbol{a}_{B_3}$, and $\boldsymbol{a}_{C_4}$.

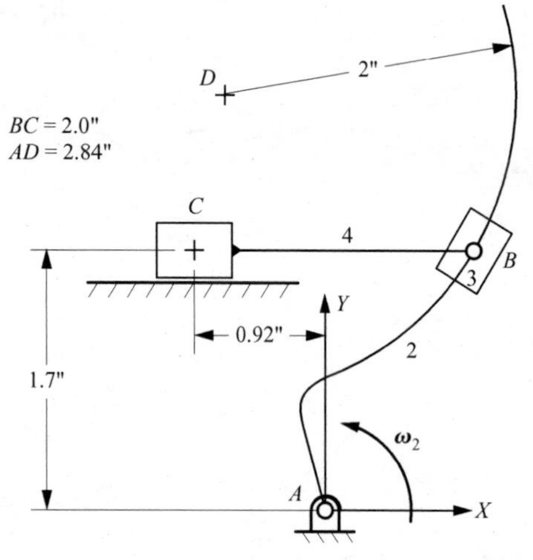

3.38 In the mechanism shown, $\boldsymbol{\omega}_2 = 10$ rad/s CW (constant). Determine the angular acceleration of link 3.

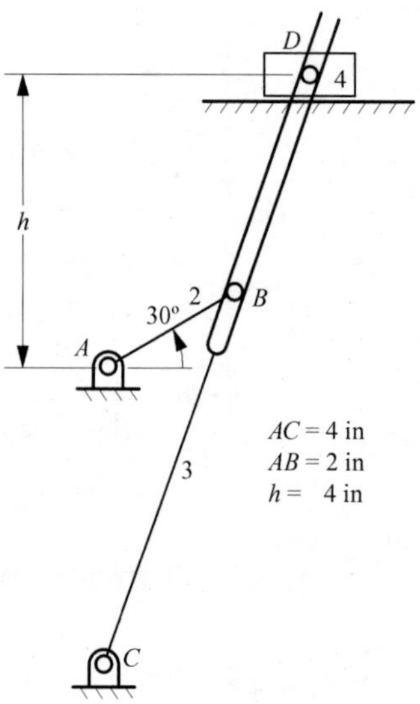

3.39 In the mechanism shown, slotted links 2 and 3 are independently driven at angular velocities of 30 and 20 rad/s CW and have angular accelerations of 900 and 400 rad/s^2 CW, respectively. Determine the acceleration of point B, the center of the pin carried at the intersection of the two slots.

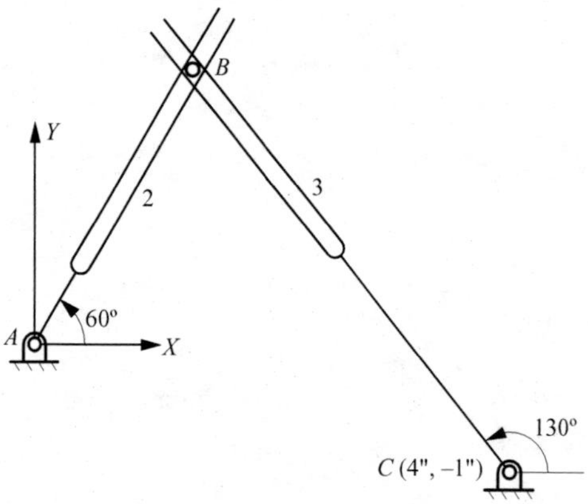

3.40 For the mechanism shown, find $\boldsymbol{\omega}_3$, $\boldsymbol{\alpha}_3$, $\boldsymbol{a}_{B_3}$, and the location of the center of curvature of the path that point B_3 traces on link 2.

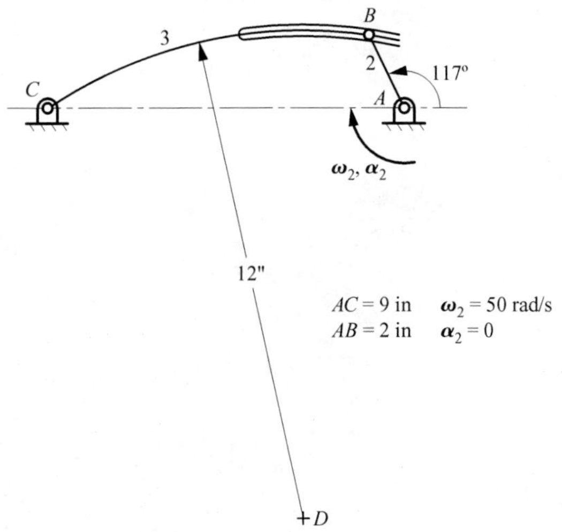

3.41 For the mechanism shown, points *C*, *B*, and *D* are collinear. Point B_2 moves in a curved slot on link 3. For the position given, find $\boldsymbol{\omega}_3$, $\boldsymbol{\alpha}_3$, $\boldsymbol{v}_{B_3}$, $\boldsymbol{a}_{B_3}$, $\boldsymbol{v}_{D_3}$, $\boldsymbol{a}_{D_3}$, and the location of the center of curvature of the path that point B_3 traces on Link 2. Assume

$AB = AC = 5\text{m},\ CD = 7\text{m},\ CE = 5.7\text{m}$

$\boldsymbol{\omega}_2 = 2$ rad/s CCW, $\boldsymbol{\alpha}_2 = 3$ rad/s^2 CCW

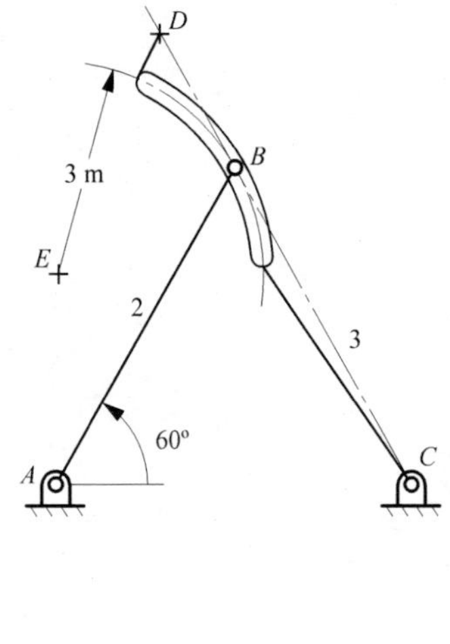

3.42 If the mechanism shown is drawn full scale, find $\boldsymbol{\omega}_3$, $\boldsymbol{\alpha}_3$, and the location of the center of curvature of the path that point B_3 traces on link 2. Assume that link 2 is driven at constant velocity.

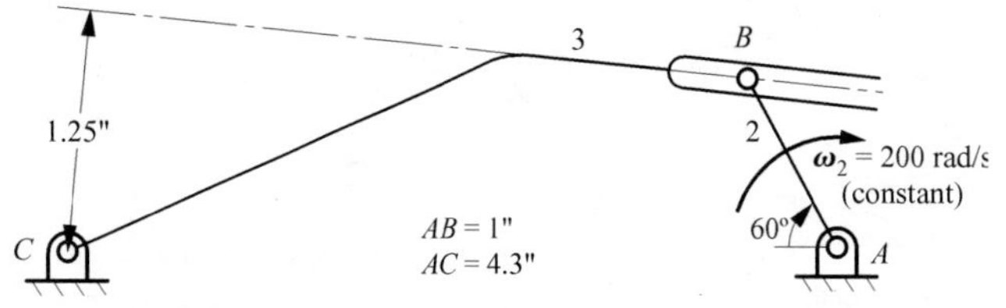

3.43 If $\boldsymbol{\omega}_2 = 20$ rad/s (constant) CCW, find $\boldsymbol{\omega}_3$, $\boldsymbol{\alpha}_3$, and the center of curvature of the path that C_3 traces on link 2.

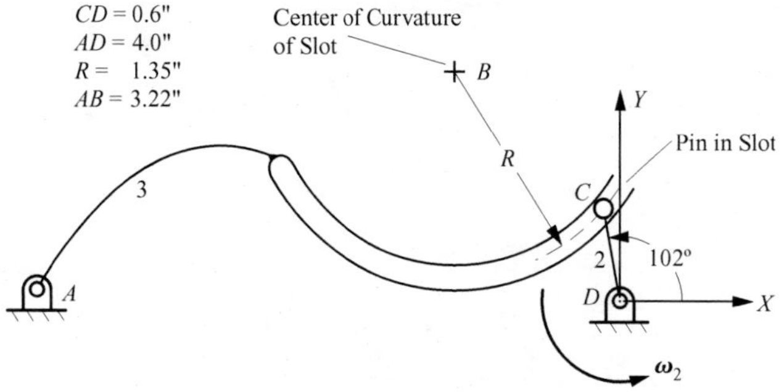

3.44 If $\boldsymbol{\omega}_2 = 10$ rad/s CW (constant), find $\boldsymbol{\alpha}_3$.

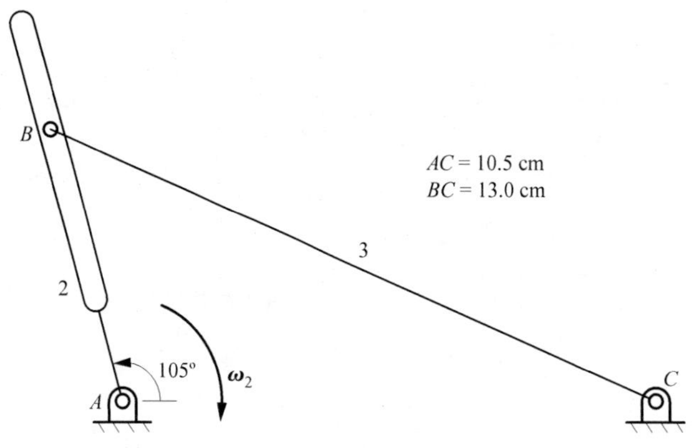

3.45 For the linkage shown, $\boldsymbol{\omega}_2 = 10$ rad/s CCW and $\boldsymbol{\alpha}_2 = 100$ rad/s^2 CCW. Determine $\boldsymbol{\omega}_3$ and $\boldsymbol{\alpha}_3$.

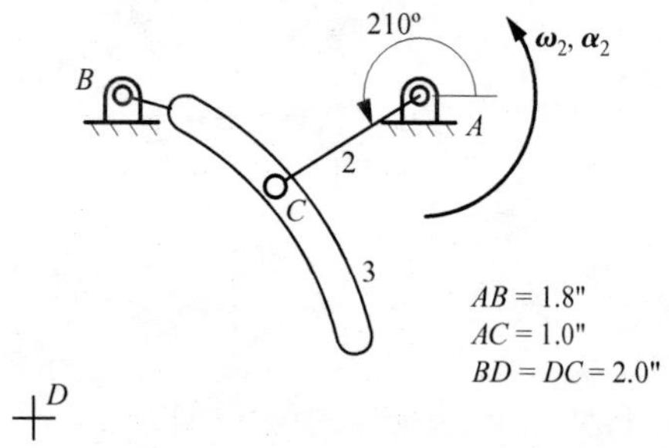

3.46 If $\boldsymbol{\omega}_2 = 10$ rad/s CW (constant), find

(a) $\boldsymbol{\omega}_3$,

(b) the center of curvature of the path that B_2 traces on link 3 (show on drawing),

(c) the center of curvature of the path that B_3 traces on link 2 (show on drawing).

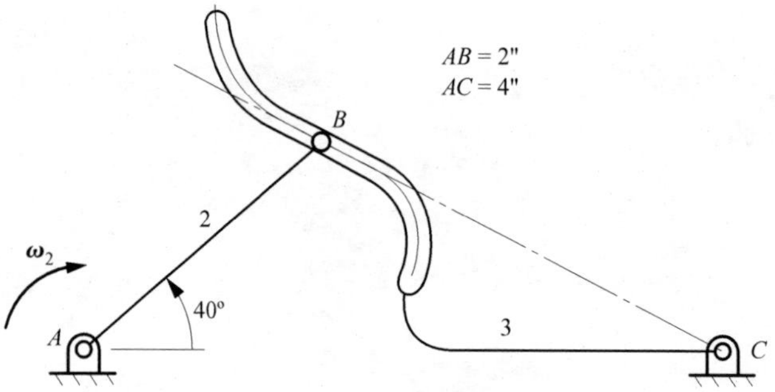

CHAPTER 4

INSTANT CENTERS OF VELOCITY

4.1 INTRODUCTION

At every instant during the motion of a rigid body in a plane, there exists a point that is instantaneously at rest. This point is called the instant center. The concept of an instant center of velocity for two bodies with planar motion was first discovered by Johann Bernoulli in 1742. This concept was later extended by Chasles in 1830 to include general spatial motion using the instantaneous screw axis concept.

The instant center technique for velocity analysis is particularly useful when only two or three velocities, or angular velocities, are of interest. It can be a very efficient technique, for example, for finding input-output velocity relationships of very complex mechanisms. When combined with virtual work, or conservation of energy (Chapter 13), it provides an efficient way to obtain input-output force or torque relationships. Instant centers are also very helpful when analyzing mechanisms with higher pairs, such as cam mechanisms, or gear trains. In principle, the instant center and velocity polygon techniques are *alternative* methods for solving the same set of problems. However, they are quite different techniques, and each is better suited to some situations than to others. Some experience is necessary to easily identify the most applicable technique for a particular problem.

It should be emphasized that instant centers of velocity are applicable to velocities only and are usually of little help if accelerations are ultimately of interest. If an acceleration analysis must be performed, then the velocity analysis should be conducted using one of the previously discussed traditional procedures based on vector methods.

Although the instant center of velocity has proved to be very useful in general mechanism velocity analysis, the corresponding instant center of acceleration has found little use. This is because, in general, more calculations are required to find the acceleration center than would be required to find the accelerations of interest using methods previously outlined. Therefore, only instant centers of velocity will be considered here.

4.2 DEFINITION

Given two bodies B and C moving with planar motion relative to each other in a reference frame R, there is, in general, only one location P in the plane of motion where the coincident points at a given instant have the same velocity with respect to the reference frame R. One coincident point is fixed to body B and the other is fixed to body C. This location is called the instant center of velocity for bodies B and C and is represented by I_{BC} or I_{CB}. If P is the instant center, then

$$^{R}\mathbf{v}_{P_B} = {}^{R}\mathbf{v}_{P_C}$$

or

$$^{R}\mathbf{v}_{P_B/P_C} = {}^{R}\mathbf{v}_{P_C/P_B} = 0$$

If the points are permanently attached to each other, they are called permanent instant centers. If the points are only momentarily coincident, the instant centers are called instantaneous instant centers.

4.3 EXISTENCE PROOF

The existence of an instant center between arbitrary links B and R may be inferred, and its location found, by the use of the relationship between the velocities of two points in body B. In the following, all velocities are defined in system R, so the left superscript designating the coordinate system will be omitted for simplicity. Then,

$$\mathbf{v}_{Q_B} = \mathbf{v}_{P_B} + \boldsymbol{\omega}_B \times \mathbf{r}_{Q/P}$$

Now, assume that Q is the instant center I_{RB}. Then, $\mathbf{v}_{Q_B} = 0 = \mathbf{v}_{I_{RB}}$ and

$$-\mathbf{v}_{P_B} = \boldsymbol{\omega}_B \times \mathbf{r}_{Q/P} \tag{4.1}$$

From Section 2.4, we know that the radial component of the relative acceleration between two points P and Q on the same rigid link B is

$$\boldsymbol{\omega}_B \times \left(\boldsymbol{\omega}_B \times \mathbf{r}_{Q/P}\right) = -\omega_B^2 \mathbf{r}_{Q/P}$$

Therefore, cross multiplication of both sides of Eq. (4.1) by $\boldsymbol{\omega}_B$ gives

$$\boldsymbol{\omega}_B \times \left(\boldsymbol{\omega}_B \times \mathbf{r}_{Q/P}\right) = -\boldsymbol{\omega}_B \times \mathbf{v}_{P_B} = -\omega_B^2 \mathbf{r}_{Q/P}$$

or

$$\mathbf{r}_{Q/P} = \frac{\boldsymbol{\omega}_B \times \mathbf{v}_{P_B}}{\omega_B^2}$$

In planar motion $\boldsymbol{\omega}_B \times \mathbf{v}_{P_B}$ is normal to $\mathbf{v}_{P_B}$ and may be written $(\omega_B)(v_{P_B})\mathbf{n}$, where $\mathbf{n}$ is a unit vector normal to $\mathbf{v}_{P_B}$ with the sense given by visualizing $\mathbf{v}_{P_B}$ rotating about its tail in the $\boldsymbol{\omega}_B$ direction. Hence

$$\mathbf{r}_{Q/P} = \frac{v_{P_B}}{\omega_B}\mathbf{n}$$

Thus, the distance, $r_{P/Q}$, in Fig. 4.1 from the instant center, I_{BR}, to point P is v_{P_B}/ω_B and the line IP is normal to $\mathbf{v}_{P_B}$. Its sense is such that rotation of $\mathbf{r}_{P/Q}$ about I in the $\boldsymbol{\omega}_B$ direction produces $\mathbf{v}_{P_B}$.

If more than one location in the plane of motion is found to be an instant center for two bodies, then those two bodies, for velocity analysis purposes, can be considered to be instantaneously fixed to each other. That is, if more than one location is an instant center, then all locations are instant centers.

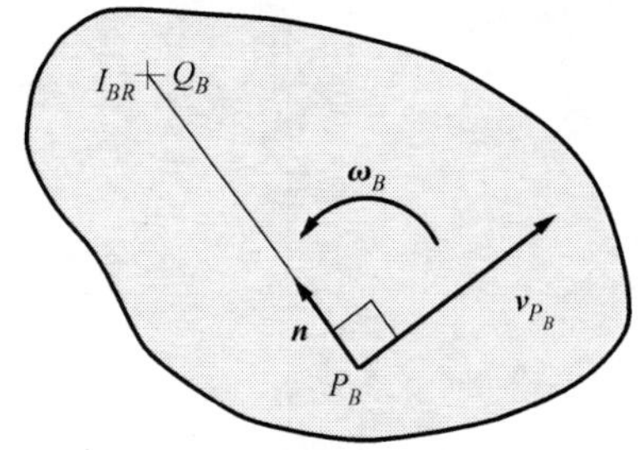

FIGURE 4.1 Proof of the existence of an instant center of velocity in planar motion.

However, if no finite location can be found that qualifies as an instant center of relative motion of two bodies, then the two bodies are translating with planar motion with respect to each other. In this case, the instant center can be considered to be located at infinity and reached by a line drawn perpendicular to the relative velocity vector between two arbitrary coincident points in the two bodies considered.

Instant centers are useful because they permit velocities to be computed easily. For example, if we know the velocity of point P_B by analysis, we know the velocity of P_R directly.

4.4 LOCATION OF AN INSTANT CENTER FROM THE DIRECTIONS OF TWO VELOCITIES

Assume that we know the velocities of two points (P and Q) in body C where the velocities are defined relative to the coordinate system in a second body B. This condition is shown in Fig. 4.2. We can then search for some point in C that has zero velocity relative to body B. The location of this point is the instant center designated by I_{BC} or, in the development here, it can be represented simply as I. To find the instant center location, let I_B be the point in body B and I_C be the coincident point in body C. We can write relative velocity expressions for points P and Q as follows:

$$^B\mathbf{v}_{P_C} = {}^B\mathbf{v}_{P_C/I_B} = {}^B\mathbf{v}_{P_C/I_C} + {}^B\mathbf{v}_{I_C/I_B}$$

and

$$^B\mathbf{v}_{Q_C} = {}^B\mathbf{v}_{Q_C/I_B} = {}^B\mathbf{v}_{Q_C/I_C} + {}^B\mathbf{v}_{I_C/I_B}$$

However, by definition of the instant center,

$$^B\mathbf{v}_{I_C/I_B} = {}^B\mathbf{v}_{I_C} = 0$$

so that

$$^B\mathbf{v}_{P_C/I_B} = {}^B\mathbf{v}_{P_C/I_C} = {}^B\boldsymbol{\omega}_C \times \mathbf{r}_{P_C/I_C}$$

and

$$^B\mathbf{v}_{Q_C/I_B} = {}^B\mathbf{v}_{Q_C/I_C} = {}^B\boldsymbol{\omega}_C \times \mathbf{r}_{Q_C/I_C}$$

By definition of the cross product, ${}^B\mathbf{v}_{P_C/I_C}$ must be perpendicular to $\mathbf{r}_{P_C/I_C}$, and ${}^B\mathbf{v}_{Q_C/I_C}$ must be perpendicular to $\mathbf{r}_{Q_C/I_C}$. The location of the instant center (I_{BC}) is given by the intersection of the two perpendicular lines as shown in Fig. 4.2.

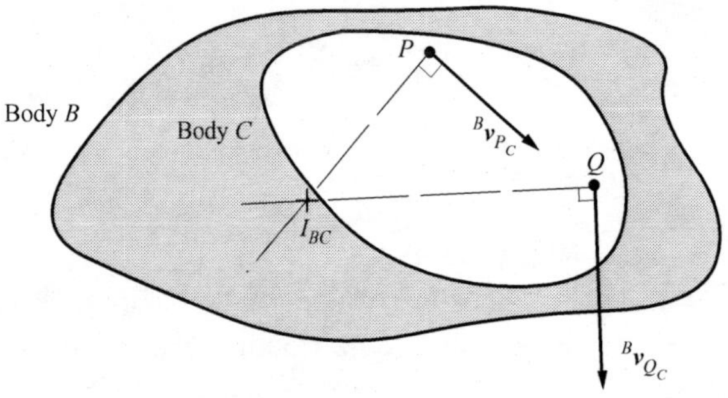

FIGURE 4.2 Location of the instant center given the directions of the velocities of two points.

4.5 INSTANT CENTER AT A REVOLUTE JOINT

The center of rotation at a revolute joint, I_{BC}, has the same velocity whether it is considered to be part of link B or link C. Therefore, it qualifies as a permanent instant center. This is indicated in Fig. 4.3.

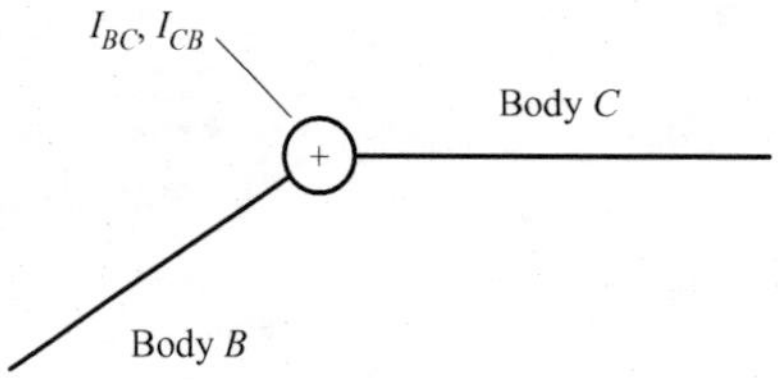

FIGURE 4.3 Permanent instant center.

4.6 INSTANT CENTER OF A CURVED SLIDER

If body B is a block moving on a circular arc on body C as shown in Fig. 4.4, then the center of the arc is a stationary location common to both bodies. Therefore, this location qualifies as a permanent instant center. If the curve is not circular at the location of interest, the curve can be replaced by its osculating circle (for velocities and accelerations) and the center of the osculating circle or center of curvature of the path at the given point would be the instant center. Actually, a circular slider is kinematically equivalent to a revolute joint. The center of the equivalent revolute is the center of curvature. That is, it is the instant center. A non-circular slide is realizable only as a higher pair, and the center of curvature is not a permanent instant center.

4.7 INSTANT CENTER OF A PRISMATIC JOINT

If the radius of curvature, ρ, in the case of the curved slider is allowed to become very large, the arc will approach a straight line. Also, the location of the instant center will tend toward infinity. However, the velocity of P relative to system B will still remain perpendicular to the line from P to the instant center. Therefore, if we know the direction of the velocity of *any* point P relative to system B, we can find one locus for the instant center; that is, it must lie on a line perpendicular to the velocity vector as shown in Fig. 4.5.

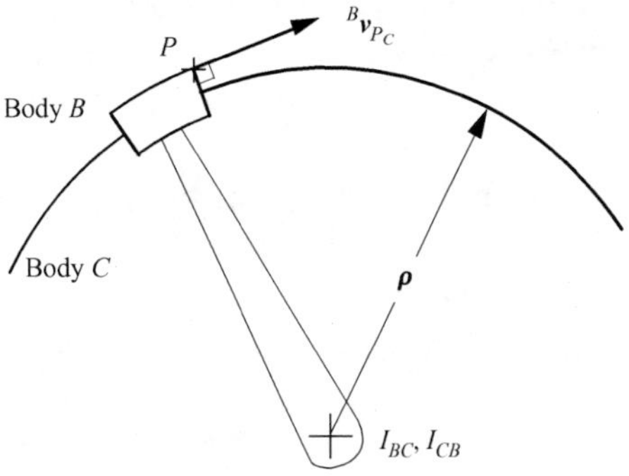

FIGURE 4.4 Instant center of a curved slide.

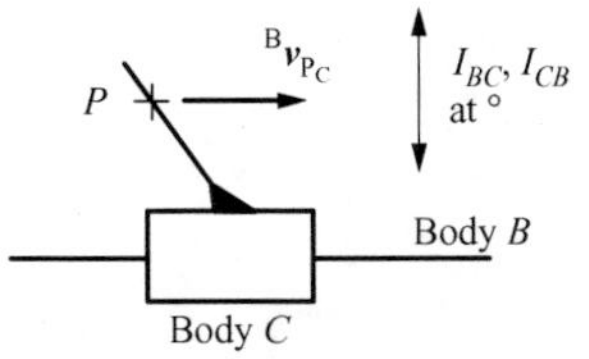

FIGURE 4.5 Instant center of a prismatic joint.

Note that the location of the line to infinity is unimportant; only the direction is defined by the velocity direction. This can be thought of as being the parallax phenomenon in which the direction to a distant object appears to remain the same, regardless of the motion of the observer.

4.8 INSTANT CENTER OF A ROLLING CONTACT PAIR

The instant center of pure rolling contact between two rigid bodies *B* and *C* is located at the point of contact of the two bodies as shown in Fig. 4.6. This is a direct consequence of the rolling condition that the two points in contact be at rest relative to one another. The instant center for the relative motion of involute spur gears is at the pitch point: the point of rolling contact between their pitch circles.

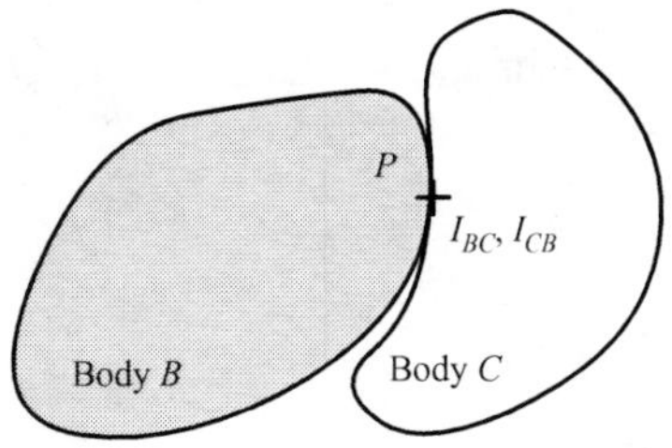

FIGURE 4.6 Instant center of a rolling contact.

4.9 INSTANT CENTER OF A GENERAL CAM-PAIR CONTACT

When two planar bodies (*B* and *C* in Fig. 4.7) are held in general cam contact, it is assumed that the bodies will neither penetrate each other nor separate. In general, the bodies both roll on each other and slide on each other. If sliding is involved, the direction of relative sliding must be along the common tangent of the profiles of the two bodies, as shown in Fig. 4.7.

If P is the contact point location, then the velocity of point P_C, relative to body B as well as the velocity of point P_B relative to body C will lie along the common tangent. Therefore, the instant center must be located on a line perpendicular to the common tangent at the contact point P. This means that the instant center must lie on a line through the centers of curvature (O_C and O_B) corresponding to P in each of the two bodies.

To locate precisely the position of I_{BC}, some further information about the relative motion of bodies B and C is required. For example, assume that body B is link 2 and body C is link 3 and that links 2 and 3 are both connected to the frame by revolute joints as shown in Fig. 4.8.

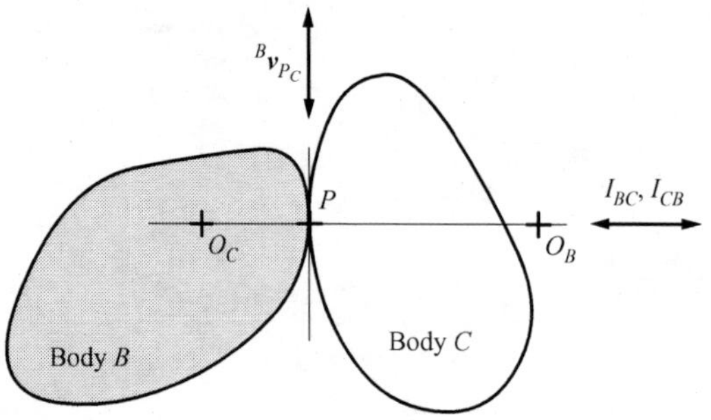

FIGURE 4.7 Relationship between instant centers and sliding velocity in cam contact.

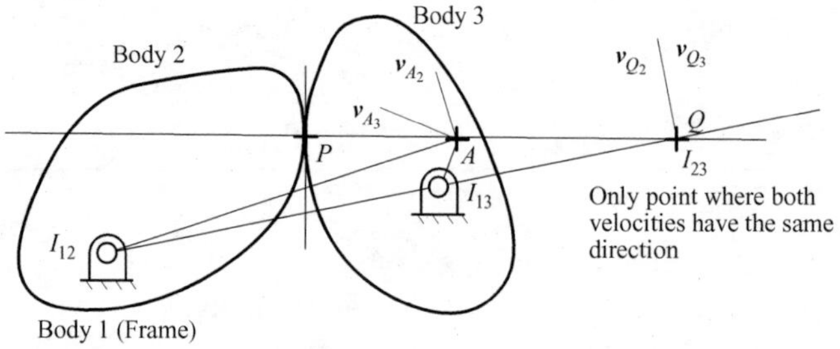

FIGURE 4.8 The instant center location between two frame-mounted cams.

If we arbitrarily pick the point A as a candidate for the instant center, we see that the velocities $\mathbf{v}_{A_2}$ and $\mathbf{v}_{A_3}$ cannot be equal because they are not in the same direction. The only location where they can be equal in direction is at the point Q on a line through the two pivots. Note that the two fixed pivots are the instant centers I_{12} and I_{13}.

4.10 CENTRODES

As two bodies, B and C, move relative to each other, I_{BC} traces a path on each of the bodies (path BC_B on body B and BC_C on body C). These paths are the centrodes for the two bodies. At any instant, the two paths will be in contact with each other at the instant center where there is zero relative velocity between the two bodies and therefore between the two centrodes. That is, the instant center acts as a point of rolling contact between the two centrodes. This means that, as the two bodies move, the two centrodes will roll on each other. Conversely, the relative motion of the two bodies can be faithfully reproduced by rolling one centrode on the other no matter how the original motion was produced. Therefore, the analysis of the relative motion of two bodies moving with planar motion can always be transformed to the study of two bodies rolling on each other. Note that as the two centrodes for links 2 and 3 roll on each other, the contact point (I_{23}) and the instant centers I_{12} and I_{13} will be collinear, as illustrated in Fig. 4.8.

These concepts can be extended into spatial motion in which the instant center becomes an instantaneous screw axis (ISA), and the loci of the ISAs in the two bodies are ruled surfaces called axodes. These axodes roll on each other in a direction perpendicular to their generating instantaneous screw axes as well as sliding relative to each other along their instantaneous screw axes.

An example of the fixed and moving centrodes associated with the coupler of a four-bar linkage is shown in Fig. 4.9. This shows the centrodes generated by instant center I_{13}. The centrodes in Fig. 4.9 are very simple, but this is not the typical case. For crank-rocker mechanisms, the centrodes will extend to infinity (when the crank and rocker are parallel) in two directions, and for drag-link mechanisms, the centrodes can form multiple loops. Typical examples are shown in Figs. 4.10 and 4.11. These centrodes were generated with the MATLAB program *centrodes.m* included on the disk with this book.

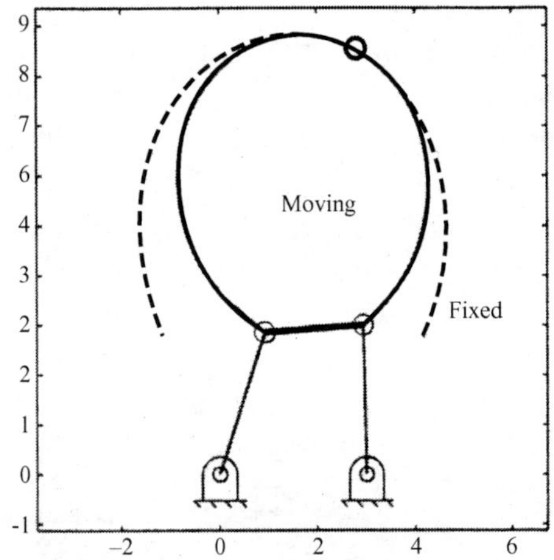

FIGURE 4.9 Centrodes associated with instant center I_{13} for a simple four-bar linkage.

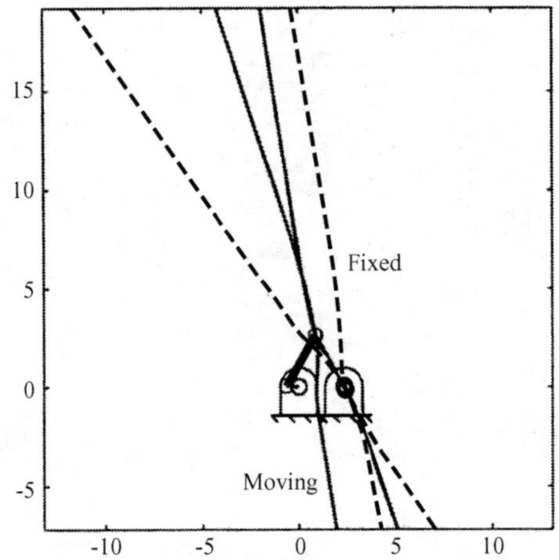

FIGURE 4.10 Centrodes associated with instant center I_{13} for a crank-rocker four-bar linkage.

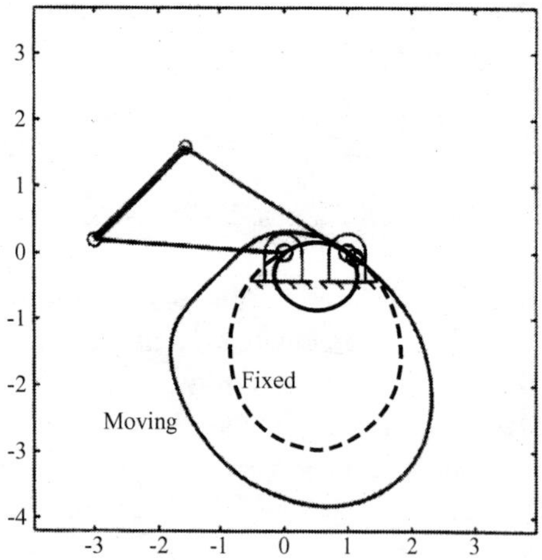

FIGURE 4.11 Centrodes associated with instant center I_{13} for a drag-link four-bar linkage.

Another example of centrodes is shown in the model in Fig. 4.12. The mechanism model is a six-bar linkage, and the noncircular gears attached to the two frame-mounted links correspond to the centrodes of relative motion of those links. The motion of the two links attached to the gears is the same relative to the frame and to each other whether the linkage is present without the gears or with the gears present but without the linkage.

FIGURE 4.12 Six-bar linkage model with centrodes represented by noncircular gears. The gears roll on each other at the pitch points, and the pitch point is the instant center between the two frame-mounted cranks.

4.11 THE KENNEDY–ARONHOLDT THEOREM

If we have n bodies and we take them two at a time such that $I_{AB} = I_{BA}$, then the total number of instant centers is given by

$$N_{IC} = \frac{n(n-1)}{2}$$

Because of the large number of instant centers (ICs) occurring in a mechanism with a large number of links, it is desirable to develop a procedure that helps to identify the locations of the instant centers in a systematic manner. This can be done using the results of the Kennedy–Aronholdt theorem.

In the late 19th century, Kennedy (England) and Aronholdt (Germany) greatly extended the usefulness of instant centers by discovering independently the theorem of three centers. The theorem is stated as follows:

If three bodies are in relative planar motion (or two bodies moving relative to each other and to the fixed reference frame), there are three instant centers pertaining to the relative motion of pairs of those bodies. Those three instant centers are collinear.

Thus, in Fig. 4.13, given three bodies A, B, and C moving with planar motion in reference frame R, the three instant centers I_{AB}, I_{AC}, and I_{BC} all lie on the same straight line in the plane. To prove the theorem, it is necessary to recognize that the instant center is really two coincident points. One of these two points is embedded in each of the two laminae for which the instant center describes the relative motion. Hence, in Fig. 4.13:

I_{AB} is two points common to A and B.

I_{AC} is two points common to A and C.

I_{BC} is two points common to B and C.

Also,

$$^R\mathbf{v}_{(I_{AB})_A} = {}^R\mathbf{v}_{(I_{AB})_B}$$
$$^R\mathbf{v}_{(I_{AC})_A} = {}^R\mathbf{v}_{(I_{AC})_C}$$
$$^R\mathbf{v}_{(I_{BC})_B} = {}^R\mathbf{v}_{(I_{BC})_C}$$

Assume that we know the locations of I_{AB} and I_{AC} and we want to find I_{BC}. Relative to link A, we can first write

$$^A\mathbf{v}_{(I_{BC})_B} = {}^A\mathbf{v}_{(I_{BC})_C}$$

or

$$^A\mathbf{v}_{(I_{BC})_B} = {}^A\mathbf{v}_{(I_{BC})_B/(I_{AB})_A} = {}^A\mathbf{v}_{(I_{BC})_B/(I_{AB})_B} = {}^A\boldsymbol{\omega}_B \times \mathbf{r}_{(I_{BC})/(I_{AB})}$$

Also,

$$^A\mathbf{v}_{(I_{BC})_C} = {}^A\mathbf{v}_{(I_{BC})_C/(I_{AC})_A} = {}^A\mathbf{v}_{(I_{BC})_C/(I_{AC})_C} = {}^A\boldsymbol{\omega}_C \times \mathbf{r}_{(I_{BC})/(I_{AC})}$$

or equating the two relationships, we get

$$ {}^{A}\boldsymbol{\omega}_C \times \boldsymbol{r}_{I_{BC}/I_{AC}} = {}^{A}\boldsymbol{\omega}_B \times \boldsymbol{r}_{I_{BC}/I_{AB}} $$

Since ${}^{B}\boldsymbol{\omega}_C$ is parallel to ${}^{A}\boldsymbol{\omega}_B$, then the $\boldsymbol{r}$'s must also be parallel to make the cross products equal. Because both of the $\boldsymbol{r}$'s pass through I_{BC}, they must be collinear. This can happen only if I_{AB}, I_{AC}, and I_{BC} all lie on the same line.

The Kennedy–Aronholdt theorem can be used in the following way to find instant centers. Assume that we have two groups of three links such that two links are common to both groups. For example, as shown in Fig. 4.14, if we have I_{45} and I_{47} and I_{35} and I_{37}, links 5 and 7 are common to both groups. We know that I_{57} must lie on a line through I_{45}, and I_{47}, and it must also lie on the line through I_{35} and I_{37}. The location is defined by the intersection of the two lines.

Therefore, by selecting two pairs of appropriate instant centers, we can locate the instant center that is common to the two groups of links. A way in which the Kennedy–Aronholdt theorem can be used is illustrated by the following example.

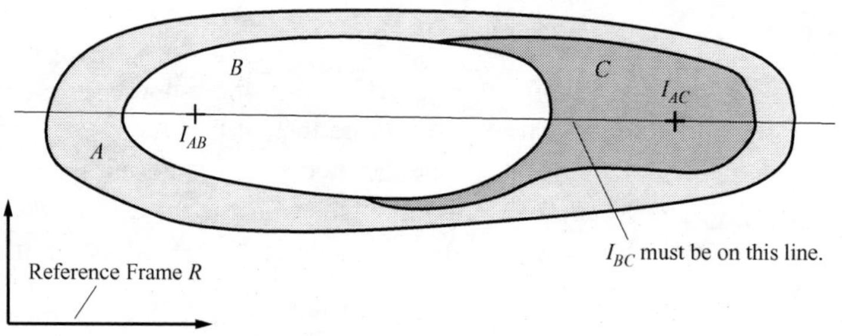

FIGURE 4.13 The Kennedy–Aronholdt theorem.

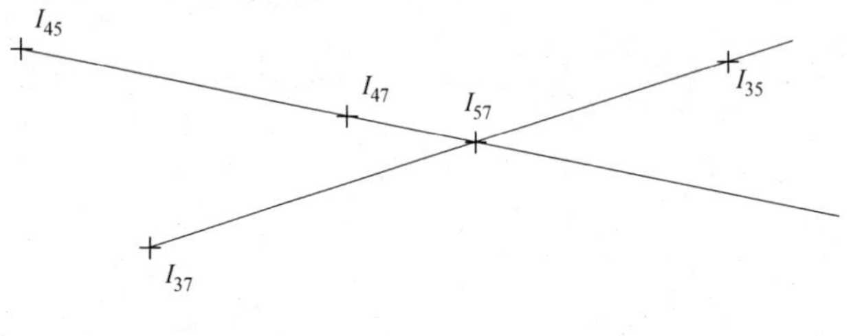

FIGURE 4.14 Triplets of instant centers.

EXAMPLE 4.1
Locating Instant Centers for a Four-Bar Linkage

Locate all instant centers of the four-bar linkage in the position shown in Fig. 4.15.

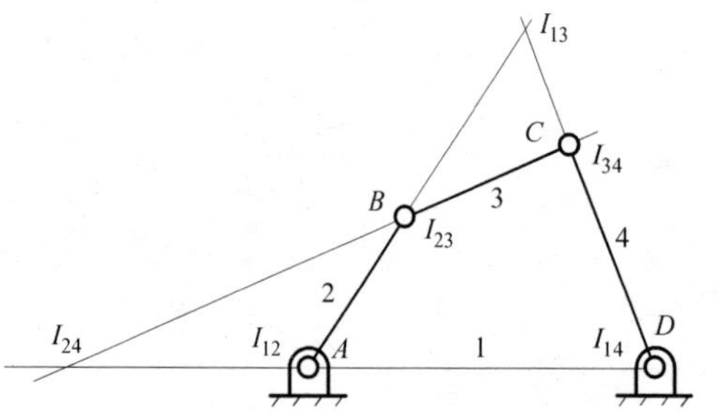

FIGURE 4.15 Application of the Kennedy–Aronholdt theorem to the location of all instant centers of a four-bar linkage.

Solution By inspection, I_{12} is at A, I_{23} at B, I_{34} at C, and I_{14} at D. Thus, four of the six instant centers are already identified. To locate I_{13}, note that it is collinear with I_{12} and I_{23} and also with I_{14} and I_{34}. Thus it is at the intersection of BC and AD. Similarly, to locate I_{24}, note that it is collinear with I_{23} and I_{34} and also with I_{12} and I_{14}.

A set of three collinear instant centers always shares the same three subscripts, each subscript appearing on two instant centers. Given two instant centers with a common subscript, the third center, which completes the collinear set, has the two subscripts that are not common to the other two centers.

4.12 CIRCLE DIAGRAM AS A STRATEGY FOR FINDING INSTANT CENTERS

When the number of bodies is large, it is helpful to use some kind of bookkeeping method to help find all of the instant centers. One such method is the circle method, which is based directly on the Kennedy–Aronholdt theorem. The procedure is illustrated on the four-bar linkage in Fig. 4.16 as follows:

1. Draw the kinematic diagram for the mechanism to be analyzed.
2. Draw a circle of arbitrary radius and place tick marks representing all of the mechanism member symbols approximately equally spaced around the perimeter of the circle.
3. By inspection, determine as many instant centers as possible, and draw a straight line between the corresponding numbers on the circle. For example, if I_{12} is known, then a line is drawn between symbols 1 and 2.
4. If a line can be drawn between two points on the circle such that the line is the only unknown side of *two* triangles, the instant center represented by that line lies at the intersection of the two lines drawn through the instant center pairs that are identified by the two known sides of each triangle. Once the instant center is located, the appropriate two points on the circle diagram are connected.
5. Repeat the procedure in step 4 until all of the instant centers of interest are found.

As a second example, consider the slider-crank mechanism shown in Fig. 4.17. Again, the instant centers to be found are I_{24} and I_{13}. These can be found directly; however, it is necessary to note that I_{14} is located at infinity along a line perpendicular to the slider velocity direction given.

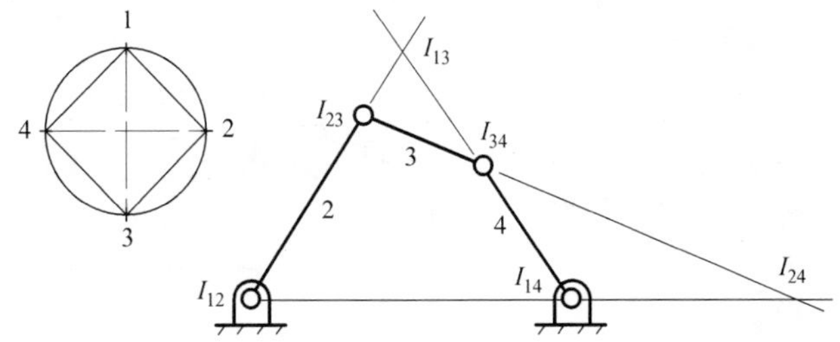

FIGURE 4.16 Use of the circle diagram when locating instant centers.

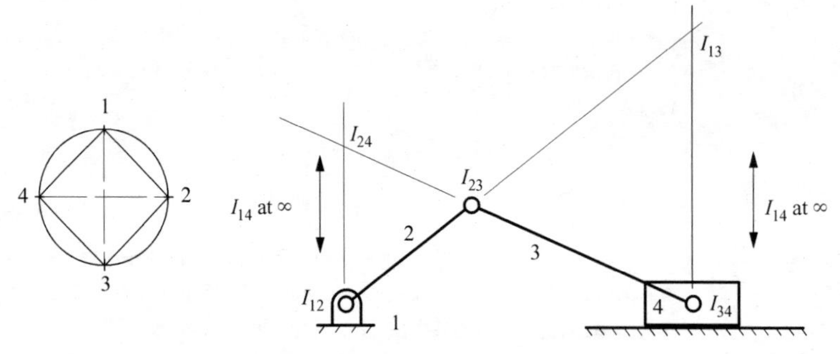

FIGURE 4.17 The instant centers of a slider-crank linkage.

4.13 USING INSTANT CENTERS: THE ROTATING-RADIUS METHOD

Once the proper instant centers are found, these can be used to find the velocities of selected points in a rigid body. This can be done analytically; however, graphical methods are generally much faster to use. An especially useful method for finding velocities is the rotating-radius method. To develop the method, assume we have an arbitrary link moving relative to the reference system. For the sake of illustration, assume that the link is 3 and the reference link is the frame (link 1). Let points P and Q be any points fixed to link 3 as shown in Fig. 4.18. Then, we can write

$$\boldsymbol{v}_{P_3/Q_3} = \boldsymbol{\omega}_3 \times \boldsymbol{r}_{P_3/Q_3} = \boldsymbol{v}_{P_3} - \boldsymbol{v}_{Q_3}$$

and this is perpendicular to the line from P to Q. If point Q_3 has zero velocity relative to link 1, then

$$\boldsymbol{v}_{P_3/Q_3} = \boldsymbol{v}_{P_3}$$

However, the only point in link 3 that has zero velocity relative to the frame is I_{13}. Therefore,

$$\boldsymbol{v}_{P_3} = \boldsymbol{\omega}_3 \times \boldsymbol{r}_{P_3/I_{13}}$$

Because point P was *any* arbitrary point in link 3, this equation holds for *all* points in link 3. Therefore, if we know the angular velocity of the link and the instant center relative to the frame, we can compute the absolute velocity of any point in the body. Furthermore, the direction of the absolute velocity is perpendicular to the line from the point to the instant center.

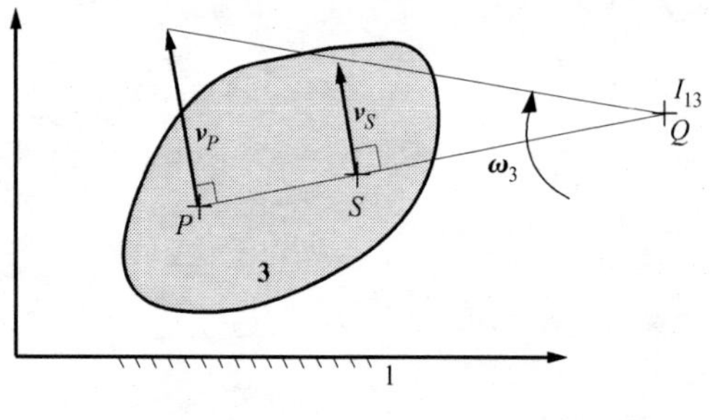

FIGURE 4.18 The rotating-radius method.

For other points, only the vector $\boldsymbol{r}_{P_3/I_{13}}$ will change as P changes. Considering the magnitude of the velocity, we have

$$\left|\boldsymbol{v}_{P_3}\right| = \left|\boldsymbol{\omega}_3\right|\left|\boldsymbol{r}_{P_3/I_{13}}\right|$$

Because $\boldsymbol{\omega}_3$ is the same for all points in the link, the magnitude of the velocity for any other point S is given by

$$\left|\boldsymbol{v}_{S_3}\right| = \left|\boldsymbol{\omega}_3\right|\left|\boldsymbol{r}_{S_3/I_{13}}\right|$$

Therefore, dividing the two equations gives

$$\frac{\left|\boldsymbol{v}_{P_3}\right|}{\left|\boldsymbol{v}_{S_3}\right|} = \frac{\left|\boldsymbol{r}_{P_3/I_{13}}\right|}{\left|\boldsymbol{r}_{S_3/I_{13}}\right|}$$

or

$$\left|\boldsymbol{v}_{S_3}\right| = \left|\boldsymbol{v}_{P_3}\right|\frac{\left|\boldsymbol{r}_{S_3/I_{13}}\right|}{\left|\boldsymbol{r}_{P_3/I_{13}}\right|}$$

This magnitude applies to any point that is the same distance from the instant center. The magnitude of the velocity is directly proportional to its distance from the instant center. Hence if two points in the rigid body have the same $|\boldsymbol{r}_{S_3/I_{13}}|$, they will have the same magnitude of velocity $|\boldsymbol{v}_{S_3}|$; however, the directions of their velocities will differ because the velocity is perpendicular to the line from the point to the instant center. This is illustrated by S and S' in Fig. 4.19. The actual direction of the velocity is obtained by recognizing that all points will appear to rotate about the instant center relative to the frame.

This theory is the basis for the rotating-radius method. The basic procedure is to find the magnitude of the velocity of one point in the rigid body and draw that velocity vector to scale on the link. The velocity of any other point on the body can then be found by recognizing that the magnitude of the velocity relative to the frame is proportional to the distance from the instant center. Proportional triangles can be drawn by using the line from the original point to the instant center as a baseline. Alternately, the line from the new point to the instant center can be used as a baseline.

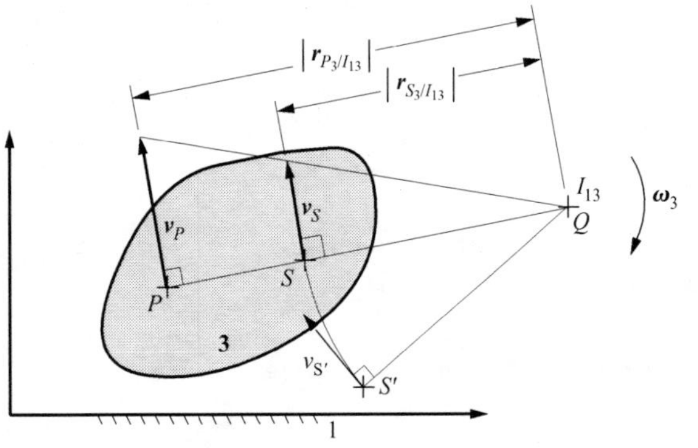

FIGURE 4.19 The rotating-radius method of obtaining the velocity of a point in a body relative to a reference frame (or another body) given the location of the instant center of the body and the velocity of some other point in the body relative to that frame.

EXAMPLE 4.2 *Using the Rotating-Radius Method for Velocities*

Given the compound linkage shown in Fig. 4.20, the velocity of point A is given as shown. Find the velocity of point B.

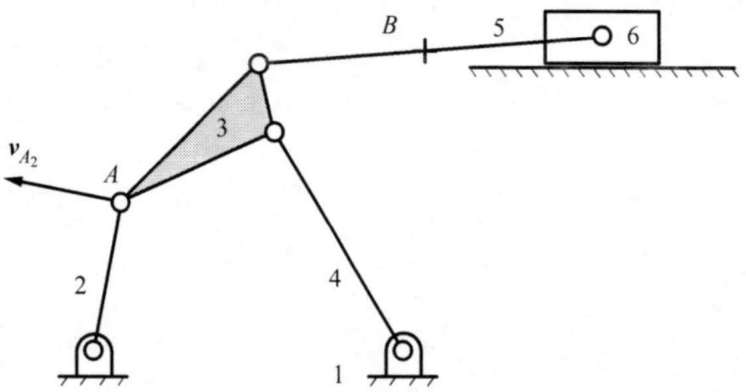

FIGURE 4.20 Compound linkage for Example 4.2.

Solution

The first step in the procedure is to determine the instant centers that are needed. This can be done by rewriting the given and desired information in terms of the link numbers and frame number. That is, we are given the velocity v_{A_2} and we want to find v_{B_5}. Here we see that the reference system is 1 and the two links involved are 2 and 5. In this problem and in general problems using instant centers, we will need to locate three instant centers:

1. I_{12}, the instant center between the reference frame and the link where the input information is given,
2. I_{15}, the instant center between the reference frame and the link where the velocity is to be found, and
3. I_{25}, the instant center between the link where a velocity is specified and the link where the velocity is to be found.

When the linkage is analyzed, it is apparent that I_{12} can be found by inspection. Therefore, only I_{25} and I_{15} need to be constructed. This is done by first locating I_{13} using I_{12} and I_{23}, and I_{14} and I_{34}. Next, I_{15} is found using I_{13} and I_{35}, and I_{16} and I_{56}. Finally, I_{25} is found using I_{15} and I_{12} and I_{23} and I_{35}. The construction lines are shown in Fig. 4.21.

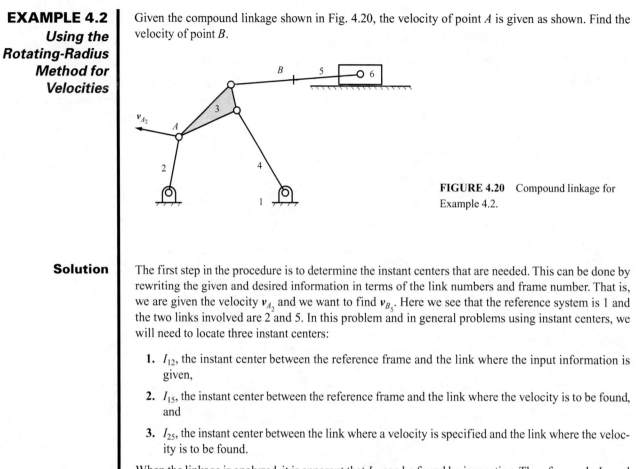

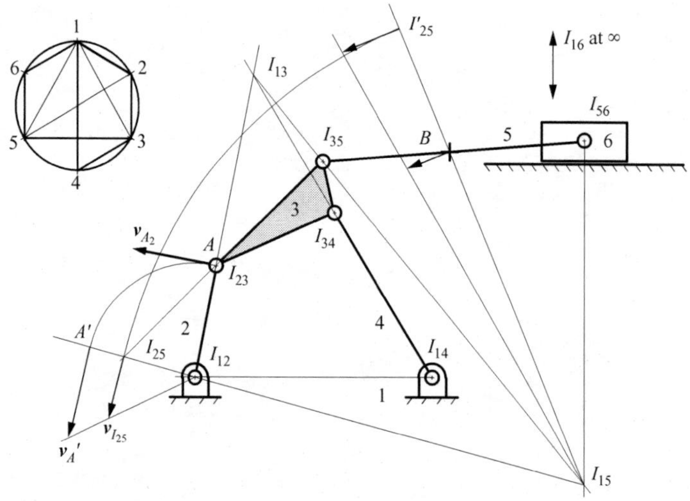

FIGURE 4.21 Use of the rotating-radius method in a compound linkage.

After I_{25} is located, the velocity of I_{25} is found by rotating the triangle formed by the sides v_{A_2} and $\overrightarrow{I_{12}A}$ about I_{12} onto the baseline through I_{12} and I_{25}. The velocity of I_{25} is then found using proportional triangles. Next, the triangle defined by sides $v_{I_{25}}$ and $\overrightarrow{I_{15}I_{25}}$ is rotated about I_{15} onto the baseline through I_{15} and B. The velocity of B is then determined using proportional triangles. Note that when the velocity of I_{25} is found, the instant center is treated as a point in link 2, that is, $(I_{25})_2$. However, when the velocity of B_5 is to be found, the instant center is treated as a point in link 5. This illustrates the fact that the instant center location defines the location of two points, one in link 2 and the other in link 5; however, both points have the same velocity.

EXAMPLE 4.3 *Using Instant Centers to Analyze a Stephenson-II Six Bar Linkage*

Consider the Stephenson-II six-bar linkage in Fig. 4.22. Assume that ω_2 is given and we want to find ω_5. This linkage has the characteristics of those described in Section 2.9; that is, the driving link is not included in any four-link loop. The following solution method should be compared to the inversion method in Section 2.9.

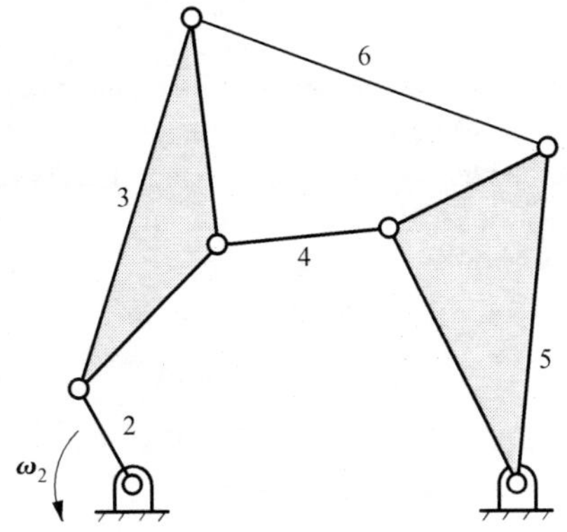

FIGURE 4.22 Stephenson-II six-bar linkage for Example 4.3.

Solution

The use of instant centers to solve this problem is especially interesting because the linkage cannot be analyzed using the usual vector polygon approach described earlier.

Again, we need to determine which instant centers are required to solve the problem. Looking at the information that is given and that is to be found, we see that three links (1, 2, 5) are identified. Therefore, we need to find I_{12}, I_{15}, and I_{25}. Of this set, only I_{25} cannot be determined by inspection. However, it can be found relatively easily from the instant centers that are available by inspection. First using I_{36} and I_{56} and I_{34} and I_{45}, I_{35} can be located. Then using I_{35} and I_{23} and I_{12} and I_{15}, I_{25} can be located. The resulting instant centers are shown in Fig. 4.23. The velocity of the coincident points at I_{25} is given by

$$v_{(I_{25})_2} = \omega_2 \times r_{I_{25}/I_{12}} = v_{(I_{25})_5} = \omega_5 \times r_{I_{25}/I_{15}}$$

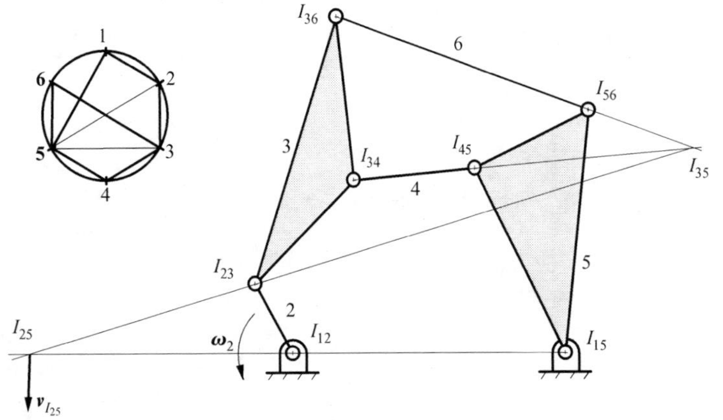

FIGURE 4.23 The instant center method applied to a Stephenson-II six-bar linkage.

Therefore, the magnitudes of the vectors are related by

$$\left|\mathbf{v}_{(I_{25})_2}\right| = \left|\boldsymbol{\omega}_2\right|\left|\mathbf{r}_{I_{25}/I_{12}}\right| = \left|\mathbf{v}_{(I_{25})_5}\right| = \left|\boldsymbol{\omega}_5\right|\left|\mathbf{r}_{I_{25}/I_{15}}\right|$$

and

$$\left|\boldsymbol{\omega}_5\right| = \left|\boldsymbol{\omega}_2\right|\frac{\left|\mathbf{r}_{I_{25}/I_{12}}\right|}{\left|\mathbf{r}_{I_{25}/I_{15}}\right|}$$

This gives the magnitude of $\boldsymbol{\omega}_5$. We can get the direction by determining the sense of the velocity of $\mathbf{v}_{(I_{25})_5}$. Because the vector is generally downward, the angular velocity must be CCW to satisfy the cross product sign convention.

EXAMPLE 4.4 *Finding Instant Centers for a Quick-Return Mechanism*

Find all the instant centers for the quick-return linkage shown in Fig. 4.24. The linkage is driven by the crank 2 rotating about the fixed revolute at point O_A. A pin fixed to link 2 at A slides in a slot in link 3. Link 3 rotates about a fixed revolute at point O_B. It is hinged at point B to the connecting link, 4. Link 4 connects to the horizontally sliding block, 5, via a revolute at point C. This type of linkage is used extensively in some machine tools (planers and shapers) because it generates a relatively slow and uniform forward, or cutting, stroke and a considerably quicker return stroke. The ratio of the durations of the two strokes can be determined by considering the angles through which the drive crank 2 rotates between the extreme positions of the rocker arm 3. The extreme positions are those in which O_AA is normal to O_BB.

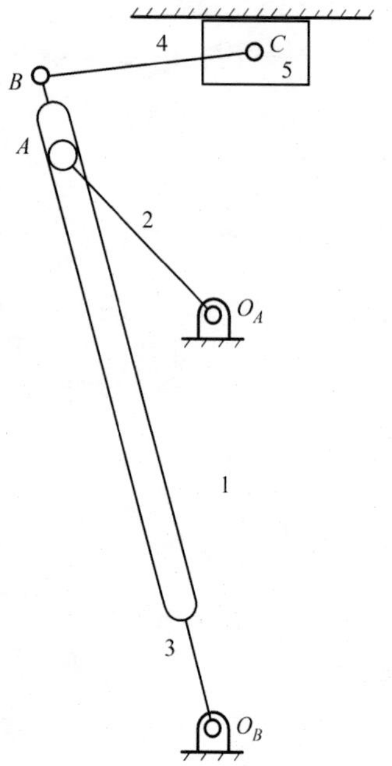

FIGURE 4.24 The linkage for Example 4.4.

Solution

The instant centers are shown in Fig. 4.25. In practice, it is seldom necessary to locate all instant centers. The great advantage of the instant center technique is its ease of use for complicated linkages, particularly when only the angular velocity of one member or the velocity of one point is to be found. For this problem only three instant centers are needed, although others may be needed in the process of locating them. The three instant centers needed are the set for the input link, output link, and base link. Here, the input link is the link whose angular velocity is given, or which contains a point whose velocity is given. The output link is the link whose angular velocity is sought, or which contains the point whose linear velocity is sought.

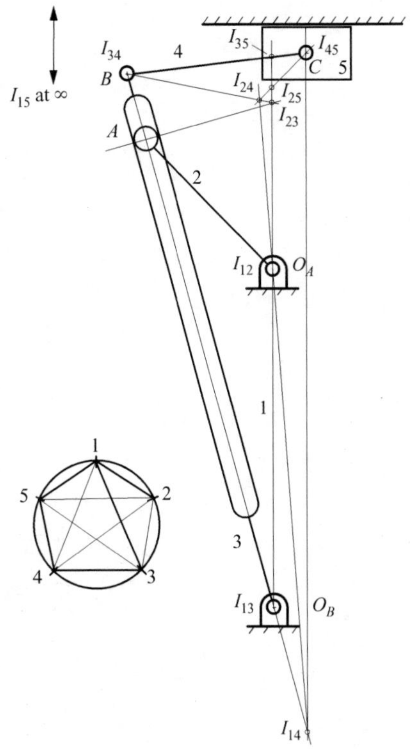

FIGURE 4.25 Location of instant centers for Example 4.4.

EXAMPLE 4.5 *Finding Instant Centers of a Quick-Return Mechanism in a Singular Position*

Find all the instant centers of the quick-return linkage in Example 4.4 when point C is collinear with O_A and O_B. This is shown in Fig. 4.26.

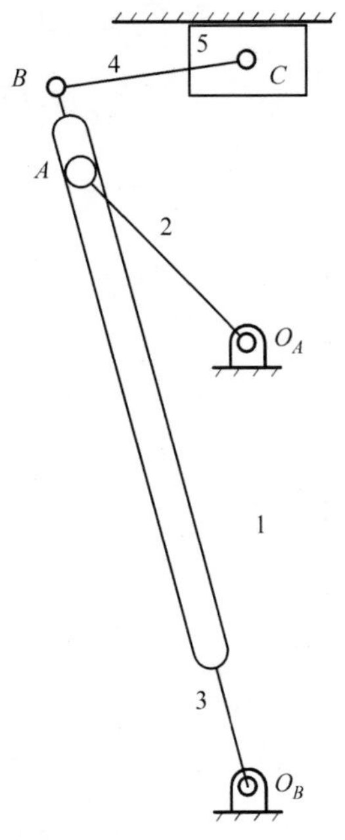

FIGURE 4.26 The linkage for Example 4.5.

Solution If an attempt is made to find the instant centers with the procedure used in Example 4.4, it will be possible to find I_{23} and I_{35} directly, as shown in Fig. 4.27. However, it is not possible to find the locations of the remaining instant centers by simple construction because all of the remaining instant centers are located on the line defined by I_{12} and I_{13}. To determine the location of the remaining instant centers, let point C be moved slightly off of the line defined by I_{12} and I_{13} and locate the instant centers. The location of the instant centers in the true position can then be determined by visualizing their movement as C approaches its actual position. This is shown in Figs. 4.28 and 4.29. Note that as C moves toward the vertical position, I_{35} becomes coincident with I_{45}, I_{14} becomes coincident with I_{13}, and I_{25} and I_{24} become coincident with I_{23}.

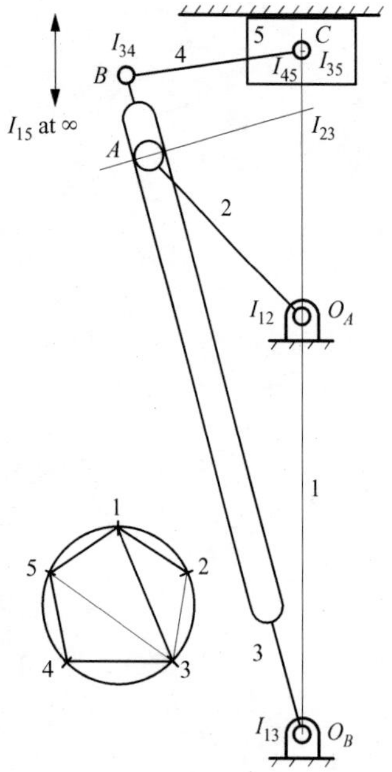

FIGURE 4.27 Location of I_{23} and I_{35} in Example 4.5.

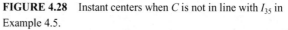

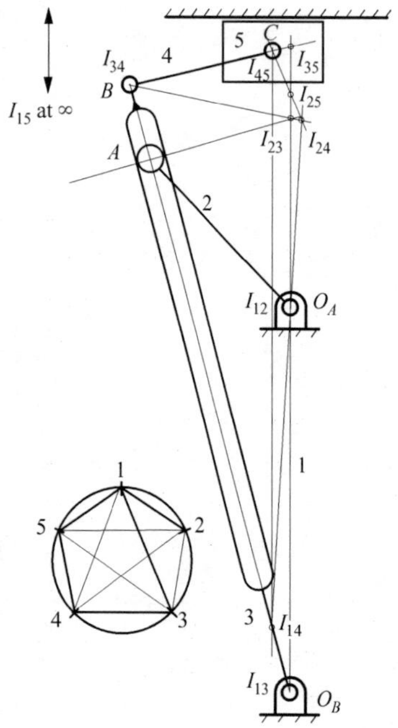

FIGURE 4.28 Instant centers when C is not in line with I_{35} in Example 4.5.

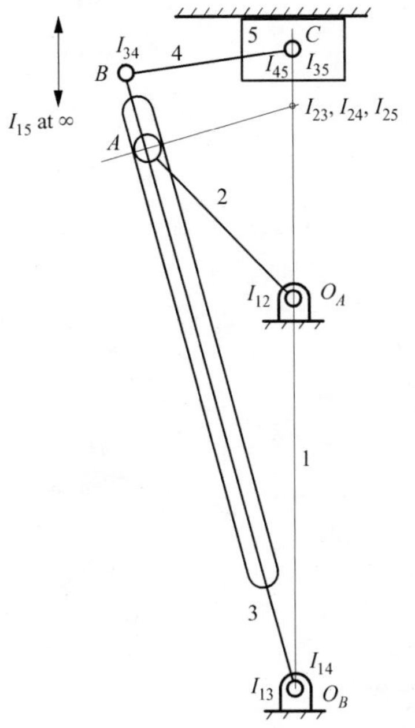

FIGURE 4.29 Actual location of I_{24}, I_{25}, and I_{14} in Example 4.5.

EXAMPLE 4.6 *Using Instant Centers to Analyze a Gear Mechanism*

Find the velocity of point C in Fig. 4.30 given that the angular velocity of gear 2 is 10 rad/s CW. B is a hinge connecting links 4 and 5 and does not connect to gear 3. Point A is a pin in link 3 that engages a slot in link 4.

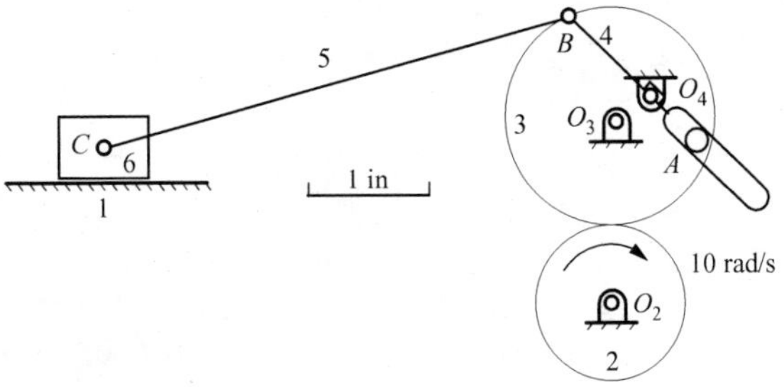

FIGURE 4.30 The linkage of Example 4.6.

Solution

To find the velocity of point C, considered as a point in link 5, from the angular velocity of link 2 relative to link 1, the instant centers I_{12}, I_{15}, and I_{25} are needed. These may be located as shown in Fig. 4.31.

Then,

$$\boldsymbol{\omega}_5 = \boldsymbol{\omega}_2 \times (I_{12}I_{25})/(I_{15}I_{25}) = 10 \times 0.940/7.261 = 1.29 \text{ rad/s CW}$$

$$\mathbf{v}_{C_5} = \boldsymbol{\omega}_5 \times (I_{15}C) = 1.29 \times 4.653 = 6.00 \text{ in/s to the left}$$

Notice that the instant center method is extremely efficient for simple input-output problems, such as this one, in which only two links are of interest.

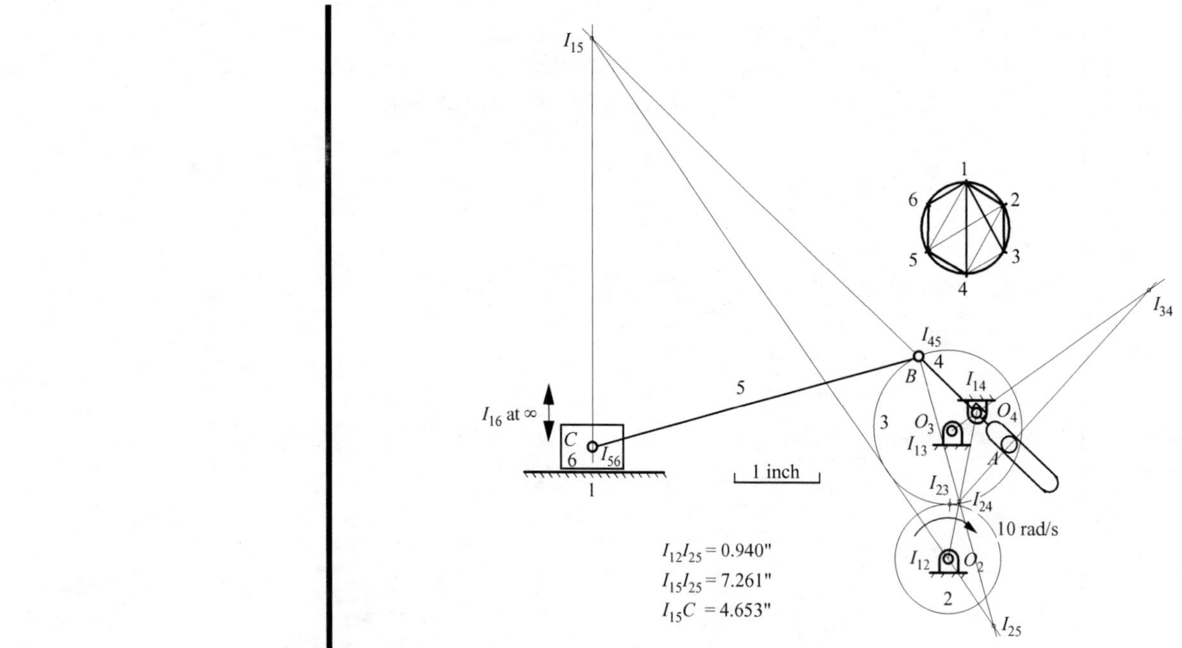

FIGURE 4.31 Location of instant centers for Example 4.6.

4.14 FINDING INSTANT CENTERS USING DRAFTING PROGRAMS

In this chapter, we have implied that the instant-center approach to velocity analysis is a purely graphical method. However, this does not mean that the actual drawings must be done on a drawing board. A better approach is to use one of the many drafting programs available on computers. The drafting package can be used to

1. draw the basic linkage to scale,
2. find the instant centers,
3. find appropriate distances using available dimension routines, and
4. determine the desired velocities by using calculators available on computers.

This procedure is relatively fast and accurate, especially if the drafting package will allow the user to draw parallel and perpendicular lines accurately. The results can be easily imported into reports and other documents. This environment also allows the user to explore other design alternatives to obtain desired velocity results. From the examples in this chapter, it is clear that significant changes in the velocity can be made by small alterations in the link lengths or pivot locations.

PROBLEMS

4.1 Locate all of the instant centers in the mechanism shown.

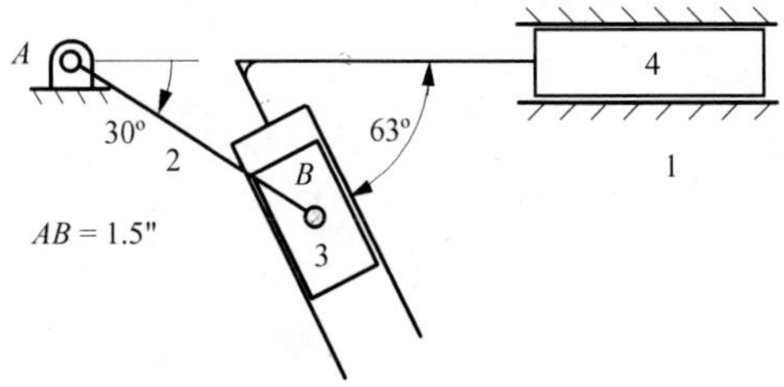

4.2 Find all of the instant centers of velocity for the mechanism shown.

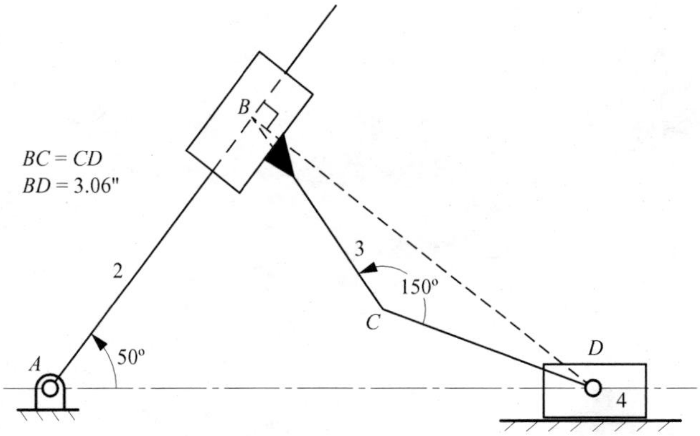

4.3 In the linkage shown, locate all of the instant centers.

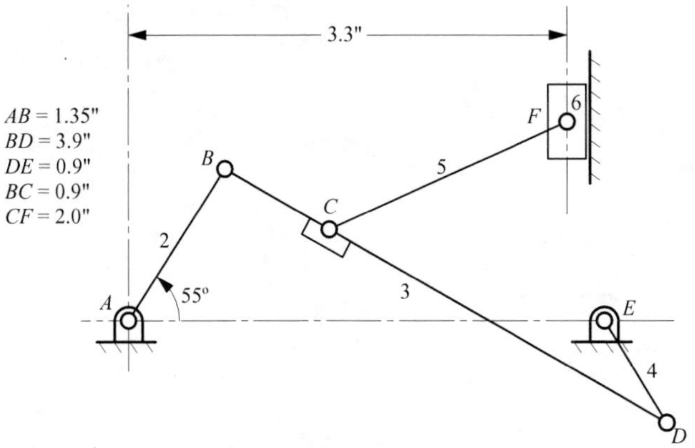

4.4 Find all of the instant centers of velocity for the mechanism shown.

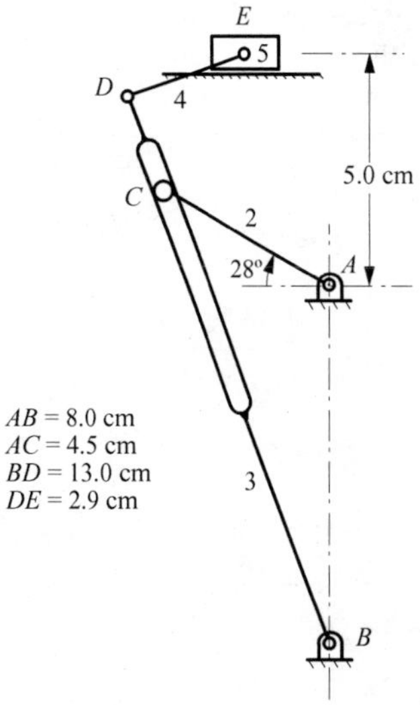

4.5 Locate all of the instant centers in the mechanism shown. If link 2 is turning CW at the rate of 60 rad/s, determine the linear velocity of points C and E using instant centers.

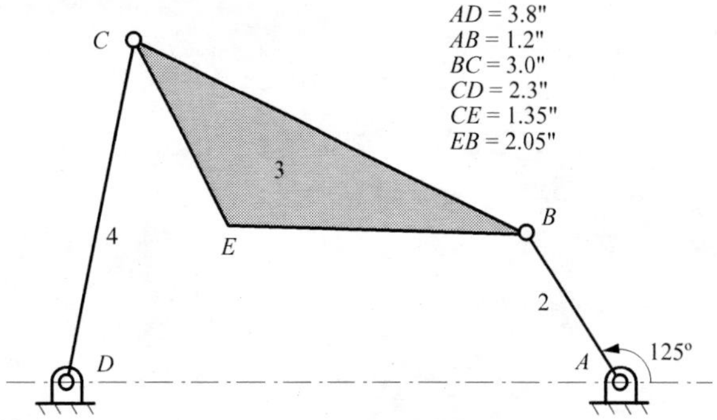

4.6 Locate all of the instant centers in the mechanism shown. If the cam (link 2) is turning CW at the rate of 900 rpm, determine the linear velocity of the follower using instant centers.

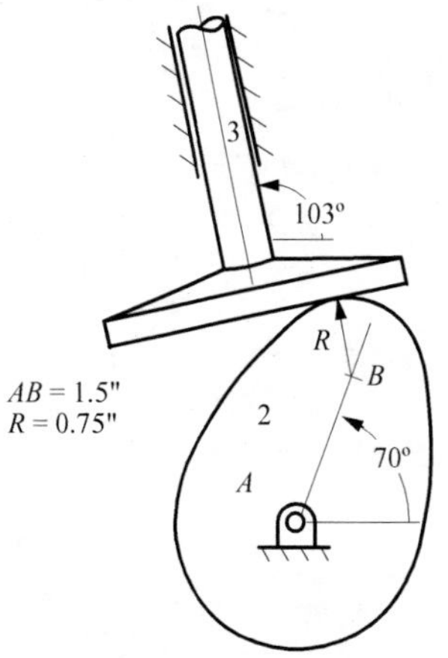

4.7 Locate all of the instant centers in the mechanism shown. If link 2 is turning CW at the rate of 36 rad/s, determine the linear velocity of point B_4 by use of instant centers. Determine the angular velocity of link 4 in rad/s and indicate the direction. Points C and E have the same vertical coordinate, and points A and C have the same horizontal coordinate.

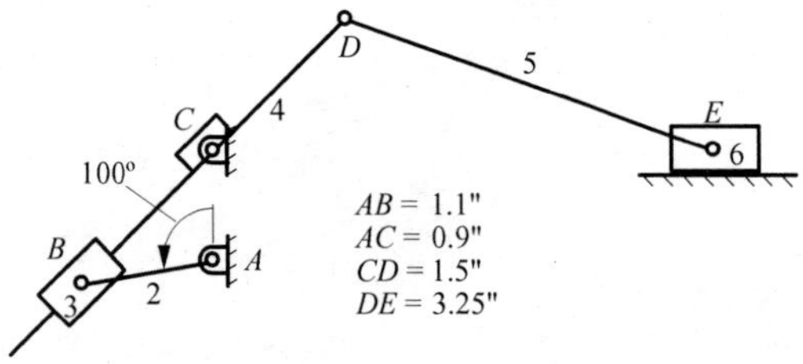

4.8 Using the instant-center method, find the angular velocity of link 6 if link 2 is rotating at 50 rpm CCW.

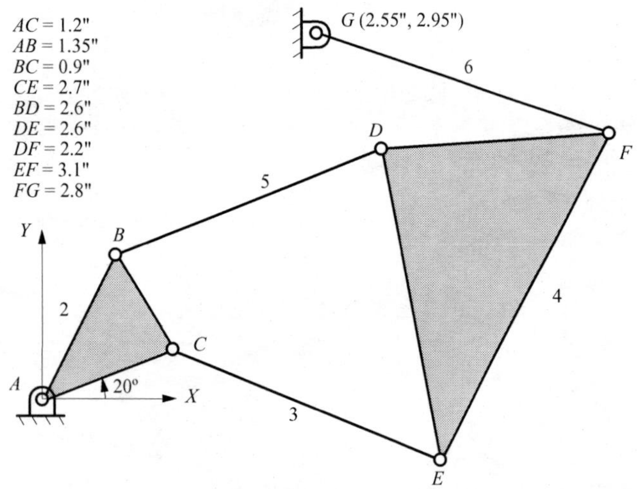

4.9 In the operation of this mechanism, link 3 strikes and trips link 5, which is initially at rest. High wear has been observed at the point of contact between links 3 and 5. As an engineer, you are asked to correct this situation. Therefore, you decide to do the following:

(a) Determine the direction of the velocity of point C on link 3 at the moment of contact.

(b) Relocate the ground pivot of link 4 to make the direction of the velocity of point C perpendicular to link 5 (hence less rubbing at the point of contact) when contact occurs.

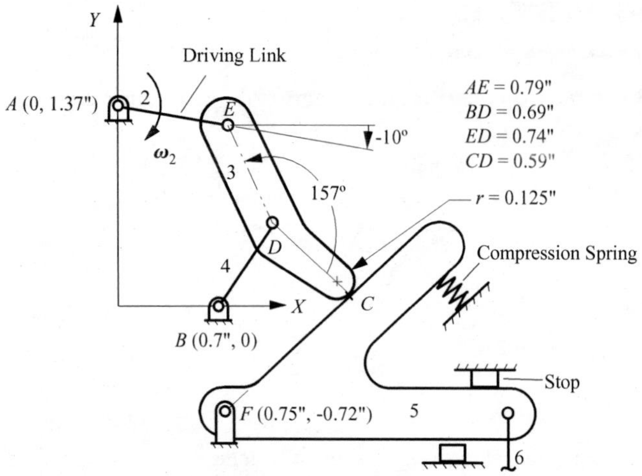

4.10 For the linkage given, $\omega_2 = 1$ rad/s CCW. Find I_{26} using the circle-diagram method. Using v_{A_2} and I_{26}, determine the magnitude and direction of v_{B_6} using the rotating-radius method.

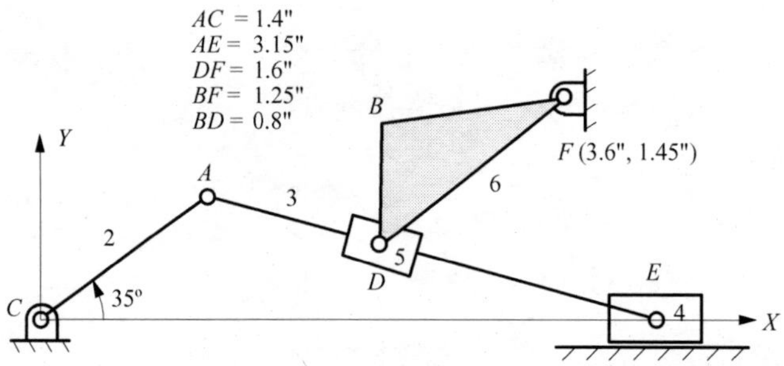

4.11 Find the velocity of point C given that the angular velocity of gear 2 is 10 rad/s CW. B is a pin joint connecting links 4 and 5. Point A is a pin in link 3 that engages a slot in link 4.

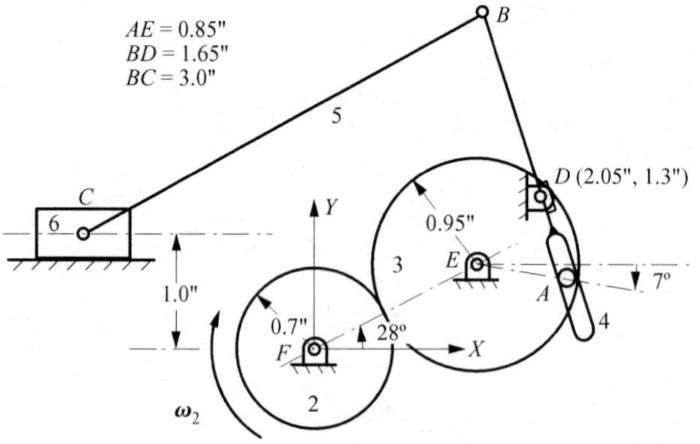

4.12 If $\omega_2 = 5$ rad/s CCW, find ω_5 using instant centers.

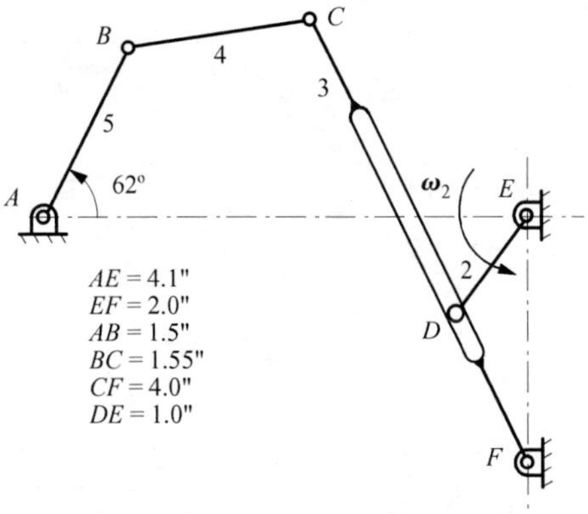

4.13 If $\omega_2 = 1$ rad/s CCW, find the velocity of point A on link 6 using the instant-center method. Show v_{A_6} on the drawing.

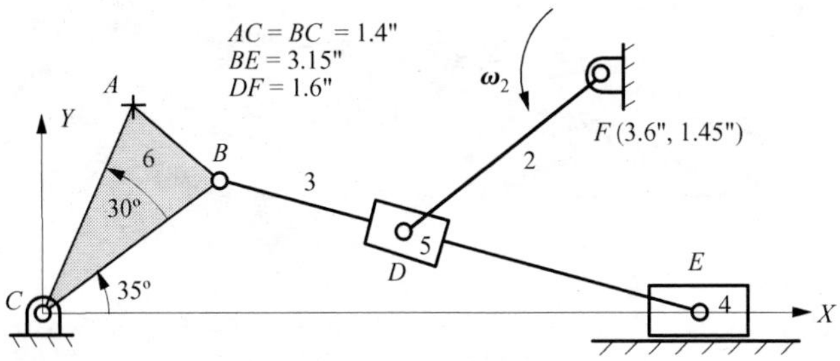

4.14 If $v_{A_2} = 10$ in/s as shown, find v_{B_4} using the instant-center method.

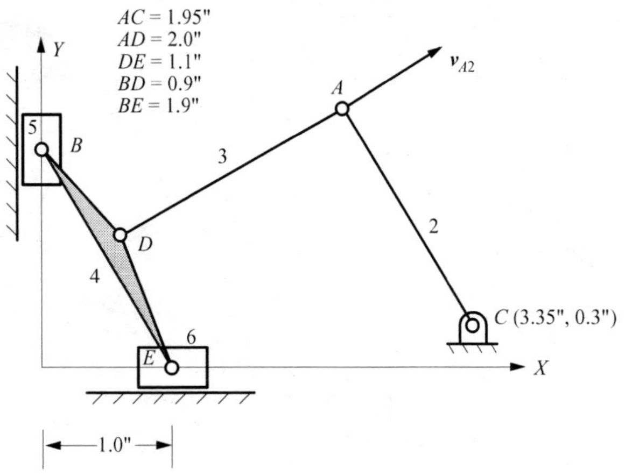

4.15 If $v_{A_2} = 10$ in/s as shown, find v_{B_4} using the instant-center method.

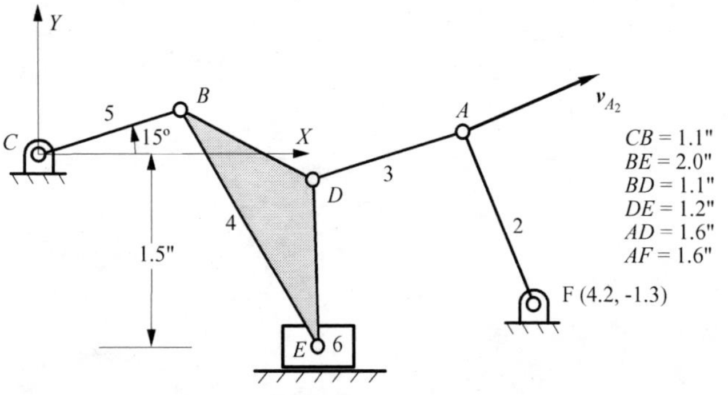

4.16 If $v_{A_6} = 10$ in/s as shown, determine the velocity vector (direction and magnitude) for point B on link 3 using the instant-center method.

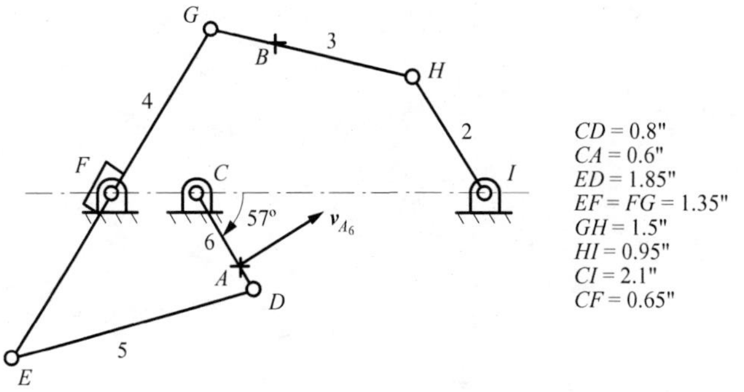

4.17 In the mechanism shown, ω_2 is 20 rad/s CCW. Find I_{26} and use it to find the angular velocity of link 6.

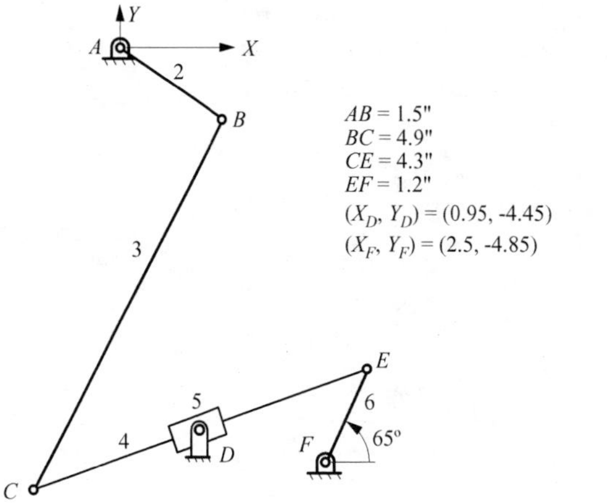

4.18 If v_{B_2} = 10 in/s as shown, determine the velocity vector (direction and magnitude) of point C_4 using the instant-center method.

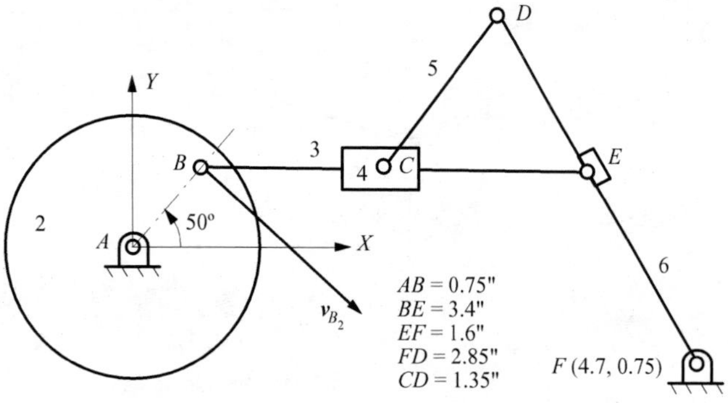

4.19 If the velocity of A_2 is 10 in/s to the right, find ω_6 using instant centers.

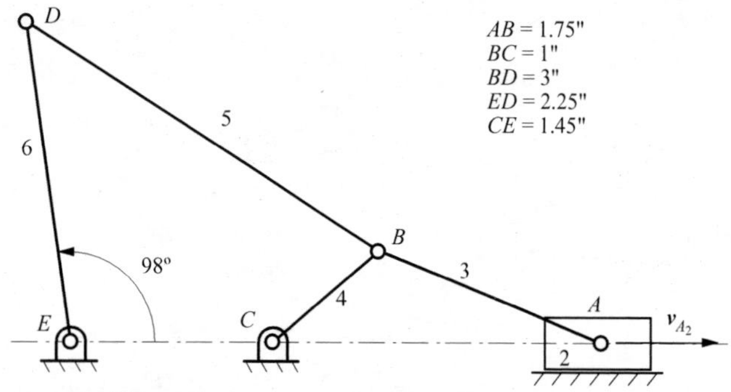

4.20 Crank 2 of the push-link mechanism shown in the figure is driven at ω_2 = 60 rad/s (CW). Find the velocity of points B and C and the angular velocity of links 3 and 4 using the instant-center method.

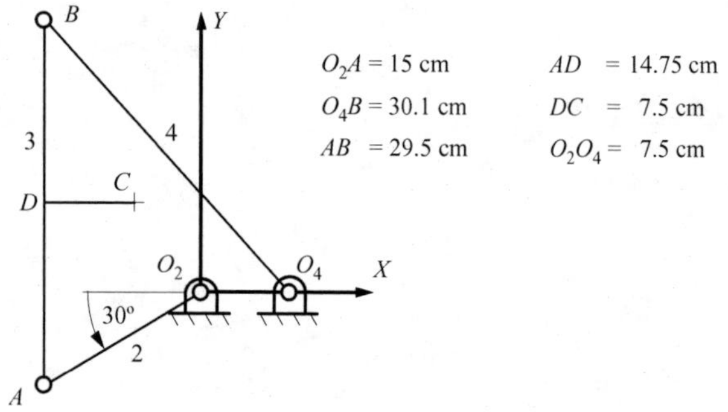

4.21 The circular cam shown is driven at an angular velocity ω_2 = 15 rad/s (CW). There is rolling contact between the cam and roller, link 3. Using the instant-center method, find the angular velocity of the oscillating follower, link 4.

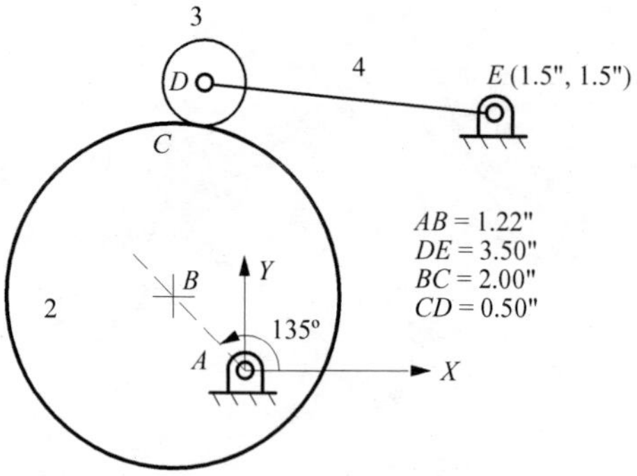

4.22 If ω_3 = 1 rad/s CCW, find the velocity of points E and F using the instant-center method. Show the velocity vectors v_{F_3} and v_{E_4} on the figure.

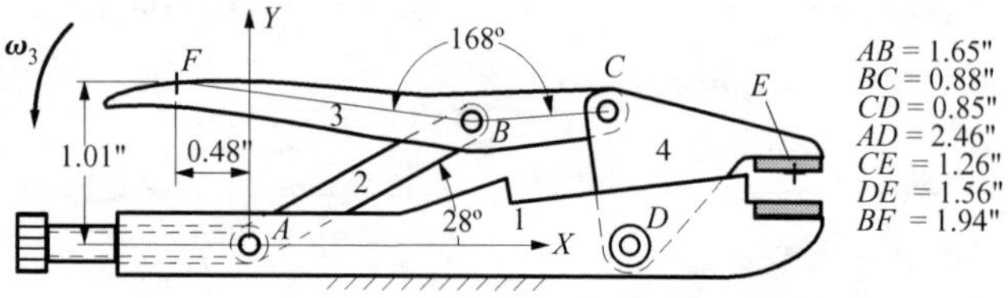

4.23 In the eight-link mechanism, most of the linkage is contained in the black box and some of the instant centers are located as shown. The velocity of point B is 100 in/s in the direction shown. Compute the velocity of point D_8 and determine the angular velocity of link 2.

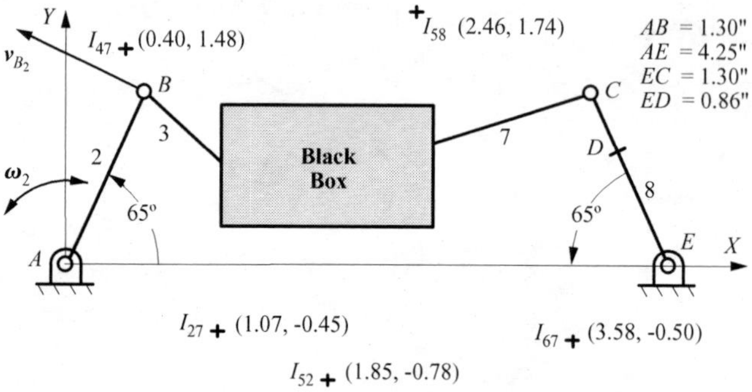

4.24 If the velocity of point A on link 2 is 10 in/s as shown, use the instant-center method to find the velocity of point C on link 5.

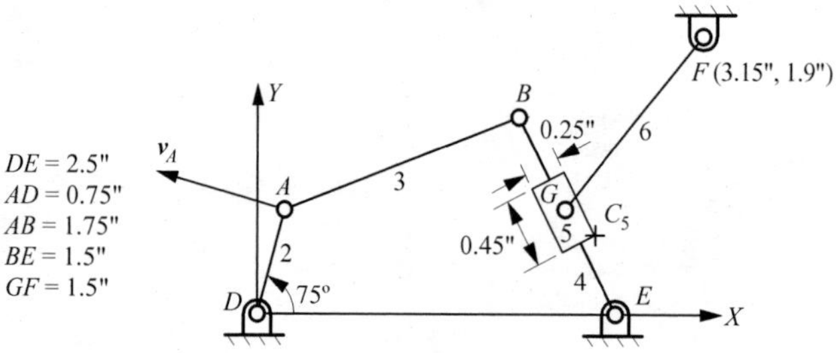

4.25 Assume that link 7 rolls on link 3 without slipping, and find the following instant centers: I_{13}, I_{15}, and I_{27}. For the given value for ω_2, find ω_7 using instant centers.

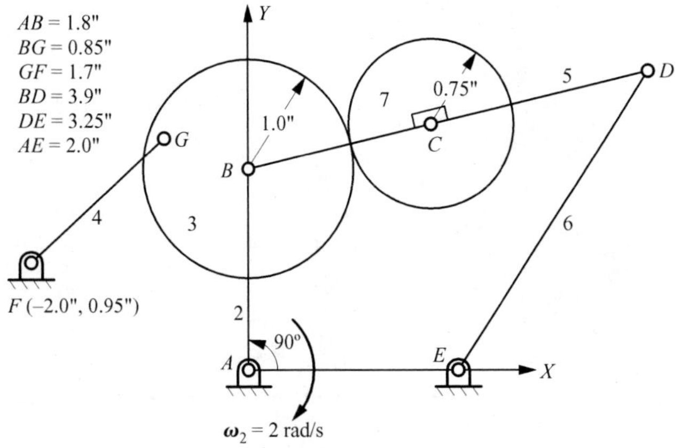

4.26 If v_{A_2} = 10 in/s as shown, find v_{C_5} using the instant-center method.

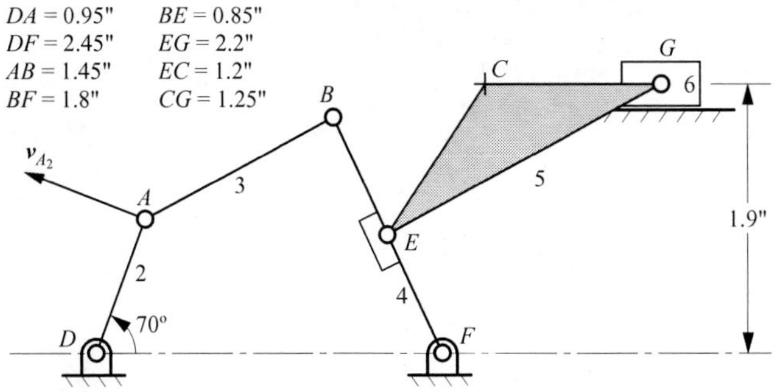

4.27 If ω_2 = 10 rad/s CCW, find the velocity of point B using the instant-center method. Show the velocity vector v_{B_3} on the figure.

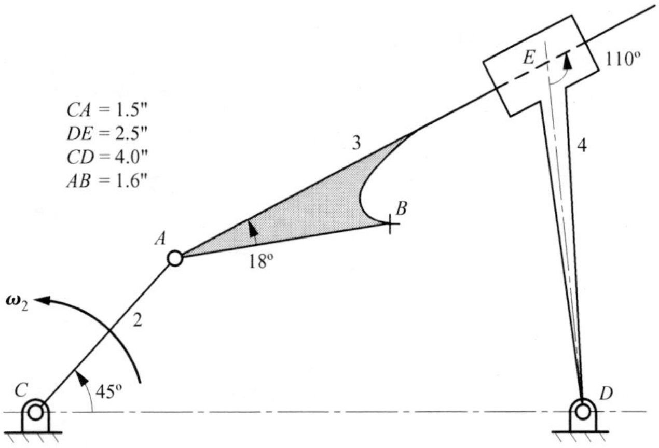

4.28 If ω_2 = 100 rad/s CCW, find the velocity of point E using the instant-center method. Show the velocity vector v_{E_4} on the figure.

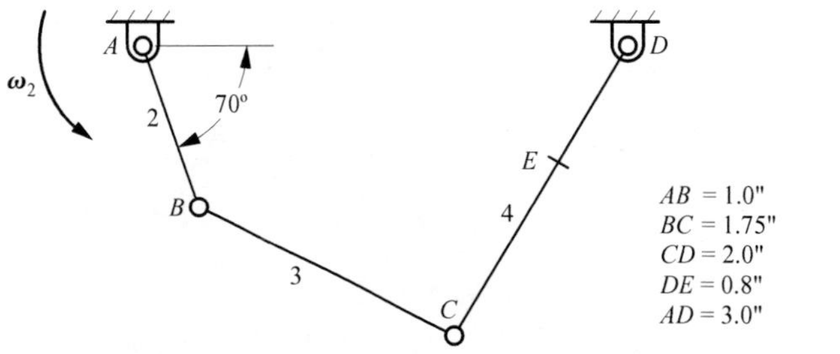

4.29 If ω_2 = 5 rad/s CCW, find ω_6 using instant centers.

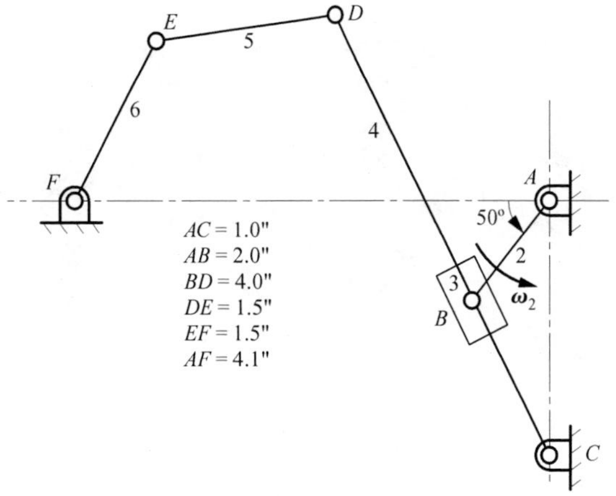

4.30 If ω_2 = 100 rad/s CCW, find v_{B_4} using instant centers and the rotating-radius method.

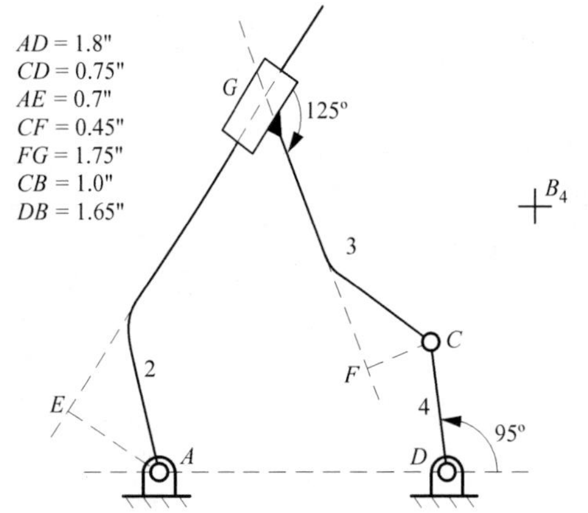

4.31 If $\boldsymbol{v}_{A_2}$ = 10 in/s as shown, find the angular velocity ($\boldsymbol{\omega}_6$) of link 6 using the instant-center method.

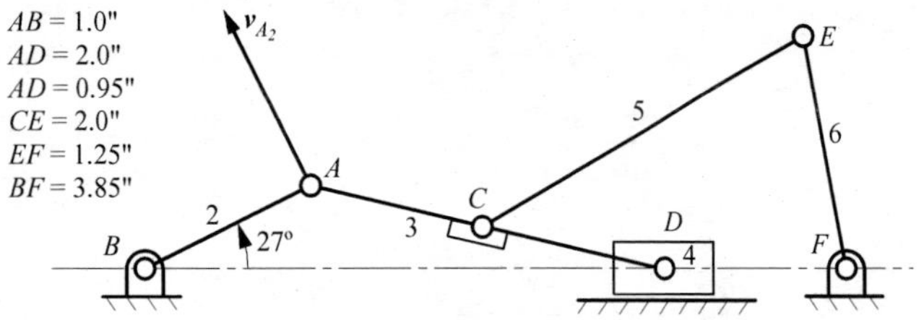

4.32 If $\boldsymbol{\omega}_2$ = 50 rad/s CCW, find the velocity of point G using the instant-center method. Show the velocity vector $\boldsymbol{v}_{G_5}$ on the figure.

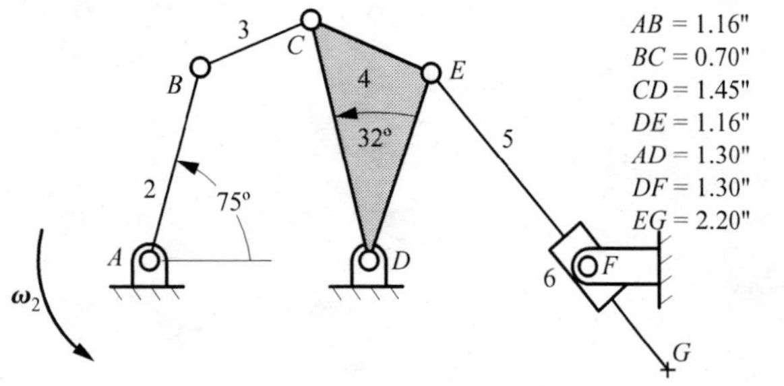

4.33 If $\boldsymbol{\omega}_2$ = 100 rad/s CCW, find $\boldsymbol{\omega}_6$.

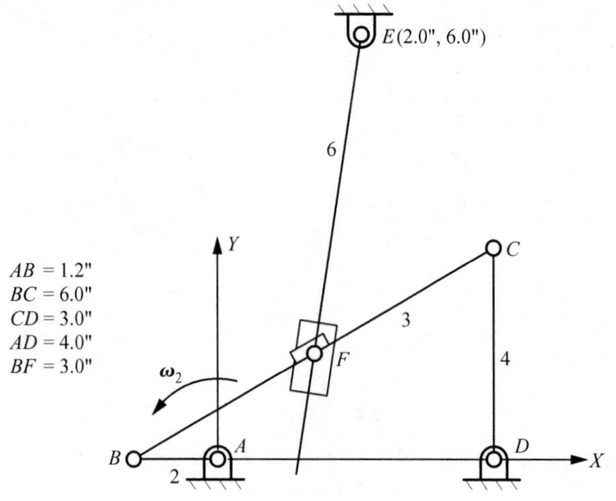

CHAPTER 5

ANALYTICAL LINKAGE ANALYSIS

5.1 INTRODUCTION

In Chapters 2 and 3, graphical techniques for position, velocity, and acceleration analysis of linkages were presented. However, as was pointed out, there are circumstances in which it is preferable to use analytical solution techniques that can be conveniently programmed on a digital computer. In any circumstance in which repetitive or extensive analyses are required, the use of computer software is highly desirable. In the present chapter, the equations used to construct analysis software are developed in detail.

The geometric constraints associated with mechanisms can be formulated using vector displacement, velocity, and acceleration closure equations. The displacement closure equations are based on the observation that there are two different but equivalent paths connecting points on the same vector loop. For example, in the four-bar linkage shown in Fig. 5.1, one can reach point C from point A either by way of point B or point D.

It is convenient to represent the terms in the closure equations by vectors, and the procedures developed in this chapter work especially well for planar problems. It is also possible to apply the same general approach to spatial linkages. Another popular method for planar mechanisms, which involves slightly more computational work, is the complex number approach, in which the Cartesian vector components are expressed in terms of the real and imaginary parts of a complex number. The use of complex numbers is advantageous in some types of problem; however, the direct vector approach is preferred here. The complex number approach is outlined briefly at the end of this chapter.

There are also specialized techniques for forming closure equations for spatial mechanisms. The general trend is to work with coordinate transformation operators. For this a set of body-fixed coordinates is established at each joint, and the product of a series of joint-to-joint coordinate transformation operators is taken. When this product is continued around the entire mechanism loop, it must be equal to the identity operator. The resulting operator equation can then be manipulated, if required, and corresponding elements can be equated. The types of operators that have been used include dual complex number 2×2 matrices, dual quaternions, real number 4×4 matrices, and dual number 3×3 matrices. A discussion of the mathematics of these operators is beyond the scope of this text. The description of spatial linkages using matrix transformations is discussed in Chapter 9.

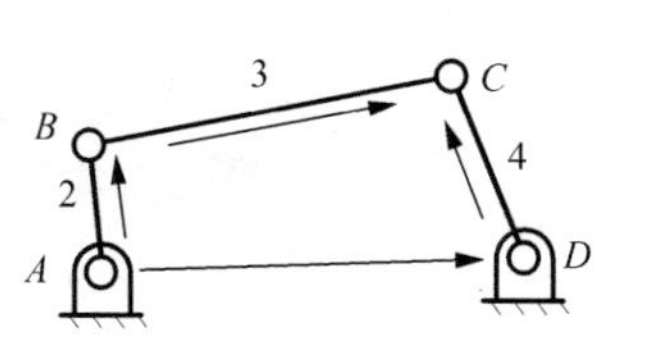

FIGURE 5.1 Closure of a four-bar linkage.

5.2 POSITION, VELOCITY, AND ACCELERATION REPRESENTATIONS

5.2.1 Position Representation

For the purpose of developing an analytical model, we can define the relative locations of a chain of points by a chain of vectors. The points will be associated with the links of a mechanism in some manner, but they do not have to be attached to specific links. An example is given in Fig. 5.2.

The position of point Q in the fixed reference frame is

$$\boldsymbol{r}_Q = \boldsymbol{r}_1 + \boldsymbol{r}_2 + \boldsymbol{r}_3 \tag{5.1}$$

Here, we will represent each vector by a length r_i and an angle θ_i, as shown in Fig. 5.3. All angles are measured counterclockwise from a line that remains parallel to the fixed x axis attached to the reference frame.

With this notation, we can resolve each of the vectors in Eq. (5.1) into x and y components making use of the unit vectors i and j as follows:

$$\left.\begin{aligned} \boldsymbol{r}_1 &= r_1\left(\cos\theta_1\boldsymbol{i} + \sin\theta_1\boldsymbol{j}\right) \\ \boldsymbol{r}_2 &= r_2\left(\cos\theta_2\boldsymbol{i} + \sin\theta_2\boldsymbol{j}\right) \\ \boldsymbol{r}_3 &= r_3\left(\cos\theta_3\boldsymbol{i} + \sin\theta_3\boldsymbol{j}\right) \end{aligned}\right\} \tag{5.2}$$

or

$$\boldsymbol{r}_k = n_k\left(\cos\theta_k\boldsymbol{i} + \sin\theta_k\boldsymbol{j}\right),\ k = 1,\ 2,\ 3 \tag{5.3}$$

5.2.2 Velocity Representation

To determine the velocity of point Q, r_Q can be differentiated. Then,

$$\boldsymbol{v}_Q = \dot{\boldsymbol{r}}_Q = \dot{\boldsymbol{r}}_1 + \dot{\boldsymbol{r}}_2 + \dot{\boldsymbol{r}}_3 \tag{5.4}$$

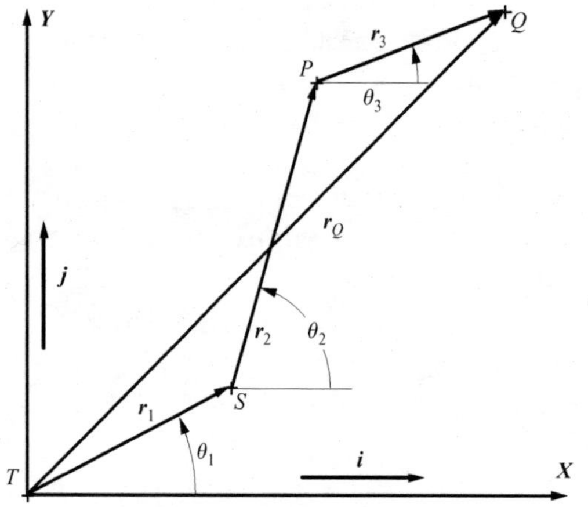

FIGURE 5.2 Representation of a chain of points by a set of vectors.

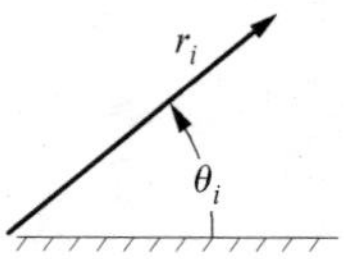

FIGURE 5.3 Notation used for vectors.

where

$$\dot{r}_k = \frac{dr_k}{dt} \tag{5.5}$$

Note that, in general, both the magnitude and direction of r_k can change. When we differentiate Eq. (5.3) using the chain rule of calculus, we obtain

$$\dot{\boldsymbol{r}}_k = \dot{r}_k\left(\cos\theta_k \boldsymbol{i} + \sin\theta_k \boldsymbol{j}\right) + r_k\left(-\dot{\theta}_k \sin\theta_k \boldsymbol{i} + \dot{\theta}_k \cos\theta_k \boldsymbol{j}\right) \tag{5.6}$$

or

$$\dot{\boldsymbol{r}}_k = \left(\dot{r}_k \cos\theta_k - r_k\dot{\theta}_k \sin\theta_k\right)\boldsymbol{i} + \left(\dot{r}_k \sin\theta_k + r_k\dot{\theta}_k \cos\theta_k\right)\boldsymbol{j} \tag{5.7}$$

If we compare the vector components indicated in Eq. (5.6) with the equations developed in Section 3.3, we will notice a similarity between corresponding terms. In particular, if $\boldsymbol{r}_k$ is the vector defining the relative position between two points P and Q, and body B is moving relative to the reference frame R as shown in Fig. 5.4, then

$$\dot{r}_k\left(\cos\theta_k \boldsymbol{i} + \sin\theta_k \boldsymbol{j}\right) = {}^B\boldsymbol{v}_{Q/P} \tag{5.8}$$

and

$$r_k\dot{\theta}_k\left(-\sin\theta_k \boldsymbol{i} + \cos\theta_k \boldsymbol{j}\right) = \boldsymbol{\omega}_B \times \boldsymbol{r}_{Q/P} \tag{5.9}$$

Equation (5.8) can be verified by recognizing that it gives the component of the velocity associated with changing the magnitude of the vector between the two points. This component is clearly in the direction of the vector r_k. The second term can be verified by computing the cross product. Recognizing that

$$\boldsymbol{\omega}_B = \dot{\theta}_k \boldsymbol{k}$$

and

$$\boldsymbol{r}_{Q/P} = \boldsymbol{r}_k = r_k\left(\cos\theta_k \boldsymbol{i} + \sin\theta_k \boldsymbol{j}\right)$$

We then have,

$$\begin{aligned}\boldsymbol{\omega}_B \times \boldsymbol{r}_{Q/P} &= \dot{\theta}_k \boldsymbol{k} \times r_k\left(\cos\theta_k \boldsymbol{i} + \sin\theta_k \boldsymbol{j}\right) = \dot{\theta}_k r_k\left(\cos\theta_k \boldsymbol{k}\times\boldsymbol{i} + \sin\theta_k \boldsymbol{k}\times\boldsymbol{j}\right)\\ &= r_k\dot{\theta}_k\left(-\sin\theta_k \boldsymbol{i} + \cos\theta_k \boldsymbol{j}\right)\end{aligned}$$

Equation (5.4) can also be expressed as

$$\boldsymbol{v}_Q = \sum_{k=1}^{3} \dot{r}_k\left(\cos\theta_k \boldsymbol{i} + \sin\theta_k \boldsymbol{j}\right) + r_k\left(-\dot{\theta}_k \sin\theta_k \boldsymbol{i} + \dot{\theta}_k \cos\theta_k \boldsymbol{j}\right) \tag{5.10}$$

or

$$\boldsymbol{v}_Q = \sum_{k=1}^{3}\left(\dot{r}_k \cos\theta_k - r_k\dot{\theta}_k \sin\theta_k\right)\boldsymbol{i} + \left(\dot{r}_k \sin\theta_k + r_k\dot{\theta}_k \cos\theta_k\right)\boldsymbol{j} \tag{5.11}$$

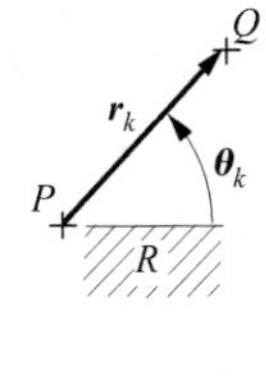

FIGURE 5.4 Position vector between two points.

5.2.3 Acceleration Representation

To obtain the acceleration expression, we need only to differentiate the velocity expression (Eq. 5.4). Symbolically, this is

$$\boldsymbol{a}_Q = \ddot{r}_Q = \ddot{r}_1 + \ddot{r}_2 + \ddot{r}_3 \tag{5.12}$$

where

$$\ddot{r}_k = \frac{d^2 \boldsymbol{r}_k}{dt^2}$$

Because the vectors have been defined in a consistent manner (Fig. 5.3), the form for the derivatives for all of the vectors will be the same. Therefore, we can develop the expression with a general vector $\boldsymbol{r}_k$.

Note again that, in general, both the magnitude and direction of $\boldsymbol{r}_k$ can change. When we differentiate Eq. (5.6) using the chain rule of calculus, we obtain

$$\begin{aligned}\ddot{r}_k &= \ddot{r}_k\left(\cos\theta_k \boldsymbol{i} + \sin\theta_k \boldsymbol{j}\right) + r_k\ddot{\theta}_k\left(-\sin\theta_k \boldsymbol{i} + \cos\theta_k \boldsymbol{j}\right) - r_k\dot{\theta}_k^2\left(\cos\theta_k \boldsymbol{i} + \sin\theta_k \boldsymbol{j}\right)\\ &\quad + 2\dot{r}_k\dot{\theta}_k\left(-\sin\theta_k \boldsymbol{i} + \cos\theta_k \boldsymbol{j}\right)\end{aligned} \tag{5.13}$$

or

$$\begin{aligned}\ddot{r}_k &= \left[\left(\ddot{r}_k - r_k\dot{\theta}_k^2\right)\cos\theta_k - \left(r_k\ddot{\theta}_k + 2\dot{r}_k\dot{\theta}_k\right)\sin\theta_k\right]\boldsymbol{i}\\ &\quad + \left[\left(\ddot{r}_k - r_k\dot{\theta}_k^2\right)\sin\theta_k - \left(r_k\ddot{\theta}_k + 2\dot{r}_k\dot{\theta}_k\right)\cos\theta_k\right]\boldsymbol{j}\end{aligned} \tag{5.14}$$

As in the case of the velocity equations, we can compare the vector components indicated in Eq. (5.13) with the acceleration equations developed in Section 3.3. Using the same nomenclature as before (Fig. 5.4), we get

$$\ddot{r}_k\left(\cos\theta_k \boldsymbol{i} + \sin\theta_k \boldsymbol{j}\right) = {}^B\boldsymbol{a}_{Q/P} \tag{5.15}$$

$$r_k\ddot{\theta}_k\left(-\sin\theta_k \boldsymbol{i} + \cos\theta_k \boldsymbol{j}\right) = \boldsymbol{\alpha}_B \times \boldsymbol{r}_{Q/P} \tag{5.16}$$

$$-r_k\dot{\theta}_k^2\left(\cos\theta_k \boldsymbol{i} + \sin\theta_k \boldsymbol{j}\right) = \boldsymbol{\omega}_B \times \left(\boldsymbol{\omega}_B \times \boldsymbol{r}_{Q/P}\right) \tag{5.17}$$

and

$$2\dot{r}_k\dot{\theta}_k\left(-\sin\theta_k \boldsymbol{i} + \cos\theta_k \boldsymbol{j}\right) = 2\boldsymbol{\omega}_B \times {}^B\boldsymbol{v}_{Q/P} \tag{5.18}$$

These can be verified by direct calculation.

If we add the individual components, we can obtain the acceleration of point Q. Then Eq. (5.12) can be expressed as

$$\boldsymbol{a}_Q = \sum_{k=1}^{3}\left\{\begin{aligned}&\ddot{r}_k\left(\cos\theta_k \boldsymbol{i} + \sin\theta_k \boldsymbol{j}\right) + r_k\ddot{\theta}_k\left(-\sin\theta_k \boldsymbol{i} + \cos\theta_k \boldsymbol{j}\right)\\ &-r_k\dot{\theta}_k^2\left(\cos\theta_k \boldsymbol{i} + \sin\theta_k \boldsymbol{j}\right) + 2\dot{r}_k\dot{\theta}_k\left(-\sin\theta_k \boldsymbol{i} + \cos\theta_k \boldsymbol{j}\right)\end{aligned}\right\} \tag{5.19}$$

or

$$a_Q = \sum_{k=1}^{3} \begin{Bmatrix} \left[\left(\ddot{r}_k - r_k \dot{\theta}_k^2 \right) \cos\theta_k - \left(r_k \ddot{\theta}_k + 2\dot{r}_k \dot{\theta}_k \right) \sin\theta_k \right] \boldsymbol{i} \\ + \left[\left(\ddot{r}_k - r_k \dot{\theta}_k^2 \right) \sin\theta_k + \left(r_k \ddot{\theta}_k + 2\dot{r}_k \dot{\theta}_k \right) \cos\theta_k \right] \boldsymbol{j} \end{Bmatrix} \tag{5.20}$$

5.2.4 Special Cases

Equations (5.6) and (5.13) or (5.7) and (5.14) are the most general forms of the velocity and acceleration equations. However, in most mechanisms usually some of the terms will be zero because of the special conditions associated with the way in which the vectors are defined. It is possible for any of the terms involved in the velocity and acceleration equations to be zero; however, a common case is to have the magnitude of a given position vector be constant. This is the case when the vector defines the relative positions of two points on a rigid link. When this happens, $\dot{r}$ and $\ddot{r}$ are zero. Then the velocity and acceleration expressions become

$$\dot{\boldsymbol{r}}_k = r_k \dot{\theta}_k \left(-\sin\theta_k \boldsymbol{i} + \cos\theta_k \boldsymbol{j} \right) \tag{5.21}$$

$$\ddot{\boldsymbol{r}}_k = r_k \ddot{\theta}_k \left(-\sin\theta_k \boldsymbol{i} + \cos\theta_k \boldsymbol{j} \right) - r_k \dot{\theta}_k^2 \left(\cos\theta_k \boldsymbol{i} + \sin\theta_k \boldsymbol{j} \right) \tag{5.22}$$

or

$$\ddot{\boldsymbol{r}}_k = \left[-r_k \dot{\theta}_k^2 \cos\theta_k - r_k \ddot{\theta}_k \sin\theta_k \right] \boldsymbol{i} + \left[-r_k \dot{\theta}_k^2 \sin\theta_k + r_k \ddot{\theta}_k \cos\theta_k \right] \boldsymbol{j} \tag{5.23}$$

5.2.5 Mechanisms to Be Considered

There are six commonly used single-loop chains with revolute and slider joints. We will look at three of these in detail to illustrate how the equations can be developed in each case. Then we will present the results for the remaining three cases. We will then discuss more complex mechanisms that require several vector loops and mechanisms that contain higher pairs.

5.3 ANALYTICAL CLOSURE EQUATIONS FOR FOUR-BAR LINKAGES

We will first give an overview of the development of the equations for the four-bar linkage using the general nomenclature just discussed. The procedures used to solve the equations for the four-bar linkage are similar to the procedures required for solving the equations associated with most other simple mechanisms.

The closure condition simply expresses the condition that a loop of a linkage closes on itself. For the four-bar linkage shown in Fig. 5.5, the closure equations would be

$$\boldsymbol{r}_P = \boldsymbol{r}_2 + \boldsymbol{r}_3 = \boldsymbol{r}_1 + \boldsymbol{r}_4 \tag{5.24}$$

or

$$r_2 \left(\cos\theta_2 \boldsymbol{i} + \sin\theta_2 \boldsymbol{j} \right) + r_3 \left(\cos\theta_3 \boldsymbol{i} + \sin\theta_3 \boldsymbol{j} \right) = r_1 \left(\cos\theta_1 \boldsymbol{i} + \sin\theta_1 \boldsymbol{j} \right) + r_4 \left(\cos\theta_4 \boldsymbol{i} + \sin\theta_4 \boldsymbol{j} \right) \tag{5.25}$$

Rewriting Eq. (5.25) in its component equations, one gets

$$r_2 \cos\theta_2 + r_3 \cos\theta_3 = r_1 \cos\theta_1 + r_4 \cos\theta_4 \tag{5.26}$$

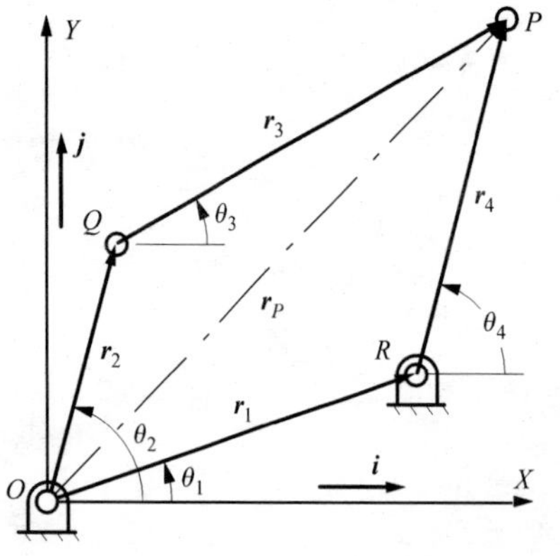

FIGURE 5.5 Vector closure condition for a four-bar loop. The position of point P obtained by adding the vectors $\boldsymbol{r}_2$ and $\boldsymbol{r}_3$ must always be the same as that obtained by adding vectors $\boldsymbol{r}_1$ and $\boldsymbol{r}_4$. Note that $\boldsymbol{r}_1$ is a constant vector that describes the base member of the linkage. Correspondingly, θ_1 is a constant angle

$$r_2 \sin\theta_2 + r_3 \sin\theta_3 = r_1 \sin\theta_1 + r_4 \sin\theta_4 \tag{5.27}$$

Equations (5.26) and (5.27) are the closure equations, and they must be satisfied throughout the motion of the linkage. The base vector will be constant, so $\boldsymbol{r}_1$ and θ_1 are constants. If θ_2 is given, that is, if crank OQ is a driving crank, it is necessary to solve Eqs. (5.26) and (5.27) for θ_3 and θ_4 in terms of θ_2. Once these expressions are obtained $\dot{\theta}_3$, $\dot{\theta}_4$, $\ddot{\theta}_3$, and $\ddot{\theta}_4$ can be obtained in terms of θ_2, $\dot{\theta}_2$, and $\ddot{\theta}_2$ by differentiation. Velocities and accelerations of points in the mechanism can then be obtained from equations like Eqs. (5.11) and (5.19), recognizing that all of the vector magnitudes are constant ($\dot{r} = \ddot{r} = 0$).

When θ_3 is given, the coupler is the driver, and we must solve Eqs. (5.26) and (5.27) for θ_2 and θ_4 in terms of θ_3. The procedure for doing this is very similar to that used when θ_2 is the input. Therefore, we will first reconsider briefly the case in which θ_2 is the input.

5.3.1 Solution of Closure Equations for Four-Bar Linkages When Link 2 Is the Driver

The analytical solution procedure follows the same major steps as in the graphical solution. That is, a position analysis must first be performed, then a velocity analysis, and finally an acceleration analysis. The position analysis, for a closed-loop linkage, comprises the solution of the closure equations for the joint angles or link orientations. Once this solution is obtained, the velocity and acceleration states are quickly obtainable using the differentiated equations. It will be seen, however, that the position analysis, which is so easily performed graphically by construction of a drawing to scale, is a complex matter when performed analytically.

For all of the simple mechanisms that we will consider initially, the first step in solving the position equations is to identify the variable to be determined first. When the position equations involve two angles as unknowns, the solution procedure is to isolate the trigonometric function involving the angle to be eliminated on the left-hand side of the equation. To eliminate θ_3 in the linkage shown in Fig. 5.5, first isolate it on one side of Eqs. (5.26) and (5.27) as follows:

$$r_3 \cos\theta_3 = r_1 \cos\theta_1 + r_4 \cos\theta_4 - r_2 \cos\theta_2 \tag{5.28}$$

$$r_3 \sin\theta_3 = r_1 \sin\theta_1 + r_4 \sin\theta_4 - r_2 \sin\theta_2 \tag{5.29}$$

Notice that the angle θ_1 is a known constant. Now square both sides of both equations, add, and simplify the result using the trigonometric identity $\sin^2\theta + \cos^2\theta = 1$. This gives

$$
\begin{aligned}
r_3^2 &= r_1^2 + r_2^2 + r_4^2 + 2r_1 r_4(\cos\theta_1 \cos\theta_4 + \sin\theta_1 \sin\theta_4) \\
&\quad -2r_1 r_2(\cos\theta_1 \cos\theta_2 + \sin\theta_1 \sin\theta_2) + 2r_2 r_4(\cos\theta_2 \cos\theta_4 + \sin\theta_2 \sin\theta_4)
\end{aligned} \tag{5.30}
$$

Equation (5.30) gives θ_4 in terms of the given angle θ_2 (and the constant angle θ_1) but not explicitly. To obtain an explicit expression, simplify Eq. (5.30) by combining the coefficients of $\cos\theta_4$ and $\sin\theta_4$ as follows:

$$
A\cos\theta_4 + B\sin\theta_4 + C = 0 \tag{5.31}
$$

where

$$
\left.
\begin{aligned}
A &= 2r_1 r_4 \cos\theta_1 - 2r_2 r_4 \cos\theta_2 \\
B &= 2r_1 r_4 \sin\theta_1 - 2r_2 r_4 \sin\theta_2 \\
C &= r_1^2 + r_2^2 + r_4^2 - r_3^2 - 2r_1 r_2(\cos\theta_1 \cos\theta_2 + \sin\theta_1 \sin\theta_2)
\end{aligned}
\right\} \tag{5.32}
$$

To solve Eq. (5.31), use the standard trigonometric identities for half angles given in the following:

$$
\sin\theta_4 = \frac{2\tan\left(\dfrac{\theta_4}{2}\right)}{1 + \tan^2\left(\dfrac{\theta_4}{2}\right)} \tag{5.33}
$$

$$
\cos\theta_4 = \frac{1 - \tan^2\left(\dfrac{\theta_4}{2}\right)}{1 + \tan^2\left(\dfrac{\theta_4}{2}\right)} \tag{5.34}
$$

After substitution and simplification, we get

$$
(C - A)t^2 + 2Bt + (A + C) = 0
$$

where

$$
t = \tan\left(\frac{\theta_4}{2}\right)
$$

Solving for t gives

$$
t = \frac{-2B + \sigma\sqrt{4B^2 - 4(C - A)(C + A)}}{2(C - A)} = \frac{-B + \sigma\sqrt{B^2 - C^2 + A^2}}{C - A} \tag{5.35}
$$

and

$$
\theta_4 = 2\tan^{-1} t \tag{5.36}
$$

where $\sigma = \pm 1$ is a sign variable identifying the assembly mode. Note that $\tan^{-1} t$ has a valid range of $-\pi/2$ ″ $\tan^{-1} t$ ″ $\pi/2$. Therefore, θ_4 will have the range $-\pi$ ″ θ_4 ″ π. Unless the linkage is a Grashof type II linkage in one of the extreme positions of its motion range, there are two solutions for θ_4 corresponding to the two values of σ, and they are both valid. These correspond to two assembly modes or branches for the linkage. Once we pick the value for σ corresponding to the desired mode, the sign normally stays the same for any value of θ_2.

Because of the square root in Eq. (5.35), the variable t can be complex $[(A^2 + B^2) < C^2]$. If this happens, the mechanism cannot be assembled in the position specified. The assembly configurations would then appear as shown in Fig. 5.6.

After θ_4 is known, equations (5.28) and (5.29) can now be solved for θ_3. Dividing Eq. (5.29) by Eq. (5.28) and solving for θ_3 gives

$$\theta_3 = \tan^{-1}\left[\frac{r_1 \sin\theta_1 + r_4 \sin\theta_4 - r_2 \sin\theta_2}{r_1 \cos\theta_1 + r_4 \cos\theta_4 - r_2 \cos\theta_2}\right] \tag{5.37}$$

Note that in Eq. (5.37), it is essential that the sign of the numerator and denominator be maintained to determine the quadrant in which the angle θ_3 lies. This can be done directly in MATLAB by using the ATAN2 function. The form of this function is

$$\text{ATAN2}(\sin\theta_3, \cos\theta_3) = \tan^{-1}\left[\frac{\sin\theta_3}{\cos\theta_3}\right]. \tag{5.38}$$

Equations (5.35) – (5.37) give a complete and consistent solution to the position problem. As indicated before, for any value of θ_2, there are typically two values of θ_3 and θ_4, given by substituting $\sigma = +1$ and -1, respectively, in Eq. (5.35). These two different solutions are shown in Fig. 5.7. The two solutions correspond to an assembly ambiguity that also appears in the graphical construction.

Note that the positions of $\boldsymbol{r}_3$ and $\boldsymbol{r}_4$ are symmetric about the line QR. Therefore, the angle $\gamma = \theta_4 - \theta_3$ has the same magnitude, but opposite sign, in each of the two positions. The sign of γ provides a useful indicator as to which of the solution branches has been drawn, from the graphical point of view.

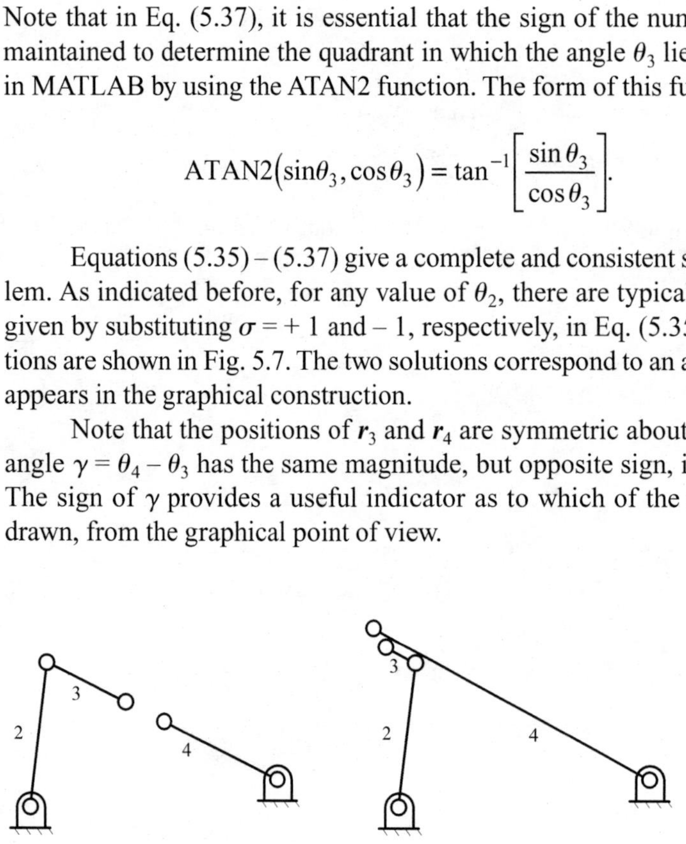

FIGURE 5.6 Grashof type II linkages cannot be placed in positions that are transitions between solution branches. The variable t would be complex in these cases

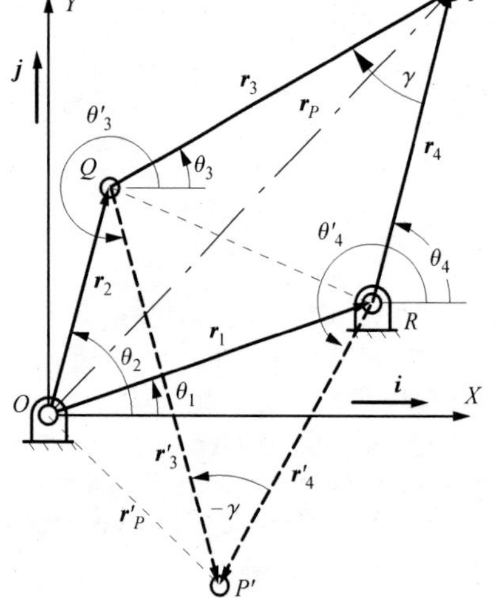

FIGURE 5.7 The two possible positions (P and P') of the point P for a given value of θ_2. Note that $QP'R$ is the mirror image of QPR about the line QR. Notice that there are two different possible values of θ_3 and two different values of θ_4 corresponding to the two possible positions of point P. The sign of the angle RPQ (γ) is reversed in the second solution, although the magnitude of $RP'Q$ is the same. The sign of γ is a useful graphical indicator of which solution is being examined (see Section 6.3.6).

Once all of the angular quantities are known, it is relatively straightforward to compute the coordinates of any point of the vector loops used in the closure equations. In particular, the coordinates of Q, P, and R are given by

$$\mathbf{r}_Q = \mathbf{r}_2 = r_2\left(\cos\theta_2 \mathbf{i} + \sin\theta_2 \mathbf{j}\right) \tag{5.39}$$

$$\begin{aligned}\mathbf{r}_P &= \mathbf{r}_2 + \mathbf{r}_3 = r_2\left(\cos\theta_2 \mathbf{i} + \sin\theta_2 \mathbf{j}\right) + r_3\left(\cos\theta_3 \mathbf{i} + \sin\theta_3 \mathbf{j}\right) \\ &= \mathbf{r}_1 + \mathbf{r}_4 = r_1\left(\cos\theta_1 \mathbf{i} + \sin\theta_1 \mathbf{j}\right) + r_4\left(\cos\theta_4 \mathbf{i} + \sin\theta_4 \mathbf{j}\right)\end{aligned} \tag{5.40}$$

and

$$\mathbf{r}_R = \mathbf{r}_1 = r_1\left(\cos\theta_1 \mathbf{i} + \sin\theta_1 \mathbf{j}\right) \tag{5.41}$$

5.3.2 Analysis When the Coupler (Link 3) Is the Driving Link

The analytical procedure just given when one of the frame-mounted links (link 2) in Fig. 5.5 is the driver is very similar to the graphical procedure. However, if the coupler is the driver, it is difficult to analyze the linkage graphically. The analytical procedure, in contrast, is very straightforward and no more difficult to conduct than when one of the frame-mounted links is the driver. The details follow exactly the same procedure as that given in Section 5.3.1. Therefore, we will simply outline the procedure and tabulate the results.

In the procedure, we can assume that in Fig. 5.5 that θ_1, θ_3, $\dot{\theta}_3$, and $\ddot{\theta}_3$ are known, and θ_2, $\dot{\theta}_2$, $\ddot{\theta}_2$, θ_4, $\dot{\theta}_4$, and $\ddot{\theta}_4$ are to be found. All of the link lengths and θ_1 are constants. For the position analysis, again begin with Eqs. (5.26) and (5.27) and isolate the terms with either θ_2 or θ_4. It is advantageous to select θ_2 for reasons that will become apparent. The resulting equations are

$$r_2\cos\theta_2 = r_1\cos\theta_1 + r_4\cos\theta_4 - r_3\cos\theta_3 \tag{5.42}$$

$$r_2\sin\theta_2 = r_1\sin\theta_1 + r_4\sin\theta_4 - r_3\sin\theta_3 \tag{5.43}$$

A comparison of Eqs. (5.42) and (5.43) with Eqs. (5.28) and (5.29) indicates that they are of exactly the same form except that the indices 2 and 3 are interchanged. Therefore, we can use directly the position solution derived in Section 5.3.1 if we interchange the indices 2 and 3.

When the coupler is the driver, there is an assembly-mode ambiguity similar to that when link 2 is the driver. This is illustrated in Fig. 5.8. It is necessary to know the appropriate mode before the analysis is begun; however, once the assembly mode is selected, it is the same for any position of the input link unless the linkage is a type 2 linkage, and passes through a singular position.

The motion of the coupler in a coupler-driven four-bar linkage will be less than 360° unless the linkage is of type 1 with the coupler or base as the shortest link. When the linkage reaches its motion limits, links 2 and 4 will be parallel.

5.3.3 Velocity Equations for Four-Bar Linkages

The analytical form of the velocity equations for the four-bar linkage of Fig. 5.5 can be developed by differentiating Eq. (5.24). The result is

$$\dot{\mathbf{r}}_P = \dot{\mathbf{r}}_2 + \dot{\mathbf{r}}_3 = \dot{\mathbf{r}}_1 + \dot{\mathbf{r}}_4 \tag{5.44}$$

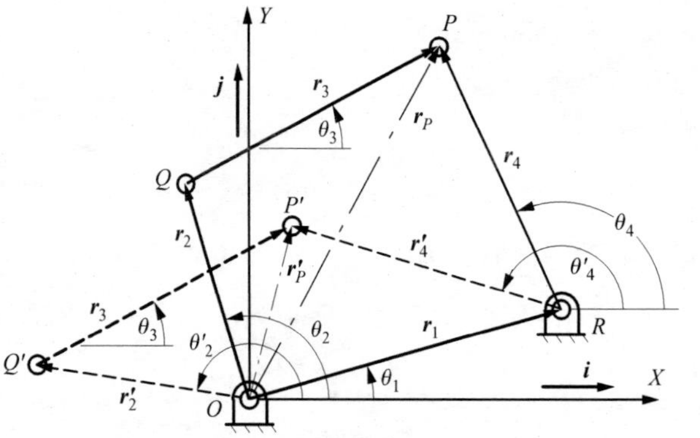

FIGURE 5.8 The two possible positions (P and P') of the point P for a given value of θ_3. There are two different possible values of θ_2 and two different values of θ_4 corresponding to the two possible positions of point P.

When this equation is written in component form, the result is the same as that of differentiating Eqs. (5.26) and (5.27). Recognizing that all of the link lengths are constant as is θ_1, we have the resulting component equations

$$r_2\dot{\theta}_2 \sin\theta_2 + r_3\dot{\theta}_3 \sin\theta_3 = r_4\dot{\theta}_4 \sin\theta_4 \tag{5.45}$$

$$r_2\dot{\theta}_2 \cos\theta_2 + r_3\dot{\theta}_3 \cos\theta_3 = r_4\dot{\theta}_4 \cos\theta_4 \tag{5.46}$$

If $\dot{\theta}_2$ is known, the only new unknowns are $\dot{\theta}_3$ and $\dot{\theta}_4$, and if $\dot{\theta}_3$ is known, the only new unknowns are $\dot{\theta}_2$ and $\dot{\theta}_4$. In either case, the equations can be solved most easily using a linear equation solver. In matrix form, Eqs. (5.45) and (5.46) can be rearranged and rewritten as

$$\begin{bmatrix} -r_J \sin\theta_J & r_4 \sin\theta_4 \\ -r_J \cos\theta_J & r_4 \cos\theta_4 \end{bmatrix} \begin{Bmatrix} \dot{\theta}_J \\ \dot{\theta}_4 \end{Bmatrix} = \begin{Bmatrix} r_M\dot{\theta}_M \sin\theta_M \\ r_M\dot{\theta}_M \cos\theta_M \end{Bmatrix} \tag{5.47}$$

where $M = 2$ and $J = 3$ for $\dot{\theta}_2$ as the input, and $M = 3$ and $J = 2$ for $\dot{\theta}_3$ as the input. The terms in the matrix and vector on the right-hand side of the equation will be known. The equation can therefore be solved manually, on a programmable calculator, or with the matrix solvers in programs such as MATLAB.

Once the angular velocities are known, it is a simple matter to compute the linear velocities of any of the points on the vector loop. The velocities of points Q and P are given by

$$\dot{\boldsymbol{r}}_Q = \dot{\boldsymbol{r}}_2 = r_2\dot{\theta}_2(-\sin\theta_2\boldsymbol{i} + \cos\theta_2\boldsymbol{j}) \tag{5.48}$$

and

$$\begin{aligned} \dot{\boldsymbol{r}}_P = \dot{\boldsymbol{r}}_2 + \dot{\boldsymbol{r}}_3 &= (-r_2\dot{\theta}_2 \sin\theta_2 - r_3\dot{\theta}_3 \sin\theta_3)\boldsymbol{i} + (r_2\dot{\theta}_2 \cos\theta_2 + r_3\dot{\theta}_3 \cos\theta_3)\boldsymbol{j} \\ = \dot{\boldsymbol{r}}_1 + \dot{\boldsymbol{r}}_4 &= (-r_4\dot{\theta}_4 \sin\theta_4)\boldsymbol{i} + (r_4\dot{\theta}_4 \cos\theta_4)\boldsymbol{j} \end{aligned} \tag{5.49}$$

5.3.4 Acceleration Equations for Four-Bar Linkages

The analytical form of the acceleration equations for the linkage of Fig. 5.5 can be developed by differentiating Eq. (5.44). The result is

$$\ddot{\boldsymbol{r}}_P = \ddot{\boldsymbol{r}}_2 + \ddot{\boldsymbol{r}}_3 = \ddot{\boldsymbol{r}}_1 + \ddot{\boldsymbol{r}}_4 \tag{5.50}$$

When this equation is written in component form, the result is the same as differentiating Eqs. (5.45) and (5.46). The resulting component equations are

$$r_2\ddot{\theta}_2 \sin\theta_2 + r_2\dot{\theta}_2^2 \cos\theta_2 + r_3\ddot{\theta}_3 \sin\theta_3 + r_3\dot{\theta}_3^2 \cos\theta_3 = r_4\ddot{\theta}_4 \sin\theta_4 + r_4\dot{\theta}_4^2 \cos\theta_4 \tag{5.51}$$

$$r_2\ddot{\theta}_2 \cos\theta_2 - r_2\dot{\theta}_2^2 \sin\theta_2 + r_3\ddot{\theta}_3 \cos\theta_3 - r_3\dot{\theta}_3^2 \sin\theta_3 = r_4\ddot{\theta}_4 \cos\theta_4 + r_4\dot{\theta}_4^2 \sin\theta_4 \tag{5.52}$$

When $\ddot{\theta}_2$ is known along with all of the position and velocity terms, the only new unknowns are $\ddot{\theta}_3$ and $\ddot{\theta}_4$, and when $\ddot{\theta}_3$ is known along with all of the position and velocity terms, the only new unknowns are $\ddot{\theta}_2$ and $\ddot{\theta}_4$. Again, because a linear problem is involved, these can be solved for most easily using a linear equation solver. In matrix form, Eqs. (5.51) and (5.52) can be rearranged and rewritten as

$$\begin{bmatrix} -r_J \sin\theta_J & r_4 \sin\theta_4 \\ -r_J \cos\theta_J & r_4 \cos\theta_4 \end{bmatrix} \begin{Bmatrix} \ddot{\theta}_J \\ \ddot{\theta}_4 \end{Bmatrix} = \begin{Bmatrix} r_M\ddot{\theta}_M \sin\theta_M + r_M\dot{\theta}_M^2 \cos\theta_M + r_J\dot{\theta}_J^2 \cos\theta_J - r_4\dot{\theta}_4^2 \cos\theta_4 \\ r_M\ddot{\theta}_M \cos\theta_M - r_M\dot{\theta}_M^2 \sin\theta_M - r_J\dot{\theta}_J^2 \sin\theta_J - r_4\dot{\theta}_4^2 \sin\theta_4 \end{Bmatrix} \tag{5.53}$$

where $M = 2$ and $J = 3$ for $\ddot{\theta}_2$ as the input, and $M = 3$ and $J = 2$ for $\ddot{\theta}_3$ as the input. The terms in the matrix and vector on the right-hand side of the equation will be known. The equation can therefore be solved manually, on a programmable calculator, or with the matrix solvers in programs such as MATLAB. Notice that the coefficient matrix is the same for both the velocities (Eq. 5.47) and the accelerations (Eq. 5.53).

Once the angular accelerations are known, it is a simple matter to compute the linear accelerations of any of the points in the linkage. The accelerations of points Q and P are given by

$$\ddot{\boldsymbol{r}}_Q = \ddot{\boldsymbol{r}}_2 = \left(-r_2\ddot{\theta}_2 \sin\theta_2 - r_2\dot{\theta}_2^2 \cos\theta_2\right)\boldsymbol{i} + \left(r_2\ddot{\theta}_2 \cos\theta_2 - r_2\dot{\theta}_2^2 \sin\theta_2\right)\boldsymbol{j} \tag{5.54}$$

and

$$\begin{aligned} \ddot{\boldsymbol{r}}_P = \ddot{\boldsymbol{r}}_2 + \ddot{\boldsymbol{r}}_3 &= -\left(r_2\ddot{\theta}_2 \sin\theta_2 + r_2\dot{\theta}_2^2 \cos\theta_2 + r_3\ddot{\theta}_3 \sin\theta_3 + r_3\dot{\theta}_3^2 \cos\theta_3\right)\boldsymbol{i} \\ &+ \left(r_2\ddot{\theta}_2 \cos\theta_2 - r_2\dot{\theta}_2^2 \sin\theta_2 + r_3\ddot{\theta}_3 \cos\theta_3 - r_3\dot{\theta}_3^2 \sin\theta_3\right)\boldsymbol{j} \\ = \ddot{\boldsymbol{r}}_1 + \ddot{\boldsymbol{r}}_4 &= -\left(r_4\ddot{\theta}_4 \sin\theta_4 + r_4\dot{\theta}_4^2 \cos\theta_4\right)\boldsymbol{i} + \left(r_4\ddot{\theta}_4 \cos\theta_4 - r_4\dot{\theta}_4^2 \sin\theta_4\right)\boldsymbol{j} \end{aligned} \tag{5.55}$$

Now that the equations have been developed, it is relatively simple to write a computer program for the analysis of a four-bar linkage. To aid in this, the equations required are summarized in Table 5.1. The authors have found that MATLAB is a very convenient language for solving simple kinematic equations, and this program runs on a variety of platforms. MATLAB routines for analyzing four-bar linkages are contained on the disk provided with this book.

TABLE 5.1 Summary of Position, Velocity, and Acceleration Equations for a Four-Bar Linkage. Link 2 Is the Input Link When $M = 2$ and $J = 3$. Link 3 Is the Input Link When $M = 3$ and $J = 2$. Link 1 Is Assumed to Be the Frame. The Link Numbers and Points Are Defined in Fig. 5.5

Position

$$A = 2r_1 r_4 \cos\theta_1 - 2r_M r_4 \cos\theta_M$$
$$B = 2r_1 r_4 \sin\theta_1 - 2r_M r_4 \sin\theta_M$$
$$C = r_1^2 + r_M^2 + r_4^2 - r_J^2 - 2r_1 r_M (\cos\theta_1 \cos\theta_M + \sin\theta_1 \sin\theta_M)$$

$$\theta_4 = 2\tan^{-1}\left[\frac{-B + \sigma\sqrt{B^2 - C^2 + A^2}}{C - A}\right]; \qquad \sigma = \pm 1$$

$$\theta_J = \tan^{-1}\left[\frac{r_1 \sin\theta_1 + r_4 \sin\theta_4 - r_M \sin\theta_M}{r_1 \cos\theta_1 + r_4 \cos\theta_4 - r_M \cos\theta_M}\right]$$

$$\boldsymbol{r}_Q = \boldsymbol{r}_2 = r_2(\cos\theta_2 \boldsymbol{i} + \sin\theta_2 \boldsymbol{j})$$

$$\begin{aligned}\boldsymbol{r}_P &= \boldsymbol{r}_2 + \boldsymbol{r}_3 = r_2(\cos\theta_2 \boldsymbol{i} + \sin\theta_2 \boldsymbol{j}) + r_3(\cos\theta_3 \boldsymbol{i} + \sin\theta_3 \boldsymbol{j}) \\ &= \boldsymbol{r}_1 + \boldsymbol{r}_4 = r_1(\cos\theta_1 \boldsymbol{i} + \sin\theta_1 \boldsymbol{j}) + r_4(\cos\theta_4 \boldsymbol{i} + \sin\theta_4 \boldsymbol{j})\end{aligned}$$

$$\boldsymbol{r}_R = \boldsymbol{r}_1 = r_1(\cos\theta_1 \boldsymbol{i} + \sin\theta_1 \boldsymbol{j})$$

Velocity

$$\begin{bmatrix} -r_J \sin\theta_J & r_4 \sin\theta_4 \\ -r_J \cos\theta_J & r_4 \cos\theta_4 \end{bmatrix} \begin{Bmatrix} \dot\theta_J \\ \dot\theta_4 \end{Bmatrix} = \begin{Bmatrix} r_M \dot\theta_M \sin\theta_M \\ r_M \dot\theta_M \cos\theta_M \end{Bmatrix}$$

$$\dot{\boldsymbol{r}}_Q = \dot{\boldsymbol{r}}_2 = r_2\dot\theta_2(-\sin\theta_2 \boldsymbol{i} + \cos\theta_2 \boldsymbol{j})$$

$$\dot{\boldsymbol{r}}_P = (-r_4\dot\theta_4 \sin\theta_4)\boldsymbol{i} + (r_4\dot\theta_4 \cos\theta_4)\boldsymbol{j}$$

Acceleration

$$\begin{bmatrix} -r_J \sin\theta_J & r_4 \sin\theta_4 \\ -r_J \cos\theta_J & r_4 \cos\theta_4 \end{bmatrix} \begin{Bmatrix} \ddot\theta_J \\ \ddot\theta_4 \end{Bmatrix} = \begin{Bmatrix} r_M \ddot\theta_M \sin\theta_M + r_M \dot\theta_M^2 \cos\theta_M + r_J \dot\theta_J^2 \cos\theta_J - r_4 \dot\theta_4^2 \cos\theta_4 \\ r_M \ddot\theta_M \cos\theta_M - r_M \dot\theta_M^2 \sin\theta_M - r_J \dot\theta_J^2 \sin\theta_J + r_4 \dot\theta_4^2 \sin\theta_4 \end{Bmatrix}$$

$$\ddot{\boldsymbol{r}}_Q = \ddot{\boldsymbol{r}}_2 = (-r_2\ddot\theta_2 \sin\theta_2 - r_2\dot\theta_2^2 \cos\theta_2)\boldsymbol{i} + (r_2\ddot\theta_2 \cos\theta_2 - r_2\dot\theta_2^2 \sin\theta_2)\boldsymbol{j}$$

$$\ddot{\boldsymbol{r}}_P = -(r_4\ddot\theta_4 \sin\theta_4 + r_4\dot\theta_4^2 \cos\theta_4)\boldsymbol{i} + (r_4\ddot\theta_4 \cos\theta_4 - r_4\dot\theta_4^2 \sin\theta_4)\boldsymbol{j}$$

EXAMPLE 5.1 *Position Analysis of a Four-Bar Linkage*

For the linkage with $r_1 = 1$, $r_2 = 2$, $r_3 = 3.5$, $r_4 = 4$, and $\theta_1 = 0$ shown in Fig. 5.9, compute the corresponding values of θ_3 and θ_4 for each of the solution branches when the driving crank is in the positions $\theta_2 = 0$, $\pi/2$, π, and $-\pi/2$. Units for the lengths are not explicitly given in this example because the angular results are independent of the units for the lengths.

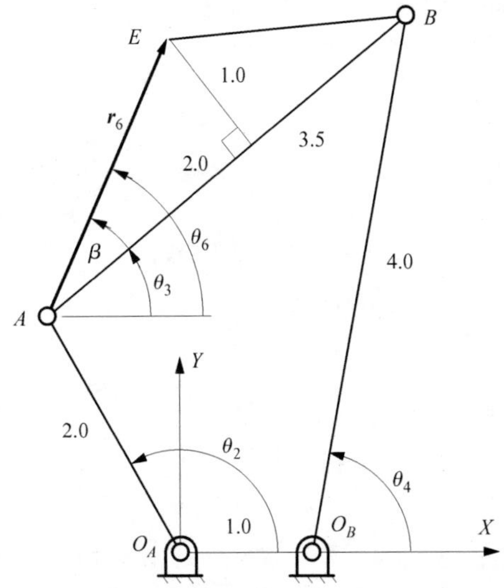

FIGURE 5.9 The linkage for Example 5.1, 5.2, and 5.3.

Solution

The solution procedure is to use the equations in Table 5.1. First compute A, B, and C for each value of θ_2 and then select σ. Next compute θ_4 and then θ_3. The calculations for $\theta_2 = 0$ are as follows:

$$A = 2r_1r_4\cos\theta_1 - 2r_2r_4\cos\theta_2 = 2(1)(4) - 2(2)(4) = -8$$

$$B = 2r_1r_4\sin\theta_1 - 2r_2r_4\sin\theta_2 = 0$$

$$C = r_1^2 + r_2^2 + r_4^2 - r_3^2 - 2r_1r_2(\cos\theta_1\cos\theta_2 + \sin\theta_1\sin\theta_2) = 1^2 + 2^2 + 4^2 - 3.5^2 - 2(1)(2) = 4.75$$

$$\theta_4 = 2\tan^{-1}\left[\frac{-B + \sigma\sqrt{B^2 - C^2 + A^2}}{C - A}\right]$$

$$= 2\tan^{-1}\left[\frac{-0 + \sqrt{0^2 - 4.75^2 + (-8)^2}}{4.75 + 8}\right] = 2\tan^{-1}(0.5049) = 53.58^\circ$$

$$\theta_3 = \tan^{-1}\left[\frac{r_1\sin\theta_1 + r_4\sin\theta_4 - r_2\sin\theta_2}{r_1\cos\theta_1 + r_4\cos\theta_4 - r_2\cos\theta_2}\right]$$

$$= \tan^{-1}\left[\frac{4\sin(53.58^\circ)}{1 + 4\cos(53.58^\circ) - 2}\right] = \tan^{-1}\left[\frac{3.2187}{1.3748}\right] = \tan^{-1}(2.3412) = 66.87^\circ$$

The remainder of the solution is summarized in Table 5.2.

TABLE 5.2 Summary of Results for Example 5.1

θ_2	σ	A	B	C	θ_4	θ_3
0	1	−8	0	4.75	53.58°	66.87°
	−1				−53.58°	−66.87°
$\pi/2$	1	87	−16	8.75	177.28°	−143.85°
	−1				55.85°	21.98°
π	1	24	0	12.75	−122.09°	−75.52°
	−1				122.09°	75.52°
$-\pi/21$	1	8	16	8.75	−55.85°	−21.98°
	−1				−177.28°	148.85°

The arithmetic may also be checked by comparing $\gamma = \theta_4 - \theta_3$ for $\sigma = \pm 1$. One value should be minus the other if both values are in the range $-\pi < \gamma'' \pi$. It may be necessary to add or subtract 2π to either value to bring γ into the range $-\pi < \gamma'' \pi$.

EXAMPLE 5.2 ***Velocity and Acceleration Analysis of a Four-Bar Linkage with Crank Input***

If, for the linkage in Example 5.1 (Fig. 5.9), $\dot{\theta}_2 = 10$ rad/s and $\ddot{\theta}_2 = 0$, compute $\dot{\theta}_3, \dot{\theta}_4, \ddot{\theta}_3, \ddot{\theta}_4$ in the first of the four positions ($\theta_2 = 0$).

Solution

Using the equations in Table 5.1, we write the velocity expression as

$$\begin{bmatrix} -r_3 \sin\theta_3 & r_4 \sin\theta_4 \\ -r_3 \cos\theta_3 & r_4 \cos\theta_4 \end{bmatrix} \begin{Bmatrix} \dot{\theta}_3 \\ \dot{\theta}_4 \end{Bmatrix} = \begin{Bmatrix} r_2\dot{\theta}_2 \sin\theta_2 \\ r_2\dot{\theta}_2 \cos\theta_2 \end{Bmatrix}$$

$$= \begin{bmatrix} -3.5\sin(66.87^\circ) & 4\sin(53.58^\circ) \\ -3.5\cos(66.87^\circ) & 4\cos(53.58^\circ) \end{bmatrix} \begin{Bmatrix} \dot{\theta}_3 \\ \dot{\theta}_4 \end{Bmatrix} = \begin{Bmatrix} 2(10)\sin(0^\circ) \\ 2(10)\cos(0^\circ) \end{Bmatrix} = \begin{bmatrix} -3.2187 & 3.2187 \\ -1.3749 & 2.3748 \end{bmatrix} \begin{Bmatrix} \dot{\theta}_3 \\ \dot{\theta}_4 \end{Bmatrix} = \begin{Bmatrix} 0 \\ 20 \end{Bmatrix}$$

Solving the linear set of equations gives $\dot{\theta}_3 = 20$ rad/s and $\dot{\theta}_4 = 20.0$ rad/s. Both values are positive, so the corresponding angular velocities are counterclockwise. The acceleration expression is

$$\begin{bmatrix} -r_3 \sin\theta_3 & r_4 \sin\theta_4 \\ -r_3 \cos\theta_3 & r_4 \cos\theta_4 \end{bmatrix} \begin{Bmatrix} \ddot{\theta}_3 \\ \ddot{\theta}_4 \end{Bmatrix} = \begin{Bmatrix} r_2\ddot{\theta}_2 \sin\theta_2 + r_2\dot{\theta}_2^2 \cos\theta_2 + r_3\dot{\theta}_3^2 \cos\theta_3 - r_4\dot{\theta}_4^2 \cos\theta_4 \\ r_2\ddot{\theta}_2 \cos\theta_2 - r_2\dot{\theta}_2^2 \sin\theta_2 - r_3\dot{\theta}_3^2 \sin\theta_3 - r_4\dot{\theta}_4^2 \sin\theta_4 \end{Bmatrix}$$

$$\begin{bmatrix} -3.2187 & 3.2187 \\ -1.3749 & 2.3748 \end{bmatrix} \begin{Bmatrix} \ddot{\theta}_3 \\ \ddot{\theta}_4 \end{Bmatrix} = \begin{Bmatrix} 0 + 2(10)^2 + 3.5(20)^2\cos(66.87^\circ) - 4(20)^2\cos(53.58^\circ) \\ 0 - 0 - 3.5(20)^2\sin(66.87^\circ) + 4(20)^2\sin(53.58^\circ) \end{Bmatrix} = \begin{Bmatrix} -200.0265 \\ -0.0363 \end{Bmatrix}$$

Solving the linear set of equations gives $\ddot{\theta}_3 = 147.5634$ rad/s^2 and $\ddot{\theta}_4 = 85.4150$ rad/s^2. Again, both values are positive, so the corresponding angular accelerations are counterclockwise.

5.4 ANALYTICAL EQUATIONS FOR A RIGID BODY AFTER THE KINEMATIC PROPERTIES OF TWO POINTS ARE KNOWN

The equations presented so far will permit the kinematic properties of the points on the vector loop to be computed directly. However, often we need to compute the position, velocity, and acceleration of points that are not directly on the vector loops. In general, given the kinematic properties of *one* point on a rigid body and the angular position, angular velocity, and angular acceleration of the body, we can compute the position, velocity, and acceleration of *any* defined point on the rigid body.

Consider the rigid body represented in Fig. 5.10. Assume that A and B are two points attached to an arbitrary link, say link 5, and a third point is defined relative to the line between points A and B by the angle β and the distance $r_{C/A}$, which is represented in Fig. 5.10 as r_6. Then the linear position, velocity, and acceleration of point C can be computed directly if the following are known: $\boldsymbol{r}_A, \dot{\boldsymbol{r}}_A, \ddot{\boldsymbol{r}}_A, \theta_5, \dot{\theta}_5$, and $\ddot{\theta}_5$.

The position of point C is given as

$$\boldsymbol{r}_C = \boldsymbol{r}_A + \boldsymbol{r}_6$$

or

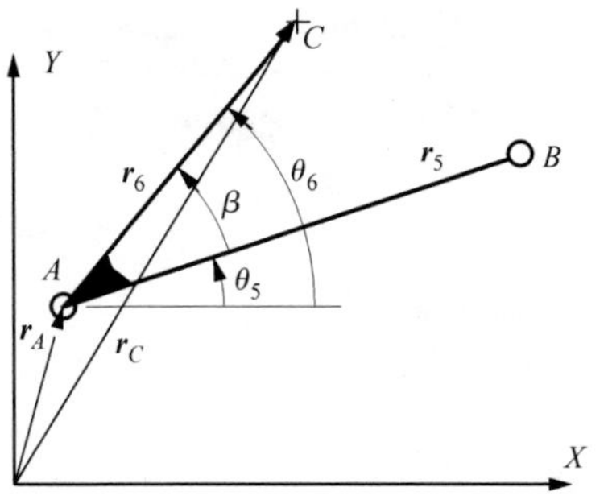

FIGURE 5.10 Calculation of the kinematic properties of a point on a link after the kinematic properties of one point and the angular velocity and acceleration of the link are known.

$$\boldsymbol{r}_C = \boldsymbol{r}_A + r_6(\cos\theta_6 \boldsymbol{i} + \sin\theta_6 \boldsymbol{j}) \tag{5.56}$$

where

$$\theta_6 = \beta + \theta_5 \tag{5.57}$$

Recognizing that β is a constant, we see that the velocity of point C is given by

$$\dot{\boldsymbol{r}}_C = \dot{\boldsymbol{r}}_A + r_6\dot{\theta}_5(-\sin\theta_6 \boldsymbol{i} + \cos\theta_6 \boldsymbol{j}) \tag{5.58}$$

and the acceleration is given by

$$\ddot{\boldsymbol{r}}_C = \ddot{\boldsymbol{r}}_A + r_6\ddot{\theta}_5(-\sin\theta_6 \boldsymbol{i} + \cos\theta_6 \boldsymbol{j}) - r_6\dot{\theta}_5^2(\cos\theta_6 \boldsymbol{i} + \sin\theta_6 \boldsymbol{j}) \tag{5.59}$$

Note that we have assumed here that θ_5, $\dot{\theta}_5$, and $\ddot{\theta}_5$ are known. Often, we will know the kinematic information for two points on a rigid link instead of these angular quantities. If we know the position, velocity, and acceleration of two points (say A and B), we can compute θ_5, $\dot{\theta}_5$, and $\ddot{\theta}_5$ and proceed as before. The angle can be computed from the x and y components of the position vectors for A and B using

$$\theta_5 = \tan^{-1}\left[\frac{r_{B_y} - r_{A_y}}{r_{B_x} - r_{A_x}}\right]$$

The angular velocity can be computed by rewriting Eq. (5.58) in terms of points A and B. That is,

$$\dot{\boldsymbol{r}}_B = \dot{\boldsymbol{r}}_A + r_5\dot{\theta}_5(-\sin\theta_5 \boldsymbol{i} + \cos\theta_5 \boldsymbol{j})$$

Therefore,

$$\dot{\theta}_5 = -\frac{\dot{r}_{B_x} - \dot{r}_{A_x}}{r_5 \sin\theta_5} = \frac{\dot{r}_{B_y} - \dot{r}_{A_y}}{r_5 \cos\theta_5}$$

Similarly, the angular acceleration can be computed by rewriting Eq. (5.59) in terms of A and B. That is,

$$\ddot{\boldsymbol{r}}_B = \ddot{\boldsymbol{r}}_A + r_5\ddot{\theta}_5(-\sin\theta_5 \boldsymbol{i} + \cos\theta_5 \boldsymbol{j}) - r_5\dot{\theta}_5^2(\cos\theta_5 \boldsymbol{i} + \sin\theta_5 \boldsymbol{j})$$

Therefore,

$$\ddot{\theta}_5 = -\frac{(\ddot{r}_{B_x} - \ddot{r}_{A_x}) + r_5\dot{\theta}_5^2 \cos\theta_5}{r_5 \sin\theta_5} = \frac{(\ddot{r}_{B_y} - \ddot{r}_{A_y}) + r_5\dot{\theta}_5^2 \sin\theta_5}{r_5 \cos\theta_5}$$

These equations are summarized in Table 5.3, and a MATLAB function routine for the calculations is included on the disk with this book.

TABLE 5.3 Summary of Position, Velocity, and Acceleration Equations for an Arbitrary Point on a Rigid Body. The Vectors and Points Are Defined in Fig. 5.10

If $\boldsymbol{r}_A$ and $\boldsymbol{r}_B$ are given instead of θ_5, $\dot{\theta}_5$, and $\ddot{\theta}_5$, first compute θ_5, $\dot{\theta}_5$, and $\ddot{\theta}_5$ using the following:

$$\theta_5 = \tan^{-1}\left[\frac{r_{B_y} - r_{A_y}}{r_{B_x} - r_{A_x}}\right],$$

$$\dot{\theta}_5 = -\frac{\dot{r}_{B_x} - \dot{r}_{A_x}}{r_5 \sin\theta_5} = \frac{\dot{r}_{B_y} - \dot{r}_{A_y}}{r_5 \cos\theta_5},$$

$$\ddot{\theta}_5 = -\frac{\left(\ddot{r}_{B_x} - \ddot{r}_{A_x}\right) + r_5\dot{\theta}_5^2 \cos\theta_5}{r_5 \sin\theta_5} = \frac{\left(\ddot{r}_{B_y} - \ddot{r}_{A_y}\right) + r_5\dot{\theta}_5^2 \sin\theta_5}{r_5 \cos\theta_5}$$

Position

$$\boldsymbol{r}_C = \boldsymbol{r}_A + r_6\left(\cos\theta_6\boldsymbol{i} + \sin\theta_6\boldsymbol{j}\right)$$

$$\theta_6 = \beta + \theta_5$$

Velocity

$$\dot{\boldsymbol{r}}_C = \dot{\boldsymbol{r}}_A + r_6\dot{\theta}_5\left(-\sin\theta_6\boldsymbol{i} + \cos\theta_6\boldsymbol{j}\right)$$

Acceleration

$$\ddot{\boldsymbol{r}}_C = \ddot{\boldsymbol{r}}_A + r_6\ddot{\theta}_5\left(-\sin\theta_6\boldsymbol{i} + \cos\theta_6\boldsymbol{j}\right) - r_6\dot{\theta}_5^2\left(\cos\theta_6\boldsymbol{i} + \sin\theta_6\boldsymbol{j}\right)$$

EXAMPLE 5.3
Velocity and Acceleration Analysis of a Coupler Point

For the linkage in Examples 5.1 and 5.2 shown in Fig. 5.9, compute the velocity and acceleration of point E_3 when $\theta_2 = 0$, $\dot{\theta}_2 = 10$ rad/s, $\ddot{\theta}_2 = 0$, and $\sigma = 1$. Assume that the lengths are given in centimeters.

Solution

First compute the angle β between the line AB and the line AE. The angle is given by

$$\beta = \tan^{-1}\left(\frac{1}{2}\right) = 26.565°$$

and the length AE is given by

$$r_6 = AE = 2.0/\cos(26.565°) = 2.236 \text{ cm}$$

Then the velocity of E_3 is given by

$$\dot{\boldsymbol{r}}_{E_3} = r_2\dot{\theta}_2\left(-\sin\theta_2\boldsymbol{i} + \cos\theta_2\boldsymbol{j}\right) + r_6\dot{\theta}_3\left(-\sin\theta_6\boldsymbol{i} + \cos\theta_6\boldsymbol{j}\right)$$

Substitution of $\theta_2 = 0$, $\theta_3 = 66.87°$, $\dot{\theta}_2 = 10.0$ rad/s, and $\dot{\theta}_3 = 20.0$ rad/s from Example 5.2 gives

$$\theta_6 = \theta_3 + \beta = 66.87° + 26.565° = 93.435°$$

and

$$\dot{\boldsymbol{r}}_{E_3} = 2(10)(0\boldsymbol{i} + \boldsymbol{j}) + 2.236(20.0)\left(-\sin(93.435°)\boldsymbol{i} + \cos(93.435°)\boldsymbol{j}\right)$$

$$= 20\boldsymbol{j} - 44.640\boldsymbol{i} - 2.679\boldsymbol{j} = -44.64\boldsymbol{i} + 17.32\boldsymbol{j} \text{ cm/s}$$

The acceleration of E_3 is given by

$$\ddot{r}_{E_3} = r_2\ddot{\theta}_2(-\sin\theta_2 \boldsymbol{i} + \cos\theta_2 \boldsymbol{j}) - r_2\dot{\theta}_2^2(\cos\theta_2 \boldsymbol{i} + \sin\theta_2 \boldsymbol{j})$$
$$+r_6\ddot{\theta}_3(-\sin\theta_6 \boldsymbol{i} + \cos\theta_6 \boldsymbol{j}) - r_6\dot{\theta}_3^2(\cos\theta_6 \boldsymbol{i} + \sin\theta_6 \boldsymbol{j})$$

Substitution of $\theta_2 = 0$, $\theta_3 = 66.87°$, $\dot{\theta}_2 = 10.0$ rad/s, $\ddot{\theta}_2 = 0$ rad/s^2, $\dot{\theta}_3 = 20.0$ rad/s, and $\ddot{\theta}_3 = 147.56$ rad/s^2 gives

$$\ddot{r}_{E_3} = 0 - 2(10)^2(\boldsymbol{i} + 0\boldsymbol{j}) + 2.236(147.56)[-\sin(93.435°)\boldsymbol{i} + \cos(93.435°)\boldsymbol{j}]$$
$$-2.236(20.0)^2[\cos(93.435°)\boldsymbol{i} + \sin(93.435°)\boldsymbol{j}] = -475.76\boldsymbol{i} - 912.56\boldsymbol{j} \text{ cm/s}^2$$

5.5 ANALYTICAL EQUATIONS FOR SLIDER-CRANK MECHANISMS

Next to the four-bar linkage, the slider-crank is probably the most commonly used mechanism. It appears in all internal combustion engines (Fig. 5.11) and in numerous industrial (Fig. 5.12) and household devices (Fig. 5.13). A general slider-crank mechanism is represented in Fig. 5.14. To develop the closure equations, locate vectors $\boldsymbol{r}_2$ and $\boldsymbol{r}_3$ as was done in the regular four-bar linkage. To form the other part of the closure equation, draw two vectors, one in the direction of the slider velocity and one perpendicular to the velocity direction. The variables associated with the problem are then located as shown in Fig. 5.14. The loop closure equation is then the same as that for the regular four-bar linkage:

$$\boldsymbol{r}_P = \boldsymbol{r}_2 + \boldsymbol{r}_3 = \boldsymbol{r}_1 + \boldsymbol{r}_4 \tag{5.60}$$

or

$$r_2(\cos\theta_2 \boldsymbol{i} + \sin\theta_2 \boldsymbol{j}) + r_3(\cos\theta_3 \boldsymbol{i} + \sin\theta_3 \boldsymbol{j}) = r_1(\cos\theta_1 \boldsymbol{i} + \sin\theta_1 \boldsymbol{j}) + r_4(\cos\theta_4 \boldsymbol{i} + \sin\theta_4 \boldsymbol{j}) \tag{5.61}$$

where

$$\theta_4 = \theta_1 + \pi/2 \tag{5.62}$$

Because θ_1 is constant, θ_4 is also constant.

Rewriting Eq. (5.61) into its component equations gives

$$r_2\cos\theta_2 + r_3\cos\theta_3 = r_1\cos\theta_1 + r_4\cos\theta_4 \tag{5.63}$$

$$r_2\sin\theta_2 + r_3\sin\theta_3 = r_1\sin\theta_1 + r_4\sin\theta_4 \tag{5.64}$$

Equations (5.62)–(5.64) must be satisfied throughout the motion of the linkage. The base vector, $\boldsymbol{r}_1$, will vary in magnitude but be constant in direction. The vector $\boldsymbol{r}_4$ will be constant. Therefore, $\boldsymbol{r}_2$, $\boldsymbol{r}_3$, $\boldsymbol{r}_4$, θ_1, and θ_4 are constants. If θ_2 is given, it is necessary to solve Eqs. (5.63) and (5.64) for θ_3 and $\boldsymbol{r}_1$ in terms of θ_2. If $\boldsymbol{r}_1$ is given, it is necessary to solve the same equations for θ_2 and θ_3. And finally, if θ_3 is given, it is necessary to solve the equations for θ_2 and $\boldsymbol{r}_1$. Once these expressions are obtained, the unknown velocities and accelerations can be computed in terms of the knowns by differentiation.

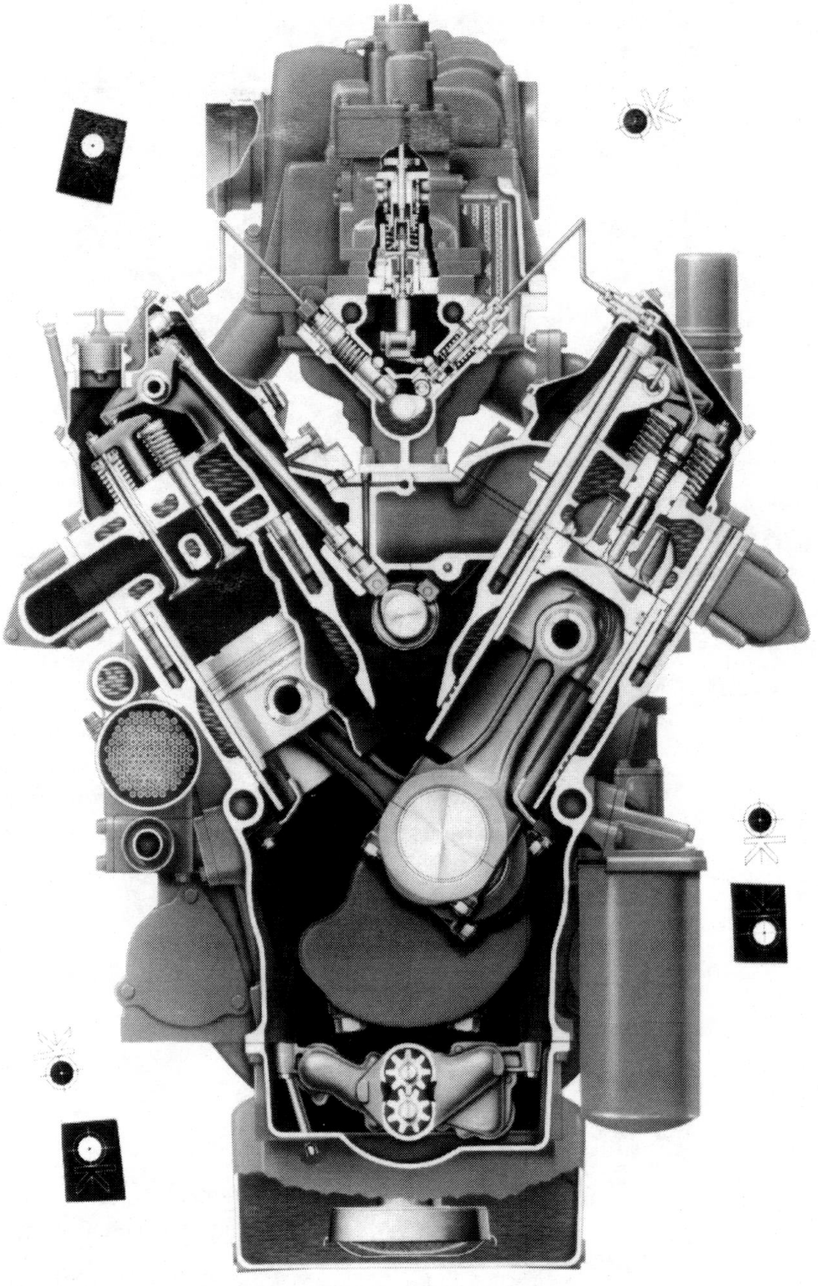

FIGURE 5.11 Internal combustion engine. An example of a slider-crank mechanism where the crank is the output link. (Courtesy of Caterpillar, Inc., Peoria, Illinois.)

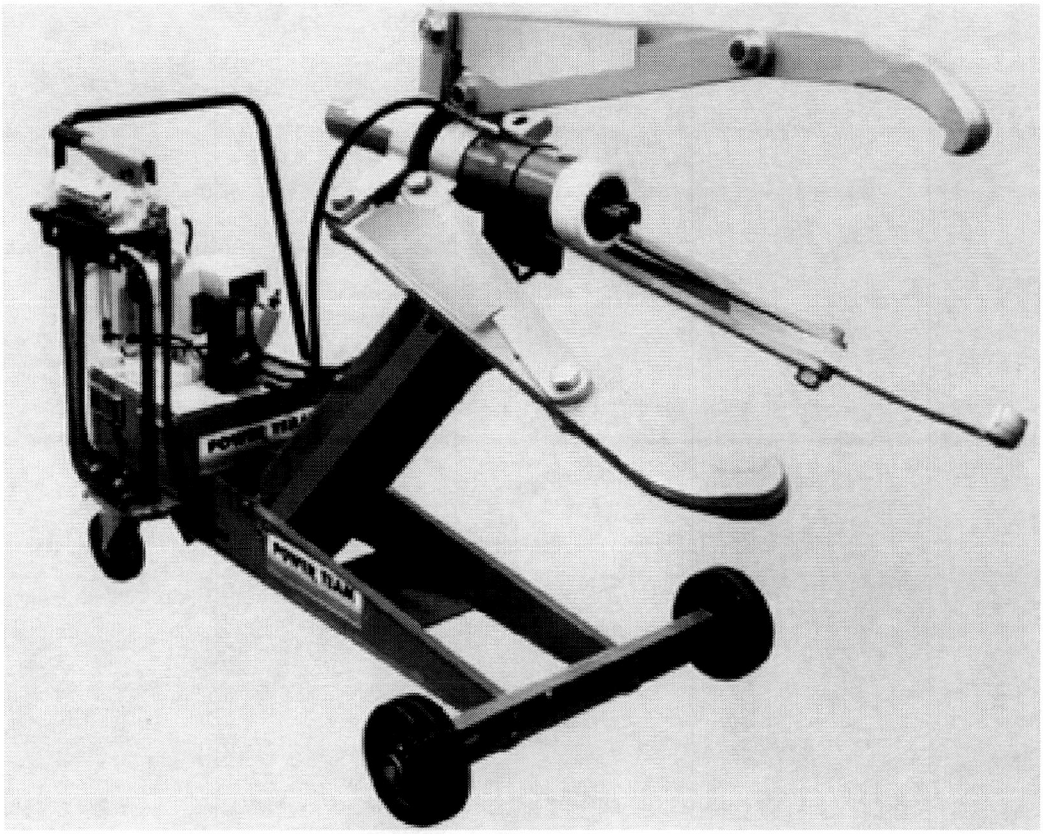

FIGURE 5.12 Hydraulic shaft puller. An example of a slider-crank mechanism where the slider is the input link. (Courtesy of Power Team, Owatonna, Minnesota.)

FIGURE 5.13 Ping-Pong table linkage. An example of a slider-crank mechanism where the coupler is the input link.

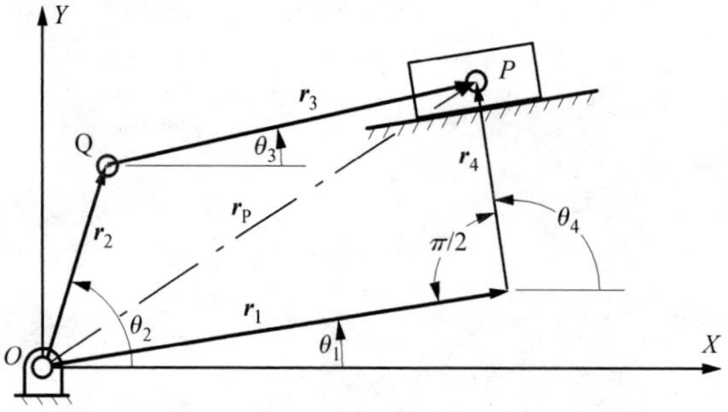

FIGURE 5.14 Vector closure condition for a slider-crank mechanism. The position of point P obtained by adding the vectors $\boldsymbol{r}_2$ and $\boldsymbol{r}_3$ is the same as that obtained by adding vectors $\boldsymbol{r}_1$ and $\boldsymbol{r}_4$.

5.5.1 Solution to Position Equations When θ_2 Is Input

The analytical solution procedure follows the same major steps as in the four-bar linkage case. To eliminate θ_3, first isolate it in Eqs. (5.63) and (5.64) as follows:

$$r_3 \cos\theta_3 = r_1 \cos\theta_1 + r_4 \cos\theta_4 - r_2 \cos\theta_2 \tag{5.65}$$

$$r_3 \sin\theta_3 = r_1 \sin\theta_1 + r_4 \sin\theta_4 - r_2 \sin\theta_2 \tag{5.66}$$

Notice that in Fig. 5.14, the angles θ_1 and θ_4 are known constants, but r_1 varies and is unknown. Now square both sides of both equations and add. This gives

$$r_3^2\left(\cos^2\theta_3 + \sin^2\theta_3\right) = \left(r_1 \cos\theta_1 + r_4 \cos\theta_4 - r_2 \cos\theta_2\right)^2 + \left(r_1 \sin\theta_1 + r_4 \sin\theta_4 - r_2 \sin\theta_2\right)^2$$

Expansion and simplification using the trigonometric identity $\sin^2\theta + \cos^2\theta = 1$ gives

$$\begin{aligned} r_3^2 = r_1^2 + r_2^2 + r_4^2 &+ 2r_1r_4\left(\cos\theta_1 \cos\theta_4 + \sin\theta_1 \sin\theta_4\right) \\ &-2r_1r_2\left(\cos\theta_1 \cos\theta_2 + \sin\theta_1 \sin\theta_2\right) - 2r_2r_4\left(\cos\theta_2 \cos\theta_4 + \sin\theta_2 \sin\theta_4\right) \end{aligned} \tag{5.67}$$

Equation (5.67) gives r_1 in a quadratic expression involving θ_2 and the other known variables. To obtain a solution, collect together the coefficients of the different powers of r_1 as follows:

$$r_1^2 + Ar_1 + B = 0 \tag{5.68}$$

where

$$\begin{aligned} A &= 2r_4\left(\cos\theta_1 \cos\theta_4 + \sin\theta_1 \sin\theta_4\right) - 2r_2\left(\cos\theta_1 \cos\theta_2 + \sin\theta_1 \sin\theta_2\right) \\ B &= r_2^2 + r_4^2 - r_3^2 - 2r_2r_4\left(\cos\theta_2 \cos\theta_4 + \sin\theta_2 \sin\theta_4\right) \end{aligned} \tag{5.69}$$

Solving for r_1 gives

$$r_1 = \frac{-A + \sigma\sqrt{A^2 - 4B}}{2} \tag{5.70}$$

where $\sigma = \pm 1$ is a sign variable identifying the assembly mode. There are two assembly modes corresponding to the two configurations shown in Fig. 5.15.

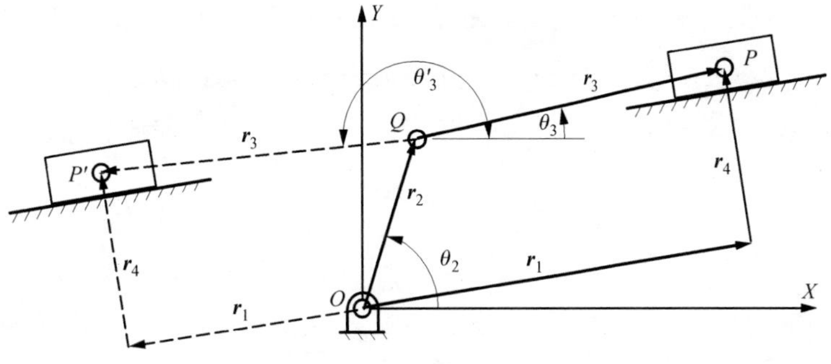

FIGURE 5.15 The two possible positions (P and P') of the point P for a given value of θ_2 in a slider-crank mechanism.

As in the case of the four-bar linkage, once we pick the value for σ corresponding to the desired mode, the sign in an actual linkage stays the same for any value of θ_2.

Because of the square root in Eq. (5.70), the variable r_1 can be complex ($A^2 < 4B$). If this happens, the mechanism cannot be assembled in the position specified. The assembly would then appear as one of the configurations shown in Fig. 5.15.

Once a value for r_1 is determined, Eqs. (5.65) and (5.66) can be solved for θ_3. Dividing Eq. (5.66) by Eq. (5.65) and solving for θ_3 gives

$$\theta_3 = \tan^{-1}\left[\frac{r_1 \sin\theta_1 + r_4 \sin\theta_4 - r_2 \sin\theta_2}{r_1 \cos\theta_1 + r_4 \cos\theta_4 - r_2 \cos\theta_2}\right] \tag{5.71}$$

As in the case of the four-bar linkage, it is essential that the signs of the numerator and denominator in Eq. (5.71) be maintained to determine the quadrant in which the angle θ_3 lies.

Once all of the angular quantities are known, it is relatively straightforward to compute the coordinates of any point on the vector loops used in the closure equations. In particular, the coordinates of Q and P are given by

$$\boldsymbol{r}_Q = \boldsymbol{r}_2 = r_2(\cos\theta_2 \boldsymbol{i} + \sin\theta_2 \boldsymbol{j}) \tag{5.72}$$

and

$$\boldsymbol{r}_P = \boldsymbol{r}_2 + \boldsymbol{r}_3 = r_2(\cos\theta_2 \boldsymbol{i} + \sin\theta_2 \boldsymbol{j}) + r_3(\cos\theta_3 \boldsymbol{i} + \sin\theta_3 \boldsymbol{j}) \tag{5.73}$$

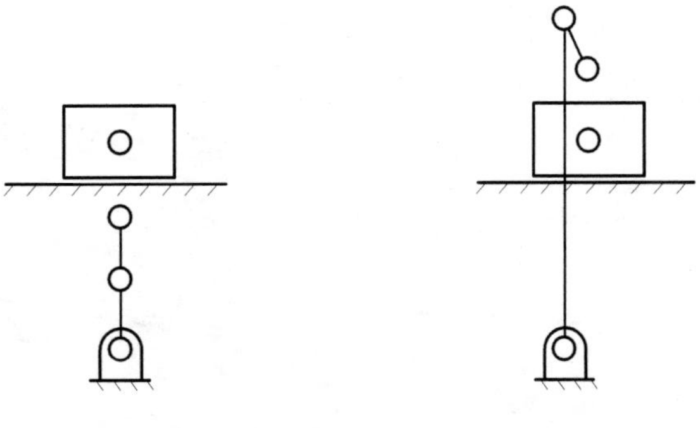

FIGURE 5.16 Configurations giving complex solutions for slider-crank position problem.

5.5.2 Solution to Position Equations When r_1 Is Input

The analytical solution procedure follows the same major steps as in the previous case. Referring to Fig. 5.14, we again start by eliminating θ_3 from Eqs. (5.63) and (5.64) to get Eq. (5.67). Then we simplify Eq. (5.67) as follows:

$$A\cos\theta_2 + B\sin\theta_2 + C = 0 \tag{5.74}$$

where

$$\left.\begin{aligned} A &= -2r_1r_2\cos\theta_1 - 2r_2r_4\cos\theta_4 \\ B &= -2r_1r_2\sin\theta_1 - 2r_2r_4\sin\theta_4 \\ C &= r_1^2 + r_2^2 + r_4^2 - r_3^2 + 2r_1r_4\left(\cos\theta_1\cos\theta_4 + \sin\theta_1\sin\theta_4\right) \end{aligned}\right\} \tag{5.75}$$

To solve Eq. (5.74), the trigonometric half-angle identities given in Eqs. (5.33–5.34) can be used. Using these identities in Eq. (5.74) and simplifying gives

$$A\left(1-t^2\right) + B\left(2t\right) + C\left(1+t^2\right) = 0$$

where

$$t = \tan\left(\frac{\theta_2}{2}\right)$$

Further simplification gives

$$\left(C-A\right)t^2 + 2Bt + \left(A+C\right) = 0$$

Solving for t gives

$$t = \frac{-2B + \sigma\sqrt{4B^2 - 4\left(C-A\right)\left(C+A\right)}}{2\left(C-A\right)} = \frac{-B + \sigma\sqrt{B^2 - C^2 + A^2}}{C-A} \tag{5.76}$$

and

$$\theta_2 = 2\tan^{-1} t \tag{5.77}$$

where $\sigma = \pm 1$ is a sign variable identifying the assembly mode. Once again, because $\tan^{-1} t$ has a valid range of values $-\pi/2$ ″ $\tan^{-1} t < \pi/2$, θ_2 will have the range $-\pi$ ″ θ_2 ″ π. Typically, there are two solutions for θ_2 corresponding to the two values of σ, and they are both valid. These correspond to the two assembly modes shown in Fig. 5.17. Once we pick the

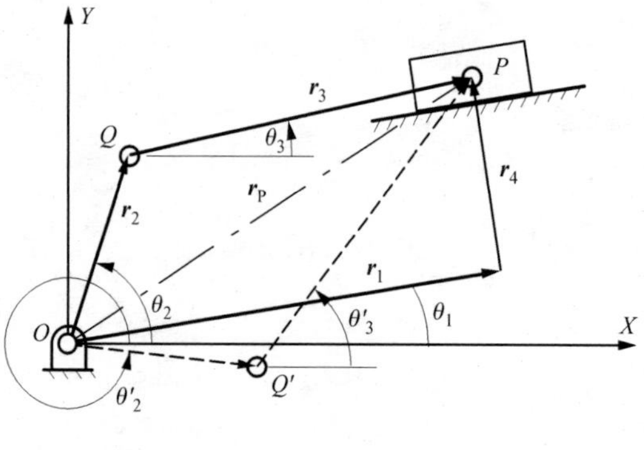

FIGURE 5.17 Two possible assembly modes when the position r_1 of the slider is given as an input.

value for σ corresponding to the desired mode, the sign in an actual linkage stays the same for any value of r_1.

Because of the square root in Eq. (5.76), the variable t can be complex $[(A^2 + B^2) < C^2]$. If this happens, the mechanism cannot be assembled for the specified value of r_1. The assembly configurations would then appear as shown in Fig. 5.18.

Knowing r_1, equations (5.65) and (5.66) can now be solved for θ_3. The resulting equation is Eq. (5.71). As in the previous cases, it is essential that the signs of the numerator and denominator in Eq. (5.71) be maintained to determine the quadrant in which the angle θ_3 lies. Note that the positions of $\mathbf{r}_2$ and $\mathbf{r}_3$ are symmetric about the line OP.

Once all of the angular quantities are known, it is relatively straightforward to compute the coordinates of any point on the vector loops used in the closure equations. The coordinates of Q and P are again given by Eqs. (5.72) and (5.73).

5.5.3 Solution to Position Equations When θ_3 Is Input

When the coupler of the linkage in Fig. 5.14 is the input link, values for θ_3 and its derivatives will be known. The analytical procedure for solving the position equations follows the same major steps as when θ_2 is the input. Therefore, we will simply outline the procedure and tabulate the results.

In the procedure, we can assume that θ_1, θ_3, θ_4, $\dot{\theta}_3$, and $\ddot{\theta}_3$ are known and θ_2, $\dot{\theta}_2$, $\ddot{\theta}_2$, r_1, $\dot{r}_1$, and $\ddot{r}_1$ are to be found. The link lengths r_2 and r_3 and the angles θ_1 and θ_4 are constants. For the position analysis, again begin with Eqs. (5.63) and (5.64) and isolate the terms with either θ_2 or θ_4. It is advantageous to select θ_2 because the resulting equations will be similar to those derived earlier. The resulting equations are

$$r_2 \cos\theta_2 = r_1 \cos\theta_1 + r_4 \cos\theta_4 - r_3 \cos\theta_3 \tag{5.78}$$

$$r_2 \sin\theta_2 = r_1 \sin\theta_1 + r_4 \sin\theta_4 - r_3 \sin\theta_3 \tag{5.79}$$

A comparison of Eqs. (5.78) and (5.79) with Eqs. (5.65) and (5.66) indicates that they are of the same form except that the indices 2 and 3 are interchanged. Therefore, we can use directly the position solution derived in Section 5.5.1 if we interchange the indices 2 and 3.

When the coupler is the driver, there is an assembly-mode ambiguity similar to that observed when link 2 is the driver. This is illustrated in Fig. 5.19. It is necessary to know the appropriate mode before the analysis can be completed; however, once the assembly mode is selected, it is the same for all positions of the input.

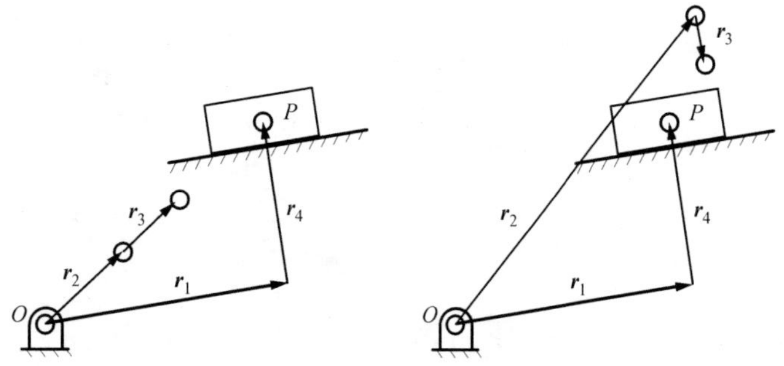

FIGURE 5.18 Slider-crank mechanisms that cannot be assembled in the position chosen for $\mathbf{r}_1$. The variable t would be complex in these cases.

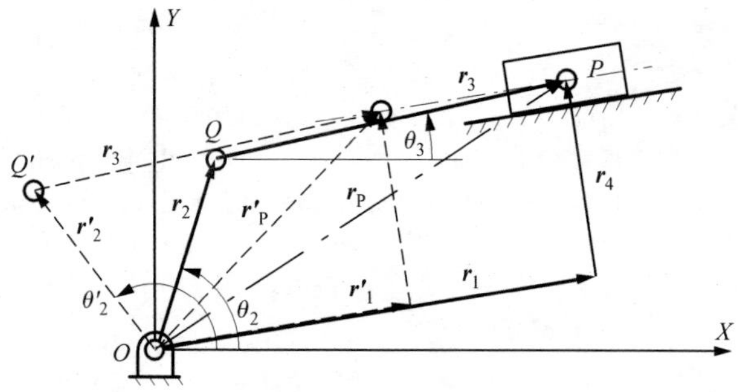

FIGURE 5.19 Two possible assembly modes when the coupler is the input link.

5.5.4 Velocity Equations for Slider-Crank Mechanism

The analytical form of the velocity equations for the linkage of Fig. 5.14 can be developed by differentiating Eq. (5.60). The result is

$$\dot{\boldsymbol{r}}_P = \dot{\boldsymbol{r}}_2 + \dot{\boldsymbol{r}}_3 = \dot{\boldsymbol{r}}_1 + \dot{\boldsymbol{r}}_4 \tag{5.80}$$

When this equation is written in component form, the result is the same as differentiating Eqs. (5.63) and (5.64). Recognizing that r_2, r_3, r_4, θ_1, and θ_4 are constants, we see the resulting component equations are

$$-r_2\dot{\theta}_2 \sin\theta_2 - r_3\dot{\theta}_3 \sin\theta_3 = \dot{r}_1 \cos\theta_1 \tag{5.81}$$

$$r_2\dot{\theta}_2 \cos\theta_2 + r_3\dot{\theta}_3 \cos\theta_3 = \dot{r}_1 \sin\theta_1 \tag{5.82}$$

The solution procedure depends on whether $\dot{r}_1$, $\dot{\theta}_2$, or $\dot{\theta}_3$ is known. If $\dot{\theta}_2$ (or $\dot{\theta}_3$) is input, then $\dot{r}_1$ and $\dot{\theta}_3$ (or $\dot{\theta}_2$) will be unknown. Therefore, the matrix equation to be solved is

$$\begin{bmatrix} \cos\theta_1 & r_J \sin\theta_J \\ \sin\theta_1 & -r_J \cos\theta_J \end{bmatrix} \begin{Bmatrix} \dot{r}_1 \\ \dot{\theta}_J \end{Bmatrix} = \begin{Bmatrix} -r_M\dot{\theta}_M \sin\theta_M \\ r_M\dot{\theta}_M \cos\theta_M \end{Bmatrix} \tag{5.83}$$

where $M = 2$ and $J = 3$ for link 2 as the input, and $M = 3$ and $J = 2$ for link 3 as the input. If $\dot{r}_1$ is input, then $\dot{\theta}_2$ and $\dot{\theta}_3$ will be unknown. The matrix equation to be solved then is

$$\begin{bmatrix} -r_2 \sin\theta_2 & -r_3 \sin\theta_3 \\ r_2 \cos\theta_2 & r_3 \cos\theta_3 \end{bmatrix} \begin{Bmatrix} \dot{\theta}_2 \\ \dot{\theta}_3 \end{Bmatrix} = \begin{Bmatrix} \dot{r}_1 \cos\theta_1 \\ \dot{r}_1 \sin\theta_1 \end{Bmatrix} \tag{5.84}$$

The terms in the matrix and in the vector on the right-hand sides of Eqs. (5.83) and (5.84) will be known. The equation can therefore be solved manually, on a programmable calculator, or numerically with the matrix solvers in programs such as MATLAB.

Once the angular velocities are known, it is a simple matter to compute the linear velocities of any of the points on the vector loop. The velocities of points Q and P are given by

$$\dot{\boldsymbol{r}}_Q = \dot{\boldsymbol{r}}_2 = r_2\dot{\theta}_2(-\sin\theta_2 \boldsymbol{i} + \cos\theta_2 \boldsymbol{j}) \tag{5.85}$$

and

$$\dot{\boldsymbol{r}}_P = \dot{\boldsymbol{r}}_2 + \dot{\boldsymbol{r}}_3 = (-r_2\dot{\theta}_2 \sin\theta_2 - r_3\dot{\theta}_3 \sin\theta_3)\boldsymbol{i} + (r_2\dot{\theta}_2 \cos\theta_2 + r_3\dot{\theta}_3 \cos\theta_3)\boldsymbol{j} \tag{5.86}$$

5.5.5 Acceleration Equations for Slider-Crank Mechanism

The analytical form of the acceleration equations for the linkage of Fig. 5.14 can be developed by differentiating Eq. (5.80). The result is

$$\ddot{r}_P = \ddot{r}_2 + \ddot{r}_3 = \ddot{r}_1 + \ddot{r}_4$$

When this equation is written in component form, the result is the same as differentiating Eqs. (5.81) and (5.82). The resulting component equations are

$$-r_2\ddot{\theta}_2 \sin\theta_2 - r_2\dot{\theta}_2^2 \cos\theta_2 - r_3\ddot{\theta}_3 \sin\theta_3 - r_3\dot{\theta}_3^2 \cos\theta_3 = \ddot{r}_1 \cos\theta_1 \tag{5.87}$$

$$r_2\ddot{\theta}_2 \cos\theta_2 - r_2\dot{\theta}_2^2 \sin\theta_2 + r_3\ddot{\theta}_3 \cos\theta_3 - r_3\dot{\theta}_3^2 \sin\theta_3 = \ddot{r}_1 \sin\theta_1 \tag{5.88}$$

As was the case for velocities, the solution procedure depends on whether $\ddot{\theta}_2$, $\ddot{\theta}_3$, or $\ddot{r}_1$ is known. If $\ddot{\theta}_2$ (or $\ddot{\theta}_3$) is input, then $\ddot{r}_1$ and $\ddot{\theta}_3$ (or $\ddot{\theta}_2$) will be unknown, and the matrix equation to be solved is

$$\begin{bmatrix} \cos\theta_1 & r_J \sin\theta_J \\ \sin\theta_1 & -r_J \cos\theta_J \end{bmatrix} \begin{Bmatrix} \ddot{r}_1 \\ \ddot{\theta}_J \end{Bmatrix} = \begin{Bmatrix} -r_M\ddot{\theta}_M \sin\theta_M - r_M\dot{\theta}_M^2 \cos\theta_M - r_J\dot{\theta}_J^2 \cos\theta_J \\ r_M\ddot{\theta}_M \cos\theta_M - r_M\dot{\theta}_M^2 \sin\theta_M - r_J\dot{\theta}_J^2 \sin\theta_J \end{Bmatrix} \tag{5.89}$$

If $\ddot{r}_1$ is input, then $\ddot{\theta}_2$ and $\ddot{\theta}_3$ will be unknown, and the matrix equation to be solved then is

$$\begin{bmatrix} -r_2 \sin\theta_2 & -r_3 \sin\theta_3 \\ r_2 \cos\theta_2 & r_3 \cos\theta_3 \end{bmatrix} \begin{Bmatrix} \ddot{\theta}_2 \\ \ddot{\theta}_3 \end{Bmatrix} = \begin{Bmatrix} r_2\dot{\theta}_2^2 \cos\theta_2 + r_3\dot{\theta}_3^2 \cos\theta_3 + \ddot{r}_1 \cos\theta_1 \\ r_2\dot{\theta}_2^2 \sin\theta_2 + r_3\dot{\theta}_3^2 \sin\theta_3 + \ddot{r}_1 \sin\theta_1 \end{Bmatrix} \tag{5.90}$$

The terms in the matrix and in the vector on the right-hand sides of Eqs. (5.89) and (5.90) will be known. The equation can therefore be solved manually, on a programmable calculator, or with the matrix solvers in programs such as MATLAB. Notice again that the coefficient matrix is the same for both the velocities (Eqs. (5.83) and (5.84) and for the accelerations (Eqs. (5.89) and (5.90)).

Once the angular accelerations are known, it is a simple matter to compute the linear acceleration of any point on the vector loop. The accelerations of points Q and P are given by

$$\ddot{r}_Q = \ddot{r}_2 = \left(r_2\ddot{\theta}_2 \sin\theta_2 - r_2\dot{\theta}_2^2 \cos\theta_2\right)\boldsymbol{i} + \left(r_2\ddot{\theta}_2 \cos\theta_2 - r_2\dot{\theta}_2^2 \sin\theta_2\right)\boldsymbol{j} \tag{5.91}$$

and

$$\ddot{r}_P = \ddot{r}_2 + \ddot{r}_3 = -\left(r_2\ddot{\theta}_2 \sin\theta_2 + r_2\dot{\theta}_2^2 \cos\theta_2 + r_3\ddot{\theta}_3 \sin\theta_3 + r_3\dot{\theta}_3^2 \cos\theta_3\right)\boldsymbol{i}$$
$$+\left(r_2\ddot{\theta}_2 \cos\theta_2 - r_2\dot{\theta}_2^2 \sin\theta_2 + r_3\ddot{\theta}_3 \cos\theta_3 - r_3\dot{\theta}_3^2 \sin\theta_3\right)\boldsymbol{j} \tag{5.92}$$

Now that the equations have been developed, it is relatively simple to write a computer program for the analysis of a slider-crank linkage. To aid in this, the equations required are summarized in Tables 5.4 and 5.5. MATLAB programs for analyzing slider-crank linkages are included on the disk with this book.

TABLE 5.4 Summary of Position, Velocity, and Acceleration Equations for a Slider-Crank Mechanism When Either the Crank or the Coupler is the Input. Link 2 Is the Input Link When $M = 2$ and $J = 3$. Link 3 Is the Input Link When $M = 3$ and $J = 2$. The Link Numbers and Points Are Defined in Fig. 5.14

Position

$$A = 2r_4(\cos\theta_1 \cos\theta_4 + \sin\theta_1 \sin\theta_4) - 2r_M(\cos\theta_1 \cos\theta_M + \sin\theta_1 \sin\theta_M)$$

$$B = r_M^2 + r_4^2 - r_J^2 - 2r_M r_4(\cos\theta_M \cos\theta_4 + \sin\theta_M \sin\theta_4)$$

$$r_1 = \frac{-A + \sigma\sqrt{A^2 - 4B}}{2}; \quad \sigma = \pm 1$$

$$\theta_J = \tan^{-1}\left[\frac{r_1 \sin\theta_1 + r_4 \sin\theta_4 - r_M \sin\theta_M}{r_1 \cos\theta_1 + r_4 \cos\theta_4 - r_M \cos\theta_M}\right]$$

$$\boldsymbol{r}_Q = \boldsymbol{r}_2 = r_2(\cos\theta_2 \boldsymbol{i} + \sin\theta_2 \boldsymbol{j})$$

$$\boldsymbol{r}_P = \boldsymbol{r}_2 + \boldsymbol{r}_3 = r_2(\cos\theta_2 \boldsymbol{i} + \sin\theta_2 \boldsymbol{j}) + r_3(\cos\theta_3 \boldsymbol{i} + \sin\theta_3 \boldsymbol{j})$$

Velocity

$$\begin{bmatrix} \cos\theta_1 & r_J \sin\theta_J \\ \sin\theta_1 & -r_J \cos\theta_J \end{bmatrix} \begin{Bmatrix} \dot{r}_1 \\ \dot{\theta}_J \end{Bmatrix} = \begin{Bmatrix} -r_M \dot{\theta}_M \sin\theta_M \\ r_M \dot{\theta}_M \cos\theta_M \end{Bmatrix}$$

$$\dot{\boldsymbol{r}}_Q = r_2\dot{\theta}_2(-\sin\theta_2 \boldsymbol{i} + \cos\theta_2 \boldsymbol{j})$$

$$\dot{\boldsymbol{r}}_P = (-r_2\dot{\theta}_2 \sin\theta_2 + r_3\dot{\theta}_3 \sin\theta_3)\boldsymbol{i} + (r_2\dot{\theta}_2 \cos\theta_2 + r_3\dot{\theta}_3 \cos\theta_3)\boldsymbol{j}$$

Acceleration

$$\begin{bmatrix} \cos\theta_1 & r_J \sin\theta_J \\ \sin\theta_1 & -r_J \cos\theta_J \end{bmatrix} \begin{Bmatrix} \ddot{r}_1 \\ \ddot{\theta}_J \end{Bmatrix} = \begin{Bmatrix} -r_M \ddot{\theta}_M \sin\theta_M - r_M \dot{\theta}_M^2 \cos\theta_M - r_J \dot{\theta}_J^2 \cos\theta_J \\ r_M \ddot{\theta}_M \cos\theta_M - r_M \dot{\theta}_M^2 \sin\theta_M - r_J \dot{\theta}_J^2 \sin\theta_J \end{Bmatrix}$$

$$\ddot{\boldsymbol{r}}_Q = (r_2\ddot{\theta}_2 \sin\theta_2 - r_2\dot{\theta}_2^2 \cos\theta_2)\boldsymbol{i} + (r_2\ddot{\theta}_2 \cos\theta_2 - r_2\dot{\theta}_2^2 \sin\theta_2)\boldsymbol{j}$$

$$\ddot{\boldsymbol{r}}_P = -(r_2\ddot{\theta}_2 \sin\theta_2 + r_2\dot{\theta}_2^2 \cos\theta_2 + r_3\ddot{\theta}_3 \sin\theta_3 + r_3\dot{\theta}_3^2 \cos\theta_3)\boldsymbol{i}$$
$$+ (r_2\ddot{\theta}_2 \cos\theta_2 - r_2\dot{\theta}_2^2 \sin\theta_2 + r_3\ddot{\theta}_3 \cos\theta_3 - r_3\dot{\theta}_3^2 \sin\theta_3)\boldsymbol{j}$$

TABLE 5.5 Summary of Position, Velocity, and Acceleration Equations for a Slider-Crank Mechanism When the Slider (Link 4) Is the Input Link. The Link Numbers and Points Are Defined in Fig. 5.14

Position

$$A = 2r_1r_2\cos\theta_1 - 2r_2r_4\cos\theta_4$$
$$B = 2r_1r_2\sin\theta_1 - 2r_2r_4\sin\theta_4$$
$$C = r_1^2 + r_2^2 + r_4^2 - r_3^2 - 2r_1r_4\left(\cos\theta_1\cos\theta_4 + \sin\theta_1\sin\theta_4\right)$$

$$\theta_2 = 2\tan^{-1}\left[\frac{-B+\sigma\sqrt{B^2-C^2+A^2}}{C-A}\right]; \quad \sigma = \pm 1$$

$$\theta_3 = \tan^{-1}\left[\frac{r_1\sin\theta_1 + r_4\sin\theta_4 - r_2\sin\theta_2}{r_1\cos\theta_1 + r_4\cos\theta_4 - r_2\cos\theta_2}\right]$$

$$\boldsymbol{r}_Q = \boldsymbol{r}_2 = r_2\left(\cos\theta_2\boldsymbol{i} + \sin\theta_2\boldsymbol{j}\right)$$

$$\boldsymbol{r}_P = \boldsymbol{r}_2 + \boldsymbol{r}_3 = r_2\left(\cos\theta_2\boldsymbol{i} + \sin\theta_2\boldsymbol{j}\right) + r_3\left(\cos\theta_3\boldsymbol{i} + \sin\theta_3\boldsymbol{j}\right)$$

Velocity

$$\begin{bmatrix} -r_2\sin\theta_2 & -r_3\sin\theta_3 \\ r_2\cos\theta_2 & r_3\cos\theta_3 \end{bmatrix}\begin{Bmatrix} \dot\theta_2 \\ \dot\theta_3 \end{Bmatrix} = \begin{Bmatrix} \dot r_1\cos\theta_1 \\ \dot r_1\sin\theta_1 \end{Bmatrix}$$

$$\dot{\boldsymbol{r}}_Q = r_2\dot\theta_2\left(-\sin\theta_2\boldsymbol{i} + \cos\theta_2\boldsymbol{j}\right)$$

$$\dot{\boldsymbol{r}}_P = \left(-r_2\dot\theta_2\sin\theta_2 - r_3\dot\theta_3\sin\theta_3\right)\boldsymbol{i} + \left(r_2\dot\theta_2\cos\theta_2 + r_3\dot\theta_3\cos\theta_3\right)\boldsymbol{j}$$

Acceleration

$$\begin{bmatrix} -r_2\sin\theta_2 & -r_3\sin\theta_3 \\ r_2\cos\theta_2 & r_3\cos\theta_3 \end{bmatrix}\begin{Bmatrix} \ddot\theta_2 \\ \ddot\theta_3 \end{Bmatrix} = \begin{Bmatrix} r_2\dot\theta_2^2\cos\theta_2 + r_3\dot\theta_3^2\cos\theta_3 + \ddot r_1\cos\theta_1 \\ r_2\dot\theta_2^2\sin\theta_2 + r_3\dot\theta_3^2\sin\theta_3 + \ddot r_1\sin\theta_1 \end{Bmatrix}$$

$$\ddot{\boldsymbol{r}}_Q = \left(-r_2\ddot\theta_2\sin\theta_2 - r_2\dot\theta_2^2\cos\theta_2\right)\boldsymbol{i} + \left(r_2\ddot\theta_2\cos\theta_2 - r_2\dot\theta_2^2\sin\theta_2\right)\boldsymbol{j}$$

$$\begin{aligned}\ddot{\boldsymbol{r}}_P = &-\left(r_2\ddot\theta_2\sin\theta_2 + r_2\dot\theta_2^2\cos\theta_2 + r_3\ddot\theta_3\sin\theta_3 + r_3\dot\theta_3^2\cos\theta_3\right)\boldsymbol{i} \\ &+\left(r_2\ddot\theta_2\cos\theta_2 - r_2\dot\theta_2^2\sin\theta_2 + r_3\ddot\theta_3\cos\theta_3 - r_3\dot\theta_3^2\sin\theta_3\right)\boldsymbol{j}\end{aligned}$$

EXAMPLE 5.4
Kinematic Analysis of a Slider-Crank Mechanism with Crank Input

In the slider-crank mechanism shown in Fig. 5.20, $\theta_2 = 45°$, $\dot{\theta}_2 = 10$ rad/s, and $\ddot{\theta}_2 = 0$. The link lengths r_2 and r_3 are as shown, and the line of motion of point C_4 is along the line AC. Find the position, velocity, and acceleration of C_4 and the angular velocity and acceleration of link 3.

Solution

For this problem, the crank is the input, and the analysis can be conducted using the equations in Table 5.4 with M=2 and J=3. The known input information is

$$\theta_1 = 0°, \quad \theta_2 = 45°, \quad \dot{\theta}_2 = 10 \text{ rad/s}, \quad \ddot{\theta}_2 = 0$$
$$r_2 = 5 \text{ in}, \quad r_3 = 8 \text{ in}, \quad r_4 = 0 \text{ in}$$

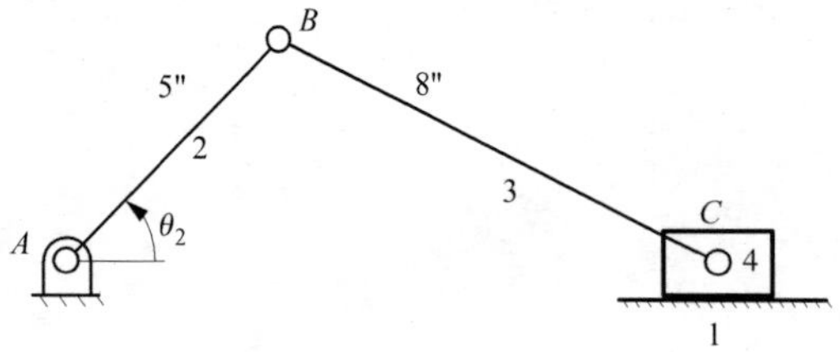

FIGURE 5.20 The slider-crank linkage to be analyzed in Example 5.4.

Start with the position analysis, and first compute the constants A and B from Eq. (5.69):

$$A = 2r_4(\cos\theta_1 \cos\theta_4 + \sin\theta_1 \sin\theta_4) - 2r_2(\cos\theta_1 \cos\theta_2 + \sin\theta_1 \sin\theta_2)$$
$$= -2(5)(\cos(0°)\cos(45°) + \sin(0°)\sin(45°)) = 7.70711$$
$$B = r_2^2 + r_4^2 - r_3^2 - 2r_2r_4(\cos\theta_2 \cos\theta_4 + \sin\theta_2 \sin\theta_4)$$
$$= (5)^2 - (8)^2 = -39$$

The desired configuration of the linkage corresponds to the position of the slider with the larger x coordinate. Therefore, $\sigma = +1$. Then,

$$r_1 = \frac{-A + \sigma\sqrt{A^2 - 4B}}{2} = \frac{-(7.70711) + \sqrt{(7.70711)^2 - 4(-39)}}{2} = 10.712 \text{ in}$$

Then θ_3 is given by

$$\theta_3 = \tan^{-1}\left[\frac{r_1 \sin\theta_1 + r_4 \sin\theta_4 - r_2 \sin\theta_2}{r_1 \cos\theta_1 + r_4 \cos\theta_4 - r_2 \cos\theta_2}\right] = \tan^{-1}\left[\frac{-5\sin(45°)}{10.712 - 5\cos(45°)}\right] = -26.228°$$

For the velocities, solve the linear set of velocity equations

$$\begin{bmatrix} \cos\theta_1 & r_3 \sin\theta_3 \\ \sin\theta_1 & -r_3 \cos\theta_3 \end{bmatrix} \begin{Bmatrix} \dot{r}_1 \\ \dot{\theta}_3 \end{Bmatrix} = \begin{Bmatrix} -r_2\dot{\theta}_2 \sin\theta_2 \\ r_2\dot{\theta}_2 \cos\theta_2 \end{Bmatrix} \text{ or } \begin{bmatrix} 1 & 8\sin(-26.228°) \\ 0 & -8\cos(-26.228°) \end{bmatrix} \begin{Bmatrix} \dot{r}_1 \\ \dot{\theta}_3 \end{Bmatrix} = \begin{Bmatrix} -5(10)\sin(45°) \\ 5(10)\cos(45°) \end{Bmatrix}$$

Then

$$\begin{bmatrix} 1 & -3.5355 \\ 0 & -7.1764 \end{bmatrix} \begin{Bmatrix} \dot{r}_1 \\ \dot{\theta}_3 \end{Bmatrix} = \begin{Bmatrix} -35.3553 \\ 35.3553 \end{Bmatrix} \text{ or } \begin{Bmatrix} \dot{r}_1 \\ \dot{\theta}_3 \end{Bmatrix} = \begin{Bmatrix} -52.774 \\ -4.927 \end{Bmatrix}$$

Therefore, $\dot{r}_1 = 52.774$ in/s and $\dot{\theta}_3 = -4.927$ rad/s CCW or 4.927 rad/s CW.

For the accelerations, solve the linear set of acceleration equations

$$\begin{bmatrix} \cos\theta_1 & r_3\sin\theta_3 \\ \sin\theta_1 & -r_3\cos\theta_3 \end{bmatrix}\begin{Bmatrix} \ddot{r}_1 \\ \ddot{\theta}_3 \end{Bmatrix} = \begin{Bmatrix} -r_2\ddot{\theta}_2\sin\theta_2 - r_2\dot{\theta}_2^2\cos\theta_2 - r_3\dot{\theta}_3^2\cos\theta_3 \\ r_2\ddot{\theta}_2\cos\theta_2 - r_2\dot{\theta}_2^2\sin\theta_2 - r_3\dot{\theta}_3^2\sin\theta_3 \end{Bmatrix}$$

or

$$\begin{bmatrix} 1 & -3.5355 \\ 0 & -7.1764 \end{bmatrix}\begin{Bmatrix} \ddot{r}_1 \\ \ddot{\theta}_3 \end{Bmatrix} = \begin{Bmatrix} -5(10)^2\cos(45°) - 8(-4.9266)^2\cos(-26.228°) \\ -5(10)^2\sin(45°) - 8(-4.9266)^2\sin(-26.228°) \end{Bmatrix} = \begin{Bmatrix} -527.7366 \\ -267.7395 \end{Bmatrix}$$

Then

$$\begin{Bmatrix} \ddot{r}_1 \\ \ddot{\theta}_3 \end{Bmatrix} = \begin{Bmatrix} -395.83 \\ 37.309 \end{Bmatrix}$$

Therefore, $\ddot{r}_1 = -395.83$ in/s^2 and $\ddot{\theta}_3 = 37.30$ rad/s^2 CCW. The results can be checked with the graphical analysis in Example 5.2.

EXAMPLE 5.5
Kinematic Analysis of a Slider-Crank Mechanism with a Slider Input

Reanalyze the slider-crank mechanism shown in Fig. 5.20 when $r_1 = 10.75$ in, $\dot{r}_1 = 50$ in/s, and $\ddot{r}_1 = 400$ in/s^2. The link lengths r_2 and r_3 are the same as in Example 5.4, and again the line of action of point C_4 is along the line AC. Find the position, angular velocity, and angular acceleration of link 2 and of link 3.

Solution

This is essentially the same problem as in Example 5.4 except that now the slider is the input link, and link 2 is the output. The analysis can be conducted using the equations in Table 5.5. The known input information is

$$\theta_1 = 0°,\quad r_1 = 10.75\text{ in},\quad \dot{r}_1 = 50\text{ in/s},\quad \ddot{r}_1 = 400\text{ in/s}^2$$
$$r_2 = 5\text{ in},\quad r_3 = 8\text{ in},\quad r_4 = 0\text{ in}$$

Start with the position analysis, and first compute constants A, B, and C:

$$A = 2r_1r_2\cos\theta_1 - 2r_2r_4\cos\theta_4 = -2(10.75)(5) = -107.5$$
$$B = 2r_1r_2\sin\theta_1 - 2r_2r_4\sin\theta_4 = 0$$
$$C = r_1^2 + r_2^2 + r_4^2 - r_3^2 - 2r_1r_4(\cos\theta_1\cos\theta_4 + \sin\theta_1\sin\theta_4) = (10.75)^2 + (5)^2 - (8)^2 = 76.56$$

For the configuration in Fig. 5.20, $\sigma = 1$. Then,

$$\theta_2 = 2\tan^{-1}\left[\frac{-B + \sigma\sqrt{B^2 - C^2 + A^2}}{C - A}\right] = 2\tan^{-1}\left[\frac{+1\sqrt{-(76.56)^2 + (-107.5)^2}}{76.56 - (-107.5)}\right] = 44.5850°$$

and

$$\theta_3 = \tan^{-1}\left[\frac{r_1\sin\theta_1 + r_4\sin\theta_4 - r_2\sin\theta_2}{r_1\cos\theta_1 + r_4\cos\theta_4 - r_2\cos\theta_2}\right] = \tan^{-1}\left[\frac{-5\sin(44.585°)}{10.75 - 5\cos(44.585°)}\right] = -26.02°$$

For the velocities, solve the linear set of velocity equations

$$\begin{bmatrix} -r_2\sin\theta_2 & -r_3\sin\theta_3 \\ r_2\cos\theta_2 & r_3\cos\theta_3 \end{bmatrix}\begin{Bmatrix} \dot{\theta}_2 \\ \dot{\theta}_3 \end{Bmatrix} = \begin{Bmatrix} \dot{r}_1\cos\theta_1 \\ \dot{r}_1\sin\theta_1 \end{Bmatrix} \text{ or } \begin{bmatrix} -5\sin(44.585°) & -8\sin(-26.02°) \\ 5\cos(44.585°) & 8\cos(-26.02°) \end{bmatrix}\begin{Bmatrix} \dot{\theta}_2 \\ \dot{\theta}_3 \end{Bmatrix} = \begin{Bmatrix} 50 \\ 0 \end{Bmatrix}$$

Then

$$\begin{bmatrix} -3.5098 & 3.5098 \\ 3.5610 & 7.189 \end{bmatrix} \begin{Bmatrix} \dot{\theta}_2 \\ \dot{\theta}_3 \end{Bmatrix} = \begin{Bmatrix} 50 \\ 0 \end{Bmatrix} \quad \text{or} \quad \begin{Bmatrix} \dot{\theta}_2 \\ \dot{\theta}_3 \end{Bmatrix} = \begin{Bmatrix} -9.527 \\ 4.719 \end{Bmatrix}$$

Therefore, $\dot{\theta}_2 = -9.527$ rad/s CCW or 9.527 rad/s CW and $\dot{\theta}_3 = 4.719$ rad/s CCW. For the accelerations, solve the linear set of acceleration equations

$$\begin{bmatrix} -r_2 \sin\theta_2 & -r_3 \sin\theta_3 \\ r_2 \cos\theta_2 & r_3 \cos\theta_3 \end{bmatrix} \begin{Bmatrix} \ddot{\theta}_2 \\ \ddot{\theta}_3 \end{Bmatrix} = \begin{Bmatrix} r_2\dot{\theta}_2^2 \cos\theta_2 + r_3\dot{\theta}_3^2 \cos\theta_3 + \ddot{r}_1 \cos\theta_1 \\ r_2\dot{\theta}_2^2 \sin\theta_2 + r_3\dot{\theta}_3^2 \sin\theta_3 + \ddot{r}_1 \sin\theta_1 \end{Bmatrix}$$

or

$$\begin{bmatrix} -3.5098 & 3.5098 \\ 3.5610 & 7.189 \end{bmatrix} \begin{Bmatrix} \ddot{\theta}_2 \\ \ddot{\theta}_3 \end{Bmatrix} = \begin{Bmatrix} 5(9.527)^2 \cos(44.585^\circ) + 8(4.719)^2 \cos(-26.02^\circ) + 400 \\ 5(9.527)^2 \sin(44.585^\circ) + 8(4.719)^2 \sin(-26.02^\circ) \end{Bmatrix} = \begin{Bmatrix} 883.309 \\ 240.381 \end{Bmatrix}$$

Then

$$\begin{Bmatrix} \ddot{\theta}_2 \\ \ddot{\theta}_3 \end{Bmatrix} = \begin{Bmatrix} -145.933 \\ 105.726 \end{Bmatrix}$$

Therefore, $\ddot{\theta}_2 = -145.933$ rad/s^2 CCW or 145.933 rad/s^2 CW and $\ddot{\theta}_3 = 105.726$ rad/s^2 CCW.

5.6 ANALYTICAL EQUATIONS FOR THE SLIDER-CRANK INVERSION

The slider-crank inversion is a common mechanism when linear actuators are involved (e.g., Figs. 1.35 and 5.21). It is also used in various pump mechanisms. As discussed in Chapter 1, for low-load conditions, the slider is often replaced by a pin-in-a-slot joint. The resulting mechanisms can be analyzed using the equations developed in this section by modeling the pin-in-a-slot joint as a revolute joint and slider joint connected by a link. A

FIGURE 5.21 Backhoe. Each joint is actuated by an inversion of the slider-crank mechanism. (Courtesy of Deere & Co., Moline, Ilinois.)

device that could be analyzed using this procedure is the walking toy shown in Fig. 5.22. To develop the closure equations, first locate vectors $\boldsymbol{r}_2$ and $\boldsymbol{r}_1$ as was done in the previous linkage. To form the other part of the closure equation, draw two vectors, one ($\boldsymbol{r}_3$) in the direction of the slider velocity from P to Q and one ($\boldsymbol{r}_4$) perpendicular to the velocity direction. The variables associated with the problem are then located as shown in Fig. 5.23, and the loop closure equation is given by

$$\boldsymbol{r}_P = \boldsymbol{r}_2 = \boldsymbol{r}_1 + \boldsymbol{r}_3 + \boldsymbol{r}_4 \tag{5.93}$$

or

$$r_2(\cos\theta_2\boldsymbol{i} + \sin\theta_2\boldsymbol{j}) = r_1(\cos\theta_1\boldsymbol{i} + \sin\theta_1\boldsymbol{j}) + r_3(\cos\theta_3\boldsymbol{i} + \sin\theta_3\boldsymbol{j}) + r_4(\cos\theta_4\boldsymbol{i} + \sin\theta_4\boldsymbol{j} \tag{5.94}$$

where

$$\theta_4 = \theta_3 - \pi/2 \tag{5.95}$$

Note that θ_4 is now a variable and that r_4 can be negative.

Rewriting Eq. (5.94) into its component equations gives

$$r_2\cos\theta_2 = r_1\cos\theta_1 + r_3\cos\theta_3 + r_4\cos\theta_4 \tag{5.96}$$

$$r_2\sin\theta_2 = r_1\sin\theta_1 + r_3\sin\theta_3 + r_4\sin\theta_4 \tag{5.97}$$

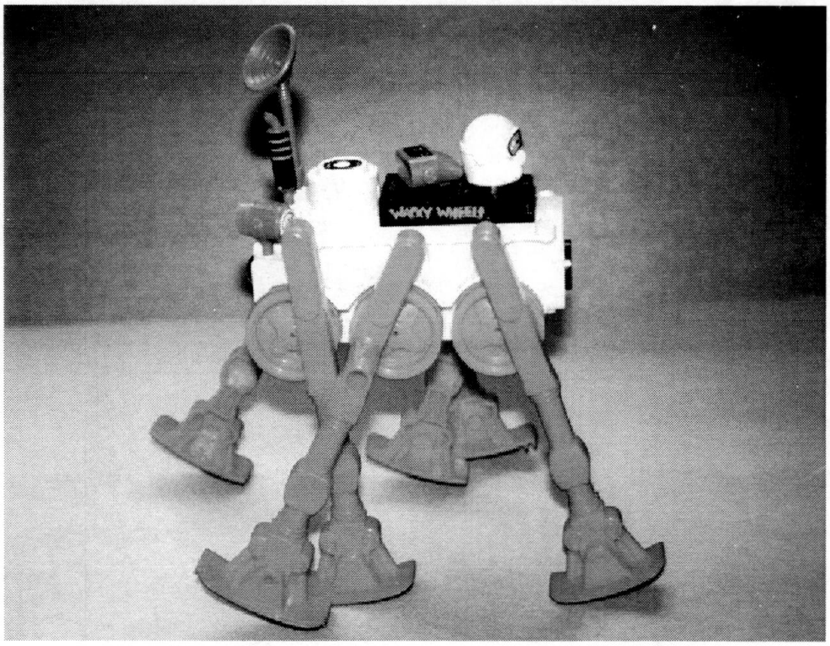

FIGURE 5.22 Walking toy. The pin-in-a-slot joints can be modeled as a separate revolute and slider joint connected by a link. The resulting mechanism can be analyzed using the equations developed in this section.

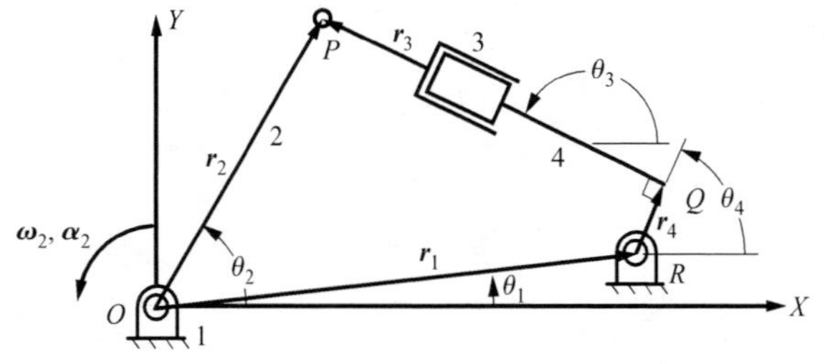

FIGURE 5.23 Vector closure condition for the slider-crank inversion. The position of point Q indicated by $\boldsymbol{r}_2 + \boldsymbol{r}_3$ is the same as that obtained by adding vectors $\boldsymbol{r}_1 + \boldsymbol{r}_4$.

Equations (5.95)–(5.97) must be satisfied throughout the motion of the linkage. The base vector $\boldsymbol{r}_1$ will be constant in direction and magnitude. The vectors $\boldsymbol{r}_2$ and $\boldsymbol{r}_4$ will be constant in magnitude, and $\boldsymbol{r}_3$ will vary in both magnitude and direction. Therefore, r_1, r_2, r_4, θ_1, and θ_4 are constants.

If θ_2 is given, it is necessary to solve Eqs. (5.95)–(5.97) for θ_2 and r_3 in terms of θ_2, and if θ_3 is given, it is necessary to solve Eqs. (5.95)–(5.97) for θ_2 and r_3 in terms of θ_3. If r_3 is given, it is necessary to solve the same equations for θ_2 and θ_3. Once the position equations are solved, the equations for the unknown velocities and accelerations can be established in terms of the knowns by differentiation.

5.6.1 Solution to Position Equations When θ_2 Is Input

The analytical solution procedure is slightly different from that used in the previous cases because θ_4 is a function of θ_3. Therefore, θ_3 cannot be eliminated without first considering θ_4. To proceed, first eliminate θ_4 from Eqs. (5.96) and (5.97) by using Eq. (5.95) and isolate the terms containing θ_3 on the right-hand side of the equations. Then,

$$r_2\cos\theta_2 - r_1\cos\theta_1 = r_3\cos\theta_3 + r_4\sin\theta_3 \tag{5.98}$$

$$r_2\sin\theta_2 - r_1\sin\theta_1 = r_3\sin\theta_3 - r_4\cos\theta_3 \tag{5.99}$$

Now square both sides of both equations and add. After simplifying using the trigonometric identity, $\sin^2\theta + \cos^2\theta = 1$, and solving for r_3, we get the resulting equation

$$r_3 = \sqrt{r_2^2 + r_1^2 - r_4^2 - 2r_1r_2\left(\cos\theta_1\cos\theta_2 + \sin\theta_1\sin\theta_2\right)} \tag{5.100}$$

To solve for θ_3, replace $\cos\theta_3$ and $\sin\theta_3$ in Eq. (5.98) by using the trigonometric half-angle identities in Eqs. (5.33–5.34). Equation (5.98) then becomes

$$A\left(1+t^2\right) - r_3\left(1-t^2\right) - r_4\left(2t\right) = 0 \tag{5.101}$$

where

$$A = r_2\cos\theta_2 - r_1\cos\theta_1$$

and

$$t = \tan\left(\frac{\theta_3}{2}\right)$$

Collecting terms in Eqs. (5.101) gives

$$\left(A + r_3\right)t^2 - 2r_4t + \left(A - r_3\right) = 0$$

This equation will give two roots for t, but one root is extraneous in this problem. The roots are

$$t = \frac{r_4 + \beta\sqrt{r_4^2 - A^2 + r_3^2}}{\left(A + r_3\right)} \tag{5.102}$$

where $\beta = \pm 1$. To determine the correct value of β for the problem, we must first compute a value of θ_3 for each value of t using

$$\theta_3 = 2\tan^{-1} t.$$

Next substitute both values of θ_3 into Eq. (5.99). The correct value of β will correspond to the value of θ_3 satisfying Eq. (5.99). The value of β must be computed for each value of θ_2 if more than one position is analyzed.

Because of the square root in Eq. (5.100), the value of r_3 can be complex $[r_2^2 + r_1^2 - r_4^2 - 2r_1r_2(\cos\theta_1\cos\theta_2 + \sin\theta_1\sin\theta_2) < 0]$. If this happens, the mechanism cannot be assembled for the value of θ_2 specified and for the given values of the link lengths. The results are summarized in Table 5.6.

TABLE 5.6 Summary of Position, Velocity, and Acceleration Equations for an Inverted Slider-Crank Mechanism When θ_2 Is the Input Variable. The Link Numbers and Points Are Defined in Fig. 5.23

Position

$$r_3 = \sqrt{r_2^2 + r_1^2 - r_4^2 - 2r_1r_2(\cos\theta_1\cos\theta_2 + \sin\theta_1\sin\theta_2)}$$

$$A = r_2\cos\theta_2 - r_1\cos\theta_1$$

$$\theta_3 = 2\tan^{-1}\left[\frac{r_4 + \beta\sqrt{r_4^2 - A^2 + r_3^2}}{(A + r_3)}\right]; \quad \beta = \pm 1$$

$$\theta_4 = \theta_3 - \pi/2$$

$$\boldsymbol{r}_P = \boldsymbol{r}_2 = r_2(\cos\theta_2\boldsymbol{i} + \sin\theta_2\boldsymbol{j})$$

$$\boldsymbol{r}_Q = \boldsymbol{r}_1 + \boldsymbol{r}_4 = r_1(\cos\theta_1\boldsymbol{i} + \sin\theta_1\boldsymbol{j}) + r_4(\cos\theta_4\boldsymbol{i} + \sin\theta_4\boldsymbol{j})$$

Velocity

$$\begin{bmatrix} \cos\theta_3 & -r_3\sin\theta_3 - r_4\sin\theta_4 \\ \sin\theta_3 & r_3\cos\theta_3 + r_4\cos\theta_4 \end{bmatrix} \begin{Bmatrix} \dot{r}_3 \\ \dot{\theta}_3 \end{Bmatrix} = \begin{Bmatrix} -r_2\dot{\theta}_2\sin\theta_2 \\ r_2\dot{\theta}_2\cos\theta_2 \end{Bmatrix}$$

$$\dot{\boldsymbol{r}}_P = \dot{\boldsymbol{r}}_2 = r_2\dot{\theta}_2(-\sin\theta_2\boldsymbol{i} + \cos\theta_2\boldsymbol{j})$$

$$\dot{\boldsymbol{r}}_Q = \dot{\boldsymbol{r}}_1 + \dot{\boldsymbol{r}}_4 = r_4\dot{\theta}_3(-\sin\theta_4\boldsymbol{i} + \cos\theta_4\boldsymbol{j})$$

Acceleration

$$\begin{bmatrix} \cos\theta_3 & -r_3\sin\theta_3 - r_4\sin\theta_4 \\ \sin\theta_3 & r_3\cos\theta_3 + r_4\cos\theta_4 \end{bmatrix} \begin{Bmatrix} \ddot{r}_3 \\ \ddot{\theta}_3 \end{Bmatrix}$$
$$= \begin{Bmatrix} -r_2\ddot{\theta}_2\sin\theta_2 - r_2\dot{\theta}_2^2\cos\theta_2 + r_3\dot{\theta}_3^2\cos\theta_3 + 2\dot{r}_3\dot{\theta}_3\sin\theta_3 + r_4\dot{\theta}_3^2\cos\theta_4 \\ r_2\ddot{\theta}_2\cos\theta_2 - r_2\dot{\theta}_2^2\sin\theta_2 + r_3\dot{\theta}_3^2\sin\theta_3 - 2\dot{r}_3\dot{\theta}_3\cos\theta_3 + r_4\dot{\theta}_3^2\sin\theta_4 \end{Bmatrix}$$

$$\ddot{\boldsymbol{r}}_P = \ddot{\boldsymbol{r}}_2 = -(r_2\ddot{\theta}_2\sin\theta_2 + r_2\dot{\theta}_2^2\cos\theta_2)\boldsymbol{i} + (r_2\ddot{\theta}_2\cos\theta_2 - r_2\dot{\theta}_2^2\sin\theta_2)\boldsymbol{j}$$

$$\ddot{\boldsymbol{r}}_Q = \ddot{\boldsymbol{r}}_1 + \ddot{\boldsymbol{r}}_4 = -(r_4\ddot{\theta}_3\sin\theta_4 + r_4\dot{\theta}_3^2\cos\theta_4)\boldsymbol{i} + (r_4\ddot{\theta}_3\cos\theta_4 - r_4\dot{\theta}_3^2\sin\theta_4)\boldsymbol{j}$$

5.6.2 Solution to Position Equations When θ_3 Is Input

When the coupler angle is the input variable for the linkage of Fig. 5.23, values for θ_3 and its derivatives will be known. The analytical procedure for solving the position equations follows the same steps as when θ_2 is the input, although the form of the equations is slightly different.

For the position analysis, again begin with Eqs. (5.63) and (5.64) and isolate the terms with θ_2. The resulting equations are

$$r_2 \cos\theta_2 = r_1 \cos\theta_1 + r_3 \cos\theta_3 + r_4 \sin\theta_3 \tag{5.103}$$

$$r_2 \sin\theta_2 = r_1 \sin\theta_1 + r_3 \sin\theta_3 - r_4 \cos\theta_3 \tag{5.104}$$

These equations can be solved first for r_3 and then for θ_2 using the procedures given in the previous sections. Two solutions are obtained corresponding to the two values of the sign variable β. The assembly positions are shown in Fig. 5.24. The results are summarized in Table 5.7.

5.6.3 Solution to Position Equations When r_3 Is Input

When r_3 is input in Fig. 5.23, we can eliminate θ_3 from the component equations as was done previously to obtain Eq. (5.91). We can solve for θ_2 and then for θ_3. Once again there are two possible solutions corresponding to the two values of the sign variable β. The assembly positions are shown in Fig. 5.25. The results are summarized in Table 5.8.

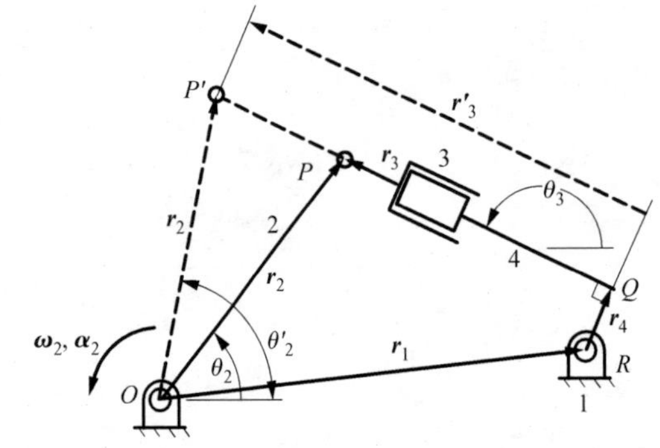

FIGURE 5.24 Two possible assembly modes for link 2 in Fig. 5.23 if θ_3 is given.

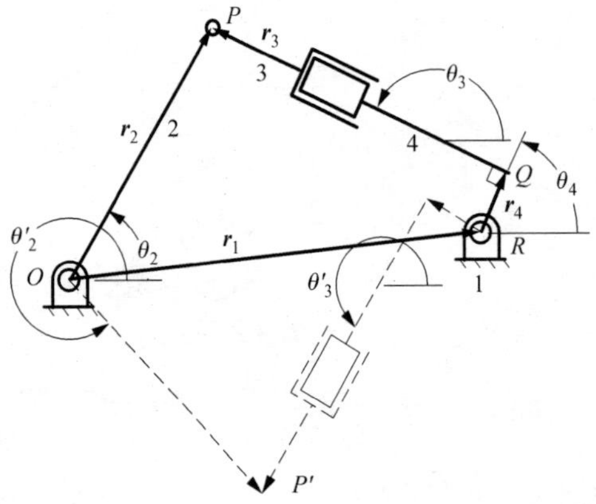

FIGURE 5.25 Two possible configurations for line PR in Fig. 5.23 if r_3 is given.

TABLE 5.7 Summary of Position, Velocity, and Acceleration Equations for an Inverted Slider-Crank Mechanism When θ_3 Is the Input Variable. The Link Numbers and Points Are Defined in Fig. 5.23

Position

$$r_3 = \frac{1}{2}\left[-B + \beta\sqrt{B^2 - 4C}\right]; \quad \beta = \pm 1$$

$$B = 2r_1(\cos\theta_1 \cos\theta_3 + \sin\theta_1 \sin\theta_3)$$

$$C = r_1^2 - r_2^2 + r_4^2 = 2r_1 r_4(\cos\theta_1 \sin\theta_3 - \sin\theta_1 \cos\theta_3)$$

$$\theta_2 = \tan^{-1}\left[\frac{r_1 \sin\theta_1 + r_3 \sin\theta_3 - r_4 \cos\theta_3}{r_1 \cos\theta_1 + r_3 \cos\theta_3 + r_4 \sin\theta_3}\right]$$

$$\theta_4 = \theta_3 - \pi/2$$

$$\boldsymbol{r}_P = \boldsymbol{r}_2 = r_2(\cos\theta_2 \boldsymbol{i} + \sin\theta_2 \boldsymbol{j})$$

$$\boldsymbol{r}_Q = \boldsymbol{r}_1 + \boldsymbol{r}_4 = r_1(\cos\theta_1 \boldsymbol{i} + \sin\theta_1 \boldsymbol{j}) + r_4(\cos\theta_4 \boldsymbol{i} + \sin\theta_4 \boldsymbol{j})$$

Velocity

$$\begin{bmatrix} -r_2 \sin\theta_2 & -\cos\theta_3 \\ r_2 \cos\theta_2 & -\sin\theta_3 \end{bmatrix} \begin{Bmatrix} \dot{\theta}_2 \\ \dot{r}_3 \end{Bmatrix} = \begin{Bmatrix} -r_3\dot{\theta}_3 \sin\theta_3 - r_4\dot{\theta}_3 \sin\theta_4 \\ r_3\dot{\theta}_3 \cos\theta_3 + r_4\dot{\theta}_3 \cos\theta_4 \end{Bmatrix}$$

$$\dot{\boldsymbol{r}}_P = \dot{\boldsymbol{r}}_2 = r_2\dot{\theta}_2(-\sin\theta_2 \boldsymbol{i} + \cos\theta_2 \boldsymbol{j})$$

$$\dot{\boldsymbol{r}}_Q = \dot{\boldsymbol{r}}_1 + \dot{\boldsymbol{r}}_4 = r_4\dot{\theta}_3(-\sin\theta_4 \boldsymbol{i} + \cos\theta_4 \boldsymbol{j})$$

Acceleration

$$\begin{bmatrix} -r_2 \sin\theta_2 & -\cos\theta_3 \\ r_2 \cos\theta_2 & -\sin\theta_3 \end{bmatrix} \begin{Bmatrix} \ddot{\theta}_2 \\ \ddot{r}_3 \end{Bmatrix}$$
$$= \begin{Bmatrix} r_2\dot{\theta}_2^2 \cos\theta_2 - r_3\ddot{\theta}_3 \sin\theta_3 - r_3\dot{\theta}_3^2 \cos\theta_3 - 2\dot{r}_3\dot{\theta}_3 \sin\theta_3 - r_4\ddot{\theta}_3 \sin\theta_4 - r_4\dot{\theta}_3^2 \cos\theta_4 \\ r_2\dot{\theta}_2^2 \sin\theta_2 + r_3\ddot{\theta}_3 \cos\theta_3 - r_3\dot{\theta}_3^2 \sin\theta_3 + 2\dot{r}_3\dot{\theta}_3 \cos\theta_3 + r_4\ddot{\theta}_3 \cos\theta_4 - r_4\dot{\theta}_3^2 \sin\theta_4 \end{Bmatrix}$$

$$\ddot{\boldsymbol{r}}_P = \ddot{\boldsymbol{r}}_2 = -(r_2\ddot{\theta}_2 \sin\theta_2 + r_2\dot{\theta}_2^2 \cos\theta_2)\boldsymbol{i} + (r_2\ddot{\theta}_2 \cos\theta_2 - r_2\dot{\theta}_2^2 \sin\theta_2)\boldsymbol{j}$$

$$\ddot{\boldsymbol{r}}_Q = \ddot{\boldsymbol{r}}_1 + \ddot{\boldsymbol{r}}_4 = -(r_4\ddot{\theta}_3 \sin\theta_4 + r_4\dot{\theta}_3^2 \cos\theta_4)\boldsymbol{i} + (r_4\ddot{\theta}_3 \cos\theta_4 - r_4\dot{\theta}_3^2 \sin\theta_4)\boldsymbol{j}$$

5.6.4 Velocity Equations for the Slider-Crank Inversion

The analytical form of the velocity equations for the linkage of Fig. 5.23 can be developed by differentiating Eq. (5.93). The result is

$$\dot{\boldsymbol{r}}_P = \dot{\boldsymbol{r}}_2 = \dot{\boldsymbol{r}}_1 + \dot{\boldsymbol{r}}_4 + \dot{\boldsymbol{r}}_3 \tag{5.105}$$

TABLE 5.8 Summary of Position, Velocity, and Acceleration Equations for Slider-Crank Inversion When r_3 is the Input Variable. The Link Numbers and Points Are Defined in Fig. 5.23

Position

$$\left.\begin{aligned} A &= -2r_1r_2\cos\theta_1 \\ B &= -2r_1r_2\sin\theta_1 \\ C &= r_2^2 + r_1^2 - r_4^2 - r_3^2 \end{aligned}\right\}$$

$$\theta_2 = 2\tan^{-1}\left[\frac{-B + \beta\sqrt{B^2 - C^2 + A^2}}{C - A}\right];\quad \beta = \pm 1$$

$$A = r_2\cos\theta_2 - r_1\cos\theta_1$$

$$\theta_3 = 2\tan^{-1}\left[\frac{r_4 + \sigma\sqrt{r_4^2 - A^2 + r_3^2}}{(A + r_3)}\right];\quad \sigma = \pm 1$$

σ is constant for a given linkage and is determined by the sign of angle PQR.

$$\theta_4 = \theta_3 - \pi/2$$

$$\boldsymbol{r}_P = \boldsymbol{r}_2 = r_2(\cos\theta_2\boldsymbol{i} + \sin\theta_2\boldsymbol{j})$$

$$\boldsymbol{r}_Q = \boldsymbol{r}_1 + \boldsymbol{r}_4 = r_1(\cos\theta_1\boldsymbol{i} + \sin\theta_1\boldsymbol{j}) + r_4(\cos\theta_4\boldsymbol{i} + \sin\theta_4\boldsymbol{j})$$

Velocity

$$\begin{bmatrix} -r_2\sin\theta_2 & r_3\sin\theta_3 + r_4\sin\theta_4 \\ r_2\cos\theta_2 & -r_3\cos\theta_3 - r_4\cos\theta_4 \end{bmatrix}\begin{Bmatrix} \dot\theta_2 \\ \dot\theta_3 \end{Bmatrix} = \begin{Bmatrix} \dot r_3\cos\theta_3 \\ \dot r_3\sin\theta_3 \end{Bmatrix}$$

$$\dot{\boldsymbol{r}}_P = \dot{\boldsymbol{r}}_2 = r_2\dot\theta_2(-\sin\theta_2\boldsymbol{i} + \cos\theta_2\boldsymbol{j})$$

$$\dot{\boldsymbol{r}}_Q = \dot{\boldsymbol{r}}_1 + \dot{\boldsymbol{r}}_4 = r_4\dot\theta_3(-\sin\theta_4\boldsymbol{i} + \cos\theta_4\boldsymbol{j})$$

Acceleration

$$\begin{bmatrix} -r_2\sin\theta_2 & r_3\sin\theta_3 + r_4\sin\theta_4 \\ r_2\cos\theta_2 & -r_3\cos\theta_3 - r_4\cos\theta_4 \end{bmatrix}\begin{Bmatrix} \ddot\theta_2 \\ \ddot\theta_3 \end{Bmatrix}$$
$$= \begin{Bmatrix} r_2\dot\theta_2^2\cos\theta_2 - r_3\dot\theta_3^2\cos\theta_3 - 2\dot r_3\dot\theta_3\sin\theta_3 + \ddot r_3\cos\theta_3 - r_4\dot\theta_3^2\cos\theta_4 \\ r_2\dot\theta_2^2\sin\theta_2 - r_3\dot\theta_3^2\sin\theta_3 + 2\dot r_3\dot\theta_3\cos\theta_3 + \ddot r_3\sin\theta_3 - r_4\dot\theta_3^2\sin\theta_4 \end{Bmatrix}$$

$$\ddot{\boldsymbol{r}}_P = \ddot{\boldsymbol{r}}_2 = -\left(r_2\ddot\theta_2\sin\theta_2 + r_2\dot\theta_2^2\cos\theta_2\right)\boldsymbol{i} + \left(r_2\ddot\theta_2\cos\theta_2 - r_2\dot\theta_2^2\sin\theta_2\right)\boldsymbol{j}$$

$$\ddot{\boldsymbol{r}}_Q = \ddot{\boldsymbol{r}}_1 + \ddot{\boldsymbol{r}}_4 = -\left(r_4\ddot\theta_3\sin\theta_4 + r_4\dot\theta_3^2\cos\theta_4\right)\boldsymbol{i} + \left(r_4\ddot\theta_3\cos\theta_4 - r_4\dot\theta_3^2\sin\theta_4\right)\boldsymbol{j}$$

When this equation is written in component form, the result is the same as differentiating Eqs. (5.96) and (5.97). Recognizing that r_1, r_2, r_4, and θ_1 are constants, and that from Eq. (5.95) $\dot{\theta}_3 = \dot{\theta}_4$, we see that the resulting component equations are

$$-r_2\dot{\theta}_2 \sin\theta_2 = -r_3\dot{\theta}_3 \sin\theta_3 + \dot{r}_3 \cos\theta_3 + r_4\dot{\theta}_3 \sin\theta_4 \tag{5.106}$$

$$r_2\dot{\theta}_2 \cos\theta_2 = r_3\dot{\theta}_3 \cos\theta_3 + \dot{r}_3 \sin\theta_3 + r_4\dot{\theta}_3 \cos\theta_4 \tag{5.107}$$

The solution procedure depends on whether $\dot{\theta}_2$, $\dot{\theta}_3$, or $\dot{r}_3$ is known. If $\dot{\theta}_2$ is input, then $\dot{r}_3$ and $\dot{\theta}_3$ will be unknown. Therefore, the matrix equation to be solved is

$$\begin{bmatrix} \cos\theta_3 & -r_3\sin\theta_3 - r_4\sin\theta_4 \\ \sin\theta_3 & r_3\cos\theta_3 + r_4\cos\theta_4 \end{bmatrix} \begin{Bmatrix} \dot{r}_3 \\ \dot{\theta}_3 \end{Bmatrix} = \begin{Bmatrix} -r_2\dot{\theta}_2\sin\theta_2 \\ r_2\dot{\theta}_2\cos\theta_2 \end{Bmatrix} \tag{5.108}$$

If $\dot{\theta}_3$ is input, then $\dot{r}_3$ and $\dot{\theta}_2$ will be unknown, and the matrix equation to be solved is

$$\begin{bmatrix} -r_2\sin\theta_2 & -\cos\theta_3 \\ r_2\cos\theta_2 & -\sin\theta_3 \end{bmatrix} \begin{Bmatrix} \dot{\theta}_2 \\ \dot{r}_3 \end{Bmatrix} = \begin{Bmatrix} -r_3\dot{\theta}_3\sin\theta_3 - r_4\dot{\theta}_3\sin\theta_4 \\ r_3\dot{\theta}_3\cos\theta_3 + r_4\dot{\theta}_3\cos\theta_4 \end{Bmatrix} \tag{5.109}$$

If $\dot{r}_3$ is input, then $\dot{\theta}_2$ and $\dot{\theta}_3$ will be unknown. The matrix equation to be solved then is

$$\begin{bmatrix} -r_2\sin\theta_2 & r_3\sin\theta_3 + r_4\sin\theta_4 \\ r_2\cos\theta_2 & -r_3\cos\theta_3 - r_4\cos\theta_4 \end{bmatrix} \begin{Bmatrix} \dot{\theta}_2 \\ \dot{\theta}_3 \end{Bmatrix} = \begin{Bmatrix} \dot{r}_3\cos\theta_3 \\ \dot{r}_3\sin\theta_3 \end{Bmatrix} \tag{5.110}$$

The terms in the matrix and vector on the right-hand sides of Eqs. (5.108)–(5.110) will be known. The equation can therefore be solved manually, on a programmable calculator, or with the matrix solvers in programs such as MATLAB.

Once the angular velocities are known, it is a simple matter to compute the linear velocities of any of the points on the vector loop. The velocities of points Q and P are given by

$$\dot{\boldsymbol{r}}_P = \dot{\boldsymbol{r}}_2 = r_2\dot{\theta}_2\left(-\sin\theta_2\boldsymbol{i} + \cos\theta_2\boldsymbol{j}\right) \tag{5.111}$$

and

$$\dot{\boldsymbol{r}}_Q = \dot{\boldsymbol{r}}_1 + \dot{\boldsymbol{r}}_4 = r_4\dot{\theta}_3\left(-\sin\theta_4\boldsymbol{i} + \cos\theta_4\boldsymbol{j}\right) \tag{5.112}$$

5.6.5 Acceleration Equations for the Slider-Crank Inversion

The analytical form of the acceleration equations for the linkage of Fig. 5.23 can be developed by differentiating Eq. (5.105). The result is

$$\ddot{\boldsymbol{r}}_P = \ddot{\boldsymbol{r}}_2 = \ddot{\boldsymbol{r}}_1 + \ddot{\boldsymbol{r}}_3 + \ddot{\boldsymbol{r}}_4 \tag{5.113}$$

When this equation is written in component form, the result is the same as differentiating Eqs. (5.106) and (5.107). The resulting component equations are

$$\begin{aligned} &-r_2\ddot{\theta}_2\sin\theta_2 - r_2\dot{\theta}_2^2\cos\theta_2 \\ &\quad = -r_3\ddot{\theta}_3\sin\theta_3 - r_3\dot{\theta}_3^2\cos\theta_3 + \ddot{r}_3\cos\theta_3 - 2\dot{r}_3\dot{\theta}_3\sin\theta_3 - r_4\ddot{\theta}_3\sin\theta_4 - r_4\dot{\theta}_3^2\cos\theta_4 \end{aligned} \tag{5.114}$$

$$\begin{aligned} &-r_2\ddot{\theta}_2\cos\theta_2 - r_2\dot{\theta}_2^2\sin\theta_2 \\ &\quad = -r_3\ddot{\theta}_3\cos\theta_3 - r_3\dot{\theta}_3^2\sin\theta_3 + \ddot{r}_3\sin\theta_3 + 2\dot{r}_3\dot{\theta}_3\cos\theta_3 + r_4\ddot{\theta}_3\cos\theta_4 - r_4\dot{\theta}_3^2\sin\theta_4 \end{aligned} \tag{5.115}$$

In a manner similar to that in the case of velocities, the solution procedure depends on whether $\ddot{r}_3$ or $\ddot{\theta}_2$ is known. If $\ddot{\theta}_2$ is input, then $\ddot{r}_3$ and $\ddot{\theta}_3$ will be unknown. Therefore, the matrix equation to be solved is

$$\begin{bmatrix} \cos\theta_3 & -r_3\sin\theta_3 - r_4\sin\theta_4 \\ \sin\theta_3 & r_3\cos\theta_3 + r_4\cos\theta_4 \end{bmatrix} \begin{Bmatrix} \ddot{r}_3 \\ \ddot{\theta}_3 \end{Bmatrix} = \begin{Bmatrix} -r_2\ddot{\theta}_2\sin\theta_2 - r_2\dot{\theta}_2^2\cos\theta_2 + r_3\dot{\theta}_3^2\cos\theta_3 + 2\dot{r}_3\dot{\theta}_3\sin\theta_3 + r_4\dot{\theta}_3^2\cos\theta_4 \\ r_2\ddot{\theta}_2\cos\theta_2 - r_2\dot{\theta}_2^2\sin\theta_2 + r_3\dot{\theta}_3^2\sin\theta_3 - 2\dot{r}_3\dot{\theta}_3\cos\theta_3 + r_4\dot{\theta}_3^2\sin\theta_4 \end{Bmatrix} \tag{5.116}$$

If $\ddot{\theta}_3$ is input, then $\ddot{r}_3$ and $\ddot{\theta}_2$ will be unknown, and the matrix equation to be solved is

$$\begin{bmatrix} -r_2\sin\theta_2 & -\cos\theta_3 \\ r_2\cos\theta_2 & -\sin\theta_3 \end{bmatrix} \begin{Bmatrix} \ddot{\theta}_2 \\ \ddot{r}_3 \end{Bmatrix} = \begin{Bmatrix} r_2\dot{\theta}_2^2\cos\theta_2 - r_3\ddot{\theta}_3\sin\theta_3 - r_3\dot{\theta}_3^2\cos\theta_3 - 2\dot{r}_3\dot{\theta}_3\sin\theta_3 - r_4\ddot{\theta}_3\sin\theta_4 - r_4\dot{\theta}_3^2\cos\theta_4 \\ r_2\dot{\theta}_2^2\sin\theta_2 + r_3\ddot{\theta}_3\cos\theta_3 - r_3\dot{\theta}_3^2\sin\theta_3 + 2\dot{r}_3\dot{\theta}_3\cos\theta_3 + r_4\ddot{\theta}_3\cos\theta_4 - r_4\dot{\theta}_3^2\sin\theta_4 \end{Bmatrix} \tag{5.117}$$

If $\ddot{r}_3$ is input, then $\ddot{\theta}_2$ and $\ddot{\theta}_3$ will be unknown. The matrix equation to be solved is then

$$\begin{bmatrix} -r_2\sin\theta_2 & r_3\sin\theta_3 + r_4\sin\theta_4 \\ r_2\cos\theta_2 & -r_3\cos\theta_3 - r_4\cos\theta_4 \end{bmatrix} \begin{Bmatrix} \ddot{\theta}_2 \\ \ddot{\theta}_3 \end{Bmatrix} = \begin{Bmatrix} r_2\dot{\theta}_2^2\cos\theta_2 - r_3\dot{\theta}_3^2\cos\theta_3 - 2\dot{r}_3\dot{\theta}_3\sin\theta_3 + \ddot{r}_3\cos\theta_3 - r_4\dot{\theta}_3^2\cos\theta_4 \\ r_2\dot{\theta}_2^2\sin\theta_2 - r_3\dot{\theta}_3^2\sin\theta_3 + 2\dot{r}_3\dot{\theta}_3\cos\theta_3 + \ddot{r}_3\sin\theta_3 - r_4\dot{\theta}_3^2\sin\theta_4 \end{Bmatrix} \tag{5.118}$$

The terms in the matrix and vector on the right-hand sides of Eqs. (5.116–5.118) will be known. The equation can therefore be solved manually, numerically on a programmable calculator, or with the matrix solvers in programs such as MATLAB. Notice again that the coefficient matrix is the same for both the velocities (Eqs. (5.108) and (5.110) and for the accelerations (Eqs. (5.116)–(5.118)).

Once the angular accelerations are known, it is a simple matter to compute the linear accelerations of any of the points on the vector loop. The accelerations of points P and Q are given by

$$\ddot{\boldsymbol{r}}_P = \ddot{\boldsymbol{r}}_2 = -\left(r_2\ddot{\theta}_2\sin\theta_2 + r_2\dot{\theta}_2^2\cos\theta_2\right)\boldsymbol{i} + \left(r_2\ddot{\theta}_2\cos\theta_2 - r_2\dot{\theta}_2^2\sin\theta_2\right)\boldsymbol{j} \tag{5.119}$$

and

$$\ddot{\boldsymbol{r}}_Q = \ddot{\boldsymbol{r}}_1 + \ddot{\boldsymbol{r}}_4 = -\left(r_4\ddot{\theta}_3\sin\theta_4 + r_4\dot{\theta}_3^2\cos\theta_4\right)\boldsymbol{i} + \left(r_4\ddot{\theta}_3\cos\theta_4 - r_4\dot{\theta}_3^2\sin\theta_4\right)\boldsymbol{j} \tag{5.120}$$

Now that the equations have been developed, it is a relatively simple matter to write a computer program for the analysis of an inverted slider-crank linkage. To aid in this, the equations required are summarized in Tables 5.6, 5.7, and 5.8. A MATLAB program for analyzing an inverted slider-crank linkage is included on the disk that accompanies this book.

EXAMPLE 5.6 *Kinematic Analysis of a Foot-Pump Mechanism*

The foot pump shown in Fig. 5.26 is to be analyzed in one position ($\theta_2 = 60°$) as an inverted slider-crank linkage. Dimensions for the mechanism are given in Fig. 5.27, and the vector diagram for the analysis is given in Fig. 5.28. Assume that the angular velocity of the driver (link 2) is constant at 2.5 rad/s CW. Conduct a position, velocity, and acceleration analysis to determine, respectively, the combined length of links 3 and 4, the angular velocity and acceleration of link 3 (or link 4), and the velocity and acceleration of point *B* observed from link 3. This information can be used to study the pumping action between links 3 and 4.

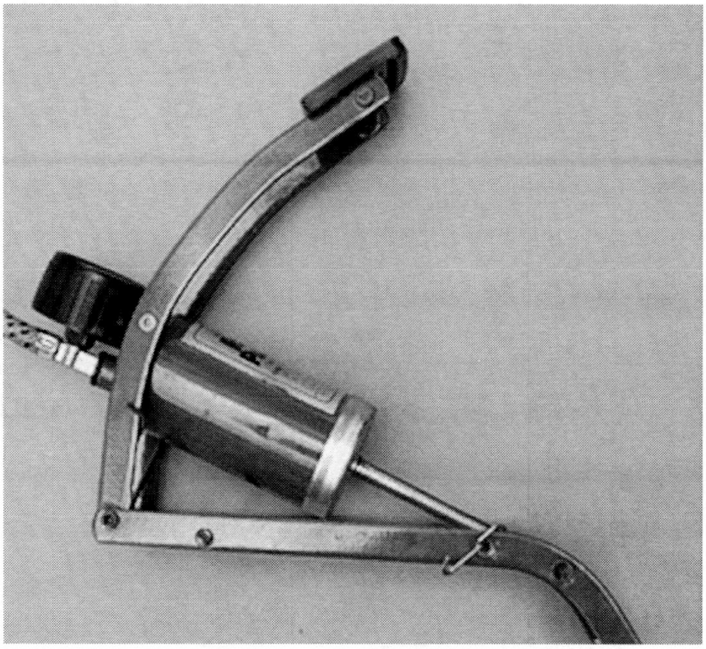

FIGURE 5.26 Foot-pump mechanism.

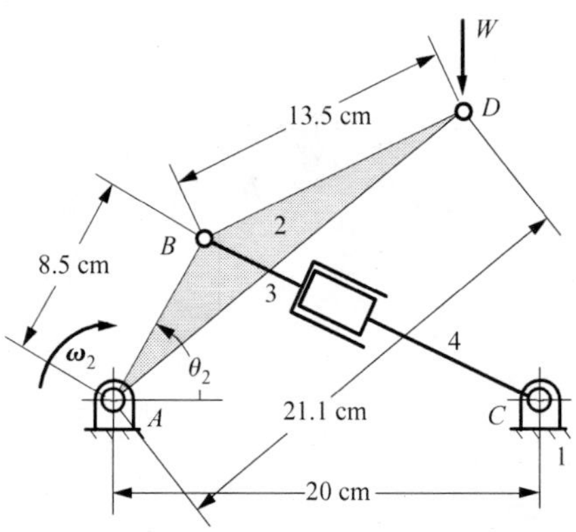

FIGURE 5.27 Kinematic model of foot-pump mechanism used in Example 5.6.

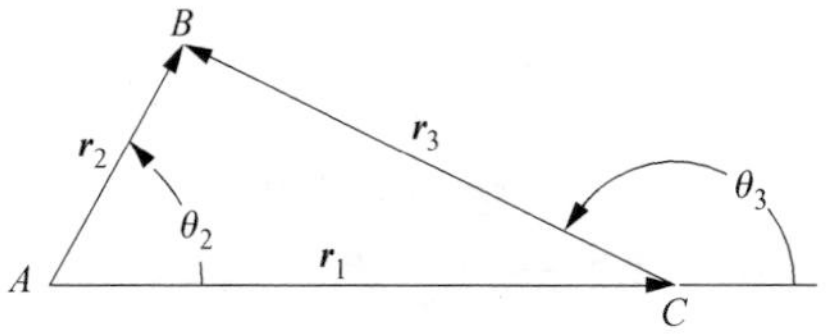

FIGURE 5.28 Position polygon for Example 5.6.

Solution

The analysis can be conducted using the equations in Table 5.6. The known input information is as follows:

$$r_1 = 20 \text{ cm}, \quad \theta_1 = 0$$
$$r_2 = 8.5 \text{ cm}, \quad \theta_2 = 60°, \quad \dot{\theta}_2 = -2.5 \text{ rad/s}, \quad \ddot{\theta}_2 = 0,$$
$$r_4 = 0, \quad \theta_4 = 60, \quad \dot{\theta}_4 = 0, \quad \ddot{\theta}_4 = 0,$$

The unknown information is: r_3, θ_3, $\dot{\theta}_3$, and $\ddot{\theta}_3$.

From Table 5.6, r_3 is given by

$$r_3 = \sqrt{r_2^2 + r_1^2 - r_4^2 - 2r_1r_2(\cos\theta_1\cos\theta_2 + \sin\theta_1\sin\theta_2)}$$
$$= \sqrt{8.5^2 + 20^2 - 2(20)(8.5)\cos(60°)} = \sqrt{302.2} = 17.38 \text{ cm}$$

Next compute θ_3. Start with the value of A:

$$A = r_2\cos\theta_2 - r_1\cos\theta_1 = 8.5\cos(60°) - 20 = -15.75 \text{ cm}$$

To determine θ_3, we need to specify β. Often, we need to compute both values of θ_3 to determine the proper value for β. Thus

$$\theta_3 = 2\tan^{-1}\left[\frac{r_4 + \beta\sqrt{r_4^2 - A^2 + r_3^2}}{(A + r_3)}\right] = 2\tan^{-1}\left[\frac{\beta\sqrt{-(-15.75)^2 + (17.38)^2}}{(-15.75 + 17.38)}\right]$$
$$= 2\tan^{-1}\left[\frac{\beta(7.3486)}{(1.63)}\right] = \pm 154.98°$$

For this problem, $\beta = +1$.

For the velocity analysis, we can use Eq. (5.108). Then,

$$\begin{bmatrix} \cos\theta_3 & -r_3\sin\theta_3 - r_4\sin\theta_4 \\ \sin\theta_3 & r_3\cos\theta_3 + r_4\cos\theta_4 \end{bmatrix}\begin{Bmatrix} \dot{r}_3 \\ \dot{\theta}_3 \end{Bmatrix} = \begin{Bmatrix} -r_2\dot{\theta}_2\sin\theta_2 \\ r_2\dot{\theta}_2\cos\theta_2 \end{Bmatrix}$$

or

$$\begin{bmatrix} \cos(154.99) & -17.38\sin(154.99) \\ \sin(154.99) & 17.38\cos(154.99) \end{bmatrix}\begin{Bmatrix} \dot{r}_3 \\ \dot{\theta}_3 \end{Bmatrix} = \begin{Bmatrix} -8.5(-2.5)\sin(60°) \\ 8.5(-2.5)\cos(60°) \end{Bmatrix}$$

or

$$\begin{bmatrix} -0.9059 & -7.3612 \\ 0.4234 & -15.750 \end{bmatrix}\begin{Bmatrix} \dot{r}_3 \\ \dot{\theta}_3 \end{Bmatrix} = \begin{Bmatrix} 18.403 \\ -10.625 \end{Bmatrix} \Rightarrow \begin{Bmatrix} \dot{r}_3 \\ \dot{\theta}_3 \end{Bmatrix} = \begin{Bmatrix} -21.171 \text{ cm/s} \\ 0.1055 \text{ rad/s}^2 \end{Bmatrix}$$

For the acceleration analysis, we can use Eq. (5.117). Then,

$$\begin{bmatrix} \cos\theta_3 & -r_3\sin\theta_3 - r_4\sin\theta_4 \\ \sin\theta_3 & r_3\cos\theta_3 + r_4\cos\theta_4 \end{bmatrix}\begin{Bmatrix} \ddot{r}_3 \\ \ddot{\theta}_3 \end{Bmatrix}$$
$$= \begin{Bmatrix} -r_2\ddot{\theta}_2\sin\theta_2 - r_2\dot{\theta}_2^2\cos\theta_2 + r_3\dot{\theta}_3^2\cos\theta_3 + 2\dot{r}_3\dot{\theta}_3\sin\theta_3 + r_4\dot{\theta}_3^2\cos\theta_4 \\ r_2\ddot{\theta}_2\cos\theta_2 - r_2\dot{\theta}_2^2\sin\theta_2 + r_3\dot{\theta}_3^2\sin\theta_3 - 2\dot{r}_3\dot{\theta}_3\cos\theta_3 + r_4\dot{\theta}_3^2\sin\theta_4 \end{Bmatrix}$$

or

$$\begin{bmatrix} -0.9059 & -7.3612 \\ 0.4234 & -15.750 \end{bmatrix} \begin{Bmatrix} \ddot{r}_3 \\ \ddot{\theta}_3 \end{Bmatrix}$$
$$= \begin{Bmatrix} -(8.5)(-2.5)^2 \cos(60°) + 17.38(0.1055)^2 \cos(154.99°) + 2(-21.171)(0.1055)\sin(154.99°) \\ -(8.5)(-2.5)^2 \sin(60°) + 17.38(0.1055)^2 \sin(154.99°) + 2(-21.171)(0.1055)\cos(154.99°) \end{Bmatrix}$$
$$= \begin{Bmatrix} -25.1851 \\ -42.6038 \end{Bmatrix} \Rightarrow \begin{Bmatrix} \ddot{r}_3 \\ \ddot{\theta}_3 \end{Bmatrix} = \begin{Bmatrix} 4.777 \ \text{cm/s}^2 \\ 2.833 \ \text{rad/s}^2 \end{Bmatrix}$$

The velocity and acceleration of point B when observed from link 4 are $\dot{r}_3$ and $\ddot{r}_3$, respectively. Note that $\dot{r}_3$ is negative when $\dot{\theta}_2$ is CW.

5.7 ANALYTICAL EQUATIONS FOR AN RPRP MECHANISM

A schematic drawing of the RPRP mechanism is shown in Fig. 5.29. In the mechanism shown, link 2 is connected to the frame by a revolute joint and to the coupler by a prismatic joint. Link 4 is connected to the frame through a prismatic joint and to the coupler by a revolute joint. This is a less common mechanism than the various four-bar linkages and slider cranks; however, it does occur in industrial machinery. For example, one variation of it, the Rapson slide, is used in marine steering gear.

When there is a slider joint between two links, the actual location of the slider does not matter from a kinematic standpoint. Therefore, for simplicity, we can analyze the mechanism as if both sliders were at point P. The resulting mechanism then appears as shown in Fig. 5.30. In Fig. 5.30, the angles are not indicated for simplicity. The angles are again always measured counterclockwise from the horizontal as shown in Fig. 5.3. To develop the closure equations, locate vectors r_1 through r_4 as shown in Fig. 5.30. By locating point P

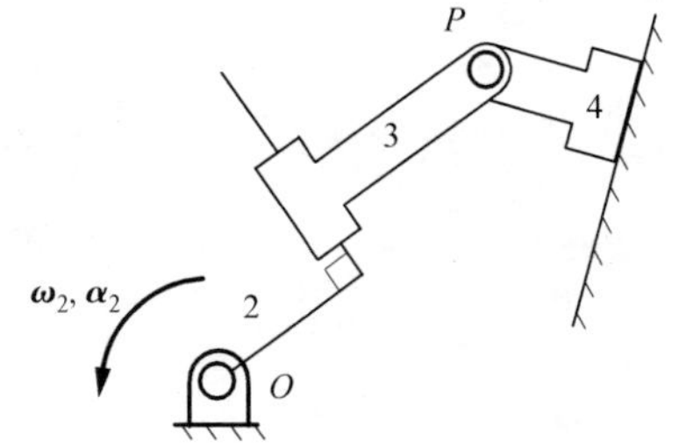

FIGURE 5.29 Schematic diagram of an RPRP mechanism.

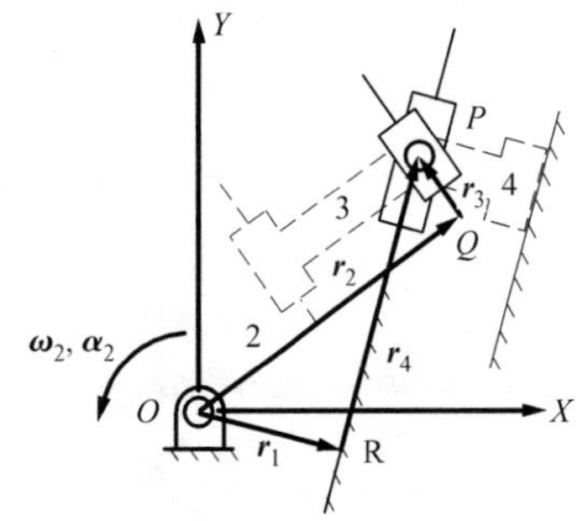

FIGURE 5.30 Vector closure condition for an RPRP mechanism. The position of point P obtained by the vectors r_2 and r_3 is the same as that obtained by adding vectors r_1 and r_4.

using two different sets of vectors, the loop closure equation is then seen to be the same as that for the regular four-bar linkage. Namely,

$$\boldsymbol{r}_P = \boldsymbol{r}_2 + \boldsymbol{r}_3 = \boldsymbol{r}_1 + \boldsymbol{r}_4 \tag{5.121}$$

or

$$r_2\left(\cos\theta_2\boldsymbol{i} + \sin\theta_2\boldsymbol{j}\right) + r_3\left(\cos\theta_3\boldsymbol{i} + \sin\theta_3\boldsymbol{j}\right) = r_1\left(\cos\theta_1\boldsymbol{i} + \sin\theta_1\boldsymbol{j}\right) + r_4\left(\cos\theta_4\boldsymbol{i} + \sin\theta_4\boldsymbol{j}\right) \tag{5.122}$$

Rewriting Eq. (5.122) in its component equations gives

$$r_2\cos\theta_2 + r_3\cos\theta_3 = r_1\cos\theta_1 + r_4\cos\theta_4 \tag{5.123}$$

$$r_2\sin\theta_2 + r_3\sin\theta_3 = r_1\sin\theta_1 + r_4\sin\theta_4 \tag{5.124}$$

Before solving the equations, it is necessary to identify the magnitudes and directions that are constants. There are eight quantities to identify: r_1 and θ_1, r_2 and θ_2, r_3 and θ_3, and r_4 and θ_4. From the diagram in Fig. 5.30, the following are constants: r_1, θ_1, r_2, and θ_4. Furthermore, we know that

$$\theta_3 = \theta_2 + \pi/2 \tag{5.125}$$

and

$$\theta_4 = \theta_1 + \pi/2 \tag{5.126}$$

The variables are r_3, θ_2, r_4, and θ_3. For a one-degree-of-freedom mechanism, one of the variables must be an input (i.e., known) variable. Therefore, there are a total of three unknowns. Because we have three equations (5.123), (5.124), and (5.125) involving the unknowns, we can solve for them.

Once all of the position variables are obtained, the unknown velocities and accelerations can be obtained by differentiating Eqs. (5.123), (5.124), and (5.125) and solving the resulting set of linear equations for the unknowns.

Before solving the equations for the unknowns, it is necessary to select an input variable. Any of r_3, θ_2, r_4, or θ_3 could be chosen. Because θ_2 and θ_3 are related by Eq. (5.125), there is no practical difference between specifying one or the other as the input. Therefore, the choices for inputs reduce to θ_2 (or θ_3) and r_4 (or r_3). The procedure for developing the equations is the same as that in Sections 5.4–5.6. Therefore, the detailed development of the equations will not be given here. Rather, an overview of each case will be given and the results will be summarized in a table.

5.7.1 Solution of Closure Equations When θ_2 Is Known

The analytical solution procedure for the linkage of Fig. 5.30 follows the same major steps as in the previous cases. That is, a position analysis must be performed first, then a velocity analysis, and finally the acceleration analysis. The case in which θ_2 is an input is especially simple because θ_3 can be computed from Eq. (5.125), and Eqs. (5.123) and (5.124) then become linear in the unknowns r_3 and r_4. The equations to be solved are

$$r_3\cos\theta_3 - r_4\cos\theta_4 = r_1\cos\theta_1 - r_2\cos\theta_2 \tag{5.127}$$

$$r_3\sin\theta_3 - r_4\sin\theta_4 = r_1\sin\theta_1 - r_2\sin\theta_2 \tag{5.128}$$

or in matrix form

$$\begin{bmatrix} \cos\theta_3 & -\cos\theta_4 \\ \sin\theta_3 & -\sin\theta_4 \end{bmatrix} \begin{Bmatrix} r_3 \\ r_4 \end{Bmatrix} = \begin{Bmatrix} r_1\cos\theta_1 - r_2\cos\theta_2 \\ r_1\sin\theta_1 - r_2\sin\theta_2 \end{Bmatrix} \tag{5.129}$$

The terms in the matrix and in the vector on the right-hand side of the equation will be known. The matrix equation can therefore be solved manually, on a programmable calculator, or with the matrix solvers in programs such as MATLAB.

Once the position equations are solved, the coordinates of points P, Q, and R can be computed directly. The equations are given in Table 5.9.

5.7.2 Solution of Closure Equations When r_4 Is Known

When r_4 is known for the linkage of Fig. 5.30, we must determine θ_2, θ_3, and r_3. Of these unknowns, θ_2 and θ_3 are related in a trivial manner through Eq. (5.125). Therefore, the principal unknowns are θ_2 and r_3. The equations to be solved are Eqs. (5.123) and (5.124). In general, there are two solutions for r_3, and they are both valid. The two assembly modes are represented in Fig. 5.31. The equations from the position analysis are summarized as part of Table 5.10. The different assembly modes are identified by selecting values of σ in Table 5.10 as either + 1 or – 1.

TABLE 5.9 Summary of Position, Velocity, and Acceleration Equations for an RPRP Mechanism When θ_2 Is the Input Variable. The Link Numbers and Points Are Defined in Fig. 5.30

Position

$$\theta_3 = \theta_2 + \pi/2$$

$$\theta_4 = \theta_1 + \pi/2$$

$$\begin{bmatrix} \cos\theta_3 & -\cos\theta_4 \\ \sin\theta_3 & -\sin\theta_4 \end{bmatrix} \begin{Bmatrix} r_3 \\ r_4 \end{Bmatrix} = \begin{Bmatrix} r_1\cos\theta_1 - r_2\cos\theta_2 \\ r_1\sin\theta_1 - r_2\sin\theta_2 \end{Bmatrix}$$

$$\begin{aligned} \boldsymbol{r}_P &= \boldsymbol{r}_2 + \boldsymbol{r}_3 = (r_2\cos\theta_2 + r_3\cos\theta_3)\boldsymbol{i} + (r_2\sin\theta_2 + r_3\sin\theta_3)\boldsymbol{j} \\ &= \boldsymbol{r}_1 + \boldsymbol{r}_4 = (r_1\cos\theta_1 + r_4\cos\theta_4)\boldsymbol{i} + (r_1\sin\theta_1 + r_4\sin\theta_4)\boldsymbol{j} \end{aligned}$$

$$\boldsymbol{r}_Q = \boldsymbol{r}_2 = (r_2\cos\theta_2)\boldsymbol{i} + (r_2\sin\theta_2)\boldsymbol{j}$$

$$\boldsymbol{r}_R = \boldsymbol{r}_1 = (r_1\cos\theta_1)\boldsymbol{i} + (r_1\sin\theta_1)\boldsymbol{j}$$

Velocity

$$\dot\theta_3 = \dot\theta_2$$

$$\begin{bmatrix} \cos\theta_3 & -\cos\theta_4 \\ \sin\theta_3 & -\sin\theta_4 \end{bmatrix} \begin{Bmatrix} \dot r_3 \\ \dot r_4 \end{Bmatrix} = \begin{Bmatrix} r_2\dot\theta_2\sin\theta_2 + r_3\dot\theta_3\sin\theta_3 \\ -r_2\dot\theta_2\cos\theta_2 - r_3\dot\theta_3\cos\theta_3 \end{Bmatrix}$$

$$\begin{aligned} \dot{\boldsymbol{r}}_P &= \dot{\boldsymbol{r}}_2 + \dot{\boldsymbol{r}}_3 = (-r_2\dot\theta_2\sin\theta_2 - r_3\dot\theta_3\sin\theta_3 + \dot r_3\cos\theta_3)\boldsymbol{i} + (r_2\dot\theta_2\cos\theta_2 + r_3\dot\theta_3\cos\theta_3 + \dot r_3\sin\theta_3)\boldsymbol{j} \\ &= \dot{\boldsymbol{r}}_4 = (\dot r_4\cos\theta_4)\boldsymbol{i} + (\dot r_4\sin\theta_4)\boldsymbol{j} \end{aligned}$$

$$\dot{\boldsymbol{r}}_Q = \dot{\boldsymbol{r}}_2 = (-r_2\dot\theta_2\sin\theta_2)\boldsymbol{i} + (r_2\dot\theta_2\cos\theta_2)\boldsymbol{j}$$

Acceleration

$$\ddot\theta_3 = \ddot\theta_2$$

$$\begin{bmatrix} \cos\theta_3 & -\cos\theta_4 \\ \sin\theta_3 & -\sin\theta_4 \end{bmatrix} \begin{Bmatrix} \ddot r_3 \\ \ddot r_4 \end{Bmatrix} = \begin{Bmatrix} r_2\ddot\theta_2\sin\theta_2 + r_2\dot\theta_2^2\cos\theta_2 + 2\dot r_3\dot\theta_3\sin\theta_3 + r_3\ddot\theta_3\sin\theta_3 + r_3\dot\theta_3^2\cos\theta_3 \\ -r_2\ddot\theta_2\cos\theta_2 + r_2\dot\theta_2^2\sin\theta_2 - 2\dot r_3\dot\theta_3\cos\theta_3 - r_3\ddot\theta_3\cos\theta_3 + r_3\dot\theta_3^2\sin\theta_3 \end{Bmatrix}$$

$$\ddot{\boldsymbol{r}}_P = \ddot{\boldsymbol{r}}_4 = (\ddot r_4\cos\theta_4)\boldsymbol{i} + (\ddot r_4\sin\theta_4)\boldsymbol{j}$$

$$\ddot{\boldsymbol{r}}_Q = \ddot{\boldsymbol{r}}_2 = (-r_2\ddot\theta_2\sin\theta_2 - r_2\dot\theta_2^2\cos\theta_2)\boldsymbol{i} + (r_2\ddot\theta_2\cos\theta_2 - r_2\dot\theta_2^2\sin\theta_2)\boldsymbol{j}$$

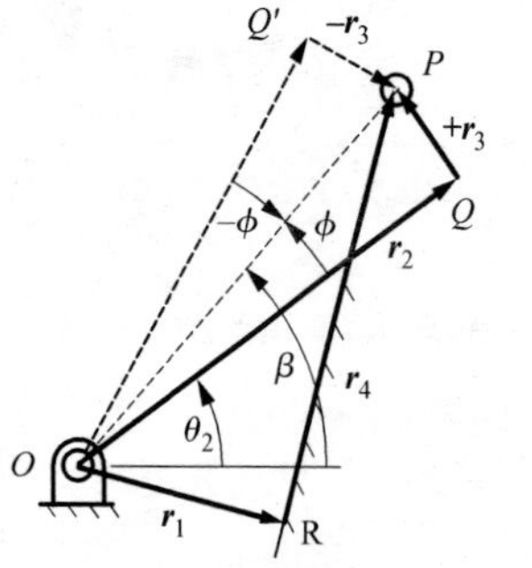

FIGURE 5.31 Two assembly modes when r_4 is input.

TABLE 5.10 Summary of Position, Velocity, and Acceleration Equations for a RPRP Mechanism When r_4 Is the Input Variable. The Link Numbers and Points Are Defined in Fig. 5.30

Position

$$r_3 = \sigma\sqrt{r_4^2 + r_1^2 - r_2^2}; \quad \sigma = \pm 1$$

$$\phi = \tan^{-1}\left(\frac{r_3}{r_2}\right)$$

$$\beta = \tan^{-1}\left(\frac{r_1 \sin\theta_1 + r_4 \sin\theta_4}{r_1 \cos\theta_1 + r_4 \cos\theta_4}\right)$$

$$\theta_2 = \beta - \phi, \qquad \theta_3 = \theta_2 + \pi/2, \qquad \theta_4 = \theta_1 + \pi/2$$

$$\begin{aligned} \boldsymbol{r}_P = \boldsymbol{r}_2 + \boldsymbol{r}_3 &= (r_2 \cos\theta_2 + r_3 \cos\theta_3)\boldsymbol{i} + (r_2 \sin\theta_2 + r_3 \sin\theta_3)\boldsymbol{j} \\ &= \boldsymbol{r}_1 + \boldsymbol{r}_4 = (r_1 \cos\theta_1 + r_4 \cos\theta_4)\boldsymbol{i} + (r_1 \sin\theta_1 + r_4 \sin\theta_4)\boldsymbol{j} \end{aligned}$$

$$\boldsymbol{r}_Q = \boldsymbol{r}_2 = (r_2 \cos\theta_2)\boldsymbol{i} + (r_2 \sin\theta_2)\boldsymbol{j}$$

Velocity

$$\begin{bmatrix} \cos\theta_3 & -(r_3 \sin\theta_3 + r_2 \sin\theta_2) \\ \sin\theta_3 & (r_3 \cos\theta_3 + r_2 \cos\theta_2) \end{bmatrix} \begin{Bmatrix} \dot{r}_3 \\ \dot{\theta}_2 \end{Bmatrix} = \begin{Bmatrix} \dot{r}_4 \cos\theta_4 \\ \dot{r}_4 \sin\theta_4 \end{Bmatrix}$$

$$\dot{\theta}_3 = \dot{\theta}_2$$

$$\begin{aligned} \dot{\boldsymbol{r}}_P = \dot{\boldsymbol{r}}_2 + \dot{\boldsymbol{r}}_3 &= (-r_2\dot{\theta}_2 \sin\theta_2 - r_3\dot{\theta}_3 \sin\theta_3 + \dot{r}_3 \cos\theta_3)\boldsymbol{i} + (r_2\dot{\theta}_2 \cos\theta_2 + r_3\dot{\theta}_3 \cos\theta_3 + \dot{r}_3 \sin\theta_3)\boldsymbol{j} \\ &= \dot{\boldsymbol{r}}_4 = (\dot{r}_4 \cos\theta_4)\boldsymbol{i} + (\dot{r}_4 \sin\theta_4)\boldsymbol{j} \end{aligned}$$

$$\dot{\boldsymbol{r}}_Q = \dot{\boldsymbol{r}}_2 = (-r_2\dot{\theta}_2 \sin\theta_2)\boldsymbol{i} + (r_2\dot{\theta}_2 \cos\theta_2)\boldsymbol{j}$$

Acceleration

$$\begin{bmatrix} \cos\theta_3 & -(r_3 \sin\theta_3 + r_2 \sin\theta_2) \\ \sin\theta_3 & (r_3 \cos\theta_3 + r_2 \cos\theta_2) \end{bmatrix} \begin{Bmatrix} \ddot{r}_3 \\ \ddot{\theta}_2 \end{Bmatrix} = \begin{Bmatrix} \ddot{r}_4 \cos\theta_4 + r_2\dot{\theta}_2^2 \cos\theta_2 + 2\dot{r}_3\dot{\theta}_3 \sin\theta_3 + r_3\dot{\theta}_3^2 \cos\theta_3 \\ \ddot{r}_4 \sin\theta_4 + r_2\dot{\theta}_2^2 \sin\theta_2 - 2\dot{r}_3\dot{\theta}_3 \cos\theta_3 + r_3\dot{\theta}_3^2 \sin\theta_3 \end{Bmatrix}$$

$$\ddot{\theta}_3 = \ddot{\theta}_2$$

$$\ddot{\boldsymbol{r}}_P = \ddot{\boldsymbol{r}}_4 = (\ddot{r}_4 \cos\theta_4)\boldsymbol{i} + (\ddot{r}_4 \sin\theta_4)\boldsymbol{j}$$

$$\ddot{\boldsymbol{r}}_Q = \ddot{\boldsymbol{r}}_2 = (-r_2\ddot{\theta}_2 \sin\theta_2 - r_2\dot{\theta}_2^2 \cos\theta_2)\boldsymbol{i} + (r_2\ddot{\theta}_2 \cos\theta_2 - r_2\dot{\theta}_2^2 \sin\theta_2)\boldsymbol{j}$$

It is also possible to specify a value for r_4 that will prevent the mechanism from being assembled. This is indicated when the argument of the square root in Table 5.10 is negative.

Once both r_3 and r_4 are known, we can find θ_2 (and θ_3) using simple geometry. First compute the angles ϕ and β shown in Fig. 5.31 using

$$\phi = \tan^{-1}\left(\frac{r_3}{r_2}\right) \tag{5.130}$$

and

$$\beta = \tan^{-1}\left(\frac{r_{P_y}}{r_{P_x}}\right) = \tan^{-1}\left(\frac{r_1 \sin\theta_1 + r_4 \sin\theta_4}{r_1 \cos\theta_1 + r_4 \cos\theta_4}\right) \tag{5.131}$$

Then

$$\theta_2 = \beta - \phi \tag{5.132}$$

and

$$\theta_3 = \theta_2 + \pi/2 \tag{5.133}$$

Equation (5.132) is valid for both the plus and minus values for r_3 because the sign of ϕ will be positive when r_3 is positive and negative when r_3 is negative.

5.7.3 Solution of Closure Equations When r_3 Is Known

When r_3 is known, we must determine θ_2, θ_3, and r_4. Of these unknowns, θ_2 and θ_3 are related in a trivial manner through Eq. (5.125). Therefore, the principal unknowns are θ_2 and r_4. The procedure for solving the position equations is very similar to that when r_4 was input. In general, there are two solutions for r_4, and they are both valid. The equations from the position analysis are summarized as part of Table 5.11. Note that it is possible to specify a value for r_3 that will prevent the mechanism from being assembled. This is indicated when the argument of the square root in Table 5.11 is negative.

TABLE 5.11 Summary of Position, Velocity, and Acceleration Equations for an RPRP Mechanism When r_3 Is the Input Variable. The Link Numbers and Points Are Defined in Fig. 5.30

Position

$$r_4 = \sigma\sqrt{r_3^2 - r_1^2 + r_2^2}; \quad \sigma = \pm 1$$

$$\phi = \tan^{-1}\left(\frac{r_3}{r_2}\right)$$

$$\beta = \tan^{-1}\left(\frac{r_1 \sin\theta_1 + r_4 \sin\theta_4}{r_1 \cos\theta_1 + r_4 \cos\theta_4}\right)$$

$$\theta_2 = \beta - \phi, \qquad \theta_3 = \theta_2 + \pi/2, \qquad \theta_4 = \theta_1 + \pi/2$$

$$\begin{aligned} \boldsymbol{r}_P &= \boldsymbol{r}_2 + \boldsymbol{r}_3 = (r_2 \cos\theta_2 + r_3 \cos\theta_3)\boldsymbol{i} + (r_2 \sin\theta_2 + r_3 \sin\theta_3)\boldsymbol{j} \\ &= \boldsymbol{r}_1 + \boldsymbol{r}_4 = (r_1 \cos\theta_1 + r_4 \cos\theta_4)\boldsymbol{i} + (r_1 \sin\theta_1 + r_4 \sin\theta_4)\boldsymbol{j} \end{aligned}$$

$$\boldsymbol{r}_Q = \boldsymbol{r}_2 = (r_2 \cos\theta_2)\boldsymbol{i} + (r_2 \sin\theta_2)\boldsymbol{j}$$

(continued)

TABLE 5.11 continued

Velocity

$$\begin{bmatrix} \cos\theta_4 & (r_3 \sin\theta_3 + r_2 \sin\theta_2) \\ \sin\theta_4 & -(r_3 \cos\theta_3 + r_2 \cos\theta_2) \end{bmatrix} \begin{Bmatrix} \dot{r}_4 \\ \dot{\theta}_2 \end{Bmatrix} = \begin{Bmatrix} \dot{r}_3 \cos\theta_3 \\ \dot{r}_3 \sin\theta_3 \end{Bmatrix}$$

$$\dot{\theta}_3 = \dot{\theta}_2$$

$$\dot{\boldsymbol{r}}_P = \dot{\boldsymbol{r}}_2 + \dot{\boldsymbol{r}}_3 = \left(-r_2\dot{\theta}_2 \sin\theta_2 - r_3\dot{\theta}_3 \sin\theta_3 + \dot{r}_3 \cos\theta_3\right)\boldsymbol{i} + \left(r_2\dot{\theta}_2 \cos\theta_2 + r_3\dot{\theta}_3 \cos\theta_3 + \dot{r}_3 \sin\theta_3\right)\boldsymbol{j}$$
$$= \dot{\boldsymbol{r}}_4 = \left(\dot{r}_4 \cos\theta_4\right)\boldsymbol{i} + \left(\dot{r}_4 \sin\theta_4\right)\boldsymbol{j}$$

$$\dot{\boldsymbol{r}}_Q = \dot{\boldsymbol{r}}_2 = \left(-r_2\dot{\theta}_2 \sin\theta_2\right)\boldsymbol{i} + \left(r_2\dot{\theta}_2 \cos\theta_2\right)\boldsymbol{j}$$

Acceleration

$$\begin{bmatrix} \cos\theta_4 & (r_3 \sin\theta_3 + r_2 \sin\theta_2) \\ \sin\theta_4 & -(r_3 \cos\theta_3 + r_2 \cos\theta_2) \end{bmatrix} \begin{Bmatrix} \ddot{r}_4 \\ \ddot{\theta}_2 \end{Bmatrix} = \begin{Bmatrix} -r_2\dot{\theta}_2^2 \cos\theta_2 - 2\dot{r}_3\dot{\theta}_3 \sin\theta_3 - r_3\dot{\theta}_3^2 \cos\theta_3 + \ddot{r}_3 \cos\theta_3 \\ -r_2\dot{\theta}_2^2 \sin\theta_2 + 2\dot{r}_3\dot{\theta}_3 \cos\theta_3 - r_3\dot{\theta}_3^2 \sin\theta_3 + \ddot{r}_3 \sin\theta_3 \end{Bmatrix}$$

$$\ddot{\theta}_3 = \ddot{\theta}_2$$

$$\ddot{\boldsymbol{r}}_P = \ddot{\boldsymbol{r}}_4 = \left(\ddot{r}_4 \cos\theta_4\right)\boldsymbol{i} + \left(\ddot{r}_4 \sin\theta_4\right)\boldsymbol{j}$$

$$\ddot{\boldsymbol{r}}_Q = \ddot{\boldsymbol{r}}_2 = \left(-r_2\ddot{\theta}_2 \sin\theta_2 - r_2\dot{\theta}_2^2 \cos\theta_2\right)\boldsymbol{i} + \left(r_2\ddot{\theta}_2 \cos\theta_2 - r_2\dot{\theta}_2^2 \sin\theta_2\right)\boldsymbol{j}$$

5.7.4 Velocity and Acceleration Equations for an RPRP Mechanism

The analytical form of the velocity equations can be developed by differentiating the position equations and solving the resulting linear set of equations for the unknowns as done in the previous examples. The acceleration equations are developed by differentiating the velocity equations. The acceleration equations are also linear and can easily be solved. The results for the RPRP mechanism are given in Tables 5.9, 5.10, and 5.11. These equations can easily be programmed, and MATLAB programs for solving the equations in the three tables are given on the disk with this book.

EXAMPLE 5.7
Kinematic Analysis of an RPRP Mechanism

In the mechanism shown in Fig. 5.32, link 3 slides on link 2, and link 4 is pinned to link 3; link 4 also slides on the frame (link 1). If $\boldsymbol{\omega}_2 = 10$ rad/s CCW and is constant, determine the velocity and acceleration of link 4 for the position defined by $\theta_2 = 60°$.

Solution

Using the nomenclature developed earlier, the basic vector closure diagram is as shown in Fig. 5.33. Note that in this example, $r_2 = 0$. From Figs. 5.32 and 5.33, the following geometric quantities can be determined:

$$r_2 = 0, \qquad r_1 = 10$$
$$\theta_1 = 90°, \qquad \theta_2 = 60°, \qquad \theta_3 = 60°, \qquad \theta_4 = 180°$$

The geometric unknowns are r_3 and r_4. Because $\theta_2 = \theta_3$ is the input variable, we can compute the results using the equations in Table 5.9. To solve for r_3 and r_4, solve

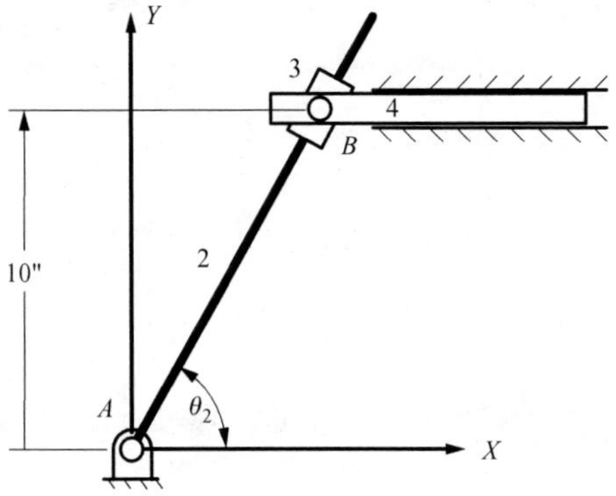

FIGURE 5.32 Mechanism for Example 5.7.

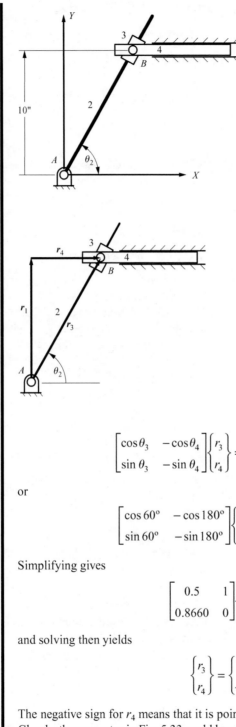

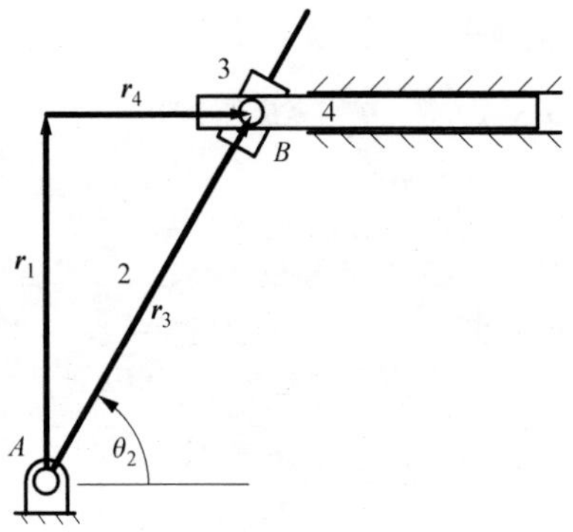

FIGURE 5.33 Vector closure diagram for Example 5.7.

$$\begin{bmatrix} \cos\theta_3 & -\cos\theta_4 \\ \sin\theta_3 & -\sin\theta_4 \end{bmatrix} \begin{Bmatrix} r_3 \\ r_4 \end{Bmatrix} = \begin{Bmatrix} r_1\cos\theta_1 - r_2\cos\theta_2 \\ r_1\sin\theta_1 - r_2\sin\theta_2 \end{Bmatrix}$$

or

$$\begin{bmatrix} \cos 60^\circ & -\cos 180^\circ \\ \sin 60^\circ & -\sin 180^\circ \end{bmatrix} \begin{Bmatrix} r_3 \\ r_4 \end{Bmatrix} = \begin{Bmatrix} 10\cos 90^\circ - 0 \\ 10\sin 90^\circ - 0 \end{Bmatrix}$$

Simplifying gives

$$\begin{bmatrix} 0.5 & 1 \\ 0.8660 & 0 \end{bmatrix} \begin{Bmatrix} r_3 \\ r_4 \end{Bmatrix} = \begin{Bmatrix} 0 \\ 10 \end{Bmatrix}$$

and solving then yields

$$\begin{Bmatrix} r_3 \\ r_4 \end{Bmatrix} = \begin{Bmatrix} 11.547 \\ -5.774 \end{Bmatrix}$$

The negative sign for r_4 means that it is pointing in the opposite direction to that given by $\theta_4 = 180°$. Clearly, the geometry in Fig. 5.33 could have been solved directly using geometry; however, the more general equations are used here to illustrate the procedure.

For the velocities, the unknowns are $\dot{r}_3$ and $\dot{r}_4$. From the problem statement, $\dot{\theta}_2 = \dot{\theta}_3 = 10$ rad/s CCW. Therefore, from Table 5.9,

$$\begin{bmatrix} \cos\theta_3 & -\cos\theta_4 \\ \sin\theta_3 & -\sin\theta_4 \end{bmatrix} \begin{Bmatrix} \dot{r}_3 \\ \dot{r}_4 \end{Bmatrix} = \begin{Bmatrix} r_2\dot{\theta}_2\sin\theta_2 + r_3\dot{\theta}_3\sin\theta_3 \\ -r_2\dot{\theta}_2\cos\theta_2 - r_3\dot{\theta}_3\cos\theta_3 \end{Bmatrix}$$

Note that the coefficient matrix on the left-hand side of the velocity equation is the same as the corresponding position matrix.

Substituting the known quantities into the matrix equation gives

$$\begin{bmatrix} 0.5 & 1 \\ 0.8660 & 0 \end{bmatrix} \begin{Bmatrix} \dot{r}_3 \\ \dot{r}_4 \end{Bmatrix} = \begin{Bmatrix} 0 + 11.547(10)\sin 60^\circ \\ 0 - 11.547(10)\cos 60^\circ \end{Bmatrix} = \begin{Bmatrix} 100 \\ -57.74 \end{Bmatrix}$$

or

$$\begin{Bmatrix} \dot{r}_3 \\ \dot{r}_4 \end{Bmatrix} = \begin{Bmatrix} -66.67 \\ 133.33 \end{Bmatrix}$$

Note that the positive value for $\dot{r}_4$ means that r_4 is increasing with time. Because r_4 is negative when it points in the positive x direction ($\theta_4 = 180^\circ$), a positive sign for $\dot{r}_4$ means that r_4 is increasing or becoming less negative with time. This means that link 4 is moving in the $-x$ direction.

For the acceleration analysis, the unknowns are $\ddot{r}_3$ and $\ddot{r}_4$. From the problem statement, $\ddot{\theta}_2 = \ddot{\theta}_3 = 0$, and from Table 5.9,

$$\begin{bmatrix} \cos\theta_3 & -\cos\theta_4 \\ \sin\theta_3 & -\sin\theta_4 \end{bmatrix} \begin{Bmatrix} \ddot{r}_3 \\ \ddot{r}_4 \end{Bmatrix} = \begin{Bmatrix} r_2\ddot{\theta}_2 \sin\theta_2 + r_2\dot{\theta}_2^2 \cos\theta_2 + 2\dot{r}_3\dot{\theta}_3 \sin\theta_3 + r_3\ddot{\theta}_3 \sin\theta_3 + r_3\dot{\theta}_3^2 \cos\theta_3 \\ -r_2\ddot{\theta}_2 \cos\theta_2 + r_2\dot{\theta}_2^2 \sin\theta_2 - 2\dot{r}_3\dot{\theta}_3 \cos\theta_3 - r_3\ddot{\theta}_3 \cos\theta_3 + r_3\dot{\theta}_3^2 \sin\theta_3 \end{Bmatrix}$$

Note again that the coefficient matrix on the left-hand side of the acceleration equation is the same as the corresponding position matrix. Substituting the known quantities into the matrix equation gives

$$\begin{bmatrix} 0.5 & 1 \\ 0.8660 & 0 \end{bmatrix} \begin{Bmatrix} \ddot{r}_3 \\ \ddot{r}_4 \end{Bmatrix} = \begin{Bmatrix} -577.4 \\ 1666.7 \end{Bmatrix}$$

or

$$\begin{Bmatrix} \ddot{r}_3 \\ \ddot{r}_4 \end{Bmatrix} = \begin{Bmatrix} 1924.5 \\ -1539.6 \end{Bmatrix}$$

Again, the positive value for $\ddot{r}_4$ means the slider is accelerating in the positive $\boldsymbol{r}_4$ direction, that is, to the left.

5.8 ANALYTICAL EQUATIONS FOR AN RRPP MECHANISM

A schematic drawing of the RRPP mechanism is shown in Fig. 5.34. In the mechanism shown, link 2 is connected to the frame and to the coupler (link 3) by revolute joints. The coupler is connected to link 4 by a prismatic joint, and link 4 is connected to the frame through a prismatic joint. This mechanism occurs frequently in industrial machinery and household appliances. A common version of it is the Scotch yoke, which is a compact mechanism for converting rotary motion to reciprocating motion.

To analyze the mechanism using vector closure equations, we must align vectors in the directions of the slider motions as shown in Fig. 5.35. Only three vectors are required to model the motion. Vector $\boldsymbol{r}_1$ is fixed at an angle θ_1 and of variable length. This vector begins at point O and ends at point Q, where Q is the intersection of a line through O and in the direction of the velocity of link 4 relative to link 1 and a second line through P in the direction of the velocity of link 3 relative to link 4. The two lines intersect at an angle β. Vector $\boldsymbol{r}_2$ is the crank and of fixed length but variable orientation. Vector $\boldsymbol{r}_3$ is measured from point Q and gives the displacement of slider 3 relative to link 4.

To develop the closure equations, locate point P with vector $\boldsymbol{r}_2$ and with vectors $\boldsymbol{r}_1 + \boldsymbol{r}_3$ as shown in Fig. 5.35. Then the vector closure equation is

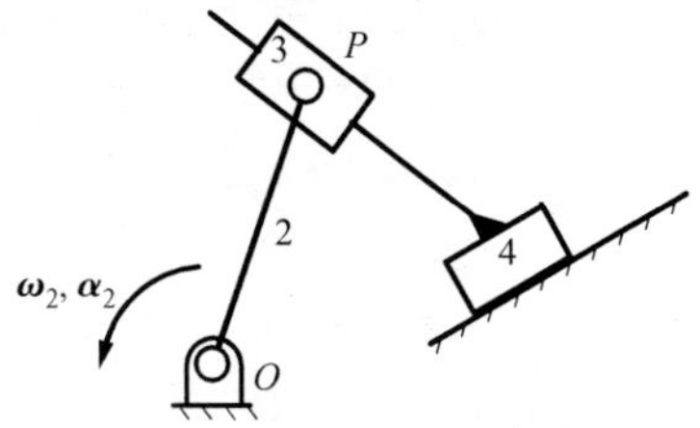

FIGURE 5.34 Schematic diagram of an RRPP mechanism.

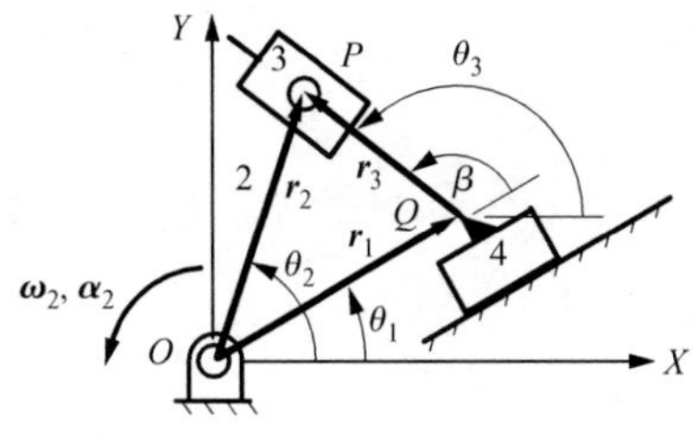

FIGURE 5.35 Vector closure diagram of an RRPP mechanism.

$$\boldsymbol{r}_P = \boldsymbol{r}_2 = \boldsymbol{r}_1 + \boldsymbol{r}_3 \tag{5.134}$$

or

$$r_2(\cos\theta_2 \boldsymbol{i} + \sin\theta_2 \boldsymbol{j}) = r_1(\cos\theta_1 \boldsymbol{i} + \sin\theta_1 \boldsymbol{j}) + r_3(\cos\theta_3 \boldsymbol{i} + \sin\theta_3 \boldsymbol{j}) \tag{5.135}$$

Rewriting the components in Eq. (5.134) as separate equations gives

$$r_2 \cos\theta_2 = r_1 \cos\theta_1 + r_3 \cos\theta_3 \tag{5.136}$$

$$r_2 \sin\theta_2 = r_1 \sin\theta_1 + r_3 \sin\theta_3 \tag{5.137}$$

Equations (5.136) and (5.137) must be satisfied throughout the motion of the linkage. There are six quantities to identify: r_1 and θ_1, r_2 and θ_2, and r_3 and θ_3. From the diagram in Fig. 5.35, θ_1, r_2, and θ_3 are constants. Furthermore, we know that

$$\theta_3 = \theta_1 + \beta \tag{5.138}$$

where β is a constant.

The variables are r_1, θ_2, and r_3. For a one-degree-of-freedom mechanism, one of the variables must be an input (i.e., a known) variable. Therefore, there are two unknowns, and we can solve for them using the two equations (5.136) and (5.137) involving the unknowns.

Once all of the position variables are obtained, the unknown velocities and accelerations can be obtained by differentiating Eqs. (5.136) and (5.137) and solving the resulting sets of linear equations for the unknowns.

Before solving the equations for the unknowns, it is necessary to select an input variable. Any of the variables r_1, θ_2, or r_3 could be chosen, and the equations have been developed for each case. Again, we will not give a detailed development of the solution procedure because it is similar to the examples discussed before. An overview of each case is given in the following, and the results are summarized in tables.

5.8.1 Solution When θ_2 Is Known

The case in which θ_2 is an input is especially simple because Eqs. (5.136) and (5.137) then become linear in the unknowns r_1 and r_3. Only one assembly mode is possible, and if r_2 is nonzero, there are no positions in which the mechanism cannot be assembled. The velocity and acceleration equations are obtained by differentiation. The solution for this case is given in Table 5.12, and a MATLAB program for solving the equations is given on the disk with this book.

TABLE 5.12 Summary of Position, Velocity, and Acceleration Equations for an RRPP Mechanism When θ_2 Is the Input Variable. The Link Numbers and Points Are Defined in Fig. 5.34

Position

$$\theta_3 = \theta_1 + \beta$$

$$\begin{bmatrix} \cos\theta_1 & \cos\theta_3 \\ \sin\theta_1 & \sin\theta_3 \end{bmatrix} \begin{Bmatrix} r_1 \\ r_3 \end{Bmatrix} = \begin{Bmatrix} r_2\cos\theta_2 \\ r_2\sin\theta_2 \end{Bmatrix}$$

$$\boldsymbol{r}_P = \boldsymbol{r}_2 = (r_2\cos\theta_2)\boldsymbol{i} + (r_2\sin\theta_2)\boldsymbol{j}$$

$$\boldsymbol{r}_Q = \boldsymbol{r}_1 = (r_1\cos\theta_1)\boldsymbol{i} + (r_1\sin\theta_1)\boldsymbol{j}$$

Velocity

$$\begin{bmatrix} \cos\theta_1 & \cos\theta_3 \\ \sin\theta_1 & \sin\theta_3 \end{bmatrix} \begin{Bmatrix} \dot{r}_1 \\ \dot{r}_3 \end{Bmatrix} = \begin{Bmatrix} -r_2\dot{\theta}_2\sin\theta_2 \\ r_2\dot{\theta}_2\cos\theta_2 \end{Bmatrix}$$

$$\dot{\boldsymbol{r}}_P = \dot{\boldsymbol{r}}_2 = (-r_2\dot{\theta}_2\sin\theta_2)\boldsymbol{i} + (r_2\dot{\theta}_2\cos\theta_2)\boldsymbol{j}$$

$$\dot{\boldsymbol{r}}_Q = \dot{\boldsymbol{r}}_1 = (\dot{r}_1\cos\theta_1)\boldsymbol{i} + (\dot{r}_1\sin\theta_1)\boldsymbol{j}$$

Acceleration

$$\begin{bmatrix} \cos\theta_1 & \cos\theta_3 \\ \sin\theta_1 & \sin\theta_3 \end{bmatrix} \begin{Bmatrix} \ddot{r}_1 \\ \ddot{r}_3 \end{Bmatrix} = \begin{Bmatrix} -r_2\ddot{\theta}_2\sin\theta_2 - r_2\dot{\theta}_2^2\cos\theta_2 \\ r_2\ddot{\theta}_2\cos\theta_2 - r_2\dot{\theta}_2^2\sin\theta_2 \end{Bmatrix}$$

$$\ddot{\boldsymbol{r}}_P = \ddot{\boldsymbol{r}}_2 = (-r_2\ddot{\theta}_2\sin\theta_2 - r_2\dot{\theta}_2^2\cos\theta_2)\boldsymbol{i} + (r_2\ddot{\theta}_2\cos\theta_2 - r_2\dot{\theta}_2^2\sin\theta_2)\boldsymbol{j}$$

$$\ddot{\boldsymbol{r}}_Q = \ddot{\boldsymbol{r}}_1 = (\ddot{r}_1\cos\theta_1)\boldsymbol{i} + (\ddot{r}_1\sin\theta_1)\boldsymbol{j}$$

5.8.2 Solution When r_1 Is Known

When r_1 is known, we must solve Eqs. (5.136) and (5.137) for θ_2 and r_3. The solution is similar to that for the slider-crank inversion. In general, there are two solutions for r_3, corresponding to the two assembly modes or branches for the linkage represented in Fig. 5.36. Also, it is possible to specify a value for r_1 that will prevent the mechanism from being assembled. After the position equations are solved, the velocity and acceleration equations are obtained by differentiation. The results are summarized in Table 5.13 and a MATLAB program for solving the equations is given on the disk with this book.

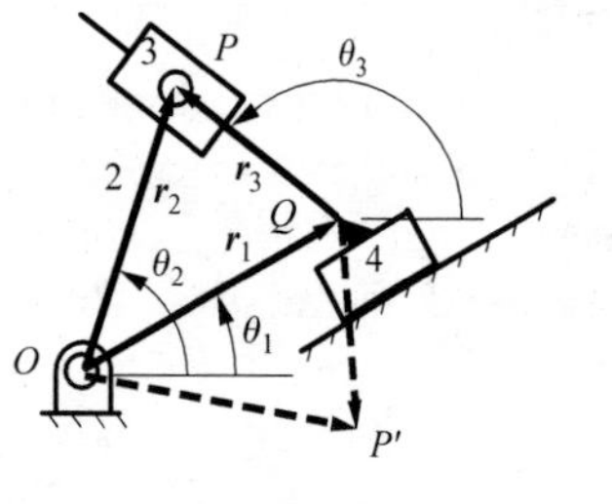

FIGURE 5.36 Two configurations possible when r_1 is input.

TABLE 5.13 Summary of Position, Velocity, and Acceleration Equations for an RRPP Mechanism When Either r_1 or r_3 is the input Variable. When r_1 Is the Input, $M = 1$ and $J = 3$. When r_3 Is the Input, $M = 3$ and $J = 1$. The Link Numbers and Points Are Defined in Fig. 5.34

Position

$$\theta_3 = \theta_1 + \beta$$

$$B = r_M\left(\cos\theta_M \cos\theta_J + \sin\theta_M \sin\theta_J\right)$$

$$C = \left(r_M^2 - r_2^2\right)$$

$$r_J = -B + \sigma\sqrt{B^2 - C}; \quad \sigma = \pm 1$$

$$\theta_2 = \tan^{-1}\frac{r_1 \sin\theta_1 + r_3 \sin\theta_3}{r_1 \cos\theta_1 + r_3 \cos\theta_3}$$

$$\boldsymbol{r}_P = \boldsymbol{r}_2 = \left(r_2 \cos\theta_2\right)\boldsymbol{i} + \left(r_2 \sin\theta_2\right)\boldsymbol{j}$$

$$\boldsymbol{r}_Q = \boldsymbol{r}_1 = \left(r_1 \cos\theta_1\right)\boldsymbol{i} + \left(r_1 \sin\theta_1\right)\boldsymbol{j}$$

Velocity

$$\begin{bmatrix} -r_2 \sin\theta_2 & -\cos\theta_J \\ r_2 \cos\theta_2 & -\sin\theta_J \end{bmatrix} \begin{Bmatrix} \dot{\theta}_2 \\ \dot{r}_J \end{Bmatrix} = \begin{Bmatrix} \dot{r}_M \cos\theta_M \\ \dot{r}_M \sin\theta_M \end{Bmatrix}$$

$$\dot{\boldsymbol{r}}_P = \dot{\boldsymbol{r}}_2 = \left(-r_2\dot{\theta}_2 \sin\theta_2\right)\boldsymbol{i} + \left(r_2\dot{\theta}_2 \cos\theta_2\right)\boldsymbol{j}$$

$$\dot{\boldsymbol{r}}_Q = \dot{\boldsymbol{r}}_1 = \left(\dot{r}_1 \cos\theta_1\right)\boldsymbol{i} + \left(\dot{r}_1 \sin\theta_1\right)\boldsymbol{j}$$

Acceleration

$$\begin{bmatrix} -r_2 \sin\theta_2 & -\cos\theta_J \\ r_2 \cos\theta_2 & -\sin\theta_J \end{bmatrix} \begin{Bmatrix} \ddot{\theta}_2 \\ \ddot{r}_J \end{Bmatrix} = \begin{Bmatrix} \ddot{r}_M \cos\theta_M + r_2\dot{\theta}_2^2 \cos\theta_2 \\ \ddot{r}_M \sin\theta_M + r_2\dot{\theta}_2^2 \sin\theta_2 \end{Bmatrix}$$

$$\ddot{\boldsymbol{r}}_P = \ddot{\boldsymbol{r}}_2 = \left(-r_2\ddot{\theta}_2 \sin\theta_2 - r_2\dot{\theta}_2^2 \cos\theta_2\right)\boldsymbol{i} + \left(r_2\ddot{\theta}_2 \cos\theta_2 - r_2\dot{\theta}_2^2 \sin\theta_2\right)\boldsymbol{j}$$

$$\ddot{\boldsymbol{r}}_Q = \ddot{\boldsymbol{r}}_1 = \left(\ddot{r}_1 \cos\theta_1\right)\boldsymbol{i} + \left(\ddot{r}_1 \sin\theta_1\right)\boldsymbol{j}$$

5.8.3 Solution When r_3 Is Known

When r_3 is known, we must solve Eqs. (5.136) and (5.137) for θ_2 and r_1. The solution is almost identical to that for the case in which r_1 is known. We need only switch the indices for 1 and 3, and the results are otherwise the same. This is indicated in Table 5.13. This case is also included in a MATLAB routine on the disk with this book.

EXAMPLE 5.8 ***Kinematic Analysis of a Scotch Yoke***

In the Scotch yoke mechanism shown in Fig. 5.37, the angular velocity of link 2 relative to the frame is 1 rad/s CCW (constant) when the angle θ_2 is 60°. Also, the length $OP = 2$ in. Determine the velocity and acceleration of link 4.

Solution

Using the nomenclature developed earlier, we can draw the basic vector closure diagram as shown in Fig. 3.38. From Figs. 5.37 and 5.38, the following geometry quantities can be determined:

$$r_2 = 2$$
$$\theta_1 = 0^\circ, \qquad \theta_2 = 60^\circ, \qquad \beta = 90^\circ, \qquad \theta_3 = 90^\circ$$
$$\dot{\theta}_2 = 1, \qquad \ddot{\theta}_2 = 0$$

Because the crank (link 2) is the driving link, we can use the equations in Table 5.12 to solve the problem. The geometric unknowns are r_1 and r_3. To determine r_1 and r_3, solve

$$\begin{bmatrix} \cos\theta_1 & \cos\theta_3 \\ \sin\theta_1 & \sin\theta_3 \end{bmatrix} \begin{Bmatrix} r_1 \\ r_3 \end{Bmatrix} = \begin{Bmatrix} r_2\cos\theta_2 \\ r_2\sin\theta_2 \end{Bmatrix}$$

or

$$\begin{bmatrix} 1 & 0 \\ 0 & 1 \end{bmatrix} \begin{Bmatrix} r_1 \\ r_3 \end{Bmatrix} = \begin{Bmatrix} r_2\cos\theta_2 \\ r_2\sin\theta_2 \end{Bmatrix}$$

Then

$$r_1 = r_2\cos\theta_2$$

and

$$r_3 = r_2\sin\theta_2$$

Notice that the motion of the slider is a sinusoidal function of the input rotation. This is one of the benefits of the Scotch yoke and is one of the reasons that it is used. For the given input values ($r_2 = 2$ and $\theta_2 = 60^\circ$) it is clear that $r_1 = 1.0$ and $r_3 = 1.732$.

For the velocities, the unknowns are $\dot{r}_1$ and $\dot{r}_3$. These can be determined from the matrix equation

$$\begin{bmatrix} \cos\theta_1 & \cos\theta_3 \\ \sin\theta_1 & \sin\theta_3 \end{bmatrix} \begin{Bmatrix} \dot{r}_1 \\ \dot{r}_3 \end{Bmatrix} = \begin{Bmatrix} -r_2\dot{\theta}_2\sin\theta_2 \\ r_2\dot{\theta}_2\cos\theta_2 \end{Bmatrix}$$

or

$$\begin{bmatrix} 1 & 0 \\ 0 & 1 \end{bmatrix} \begin{Bmatrix} \dot{r}_1 \\ \dot{r}_3 \end{Bmatrix} = \begin{Bmatrix} -2(1)\sin 60^\circ \\ 2(1)\cos 60^\circ \end{Bmatrix} = \begin{Bmatrix} -1.732 \\ 1 \end{Bmatrix}$$

or

$$\dot{r}_1 = -1.732 \text{ in/s}$$

and

$$\dot{r}_3 = 1 \text{ in/s}$$

The negative sign means that r_1 is decreasing in length with increasing time.

For the accelerations, the unknowns are $\ddot{r}_1$ and $\ddot{r}_3$. These can be determined by solving

$$\begin{bmatrix} \cos\theta_1 & \cos\theta_3 \\ \sin\theta_1 & \sin\theta_3 \end{bmatrix} \begin{Bmatrix} \ddot{r}_1 \\ \ddot{r}_3 \end{Bmatrix} = \begin{Bmatrix} -r_2\ddot{\theta}_2\sin\theta_2 - r_2\dot{\theta}_2^2\cos\theta_2 \\ r_2\ddot{\theta}_2\cos\theta_2 - r_2\dot{\theta}_2^2\sin\theta_2 \end{Bmatrix}$$

Substituting into the equation the known values, we get

$$\begin{bmatrix} 1 & 0 \\ 0 & 1 \end{bmatrix} \begin{Bmatrix} \ddot{r}_1 \\ \ddot{r}_3 \end{Bmatrix} = \begin{Bmatrix} 0 - 2(1)^2\cos 60^\circ \\ 0 - 2(1)^2\sin 60^\circ \end{Bmatrix} = \begin{Bmatrix} -1 \\ -1.732 \end{Bmatrix}$$

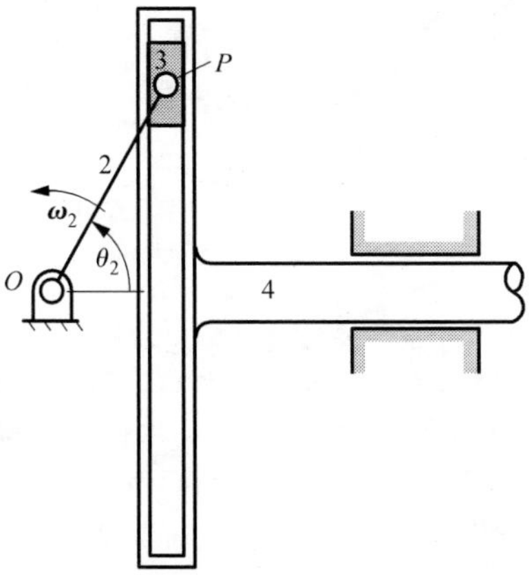

FIGURE 5.37 Scotch yoke mechanism.

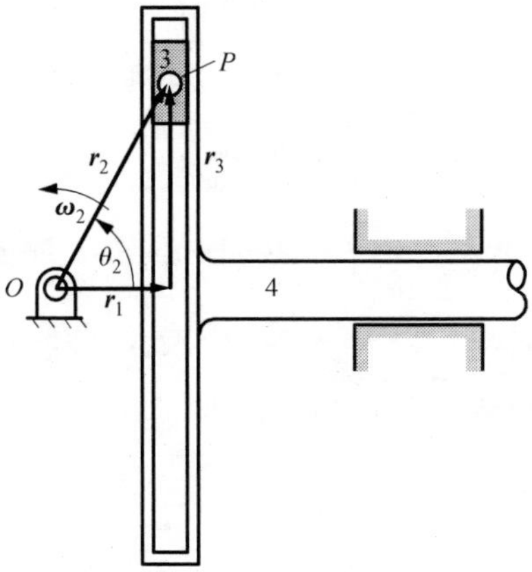

FIGURE 5.38 Vector diagram for Scotch yoke mechanism.

or

$$\ddot{r}_1 = -1 \ \text{in/s}^2$$

and

$$\ddot{r}_3 = -1.732 \ \text{in/s}^2$$

5.9 ANALYTICAL EQUATIONS FOR ELLIPTIC TRAMMEL

The elliptic trammel is an inversion of the RRPP mechanism, and a schematic drawing of this mechanism is shown in Fig. 5.39. In the mechanism, links 2 and 4 are connected to the frame by prismatic joints and to the coupler by revolute joints. A significant feature of this mechanism is that coupler points trace ellipses on the frame, and it is used in machine tools for this purpose.

To analyze the mechanism using vector closure equations, we must again align vectors in the directions of the slider motions as shown in Fig. 5.40. As in the case of the RRPP mechanism, only three vectors are required to model the motion. Vector $\boldsymbol{r}_1$ is fixed at an

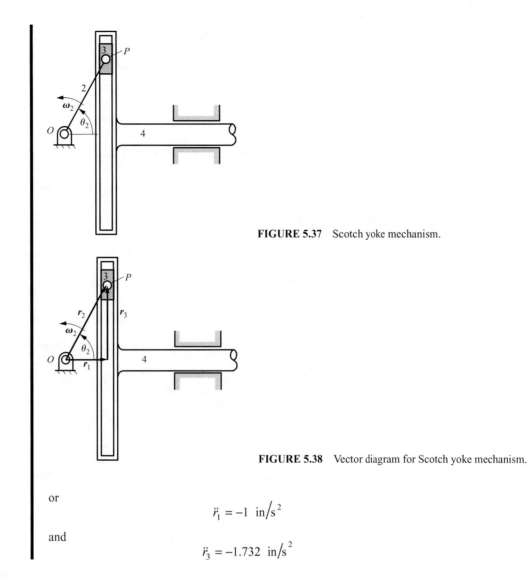

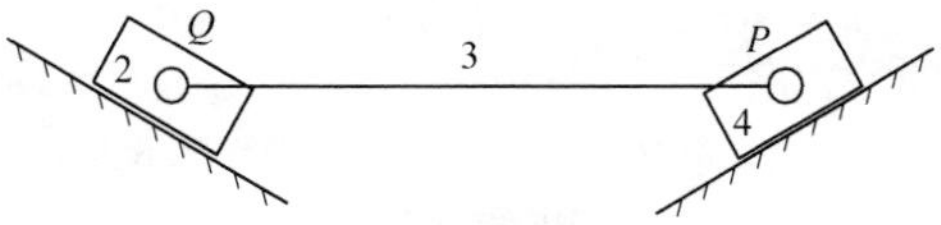

FIGURE 5.39 Schematic diagram of elliptic trammel.

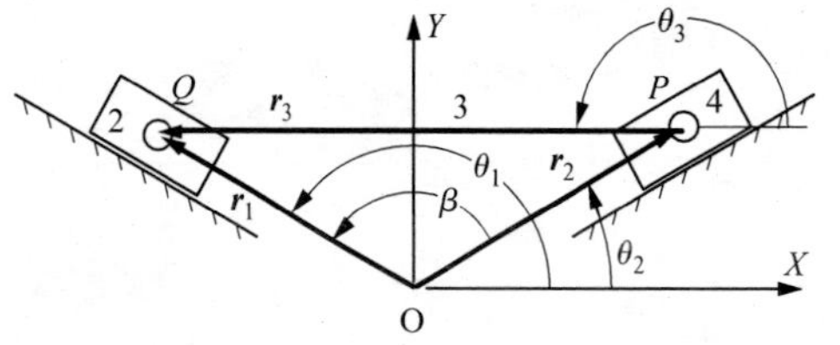

FIGURE 5.40 Vector closure diagram for elliptic trammel mechanism.

angle θ_1 and of variable length. This vector begins at point O and ends at point Q, where O is the intersection of a line through Q and in the direction of the velocity of link 2 relative to link 1 and a second line through P in the direction of the velocity of link 4 relative to link 1. Point O is the origin of the frame coordinate system. The two lines intersect at an angle β, measured from $\boldsymbol{r}_2$ to $\boldsymbol{r}_1$. Vector $\boldsymbol{r}_2$ is fixed at an angle θ_2 and of variable length. Vector $\boldsymbol{r}_3$ is measured from point P to point Q.

As shown in Fig. 5.40, to develop the closure equations, locate point Q with vector $\boldsymbol{r}_1$ and with vectors $\boldsymbol{r}_2 + \boldsymbol{r}_3$. Then the vector closure equation is

$$r_Q = r_1 = r_2 + r_3 \tag{5.139}$$

or

$$r_1\left(\cos\theta_1\boldsymbol{i} + \sin\theta_1\boldsymbol{j}\right) = r_2\left(\cos\theta_2\boldsymbol{i} + \sin\theta_2\boldsymbol{j}\right) + r_3\left(\cos\theta_3\boldsymbol{i} + \sin\theta_3\boldsymbol{j}\right) \tag{5.140}$$

Rewriting the components in Eq. (5.139) as separate equations gives

$$r_1\cos\theta_1 = r_2\cos\theta_2 + r_3\cos\theta_3 \tag{5.141}$$

$$r_1\sin\theta_1 = r_2\sin\theta_2 + r_3\sin\theta_3 \tag{5.142}$$

Equations (5.141) and (5.142) must be satisfied throughout the motion of the linkage. As in the case of the RRPP mechanism, there are six quantities to identify: r_1 and θ_1, r_2 and θ_2, and r_3 and θ_3. From the diagram in Fig. 5.40, the following are constants: θ_1, r_3, and θ_2. Furthermore, we know that

$$\theta_1 = \theta_2 + \beta \tag{5.143}$$

where β is a constant.

The variables are r_1, θ_3, and r_2. For a one-degree-of-freedom mechanism, one of the variables must be an input (i.e., known) variable. Therefore, there are a total of two unknowns, and we can solve for them using the two equations (5.141) and (5.142) involving the unknowns. Once all of the position variables are obtained, the unknown velocities and accelerations can be found by differentiating Eqs. (5.141) and (5.142) and solving the resulting set of linear equations for the unknowns.

Before solving the equations for the unknowns it is necessary to select an input variable from r_1, θ_3, and r_2. Because of the symmetry of the mechanism, choosing r_1 or r_2 will give a similar set of equations. That is, if we establish the input–output relationships for r_1 as the input, we can derive the relationships for r_2 as the input by simply interchanging the subscripts 1 and 2 in the relationships derived for r_1 as the driver. Therefore, we need to consider only the cases for θ_3 and r_1 as input variables.

5.9.1 Analysis When θ_3 Is Known

The analytical solution procedure follows the same major steps as were followed in the case of the RRPP mechanism. When θ_3 is an input, Eqs. (5.141) and (5.142) become linear in the unknowns r_1 and r_2, and the equations for position, velocity, and acceleration can be solved easily. The resulting equations are summarized in Table 5.14.

TABLE 5.14 Summary of Position, Velocity, and Acceleration Equations for an Elliptic Trammel Mechanism When θ_3 Is the Input Variable. The Link Numbers and Points Are Defined in Fig. 5.40

Position

$$\theta_1 = \theta_2 + \beta$$

$$\begin{bmatrix} \cos\theta_1 & -\cos\theta_2 \\ \sin\theta_1 & -\sin\theta_2 \end{bmatrix} \begin{Bmatrix} r_1 \\ r_2 \end{Bmatrix} = \begin{Bmatrix} r_3\cos\theta_3 \\ r_3\sin\theta_3 \end{Bmatrix}$$

$$\boldsymbol{r}_P = \boldsymbol{r}_2 = (r_2\cos\theta_2)\boldsymbol{i} + (r_2\sin\theta_2)\boldsymbol{j}$$

$$\boldsymbol{r}_Q = \boldsymbol{r}_1 = (r_1\cos\theta_1)\boldsymbol{i} + (r_1\sin\theta_1)\boldsymbol{j}$$

Velocity

$$\begin{bmatrix} \cos\theta_1 & -\cos\theta_2 \\ \sin\theta_1 & -\sin\theta_2 \end{bmatrix} \begin{Bmatrix} \dot{r}_1 \\ \dot{r}_2 \end{Bmatrix} = \begin{Bmatrix} -r_3\dot{\theta}_3\sin\theta_3 \\ r_3\dot{\theta}_3\cos\theta_3 \end{Bmatrix}$$

$$\dot{\boldsymbol{r}}_P = \dot{\boldsymbol{r}}_2 = (\dot{r}_2\cos\theta_2)\boldsymbol{i} + (\dot{r}_2\sin\theta_2)\boldsymbol{j}$$

$$\dot{\boldsymbol{r}}_Q = \dot{\boldsymbol{r}}_1 = (\dot{r}_1\cos\theta_1)\boldsymbol{i} + (\dot{r}_1\sin\theta_1)\boldsymbol{j}$$

Acceleration

$$\begin{bmatrix} \cos\theta_1 & -\cos\theta_2 \\ \sin\theta_1 & -\sin\theta_2 \end{bmatrix} \begin{Bmatrix} \ddot{r}_1 \\ \ddot{r}_2 \end{Bmatrix} = \begin{Bmatrix} -r_3\ddot{\theta}_3\sin\theta_3 - r_3\dot{\theta}_3^2\cos\theta_3 \\ r_3\ddot{\theta}_3\cos\theta_3 - r_3\dot{\theta}_3^2\sin\theta_3 \end{Bmatrix}$$

$$\ddot{\boldsymbol{r}}_P = \ddot{\boldsymbol{r}}_2 = (\ddot{r}_2\cos\theta_2)\boldsymbol{i} + (\ddot{r}_2\sin\theta_2)\boldsymbol{j}$$

$$\ddot{\boldsymbol{r}}_Q = \ddot{\boldsymbol{r}}_1 = (\ddot{r}_1\cos\theta_1)\boldsymbol{i} + (\ddot{r}_1\sin\theta_1)\boldsymbol{j}$$

5.9.2 Analysis When r_1 Is Known

When r_1 is known, we must determine θ_3 and r_2. Two solutions result corresponding to the assembly modes shown in Fig. 5.41. It is also possible to specify values for r_1 for which the mechanism cannot be assembled. The analytical form of the velocity and acceleration

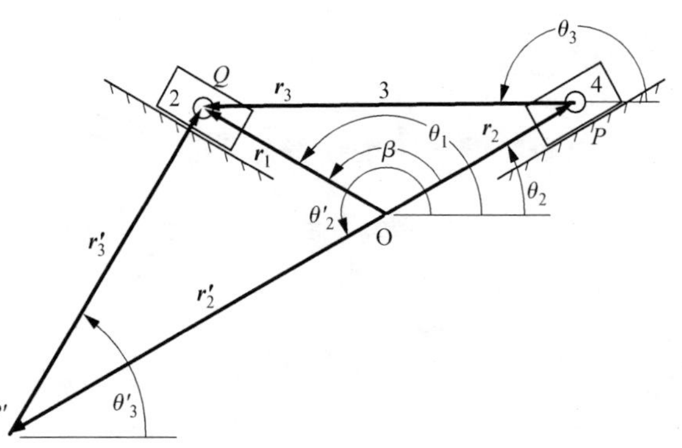

FIGURE 5.41 Two configurations possible for elliptic trammel when $\boldsymbol{r}_1$ is input.

equations can be developed by differentiating the position equations and solving the resulting linear equations for the unknowns. The results for r_1 as the input are summarized in Table 5.15.

TABLE 5.15 Summary of Position, Velocity, and Acceleration Equations for an Elliptic Trammel Mechanism When r_1 Is the Input. The Link Numbers and Points Are Defined in Fig. 5.40

Position

$$\theta_1 = \theta_2 + \beta$$

$$B = -r_1\left(\cos\theta_1 \cos\theta_2 + \sin\theta_1 \sin\theta_2\right)$$

$$C = \left(r_1^2 - r_3^2\right)$$

$$r_2 = -B + \sigma\sqrt{B^2 - C}$$

$$\theta_3 = \tan^{-1}\frac{r_1 \sin\theta_1 - r_2 \sin\theta_2}{r_1 \cos\theta_1 - r_2 \cos\theta_2}$$

$$\mathbf{r}_P = \mathbf{r}_2 = \left(r_2 \cos\theta_2\right)\mathbf{i} + \left(r_2 \sin\theta_2\right)\mathbf{j}$$

$$\mathbf{r}_Q = \mathbf{r}_1 = \left(r_1 \cos\theta_1\right)\mathbf{i} + \left(r_1 \sin\theta_1\right)\mathbf{j}$$

Velocity

$$\begin{bmatrix} \cos\theta_2 & -r_3 \sin\theta_3 \\ \sin\theta_2 & r_3 \cos\theta_3 \end{bmatrix} \begin{Bmatrix} \dot{r}_2 \\ \dot{\theta}_3 \end{Bmatrix} = \begin{Bmatrix} \dot{r}_1 \cos\theta_1 \\ \dot{r}_1 \sin\theta_1 \end{Bmatrix}$$

$$\dot{\mathbf{r}}_P = \dot{\mathbf{r}}_2 = \left(\dot{r}_2 \cos\theta_2\right)\mathbf{i} + \left(\dot{r}_2 \sin\theta_2\right)\mathbf{j}$$

$$\dot{\mathbf{r}}_Q = \dot{\mathbf{r}}_1 = \left(\dot{r}_1 \cos\theta_1\right)\mathbf{i} + \left(\dot{r}_1 \sin\theta_1\right)\mathbf{j}$$

Acceleration

$$\begin{bmatrix} \cos\theta_2 & -r_3 \sin\theta_3 \\ \sin\theta_2 & r_3 \cos\theta_3 \end{bmatrix} \begin{Bmatrix} \ddot{r}_2 \\ \ddot{\theta}_3 \end{Bmatrix} = \begin{Bmatrix} \ddot{r}_1 \cos\theta_1 + r_3\dot{\theta}_3^2 \cos\theta_3 \\ \ddot{r}_1 \sin\theta_1 + r_3\dot{\theta}_3^2 \sin\theta_3 \end{Bmatrix}$$

$$\ddot{\mathbf{r}}_P = \ddot{\mathbf{r}}_2 = \left(\ddot{r}_2 \cos\theta_2\right)\mathbf{i} + \left(\ddot{r}_2 \sin\theta_2\right)\mathbf{j}$$

$$\ddot{\mathbf{r}}_Q = \ddot{\mathbf{r}}_1 = \left(\ddot{r}_1 \cos\theta_1\right)\mathbf{i} + \left(\ddot{r}_1 \sin\theta_1\right)\mathbf{j}$$

EXAMPLE 5.9 *Kinematic Analysis of an Elliptic Trammel*

In the elliptic trammel mechanism shown in Fig. 5.42a, the angular velocity of link 3 relative to the frame is 10 rad/s CCW (constant). Also, the length $QP = 10$ cm and QR is 20 cm. Determine the position of point R and the velocity and acceleration of point P for a full rotation of the coupler.

Solution

Using the nomenclature developed earlier, the basic vector closure diagram for the linkage is as shown in Fig. 5.42a. From Figs. 5.41 and 5.42, the following geometric quantities can be determined:

$$r_3 = 10$$
$$\theta_1 = 90°, \qquad \theta_2 = 0°, \qquad \beta = 90°$$
$$\dot{\theta}_3 = 10, \qquad \ddot{\theta}_3 = 0$$

Because we are interested in the behavior of the mechanism for its full range of motion, we must solve the position, velocity, and acceleration equations in terms of θ_3. The vector diagram establishing the quantities involved is shown in Fig. 5.42b.

The position of R_3 is given by

$$\boldsymbol{r}_{R_3} = \boldsymbol{r}_1 + \boldsymbol{r}_4$$

or, in component form,

$$\boldsymbol{r}_{R_3} = \left(r_1 \cos\theta_1 + r_4 \cos\theta_4\right)\boldsymbol{i} + \left(r_1 \sin\theta_1 + r_4 \sin\theta_4\right)\boldsymbol{j} \tag{5.144}$$

From Fig. 5.42b, $\theta_4 = \theta_3 + \pi$. Therefore, Eq. (5.144) becomes

$$\boldsymbol{r}_{R_3} = \left(r_1 \cos\theta_1 - r_4 \cos\theta_3\right)\boldsymbol{i} + \left(r_1 \sin\theta_1 - r_4 \sin\theta_3\right)\boldsymbol{j} \tag{5.145}$$

To solve for the position, velocity, and acceleration of P_3, we must determine the corresponding values for r_1. From Table 5.14, the equations to be solved are

$$\begin{bmatrix} 0 & -1 \\ 1 & 0 \end{bmatrix} \begin{Bmatrix} r_1 \\ r_2 \end{Bmatrix} = \begin{Bmatrix} r_3 \cos\theta_3 \\ r_3 \sin\theta_3 \end{Bmatrix} \tag{5.146}$$

$$\begin{bmatrix} 0 & -1 \\ 1 & 0 \end{bmatrix} \begin{Bmatrix} \dot{r}_1 \\ \dot{r}_2 \end{Bmatrix} = \begin{Bmatrix} -r_3\dot{\theta}_3 \sin\theta_3 \\ r_3\dot{\theta}_3 \cos\theta_3 \end{Bmatrix} \tag{5.147}$$

and

$$\begin{bmatrix} 0 & -1 \\ 1 & 0 \end{bmatrix} \begin{Bmatrix} \ddot{r}_1 \\ \ddot{r}_2 \end{Bmatrix} = \begin{Bmatrix} -r_3\ddot{\theta}_3 \sin\theta_3 - r_3\dot{\theta}_3^2 \cos\theta_3 \\ r_3\ddot{\theta}_3 \cos\theta_3 - r_3\dot{\theta}_3^2 \sin\theta_3 \end{Bmatrix} \tag{5.148}$$

From Eqs. (5.146)–(5.148),

$$r_1 = r_3 \sin\theta_3 \tag{5.149}$$

$$\dot{r}_1 = r_3\dot{\theta}_3 \cos\theta_3 \tag{5.150}$$

and

$$\ddot{r}_1 = r_3\ddot{\theta}_3 \cos\theta_3 - r_3\dot{\theta}_3^2 \sin\theta_3 \tag{5.151}$$

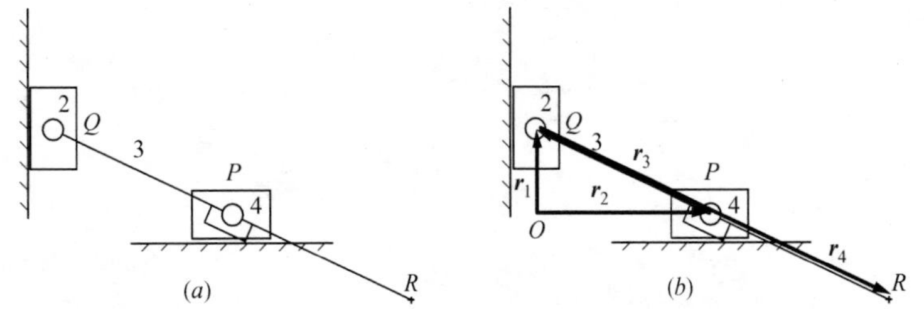

FIGURE 5.42 Elliptic trammel mechanism (a) and vector diagram (b) for Example 5.9.

Equations (5.149)–(5.151) can be combined with Eq. (5.145) to solve for the position of R_3 and for the velocity and acceleration of P_3 as a function of θ_3. The equations can be computed easily, and the results are plotted in Fig. 5.43. The MATLAB program used to generate the curves is included on the disk with this book. Notice that the path of R_3 is an ellipse.

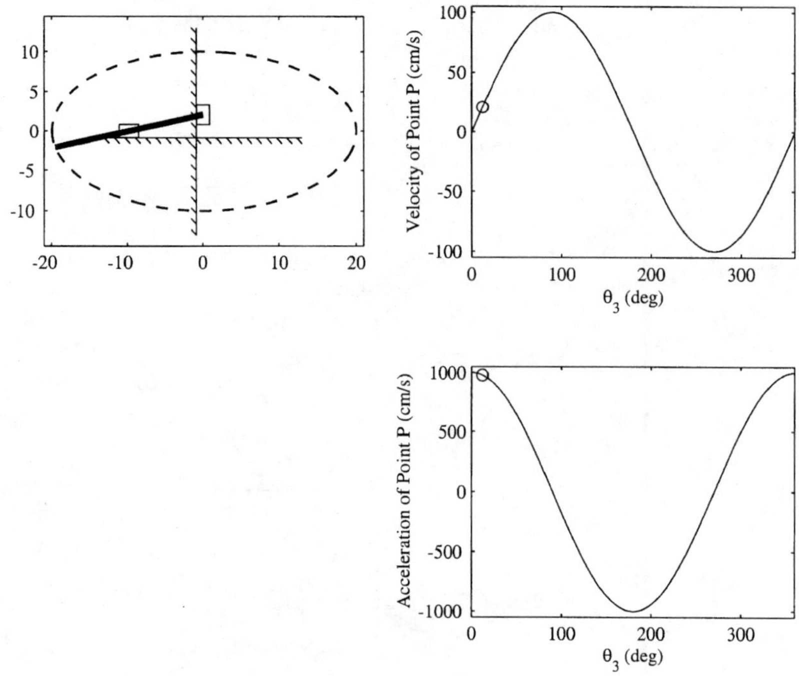

FIGURE 5.43 Results for Example 5.9.

5.10 ANALYTICAL EQUATIONS FOR THE OLDHAM MECHANISM

The Oldham (RPPR) mechanism is another inversion of the RRPP mechanism, and a schematic drawing of this mechanism is shown in Fig. 5.44. In the mechanism, links 2 and 4 are connected to the frame by revolute joints and to the coupler by prismatic joints. Therefore, the angle β between links 2 and 4 is fixed.

To analyze the mechanism using vector closure equations, we must again align vectors in the directions of the slider motions as shown in Fig. 5.45. As in the case of the elliptic trammel, only three vectors are required to model the motion. Vector $\boldsymbol{r}_1$ is fixed at an angle θ_1 and of constant length. Point O is the origin of the frame coordinate system. Links

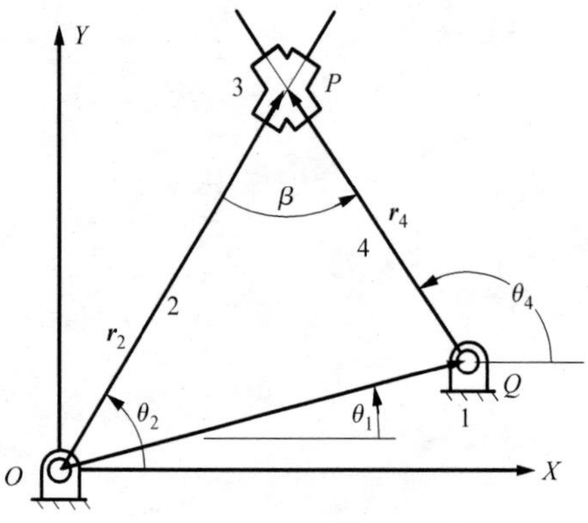

FIGURE 5.44 Schematic diagram of Oldham mechanism.

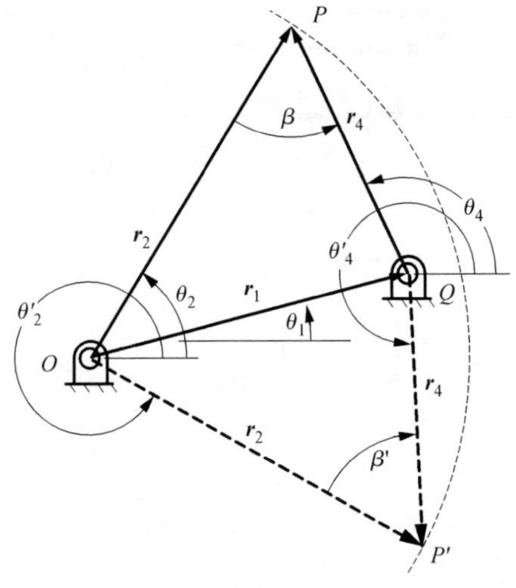

FIGURE 5.45 Two assembly modes for Oldham mechanism when r_2 is the input variable.

2 and 4 intersect at an angle β, where β is measured from $\boldsymbol{r}_2$ to $\boldsymbol{r}_4$. Vector $\boldsymbol{r}_2$ is at an angle θ_2 with respect to a horizontal line and is of variable length. Vector $\boldsymbol{r}_4$ is at an angle θ_4 with respect to a horizontal line and of variable length.

As shown in Fig. 5.44, to develop the closure equations, locate point P with vector $\boldsymbol{r}_2$ and with vectors $\boldsymbol{r}_1 + \boldsymbol{r}_4$. Then the vector closure equation is

$$\boldsymbol{r}_P = \boldsymbol{r}_2 = \boldsymbol{r}_1 + \boldsymbol{r}_4 \tag{5.152}$$

or

$$r_2\left(\cos\theta_2\boldsymbol{i} + \sin\theta_2\boldsymbol{j}\right) = r_1\left(\cos\theta_1\boldsymbol{i} + \sin\theta_1\boldsymbol{j}\right) + r_4\left(\cos\theta_4\boldsymbol{i} + \sin\theta_4\boldsymbol{j}\right) \tag{5.153}$$

Rewriting the components in Eq. (5.153) as separate equations gives

$$r_2\cos\theta_2 = r_1\cos\theta_1 + r_4\cos\theta_4 \tag{5.154}$$

$$r_2\sin\theta_2 = r_1\sin\theta_1 + r_4\sin\theta_4 \tag{5.155}$$

As was the case for the other RRPP mechanisms, there are six quantities to identify: r_1 and θ_1, r_2 and θ_2, and r_4 and θ_4. From Fig. 5.44, θ_1, and r_1 are constants. Furthermore, we know that

$$\theta_4 = \theta_2 + \beta \tag{5.156}$$

where β is a constant.

The variables are θ_2, θ_4, r_2, and r_4. For a one-degree-of-freedom mechanism, one of the variables must be an input (i.e., known) variable, and there are three unknowns. We can solve for them using the three equations (5.154)–(5.156) involving the unknowns. Once all of the position variables are obtained, the unknown velocities and accelerations can be found by differentiating Eqs. (5.154)–(5.156) and solving the resulting set of linear equations for the unknowns.

Before solving the equations for the unknowns, it is necessary to select an input variable from among r_2, r_4, θ_2, and θ_4. The equations will be similar when either r_2 or r_4 is selected, and when either θ_2 and θ_4 are selected. Therefore, we will consider only the two cases when r_2 is a variable and when θ_2 is a variable.

5.10.1 Analysis When θ_2 Is Known

When θ_2 is the input variable, Eqs. (5.154) and (5.155) become linear in the unknowns r_2 and r_4, and the equations for position, velocity, and acceleration can be easily solved. The resulting equations are summarized in Table 5.16. The equations can be programmed easily,

TABLE 5.16 Summary of Position, Velocity, and Acceleration Equations for an Oldham Mechanism When θ_2 Is the Input Variable. The Link Numbers and Points Are Defined in Fig. 5.44

Position

$$\theta_4 = \theta_2 + \beta$$

$$\begin{bmatrix} \cos\theta_2 & -\cos\theta_4 \\ \sin\theta_2 & -\sin\theta_4 \end{bmatrix} \begin{Bmatrix} r_2 \\ r_4 \end{Bmatrix} = \begin{Bmatrix} r_1 \cos\theta_1 \\ r_1 \sin\theta_1 \end{Bmatrix}$$

$$\boldsymbol{r}_P = \boldsymbol{r}_2 = (r_2 \cos\theta_2)\boldsymbol{i} + (r_2 \sin\theta_2)\boldsymbol{j}$$

$$\boldsymbol{r}_Q = \boldsymbol{r}_1 = (r_1 \cos\theta_1)\boldsymbol{i} + (r_1 \sin\theta_1)\boldsymbol{j}$$

Velocity

$$\dot\theta_4 = \dot\theta_2$$

$$\begin{bmatrix} \cos\theta_2 & -\cos\theta_4 \\ \sin\theta_2 & -\sin\theta_4 \end{bmatrix} \begin{Bmatrix} \dot r_2 \\ \dot r_4 \end{Bmatrix} = \begin{Bmatrix} r_2\dot\theta_2 \sin\theta_2 - r_4\dot\theta_2 \sin\theta_4 \\ -r_2\dot\theta_2 \cos\theta_2 + r_4\dot\theta_2 \cos\theta_4 \end{Bmatrix}$$

$$\dot{\boldsymbol{r}}_{P_2} = (-r_2\dot\theta_2 \sin\theta_2)\boldsymbol{i} + (r_2\dot\theta_2 \cos\theta_2)\boldsymbol{j}$$

$$\dot{\boldsymbol{r}}_{P_3} = (\dot r_2 \cos\theta_2 - r_2\dot\theta_2 \sin\theta_2)\boldsymbol{i} + (\dot r_2 \sin\theta_2 + r_2\dot\theta_2 \cos\theta_2)\boldsymbol{j}$$

Acceleration

$$\ddot\theta_4 = \ddot\theta_2$$

$$\begin{bmatrix} \cos\theta_2 & -\cos\theta_4 \\ \sin\theta_2 & -\sin\theta_4 \end{bmatrix} \begin{Bmatrix} \ddot r_2 \\ \ddot r_4 \end{Bmatrix}$$

$$= \begin{Bmatrix} (r_2\ddot\theta_2 + 2\dot r_2\dot\theta_2)\sin\theta_2 - (r_4\ddot\theta_2 + 2\dot r_4\dot\theta_2)\sin\theta_4 + r_2\dot\theta_2^2 \cos\theta_2 - r_4\dot\theta_2^2 \cos\theta_4 \\ -(r_2\ddot\theta_2 + 2\dot r_2\dot\theta_2)\cos\theta_2 + (r_4\ddot\theta_2 + 2\dot r_4\dot\theta_2)\cos\theta_4 + r_2\dot\theta_2^2 \sin\theta_2 - r_4\dot\theta_2^2 \sin\theta_4 \end{Bmatrix}$$

$$\ddot{\boldsymbol{r}}_{P_2} = (-r_2\ddot\theta_2 \sin\theta_2 - r_2\dot\theta_2^2 \cos\theta_2)\boldsymbol{i} + (r_2\ddot\theta_2 \cos\theta_2 - r_2\dot\theta_2^2 \sin\theta_2)\boldsymbol{j}$$

$$\ddot{\boldsymbol{r}}_{P_3} = (\ddot r_2 \cos\theta_2 - 2\dot r_2\dot\theta_2 \sin\theta_2 - r_2\ddot\theta_2 \sin\theta_2 - r_2\dot\theta_2^2 \cos\theta_2)\boldsymbol{i}$$
$$+ (\ddot r_2 \sin\theta_2 + 2\dot r_2\dot\theta_2 \cos\theta_2 + r_2\ddot\theta_2 \cos\theta_2 - r_2\dot\theta_2^2 \sin\theta_2)\boldsymbol{j}$$

and a MATLAB program for analyzing the mechanism when θ_2 is the driver is included on the disk with this book.

5.10.2 Analysis When r_2 Is Known

When r_2 is known, we must determine θ_2, θ_4 and r_4, and the equations required for the analysis are given in Table 5.17. Two solutions corresponding to the assembly modes shown

TABLE 5.17 Summary of Position, Velocity, and Acceleration Equations for an Oldham Mechanism When r_2 Is the Input Variable. The Link Numbers and Points Are Defined in Fig. 5.44

Position

$$r_4 = r_2 \cos\beta + \sigma\sqrt{r_2^2\left(\cos^2\beta - 1\right) + r_1^2}; \quad \sigma = \pm 1$$

$$A = r_1 \sin\theta_1 - r_4 \sin\beta$$
$$B = -2\left(r_2 - r_4 \cos\beta\right)$$
$$C = r_4 \sin\beta + r_1 \sin\theta_1$$

$$\theta_2 = 2\tan^{-1}\left[\frac{-B + \gamma\sqrt{B^2 - C^2 + A^2}}{(C - A)}\right]; \quad \gamma = +1 \text{ or } -1; \text{ valid value satisfies Eq. } (5.153)$$

$$\theta_4 = \theta_2 + \beta$$

$$\boldsymbol{r}_P = \boldsymbol{r}_2 = \left(r_2 \cos\theta_2\right)\boldsymbol{i} + \left(r_2 \sin\theta_2\right)\boldsymbol{j}$$

$$\boldsymbol{r}_Q = \boldsymbol{r}_1 = \left(r_1 \cos\theta_1\right)\boldsymbol{i} + \left(r_1 \sin\theta_1\right)\boldsymbol{j}$$

Velocity

$$\dot\theta_4 = \dot\theta_2$$

$$\begin{bmatrix} -r_2 \sin\theta_2 + r_4 \sin\theta_4 & -\cos\theta_4 \\ r_2 \cos\theta_2 - r_4 \cos\theta_4 & -\sin\theta_4 \end{bmatrix}\begin{Bmatrix} \dot\theta_2 \\ \dot r_4 \end{Bmatrix} = \begin{Bmatrix} -\dot r_2 \cos\theta_2 \\ -\dot r_2 \sin\theta_2 \end{Bmatrix}$$

$$\dot{\boldsymbol{r}}_{P_2} = \left(-r_2\dot\theta_2 \sin\theta_2\right)\boldsymbol{i} + \left(r_2\dot\theta_2 \cos\theta_2\right)\boldsymbol{j}$$

$$\dot{\boldsymbol{r}}_{P_3} = \left(\dot r_2 \cos\theta_2 - r_2\dot\theta_2 \sin\theta_2\right)\boldsymbol{i} + \left(\dot r_2 \sin\theta_2 + r_2\dot\theta_2 \cos\theta_2\right)\boldsymbol{j}$$

Acceleration

$$\ddot\theta_4 = \ddot\theta_2$$

$$\begin{bmatrix} -r_2 \sin\theta_2 + r_4 \sin\theta_4 & -\cos\theta_4 \\ r_2 \cos\theta_2 - r_4 \cos\theta_4 & -\sin\theta_4 \end{bmatrix}\begin{Bmatrix} \ddot\theta_2 \\ \ddot r_4 \end{Bmatrix}$$
$$= \begin{Bmatrix} 2\dot r_2\dot\theta_2 \sin\theta_2 - 2\dot r_4\dot\theta_2 \sin\theta_4 + r_2\dot\theta_2^2 \cos\theta_2 - \ddot r_2 \cos\theta_2 - r_4\dot\theta_2^2 \cos\theta_4 \\ -2\dot r_2\dot\theta_2 \cos\theta_2 + 2\dot r_4\dot\theta_2 \cos\theta_4 + r_2\dot\theta_2^2 \sin\theta_2 - \ddot r_2 \sin\theta_2 - r_4\dot\theta_2^2 \sin\theta_4 \end{Bmatrix}$$

$$\ddot{\boldsymbol{r}}_{P_2} = \left(-r_2\ddot\theta_2 \sin\theta_2 - r_2\dot\theta_2^2 \cos\theta_2\right)\boldsymbol{i} + \left(r_2\ddot\theta_2 \cos\theta_2 + r_2\dot\theta_2^2 \sin\theta_2\right)\boldsymbol{j}$$

$$\ddot{\boldsymbol{r}}_{P_3} = \left(\ddot r_2 \cos\theta_2 - 2\dot r_2\dot\theta_2 \sin\theta_2 - r_2\ddot\theta_2 \sin\theta_2 - r_2\dot\theta_2^2 \cos\theta_2\right)\boldsymbol{i}$$
$$+\left(\ddot r_2 \sin\theta_2 + 2\dot r_2\dot\theta_2 \cos\theta_2 + r_2\ddot\theta_2 \cos\theta_2 - r_2\dot\theta_2^2 \sin\theta_2\right)\boldsymbol{j}$$

in Fig. 5.45 result. Note that in one assembly mode, β is positive, and in the other, β is negative. If the sign of β must be positive, the solution corresponding to a minus angle would be discarded. The value of γ that is valid is the one satisfying Eqs. (5.154) and (5.155). It is also possible to specify values for r_2 for which the mechanism cannot be assembled. The analytical form of the velocity and acceleration equations can be developed by differentiating the position equations and solving the resulting linear equations for the unknowns. Again, the equations can be easily programmed, and a MATLAB program for analyzing the mechanism when r_2 is the driver is included on the disk with this book.

EXAMPLE 5.10 *Kinematic Analysis of the Oldham Mechanism*

In the Oldham mechanism shown in Fig. 5.46a, the angular velocity of link 2 relative to the frame is 10 rad/s CCW and the angular acceleration is 100 rad/s^2 CCW. Also, the length $OQ = 10$ cm and the angle β is 45°. Determine the position of point P and the velocity and acceleration of points P_2 and P_3 in the position given.

Solution

Using the nomenclature developed earlier, we can draw the basic vector closure diagram for the linkage shown in Fig. 5.46b. From Fig. 5.46, the following geometry quantities can be determined:

$$\theta_1 = 0°, \qquad \theta_2 = 60°, \qquad \theta_4 = 105°$$
$$r_1 = 10 \text{ cm}$$

To perform the analysis, we can use the equations in Table 5.16. For the position analysis, we need to solve

$$\begin{bmatrix} \cos\theta_2 & -\cos\theta_4 \\ \sin\theta_2 & -\sin\theta_4 \end{bmatrix} \begin{Bmatrix} r_2 \\ r_4 \end{Bmatrix} = \begin{Bmatrix} r_1 \cos\theta_1 \\ r_1 \sin\theta_1 \end{Bmatrix} \quad \text{or} \quad \begin{bmatrix} \cos(60°) & -\cos(105°) \\ \sin(60°) & -\sin(105°) \end{bmatrix} \begin{Bmatrix} r_2 \\ r_4 \end{Bmatrix} = \begin{Bmatrix} 10\cos 0° \\ 10\sin 0° \end{Bmatrix}$$

or

$$\begin{bmatrix} 0.500 & 0.2588 \\ 0.8660 & -0.9659 \end{bmatrix} \begin{Bmatrix} r_2 \\ r_4 \end{Bmatrix} = \begin{Bmatrix} 10 \\ 0 \end{Bmatrix} \Rightarrow \begin{Bmatrix} r_2 \\ r_4 \end{Bmatrix} = \begin{Bmatrix} 13.6603 \\ 12.2474 \end{Bmatrix}$$

The positions of P and Q are given by

$$\boldsymbol{r}_P = (r_2 \cos\theta_2)\boldsymbol{i} + (r_2 \sin\theta_2)\boldsymbol{j} = 6.8301\boldsymbol{i} + 11.8301\boldsymbol{j}$$

and

$$\boldsymbol{r}_Q = (r_1 \cos\theta_1)\boldsymbol{i} + (r_1 \sin\theta_1)\boldsymbol{j} = 10\boldsymbol{i}$$

For the velocity analysis, solve

$$\begin{bmatrix} \cos\theta_2 & -\cos\theta_4 \\ \sin\theta_2 & -\sin\theta_4 \end{bmatrix} \begin{Bmatrix} \dot{r}_2 \\ \dot{r}_4 \end{Bmatrix} = \begin{Bmatrix} r_2\dot{\theta}_2 \sin\theta_2 - r_4\dot{\theta}_2 \sin\theta_4 \\ -r_2\dot{\theta}_2 \cos\theta_2 + r_4\dot{\theta}_2 \cos\theta_4 \end{Bmatrix} \Rightarrow \begin{bmatrix} 0.500 & 0.2588 \\ 0.8660 & -0.9659 \end{bmatrix} \begin{Bmatrix} \dot{r}_2 \\ \dot{r}_4 \end{Bmatrix} = \begin{Bmatrix} 0 \\ -100 \end{Bmatrix}$$

or

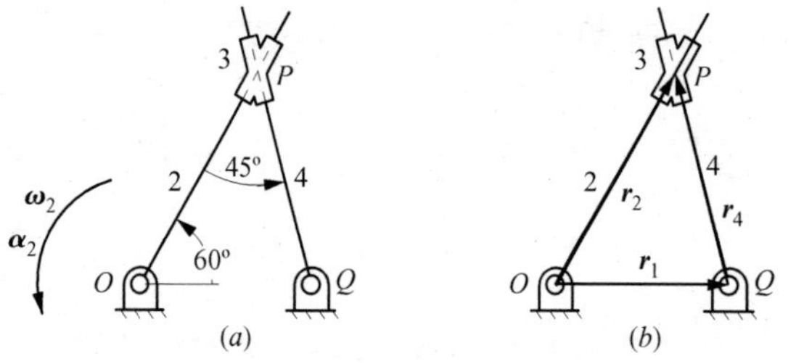

FIGURE 5.46 Oldham mechanism (a) and vector diagram (b) for Example 5.10.

$$\begin{Bmatrix} \dot{r}_2 \\ \dot{r}_4 \end{Bmatrix} = \begin{Bmatrix} -36.6025 \\ 70.7107 \end{Bmatrix}$$

The velocities of points P_2 and P_3 are

$$\dot{\boldsymbol{r}}_{P_2} = \left(-r_2\dot{\theta}_2 \sin\theta_2\right)\boldsymbol{i} + \left(r_2\dot{\theta}_2 \cos\theta_2\right)\boldsymbol{j} = -118.3031\boldsymbol{i} + 68.3013\boldsymbol{j}$$

and

$$\dot{\boldsymbol{r}}_{P_3} = \left(\dot{r}_2 \cos\theta_2 - r_2\dot{\theta}_2 \sin\theta_2\right)\boldsymbol{i} + \left(\dot{r}_2 \sin\theta_2 + r_2\dot{\theta}_2 \cos\theta_2\right)\boldsymbol{j} = -136.6025\boldsymbol{i} + 36.6025\boldsymbol{j}$$

For the acceleration analysis, solve

$$\begin{bmatrix} \cos\theta_2 & -\cos\theta_4 \\ \sin\theta_2 & -\sin\theta_4 \end{bmatrix} \begin{Bmatrix} \ddot{r}_2 \\ \ddot{r}_4 \end{Bmatrix}$$
$$= \begin{Bmatrix} \left(r_2\ddot{\theta}_2 + 2\dot{r}_2\dot{\theta}_2\right)\sin\theta_2 - \left(r_4\ddot{\theta}_2 + 2\dot{r}_4\dot{\theta}_2\right)\sin\theta_4 + r_2\dot{\theta}_2^2 \cos\theta_2 - r_4\dot{\theta}_2^2 \cos\theta_4 \\ -\left(r_2\ddot{\theta}_2 + 2\dot{r}_2\dot{\theta}_2\right)\cos\theta_2 + \left(r_4\ddot{\theta}_2 + 2\dot{r}_4\dot{\theta}_2\right)\cos\theta_4 + r_2\dot{\theta}_2^2 \sin\theta_2 - r_4\dot{\theta}_2^2 \sin\theta_4 \end{Bmatrix}$$

or

$$\begin{bmatrix} 0.500 & 0.2588 \\ 0.8660 & -0.9659 \end{bmatrix} \begin{Bmatrix} \ddot{r}_2 \\ \ddot{r}_4 \end{Bmatrix} = \begin{Bmatrix} -1000 \\ -1000 \end{Bmatrix}$$

Then,

$$\begin{Bmatrix} \ddot{r}_2 \\ \ddot{r}_4 \end{Bmatrix} = \begin{Bmatrix} -1732.1 \\ -517.6 \end{Bmatrix}$$

Also,

$$\ddot{\boldsymbol{r}}_{P_2} = \left(-r_2\ddot{\theta}_2 \sin\theta_2 - r_2\dot{\theta}_2^2 \cos\theta_2\right)\boldsymbol{i} + \left(r_2\ddot{\theta}_2 \cos\theta_2 + r_2\dot{\theta}_2^2 \sin\theta_2\right)\boldsymbol{j} = -1866\boldsymbol{i} - 500\boldsymbol{j}$$

and

$$\ddot{\boldsymbol{r}}_{P_3} = \left(\ddot{r}_2 \cos\theta_2 - 2\dot{r}_2\dot{\theta}_2 \sin\theta_2 - r_2\ddot{\theta}_2 \sin\theta_2 - r_2\dot{\theta}_2^2 \cos\theta_2\right)\boldsymbol{i}$$
$$+\left(\ddot{r}_2 \sin\theta_2 + 2\dot{r}_2\dot{\theta}_2 \cos\theta_2 + r_2\ddot{\theta}_2 \cos\theta_2 - r_2\dot{\theta}_2^2 \sin\theta_2\right)\boldsymbol{j} = -2098.1\boldsymbol{i} - 2366\boldsymbol{j}$$

5.11 CLOSURE OR LOOP-EQUATION APPROACH FOR COMPOUND MECHANISMS

As in the case of simple, single-loop mechanisms, each vector is represented by a length r_i and an angle θ_i. All angles are measured counterclockwise from a fixed line parallel to the x axis attached to the frame as shown in Fig. 5.47.

To illustrate the method for compound mechanisms, consider the kinematic diagram of the mechanism given in Fig. 5.47. Each member is represented by a directed length and an angle. The formulation of the analytical procedure based on vector loops for compound mechanisms is straightforward, but it requires a system if results are to be meaningful. A procedure will be outlined in the following and illustrated on the mechanism in Fig. 5.47. It will be noted that the procedure presented is a generalization of that used for the single-loop mechanisms. In the mechanism shown, assume that θ_2, $\boldsymbol{\omega}_2$, and $\boldsymbol{\alpha}_2$ are known values.

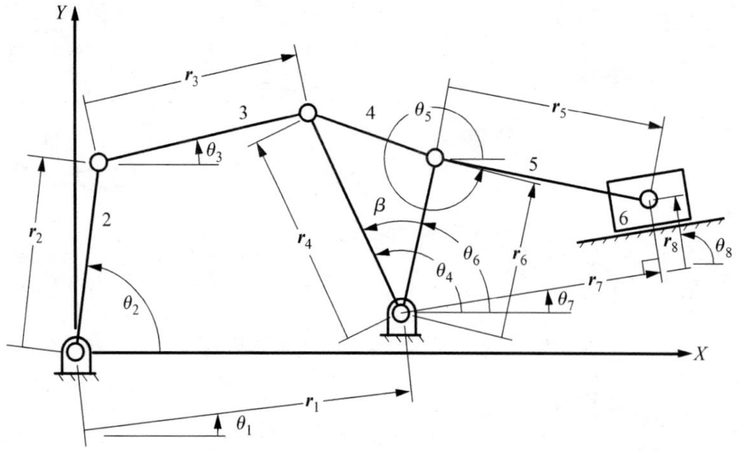

FIGURE 5.47 Example of formulation of solution procedure using vector loops.

Procedure

1. Draw a kinematic sketch of the mechanism. The sketch need not be to scale; however, it must be sufficiently accurate that the assembly mode can be determined by inspection.
2. Establish a global coordinate system for the mechanism. This will establish the horizontal axis from which all angles will be measured and identify the system from which all global coordinates will be determined.
3. Represent the link between adjacent joints by a vector $\boldsymbol{r}_i$ defined by a directed line and an angle measured positive CCW from the x axis (or a line parallel to the x axis):

$$\boldsymbol{r}_i = r_i \angle \theta_i$$

4. If sliders are involved, locate the slider by two vectors, one in the direction of the relative velocity between the slider and the slide and the second in a direction perpendicular to the direction of the velocity (see $\boldsymbol{r}_7$ and $\boldsymbol{r}_8$ in Fig. 5.47).
5. Note which lengths and angles are fixed and which are variable. In the mechanism above, r_7 is the only *variable* length and θ_1, θ_7, θ_8, and β are the only *fixed* angles.

   If the vectors are properly defined, they will all be expressible as

$$\boldsymbol{r}_i = r_i\left(\cos\theta_i \boldsymbol{i} + \sin\theta_i \boldsymbol{j}\right)$$

   The cosine term will always go with **i** and the sine term will go with **j**. Some angles may be functions of others. For example, $\theta_5 = \theta_4 - \beta$.

6. Identify all of the joints on the linkage, and be sure that each one is located at the end of one of the vectors. Then identify all of the independent vector loops in the linkage, and write a vector equation for each loop. For the mechanism in Fig. 5.47, there are two obvious vector loops represented by the following equations:

$$\boldsymbol{r}_1 + \boldsymbol{r}_4 = \boldsymbol{r}_2 + \boldsymbol{r}_3 \tag{5.157}$$

$$\boldsymbol{r}_5 + \boldsymbol{r}_6 = \boldsymbol{r}_7 + \boldsymbol{r}_8 \tag{5.158}$$

7. Write the x, y scalar equations for each vector equation. Notice that the form of the equations is consistent, and once the basic vector equations are given (e.g., Eqs. (5.157) and (5.158)), it is not even necessary to look at the mechanism to be able to write the component equations.

$$x \Rightarrow r_1 \cos\theta_1 + r_4 \cos\theta_4 = r_2 \cos\theta_2 + r_3 \cos\theta_3 \tag{5.159}$$

$$y \Rightarrow r_1 \sin\theta_1 + r_4 \sin\theta_4 = r_2 \sin\theta_2 + r_3 \sin\theta_3 \tag{5.160}$$

$$x \Rightarrow r_5 \cos\theta_5 + r_6 \cos\theta_6 = r_7 \cos\theta_7 + r_8 \cos\theta_8 \tag{5.161}$$

$$y \Rightarrow r_5 \sin\theta_5 + r_6 \sin\theta_6 = r_7 \sin\theta_7 + r_8 \sin\theta_8 \tag{5.162}$$

8. Identify any constraints among the lengths or angles that are not identified by the vector loops. In the mechanism in Fig. 5.47, θ_7 is related to θ_8 by $\pi/2$, and θ_6 is related to θ_4 through β. Therefore, the extra constraint equations are

$$\theta_8 = \theta_7 + \pi/2 \tag{5.163}$$

and

$$\theta_6 = \theta_4 - \beta \tag{5.164}$$

9. Count the total number of variables in the component equations and the extra constraint equations. If n is the total number of equations and f is the number of degrees of freedom for the mechanism, the total number of unknowns should be $n + f$. If the number of unknowns is larger than this, it is necessary to identify additional constraints or to reformulate the loop closure equations. In the mechanism in Fig. 5.47, the total number of unknowns is seven (θ_2, θ_3, θ_4, θ_5, θ_6, θ_8, and r_7), and the mechanism has only one degree of freedom. Therefore, $n + f = 7$, which indicates that the problem should be solvable. Note that the number of unknowns and the number of variables are not necessarily the same. In this mechanism, θ_8 is a constant but initially unknown. It must be computed using Eq. (5.163). Equations (5.159)–(5.164) are nonlinear in the unknowns (θ_2, θ_3, θ_4, θ_5, θ_6, and r_7), and most of the analysis difficulties are concentrated here.

10. For velocities, differentiate the position equations (x and y components) term by term. In the example case, the velocity equations are

$$\dot{\mathbf{r}}_1 + \dot{\mathbf{r}}_4 = \dot{\mathbf{r}}_2 + \dot{\mathbf{r}}_3 \tag{5.165}$$

$$\dot{\mathbf{r}}_5 + \dot{\mathbf{r}}_6 = \dot{\mathbf{r}}_7 + \dot{\mathbf{r}}_8 \tag{5.166}$$

and recognizing which terms are constants and which are variables, one gets

$$x \Rightarrow -r_4\dot{\theta}_4 \sin\theta_4 = -r_2\dot{\theta}_2 \sin\theta_2 - r_3\dot{\theta}_3 \sin\theta_3 \tag{5.167}$$

$$y \Rightarrow r_4\dot{\theta}_4 \cos\theta_4 = r_2\dot{\theta}_2 \cos\theta_2 + r_3\dot{\theta}_3 \cos\theta_3 \tag{5.168}$$

$$\dot{\theta}_6 = \dot{\theta}_4 \tag{5.169}$$

$$x \Rightarrow -r_5\dot{\theta}_5 \sin\theta_5 - r_6\dot{\theta}_6 \sin\theta_6 = \dot{r}_7 \cos\theta_7 \tag{5.170}$$

$$y \Rightarrow r_5\dot{\theta}_5 \cos\theta_5 + r_6\dot{\theta}_6 \cos\theta_6 = \dot{r}_7 \sin\theta_7 \tag{5.171}$$

Note that once we have solved the position equations, only the angle and length derivatives will be unknown. Hence the equations are linear in the unknowns and can be easily solved. There are five linear equations in five unknowns ($\dot{\theta}_3$, $\dot{\theta}_4$, θ_5, $\dot{\theta}_6$, $\dot{r}_7$). These can be solved directly by Gaussian elimination, by using a programmable calculator, or by using a matrix solver such as MATLAB.

11. For accelerations, differentiate the velocity equations (x and y components) term by term. In the example case, the acceleration equations are

$$\ddot{\mathbf{r}}_1 + \ddot{\mathbf{r}}_4 = \ddot{\mathbf{r}}_2 + \ddot{\mathbf{r}}_3 \tag{5.172}$$

$$\ddot{r}_5 + \ddot{r}_6 = \ddot{r}_7 + \ddot{r}_8 \tag{5.173}$$

and, in terms of components,

$$x \Rightarrow -r_4\ddot{\theta}_4 \sin\theta_4 - r_4\dot{\theta}_4^2 \cos\theta_4 = -r_2\ddot{\theta}_2 \sin\theta_2 - r_4\dot{\theta}_2^2 \cos\theta_2 - r_3\ddot{\theta}_3 \sin\theta_3 - r_3\dot{\theta}_3^2 \cos\theta_3 \tag{5.174}$$

$$y \Rightarrow r_4\ddot{\theta}_4 \cos\theta_4 - r_4\dot{\theta}_4^2 \sin\theta_4 = r_2\ddot{\theta}_2 \cos\theta_2 - r_4\dot{\theta}_2^2 \sin\theta_2 + r_3\ddot{\theta}_3 \cos\theta_3 - r_3\dot{\theta}_3^2 \sin\theta_3 \tag{5.175}$$

$$\ddot{\theta}_6 = \ddot{\theta}_4 \tag{5.176}$$

$$x \Rightarrow -r_5\ddot{\theta}_5 \sin\theta_5 - r_5\dot{\theta}_5^2 \cos\theta_5 - r_6\ddot{\theta}_6 \sin\theta_6 - r_6\dot{\theta}_6^2 \cos\theta_6 = \ddot{r}_7 \cos\theta_7 \tag{5.177}$$

$$y \Rightarrow r_5\ddot{\theta}_5 \cos\theta_5 - r_5\dot{\theta}_5^2 \sin\theta_5 + r_6\ddot{\theta}_6 \cos\theta_6 - r_6\dot{\theta}_6^2 \sin\theta_6 = \ddot{r}_7 \sin\theta_7 \tag{5.178}$$

Note that once we have solved the position and velocity equations, only the derivatives of velocity will be unknown. Hence, the equations are linear in the unknowns and can be easily solved. There are five linear equations in five unknowns $\ddot{\theta}_3$, $\ddot{\theta}_4$, $\ddot{\theta}_5$, $\ddot{\theta}_6$, and $\ddot{r}_7$. Once again, these can be solved directly by Gaussian elimination, by using a programmable calculator, or by using a matrix solver such as MATLAB.

5.11.1 Handling Points Not on the Vector Loops

The solution procedure outlined in the preceding section will give the position, velocity, and acceleration of each point at a vertex of a vector loop in addition to the angular velocity and acceleration of each link. The angular velocities and accelerations are the $\dot{\theta}_i$ and $\ddot{\theta}_i$ terms, respectively. In general,

$$\boldsymbol{\omega}_i = \dot{\theta}_i \boldsymbol{k}$$

and

$$\boldsymbol{\alpha}_i = \ddot{\theta}_i \boldsymbol{k}$$

Once the basic analysis is completed by solving the vector loop equations, we will be able to locate at least one point on each rigid body (link) as a function of time. We will also be able to determine the orientation of each rigid body as a function of time, that is, θ_i, $\boldsymbol{\omega}_i$, and α_i will be known or can be determined for each link.

Points that are not vertices of the vector loops must be associated with one of the rigid bodies in the mechanism. To determine the kinematic properties of a given point, we simply identify the point by a vector in terms of the known quantities, determine the x, y components of the vector, and differentiate. For example, assume that we want to know the kinematic properties of a point Q on link 3 as shown in Fig. 5.48. Then,

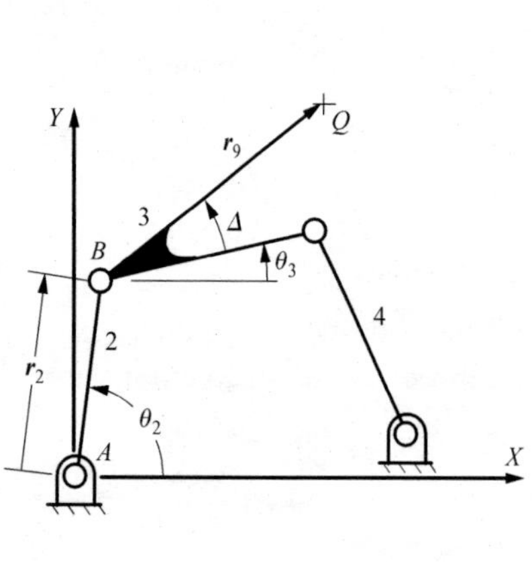

FIGURE 5.48 Determination of velocity and acceleration of a point Q that is not a vertex of a vector loop.

$$r_{Q_3/A_2} = r_2 + r_9$$

or

$$\begin{aligned} r_{Q_3/A_2} &= r_2(\cos\theta_2 \boldsymbol{i} + \sin\theta_2 \boldsymbol{j}) + r_9[\cos(\Delta+\theta_3)\boldsymbol{i} + \sin(\Delta+\theta_3)\boldsymbol{j}] \\ &= [r_2\cos\theta_2 + r_9\cos(\Delta+\theta_3)]\boldsymbol{i} + [r_2\sin\theta_2 + r_9\sin(\Delta+\theta_3)]\boldsymbol{j} \end{aligned} \tag{5.179}$$

All terms on the right-hand side of Eq. (5.179) will be known. Therefore, the position vector can be computed directly. The velocity is given by

$$v_{Q_3/A_2} = \dot{r}_2 + \dot{r}_9$$

and

$$\begin{aligned} v_{Q_3/A_2} &= r_2\dot{\theta}_2(-\sin\theta_2 \boldsymbol{i} + \cos\theta_2 \boldsymbol{j}) + r_9\dot{\theta}_3[-\sin(\Delta+\theta_3)\boldsymbol{i} + \cos(\Delta+\theta_3)\boldsymbol{j}] \\ &= -[r_2\dot{\theta}_2\sin\theta_2 + r_9\dot{\theta}_3\sin(\Delta+\theta_3)]\boldsymbol{i} + [r_2\dot{\theta}_2\cos\theta_2 + r_9\dot{\theta}_3\cos(\Delta+\theta_3)]\boldsymbol{j} \end{aligned} \tag{5.180}$$

Again, all quantities on the right-hand side of Eq. (5.180) are known, and so the velocity of point Q can be computed without difficulty. For the acceleration, differentiate the velocity expression. Then,

$$a_{Q_3/A_2} = \ddot{r}_2 + \ddot{r}_9$$

and

$$\begin{aligned} a_{Q_3/A_2} &= r_2\ddot{\theta}_2(-\sin\theta_2 \boldsymbol{i} + \cos\theta_2 \boldsymbol{j}) - r_2(\dot{\theta}_2)^2(\cos\theta_2 \boldsymbol{i} + \sin\theta_2 \boldsymbol{j}) \\ &\quad + r_9\ddot{\theta}_3[-\sin(\Delta+\theta_3)\boldsymbol{i} + \cos(\Delta+\theta_3)\boldsymbol{j}] - r_9(\dot{\theta}_3)^2[\cos(\Delta+\theta_3)\boldsymbol{i} + \sin(\Delta+\theta_3)\boldsymbol{j}] \\ &= \left[-r_2\ddot{\theta}_2\sin\theta_2 - r_9\ddot{\theta}_3\sin(\Delta+\theta_3) - r_2(\dot{\theta}_2)^2\cos\theta_2 - r_9(\dot{\theta}_3)^2\cos(\Delta+\theta_3)\right]\boldsymbol{i} \\ &\quad + \left[r_2\ddot{\theta}_2\cos\theta_2 + r_9\ddot{\theta}_3\cos(\Delta+\theta_3) - r_2(\dot{\theta}_2)^2\sin\theta_2 - r_9(\dot{\theta}_3)^2\sin(\Delta+\theta_3)\right]\boldsymbol{j} \end{aligned} \tag{5.181}$$

Again, all quantities on the right-hand side of Eq. (5.181) are known and so the acceleration of point Q can be computed without difficulty. Note that this procedure is simply a variation on the rigid-body analysis given in Section 5.4.

5.11.2 Solving the Position Equations

A review of the analysis just developed shows that only the position equations are nonlinear in the unknowns. Therefore specialized techniques are required to solve them. If a numerical solution is chosen, then an initial guess for the variables is required. This is best obtained by sketching the mechanism to scale. A numerical iteration method such as the Newton–Rapson method can be used to obtain refined values. If a series of input angles is to be investigated, then the final variable values for the previous input value can be used as the initial estimates of the variables for the next input value provided that the input angle increments are relatively small (i.e., within about 10° of each other).

Another numerical approach that is computationally more efficient than using Newton's method, but sometimes has convergence problems at end-of-travel positions, is to numerically integrate the velocity equations after a precise set of values for the variables is obtained by Newton's method. The input step size for this integration should not exceed 2°. This method is very convenient if a numerical integration is already needed for dynamic problems in which the equations of motion are required.

When it is possible, it is preferable to solve the displacement equations analytically This method eliminates the numerical instability problems present in both Newton's method and numerical integration. In general, it is always possible to solve the equations analytically if the mechanism can be analyzed by hand using traditional graphical methods with vector polygons as presented in Chapters 2 and 3. When it is possible to do this, the position equations can be solved in sets of two equations in two unknowns as was done in Sections 5.3–5.10. If it is not possible to reduce the equations to a series of two equations in two unknowns, the equations must be solved iteratively using a numerical procedure such as Newton's method.

When it is possible to solve the position equations algebraically, one of two situations will usually occur. In the first situation, the compound mechanism can be treated as a series of simple mechanisms. In the second situation, the compound mechanism cannot be represented as a series of simple mechanisms; however, the equations can be partitioned into a sequential set of two equations in two unknowns. These two situations will be presented separately.

Compound Linkage as a Series of Simple Mechanisms When the compound linkage is a series of simple mechanisms, we can analyze each mechanism in sequence. The output for one mechanism is the input to the next mechanism. If we have computer routines to analyze the single-loop mechanisms, the routines can be concatenated to analyze the entire linkage. This is the case that exists in the mechanism of Fig. 5.47. When we examine the mechanism, we find that the first linkage is a four-bar linkage defined by vectors $\boldsymbol{r}_1$, $\boldsymbol{r}_2$, $\boldsymbol{r}_3$, and $\boldsymbol{r}_4$. This mechanism can be analyzed using the equations developed in Section 5.3. The four-bar loop drives link 4. Therefore, once the position, velocity, and acceleration for $\boldsymbol{r}_4$ are known, the corresponding values for $\boldsymbol{r}_6$ can be found using rigid-body conditions (Section 5.4). Link 4 is the input for the slider-crank mechanism defined by $\boldsymbol{r}_5$, $\boldsymbol{r}_6$, $\boldsymbol{r}_7$, and $\boldsymbol{r}_8$. This mechanism can be analyzed using the equations in Section 5.5 to determine the kinematic properties of the slider.

EXAMPLE 5.11
Kinematic Analysis of a Compound Linkage Mechanism

Determine the angular position, velocity, and acceleration of link 6 in the mechanism in Fig. 5.49 if the slider is moving at 10 cm/s (constant) to the right. The following dimensions are known:

$$AB = 22.7 \text{ cm}, \quad CD = 7.5 \text{ cm}, \quad EF = 10.6 \text{ cm}$$
$$BC = 10.6 \text{ cm}, \quad CF = 14.6 \text{ cm}$$
$$AC = 28 \text{ cm}, \quad DE = 11.4 \text{ cm}$$

Solution

We will analyze the mechanism as three linkage systems in series. First we will analyze the slider-crank mechanism using the equations in Table 5.5. Next we will compute the position of *CD* from rigid-body conditions (Table 5.3). Last, the four-bar linkage (*CDEF*) can be analyzed using Table 5.1. The actual numerical calculations can be made using the MATLAB routines included on the disk with this book.

To facilitate the analysis, the mechanism in Fig. 5.49 is represented by the vectors indicated in Fig. 5.50.

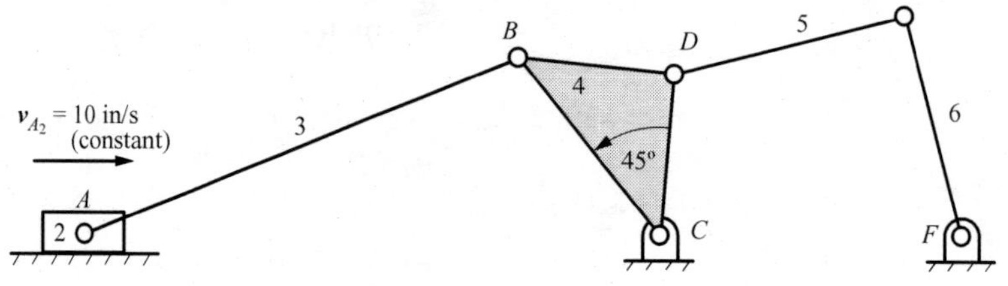

FIGURE 5.49 Mechanism for Example 5.11.

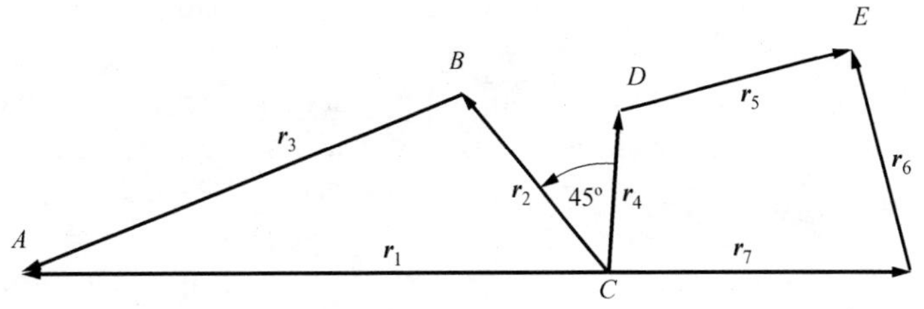

FIGURE 5.50 Vectors representing mechanism in Fig. 5.49.

For the slider-crank part of the mechanism, the following magnitudes and directions are known:

$$r_1 = 28, \quad \theta_1 = 180^\circ, \quad \dot{r}_1 = 10, \quad \ddot{r}_1 = 0$$
$$r_2 = 10.6$$
$$r_3 = 22.7$$

The unknowns are: $\theta_2, \dot{\theta}_2, \ddot{\theta}_2, \theta_3, \dot{\theta}_3, \ddot{\theta}_3$. For this set of values, the equations in Table 5.5 can be used. The value of σ is -1 for the geometry given, and the results are

$$\theta_1 = 180^\circ, \quad \dot{\theta}_1 = 0 \text{ rad/s}, \quad \ddot{\theta}_1 = 0 \text{ rad/s}^2$$
$$\theta_2 = 129.94^\circ, \quad \dot{\theta}_2 = -0.9314 \text{ rad/s}, \quad \ddot{\theta}_2 = 0.5005 \text{ rad/s}^2$$
$$\theta_3 = -159.02^\circ, \quad \dot{\theta}_3 = 0.299 \text{ rad/s}, \quad \ddot{\theta}_3 = -0.459 \text{ rad/s}^2$$

The orientation of the vector $\boldsymbol{r}_4$ will be related to that of the vector $\boldsymbol{r}_2$ through the equation

$$\theta_4 = \theta_2 - 45^\circ$$

Therefore, the magnitudes and directions for the vectors defining the four-bar linkage are

$$r_4 = 7.5, \quad \theta_4 = 84.94^\circ, \quad \dot{\theta}_4 = -0.9314 \text{ rad/s}, \quad \ddot{\theta}_4 = 0.5005 \text{ rad/s}^2$$
$$r_5 = 11.4,$$
$$r_6 = 10.6,$$
$$r_7 = 14.6, \quad \theta_7 = 0^\circ$$

The unknowns are: $\theta_5, \dot{\theta}_5, \ddot{\theta}_5, \theta_6, \dot{\theta}_6, \ddot{\theta}_6$. For this set of values, the equations in Table 5.1 can be used. The value of σ is again -1 for the geometry given, and the results are

$$\theta_4 = 84.94^\circ, \quad \dot{\theta}_4 = -0.9314 \text{ rad/s}, \quad \ddot{\theta}_4 = 0.5005 \text{ rad/s}^2$$
$$\theta_5 = 13.87^\circ, \quad \dot{\theta}_5 = 0.2175 \text{ rad/s}, \quad \ddot{\theta}_5 = 0.0536 \text{ rad/s}^2$$
$$\theta_6 = 105.7146^\circ, \quad \dot{\theta}_6 = -0.6237 \text{ rad/s}, \quad \ddot{\theta}_6 = 0.5978 \text{ rad/s}^2$$
$$\theta_7 = 0^\circ, \quad \dot{\theta}_7 = 0 \text{ rad/s}, \quad \ddot{\theta}_7 = 0 \text{ rad/s}^2$$

General Cases In Which Two Equations in Two Unknowns Result For simple lower pair mechanisms with one vector loop, the position analysis will reduce to two scalar equations in two unknowns, and it is relatively easy to develop closed-form equations for the unknown variables. However, when analyzing more complex lower pair mechanisms with n loop equations, the number of equations and the number of variable unknowns are both $2n$, and the solution can become much more complicated. However, not all the pair variables appear in each of the equations. Fortunately, it is often possible to group the equations into smaller sets that can be solved independently in a serial fashion.

If a given lower pair mechanism can be analyzed using the traditional vector-polygon approach, it is always possible to group the position equations in such a way that no more than two equations in two unknowns must be solved at any one time. For such mechanisms, the position equations can always be solved in closed form, and these types of mechanisms form the vast majority of the linkages that an engineer might design. For complex mechanisms that cannot be analyzed entirely using closed-form equations, it is often possible to analyze a part of the mechanism with closed-form equations after other parts are analyzed numerically.

For simplicity, the vector form of the loop closure equation for each loop will be represented in homogeneous form as

$$\sum_{i=1}^{k} \sigma_i \boldsymbol{r}_i = 0$$

where $\sigma_i = \pm 1$. This equation can be divided into x and y components, and the corresponding component equations are

$$\sum_{i=1}^{k} \sigma_i r_i \cos\theta_i = 0 \tag{5.182}$$

$$\sum_{i=1}^{k} \sigma_i r_i \sin\theta_i = 0 \tag{5.183}$$

where r_i is the length of vector i, θ_i is the angle (measured CCW) between link i and a horizontal line, and k is the number of vectors in a given loop. Equations (5.182) and (5.183) are written for each closure loop of the mechanism, and for n loops there will be $2n$ equations and $2n$ unknowns. When the links contain more than two joints, there will also be auxiliary equations that relate joint angles. As shown in Fig. 5.51, these auxiliary equations can generally be written as

$$\theta_q = \theta_r - \Delta \tag{5.184}$$

where Δ is a constant. When such equations are necessary, the equations can be written such that θ_r is solved first so that it is a trivial matter to solve for θ_q. Note that Eq. (5.184) is linear.

When all of the equations of the forms given by Eqs. (5.182)–(5.184) are considered as a set, it is usually possible to separate the $2n$ nonlinear equations into smaller groups that can be solved serially, and in most cases the nonlinear equations can be grouped into sets of two equations and two unknowns of the following form:

$$\sigma_p r_p \cos\theta_p + \sigma_m r_m \cos\theta_m + \sum_{i=1}^{p-1} \sigma_i r_i \cos\theta_i + \sum_{i=p+1}^{m-1} \sigma_i r_i \cos\theta_i + \sum_{i=m+1}^{k} \sigma_i r_i \cos\theta_i = 0 \tag{5.185}$$

$$\sigma_p r_p \sin\theta_p + \sigma_m r_m \sin\theta_m + \sum_{i=1}^{p-1} \sigma_i r_i \sin\theta_i + \sum_{i=p+1}^{m-1} \sigma_i r_i \sin\theta_i + \sum_{i=m+1}^{k} \sigma_i r_i \sin\theta_i = 0 \tag{5.186}$$

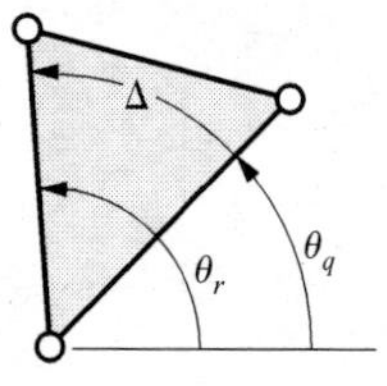

FIGURE 5.51 Geometry described by auxiliary equations.

where $\sigma_p = \sigma_m$, and all variables in the summation terms are known.

Then,

$$r_p \cos\theta_p + r_m \cos\theta_m = C_1 \tag{5.187}$$

$$r_p \sin\theta_p + r_m \sin\theta_m = C_2 \tag{5.188}$$

where

$$C_1 = -\frac{1}{\sigma_m}\left(\sum_{i=1}^{p-1}\sigma_i r_i \cos\theta_i + \sum_{i=p+1}^{m-1}\sigma_i r_i \cos\theta_i + \sum_{i=m+1}^{k}\sigma_i r_i \cos\theta_i\right)$$

and

$$C_2 = -\frac{1}{\sigma_m}\left(\sum_{i=1}^{p-1}\sigma_i r_i \sin\theta_i + \sum_{i=p+1}^{m-1}\sigma_i r_i \sin\theta_i + \sum_{i=m+1}^{k}\sigma_i r_i \sin\theta_i\right)$$

In Eqs. (5.187) and (5.188), two of the four variables r_p, θ_p, r_m, and θ_m can be unknown, resulting in six possible combinations; however, only four of these six combinations are unique. The four cases that must be considered are 1. r_p and θ_p or r_m and θ_m are the unknowns, 2. r_p and θ_m or r_m and θ_p are the unknowns, 3. r_p and r_m are the unknowns, and 4. θ_p and θ_m are the unknowns. The rest of the variables in the four cases are known for each position of the mechanism. When solving each of the cases, the three trigonometric identities discussed earlier for $\sin\theta$, $\cos\theta$, and $\tan\frac{\theta}{2}$ are used:

$$\cos^2\theta + \sin^2\theta = 1 \tag{5.189}$$

$$\cos\theta = \frac{1-\tan^2\left(\dfrac{\theta}{2}\right)}{1+\tan^2\left(\dfrac{\theta}{2}\right)} \tag{5.190}$$

and

$$\sin\theta = \frac{2\tan\left(\dfrac{\theta}{2}\right)}{1+\tan^2\left(\dfrac{\theta}{2}\right)} \tag{5.191}$$

The equations for calculating the unknown variables in each of these cases are developed in the following:

Case 1: r_p and θ_p Unknown To solve this case, the terms $r_p \cos\theta_p$ and $r_p \sin\theta_p$ are first isolated on the left-hand side of Eqs. (5.187) and (5.188).

$$r_p \cos\theta_p = C_1 - r_m \cos\theta_m \tag{5.192}$$

$$r_p \sin\theta_p = C_2 - r_m \sin\theta_m \tag{5.193}$$

Equation (5.193) is then divided by Eq. (5.192) to provide the solution for θ_p. Next the two equations are squared, added together, and simplified using Eq. (5.189) to obtain a solution for r_p. The resulting expressions for r_p and θ_p are

$$r_p = \sqrt{C_1^2 + C_2^2 + r_m^2 - 2C_1 r_m \cos\theta_m - 2C_2 r_m \sin\theta_m} \tag{5.194}$$

$$\theta_p = \tan^{-1}\left[\frac{C_2 - r_m \sin\theta_m}{C_1 - r_m \cos\theta_m}\right] \tag{5.195}$$

Case 2: r_p and θ_m Unknown To solve for the two unknown variables, r_p and θ_m, the terms $r_m \cos\theta_m$ and $r_m \sin\theta_m$ are first isolated on the left-hand side of Eqs. (5.187) and (5.188).

$$r_m \cos\theta_m = C_1 - r_p \cos\theta_p \tag{5.196}$$

$$r_m \sin\theta_m = C_2 - r_p \sin\theta_p \tag{5.197}$$

Equations (5.196) and (5.197) are then squared, added together, and simplified using Eq. (5.189) to give a quadratic equation in the variable r_p. The solution to the resulting equation is

$$r_p = \frac{-b \pm \sqrt{b^2 - 4c}}{2} \tag{5.198}$$

where

$$b = -2C_1 \cos\theta_p - 2C_2 \sin\theta_p$$

and

$$c = C_1^2 + C_2^2 - r_m^2$$

The angle θ_m is found by dividing Eq. (5.197) by Eq. (5.196) and solving for θ_m:

$$\theta_m = \tan^{-1}\left[\frac{-r_p \sin\theta_p + C_2}{-r_p \cos\theta_p + C_1}\right] \tag{5.199}$$

Equations (5.198) and (5.199) each have two solutions corresponding to the two assembly modes of this part of the linkage. The proper mode must be specified at the time of the analysis. This can be done directly or by providing an initial estimate of the position of the mechanism and determining which solution is closest to that indicated by the initial estimate. In practice, the initial estimate of the position of the mechanism could be provided by an approximate sketch drawn on a computer screen.

Case 3: r_p and r_m Unknown To solve for r_p, Eq. (5.187) is first multiplied by $\sin\theta_m$ and the result is then simplified. Equation (5.188) is then multiplied by $\cos\theta_m$ and the resulting equations from the two operations are subtracted. After simplification, the expression for r_p is

$$r_p = \frac{C_1 \sin\theta_m - C_2 \cos\theta_m}{\sin(\theta_m - \theta_p)} \tag{5.200}$$

After r_p is known, Eqs. (5.187) and (5.188) can be solved directly for r_m:

$$r_m = \frac{C_1 - r_p \cos\theta_p}{\cos\theta_m} = \frac{C_2 - r_p \sin\theta_p}{\sin\theta_m} \tag{5.201}$$

Case 4: θ_p and θ_m Unknown To solve for θ_m, Eqs. (5.192) and (5.193) are squared, added together, and simplified with the aid of Eqs. (5.189)–(5.191) to give a quadratic equation in the variable $\tan(\theta_m/2)$. The resulting solution is

$$\theta_m = 2\tan^{-1}\left(\frac{-C_4 \pm \sqrt{C_4^2 - 4C_3C_5}}{2C_3}\right) \tag{5.202}$$

where

$$C_3 = r_p^2 - C_1^2 - C_2^2 - r_m^2 - 2C_1r_m$$
$$C_4 = 4C_2r_m$$

and

$$C_5 = r_p^2 - C_1^2 - C_2^2 - r_m^2 + 2C_1r_m$$

Given θ_m, an expression for θ_p can be found by dividing Eq. (5.193) by Eq. (5.192) and simplifying,

$$\theta_p = \tan^{-1}\left(\frac{C_2 - r_m \sin\theta_m}{C_1 - r_m \cos\theta_m}\right) \tag{5.203}$$

Equations (5.202) and (5.203) each have two solutions, corresponding to the two assembly modes of this part of the linkage. As with case 2, the proper assembly mode must be identified before the analysis can be conducted.

5.12 CLOSURE EQUATIONS FOR MECHANISMS WITH HIGHER PAIRS

The closure equation approach can also be used for mechanisms with higher pairs if we use the centers of curvature of the contact surfaces corresponding to the contact points. This is exactly the approach employed when equivalent mechanisms are used, and, in fact, we could represent the higher pair mechanisms by their equivalent lower pair mechanism and determine the kinematic properties by analyzing the corresponding lower pair mechanism. By using the centers of curvature, however, we can also approach the problem without using equivalent mechanisms directly.

The approach using centers of curvature can be applied directly to mechanisms with cam joints and to mechanisms with rolling joints if the contact points (and the corresponding centers of curvature) are known. With rolling contact, locating the contact point as a function of the input motion requires that we know the initial contact point when the mechanism begins to move. Subsequent contact points are then located by enforcing the constraint that there is no slipping at the contacting surfaces. If circle arcs are involved, the resulting constraint equations are simple; however, if general surfaces are involved, the constraint equations require that the arc length on each contacting surface be determined by integration. For simplicity, we will limit the discussions here to cases in which the contact point either is known or can be determined simply.

For higher pair mechanisms, the vector closure diagrams are set up using the same procedure as would be used when the mechanism is drawn. In general, the same points and vectors will be used. The procedure will be illustrated with three examples.

EXAMPLE 5.12 *Kinematic Analysis of a Mechanism with Cam Contact*

In the mechanism shown in Fig. 5.52, $\boldsymbol{\omega}_2 = 10$ rad/s CW and is constant. Determine v_{C_3/C_2}, v_{C_3}, a_{C_3/C_2} and a_{C_3} using vector closure equations.

Solution

To solve the problem, set up four vectors as shown in Fig. 5.53. The vector $\boldsymbol{r}_2$ is from point B to point A, the center of curvature of link 2 corresponding to the contact point at C. Vector $\boldsymbol{r}_1$ is from point A to point C, the contact location. The vector $\boldsymbol{r}_1$ is constant in both direction and magnitude. Vector $\boldsymbol{r}_3$ is from point B to the face of the cam follower. The direction of $\boldsymbol{r}_3$ is constant, but the magnitude varies. Because $\boldsymbol{r}_3$ is measured from a fixed point on the frame (point B) to the face of the cam follower, the first and second derivatives of $\boldsymbol{r}_3$ correspond to the velocity and acceleration, respectively, of the cam follower. Vector $\boldsymbol{r}_4$ is measured from the contact point to a line through B and in the direction of travel of the cam.

The vector closure equation for the mechanism is

$$\boldsymbol{r}_3 = \boldsymbol{r}_2 + \boldsymbol{r}_1 + \boldsymbol{r}_4 \tag{5.204}$$

and the corresponding velocity and acceleration expressions are given by

$$\dot{\boldsymbol{r}}_3 = \dot{\boldsymbol{r}}_2 + \dot{\boldsymbol{r}}_1 + \dot{\boldsymbol{r}}_4 \tag{5.205}$$

and

$$\ddot{\boldsymbol{r}}_3 = \ddot{\boldsymbol{r}}_2 + \ddot{\boldsymbol{r}}_1 + \ddot{\boldsymbol{r}}_4 \tag{5.206}$$

Before actually solving the equations, we can summarize the variables that are known and unknown. These are

$$\begin{array}{llll}
r_1 = 1.0 \text{ in}, & \theta_1 = 0°, & \dot{\theta}_1 = 0 \text{ rad/s}, & \ddot{\theta}_1 = 0 \\
r_2 = 0.5 \text{ in}, & \theta_2 = 225°, & \dot{\theta}_2 = -10 \text{ rad/s}, & \ddot{\theta}_2 = 0 \\
r_3 = ?, & \theta_3 = 0°, & \dot{\theta}_3 = 0 \text{ rad/s}, & \ddot{\theta}_3 = 0 \\
r_4 = ?, & \theta_4 = 90°, & \dot{\theta}_4 = 0 \text{ rad/s}, & \ddot{\theta}_4 = 0
\end{array}$$

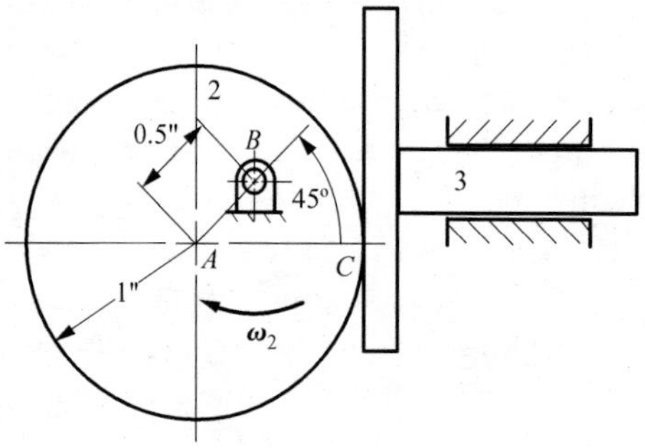

FIGURE 5.52 Figure for Example 5.12.

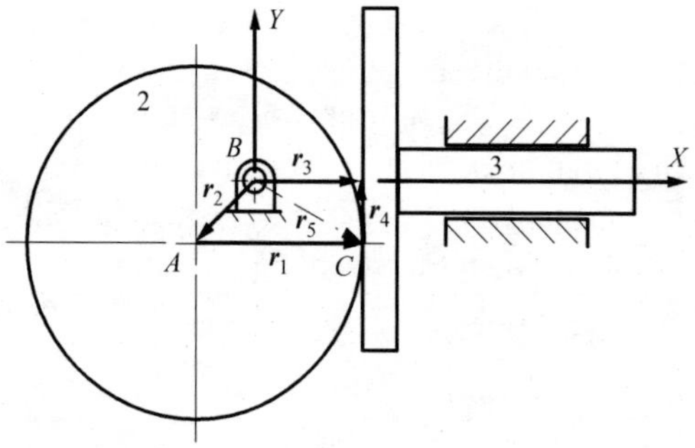

FIGURE 5.53 Vector closure for Example 5.12.

As in the cases of lower pair mechanisms, the position equation must be solved first. The resulting linear velocity and acceleration equations can then be solved easily. Rewriting the position closure equation in component form gives

$$r_3\cos\theta_3 = r_2\cos\theta_2 + r_1\cos\theta_1 + r_4\cos\theta_4$$
$$r_3\sin\theta_3 = r_2\sin\theta_2 + r_1\sin\theta_1 + r_4\sin\theta_4$$

Simplifying based on the input values, we get

$$r_3 = r_2\cos\theta_2 + r_1$$
$$0 = r_2\sin\theta_2 + r_4 \tag{5.207}$$

Equations (5.207) are linear in the unknowns (r_3 and r_4) and can easily be solved. The results are

$$r_3 = r_2\cos\theta_2 + r_1 = 0.5\cos(225^\circ) + 1.0 = 0.646 \text{ in}$$

and

$$r_4 = -r_2\sin\theta_2 = 0.354 \text{ in}$$

To conduct the velocity analysis, rewrite Eq. (5.205) in component form and simplify or differentiate Eqs. (5.207) and simplify. In either case, the results are

$$\dot{r}_3 = -r_2\dot{\theta}_2\sin\theta_2$$
$$\dot{r}_4 = -r_2\dot{\theta}_2\cos\theta_2 \tag{5.208}$$

Substituting in the known values, we obtain

$$\dot{r}_3 = -r_2\dot{\theta}_2\sin\theta_2 = -0.5(-10)\sin(225^\circ) = -3.535 \text{ in/s}$$
$$\dot{r}_4 = -r_2\dot{\theta}_2\cos\theta_2 = -0.5(-10)\cos(225^\circ) = -3.535 \text{ in/s}$$

The location of both C_2 and C_3 is given by $\boldsymbol{r}_5 = \boldsymbol{r}_1 + \boldsymbol{r}_2$ in Fig. 5.53. Both points momentarily have the same coordinates. However, the velocities of the corresponding points are different. To determine the velocities, we must carefully interpret the vectors. The velocity of all points on the follower is the same. Therefore, the velocity of C_3 is given by $\dot{\boldsymbol{r}}_3$ if $\boldsymbol{r}_3$ remains horizontal. The velocity of C_2 is given by the derivative of a vector fixed to link 2 and directed from point B to C. This is $\dot{\boldsymbol{r}}_3$ if we assume $\boldsymbol{r}_5$ is fixed to link 2. Then the velocity of C_2 is given by $\dot{\boldsymbol{r}}_5 = \dot{\boldsymbol{r}}_1 + \dot{\boldsymbol{r}}_2$ if we assume that both $\boldsymbol{r}_1$ and $\boldsymbol{r}_2$ are fixed to (i.e., rotate with) link 2. Then the components of the velocity of C_2 will be given by

$$\boldsymbol{v}_{C_2} = \dot{r}_5 = \dot{r}_1 + \dot{r}_2 = \left(-r_1\dot{\theta}_2\sin\theta_1 - r_2\dot{\theta}_2\sin\theta_2\right)\boldsymbol{i} + \left(r_1\dot{\theta}_2\cos\theta_1 + r_2\dot{\theta}_2\cos\theta_2\right)\boldsymbol{j}$$

The relative velocity is given by

$$\boldsymbol{v}_{C_3/C_2} = \boldsymbol{v}_{C_3} - \boldsymbol{v}_{C_2} = \left(\dot{r}_3 + r_1\dot{\theta}_2\sin\theta_1 + r_2\dot{\theta}_2\sin\theta_2\right)\boldsymbol{i} - \left(r_1\dot{\theta}_2\cos\theta_1 + r_2\dot{\theta}_2\cos\theta_2\right)\boldsymbol{j}$$

Substituting values for the variables gives

$$\boldsymbol{v}_{C_3/C_2} = \boldsymbol{v}_{C_3} - \boldsymbol{v}_{C_2} = [0]\boldsymbol{i} - [1.0(-10)\cos(0^\circ) + 0.5(-10)\cos(225^\circ)]\boldsymbol{j} = 6.464\boldsymbol{j} \text{ in/s}$$

For the acceleration analysis, differentiate Eqs. (5.208) and simplify. Then,

$$\ddot{r}_3 = -r_2\ddot{\theta}_2\sin\theta_2 - r_2\dot{\theta}_2^2\cos\theta_2$$
$$\ddot{r}_4 = -r_2\ddot{\theta}_2\cos\theta_2 + r_2\dot{\theta}_2^2\sin\theta_2 \tag{5.209}$$

Substituting in the known values gives

$$\ddot{r}_3 = -r_2\ddot{\theta}_2\sin\theta_2 - r_2\dot{\theta}_2^2\cos\theta_2 = 0 - 0.5(-10)^2\cos(225^\circ) = 35.35 \text{ in/s}^2$$

$$\ddot{r}_4 = -r_2\ddot{\theta}_2 \cos\theta_2 + r_2\dot{\theta}_2^2 \sin\theta_2 = 0 + 0.5(-10)^2 \sin(225°) = -35.35 \text{ in/s}^2$$

Finally, we obtain

$$\begin{aligned}\boldsymbol{a}_{C_2} = \ddot{\boldsymbol{r}}_5 = \ddot{\boldsymbol{r}}_1 + \ddot{\boldsymbol{r}}_2 &= \left(-r_1\ddot{\theta}_2 \sin\theta_1 - r_2\ddot{\theta}_2 \sin\theta_2 - r_1\dot{\theta}_2^2 \cos\theta_1 - r_2\dot{\theta}_2^2 \cos\theta_2\right)\mathbf{i} \\ &+\left(r_1\ddot{\theta}_2 \cos\theta_1 + r_2\ddot{\theta}_2 \cos\theta_2 - r_1\dot{\theta}_2^2 \sin\theta_1 - r_2\dot{\theta}_2^2 \sin\theta_2\right)\mathbf{j} \\ &= \left[0 - 0 - 1(-10)^2 - 0.5(-10)^2 \cos(225°)\right]\mathbf{i} + \left[0 + 0 - 0 - 0.5(-10)^2 \sin(225°)\right]\mathbf{j} \\ &= \left[-100 + 35.35\right]\mathbf{i} + \left[35.35\right]\mathbf{j} = -64.65\mathbf{i} + 35.35\mathbf{j}\end{aligned}$$

and

$$\boldsymbol{a}_{C_3/C_2} = \boldsymbol{a}_{C_3} - \boldsymbol{a}_{C_2} = \left[35.35 + 64.65\right]\mathbf{i} - 35.35\mathbf{j} = 100\mathbf{i} - 35.35\mathbf{j} \text{ in/s}^2$$

EXAMPLE 5.13 *Kinematic Analysis of a Mechanism with a Pin-in-a-Slot Joint*

For the mechanism shown in Fig. 5.54, find $\boldsymbol{\omega}_3$ and $\boldsymbol{\alpha}_3$ if $\theta_2 = 100°$ and $\boldsymbol{\omega}_2 = 50$ rad/s CCW and is constant.

Solution

To solve the problem, set up four vectors as shown in Fig. 5.55. The vector $\boldsymbol{r}_1$ is from point A to D, and $\boldsymbol{r}_2$ is from point A to B. The other two vectors involve the center of curvature, C, of the path that point B_2 traces on link 3. Vector $\boldsymbol{r}_3$ is from point B to C, and $\boldsymbol{r}_4$ is from point D to C. Both points D and C are fixed to link 3; therefore, $\boldsymbol{r}_4$ is fixed to link 3. All of the vectors have constant lengths. The unknown

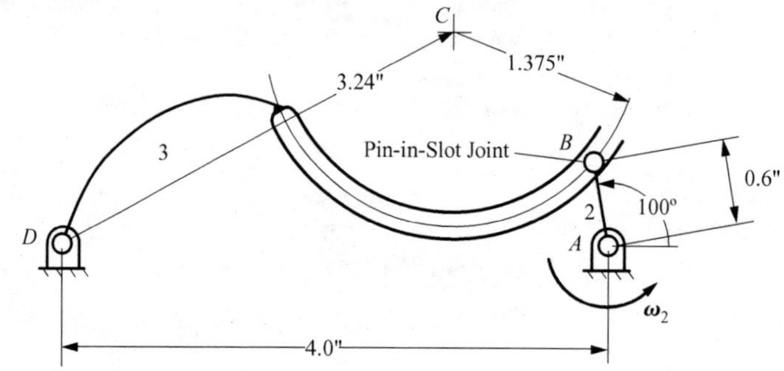

FIGURE 5.54 Mechanism for Example 5.13.

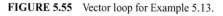

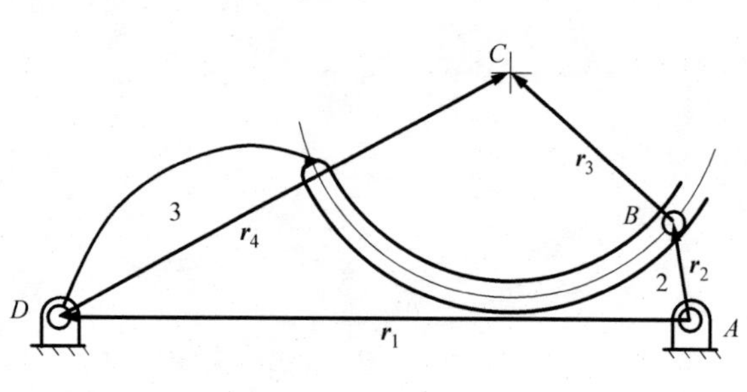

FIGURE 5.55 Vector loop for Example 5.13.

angles are θ_3 and θ_4 because θ_1 is fixed and θ_2 is the known input angle. The known and unknown information can be summarized as follows:

$$r_1 = 4.0 \text{ in}, \quad \theta_1 = 180°, \quad \dot{\theta}_1 = 0 \text{ rad/s}, \quad \ddot{\theta}_1 = 0 \text{ rad/s}^2$$
$$r_2 = 0.6 \text{ in}, \quad \theta_2 = 100°, \quad \dot{\theta}_2 = 50 \text{ rad/s}, \quad \ddot{\theta}_2 = 0 \text{ rad/s}^2$$
$$r_3 = 1.375 \text{ in}, \quad \theta_3 = ?, \quad \dot{\theta}_3 = ?, \quad \ddot{\theta}_3 = ?$$
$$r_4 = 3.24 \text{ in}, \quad \theta_4 = ?, \quad \dot{\theta}_4 = ?, \quad \ddot{\theta}_4 = ?$$

Based on Fig. 5.55, the vector closure equation for this mechanism is

$$\mathbf{r}_2 + \mathbf{r}_3 = \mathbf{r}_1 + \mathbf{r}_4 \tag{5.210}$$

This equation is exactly the same as that for a four-bar linkage (Eq. 5.24). Therefore, the equations developed for a four-bar linkage and summarized in Table 5.1 can be applied directly to this example. The results are

$$\theta_3 = 138.31°, \quad \dot{\theta}_3 = -22.21 \text{ rad/s}, \quad \ddot{\theta}_3 = 73.77 \text{ rad/s}^2$$
$$\theta_4 = 27.69°, \quad \dot{\theta}_4 = 6.133 \text{ rad/s}, \quad \ddot{\theta}_4 = -625.98 \text{ rad/s}^2$$

In the mechanism, vector $\mathbf{r}_4$ is fixed to link 3. Therefore,

$$\boldsymbol{\omega}_3 = 6.133 \text{ rad/s CCW}$$
$$\boldsymbol{\alpha}_3 = -625.98 \text{ rad/s}^2 \text{ CW}$$

EXAMPLE 5.14 *Kinematic Analysis of a Mechanism with Rolling Contact*

In the mechanism shown in Fig. 5.56, link 2 is turning with a constant angular velocity of 200 rpm CCW. Determine the angular velocity and acceleration of link 4.

Solution

This mechanism involves rolling contact at point *E*. It is relatively straightforward to determine the angular quantities associated with link 4 if we locate the vectors for the closure equations using the centers of curvature of links 2 and 3 corresponding to the contact location *E*. This approach will not yield any angular information for link 3, however. In fact, the velocity and acceleration of link 4 are the same whether there is rolling or slipping at *E*.

The vector closure diagram is given in Fig. 5.57. The vector $\mathbf{r}_1$ is from point *A* to *D*, and $\mathbf{r}_2$ is from point *A* to *B*. The other two vectors involve the center of curvature, *C*, of the path that point B_2 traces

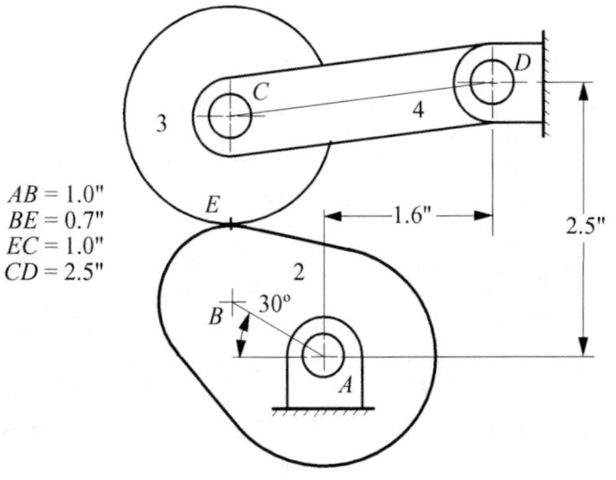

FIGURE 5.56 Mechanism for Example 5.14.

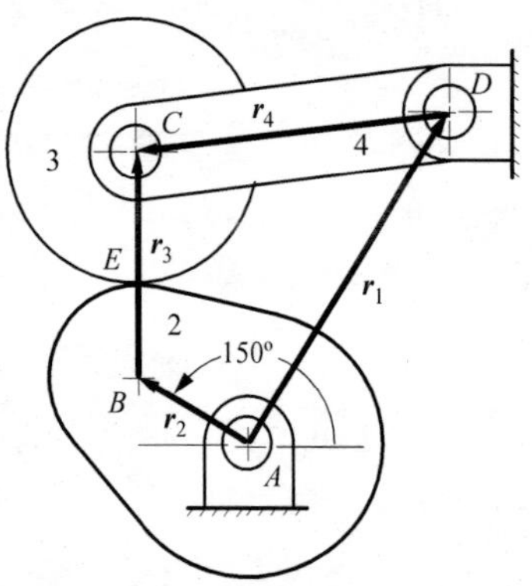

FIGURE 5.57 Vector loop for Example 5.14.

on link 3. Vector $\boldsymbol{r}_3$ is from point B to C, the centers of curvature corresponding to E_2 and E_3, respectively, and $\boldsymbol{r}_4$ is from point D to C. Note that the points D and C of interest are those fixed to link 4. Therefore, $\boldsymbol{r}_4$ can be treated as a vector fixed to link 4.

All of the vectors have constant lengths. The unknown angles are θ_3 and θ_4 because θ_1 is fixed and θ_2 is the known input angle. The angle θ_1 can be computed from

$$\theta_1 = \tan^{-1}\left[\frac{2.5}{1.6}\right] = 57.38°$$

The known and unknown information can be summarized as follows:

$$r_1 = \sqrt{2.5^2 + 1.6^2} = 2.968 \text{ in}, \quad \theta_1 = 57.38°, \quad \dot{\theta}_1 = 0 \text{ rad/s}, \quad \ddot{\theta}_1 = 0$$

$$r_2 = 1.0 \text{ in}, \quad \theta_2 = 150°, \quad \dot{\theta}_2 = 200\left(\frac{2\pi}{60}\right) = 20.94 \text{ rad/s}, \quad \ddot{\theta}_2 = 0$$

$$r_3 = (0.7 + 1.0) = 1.7 \text{ in}, \quad \theta_3 = ?, \quad \dot{\theta}_3 = ?, \quad \ddot{\theta}_3 = ?$$

$$r_4 = 2.5 \text{ in}, \quad \theta_4 = ?, \quad \dot{\theta}_4 = ?, \quad \ddot{\theta}_4 = ?$$

Based on Fig. 5.57, the vector closure equation for this mechanism is

$$\boldsymbol{r}_2 + \boldsymbol{r}_3 = \boldsymbol{r}_1 + \boldsymbol{r}_4$$

This equation is again exactly the same as for a four-bar linkage (Eq. 5.24). Therefore, the equations developed for a four-bar linkage and summarized in Table 5.1 can again be applied directly to this example. The results are

$$\theta_3 = 138.31°, \quad \dot{\theta}_3 = -22.21 \text{ rad/s}, \quad \ddot{\theta}_3 = -73.77 \text{ rad/s}^2$$

$$\theta_4 = 27.69°, \quad \dot{\theta}_4 = 6.133 \text{ rad/s}, \quad \ddot{\theta}_4 = -625.98 \text{ rad/s}^2$$

In the mechanism, vector $\boldsymbol{r}_4$ is fixed to link 4. Therefore, $\boldsymbol{\omega}_4 = 6.133$ rad/s CCW and $\boldsymbol{\alpha}_4 = 625.98$ rad/s^2 CW.

5.13 NOTATIONAL DIFFERENCES: VECTORS AND COMPLEX NUMBERS

Several different notations are in widespread use for analytical solution of planar kinematic problems. The two principal notations are based on vectors and complex numbers. It is the purpose of this section to compare these two notations. In principle, they are completely equivalent to one another, with every relationship written in one notation directly translatable to the other. Nevertheless, some relationships are more easily discerned when using one in preference to the other. Broadly speaking, the complex number notation tends to be most compatible with relationships that are most naturally expressed in polar coordinates. This includes most relationships describing the instantaneous motion state of a rigid body. These relationships are usually most compactly expressed in complex notation. Vector notation is, again broadly speaking, most compatible with relationships that are most naturally expressed in Cartesian coordinates. This is usually true whenever there is no single point that dominates the geometry of the system. In the opinion of the authors of this book, this includes the majority of situations to be studied. Also, planar vector notation is fully compatible with the corresponding techniques used for three-dimensional representation. Therefore, if only one notation is to be used, it should be the vector notation. For this reason, this text is based on the use of vector notation. Of course, advanced students of the subject should seek proficiency in both types of notation.

In complex number notation, planar vector quantities are represented by identifying the real and imaginary parts with orthogonal components. Normally, the x component is represented by the real part and the y component by the imaginary part. That is, the complex number

$$z = x + iy$$

represents the vector (x, y). An important alternative form for z is

$$z = re^{i\theta} = r\left(\cos\theta + i\sin\theta\right) \tag{5.211}$$

where r is the length of the vector and θ is its direction relative to the x axis. That is

$$r = \sqrt{x^2 + y^2}$$

and

$$\theta = \tan^{-1}\left(y/x\right)$$

It is this form that is effective in expressing polar relationships.

Referring to Fig. 5.58, we can write the basic closure equation for the four-bar linkage with the vectors $\boldsymbol{a}$, $\boldsymbol{b}$, $\boldsymbol{c}$, and $\boldsymbol{d}$ interpreted as complex numbers. Then

$$\boldsymbol{b} + \boldsymbol{c} = \boldsymbol{a} + \boldsymbol{d}$$

Using the form of Eq. (5.211), this can be written

$$be^{i\theta} + ce^{i\psi} = a + de^{i\phi} \tag{5.212}$$

Decomposition of this expression into its real and imaginary parts, respectively, gives

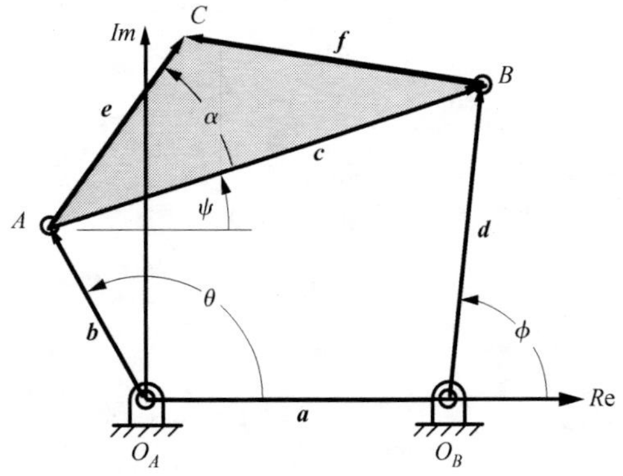

FIGURE 5.58 The real and imaginary axes used in setting up a complex number solution of the four-bar loop.

$$b\cos\theta + c\cos\psi = a + d\cos\phi$$
$$b\sin\theta + c\sin\psi = d\sin\phi$$

which are identical to the component equations developed using the vector formulation. The development of a position solution and of the velocity and acceleration solutions of this chapter is then identical to that given earlier.

Alternatively, the elimination of one of the variables may be pursued in the complex variable form. Equation (5.212) may be written in the form

$$\mathbf{b} + \mathbf{c} - \mathbf{a} = \mathbf{d} \tag{5.213}$$

Now, the conjugates of $\mathbf{b}$, $\mathbf{c}$, and $\mathbf{d}$ are, respectively,

$$\tilde{\mathbf{b}} = be^{-i\theta}, \quad \tilde{\mathbf{c}} = ce^{-i\psi}, \quad \text{and } \tilde{\mathbf{d}} = de^{-i\phi}$$

Also, the conjugate of $\boldsymbol{a}$ is $\boldsymbol{a}\ i$ since $\boldsymbol{a}$ is a real number. The conjugate of Eq. (5.213)

$$\tilde{\mathbf{b}} + \tilde{\mathbf{c}} - \tilde{\mathbf{a}} = \tilde{\mathbf{d}}$$

is also true since the process of forming the conjugate simply changes the signs on all imaginary parts.

Multiplication of each side of Eq. (5.213) by its conjugate gives

$$\left(\mathbf{b} + \mathbf{c} - \mathbf{a}\right)\left(\tilde{\mathbf{b}} + \tilde{\mathbf{c}} - \tilde{\mathbf{a}}\right) = \mathbf{d}\tilde{\mathbf{d}}$$

Now, referring to Eq. (5.212), we get

$$z\tilde{z} = re^{i\theta}re^{-i\theta} = r^2$$

Also

$$z + \tilde{z} = re^{i\theta} + re^{-i\theta} = r\left(\cos\theta + i\sin\theta\right) + r\left(\cos\theta - i\sin\theta\right) = 2r\cos\theta$$

Hence

$$\mathbf{b}\tilde{\mathbf{b}} = b^2, \quad \mathbf{c}\tilde{\mathbf{c}} = c^2, \quad \text{and } \mathbf{d}\tilde{\mathbf{d}} = d^2$$

Thus, expansion of the foregoing expression gives

$$\mathbf{b}\tilde{\mathbf{b}} + \mathbf{c}\tilde{\mathbf{c}} + \mathbf{a}\tilde{\mathbf{a}} + \mathbf{b}\tilde{\mathbf{c}} + \tilde{\mathbf{b}}\mathbf{c} - \mathbf{b}\tilde{\mathbf{a}} - \tilde{\mathbf{b}}\mathbf{a} - \mathbf{c}\tilde{\mathbf{a}} - \tilde{\mathbf{c}}\mathbf{a} = \mathbf{d}\tilde{\mathbf{d}}$$

or

$$b^2 + c^2 + a^2 + be^{i\theta}ce^{-i\psi} + be^{-i\theta}ce^{i\psi} - abe^{i\theta} - abe^{-i\theta} - ace^{i\psi} - ace^{-i\psi} = d^2$$

or

$$b^2 + c^2 + a^2 + bce^{i(\theta-\psi)} + bce^{-i(\theta-\psi)} - abe^{i\theta} - abe^{-i\theta} - ace^{i\psi} - ace^{-i\psi} = d^2$$

or

$$b^2 + c^2 + a^2 + 2bc\cos\left(\theta - \psi\right) - 2ab\cos\theta - 2ac\cos\psi = d^2$$

which is the same as the form derived earlier.

Similarly, multiplying each side of the equation

$$\mathbf{b} - \mathbf{d} - \mathbf{a} = -\mathbf{c}$$

by its conjugate gives

$$\mathbf{b}\tilde{\mathbf{b}} + \mathbf{d}\tilde{\mathbf{d}} + \mathbf{a}\tilde{\mathbf{a}} - \mathbf{b}\tilde{\mathbf{d}} - \tilde{\mathbf{b}}\mathbf{d} - \mathbf{b}\tilde{\mathbf{a}} - \tilde{\mathbf{b}}\mathbf{a} + \mathbf{d}\tilde{\mathbf{a}} + \tilde{\mathbf{d}}\mathbf{a} = \mathbf{c}\tilde{\mathbf{c}}$$

or

$$b^2 + d^2 + a^2 - bde^{i(\theta-\phi)} - bde^{-i(\theta-\phi)} - abe^{i\theta} - abe^{-i\theta} + ade^{i\phi} + ade^{-i\phi} = c^2$$

giving

$$b^2 + d^2 + a^2 - 2bd\cos(\theta-\phi) - 2ab\cos\theta + 2ad\cos\phi = c^2$$

which is also the same as the form derived earlier

Equation (5.212) lends itself to development of velocity and acceleration expressions. Differentiation with respect to time gives

$$ib\dot{\theta}e^{i\theta} + ic\dot{\psi}e^{i\psi} = id\dot{\phi}e^{i\phi}$$

or, removing the common factor i, we get

$$b\dot{\theta}e^{i\theta} + c\dot{\psi}e^{i\psi} = d\dot{\phi}e^{i\phi} \tag{5.214}$$

Separation into the real and imaginary parts gives, respectively,

$$b\dot{\theta}\cos\theta + c\dot{\psi}\cos\psi = d\dot{\phi}\cos\phi$$

and

$$b\dot{\theta}\sin\theta + c\dot{\psi}\sin\psi = d\dot{\phi}\sin\phi$$

which may be recognized as the same form as given in Table 5.1.

Differentiation of Eq. (5.214) with respect to time gives

$$b\ddot{\theta}e^{i\theta} + ib\dot{\theta}^2e^{i\theta} + c\ddot{\psi}e^{i\psi} + ic\dot{\psi}^2e^{i\psi} = d\ddot{\phi}e^{i\phi} + id\dot{\phi}^2e^{i\phi}$$

Expansion of the $e^i\theta$ terms gives

$$b\ddot{\theta}(\cos\theta + i\sin\theta) + b\dot{\theta}^2(i\cos\theta - \sin\theta) + c\ddot{\psi}(\cos\psi + i\sin\psi) + c\dot{\psi}^2(i\cos\psi - \sin\psi)$$
$$= d\ddot{\phi}(\cos\phi + i\sin\phi) + d\dot{\phi}^2(i\cos\phi - \sin\phi)$$

Hence, separation into the real and imaginary parts gives

$$b\ddot{\theta}\cos\theta - b\dot{\theta}^2\sin\theta + c\ddot{\psi}\cos\psi - c\dot{\psi}^2\sin\psi = d\ddot{\phi}\cos\phi - d\dot{\phi}^2\sin\phi$$

and

$$b\ddot{\theta}\sin\theta + b\dot{\theta}^2\cos\theta + c\ddot{\psi}\sin\psi + c\dot{\psi}^2\cos\psi = d\ddot{\phi}\sin\phi + d\dot{\phi}^2\cos\phi$$

which can be recognized as the same form as those given in Table 5.1.

The foregoing illustrates the equivalence of the vector and complex number representations for simple planar mechanisms.

PROBLEMS

5.1 For the mechanism shown, do the following:

(a) Write the vector equation of the linkage shown.

(b) Write the x and y displacement equations.

(c) Find the velocity component equations.

(d) Find the acceleration component equations.

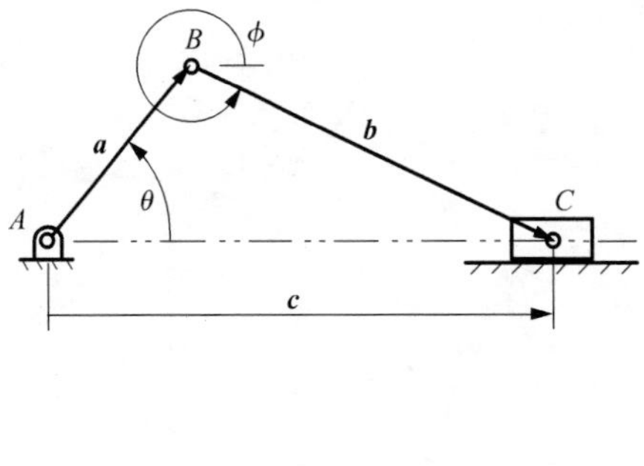

5.2 In the mechanism in Problem 5.1, determine $\dot{\phi}$ analytically for the following values:

$$a = 1 \text{ cm}, \quad b = 4 \text{ cm}, \quad \theta = 60^\circ, \quad \dot{\theta} = 10 \text{ rad/s}$$

5.3 In the mechanism shown, $\dot{s} = -10$ in/s and $\ddot{s} = 0$ for the position corresponding to $\phi = 60^\circ$. Find $\dot{\phi}$ and $\ddot{\phi}$ for that position using the loop-equation approach.

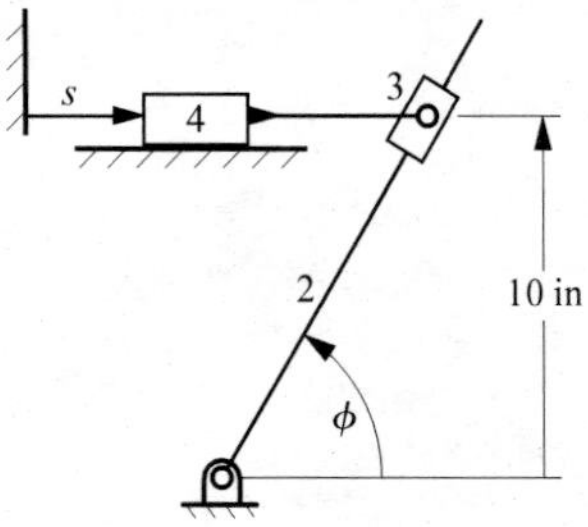

5.4 In the mechanism in Problem 5.3 assume that $\dot{\phi}$ is 10 rad/s CCW. Use the loop-equation approach to determine the velocity of point B_4 for the position defined by $\phi = 60^\circ$.

5.5 In the mechanism given, point A is moving to the right with a velocity of 10 cm/s. Use the loop-equation approach to determine the angular velocity of link 3. Link 3 is 10 cm long, and ϕ is 120° in the position shown.

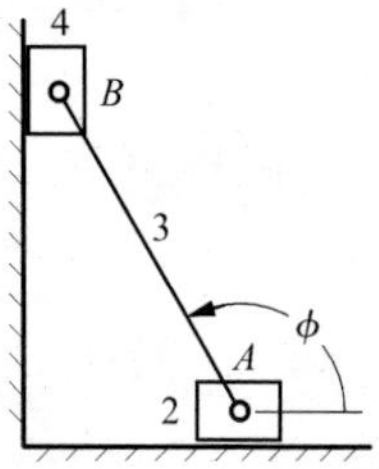

5.6 Re-solve Problem 5.5 if ϕ is 150°.

5.7 The mechanism shown is a marine steering gear called Rapson's slide. AB is the tiller, and CD is the actuating rod. If the velocity of rod CD is a constant 10 in/min to the right, and $\theta = 300^\circ$, use the loop-equation approach to determine the angular acceleration of the tiller.

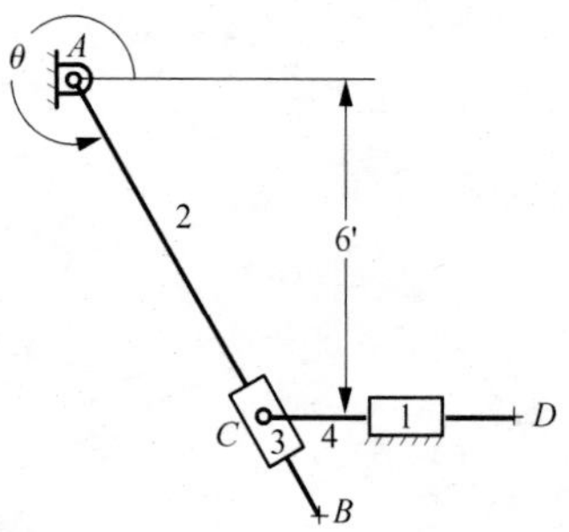

5.8 Use loop equations to determine the velocity and acceleration of point B on link 2 when $\theta = 30^\circ$, $\boldsymbol{\omega}_4 = 1$ rad/s CCW, and $\boldsymbol{\alpha}_4 = 0$. Make point A the origin of your reference coordinate system.

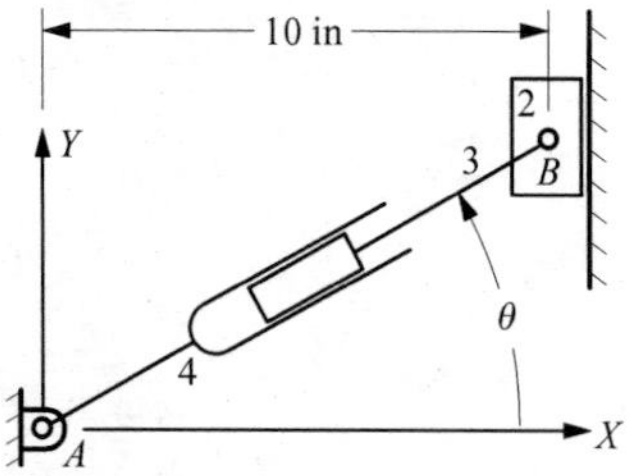

5.9 In the mechanism shown, $\theta = 30^\circ$, $\boldsymbol{\omega}_2 = 1$ rad/s CCW, and $\boldsymbol{\alpha}_2 = 0$. Use loop equations to determine the velocity and acceleration of point B on link 4.

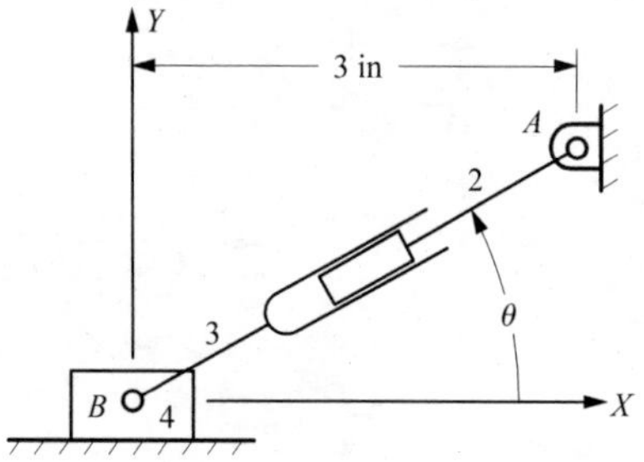

5.10 In the mechanism for Problem 5.9, assume that v_{B_4} is a constant 10 in/s to the left and θ is 45°. Use loop equations to determine the angular velocity and acceleration of link 3.

5.11 For the mechanism in the position shown, link 2 is the driver and rotates with a constant angular velocity of 100 rad/s CCW. Write vector loop equations for position, velocity, and acceleration, and solve for the velocity and acceleration of point C on link 4.

$AB = 0.9$", $AD = 1.7$", $BC = 2.6$", $h = 0.8$", $\theta_1 = 6^\circ$, $\phi = 120^\circ$

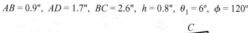

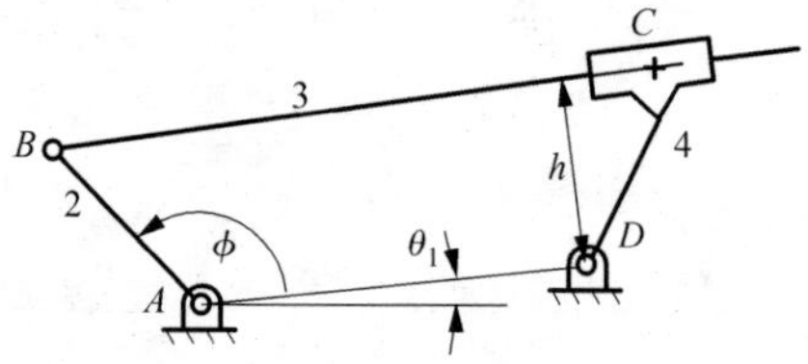

5.12 For the mechanism in the position shown, link 2 is the driver and rotates with a constant angular velocity of 50 rad/s CCW. Write vector loop equations for position, velocity, and acceleration, and solve for the velocity and acceleration of point C on link 3.

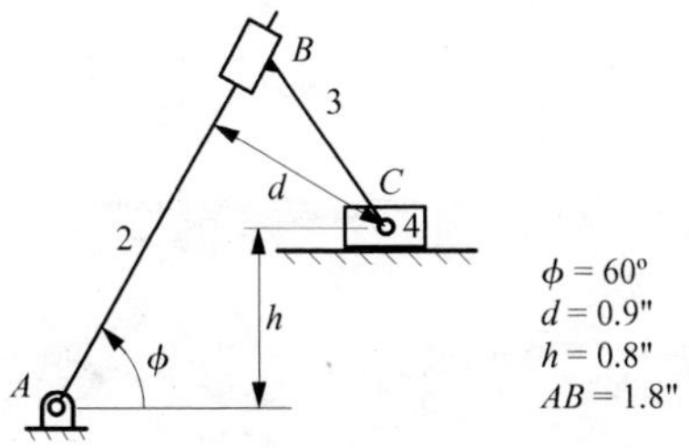

5.13 In the mechanism shown, link 3 slides on link 2, and link 4 is pinned to link 3 and slides on the frame. If $\omega_2 = 10$ rad/s CCW (constant), use loop equations to find the acceleration of link 4 for the position defined by $\phi = 90°$.

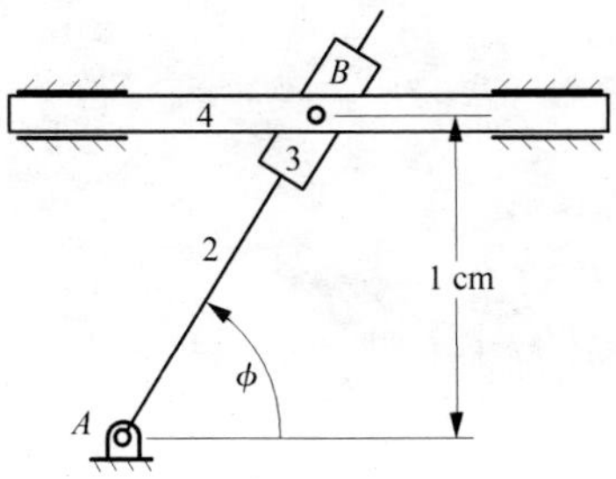

5.14 For the mechanism in the position shown, the cam (link 2) rotates with an angular velocity of 200 rad/s. Write the vector loop equations for position, velocity, and acceleration, and determine the angular velocity and acceleration of the follower (link 3). Use $\phi = 60°$ and neglect the follower thickness (i.e., assume that it is zero).

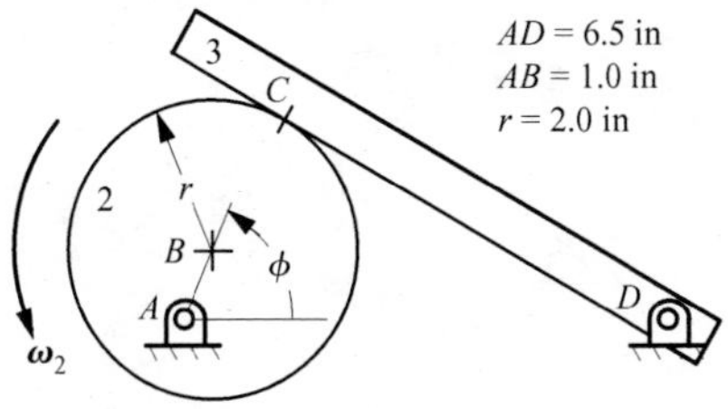

5.15 In the mechanism shown, link 3 is perpendicular to link 2. Write the vector loop equations for position and velocity. If the angular velocity of link 2 is 100 rad/s CCW, use the vector loop equations to solve for the velocity of point C_4 for the position corresponding to $\phi = 60°$.

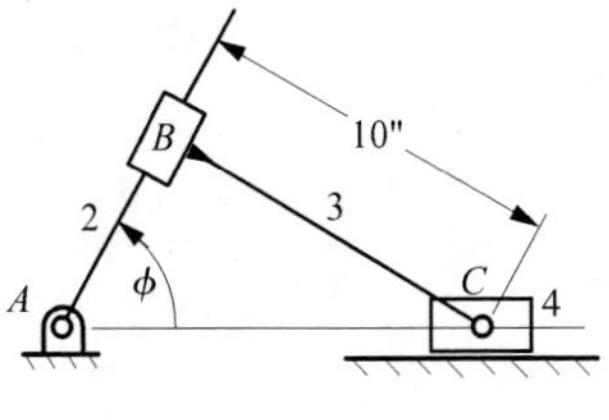

5.16 In the simple, two-link mechanism given, v_{B_2} is 10 in/s to the right. Use the loop-equation approach to determine v_{A_2} and ω_2.

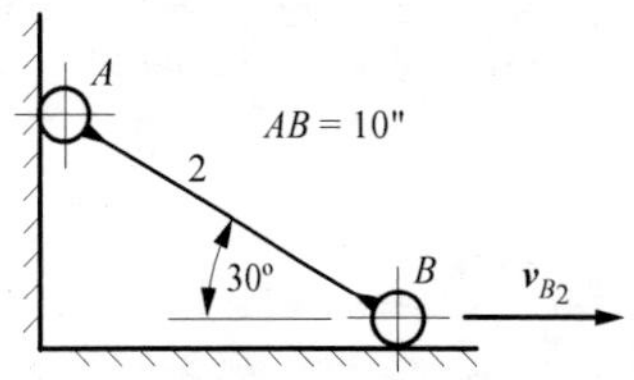

5.17 In the mechanism shown, the angular velocity of link 2 is 100 rad/s CCW and the dimensions of various links are given. Use loop equations to find the position and velocity of point D on link 3 when θ_2 is 90°.

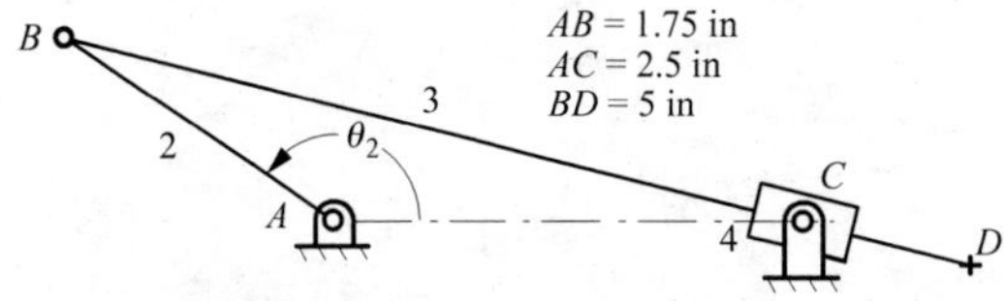

5.18 In the Scotch yoke mechanism shown, $\omega_2 = 10$ rad/s, $\alpha_2 = 100$ rad/s^2, and $\theta_2 = 60°$. Also, length $OA = 20$ in. Determine v_{A_4} and a_{A_4} using loop equations.

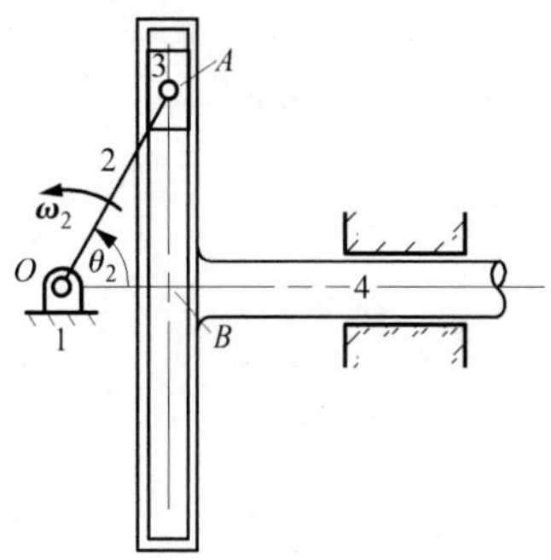

5.19 Use loop equations to determine the velocity and acceleration of point B on link 4. The angular velocity of link 2 is constant at 10 rad/s CCW.

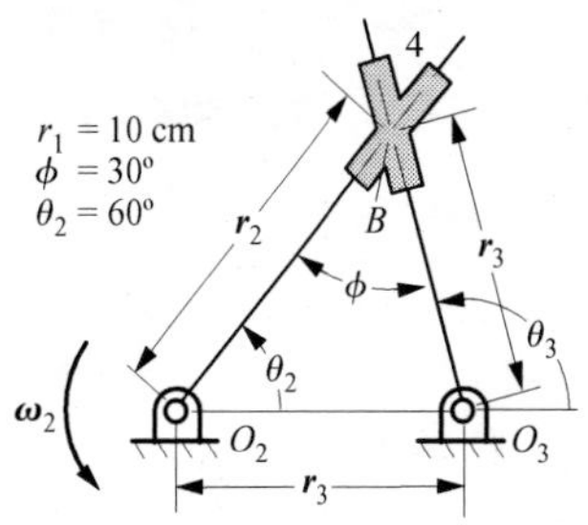

5.20 The oscillating fan shown is to be analyzed as a double-rocker. The fan is link 2, the motor shaft is connected to link 3, and link 4 is connected from the coupler to the frame. The actual input of the mechanism is the coupler, and ${}^2\boldsymbol{\omega}_3$ is a constant 956 (rad/s) in the counterclockwise direction. Compute the angular velocity and angular acceleration of link 2 if $\theta = 120°$, $AD = 0.75$ in, $AB = DC = 3.0$ in, and $BC = 0.50$ in.

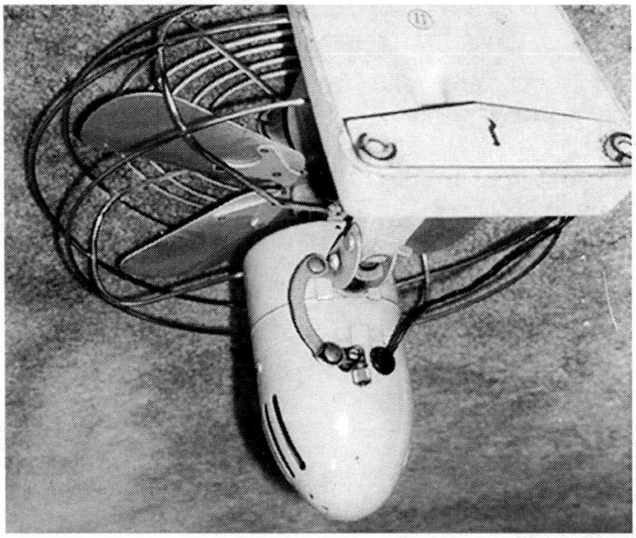

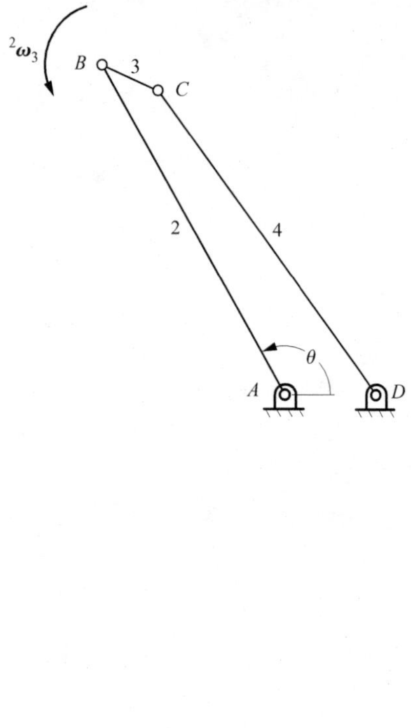

5.21 The rear suspension of a motorcycle can be analyzed as an inverted slider-crank mechanism. The frame of the motorcycle is link 1, and the tire assembly is attached to link 2 at point C. The shock absorber comprises links 3 and 4. As the motorcycle goes over a bump in the position shown, the angular velocity of link 2 relative to the frame, $\boldsymbol{\omega}_2$, is 5 rad/s CW, and the angular acceleration, $\boldsymbol{\alpha}_2$, is 45 rad/s^2 CW. Compute the angular velocity and angular acceleration of link 3 for the position defined by $\theta = 187°$.

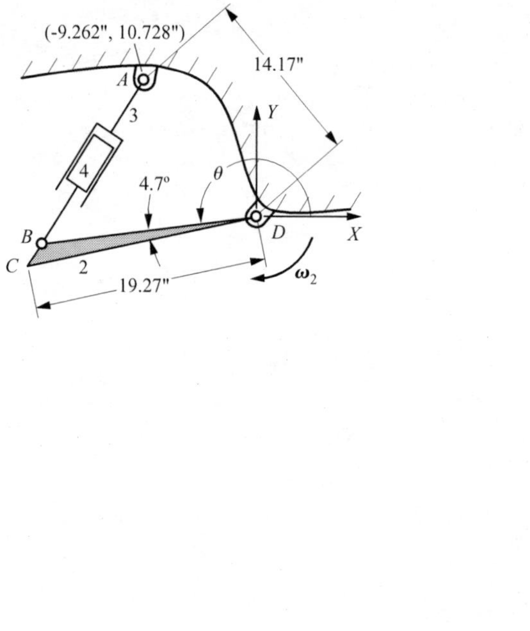

5.22 The door-closing linkage shown is to be analyzed as a slider-crank linkage. Link 2 is the door, and links 3 and 4 are the two links of the door closer. Assume that the angular velocity of the door (link 2) is a constant at 3.71 rad/s CW. Compute the angular velocity and angular acceleration of link 4 if the dimensions are as follows:

Coordinates of D (– 2.5", – 3.0")

AB = 17.0"

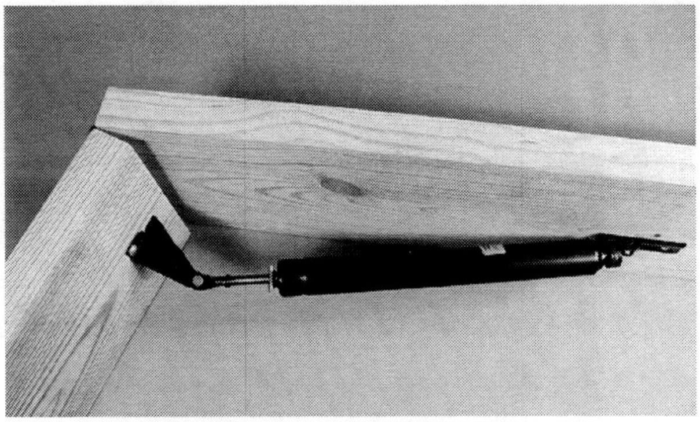

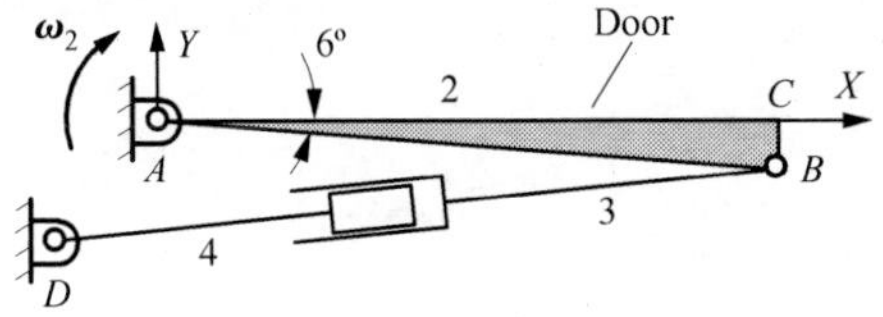

5.23 The general action of a person who is doing pushups can be modeled as a four-bar linkage as shown. The floor is the base link, and link 4 comprises the back and legs. Link 2 is the forearm, and link 3 is the upper arm. For the purposes of analysis, the motion that is controlled is the motion of link 3 relative to link 2 (elbow joint). Assume that ${}^2\boldsymbol{\omega}_3$ is a constant 6.0 rad/s CCW. Compute the angular velocity and angular acceleration of link 4 if link 2 is oriented at 45° to the horizontal.

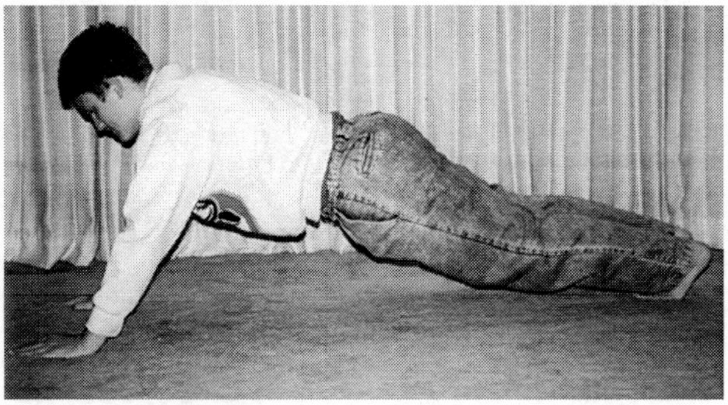

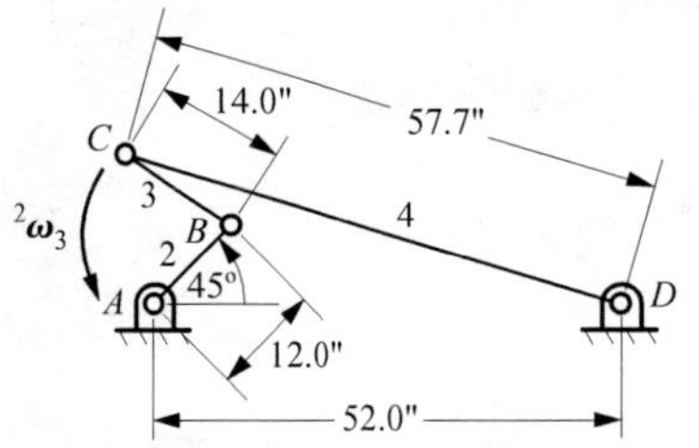

5.24 A carousel mechanism can be modeled as an inverted slider-crank mechanism as shown. Point D is the location of the saddle on the horse. Assume that the angular velocity of the driver (link 2) is a constant 2 rad/s CCW. Compute the velocity and acceleration of D_3 in the position shown if $AB = 8.0$ in, $BC = 96.0$ in, and $BD = 54$ in.

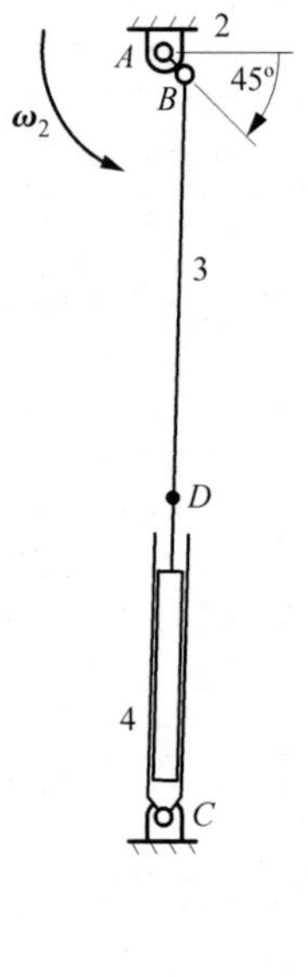

5.25 The shock-absorber mechanism on a mountain bicycle is a four-bar linkage as shown. The frame of the bike is link 1, the fork and tire assembly comprise link 3, and the connecting linkage comprises links 2 and 4. As the bicycle goes over a bump in the position shown, the angular velocity of link 2 relative to the frame, $\boldsymbol{\omega}_2$, is 205 rad/s CW, and the angular acceleration, $\boldsymbol{\alpha}_2$, is 60 rad/s^2 CW. Compute the angular velocity and angular acceleration of link 3 for the position shown.

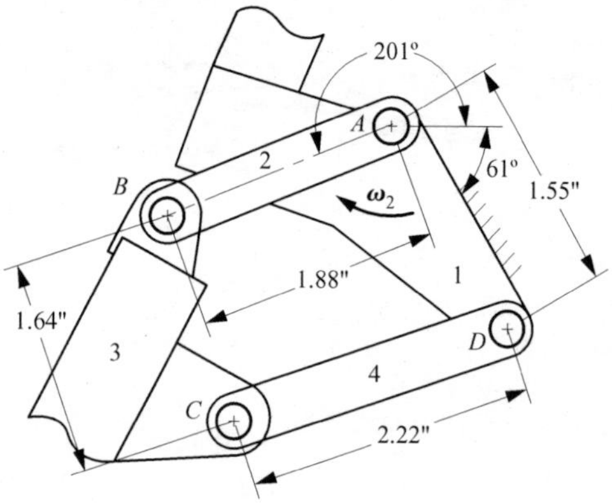

CHAPTER 6

PLANAR LINKAGE DESIGN

6.1 INTRODUCTION

The machine designer is often called upon to provide a means of generating an irregular motion. For our purposes, an irregular motion can be regarded as anything except either uniform rotation about a fixed axis or uniform rectilinear translation. There are two means of generating irregular motions by one-degree-of-freedom mechanisms: cams and linkages. As irregular motion generators, they each have advantages and disadvantages. In general, cams are easily designed but are relatively difficult, and therefore expensive, to manufacture. They are also relatively unreliable owing to wear problems. Linkages are difficult to design but are inexpensive to manufacture and relatively reliable. The subject of this chapter is linkage design.

One naturally attempts to use the simplest mechanism capable of performing the desired function. For this reason, four-link mechanisms are by far the most widely used. The techniques used for the design of five- and six-bar mechanisms are basically extensions of those used for four-link mechanisms. Thus, the primary emphasis of this chapter will be on four-link mechanism synthesis.

The joints most commonly used in mechanisms are those in which the joint constraints are provided by two surfaces in contact, which, ideally, occurs over an area. This is as opposed to point or line contact as is used in cams and gears. Surface contact is desirable from the point of view of lubrication and wear resistance. The only surface contact, or lower pair, joints that are available for use in planar mechanisms are hinges and prismatic slides. There are, therefore, four possible basic types of four-link mechanisms with surface contact joints.

1. **The four-bar linkage.** In this linkage, all four joints are hinges as shown in Fig. 6.1. This is by far the most widely used linkage for irregular motion generation.
2. **The slider-crank (and its inversions).** The slider-crank chain is shown schematically in Fig. 6.2. Linkages based on this chain are very commonly used to convert linear to rotary motion and vice versa. It is little used when neither a linear input nor a linear output is needed.
3. **The elliptic trammel (and its inversions).** The chain for the elliptic trammel is shown in Fig. 6.3. Except for the Scotch yoke and Oldham inversions, the elliptic trammel is

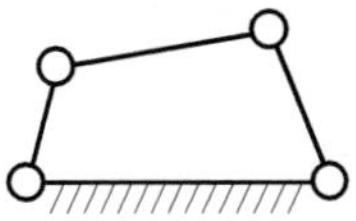

FIGURE 6.1 The four revolute four-bar linkage. This is one of four basic planar single-loop linkages. It is the most commonly used mechanism for generating irregular motions.

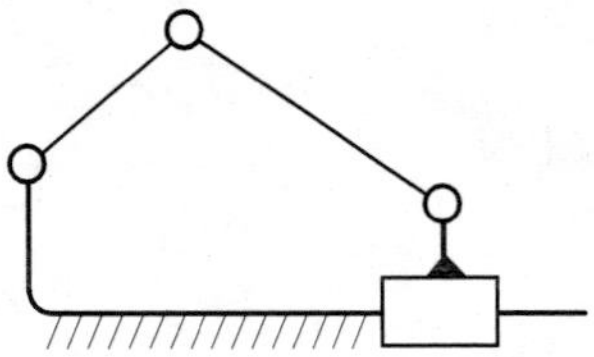

FIGURE 6.2 The slider-crank linkage is obtained by replacing one revolute joint in a four-bar linkage with a prismatic joint. When inverted onto the crank, or the coupler, so that the slide rotates, the linkage becomes a turning block linkage.

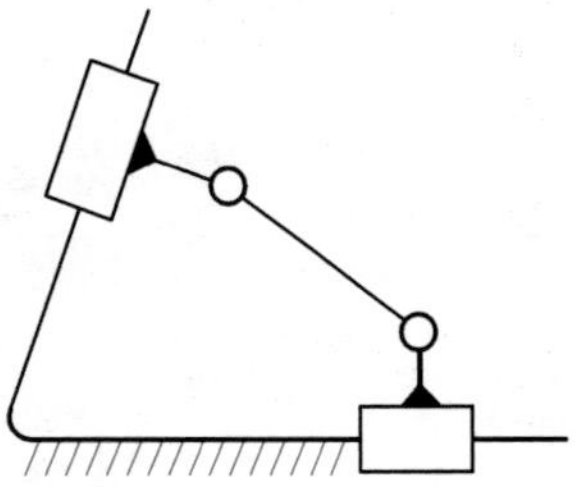

FIGURE 6.3 Elliptic trammel linkage. The paths of all points in the coupler are ellipses. When inverted onto one of the revolute-prismatic members, this becomes a Scotch yoke linkage. The Scotch yoke is sometimes used as a harmonic motion generator. The other possible inversion, onto the coupler, is used in practice as the Oldham coupling. This is a simple mechanism for accommodating misalignment between shafts.

little used because of slip–stick friction problems in the two slides. Analysis equations for two inversions of this linkage are given in Sections 5.9 and 5.10.

4. **The Rapson slide.** A schematic diagram of the chain for the Rapson slide is shown in Fig. 6.4. There are two sliders that must be carefully designed if mechanisms based on the chain are to work properly. In practice, the Rapson slide is used much less frequently than the four-bar linkage or slider-crank because neither rotary joint can be made to rotate 360°o and because of slip–stick friction in the two slides. The analysis equations for one inversion of this mechanism are given in Section 5.7.

The majority of the techniques discussed in this book are intended for four-bar linkage synthesis. This is primarily because of the large number of dimensions that can be varied, allowing more flexibility in design. Unfortunately, it also results in more complicated design techniques. When the techniques are applied to linkages having one or more slider joints, the results are somewhat simpler.

It is very rare for the desired motion to be exactly producible by a four-bar linkage. Thus, we can typically only approximate the desired motion. One approach is to select a number of positions (precision points) along the desired path and compel the linkage to move exactly through those positions. Using this method, one has no direct control over the behavior of the linkage between the design positions. One works in the (sometimes pious) hope that the linkage movement will not deviate too far from that desired between the design positions. It is, in fact, remarkable how accurate this method can be in favorable circumstances. It is possible to design a four-bar linkage for which the path of a point on the coupler deviates no more than $\frac{1}{1000}$ of an inch from a straight line over a 10-in line length in this way.

The types of problems most usually tackled using the precision position approach permit a graphical solution. This is straightforward for problems with two and three design positions but becomes complex and laborious for four or five design positions. Most precision position problems do not admit more than five design positions. Computer packages,

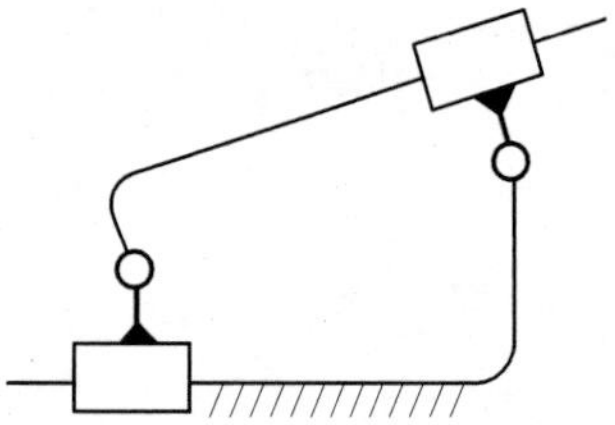

FIGURE 6.4 The Rapson slide linkage. Its inversions are also Rapson slide linkages.

such as KINSYN,[1] RECSYN,[2] and LINCAGES,[3] have been developed to automate the solution of precision position problems. Graphical techniques that are useful for small numbers of design positions will be described in this chapter. They form a basis for understanding the techniques of computer-aided synthesis required for more demanding problems.

The second basic approach is to select a rather large number of design positions and, instead of requiring the mechanism to pass through them exactly, minimize the sum of the squares of the deviations of the mechanism position from those positions. Thus, the linkage motion approaches the design positions but does not exactly pass through any of them. This method makes use of numerical optimization techniques to produce solution linkages. Consequently, the use of a computer is essential. Used directly, this type of approach requires the user to manipulate the mathematical constraints to obtain control over the type and properties of the solution linkage. Some packages, such as the automatic synthesis module of RECSYN, attempt to provide that control in a user-friendly form.

In a given problem, either of these approaches may yield good results. The choice is most often decided by the techniques with which the designer is most familiar and by what aids, such as synthesis programs, he or she has available.

The range of synthesis problems that arise is infinite. We will restrict our study to a few classes of problems that, because of a combination of practical importance and a well-developed theory, are most usually treated. They are as follows:

1. **The double-rocker problem.** This is one of the simplest linkage design problems. The problem is to design a four-bar linkage that will move its output link through an angle ϕ while the input link moves through an angle θ.
2. **The motion generation problem.** A linkage is to be synthesized whose coupler, as a whole, is to follow a desired trajectory. That is, the movement of the coupler as a whole is specified, not just that of a point or line lying on it.
3. **The function generation problem.** In this case the angles of the two cranks are to be coordinated. The name "function generation" originated in the days in which mechanical analog computers were used to perform complex mathematical calculations in such devices as naval gunsights. Linkages were used to generate angular relationships approximating logarithms, trigonometric functions, and so forth.
4. **The rocker amplitude problem.** In the rocker amplitude problem, the output link is to oscillate through a specified angular amplitude. Typically, the required linkage is a crank-rocker with continuously rotating driving crank. An oscillatory output motion of specified amplitude is required.
5. **The point path problem.** A single point on the coupler is to follow a nominated curve. In this form the problem does not admit a direct graphical solution. However, this class of problem is important from a practical point of view, and design methods will be presented. These are trial-and-error techniques starting with selection of an approximate coupler point path from an atlas of coupler curves or from curves generated with a computer program. Simple computer programs can be important aids in the trial-and-error process.

A modified type of point path problem in which the progression of the coupler point between design positions is coordinated with the corresponding angular displacements of the driving crank does permit direct graphical solution. This is referred to as the path–angle problem type. The techniques required for solution of this type of problem are beyond the scope of this book. KINSYN, RECSYN, and LINCAGES do provide the capability for its solution.

6.2 TWO-POSITION DOUBLE-ROCKER DESIGN

A common problem in kinematics is the design of a double-lever or double-rocker mechanism. The design situation is shown in Fig. 6.5a. The problem is to design a four-bar linkage such that the output link will rotate through an angle ϕ when the input link rotates through an angle θ. For the problem we will consider here, the distance between the fixed pivots O_2 and O_4 is given as is the length of the output link O_4B. To complete the design, we must determine the length of the input link O_2A and of the coupler AB.

6.2.1 Graphical Solution Procedure

The basis for solving the problem is to invert the mechanism and visualize the motion of the mechanism when the observer is fixed to the input link. This apparent motion is shown in Fig. 6.5b. As observed from the ground or link 1, points A and B appear to move from position 1 to position 2 through their respective angles, θ and ϕ. However, if link 2 is the reference, then link 2 appears not to move and the other links, including the frame, appear to move relative to link 2 in the direction of $-\theta$. In a given position, the relative geometry is the same regardless of which link is the reference link. Therefore, the quadrilateral $O_2A_2B_2O_4$ is the same whether link 1 is the reference or link 2 is the reference. To show the apparent position of the links relative to link 2, we need only rotate the quadrilateral $O_2A_2B_2O_4$ through an angle of $-\theta$ about pivot O_2. When this is done, note that lines O_2O_4 and O_2B_2 are both rotated by the angle $-\theta$. This observation is the basis for the design procedure given in the following.

The design procedure is illustrated in Fig. 6.6. We begin knowing the distance between the frame pivots O_2 and O_4 and the length of the output link, O_4B. First draw the line O_2B_2 and rotate it by $-\theta$ about the pivot O_2. This will locate B'_2, which is where B_2 would appear to be if the observer were on link 2. Relative to the input link in position 1, B appears to rotate on a circular arc about A_1 as B travels from B_1 to B'_2. Therefore, A_1 must lie on the perpendicular bisector of the line segment $B_1B'_2$. Also, A_1 will lie on the designated line through O_2 shown in Fig. 6.6a.

Once A_1 is determined, the lengths of the input rocker and of the coupler will be known. The input rocker length is O_2A_1 and the coupler length is A_1B_1 (or $A_1B'_2$).

Note that the solution to this problem makes use of inversion. We will use this concept of inversion again when we consider the design of linkages for motion generation or rigid-body guidance.

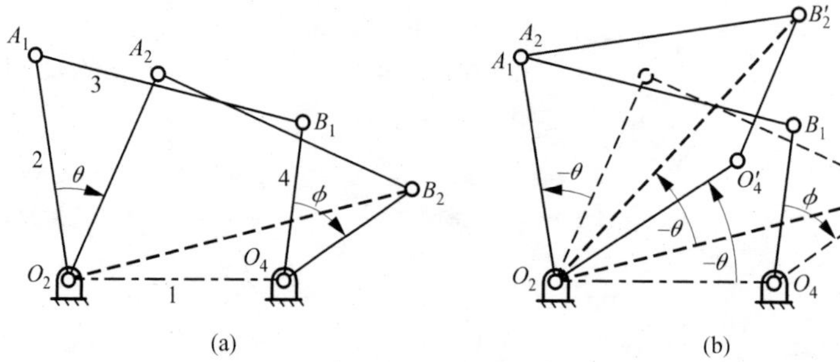

FIGURE 6.5 Two positions of the rockers of a four-bar linkage. (a) shows the positions relative to the frame, and (b) shows the positions relative to the input rocker.

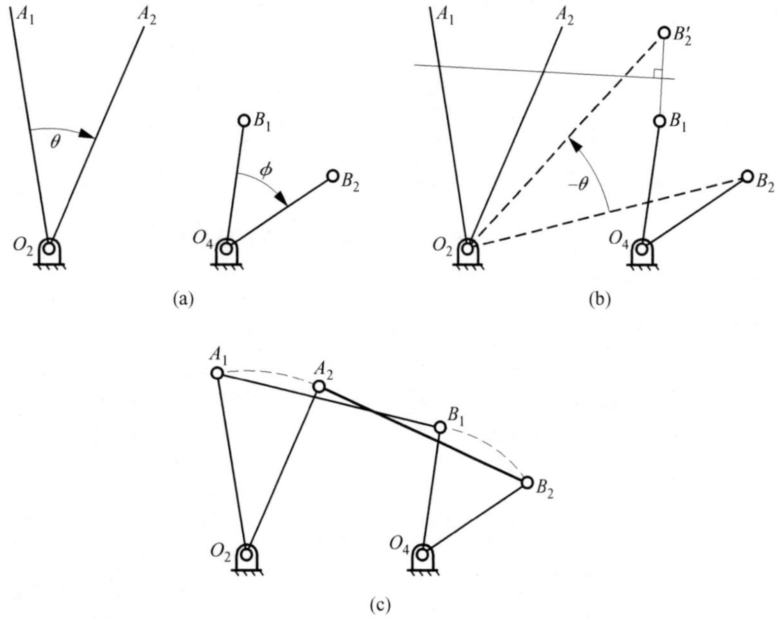

FIGURE 6.6 Locating point A_1, which in turn determines the length of the coupler and the input rocker.

6.2.2 Analytical Solution Procedure

The double-rocker problem can be solved analytically so that the design procedure can be easily programmed. To begin, locate the origin of the coordinate system at O_2 and orient the x axis through O_4 as shown in Fig. 6.7. Note that in Fig. 6.7, we have assumed that the direction of rotation is counterclockwise. This will allow us to use the standard positive sign convention for angles that was employed in Chapter 5. Using the variables represented in Fig. 6.7, we can compute the (x, y) coordinates of B_1 and B_2.

For B_1,

$$
\begin{aligned}
x_{B_1} &= r_1 + r_4\cos\phi_1 \\
y_{B_1} &= r_4\sin\phi_1
\end{aligned}
\tag{6.1}
$$

To simplify the resulting expression, let

$$
\begin{aligned}
\theta_2 &= \theta_1 + \theta \\
\phi_2 &= \phi_1 + \phi
\end{aligned}
$$

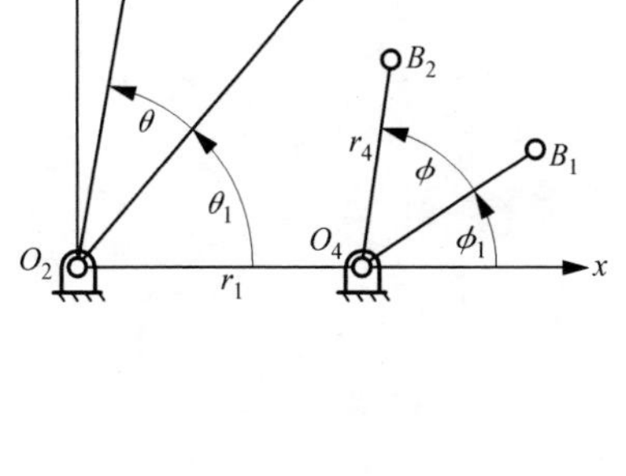

FIGURE 6.7 Parameters for analytical solution procedure.

Then for B_2,

$$x_{B_2} = r_1 + r_4\cos\phi_2$$
$$y_{B_2} = r_4\sin\phi_2 \tag{6.2}$$

Similarly, the coordinates of A_1 and A_2 can be written in terms of the input crank r_2. For A_1,

$$x_{A_1} = r_2\cos\theta_1$$
$$y_{A_1} = r_2\sin\theta_1 \tag{6.3}$$

and for A_2,

$$x_{A_2} = r_2\cos\theta_2$$
$$y_{A_2} = r_2\sin\theta_2 \tag{6.4}$$

The distance between A and B is a constant (r_3) for all positions of A and B. Therefore, we can write

$$r_3 = \sqrt{\left(x_{A_1} - x_{B_1}\right)^2 + \left(y_{A_1} - y_{B_1}\right)^2} = \sqrt{\left(x_{A_2} - x_{B_2}\right)^2 + \left(y_{A_2} - y_{B_2}\right)^2} \tag{6.5}$$

or

$$\left(x_{A_1} - x_{B_1}\right)^2 + \left(y_{A_1} - y_{B_1}\right)^2 = \left(x_{A_2} - x_{B_2}\right)^2 + \left(y_{A_2} - y_{B_2}\right)^2$$

Substituting values for the x's and y's in Eqs. (6.1–6.5), we get

$$\left(r_2\cos\theta_1 - r_1 - r_4\cos\phi_1\right)^2 + \left(r_2\sin\theta_1 - r_4\sin\phi_1\right)^2$$
$$= \left(r_2\cos\theta_2 - r_1 - r_4\cos\phi_2\right)^2 + \left(r_2\sin\theta_2 - r_4\sin\phi_2\right)^2$$

Expanding and simplifying using $\sin^2\theta + \cos^2\theta = 1$, we get

$$-r_1r_2\cos\theta_1 - r_2r_4\cos\theta_1\cos\phi_1 + r_1r_4\cos\phi_1 - r_2r_4\sin\theta_1\sin\phi_1$$
$$= -r_1r_2\cos\theta_2 - r_2r_4\cos\theta_2\cos\phi_2 + r_1r_4\cos\phi_2 - r_2r_4\sin\theta_2\sin\phi_2$$

In this equation, the only unknown is r_2. The equation is linear in the unknown and can be easily solved for r_2. Collecting terms, we obtain

$$r_1r_4\cos\phi_2 - r_1r_4\cos\phi_1$$
$$= r_2\left[-r_1\cos\theta_1 - r_4\cos\theta_1\cos\phi_1 - r_4\sin\theta_1\sin\phi_1 + r_1\cos\theta_2 + r_4\cos\theta_2\cos\phi_2 + r_4\sin\theta_2\sin\phi_2\right]$$

Then using the identity $\cos(a + b) \equiv \cos a\cos b - \sin a\sin b$, and solving for r_2, we get

$$r_2 = \frac{r_1r_4\left[\cos\phi_2 - \cos\phi_1\right]}{-r_4\left[\cos\left(\theta_1 - \phi_1\right)\right] + r_1\left[\cos\theta_2 - \cos\theta_1\right] + r_4\left[\cos\left(\theta_2 - \phi_2\right)\right]}$$

Knowing r_2, we can compute r_3 from Eq. (6.5); that is,

$$r_3 = \sqrt{\left(r_2\cos\theta_1 - r_1 - r_4\cos\phi_1\right)^2 + \left(r_2\sin\theta_1 - r_4\sin\phi_1\right)^2}$$
$$= \sqrt{\left(r_2\cos\theta_2 - r_1 - r_4\cos\phi_2\right)^2 + \left(r_2\sin\theta_2 - r_4\sin\phi_2\right)^2}$$

6.3 MOTION GENERATION

6.3.1 Introduction

Figure 6.8 shows the path of a moving lamina as described by the paths of three points embedded in it: A, B, and C. That is, A_1 is the first position of point A, A_2 is its second position, and A_3 is its third position, and similarly for points B and C. We will use this notation extensively in the following. As viewed in the moving lamina, there is only one point, A. As seen from the fixed reference frame, this point assumes three different positions, A_1, A_2, and A_3, as the moving lamina moves through the three positions shown.

Actually, only the path of one point and the changes in the orientation of a line drawn on the lamina are needed to describe its motion. To synthesize a four-bar linkage whose coupler will approximate the given motion, we choose a number of positions on the trajectory, such as $A_1B_1C_1$, $A_2B_2C_2$, and $A_3B_3C_3$, as design positions. This is shown in Fig. 6.8. The coupler will be made to pass through these positions precisely. Depending on the degree of accuracy required, a larger or smaller number of design positions should be chosen. Synthesis of the linkage is easier and the flexibility available to the designer is greater if fewer positions are used. Five is the upper limit to the number of design positions that can be used.

Geometrically, a crank has the effect of constraining the center of its moving pivot to move on a circle. The fixed pivot is at the center of that circle and is sometimes called a center point. Consequently, the problem of synthesizing a four-bar linkage to move its coupler through the design positions is basically the problem of locating two points in the moving lamina. Successive positions of each point all lie on the same circle. These points are sometimes called circle points. These points are taken as the locations of the moving pivots of the two cranks. The centers of the two circles on which their successive positions lie become the fixed pivots of the cranks.

6.3.2 Two Positions

Because an infinite number of circles can be drawn through any two points, any point in the moving lamina can be chosen as a moving pivot when two positions are of interest. In the example shown in Fig. 6.9, the two positions of the lamina are defined relative to the fixed frame by the line segments A_1B_1 and A_2B_2, which are two positions of the line segment AB

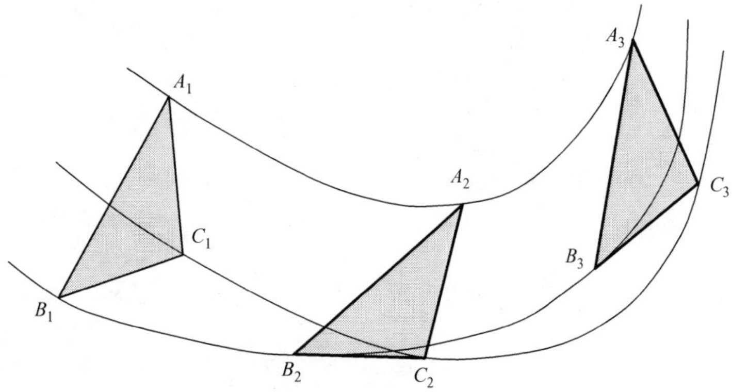

FIGURE 6.8 Motion of a lamina along a continuous trajectory. Each point in the lamina moves along a continuous curve. The triangle ABC drawn on the lamina is shown in three different positions along the trajectory: $A_1B_1C_1$, $A_2B_2C_2$, and $A_3B_3C_3$.

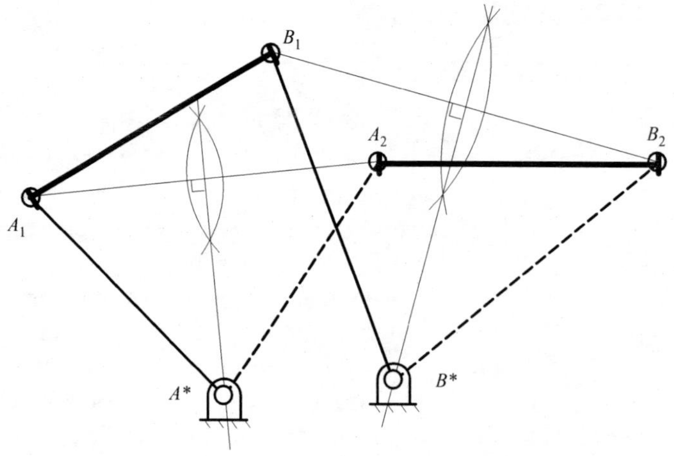

FIGURE 6.9 Construction of a four-bar linkage that moves its coupler plane through the positions A_1B_1 and A_2B_2.

drawn on the moving lamina. Since any point in the lamina can be a moving pivot or circle point, we might as well choose A and B. In each case, we then have an infinite number of points that can be the fixed pivots or center points, namely all points on the perpendicular bisector of A_1A_2 for the fixed pivot corresponding to A and all points on the perpendicular bisector of B_1B_2 for the fixed pivot corresponding to B.

The perpendicular bisector of A_1A_2 can be constructed by setting any convenient radius on a pair of compasses and drawing two arcs. The first arc is centered on A_1, and the second is centered on A_2. The perpendicular bisector is the line drawn through the two intersections of these two arcs. In practice, only small portions of the two arcs are drawn in the neighborhoods in which the intersections are expected, as shown in Fig. 6.9. This operation of constructing a perpendicular bisector will be used extensively in the following.

The four-bar linkage that results from this construction is, in its first position, $A^*A_1B_1B^*$. The base link is A^*B^*. The coupler is A_1B_1. That is, in this case, the coupler is simply the line segment used to define the positions of the moving lamina. This need not be so.

Any point in the moving lamina, not just A or B, can be chosen as a moving pivot. This is shown in Fig. 6.10, in which point C is chosen as the second moving pivot, rather than point B. The first step, in this case, is to locate the two positions C_1 and C_2 of this point. The convention for showing points on the moving plane that is used almost universally in the literature, and that is followed here, is that the moving lamina is drawn in its *first position*. Therefore, point C drawn on the moving lamina is identical to point C_1. To locate point C_2, we note that ABC is a triangle drawn on the rigid, moving lamina. It does not change shape, regardless of the motion. Therefore triangle $A_2B_2C_2$ is congruent to triangle $A_1B_1C_1$. Consequently, C_2 can be located by completing triangle $A_2B_2C_2$.

In practice, this is accomplished by setting radius A_1C_1 on a pair of compasses and drawing an arc with center A_2. The compasses are then set to radius B_1C_1, and an arc is drawn with center B_2. The intersection of the two arcs is point C_2. It is important to note that there are actually two possible intersections of these two arcs. One gives triangle $A_2B_2C_2$ congruent to triangle $A_1B_1C_1$, but the other gives the mirror image of that triangle. This

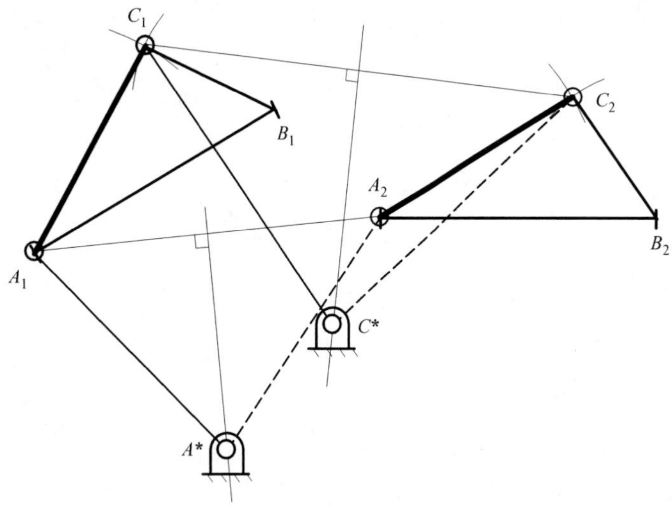

FIGURE 6.10 Solution of the same two-position problem shown in Fig. 6.9 with a different point: C_1 chosen as the second moving pivot.

second possibility will give incorrect results. Care is necessary to ensure that the correct intersection is used. In some cases, the correct solution is not obvious. A simple check is to count off the vertices A_1, B_1, C_1 when proceeding in a counterclockwise direction around the triangle. Counting off A_2, B_2, C_2, when proceeding around the triangle in its second position in the same direction, should give the same order. If the order is $A_2C_2B_2$, the triangle is the mirror image, and the solution is incorrect.

The problem can now be solved in exactly the same manner as it was before, except that C_1 and C_2 are used instead of B_1 and B_2. That is, the perpendicular bisector of A_1A_2 is constructed, and any point A^* is selected on that perpendicular bisector to be the fixed pivot corresponding to the moving pivot A. The perpendicular bisector of C_1C_2 is then constructed, and any point C^* on that bisector is chosen to be the fixed pivot corresponding to the moving pivot C. The resulting four-bar linkage is, in its first position, $A^*A_1C_1C^*$. In its second position it is $A^*A_2C_2C^*$.

Actually, for two positions, it is possible to locate a unique point such that the moving lamina can be attached to a single, fixed pivot at that point and will rotate through the two design positions. This is shown in Fig. 6.11. This point, P_{12}, is called the displacement pole for the two positions. One position can be reached from the other by means of a pure rotation about the pole.

The construction for locating the pole is as shown in Fig. 6.11. Since P_{12} lies on the perpendicular bisector of A_1A_2, it is equidistant from A_1 and A_2. Similarly, it is equidistant from B_1 and B_2. Thus position 2 can be reached from position 1 by a pure rotation about P_{12}. Note that we can use the two positions of any two points on the moving body to locate the pole. For example, we could also have used points A and C or C and B.

If more than two positions are involved, as is the case in the next section, there will be a rotation pole for every two positions. For example, for three positions, there will be three poles P_{12}, P_{13}, and P_{23}. In each case, the poles will be located using the procedure shown in Fig. 6.11.

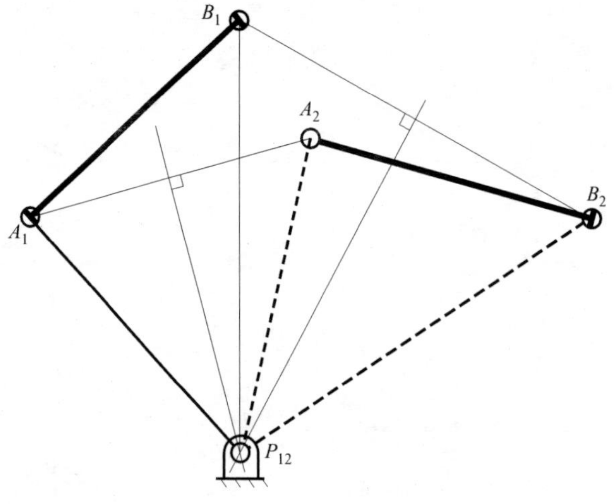

FIGURE 6.11 Location of the pole, P_{12}, of displacement of the moving lamina from position 1 to position 2. P_{12} is located at the intersection of the perpendicular bisectors of A_1A_2 and B_1B_2. The moving lamina can be displaced from position 1 to position 2 by a pure rotation about P_{12}.

6.3.3 Three Positions with Selected Moving Pivots

Because a circle can be drawn through any three points, any point on the moving lamina can be a moving pivot. The corresponding fixed pivot is at the center of the circle on which the three positions of the point lie. Taking A as one moving pivot, the corresponding fixed pivot A^* is located at the center of the circle upon which A_1, A_2, and A_3, the three positions of point A, lie. Notice that A_1, A_2, and A_3 represent the three positions of *a single point, A*, in the moving plane. They are the positions of that point *as seen from the fixed plane*. The positions of points and lines in the moving plane are, by convention, drawn on the first position of the moving plane. Thus, points A and A_1 can be regarded as being identical, as can B and B_1.

The center of the circle, A^*, can be found at the intersection of the perpendicular bisectors of A_1A_2 and A_2A_3. Similarly, B^* is located at the center of the circle on which B_1, B_2, and B_3 lie. That is, B^* is at the intersection of the perpendicular bisectors of B_1B_2 and B_2B_3. The solution linkage is then the four-bar $A^*A_1B_1B^*$ as shown in position 1. This construction is shown in Fig. 6.12.

As pointed out in the two-position case, it is not necessary for A and B to be chosen as the moving pivots. If a third point, $C\,(\equiv C_1)$, is chosen as a moving pivot, its second and third positions may be found by constructing triangles $A_2B_2C_2$ and $A_3B_3C_3$ congruent to triangle $A_1B_1C_1$. Figure 6.13 shows the synthesis of a four-bar linkage that moves its coupler through the three positions in Fig. 6.12. The points C and D that do not lie on the line AB are chosen as the moving pivots. Points C_2 and C_3 are located by constructing congruent triangles. Likewise, points D_2 and D_3 are located by constructing triangles $A_2B_2D_2$ and $A_3B_3D_3$ congruent to triangle $A_1B_1D_1$. Notice that, although we represent the moving lamina by means of the line segment AB, the moving lamina is a *plane*, not a line, and we are at liberty to draw points and lines on it that do not lie on AB.

6.3.4 Synthesis of a Crank with Chosen Fixed Pivots

The procedure just given allows us to synthesize a crank with any chosen moving pivot. If we wish to choose the fixed pivot rather than the moving pivot, the linkage must be inverted

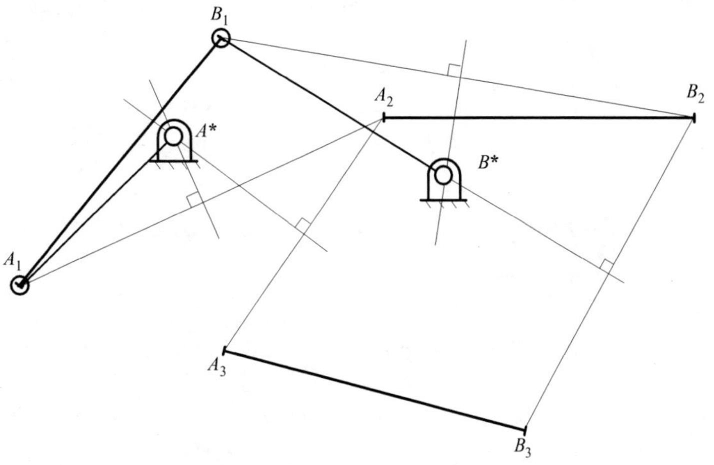

FIGURE 6.12 Synthesis of a four-bar linkage that moves its coupler plane through three nominated positions. The line segment AB defines the three positions of the moving plane. The points A and B are also chosen as the moving pivots of the two cranks. A^* and B^* are the fixed pivots of those cranks.

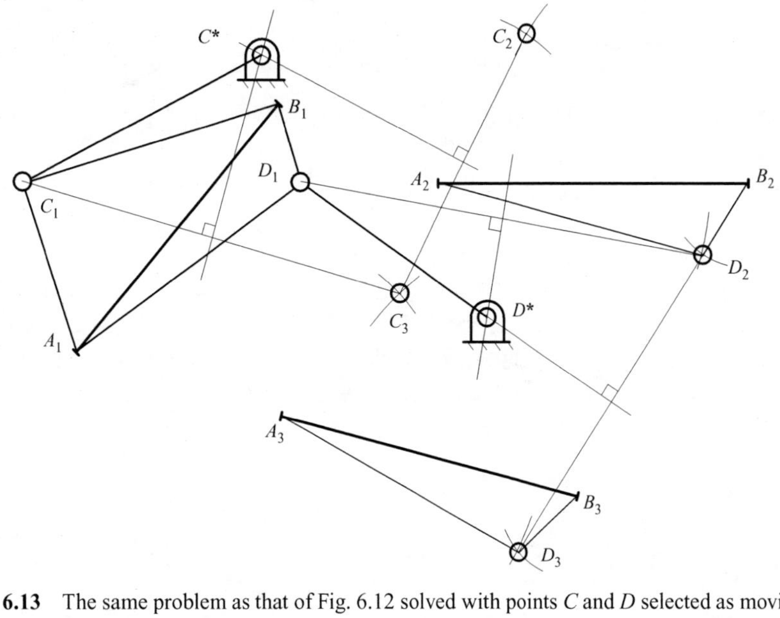

FIGURE 6.13 The same problem as that of Fig. 6.12 solved with points C and D selected as moving pivots, rather than A and B. Triangles $A_2B_2D_2$ and $A_3B_3D_3$ are congruent to $A_1B_1D_1$. The solution linkage, shown in its first position, is $C^*C_1D_1D^*$.

with the coupler becoming the reference frame. When this is done, the chosen fixed pivot is observed to move through three apparent positions as seen by the observer on the coupler. The resulting construction is shown in Fig. 6.14.

The three positions assumed by the chosen fixed pivot C^* relative to the moving lamina are plotted on the first position of that lamina. The apparent position of C^* when the lamina is in the first position is then its true position. Its apparent positions C^*_2 and C^*_3 when the lamina is in its second and third positions are obtained by constructing triangle $A_1B_1C^*_2$ congruent to $A_2B_2C^*$ and triangle $A_1B_1C^*_3$ congruent to triangle $A_3B_3C^*$. The location, C_1, of the moving pivot in the first position is obtained as the center of the circle on which C^*, C^*_2, and C^*_3 lie. This defines the crank C^*C_1 in its first position. If needed, the second and third positions (C_2, C_3) of the moving pivot can be located by constructing triangle $A_2B_2C_2$ congruent to triangle $A_1B_1C_1$ and triangle $A_3B_3C_3$ congruent to triangle $A_1B_1C_1$.

This technique gives, of course, only one crank. If both cranks are to have nominated fixed pivots, the construction must be repeated for the second crank. If the moving pivot of the second crank is to be chosen, then the earlier construction is used.

6.3.5 Design of Slider Cranks and Elliptic Trammels

To design a linkage that has a slider moving on a straight line, we must find a coupler point that has three positions on a straight line. This is shown in Fig. 6.15. The points having three points on a straight line are those special circle points that move on a circle of infinite radius. Therefore, the points satisfying this condition are a select set of points. The procedure for finding these special points is described in the following:

1. Locate the poles P_{12}, P_{13}, and P_{23} for positions 1 and 2, 1 and 3, and 2 and 3, respectively.
2. Locate the point P'_{23} called an image pole by making triangle $P_{12}P_{13}P'_{23}$ the mirror image of triangle $P_{12}P_{13}P_{23}$ about the line through poles P_{12} and P_{13}. The image pole P'_{ij} is the point in the coupler about which the frame appears to pivot as the coupler moves from position i to position j. Poles P_{12} and P_{13} are both poles and image poles.
3. Locate the center of the circle circumscribing the image pole triangle $P_{12}P_{13}P'_{23}$ by drawing the perpendicular bisectors of $P_{12}P_{13}$ and $P_{13}P'_{23}$ or $P_{12}P'_{23}$.
4. Draw the circle through P_{12}, P_{13}, and P'_{23}. This circle is fixed to the coupler and is called the circle of sliders. Any point on this circle has all three of its positions collinear. Hence, any point on this circle can be used as the moving pivot of a slider-hinge link.
5. Select a point on the circle of sliders and construct the three positions of that point (the moving pivot). These three positions will be collinear. The slide direction is parallel to the line on which all three positions lie. Actually, in this construction, one needs to construct only two of the three positions since any two positions will determine the slider line. Three positions of the coupler triangle (ABC) are shown in Fig. 6.16. Note that the three triangles $A_1B_1C_1$, $A_2B_2C_2$, and $A_3B_3C_3$ are congruent.

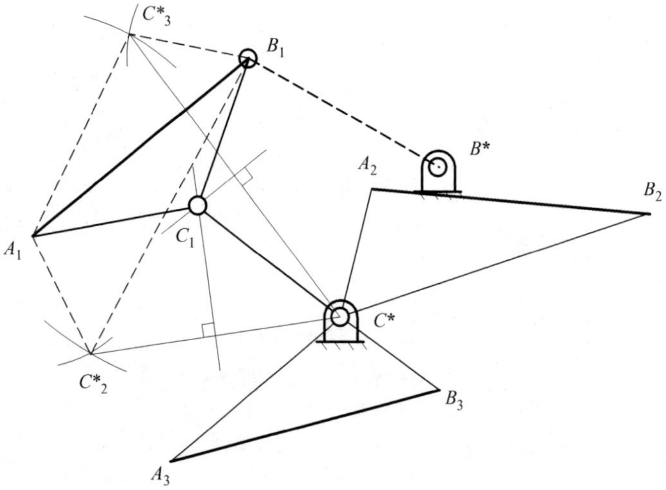

FIGURE 6.14 Synthesis of a crank with a selected fixed pivot C^*. C^*_2 and C^*_3 are, respectively, the second and third positions of point C^* as seen from the moving lamina. C_1 is the center of the circle passing through C^*, C^*_2, and C^*_3. After the crank C^*C_1 has been synthesized, the linkage may be completed by designing a second crank by any method. The dashed crank is the result of choosing B_1 as the moving pivot of the second

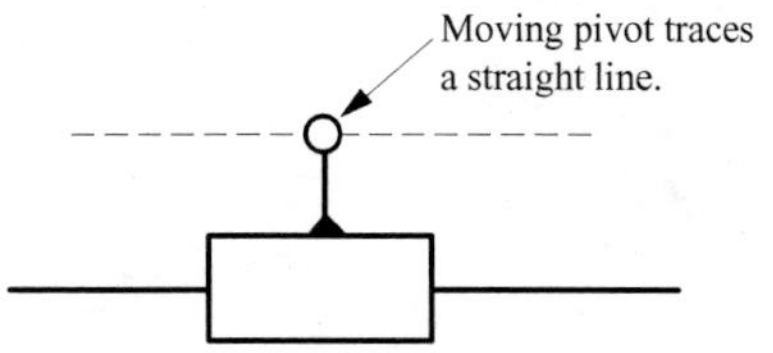

FIGURE 6.15 Geometric effect of replacing the fixed revolute of a crank by a prismatic joint.

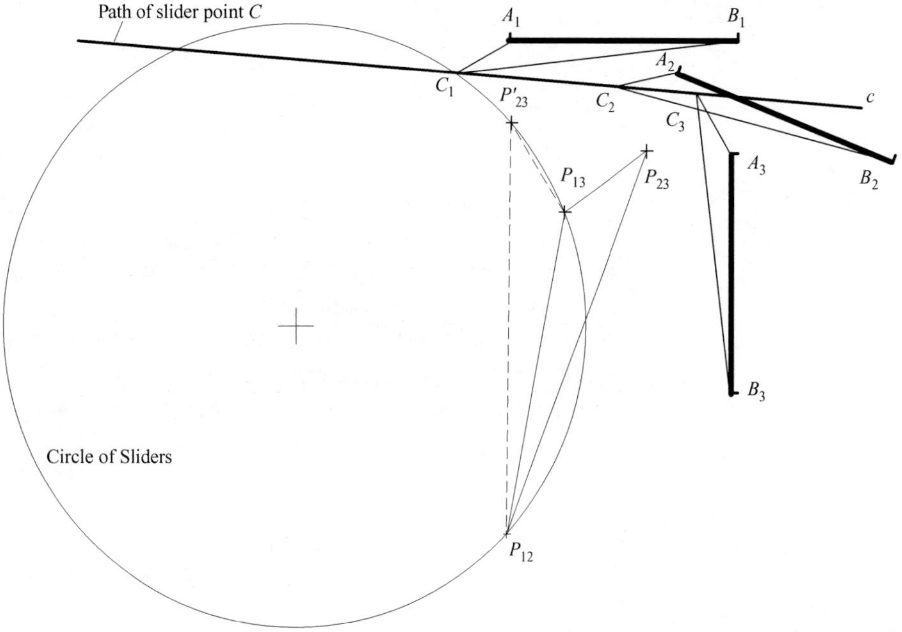

FIGURE 6.16 Construction of slider link and slider line. The three design positions are A_1B_1, A_2B_2, and A_3B_3. The slider point, C_1, is chosen from the circle that passes through the points P_{12}, P_{13}, and P_{23}'. C_2 and C_3 are the second and third positions of the slider point. c is the line in the direction of sliding.

That this construction will give slider points can be proved as follows (also, see Hall[4]):

1. The angle subtended at the pole P_{1i} by any crank is $\theta_{1i}/2$, where θ_{1i} is the rotation of the moving plane between positions 1 and i. This is shown in Fig. 6.17. This follows because the circle point, X, being a point in the moving plane, rotates through angle θ_{1i} about P_{1i} in moving from position 1 to position i. Since $P_{1i}X^*$ is common for both positions, and $X^*X_i = X^*X_1$, and $P_{1i}X_1 = P_{1i}X_i$, it follows that triangle $P_{1i}X^*X_i$ is the mirror image of $P_{1i}X^*X_1$. Therefore, $\angle X_1P_{1i}X^* = \angle X^*P_{1i}X_i = \theta_{1i}/2$.
2. A slider-hinge link can be thought of as a crank with its center point at infinity. If we draw a line from P_{1i} toward the center point at infinity, that line will be perpendicular to the slider line. From the result in item 1, the angle at the pole P_{1i} between the line joining P_{1i} to the circle point and a line normal to the slide is $\theta_{1i}/2$. Thus, given the direction c of the slide, the circle point C_1 whose three positions lie on a line parallel to c is located by drawing normals from c to P_{12} and P_{13} as shown in Fig. 6.18, and constructing lines at angles $\theta_{12}/2$ and $\theta_{13}/2$, respectively, to those normals. These lines intersect at the required point C_1, as shown in Fig. 6.18. The angle $P_{12}C_1P_{13}$ is $(\theta_{13}/2–\theta_{12}/2)$.

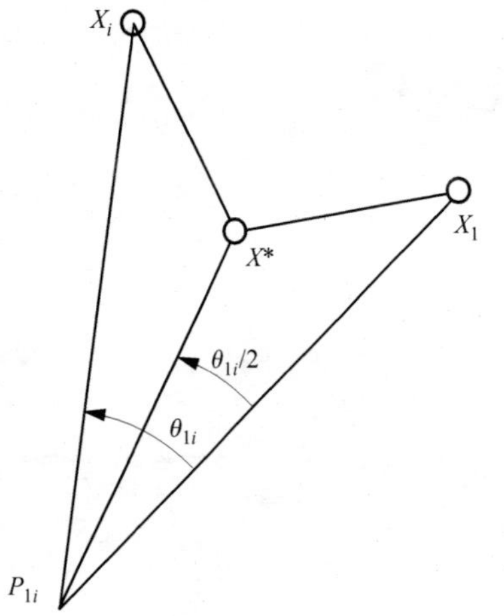

FIGURE 6.17 Relationship of angle subtended by a crank at a pole to the angular displacement about that pole.

3. The three poles, P_{12}, P_{23}, and P_{13}, form a triangle called a pole triangle as shown in Fig. 6.19. From Fig. 6.18, the angle $P_{12}C_1P_{13}$ is $(\theta_{13}/2 - \theta_{12}/2)$; and from the pole triangle, $(\theta_{13}/2 - \theta_{12}/2) = \theta_{23}/2$ (since the exterior angle of a triangle is equal to the sum of the opposite interior angles). Hence, the angle $P_{12}C_1P_{13}$ is equal to $\theta_{23}/2$ regardless of the direction of c, making the angle $P_{12}C_1P_{13}$ independent of the direction of c, and the locus of all points having three positions collinear is the locus of all points C_1 forming the angle $(P_{12}C_1P_{13})/2$. This is a circle passing through poles P_{12} and P_{13} with the central angle subtended by $P_{12}P_{13}$ equal to θ_{23}. The image pole, P'_{23}, also lies on this circle because it rotates with the body to P_{23} through the angle θ_{13} about P_{13}. Thus, the angle $P_{12}P'_{23}P_{13}$ is $\theta_{23}/2$. Hence, the required circle is the circle that circumscribes $P_{12}P_{13}P'_{23}$.

6.3.6 Order Problem and Change of Branch

Note that the preceding techniques really only guarantee that the mechanism can be assembled in the design positions; they do not guarantee that the mechanism will function correctly between different design positions. It is confusing, but it is quite possible for the simple graphical procedures developed here to produce spurious solutions. These are solutions that do not physically pass through the design positions or pass through the design positions in the wrong order. Thus, two problems can occur that may make the design unacceptable.

The first problem arises because there are two possible assembly modes for a four-bar linkage of given link lengths corresponding to a given value of the driving-crank angle. These are termed "assembly configurations" or "solution branches." If the solution linkage for a motion generation problem is such that some of the design positions lie on one assembly configuration and others on the other assembly configuration, it may not be possible to move the linkage through all design positions without physically disconnecting it and reassembling it in the other assembly configuration. Fortunately, there is a simple graphical test to identify this problem.

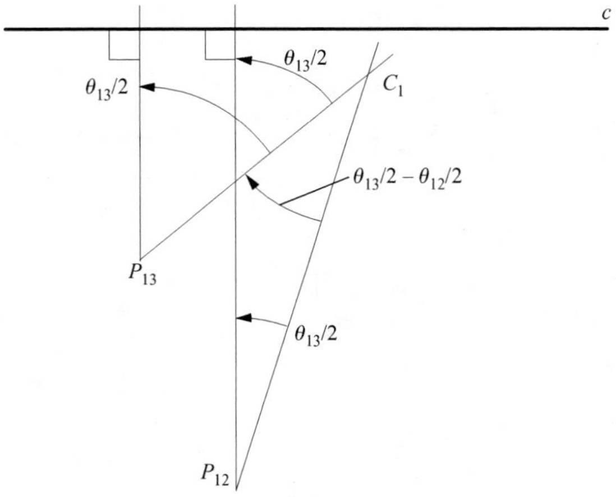

FIGURE 6.18 Relationship of sliding direction c and slider point C_1 to the poles P_{12} and P_{13}.

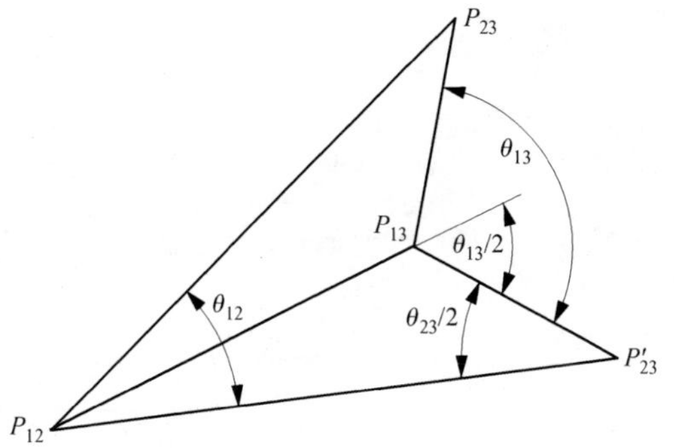

FIGURE 6.19 Angular relationships of pole triangle and image pole triangle. The triangles are mirror images of each other.

To detect whether a mechanism must change branches to pass through all of the positions, it is necessary only to assemble the mechanism in one position and determine whether it can be moved through the other two positions. This can be done conveniently if the linkage can be animated on a computer screen. If one position is missed, then a change of branch is indicated.

Another way to determine whether a change of branch is indicated is to examine the angle ψ between the coupler and the output link. Because an extreme position of the driving joint corresponds to the angle ψ passing through an angle of either 0 or π, the key to determining the branch change is the sign of that angle. A convenient method is to construct the cranks and coupler in all design positions and inspect the angle ψ between the driven crank (the longer of the two cranks) and the coupler. A change in direction of this angle indicates a change of branch in a crank-rocker or drag-link type of mechanism and a drive failure in a double-rocker type of linkage. In either case, the solution linkage is not usable. An example of this condition is shown in Fig. 6.20. There the direction of the angle $D^*D_1C_1$ is opposite to that of angles $D^*D_2C_2$ and $D^*D_3C_3$. Hence the linkage passes through a position in which the driving joint C^* is at a motion limit.

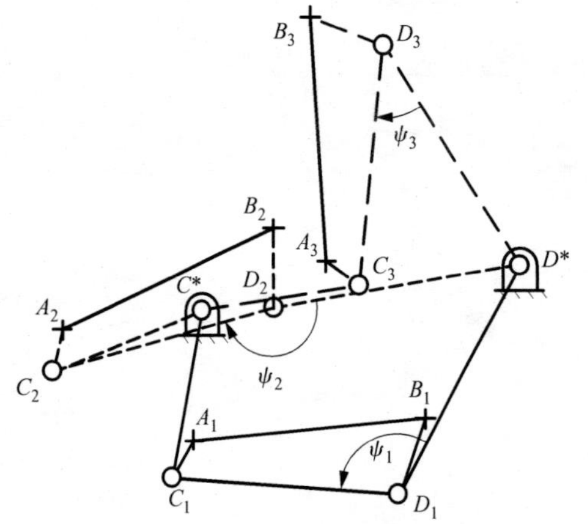

FIGURE 6.20 An example in which the solution linkage is incapable of moving through the design positions without being disconnected and reassembled. The solution linkage is shown in all three design positions as $C^*C_1D_1D^*$, $C^*C_2D_2D^*$, and $C^*C_3D_3D^*$, respectively. The angles between the driven (longer) crank and the coupler are examined in all three positions. These are the angles $D^*D_1C_1 = \psi_1$, $D^*D_2C_2 = \psi_2$, and $D^*D_3C_3 = \psi_3$ respectively. ψ_1 is counterclockwise, and ψ_2 and ψ_3 are clockwise. Thus the angle ψ changes sign, indicating a change of branch in the solution.

EXAMPLE 6.1 *Position Synthesis of a Four-Bar Linkage*

Design a four-bar linkage whose coupler moves through the three positions indicated by the line segment AB in Fig. 6.21. Point B is to be one moving pivot and point X^* is to be one fixed pivot.

Solution

1. The procedure for locating the fixed pivot B^* is shown in Fig. 6.22. The construction used is that of Fig. 6.12.
2. The procedure for the location of moving pivot X is shown in Fig. 6.23. The construction used is that of Fig. 6.14.

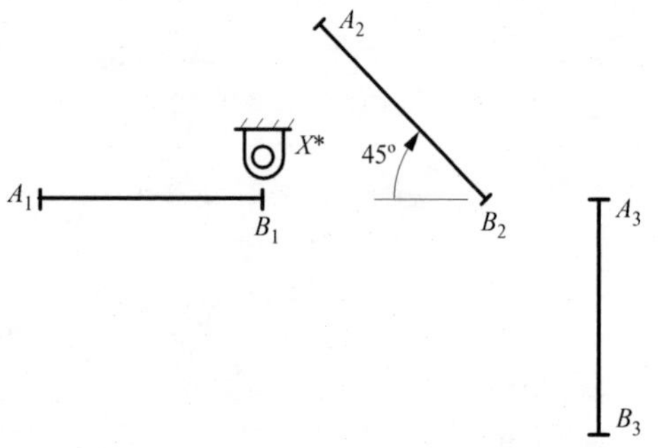

FIGURE 6.21 The problem of Example 6.1.

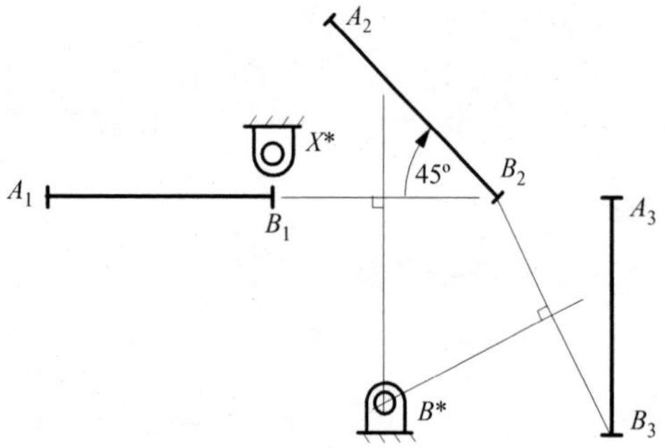

FIGURE 6.22 Location of the fixed pivot, B^*, given the moving pivot, B_1.

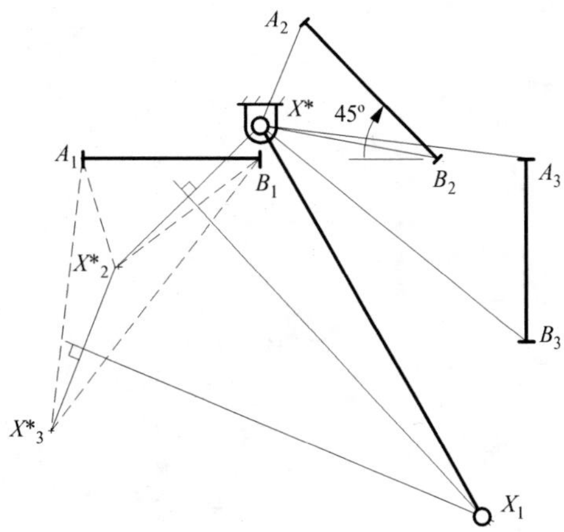

FIGURE 6.23 Location of the moving pivot, X_1, given the location of the fixed pivot, X^*. Triangles $A_1B_1X_2^*$ and $A_2B_2X^*$ are congruent, as are triangles $A_1B_1X_3^*$ and $A_3B_3X^*$.

Triangle $A_1B_1X_2^*$ is congruent to triangle $A_2B_2X^*$, and triangle $A_1B_1X_3^*$ is congruent to triangle $A_3B_3X^*$.

X_1 is located at the center of the circle $X^*X_2^*X_3^*$.

The other two positions of point X (X_2 and X_3) can then be located by constructing triangles $A_2B_2X_2$ and $A_3B_3X_3$ congruent to triangle $A_1B_1X_1$.

3. Check the solution.

We first check the Grashof type of the linkage:

$X^*B^* = 2.41 = p$

$B_1X_1 = 4.28 = q$

$B^*B_1 = 2.06 = s$

$X^*X_1 = 4.62 = l$

$l + s = 6.68, \ p - q = 6.69$

so

$l + s < p + q$ (barely)

The shortest link, s, is a crank, so the linkage is a crank-rocker.

To check for change of branch, we draw the linkage in all three of the design positions, as shown in Fig. 6.24. All of the information necessary to do this has already been generated in previous stages of the construction procedure.

Because X^*X_1 is the longer of the two cranks, assume that it is the driven link, and B^*B is the driver link. We can then check the signs of the angles $X^*X_1B_1$, $X^*X_2B_2$, and $X^*X_3B_3$ to check for branching. $\angle X^*X_1B_1$ is counterclockwise whereas $\angle X^*X_2B_2$ and $\angle X^*X_3B_3$ are clockwise. Hence a change of branch must occur.

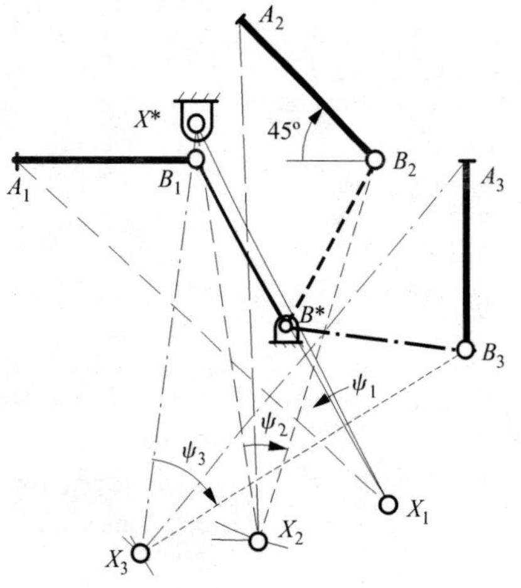

FIGURE 6.24 Construction of the solution linkage and verification that it satisfies the design positions without disconnection. In this case, the linkage fails the test because $\psi_1 = \angle X^*X_1B_1$ is counterclockwise whereas ψ_2 and ψ_3 are clockwise. Hence, the linkage cannot be moved through the design positions by rotation of the crank B^*B.

EXAMPLE 6.2 *Position Synthesis of a Slider-Crank Mechanism*

Design a slider-crank mechanism to move a coupler containing the line AB through the three positions shown in Fig. 6.25. Use point B as a circle point.

Solution

To design a slider-crank mechanism, it is necessary to identify a circle point and the corresponding center point (or vice versa) and a slider point. We must also identify the direction of the slider line. In this problem, point B has been identified as the circle point for the crank. Therefore, to locate the center point, we need only find the center of the circle on which the three positions of B lie. The construction for finding the center point (B^*) and the crank in position 1 is shown in Fig. 6.26.

To locate the slider point, we must locate the poles, the image pole P'_{23}, and the circle of sliders in position 1. This circle is attached to the coupler. The construction of the poles is shown in Fig. 6.27, and the locations of the image pole and circle of sliders are shown in Fig. 6.28. We can select any point on the slider circle as a slider point. The point chosen is C. To complete the design, we need to locate the slider point in positions 2 and 3. The three positions, C_1, C_2, and C_3, will be collinear on the slider line. The construction of the slider line is also shown in Fig. 6.28.

From the three positions of C shown in Fig. 6.28, it is clear that the linkage does go through the three positions in the correct order. However, in general it is necessary to check for both order and branch problems.

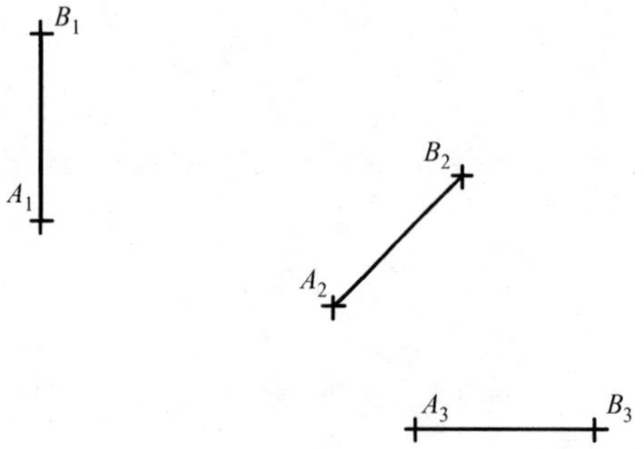

FIGURE 6.25 Design positions for Example 6.2.

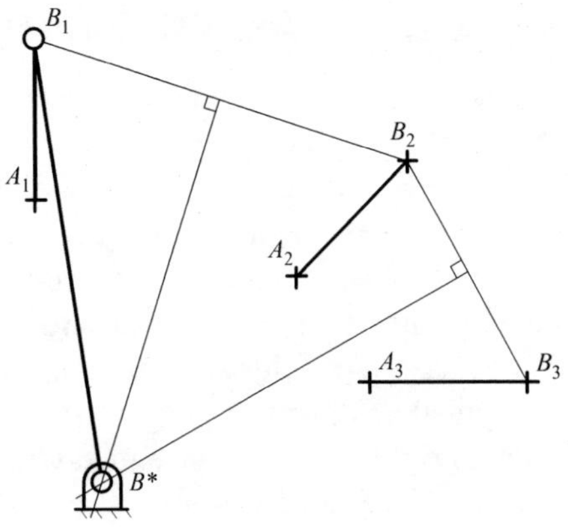

FIGURE 6.26 Construction of crank of slider-crank mechanism for Example 6.2.

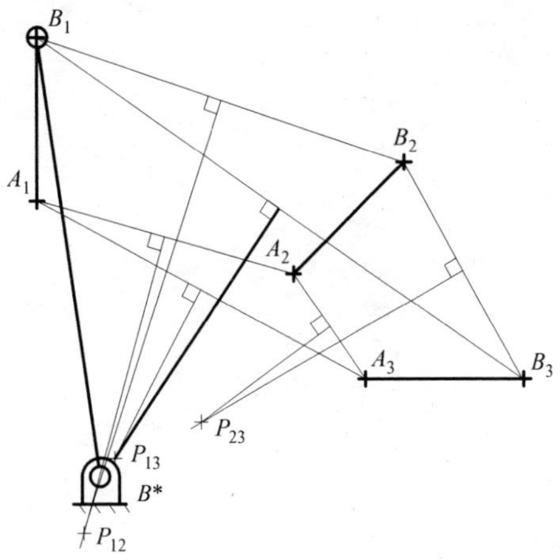

FIGURE 6.27 Construction of the poles for Example 6.2.

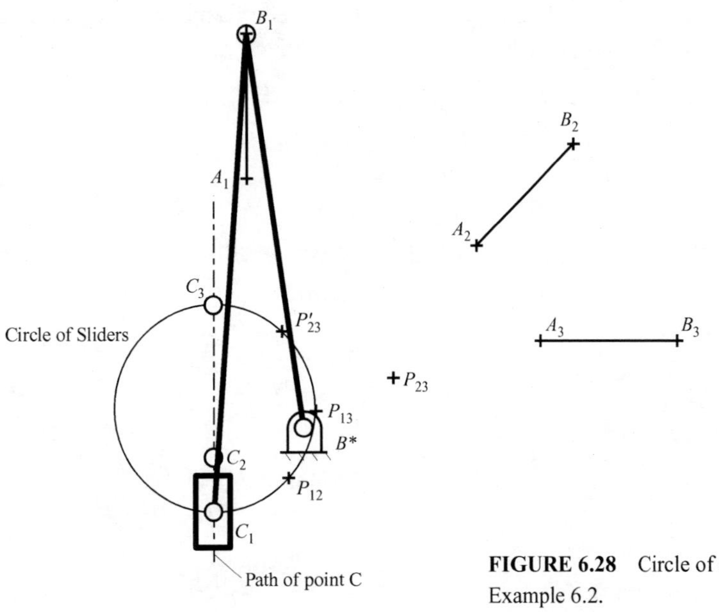

FIGURE 6.28 Circle of sliders and final linkage for Example 6.2.

6.3.7 Analytical Approach to Rigid-Body Guidance

Rigid-body guidance can be approached analytically in two ways. The first procedure requires coordinate transformations and is more general. It can be extended easily to four positions, and the different elements (such as the circle of sliders) developed in the graphical procedure arise naturally from the mathematics. However, for three positions, the first procedure is more involved than the second procedure, which is a mathematical representation of the graphical procedure. Therefore, only the second procedure will be presented here. Readers are referred to works by Sandor and Erdman,[7] Waldron,[9] or Suh and Radcliffe[8] for a more general analytical treatment.

The analytical approach to rigid-body guidance involves coordinate transformations when center points are selected. Therefore, before addressing the topic directly, let us develop the equations for the needed coordinate transformations between the coupler and frame coordinate systems.

Coordinate Transformations The general relationship between the coupler and frame systems is indicated in Fig. 6.29. From Fig. 6.29, we can write the vector equations as

$$\boldsymbol{r}_{P/O} = \boldsymbol{r}_{P/A} + \boldsymbol{r}_{A/O}$$

In this equation, $\boldsymbol{r}_{P/O}$ and $\boldsymbol{r}_{A/O}$ are defined in the frame coordinate system, and $\boldsymbol{r}_{P/A}$ is defined in the coupler coordinate system. Therefore, only $\boldsymbol{r}_{P/A}$ needs to be transformed to the frame coordinate system. This is shown in Fig. 6.30.

In matrix form, the coordinate transformation from the coupler to the frame system is

$$\begin{Bmatrix} x \\ y \end{Bmatrix} = [R]\begin{Bmatrix} X \\ Y \end{Bmatrix} + \begin{Bmatrix} a_x \\ a_y \end{Bmatrix} \tag{6.6}$$

In Eq. (6.6), the matrix R indicates the orientation (rotation) of the coupler coordinate system relative to the frame coordinate system. The vector $\{a_x\ a_y\}^T$ gives the origin of the coupler coordinate system relative to the frame system. We need to determine the rotation matrix $[R]$ first. From Fig. 6.30, we have

$$x_{P/A} = X\cos\theta - Y\sin\theta$$

$$y_{P/A} = Y\cos\theta + X\sin\theta$$

or

$$\begin{Bmatrix} x_{P/A} \\ y_{P/A} \end{Bmatrix} = \begin{bmatrix} \cos\theta & -\sin\theta \\ \sin\theta & \cos\theta \end{bmatrix}\begin{Bmatrix} X \\ Y \end{Bmatrix}$$

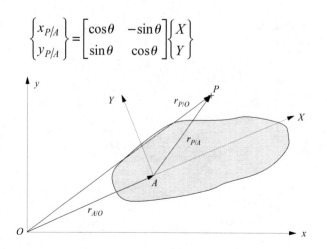

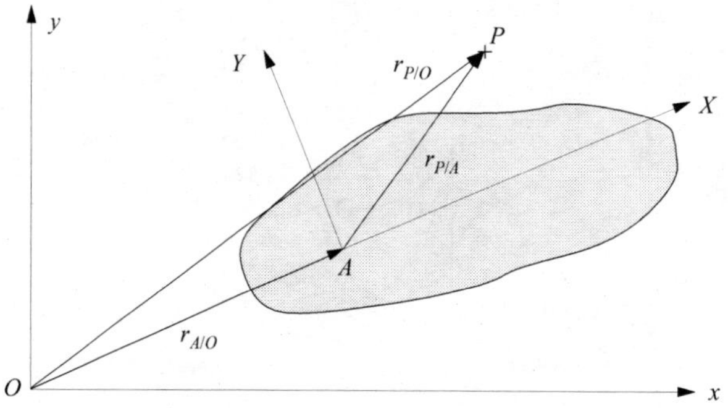

FIGURE 6.29 Relationship between coupler and frame coordinate systems.

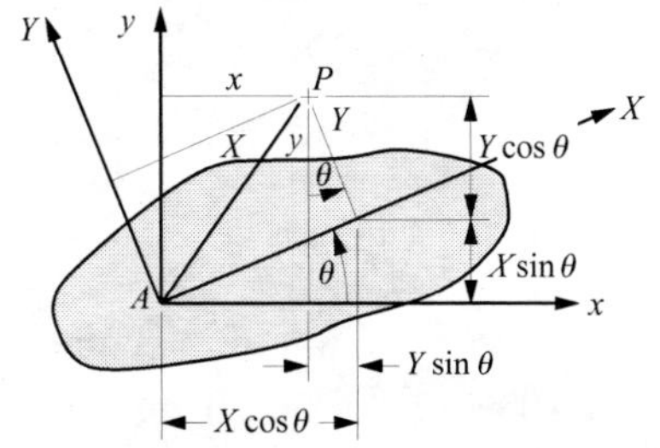

FIGURE 6.30 Transformation from coupler system *XY* to frame system *xy*.

For any general point with coordinates (*X*, *Y*) relative to the coupler, the coordinates (*x*, *y*) relative to the frame are given by Eq. (6.6) or

$$\begin{Bmatrix} x \\ y \end{Bmatrix} = \begin{bmatrix} \cos\theta & -\sin\theta \\ \sin\theta & \cos\theta \end{bmatrix} \begin{Bmatrix} X \\ Y \end{Bmatrix} + \begin{Bmatrix} a_x \\ a_y \end{Bmatrix} = [R] \begin{Bmatrix} X \\ Y \end{Bmatrix} + \begin{Bmatrix} a_x \\ a_y \end{Bmatrix}$$

Therefore,

$$[R] = \begin{bmatrix} \cos\theta & -\sin\theta \\ \sin\theta & \cos\theta \end{bmatrix} \tag{6.7}$$

We can also transform from the frame coordinate system to the coupler coordinate system. This is shown in Fig. 6.31. From that figure it is clear that

$$X_{P/A} = x_{P/A}\cos\theta + y_{P/A}\sin\theta$$
$$Y_{P/A} = y_{P/A}\cos\theta - x_{P/A}\sin\theta$$

or

$$\begin{Bmatrix} X_{P/A} \\ Y_{P/A} \end{Bmatrix} = \begin{bmatrix} \cos\theta & \sin\theta \\ -\sin\theta & \cos\theta \end{bmatrix} \begin{Bmatrix} x_{P/A} \\ y_{P/A} \end{Bmatrix} = [A] \begin{Bmatrix} x_{P/A} \\ y_{P/A} \end{Bmatrix} \tag{6.8}$$

where

$$[A] = \begin{bmatrix} \cos\theta & \sin\theta \\ -\sin\theta & \cos\theta \end{bmatrix} \tag{6.9}$$

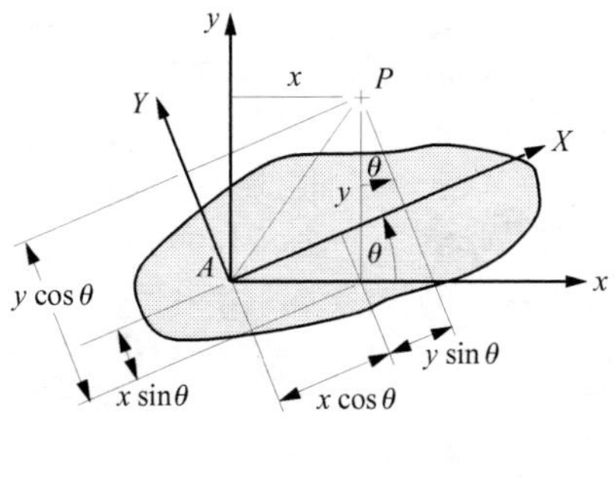

FIGURE 6.31 Transformation from frame system *xy* and coupler system *XY*.

When we compare Eqs. (6.8) and (6.9), it is clear that

$$\begin{bmatrix} \cos\theta & \sin\theta \\ -\sin\theta & \cos\theta \end{bmatrix} = \begin{bmatrix} \cos\theta & -\sin\theta \\ \sin\theta & \cos\theta \end{bmatrix}^{\mathrm{T}} = \begin{bmatrix} \cos\theta & -\sin\theta \\ \sin\theta & \cos\theta \end{bmatrix}^{-1}$$

Therefore,

$$[A] = [R]^{-1} = [R]^{\mathrm{T}} \tag{6.10}$$

Now assume that we have specified the position of the coupler coordinate system by the origin of the moving system (a_x, a_y) and the rotation angle θ for the X axis. To transform from the coupler system (X, Y) to the frame coordinate system (x, y), use

$$\begin{Bmatrix} x \\ y \end{Bmatrix} = \begin{bmatrix} \cos\theta & -\sin\theta \\ \sin\theta & \cos\theta \end{bmatrix} \begin{Bmatrix} X \\ Y \end{Bmatrix} + \begin{Bmatrix} a_x \\ a_y \end{Bmatrix} \tag{6.11}$$

To transform from the frame system to the coupler system, use

$$\begin{Bmatrix} X \\ Y \end{Bmatrix} = \begin{bmatrix} \cos\theta & \sin\theta \\ -\sin\theta & \cos\theta \end{bmatrix} \begin{Bmatrix} x - a_x \\ y - a_y \end{Bmatrix} = \begin{bmatrix} \cos\theta & \sin\theta \\ -\sin\theta & \cos\theta \end{bmatrix} \begin{Bmatrix} x \\ y \end{Bmatrix} - \begin{bmatrix} \cos\theta & \sin\theta \\ -\sin\theta & \cos\theta \end{bmatrix} \begin{Bmatrix} a_x \\ a_y \end{Bmatrix} \tag{6.12}$$

In the following, we will assume that each position of the coupler is given by the coordinates (a_x, a_y) of the origin of the coupler coordinate system relative to the frame and by the angle θ for the X axis. If instead of the angle θ, the coordinates (b_x, b_y) of a second point B in the coupler are given, we must first compute the angle θ from the equation

$$\theta = \tan^{-1}\left[\frac{b_y - a_y}{b_x - a_x}\right] \tag{6.13}$$

When a circle point is selected, the coordinates of that point are given relative to the coupler coordinate system (X, Y). The coordinates of the three positions of that point relative to the frame coordinate system can be computed using Eq. (6.11). The corresponding center point is located by finding the center of the circle (analytically) on which the three positions of the circle point lie. The coordinates of the center of the circle will be defined in the frame coordinate system.

If a center point is given, the coordinates will be in the frame coordinate system (x, y). To find the corresponding circle point, the three apparent positions of the center point relative to the coupler coordinate system must be found. This is done using Eq. (6.12). The corresponding circle point is located by finding the center of the circle (analytically) on which the three positions of the center point lie. The coordinates of the center of the circle will be defined in the coupler coordinate system. The coordinates of this point in any of the positions can be found relative to the frame using Eq. (6.11). The crank length can be determined by computing the distance between the circle and center points once both are defined relative to the same coordinate system.

Locating center points given circle points and vice versa requires that the center of the circle corresponding to three positions of a point be found. To find the circle of sliders, the locations of the poles and the image pole must be found. We will discuss an analytical procedure for finding poles first. After this is done, it will be apparent that the same procedure can be used to find the center of a circle given three positions of a point.

Finding Poles Let A_i and A_j and B_i and B_j be vectors defining the locations of two points in two positions. The x and y coordinates of each point are assumed to be known. As indicated in Fig. 6.11, the pole is the point that lets us move the rigid body from position i to position j by a simple rotation. To determine the location of the pole analytically, let r_A be the distance from the pole to point A and r_B be the distance from B to the pole P_{ij} as shown in Fig. 6.32a. The following geometric relationships then hold.

$$\left.\begin{aligned}\left(A_{x_i}-p_{ij_x}\right)^2+\left(A_{y_i}-p_{ij_y}\right)^2=\left(r_A\right)^2=\left(A_{x_j}-p_{ij_x}\right)^2+\left(A_{y_j}-p_{ij_y}\right)^2\\ \left(B_{x_i}-p_{ij_x}\right)^2+\left(B_{y_i}-p_{ij_y}\right)^2=\left(r_B\right)^2=\left(B_{x_j}-p_{ij_x}\right)^2+\left(B_{y_j}-p_{ij_y}\right)^2\end{aligned}\right\} \tag{6.14}$$

Expanding Eqs. (6.14) gives

$$A_{x_i}^2-2A_{x_i}p_{ij_x}+p_{ij_x}^2+A_{y_i}^2-2A_{y_i}p_{ij_y}+p_{ij_y}^2=A_{x_j}^2-2A_{x_j}p_{ij_x}+p_{ij_x}^2+A_{y_j}^2-2A_{y_j}p_{ij_y}+p_{ij_y}^2$$

$$B_{x_i}^2-2B_{x_i}p_{ij_x}+p_{ij_x}^2+B_{y_i}^2-2B_{y_i}p_{ij_y}+p_{ij_y}^2=B_{x_j}^2-2B_{x_j}p_{ij_x}+p_{ij_x}^2+B_{y_j}^2-2B_{y_j}p_{ij_y}+p_{ij_y}^2$$

These equations can be simplified to give

$$\begin{aligned}\left(A_{x_i}^2+A_{y_i}^2\right)-\left(A_{x_j}^2+A_{y_j}^2\right)=2\left(A_{x_i}-A_{x_j}\right)p_{ij_x}+2\left(A_{y_i}-A_{y_j}\right)p_{ij_y}\\ \left(B_{x_i}^2+B_{y_i}^2\right)-\left(B_{x_j}^2+B_{y_j}^2\right)=2\left(B_{x_i}-B_{x_j}\right)p_{ij_x}+2\left(B_{y_i}-B_{y_j}\right)p_{ij_y}\end{aligned} \tag{6.15}$$

These equations are linear in the unknown pole coordinates and can easily be solved. In matrix form, the equations become

$$\begin{bmatrix}2\left(A_{x_i}-A_{x_j}\right) & 2\left(A_{y_i}-A_{y_j}\right)\\ 2\left(B_{x_i}-B_{x_j}\right) & 2\left(B_{y_i}-B_{y_j}\right)\end{bmatrix}\begin{Bmatrix}p_{ij_x}\\ p_{ij_y}\end{Bmatrix}=\begin{Bmatrix}\left(A_{x_i}^2+A_{y_i}^2\right)-\left(A_{x_j}^2+A_{y_j}^2\right)\\ \left(B_{x_i}^2+B_{y_i}^2\right)-\left(B_{x_j}^2+B_{y_j}^2\right)\end{Bmatrix} \tag{6.16}$$

Equations (6.16) can be solved using a calculator or a matrix equation solver such as MATLAB.

Equations (6.16) apply to most types of positions; however, there are three special cases that will make the matrix singular. These are shown in Fig. 6.32 and identified in the following:

1. Two positions of the coupler are parallel (Fig. 6.32b).
2. Lines linking the successive positions of two points are parallel (Fig. 6.32c).
3. Two successive positions of a point are coincident (Fig. 6.32d).

Each of these conditions can be handled separately.

Two Parallel Positions When two positions are parallel, the resulting pole is at infinity in the direction given by the angle γ where

$$\gamma=\frac{\pi}{2}+\tan^{-1}\left(\frac{A_{y_j}-A_{y_i}}{A_{x_j}-A_{x_i}}\right)=\frac{\pi}{2}+\tan^{-1}\left(\frac{B_{y_j}-B_{y_i}}{B_{x_j}-B_{x_i}}\right)$$

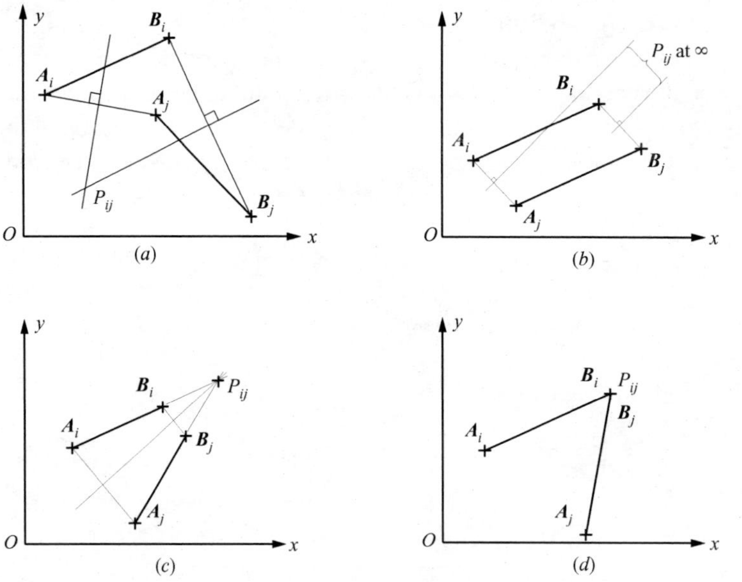

FIGURE 6.32 Location of pole P_{ij}: (a) general case, (b) parallel positions, (c) symmetric positions, (d) intersecting positions at B (or A).

Lines A_iA_j and B_iB_j are Parallel When this situation occurs, the pole is located at the intersection of the lines defined by A_iB_i and A_jB_j. The location of the pole is then given by solving the following simultaneous equations:

$$\left(\frac{p_{ij_x} - A_{x_i}}{B_{x_i} - A_{x_i}}\right) = \left(\frac{p_{ij_y} - A_{y_i}}{B_{y_i} - A_{y_i}}\right)$$

and

$$\left(\frac{p_{ij_x} - A_{x_j}}{B_{x_j} - A_{x_j}}\right) = \left(\frac{p_{ij_y} - A_{y_j}}{B_{y_j} - A_{y_j}}\right)$$

The equations can be simplified and rewritten as

$$p_{ij_x}\left(B_{y_i} - A_{y_i}\right) - p_{ij_y}\left(B_{x_i} - A_{x_i}\right) = A_{x_i}\left(B_{y_i} - A_{y_i}\right) - A_{y_i}\left(B_{x_i} - A_{x_i}\right)$$
$$p_{ij_x}\left(B_{y_j} - A_{y_j}\right) - p_{ij_y}\left(B_{x_j} - A_{x_j}\right) = A_{x_j}\left(B_{y_j} - A_{y_j}\right) - A_{y_j}\left(B_{x_j} - A_{x_j}\right)$$

or in matrix form,

$$\begin{bmatrix} \left(B_{y_i} - A_{y_i}\right) & -\left(B_{x_i} - A_{x_i}\right) \\ \left(B_{y_j} - A_{y_j}\right) & -\left(B_{x_j} - A_{x_j}\right) \end{bmatrix} \begin{Bmatrix} p_{ij_x} \\ p_{ij_y} \end{Bmatrix} = \begin{Bmatrix} A_{x_i}\left(B_{y_i} - A_{y_i}\right) - A_{y_i}\left(B_{x_i} - A_{x_i}\right) \\ A_{x_j}\left(B_{y_j} - A_{y_j}\right) - A_{y_j}\left(B_{x_j} - A_{x_j}\right) \end{Bmatrix} \quad (6.17)$$

Equations (6.17) can be solved using a calculator or a matrix equation solver such as MATLAB.

Two Successive Positions Coincident When a point on the coupler does not move in successive coupler positions, that point is identical to the pole. Therefore, if $\boldsymbol{A}_i = \boldsymbol{A}_j$ then both equal $\boldsymbol{p}_{ij}$, or if $\boldsymbol{B}_i = \boldsymbol{B}_j$ then both equal $\boldsymbol{p}_{ij}$.

Finding the Center of a Circle on Which Three Points Lie The procedure given for finding poles can be used to find the center of the circle that passes through three points. To do this, simply treat $\boldsymbol{B}_i$ and $\boldsymbol{A}_j$ as the same point. This is shown schematically in Fig. 6.33 to find $\boldsymbol{A}^*$ given three positions of $\boldsymbol{A}$.

Image Pole The image pole is found by reflecting the pole about a line through the two other poles. To find the image pole P'_{23}, we reflect the pole P_{23} about the line through poles P_{12} and P_{13}. This is shown in Fig. 6.34. Given the coordinates of poles P_{12}, P_{23}, and P_{13}, the coordinates of the image pole, P'_{23}, can be found as follows. First define

$$\boldsymbol{g} = (\boldsymbol{p}_{13} - \boldsymbol{p}_{12}) = (g_x, g_y)$$

and

$$\boldsymbol{h} = (\boldsymbol{p}_{23} - \boldsymbol{p}_{12}) = (h_x, h_y)$$

Then,

$$\beta = \tan^{-1}\left(\frac{h_y}{h_x}\right)$$

and

$$\theta = \tan^{-1}\left(\frac{g_y}{g_x}\right) - \beta$$

Let

$$r = \sqrt{h_x^2 + h_y^2}$$

Then, the coordinates of the image pole are given by

$$\boldsymbol{p}'_{23} = \boldsymbol{p}_{12} + \left(r\cos(\beta + 2\theta)\boldsymbol{i} + r\sin(\beta + 2\theta)\boldsymbol{j}\right)$$

MATLAB functions for the pole and image pole routines are given on the disk included with this book.

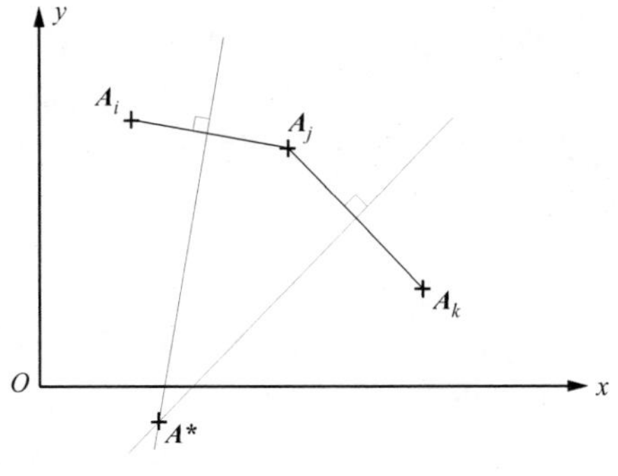

FIGURE 6.33 Locating the center of a circle using the pole procedure. Compare this figure with Fig. 6.32a.

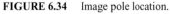

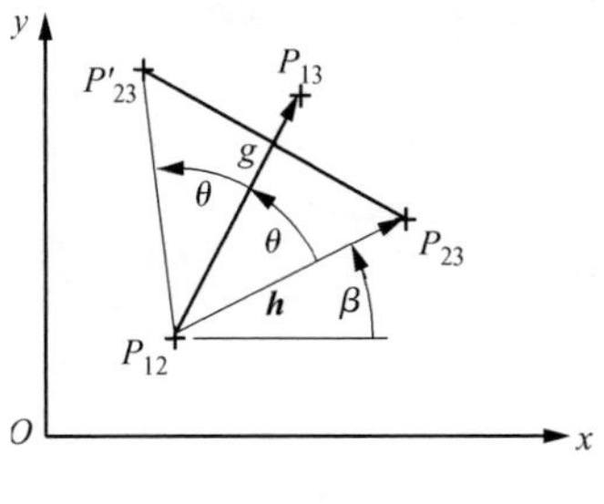

FIGURE 6.34 Image pole location.

Crank Design Given Circle Point If the circle point is specified, the circle point coordinates (X, Y) will be given relative to the coupler coordinate system. The procedure for finding the corresponding center point and the resulting crank is given in the following.

1. Transform the coordinates of the circle point to the frame coordinate system using Eq. (6.11) for each position of the coupler. This will give three pairs of points, (x_1, y_1), (x_2, y_2), and (x_3, y_3) relative to the frame coordinate system.
2. Set $\boldsymbol{A}_1 = (x_1, y_1)$; $\boldsymbol{A}_2 = (x_2, y_2)$; and $\boldsymbol{A}_3 = (x_3, y_3)$. Then use the procedure in the subsection "Finding Poles" to find the location of the center point in the frame coordinate system. Call this point (x^*, y^*).
3. The crank in position 1 is located by the line from (x^*, y^*) to (x_1, y_1).
4. Locate the second crank using the same procedure and complete the linkage.

Crank Design Given Center Point If the center point is specified, the center point coordinates (x^*, y^*) will be given relative to the frame coordinate system. The procedure for finding the corresponding circle point relative to the coupler coordinate system and the subsequent crank is given in the following.

1. Transform the coordinates of the center point to the coupler coordinate system using Eq. (6.12) for each position of the coupler. This will give three pairs of points, (X_1^*, Y_1^*), (X_2^*, Y_2^*), and (X_3^*, Y_3^*), relative to the coupler coordinate system.
2. Set $\boldsymbol{A}_1 = (X_1^*, Y_1^*)$; $\boldsymbol{A}_2 = X_2^*, Y_2^*)$; and $\boldsymbol{A}_3 = (X_3^*, Y_3^*)$. Then use the procedure in subsection "Finding Poles" to find the location of the circle point relative to the coupler coordinate system. Call this point (X, Y).
3. Identify the position i in which the linkage is to be displayed. Transform the coordinates of point (X, Y) to the frame coordinate system using Eq. (6.11) for position i. Call the transformed point (x_i, y_i).
4. The crank in position i is located by the line from (x^*, y^*) to (x_i, y_i).
5. Locate the second crank and complete the linkage.

Design of a Slider If a slider is to be used, we must find the circle of sliders and two of the three positions of the slider point. The procedure is given in the following.

1. Let two points in the coupler be given as $A = (0, 0)$ and $B = (1, 0)$ relative to the coupler coordinate system. Transform the coordinates of both points to the frame coordinate system using Eq. (6.11) for each position of the coupler. This will give three pairs of coordinates for A and three for B relative to the frame coordinate system. Call the point locations A_1, A_2, A_3, B_1, B_2, and B_3.
2. Compute the coordinates of the poles p_{12}, p_{13}, and p_{23} using the coordinates of A and B and the procedure given in subsection "Finding Poles." The resulting coordinates will be in the frame coordinate system.
3. Compute the coordinates of the image pole p'_{23} using the procedure given in the subsection "Image Pole." The coordinates of P'_{23} will also be in the frame coordinate system.
4. Set $\boldsymbol{C}_i = p_{12}$; $\boldsymbol{C}_j = p_{13}$; and $\boldsymbol{C}_k = p'_{23}$. Then use the procedure in subsection "Finding Poles" to find the location of the center (x_c, y_c) of the slider circle in the frame coordinate system. Compute the radius of the circle using

$$r_c = \sqrt{\left(C_{i_x} - x_c\right)^2 + \left(C_{i_y} - y_c\right)^2}$$

The center (x_c, y_c) and radius r_c will correspond to the circle of sliders in position 1.

5. Select the x coordinate of the slider point. Call this coordinate x_s. Solve for the coordinate y_s using

$$y_s = y_c \pm \sqrt{r_c^2 - (x_s - x_c)^2}$$

Notice that there will be two possible values for y_s for each value of x_s. It is necessary to select the specific point desired by identifying which sign (+ or –) gives the proper configuration for the linkage. The resulting point $(x_s, y_s)_1$ will be the coordinates of the slider point in position 1 in the frame coordinate system.

6. Transform the point $(x_s, y_s)_1$ to the coupler coordinate system using Eq. (6.12) and $(a_x, a_y)_1$ and the rotation angle θ_1. Call this point (X_s, Y_s). It identifies the slider point relative to the coupler coordinate system.
7. Determine the coordinates of point (X_s, Y_s) in the frame coordinate system for positions 2 and 3 of the coupler. Call these positions $(x_s, y_s)_2$ and $(x_s, y_s)_3$.
8. Define the slider line parametrically by

$$(x, y) = (x_s, y_s)_1 + \beta\left[(x_s, x_s)_3 - (x_s, y_s)_1\right] \tag{6.18}$$

where points along the slider line are a function of the single variable β. Note that $\beta = 0$ at the first position $(x_s, y_s)_1$ and $\beta = 1$ at the third position $(x_s, y_s)_3$.

Compute β corresponding to the distance to the slider point in the second position using

$$\beta_2 = \frac{\left[(x_s, y_s)_2 - (x_s, y_s)_1\right]}{\left[(x_s, y_s)_3 - (x_s, y_s)_1\right]} \tag{6.19}$$

10. Check to ensure that the linkage goes through the positions in the correct order. For this to occur, position 2 must lie between positions 1 and 3 or $0 < \beta_2 < 1$.

Implementing the Analytical Approach to Rigid-Body Guidance The procedures given in the previous subsections can be used with a calculator to design four-bar linkages with revolute joints and sliders sliding on the frame. The procedures can also be programmed easily on a computer using any of the various languages. It is especially easy to program the procedure in MATLAB because of the ease with which matrix and vector manipulations may be carried out. A program that implements the procedure with limited graphical output is given on the disk included with this book.

6.4 FUNCTION GENERATION

The procedure developed here will use a four-bar linkage to generate the desired function; however, the general ideas presented can be used for any system for which a functional relationship can be derived between two variables. For example, assume that a "black box" is given such that the functional relationship between the two variables α and ρ is

$$f(\alpha, \rho, a_1, a_2, a_3, a_4) = 0 \tag{6.20}$$

where a_1, a_2, a_3, and a_4 are design variables defining the system. To design the system to approximate the function

$$g(\alpha, \rho) = 0 \tag{6.21}$$

we simply need to solve Eq. (6.21) four times to obtain four pairs of values for α and ρ. We can designate these as (α_1, ρ_1), (α_2, ρ_2), (α_3, ρ_3), and (α_4, ρ_4). The points chosen where the approximate solution matches the exact solution are called precision points. Next rewrite Eq. (6.20) four times (corresponding to the number of design variables), one for each pair of (α_i, ρ_i), and solve the resulting set of equations for a_1, a_2, a_3, and a_4. Note that the equations may be nonlinear, requiring the use of numerical techniques.

EXAMPLE 6.3 *Function Generation with a General Device*

A mechanical device characterized by the input–output relationship $\phi = 2a_1 + a_2 \tan\theta$ is to be used to generate (approximately) the function $\phi = 2\theta_3$ (with θ and ϕ both in radians) over the range 0 ″ θ ″ $\pi/3$.

a. Determine the number of precision points required to complete the design of the system.

b. Choose reasonable precision points and determine the values for the unknown design variables that will allow the device to approximate the function.

Solution

There are two unknowns $(a_1$ and $a_2)$, so the number of precision points is two. We will determine a systematic way to locate the precision points later in this section, but for now, let us choose the two points to be at the quarter and three-quarter points of the range. Then

$$\theta_1 = \theta_{\min} + \frac{(\theta_{\max} - \theta_{\min})}{4} = 0 + \frac{(\pi/3 - 0)}{4} = 0 + \frac{\pi}{12} = 0.2618$$

and

$$\theta_2 = \theta_{\min} + \frac{(\theta_{\max} - \theta_{\min})}{4} = 0 + \frac{3(\pi/3 - 0)}{4} = 0 + \frac{\pi}{4} = 0.7854$$

The corresponding values of ϕ are

$$\phi_1 = 2\theta_1^3 = 2(0.2618)^3 = 0.03589, \quad \phi_2 = 2\theta_2^3 = 2(0.7854)^3 = 0.9689$$

We can now solve for a_1 and a_2 using the desired input–output relationship,

$$\phi = 2a_1 + a_2 \tan\theta$$

Substituting into the equation the values for θ and ϕ at the two precision points gives

$$0.03589 = 2a_1 + a_2 \tan(0.2618) = 2a_1 + 0.2679a_2$$

and

$$0.9689 = 2a_1 + a_2 \tan(0.7854) = 2a_1 + 1.0000a_2$$

Subtracting the two equations gives,

$$0.9330 = 0.7321a_2 \text{ resulting in } a_2 = 1.2746$$

Backsubstituting to determine a_1 gives

$$2a_1 = 0.03589 - a_2 \tan(0.2618) = 0.03589 - 0.2679(1.2746) = -0.3055 \text{ resulting in } a_1 = -0.1528$$

The final equation for the device is

$$\phi = 2a_1 + a_2 \tan\theta = -0.3055 + 1.2746 \tan\theta$$

In the following example, the function *f* in Eq. (6.20) will be the governing position equation for a four-bar linkage. The function *g* will be an arbitrary function that is specified at the beginning of the analysis.

6.4.1 Function Generation Using a Four-Bar Linkage

Analytical function generation using a four-bar linkage was developed by Freudenstein,[13] and the basic equation relating the input and output variables for the four-bar linkage is called Freudenstein's equation.

Given three pairs of values for θ and ϕ in Fig. 6.35, the objective for the case considered here is to find r_2, r_3, and r_4 for the four-bar linkage. This is the linkage that will approximate the function implied by the three pairs of values for θ and ϕ. In the three-position function generation problem, the size of the linkage does not affect the functional relationship between θ and ϕ. Therefore, the frame link (r_1) can be taken to initially have length 1, and the entire linkage can be scaled to any desired size after the basic design is established.

To develop the governing equation relating the input and output variables for the linkage, first determine expressions for the *x* and *y* components of the vectors corresponding to each link length. For the *x* direction,

$$r_2 \cos\theta + r_3 \cos\psi = 1 + r_4 \cos\phi \tag{6.22}$$

and for the *y* direction,

$$r_2 \sin\theta + r_3 \sin\psi = r_4 \sin\phi \tag{6.23}$$

We do not want ψ in the final equation. Therefore, isolate the terms involving ψ so that this angle can be eliminated. Then

$$\begin{aligned} r_3 \cos\psi &= 1 + r_4 \cos\phi - r_2 \cos\theta \\ r_3 \sin\psi &= r_4 \sin\phi - r_2 \sin\theta \end{aligned} \tag{6.24}$$

Square both equations and add to get

$$r_3^2\left(\cos^2\psi + \sin^2\psi\right) = \left(1 + r_4 \cos\phi - r_2 \cos\theta\right)^2 + \left(r_4 \sin\phi - r_4 \sin\theta\right)^2$$

Expanding the equation and simplifying gives

$$r_3^2 = 1 + r_4^2 + r_2^2 + 2r_4 \cos\phi - 2r_2 \cos\theta - 2r_4 r_2 \cos(\theta - \phi)$$

Because we have three pairs of values for θ and ϕ, this equation can be written three times as

$$\begin{aligned} r_3^2 &= 1 + r_4^2 + r_2^2 + 2r_4 \cos\phi_1 - 2r_2 \cos\theta_1 - 2r_4 r_2 \cos(\theta_1 - \phi_1) \\ r_3^2 &= 1 + r_4^2 + r_2^2 + 2r_4 \cos\phi_2 - 2r_2 \cos\theta_2 - 2r_4 r_2 \cos(\theta_2 - \phi_2) \\ r_3^2 &= 1 + r_4^2 + r_2^2 + 2r_4 \cos\phi_3 - 2r_2 \cos\theta_3 - 2r_4 r_2 \cos(\theta_3 - \phi_3) \end{aligned} \tag{6.25}$$

Equations (6.25) can be solved for r_2, r_3, and r_4. The procedure used to solve the equations depends on the tools that are available.

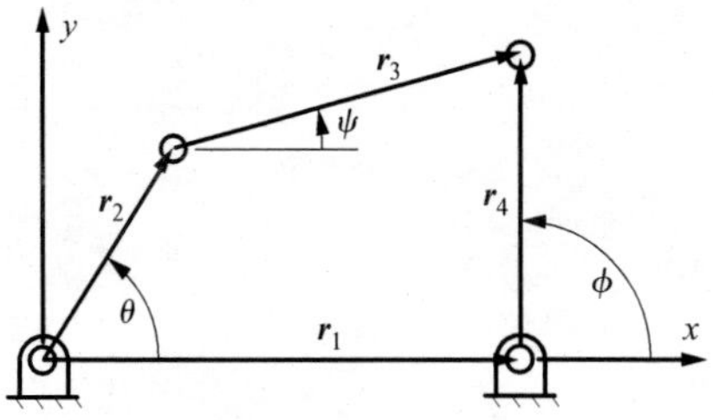

FIGURE 6.35 Four-bar linkage used for function generation.

Solution by Matrices The equations can be written simply in matrix form. To simplify the result, first rearrange the terms and divide each equation in Eqs. (6.25) by $2r_2r_4$ and define the new unknowns as

$$z_1 = \frac{1 + r_2^2 + r_4^2 - r_3^2}{2r_2r_4} \tag{6.26}$$

$$z_2 = \frac{1}{r_2} \tag{6.27}$$

and

$$z_3 = \frac{1}{r_4} \tag{6.28}$$

We can then write the resulting equations as

$$\begin{aligned} z_1 + z_2 \cos\phi_1 - z_3 \cos\theta_1 &= \cos(\theta_1 - \phi_1) \\ z_1 + z_2 \cos\phi_2 - z_3 \cos\theta_2 &= \cos(\theta_2 - \phi_2) \\ z_1 + z_2 \cos\phi_3 - z_3 \cos\theta_3 &= \cos(\theta_3 - \phi_3) \end{aligned} \tag{6.29}$$

or in matrix form,

$$\begin{bmatrix} 1 & \cos\phi_1 & -\cos\theta_1 \\ 1 & \cos\phi_2 & -\cos\theta_2 \\ 1 & \cos\phi_3 & -\cos\theta_3 \end{bmatrix} \begin{Bmatrix} z_1 \\ z_2 \\ z_3 \end{Bmatrix} = \begin{Bmatrix} \cos(\theta_1 - \phi_1) \\ \cos(\theta_2 - \phi_2) \\ \cos(\theta_3 - \phi_3) \end{Bmatrix} \tag{6.30}$$

We can solve for z_1, z_2, and z_3 using MATLAB or some other matrix solver. Symbolically,

$$\begin{Bmatrix} z_1 \\ z_2 \\ z_3 \end{Bmatrix} = \begin{bmatrix} 1 & \cos\phi_1 & -\cos\theta_1 \\ 1 & \cos\phi_2 & -\cos\theta_2 \\ 1 & \cos\phi_3 & -\cos\theta_3 \end{bmatrix}^{-1} \begin{Bmatrix} \cos(\theta_1 - \phi_1) \\ \cos(\theta_2 - \phi_2) \\ \cos(\theta_3 - \phi_3) \end{Bmatrix} \tag{6.31}$$

Knowing z_1, z_2, and z_3, we can solve for the unknown link lengths using Eqs. (6.26), (6.27), and (6.28). Then,

$$r_2 = \frac{1}{z_2} \tag{6.32}$$

$$r_4 = \frac{1}{z_3} \tag{6.33}$$

and

$$r_3 = \sqrt{1 + r_2^2 + r_4^2 - 2r_2r_4z_1} \tag{6.34}$$

Note that the square root used to compute r_3 can be plus or minus. Only the plus sign has a physical meaning, however, since r_3 is physically the distance from the end of link 2 to the end of link 4.

Unscaling the Solution In the previous derivation, it is assumed that the length of the base link (r_1) is 1. This is not generally the case. However, to determine the true size of the links, it is necessary to know the size of just one of the links initially. Through a scaling factor, we can determine the size of the other links.

Assume that the actual link lengths are R_1, R_2, R_3, and R_4, where the R's are related to the computed r's through the following:

$$\left.\begin{aligned} R_1 &= Kr_1 \\ R_2 &= Kr_2 \\ R_3 &= Kr_3 \\ R_4 &= Kr_4 \end{aligned}\right\} \tag{6.35}$$

where K is the scale factor for the linkage. From Eq. (6.35), we have

$$K = R_1/r_1 = R_2/r_2 = R_3/r_3 = R_4/r_4 \tag{6.36}$$

After the design procedure is completed, we will know r_1, r_2, r_3, and r_4. Therefore, we need to specify only *one* of R_1, R_2, R_3, or R_4 to find K using Eq. (6.36). Knowing K, we can compute the actual link lengths using Eq. (6.35).

6.4.2 Design Procedure When $y = y(x)$ Is to Be Generated

Generally, in function generation, θ and ϕ will not be given directly. Instead, the linkage will be designed to approximate a function $y = y(x)$, where y corresponds to ϕ (the output) and x corresponds to θ (the input). The angles θ and ϕ will be related to x and y such that, given θ and ϕ, x and y can be computed. The functional relationships between ϕ and y and θ and x are somewhat arbitrary; however, the problem is most easily solved if linear relationships are used. The most common relationships are

$$\frac{x - x_0}{x_f - x_0} = \frac{\theta - \theta_0}{\theta_f - \theta_0}$$

and

$$\frac{y - y_0}{y_f - y_0} = \frac{\phi - \phi_0}{\phi_f - \phi_0}$$

or

$$x = \frac{x_f - x_0}{\theta_f - \theta_0}\left(\theta - \theta_0\right) + x_0 \tag{6.37}$$

$$y = \frac{y_f - y_0}{\phi_f - \phi_0}\left(\phi - \phi_0\right) + y_0 \tag{6.38}$$

and

$$\theta = \frac{\theta_f - \theta_0}{x_f - x_0}\left(x - x_0\right) + \theta_0 \tag{6.39}$$

$$\phi = \frac{\phi_f - \phi_0}{y_f - y_0}\left(y - y_0\right) + \phi_0 \tag{6.40}$$

When the design problem is formulated, we will know $y = y(x)$ and the range for x (x_0 ″ x ″ x_f). Given x_0 and x_f, we can compute y_0 and y_f. We must then pick θ_0 and θ_f and ϕ_0 and ϕ_f. Then, given three design positions for x, three values for y, θ and ϕ can be computed, and given the three values for θ and ϕ, the link lengths can be computed using the procedure given here.

Often, instead of selecting θ_0, θ_f, ϕ_0, and ϕ_f directly, θ_0, ϕ_0, and $\Delta\theta = \theta_f - \theta_0$ and $\Delta\phi = \phi_f - \phi_0$ are selected. Typically, choosing $\Delta\theta$ and $\Delta\phi$ to be between 60° and 120° usually works well. It is also usually better to avoid having either the driver or the output link pass below the line defined by the two fixed pivots (line of centers) in the range where the function is to be matched; that is, make 0° ″ θ_0 ″ θ ″ θ_f ″ 180° and 0° ″ ϕ_0 ″ ϕ ″ ϕ_f ″ 180°.

6.4.3 Selection of Design Positions

In general, the function generated by the linkage will match the actual function only at the precision points, and the error between the precision points will vary depending on where the precision points are placed in the range x_0 ″ x ″ x_f. Therefore, when trying to match the function $y = y(x)$ over the range x_0 ″ x ″ x_f, the objective is to select the precision points so that the deviation of the function actually generated from that desired between the design positions is minimized. The difference between the actual function generated and the desired function is called the *structural error e*. If this error is plotted as a function of x, it can be shown that the maximum structural error (e^*) is minimized when it takes the form shown in Fig. 6.36. Ideally, the maximum errors between the precision points are both equal in magnitude to the errors at the ends of the range.

It is usually difficult to locate the precision points so that this criterion for the error is met for an arbitrary function; however, a useful approximate solution is obtained by approximating the error function by a Chebyshev polynomial of order N, where N is equal to the number of precision points. If the approximation were exact, the optimum locations of the precision points are given by

$$x_i = \frac{x_f + x_0}{2} - \frac{x_f - x_0}{2}\cos\left(\frac{\pi i}{N} - \frac{\pi}{2N}\right) = \frac{x_f + x_0}{2} - \frac{x_f - x_0}{2}\cos\left\{\frac{\pi}{2N}\left(2i - 1\right)\right\} \tag{6.41}$$

where $i = 1, 2, \ldots, N$. These values for x_i are the roots of the Chebyshev polynomial of order N. As already noted, Eq. (6.41) approximates only the optimum locations of the precision points, but it is still a useful starting solution to use, especially when there is no other basis upon which to choose design positions.

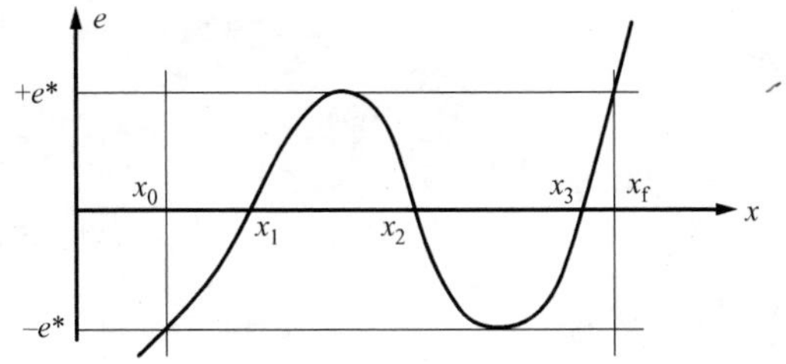

FIGURE 6.36 Optimum error distribution.

The roots of the Chebyshev polynomial can be given a geometric interpretation that makes it easy to derive Eq. (6.41) if the form of the equation is forgotten. For this, draw a circle of radius $(x_f - x_0)/2$ with its center at $(x_f + x_0)/2$. Then divide the circle into a regular polygon with $2N$ sides. The projection of the vertices of the polygon onto the x axis will give the locations of the precision points. This is shown in Fig. 6.37. When Chebyshev spacing is used, the center point, $(x_f + x_0)/2$, will be a precision point *only* when N is odd, and the extremes (x_f and x_0) of the range will *never* be chosen as precision points.

6.4.4 Summary of Solution Procedure for Four-Bar Linkage and Three Precision Points

Let $y = y(x)$ be the function to be generated over the range x_0 ″ x ″ x_f. The design positions should be placed inside the range x_0 ″ x ″ x_f, and as a rule, for the three positions use

$$x_1 = \frac{x_f + x_0}{2} - \frac{x_f - x_0}{2}\cos 30^\circ$$

$$x_2 = \frac{x_f + x_0}{2}$$

$$x_3 = \frac{x_f + x_0}{2} - \frac{x_f - x_0}{2}\cos 150^\circ$$

Choose the angular range $\Delta\theta$ of the input crank that is to correspond to the range x_0 ″ x ″ x_f for x. Also, choose the angle θ_0 corresponding to x_0 from which this range is to start.

Choose the angular range $\Delta\phi$ of the output crank that is to correspond to the range y_0 ″ y ″ y_f for y where $y_0 = y(x_0)$ and $y_f = y(x_f)$. Also, choose the angle ϕ_0 corresponding to y_0 from which the output range will start.

Compute the values of θ and ϕ that represent the precision points from the equations

$$\theta_i = \frac{\theta_f - \theta_0}{x_f - x_0}\left(x_i - x_0\right) + \theta_0 = \frac{x_i - x_0}{x_f - x_0}\Delta\theta + \theta_0$$

and

$$\phi_i = \frac{\phi_f - \phi_0}{y_f - y_0}\left(y_i - y_0\right) + \phi_0 = \frac{y_i - y_0}{y_f - y_0}\Delta\phi + \phi_0$$

where $y_i = y(x_i)$.

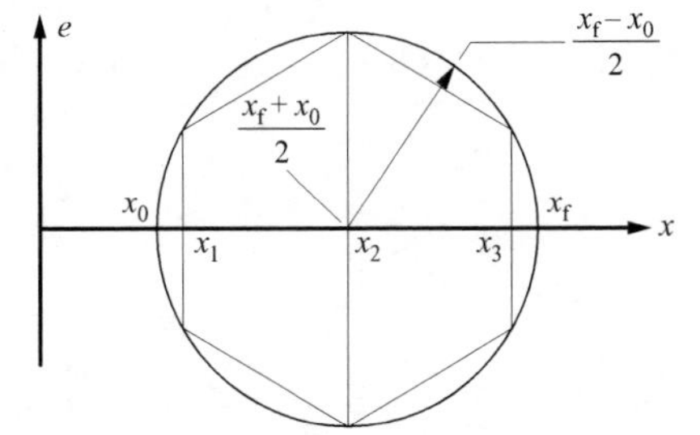

FIGURE 6.37 Chebyshev spacing for precision points.

Next let the base length be unity and calculate the lengths for the driver, coupler, and output links using Eqs. (6.31)–(6.34). To do this, solve

$$\begin{Bmatrix} z_1 \\ z_2 \\ z_3 \end{Bmatrix} = \begin{bmatrix} 1 & \cos\phi_1 & -\cos\theta_1 \\ 1 & \cos\phi_2 & -\cos\theta_2 \\ 1 & \cos\phi_3 & -\cos\theta_3 \end{bmatrix}^{-1} \begin{Bmatrix} \cos(\theta_1-\phi_1) \\ \cos(\theta_2-\phi_2) \\ \cos(\theta_3-\phi_3) \end{Bmatrix}$$

for z_1, z_2, and z_3. Then solve for r_1 , r_3, and r_4 from

$$r_2 = \frac{1}{z_2}$$

$$r_4 = \frac{1}{z_3}$$

and

$$r_3 = \sqrt{1 + r_2^2 + r_4^2 - 2r_2r_4z_1}$$

Note that r_2 and r_4 can be negative. When r_2 or r_4 is negative, the direction for the vector representing the link length is reversed (see Fig. 6.38).

After the scaled link lengths are determined, determine the scale factor using

$$K = R_1/r_1 = R_2/r_2 = R_3/r_3 = R_4/r_4$$

and the true value of one of the link lengths. Then determine the true value for all of the link lengths using Eqs. (6.35).

Draw the linkage to scale, and check that a linkage with the calculated dimensions will pass through the design positions (θ_1, ϕ_1), (θ_2, ϕ_2), (θ_3, ϕ_3). The procedure guarantees only that the linkage can be assembled in the design positions. It may not be able to move from one position to another without changing branches. It is also important to check the force and torque transmission characteristics of the linkage at each design position. As will be discussed when crank-rocker mechanisms are considered, the force transmission characteristics of a four-bar linkage can change greatly from position to position.

If for some reason the linkage is unacceptable, change either the range or starting point for either θ or ϕ and solve for another design.

Note that it is possible to choose different combinations of variables other than x_1, x_2, and x_3 when selecting the precision points. If we let

$$x_f - x_0 = \Delta x$$

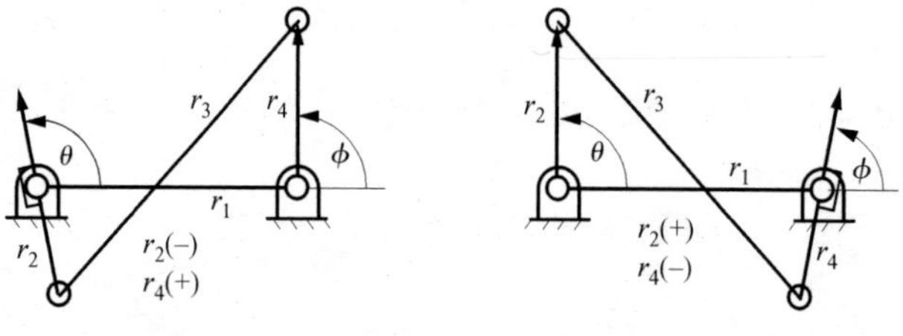

FIGURE 6.38 Interpretation of negative values for r_4 and r_2.

then the basic equations for selecting the precision points can be written as

$$x_1 = \frac{x_f + x_0}{2} - \frac{\Delta x}{2}\cos 30^\circ$$

$$x_2 = \frac{x_f + x_0}{2}$$

$$x_3 = \frac{x_f + x_0}{2} + \frac{\Delta x}{2}\cos 30^\circ$$

From this it is clear that we can select any three from the list of variables, x_1, x_2, x_3, x_f, x_0, or Δx and solve for the other three.

The function generation equations have been programmed using MATLAB in the routine *fungen.m* provided on the disk with this book. This routine can be easily modified to handle a relatively wide range of function generation problems involving a four-bar linkage.

EXAMPLE 6.4
Function Generation Using a Four-Bar Linkage

Design a linkage to generate the function $y = \log_{10}x$ over the range 1 ″ x ″ 2.

Solution

From the given information,

$$x_0 = 1 \text{ and } x_f = 2$$

Using Chebyshev spacing for the precision points, we have

$$x_1 = \frac{x_f + x_0}{2} - \frac{x_f - x_0}{2}\cos 30^\circ = \frac{2+1}{2} - \frac{2-1}{2}\cos 30^\circ = 1.06699$$

Similarly, $x_2 = 1.5$ and $x_3 = 1.93301$. Then, the corresponding values for y are

$$y_f = \log_{10}2 = 0.30103$$

$$y_0 = \log_{10}1 = 0$$

$$y_1 = \log_{10}x_1 = 0.028160$$

$$y_2 = \log_{10}x_2 = 0.176091$$

$$y_3 = \log_{10}x_3 = 0.28623$$

Note that a minimum of five decimal places is needed to ensure adequate solution accuracy. To identify the linkage angles, choose

$$\theta_0 = 45^\circ, \quad \Delta\theta = 60^\circ$$

and

$$\phi_0 = 0^\circ, \quad \Delta\phi = 60^\circ$$

Note that these values are somewhat arbitrary. If the resulting linkage is unacceptable, we can try other values. The precision points in terms of θ are

$$\theta_1 = \frac{x_1 - x_0}{x_f - x_0}\Delta\theta + \theta_0 = \frac{1.06699 - 1}{1} 60° + 45° = 49.019°$$

$$\theta_2 = \frac{x_2 - x_0}{x_f - x_0}\Delta\theta + \theta_0 = \frac{1.5 - 1}{1} 60° + 45° = 75.000°$$

$$\theta_3 = \frac{x_3 - x_0}{x_f - x_0}\Delta\theta + \theta_0 = \frac{1.93301 - 1}{1} 60° + 45° = 100.981°$$

Similarly,

$$\phi_1 = \frac{y_1 - y_0}{y_f - y_0}\Delta\phi + \phi_0 = \frac{0.028160 - 1}{0.30103} 60° + 0 = 5.612°$$

$$\phi_2 = \frac{y_2 - y_0}{y_f - y_0}\Delta\phi + \phi_0 = \frac{0.176091 - 1}{0.30103} 60° + 0° = 35.098°$$

$$\phi_3 = \frac{y_3 - y_0}{y_f - y_0}\Delta\phi + \phi_0 = \frac{0.28623 - 1}{0.30103} 60° + 0 = 57.050°$$

Using the matrix solution procedure, we get

$$\begin{Bmatrix} z_1 \\ z_2 \\ z_3 \end{Bmatrix} = \begin{bmatrix} 1 & \cos\phi_1 & -\cos\theta_1 \\ 1 & \cos\phi_2 & -\cos\theta_2 \\ 1 & \cos\phi_3 & -\cos\theta_3 \end{bmatrix}^{-1} \begin{Bmatrix} \cos(\theta_1 - \phi_1) \\ \cos(\theta_2 - \phi_2) \\ \cos(\theta_3 - \phi_3) \end{Bmatrix} = \begin{bmatrix} 1 & 0.9952 & -0.6558 \\ 1 & 0.8182 & -0.2588 \\ 1 & 0.5439 & -0.1905 \end{bmatrix}^{-1} \begin{Bmatrix} 0.7265 \\ 0.7671 \\ 0.7202 \end{Bmatrix} = \begin{Bmatrix} 0.6383 \\ 0.2210 \\ 0.2008 \end{Bmatrix}$$

and

$$r_2 = \frac{1}{z_2} = \frac{1}{1.2574} = 0.7953$$

$$r_4 = \frac{1}{z_3} = \frac{1}{0.6631} = 1.5080$$

and

$$r_3 = \sqrt{1 + r_2^2 + r_4^2 - 2r_2r_4z_1} = \sqrt{1 + 0.7953^2 + 1.5080^2 - 2(0.7953)(1.5080)(-0.0900)} = 2.0304$$

For the overall size of the linkage, use a base link length of 2 in. Then the lengths of the other links become

$$R_1 = 1(2) = 2.0000 \text{ in}$$

$$R_2 = 0.7953(2) = 1.5905 \text{ in}$$

$$R_4 = 1.5080(2) = 3.0160 \text{ in}$$

$$R_3 = 2.0304(2) = 4.0608 \text{ in}$$

The linkage is drawn to scale in Fig. 6.39.

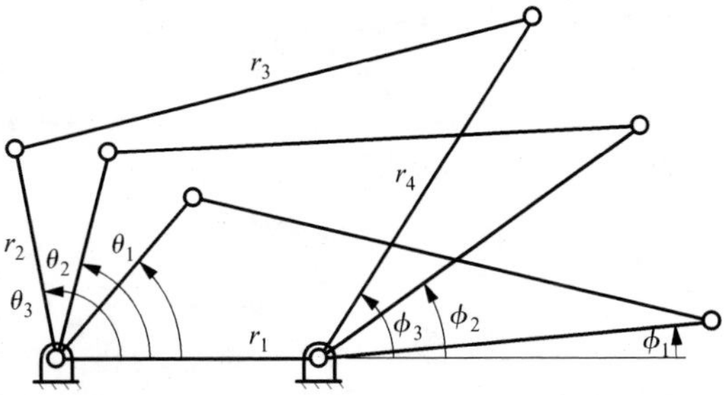

FIGURE 6.39 Final linkage for Example 6.4.

6.4.5 Graphical Approach to Function Generation

The function generation problem can be solved graphically if the linkage is inverted so that the crank becomes the temporary frame. We can choose any position of the crank to start the construction, but position 1 is the most common position to choose. To illustrate the procedure, the problem in Example 6.4 will be used again. That is, it will be assumed that three pairs of points, (θ_1, ϕ_1), (θ_2, ϕ_2), and (θ_3, ϕ_3) are known. The input and output cranks in the three positions are shown in Fig. 6.40. Note that the base link (r_1) has been chosen, but the lengths of the input and output links (r_2 and r_4) have not been specified.

The next step is to invert the linkage so that the driver (r_2) becomes the frame. To do this, treat the group of links, r_1, r_2, and r_4, as a rigid body in each position and rotate the group of links such that r_2 is in the same location for each position. This is shown in Fig. 6.41. In the inverted linkage, r_2 is the frame, r_3, the original coupler, is the output link, and r_4, the original output link, becomes the coupler. For the inverted linkage, one crank is known, so we need only establish the other crank (r_3 for the original linkage), and the linkage geometry is established. The problem has therefore been converted to a rigid-body guidance problem where r_4 is the coupler to be guided. One crank (r_1) has already been established. To find the other crank, choose a point C on link 4. The center of the circle on which C_1, C_2, and C_3 lie is C^*. The synthesized linkage in position 1 is A, B_1, C_1, C^* as shown in Fig. 6.42. When inverted back to the original base, we have the solution of the function generation problem. The final solution linkage is shown in Fig 6.43. Note that θ_0 and θ_f are different in this solution compared with the analytical solution, but $\Delta\theta$ is the same for both solutions. Here, we chose the position of C (that is, the length of r_4) rather than θ_0.

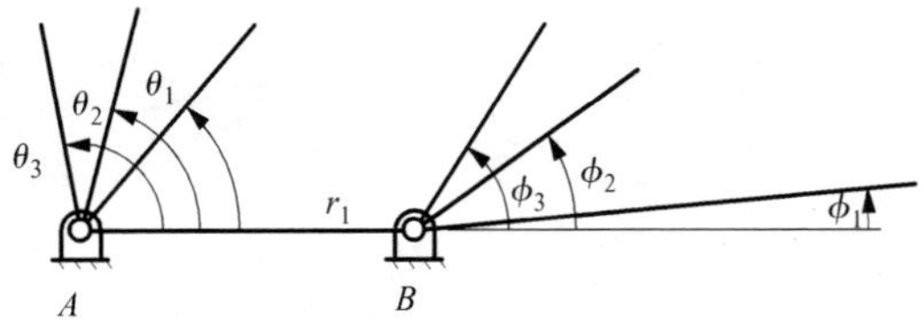

FIGURE 6.40 Three positions for input and output links for graphical synthesis.

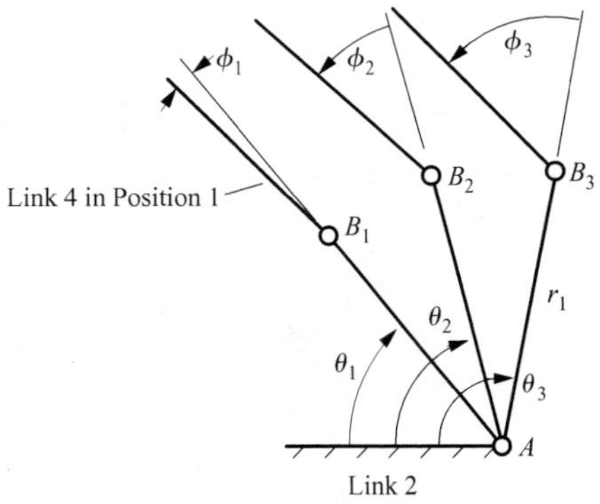

FIGURE 6.41 Inversion of linkage making r_2 the frame. The original linkage is inverted onto its driving crank to convert the function generation problem into a motion generation problem.

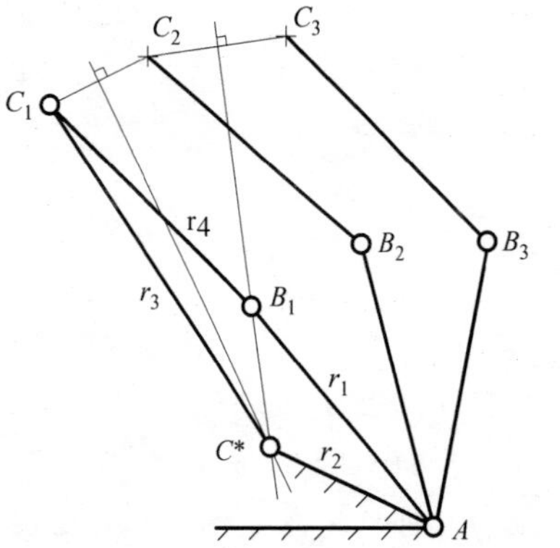

FIGURE 6.42 Construction of center point C^* given three positions of C.

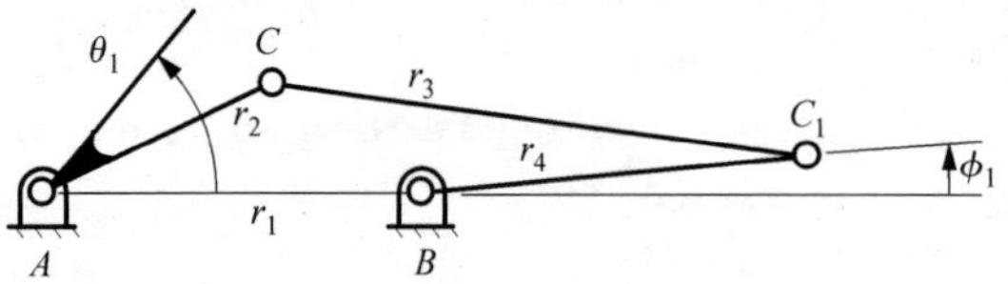

FIGURE 6.43 Final solution linkage.

6.5 SYNTHESIS OF CRANK-ROCKER LINKAGES FOR SPECIFIED ROCKER AMPLITUDE

In a crank-rocker mechanism, the crank rotates through 360°, and the rocker oscillates through an angle θ. This mechanism is often used interchangeably with cam mechanisms for the same function; however, there are many cases in which a crank-rocker mechanism is superior to a cam–follower mechanism. Among the advantages over cam systems are the smaller contact forces involved, the elimination of the retaining spring, and the closer clearances achieved because of the use of revolute joints.

6.5.1 Extreme Rocker Positions and Simple Analytical Solution

The maximum and minimum rocker angles occur in the positions shown in Fig. 6.44. Using the cosine rule, we have

$$(r_2 + r_3)^2 = r_1^2 + r_4^2 - 2r_1r_4\cos\rho \tag{6.42}$$

and

$$(r_3 - r_2)^2 = r_1^2 + r_4^2 - 2r_1r_4\cos\beta \tag{6.43}$$

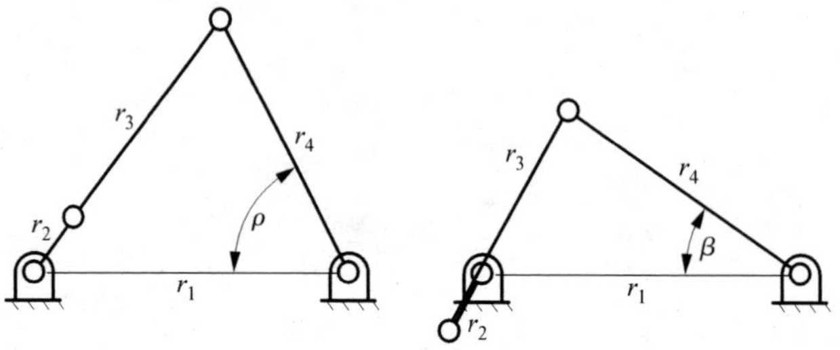

FIGURE 6.44 The positions of a crank-rocker linkage in which the rocker is at the extremes of its motion range.

Since we have two equations in six variables, r_1, r_2, r_3, r_4, ρ, and β, the values of four variables can be specified. As in the case of function generation, the angles in the triangles are independent of the size of the triangles. Therefore, r_1 is usually taken as 1. Usually, the design problem requires only a specified value for the difference $\beta - \rho$. Nevertheless, the solution is much simpler if both ρ and β are specified. Since a crank-rocker linkage is sought, it is also helpful to specify r_2. Values in the range 0.1 ″ r^2 ″ 0.4 will usually give good results when $r_1 = 1$. Assuming ρ, β, r_1 and r_2 are specified, we can solve Eqs. (6.42) and (6.43) for r_3 and r_4. Adding the equations and simplifying, we get

$$r_2^2 + r_3^2 = r_1^2 + r_4^2 - r_1 r_4(\cos\rho + \cos\beta) \tag{6.44}$$

Subtracting Eq. (6.44) from (6.42), we get

$$2r_2 r_3 = r_1 r_4(\cos\beta - \cos\rho) \tag{6.45}$$

Hence

$$r_3 = \frac{r_1 r_4(\cos\beta - \cos\rho)}{2r_2} \tag{6.46}$$

Substitution into Eq. (6.44) gives, after some manipulation,

$$Pr_4^2 + Qr_4 + R = 0 \tag{6.47}$$

where

$$P = 1 - \frac{r_1^2(\cos\beta - \cos\rho)^2}{4r_2^2}$$

$$Q = -r_1(\cos\beta + \cos\rho)$$

$$R = r_1^2 - r_2^2 \tag{6.48}$$

The solution to the quadratic equation Eq. (6.47) gives a positive root and a negative root for r_4. The negative root can be discarded. If no real roots exist, it is necessary to choose a new value of β and try again. Once r_4 is known, r_3 can be found from Eq. (6.46). The formulation of the problem guarantees that the joint between r_2 and r_3 will rotate completely, but this still does not guarantee a crank-rocker solution (it could be a type 1 double-rocker). Thus, although it is a type 1 linkage, it is necessary to check that $r_3 > r_2$. The Grashof inequality can be used as a simple check on arithmetic.

The simplified procedure given here can be used if the oscillation amplitude $(\rho - \beta)$ is the only quantity of interest. The procedure gives no control over the time ratio of the forward oscillation to the reverse oscillation. This time ratio is often of interest, however, and the following procedure gives a means of incorporating it in the basic design procedure.

6.5.2 The Rocker Amplitude Problem: Graphical Approach

As the crank in a crank-rocker mechanism rotates through 360°, the output link or rocker will oscillate through an angle θ. The limiting positions of the rocker occur when the crank and coupler are collinear as shown in Fig. 6.45. In general, the time required for the rocker oscillation in one direction will be different from the time required for the other direction. As previously indicated, the ratio of the times required for the forward and return motions is called the time ratio. An expression for the time ratio can be developed by using the nomenclature defined in Fig. 6.45.

In the crank-rocker, the crank moves through the angle ψ while the rocker moves from B_1 to B_2 through the angle θ. On the return stroke, the crank moves through the angle 360° – ψ and the rocker moves from B_2 to B_1 through the same angle θ.

Assuming that the crank moves with constant angular velocity, the ratio of the times for the forward and reverse strokes of the follower can be related directly to the angles in Fig. 6.45. The crank angle for the forward stroke is ψ or 180° + α. The crank angle for the return stroke is 360° – ψ or 180° – α. Therefore, the time ratio, Q, can be written as

$$Q = \frac{180 + \alpha}{180 - \alpha} \tag{6.49}$$

where α is given in degrees.

The most common problem associated with the synthesis of crank-rocker mechanisms is that of designing the linkage for a given oscillation angle and a given time ratio. For the discussion here, assume that the time ratio Q has been given. The first step in the synthesis is to compute the angle α. This can be done by rewriting the basic equation for Q. Then,

$$\alpha = 180\frac{(Q-1)}{(Q+1)} \tag{6.50}$$

Note that α is positive when Q is greater than 1 and negative when Q is less than 1. Examples of positive and negative α are shown in Fig. 6.46.

Once α is known, there are a number of ways to proceed with the design. The simplest way is to choose a location for O_4, select a trial value for ϕ, and draw the two positions of the rocker (r_4) separated by the angle θ. Draw any line x through the pivot at B_1, and construct a second line at an angle of α to the line x and through the pivot at B_2. Call the second line y. The intersection of lines x and y defines the location of the second fixed pivot (O_2).

Next compute the values of r_2 and r_3. This is done by using the geometric relationships in Fig. 6.45. That is,

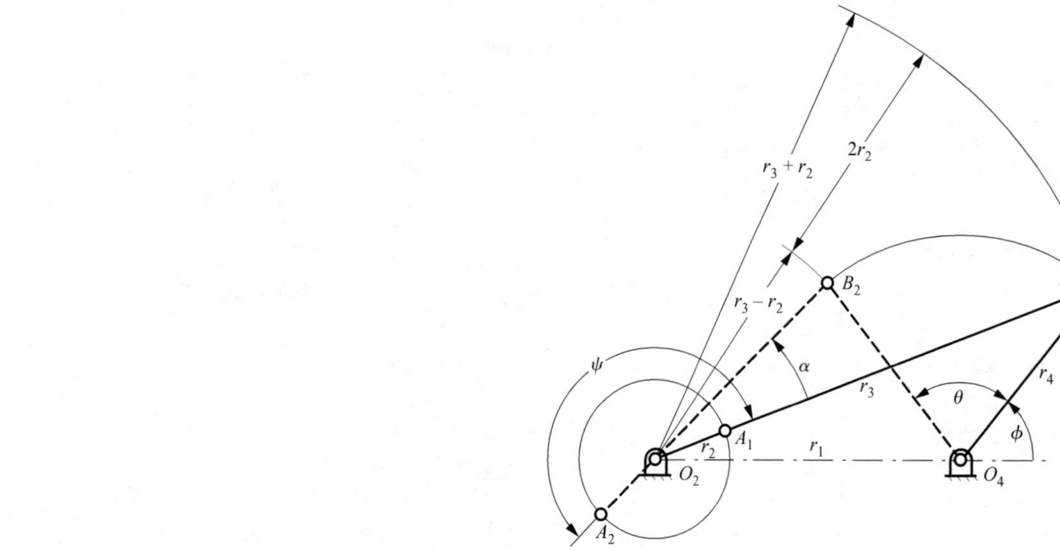

FIGURE 6.45 crank-rocker mechanism in extreme positions.

$$r_2 + r_3 = \overline{O_2B_1}$$

and

$$r_3 - r_2 = \overline{O_2B_2}$$

Therefore,

$$r_2 = \frac{\overline{O_2B_1} - \overline{O_2B_2}}{2} \tag{6.51}$$

and

$$r_3 = \frac{\overline{O_2B_1} + \overline{O_2B_2}}{2} \tag{6.52}$$

Note that during the design procedure, several choices were made. Among these were the starting angle ϕ for the line O_4B_1 and the slope of the line x. There are an infinite number of choices for each, and each choice will give a different linkage.

Note also that not all solutions are valid. In particular, the pivots B_1 and B_2 may not extend below the line of centers defined by a line through the fixed pivots O_2 and O_4. If this happens, the linkage must change branch to reach the two positions, and the desired oscillation angle will not be achieved. As indicated by Hall,[4] once α and θ are known, the locus of acceptable positions for O_2 must lie on circle arcs represented by the heavy sections of the circles shown in Fig. 6.47. The locus of O_2 must be on a circle arc because the triangle $B_2B_1O_2$ has a fixed base and a constant apex angle (α). If O_2 is chosen in the light part of the circles, the two positions of B will be on opposite sides of the line of centers.

In some instances, the length of one of the links must be a specific value. However, the procedure outlined here will permit only the length of the rocker to be specified directly. If the length of one of the other links is known, the lengths of the links in the linkage can be scaled using the procedure given in Section 6.4.1.

Range for α A study of Fig. 6.47 will indicate the extreme values for the angle α. When the time ratio is 1, then $\alpha = 0$. This case is shown in Fig. 6.48. When $\alpha = 0$, the limiting circles shown in Fig. 6.47 converge to a straight line through B_1 and B_2. Any point outside the span between B_1 and B_2 may be chosen as the fixed pivot for the crank. Note that, for this case, the distance between B_1 and B_2 is equal to $2r_2$. [See Eq. (6.51).]

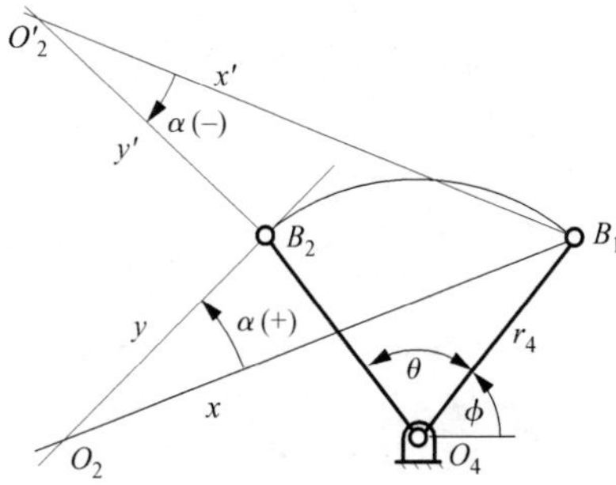

FIGURE 6.46 Locations of O_2 given θ and $\pm\,\alpha$.

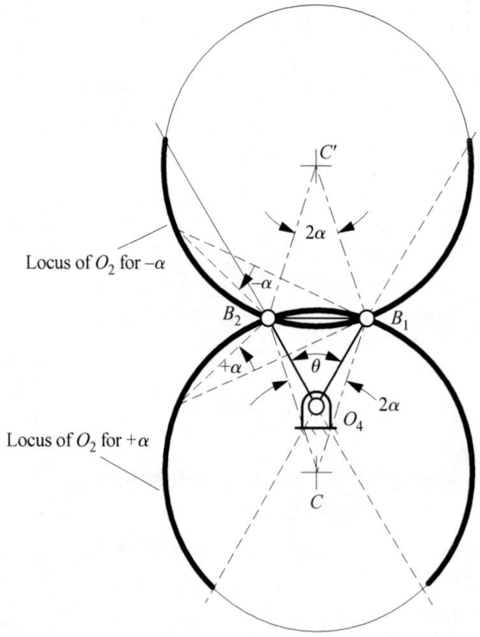

FIGURE 6.47 Possible locations for O_2 given θ and α.

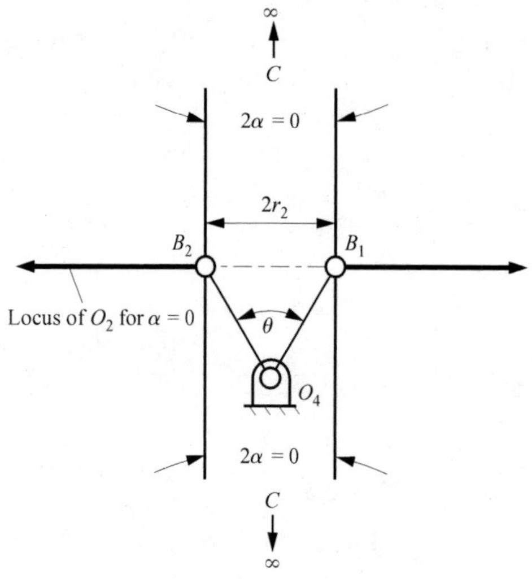

FIGURE 6.48 Limiting case when $\alpha = 0$ or $Q = 1$.

As $+\alpha$ increases from 0, the center C of the bottom circle in Fig. 6.47 will move from $-\infty$ toward the pivot O_4. The highest location possible for the circle is when it is tangent to B_1 and B_2 at the two extreme locations of r_4. This is shown in Fig. 6.49. In this position, there are no solutions possible, but if C is only slightly lower than the location C_m shown in Fig. 6.49, solutions exist for O_2 for positive α. When C moves above the line between B_1 and B_2, the angle 2α is the obtuse angle shown in Fig. 6.49. From the geometry shown in Fig. 6.49, the maximum value for α will be $\pi/2 + \theta/2$.

As α decreases from 0 (i.e., α becomes more negative), the center C' of the top circle in Fig. 6.47 will move from $+\infty$ toward the pivot O_4. The lowest location possible for the circle is again when it is tangent to r_4 at B_1 and B_2 for the two extreme locations of r_4. Again, in this position, no solutions are possible, but if C is moved only slightly *higher* than the location C_m shown in Fig. 6.49, solutions will exist for O_2. When C' moves above C_m, the angle -2α is the acute angle at C_m as shown. From the geometry shown in Fig. 6.49, the minimum value for α shown in Fig. 6.47 will be $-(\pi/2 - \theta/2)$.

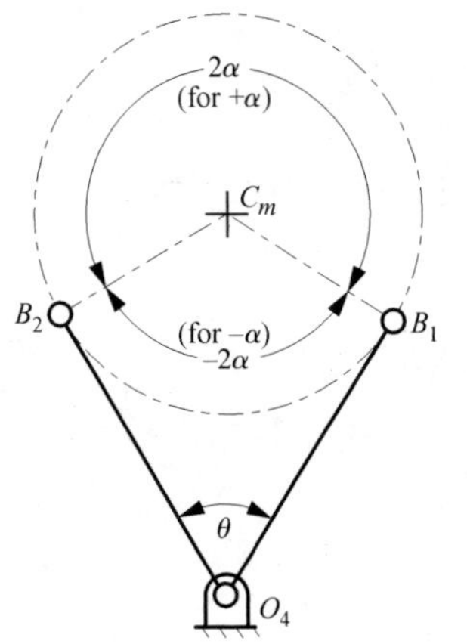

FIGURE 6.49 Limiting values for $\pm\alpha$. The maximum value when α is positive is $\pi/2 + \theta/2$. The minimum value when α is negative is $-(\pi/2 - \theta/2)$.

EXAMPLE 6.5 *Crank-rocker Design (Graphical)*

A crank-rocker is to be used in the transmission of an automatic washing machine to drive the agitator. The rocker link is attached to a gear sector, which drives a pinion gear attached to the agitator shaft. The radius of the sector gear is 3 in., and the pinion radius is 1 in. The pivot for the output link is at O_4. The sector gear is to oscillate 90°. The times for the forward and return stroke for the sector are the same. If the base link (r_1) of the mechanism is to be 10-cm long, determine the lengths of the other links (r_2, r_3, and r_4).

Solution

A sketch of the mechanism is shown in Fig. 6.50. We must determine the four-bar linkage defined by O_2, O_4, A, and B. The sector gear is attached to the output link, which rotates through an angle θ of 90°. The time ratio is 1 so

$$\alpha = 180^\circ\left[\frac{Q-1}{Q+1}\right] = 180^\circ\left[\frac{0}{2}\right] = 0$$

Therefore, the locus for O_2 corresponds to that shown in Fig. 6.48. For the construction, let r_4 be 1 in. Then a solution for the linkage can be constructed as shown in Fig. 6.51.

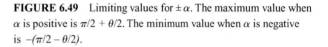

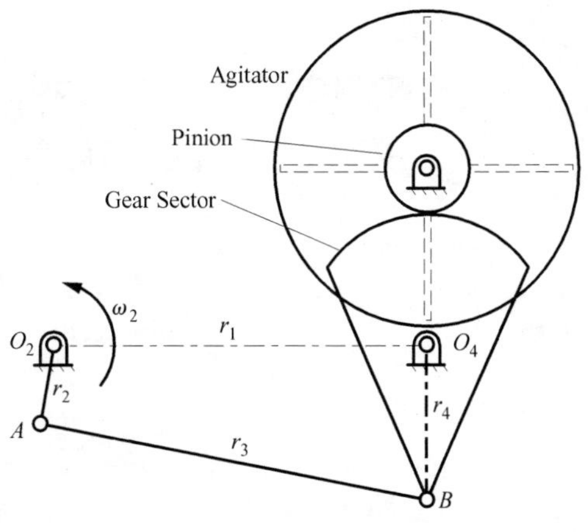

FIGURE 6.50 Sketch of linkage for Example 6.5.

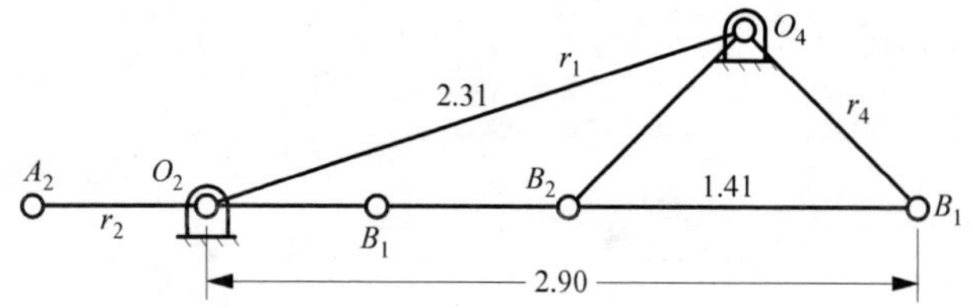

FIGURE 6.51 A solution to Example 6.5.

From Fig. 6.51, we have

$$r_4 = 1 \text{ in}$$

$$r_1 = 2.31 \text{ in}$$

$$r_2 + r_3 = O_2B_1$$
$$r_3 - r_2 = O_2B_2$$

or

$$r_2 = (O_2B_1 - O_2B_2)/2 = (2.90 - 1.49)/2 = 0.70 \text{ in}$$
$$r_3 = (O_2B_1 - O_2B_2)/2 = (2.90 + 1.49)/2 = 2.20 \text{ in}$$

Determining the scaling factor, we get

$$K = \frac{R_1}{r_1} = \frac{10}{3.31} = 3.021 = \frac{R_2}{r_2} = \frac{R_3}{r_3} = \frac{R_4}{r_4}$$

Using the unscaled lengths from the figure gives

$$R_2 = 3.021\, r_2 = 3.021(0.70) = 2.11 \text{ cm}$$

$$R_3 = 3.021\, r_3 = 3.021(2.20) = 6.65 \text{ cm}$$

$$R_4 = 3.021\, r_4 = 3.021(1) = 3.02 \text{ cm}$$

The mechanism is drawn to scale in Fig. 6.52.

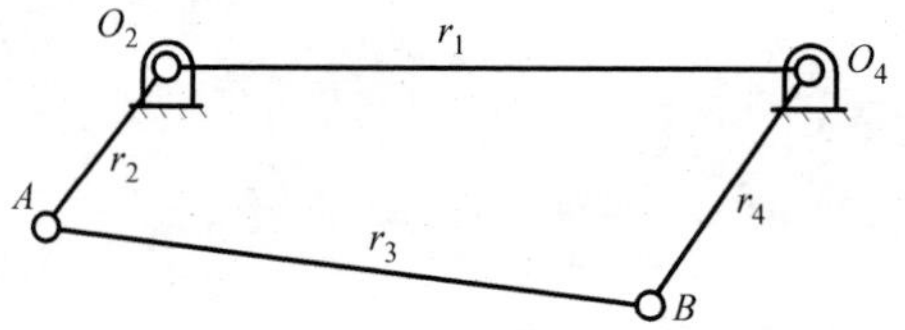

FIGURE 6.52 Final linkage for Example 6.5.

6.5.3 Transmission Angle

Ultimately, the design of the crank-rockers reduces to an optimization problem because a single design based on the construction discussed above will usually have poor transmission angle characteristics. The maximum (η_{max}) and minimum (η_{min}) transmission angles are shown in Fig. 6.53. Typically, a poor transmission angle corresponds to a large value of $|(\pi/2 - \eta_{max/min})|$. Note that the maximum and minimum values for the transmission angle do not occur at the extreme positions of r_4, but η_{max} and η_{min} can be easily computed using the geometry in Fig. 6.53. The equations are

$$\eta'_{max} = \cos^{-1}\left[\frac{r_4^2 - (r_1 + r_2)^2 + r_3^2}{2r_4r_3}\right] \tag{6.53}$$

$$\eta'_{min} = \cos^{-1}\left[\frac{r_4^2 - (r_1 - r_2)^2 + r_3^2}{2r_4r_3}\right] \tag{6.54}$$

If η_{max} is negative, then $\eta_{max} = \pi + \eta'_{max}$. Otherwise, $\eta_{max} = \eta'_{max}$. Similar conditions apply to η_{min}.

6.5.4 Alternative Graphical Design Procedure Based on Specification of O_2–O_4

The graphical procedure developed earlier could be programmed if desired. However, it has the undesirable characteristic of a variable length for the frame. An approach developed by Hall[4] is easier to program, and it will be discussed here. In this procedure, we will select the length of the frame link initially (instead of link 4). This approach reduces the design problem to a one-dimensional problem where well-defined limits are known for the design variable.

Assuming θ and α are known, the following procedure, represented in Fig. 6.54, provides a means for determining all of the linkages satisfying the design requirements. The approach is to determine the locus for all possible values of B_2 relative to the frame. To construct the locus, do the following:

1. Pick the base link and locate the ground pivots O_2 and O_4. The distance O_2O_4 determines the scale for the linkage.
2. Draw the line O_2G at an angle $\theta/2 - \alpha$ (positive clockwise) relative to O_2O_4.
3. Draw the line O_4G at an angle of $\theta/2$ (positive counterclockwise) relative to O_2O_4.

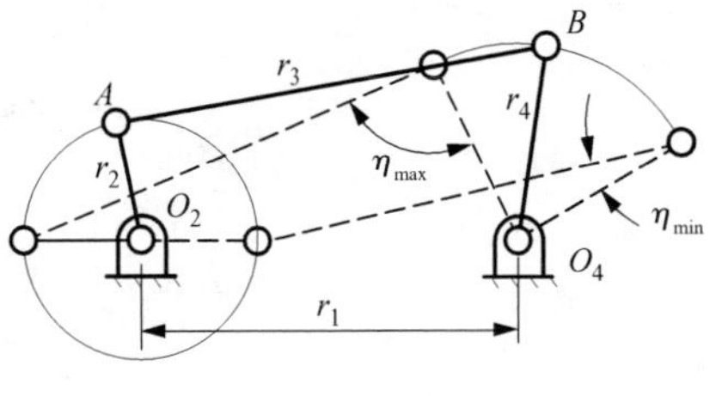

FIGURE 6.53 Maximum and minimum transmission angles.

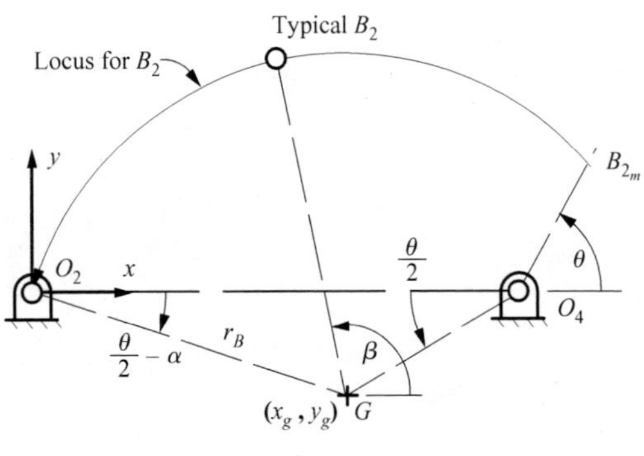

FIGURE 6.54 Construction of the circle arc giving the locus B_2 and B_1.

4. Draw the circle of radius GO_2 centered at G.
5. Draw a line ($O_4B_{2_m}$) through O_4 at an angle of θ (positive counterclockwise) relative to O_2O_4.
6. The circle arc starting at O_2 and ending at the intersection with either $O_4B_{2_m}$ or O_2O_4 (whichever occurs first) gives the locus of the point B in the second extreme position of the rocker. The point (B_1) located at an angle θ relative to the line O_4B_2 is the other extreme position. The locus of B_1 will be a second circle that has the same radius as the B_2 circle, and the center for the B_1 circle will be the reflection of point G about the O_2O_4 axis. The length r_4 is equal to O_4B.

After B_2 is chosen and B_1 is located, the remaining link lengths can then be computed by solving Eqs. (6.51) and (6.52). The transmission angle limits can be measured after drawing the linkage in the extreme positions shown in Fig. 6.53.

EXAMPLE 6.6
Crank-Rocker Design Using Alternate Graphical Procedure

A crank-rocker mechanism is to have an oscillation angle of 80° and a time ratio of 1.3. The base length is to be 2 in. Design a linkage that will satisfy these conditions.

Solution

The time ratio is 1.3 so

$$\alpha = 180^\circ\left[\frac{Q-1}{Q+1}\right] = 180^\circ\left[\frac{1.3-1}{1.3+1}\right] = 23.47^\circ$$

We will begin the design procedure by drawing the two fixed pivots, locating point G, and drawing the arc corresponding to the locus for B_2. The angles needed to locate G are

$$\frac{\theta}{2} = 40^\circ$$

and

$$\frac{\theta}{2} - \alpha = 40^\circ - 23.47 = 16.53^\circ$$

The construction is shown in Fig. 6.55.

Now we need to select any point on the locus for B_2. Once B_2 is selected, B_1 can be found. This is shown in Fig. 6.56. Given B_1 and B_2, the link lengths can be found using Eqs. (6.51) and 6.52).

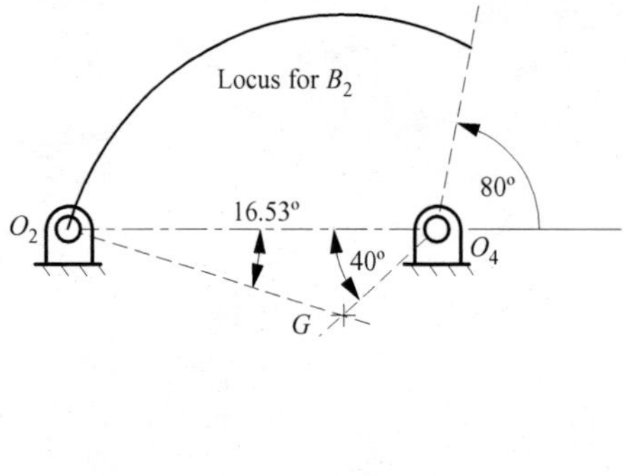

FIGURE 6.55 Construction showing the locus of B_2 for Example 6.6.

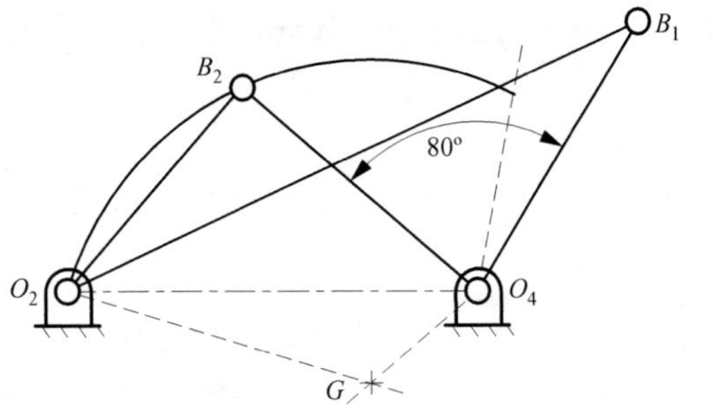

FIGURE 6.56 Construction of B_2 and B_1 for Example 6.6.

From Fig. 6.56, we have

$$r_4 = 1.51 \text{ in}$$

$$r_1 = 2 \text{ in}$$

$$r_2 + r_3 = O_2B_1$$
$$r_3 - r_2 = O_2B_2$$

$$r_2 = (O_2B_1 - O_2B_2)/2 = (3.09 - 1.29)/2 = 0.90 \text{ in}$$
$$r_3 = (O_2B_1 + O_2B_2)/2 = (3.06 + 1.29)/2 = 2.18 \text{ in}$$

The mechanism is drawn to scale in Fig. 6.57

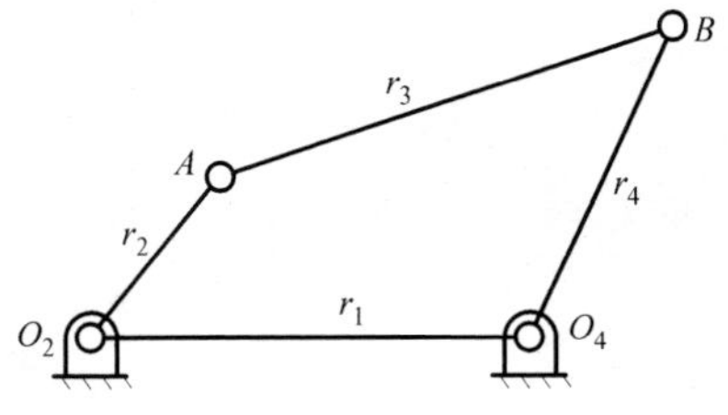

FIGURE 6.57 Final linkage for Example 6.6.

Reviewing the graphical procedure represented in Fig. 6.54, we see that once θ and α are known, the arc defining the loci for B_2 is defined. Locating a point on the arc requires the specification of only one additional parameter (β). Therefore, different designs can be developed by adjusting this single variable. Furthermore, because the locus for B_2 is the circle arc between O_2 and B_{2_m}, the limits for β can be established at the beginning of the design procedure.

The geometry shown in Fig. 6.54 is the general geometry for the design procedure. However, depending on the values of α and θ, four cases need to be considered. These are represented in Figs. 6.48a–6.48d. The four cases are characterized by the following:

a. $0 < \alpha < \theta$ (the general case and the one represented in Figs. 6.54 and 6.58a),

b. $-(\pi/2 - \theta/2) < \alpha < 0$ (Fig. 6.58b),

c. $\alpha = \theta$ (Fig. 6.58c), and

d. $\pi/2 + \theta/2 > \alpha > \theta$ (Fig. 6.58d).

6.5.5 Analytical Design Procedure Based on Specification of O_2–O_4

Case a ($0 < \alpha < \theta$) To determine the analytical equations for the arc giving the locus of B_2 in Fig. 6.58a, it is necessary only to find the coordinates of the circle center G and the limits β_1 and β_2. Locating the x and y axes as shown in Fig. 6.54, we define the center (x_g, y_g) by the triangle O_2O_4G, which has one known side (O_2O_4) and two known included angles ($\theta/2 - \alpha$ and $\theta/2$). By simple plane geometry, the coordinates of the center of the B_2 circle are

$$x_g = O_2O_4\left[\frac{\tan(\theta/2)}{\tan(\theta/2)+\tan(\theta/2-\alpha)}\right] \tag{6.55}$$

and

$$y_g = (O_2O_4 - x_g)\tan(\theta/2)$$

and the radius of the circle arc is

$$r_B = \sqrt{x_g^2 + y_g^2} \tag{6.56}$$

A given point on the B_2 circle can be found using r_B and the angle β; however, the allowable range for β must be determined first. The point B on the rocker cannot lie below the line defined by O_2O_4. Therefore, one extreme position of the locus for B_2 is O_2.

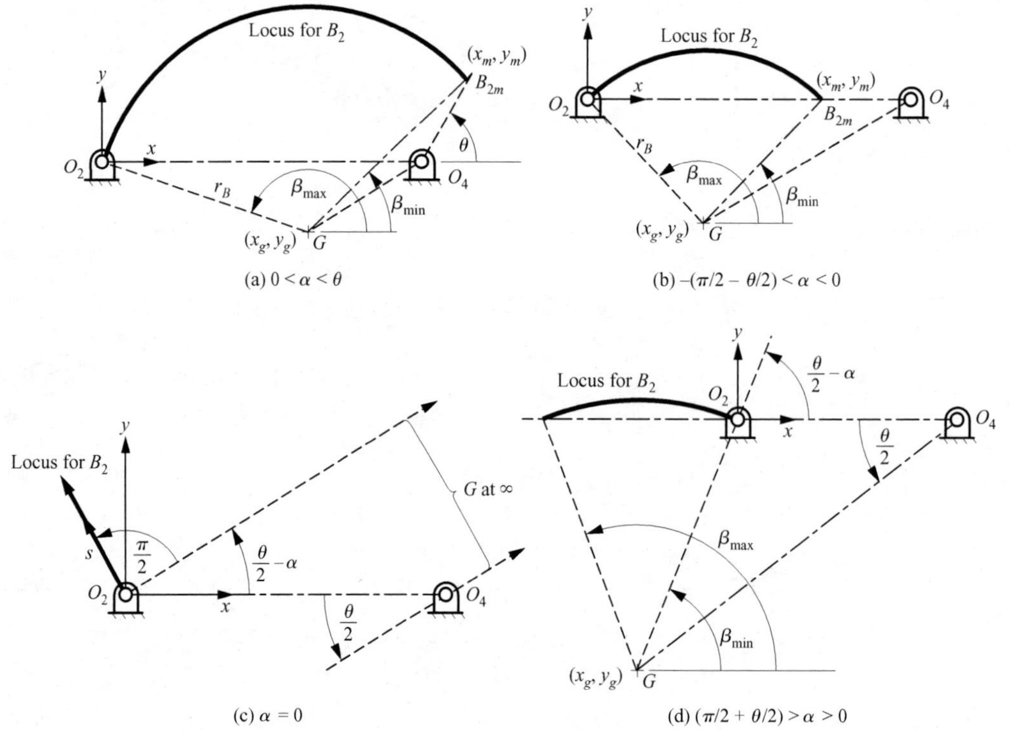

FIGURE 6.58 Different geometries based on relative values of α and θ.

In Fig. 6.58a, the other extreme position is found by noting that B_1 cannot lie below the extension of O_2O_4. Therefore, the other extreme position of the B_2 locus is at the intersection of the B_2 circle and the line through O_4 at an angle of θ with the horizontal. The coordinates of this intersection point are found most easily if we first scale the linkage by setting $O_2O_4 = 1$. Then

$$r_B \cos\left(\beta_{\min}\right) = x_m - x_g \tag{6.57}$$

$$r_B \sin\left(\beta_{\min}\right) = y_m - y_g \tag{6.58}$$

and

$$\frac{y_m}{x_m - 1} = \tan\theta \tag{6.59}$$

If Eqs. (6.57) and (6.58) are squared and added and Eq. (6.59) is used to eliminate x_m from the result, the following quadratic equation results for y_m:

$$\left[\frac{1}{\tan^2\theta} + 1\right]y_m^2 - 2\left[\frac{x_g - 1}{\tan\theta} + y_g\right]y_m + \left[1 + y_g^2 + x_g^2 - 2x_g - r_B^2\right] = 0$$

or

$$y_m = \left[-B \pm \sqrt{B^2 - 4AC}\right]\Big/2A \tag{6.60}$$

where

$$A = \frac{1}{\tan^2\theta} + 1$$

$$B = -2\left[\frac{x_g - 1}{\tan\theta} + y_g\right]$$

$$C = \left[1 + y_g^2 + x_g^2 - 2x_g - r_B^2\right]$$

Two values for y are mathematically possible, but there will be a maximum of one positive root. Only positive values for y_m are of interest. If both values of y are negative, the condition in Fig. 6.58b is indicated. If one y_m is positive, then x_m can be computed using Eq. (6.59) or

$$x_m = 1 + \frac{y_m}{\tan\theta} \tag{6.61}$$

Note that $B^2 - 4AC$ must be positive for a valid solution to exist.

The minimum β is

$$\beta_{\min} = \tan^{-1}\left[\frac{y_m - y_g}{x_m - x_g}\right] \tag{6.62}$$

and the maximum value for β is

$$\beta_{\max} = \pi + \alpha - \frac{\theta}{2} \tag{6.63}$$

For a valid design, $\beta_{\min}$ ″ β ″ $\beta_{\max}$.

Case b [(π/2 – θ/2) < α < 0] For the case when α is negative (Fig. 6.58b), the coordinates of G and the radius r_B are the same as in Case a. The coordinates at the extreme location B_{2_m} are given by

$$y_m = 0 \tag{6.64}$$

and

$$x_m = 2r_B \cos\left(\frac{\theta}{2} - \alpha\right) \tag{6.65}$$

The equations for $\beta_{\min}$ and $\beta_{\max}$ and are given by Eqs (6.62) and (6.63).

Case c (α = θ) When $\alpha = \theta$, the center G will be at infinity, as shown in Fig. 6.58c. This is indicated by Eq. (6.55) because the denominator in the expression for x_g becomes 0. Therefore, the locus for B_2 is a straight line through O_2 at an angle of $\pi/2 + \theta/2 - \alpha$ to the horizontal. B_2 can be located anywhere along the straight line, including at infinity. When B_2 is located at infinity, the coupler becomes a slider and the mechanism becomes an inverted slider-crank mechanism (see Hall[4]). Computationally, this case can be best treated separately. Points on the locus for B_2 are given by

$$x = s\cos(\theta/2 - \pi/2 + \alpha) \tag{6.66}$$

and

$$y = s\sin(\theta/2 - \pi/2 + \alpha) \tag{6.67}$$

where s is the distance measured from the pivot O_2. It is not necessary to compute $\beta_{\min}$ and $\beta_{\max}$.

Case d (π/2 + θ/2 > α > θ) When $\alpha > \theta$, the center G will be located to the left of the pivot O_2, as shown in Fig. 6.58d. The center of the circle is given by the intersection of the line through O_4 with the line through O_2. The coordinates of the center G are given by

$$x_g = O_2O_4\left[\frac{\tan(\theta/2)}{\tan(\theta/2) + \tan(\theta/2 - \alpha)}\right]$$

and

$$y_g = -(O_2O_4 - x_g)\tan(\theta/2)$$

and the radius is given by

$$r_B = \sqrt{x_g^2 + y_g^2}$$

Note that both x_g and y_g will be negative. The locus for B_2 will begin at O_2 and end at B_{2_m}, where

$$y_m = 0$$

and

$$x_m = -2r_B \cos\left(\frac{\theta}{2} - \alpha\right)$$

The extreme values for β are given by

$$\beta_{\min} = \alpha - \frac{\theta}{2}$$

and

$$\beta_{\max} = \tan^{-1}\left[\frac{y_m - y_g}{x_m - x_g}\right]$$

For Cases a, b, and d, we can locate B_2 using any value of β between $\beta_{\min}$ and $\beta_{\max}$. The link lengths are computed using Eqs. (6.51) and (6.52) together with the following:

$$x = r_B \cos\beta + x_g$$

$$y = r_B \sin\beta + y_g$$

$$r_4 = \sqrt{(x-1)^2 + y^2} \tag{6.68}$$

$$O_2B_2 = \sqrt{x^2 + y^2} \tag{6.69}$$

$$\phi = \tan^{-1}\left(\frac{y}{x-1}\right) \tag{6.70}$$

$$O_2B_1 = \sqrt{\left[1 + r_4\cos(\phi - \theta)\right]^2 + \left[r_4\sin(\phi - \theta)\right]^2} \tag{6.71}$$

In Eq. (6.70), it is important to preserve the signs of both the numerator and denominator since ϕ may be greater than $\pi/2$.

For Case c, we can locate values of B_2 by using the distance s from the pivot O_2. For a given value of s, we can compute the location (x,y) of B_2 using Eqs. (6.66) and (6.67). Equations (6.68)–(6.71) can then be used to compute the remaining quantities needed to determine O_2B_2 and O_2B_1.

The crank-rocker design equations are coded in MATLAB and included on the disk with this book.

6.5.6 Use of Analytical Design Procedure for Optimization

Using the procedure developed, any value of β satisfying $\beta_{\min}$ ″ β ″ $\beta_{\max}$ will produce a linkage that satisfies the basic design requirements for θ and α (or Q). To choose the best linkage, we must select a criterion to optimize. If the output link of the linkage is subjected to a constant torque and we wish to design a linkage that can be driven with the smallest motor possible, it is reasonable to optimize the linkage based on the transmission angle. Therefore, we will use this as an example of the procedure that would be used for optimization. Referring to Fig. 6.53, we see that the maximum and minimum values for the transmission angle are given by Eqs. (6.53) and (6.54).

The basic objective function to be minimized during the optimization procedure is

$$U' = \max\left[\left|\frac{\pi}{2} - \mu_{\max}\right|, \left|\frac{\pi}{2} - \mu_{\min}\right|\right]$$

However, if U' is used directly, the optimum linkage will occasionally be one where r_2 is very small compared with one of the other link lengths. Therefore, it is convenient to include the link length ratio as part of the objective function. Because r_2 will be the shortest link, this function can be written as

$$F = \max\left[\frac{r_1}{r_2}, \frac{r_3}{r_2}, \frac{r_4}{r_2}\right]$$

and

$$U'' = e^{(F-n)}$$

where n is an integer that represents the largest acceptable value for the link length ratio. Here, it is assumed that length ratios less than n are acceptable. A typical value for n is 5.

The combined objective function is

$$U = U' + WU''$$

where W is a weighting factor that can be chosen to adjust the relative importance of the length ratio. In many problems, the value chosen for W is not important because linkages that have good transmission angles often have good link length ratios. When n is 5, values between 1 and 5 for W will generally give good results.

Once β is selected, the crank-rocker linkage is completely defined, and a value for U can be computed. Therefore, U is a function of β only, and well-established limits for β are known. The optimization can then be easily accomplished by varying β and computing U until U is minimized. This can be done manually, interactively, or by using any one-dimensional (line search) optimization routine. Several such one-dimensional routines are described by Arora.[6]

6.6 PATH SYNTHESIS

The path synthesis problem is that of specifying the path taken by a single point fixed in some member of a mechanism. There may also be a requirement for faster or slower speeds along different portions of the path. Although many research papers have been written on the subject of path synthesis, designers usually use a trial-and-error approach in practice. The traditional tool for this purpose is the Hrones and Nelson coupler-curve atlas.[10] This is a large book containing plots of four-bar linkage coupler curves for a large variety of points located in the coupler plane and a large range of link length variations. The approach is to leaf through the coupler-curve atlas and pick out a curve that has more or less the right shape and then refine it by trial and error, testing the effect of small variations in the position of the coupler point or small variations in the link lengths. This gets quite laborious if done manually.

Use of either a simple program based on the theory presented in Chapter 5 or professionally written linkage analysis software can make this task much easier. Coupler-curve programs written in MATLAB for both four-bar linkages and slider-crank mechanisms are included on the disk provided with this book. These programs use the same nomenclature as the Hrones and Nelson atlas. Using these programs, it is possible to review quickly the coupler curves available and to determine the link lengths and coupler point that will generate the curve.

6.6.1 Design of Six-Bar Linkages Using Coupler Curves

Coupler curves from four-bar linkages and slider-crank mechanisms are used in two main ways. The first is to use the motion of the coupler in the area of the curve to perform some function. A common use for such points is in packaging and conveying equipment. Figure 6.59 shows a coupler mechanism design for packing hay in a round baler.[11] Figure 6.60 shows a mechanism that has been used to feed film in a motion picture projector.[12]

A second use for coupler curves is to facilitate the design of six- and eight-link mechanisms where the output link is to have a prescribed motion relative to the input link. A six-link mechanism is represented schematically in Fig. 6.61, where link 2 is the input and link 6 is the output. The output dyad (links 5 and 6) is driven by the coupler point (E) of the four-bar linkage. By properly selecting the coupler curve, different functional relationships between ϕ and θ can be achieved. The design of six-link mechanisms using coupler curves is discussed extensively by Soni.[5] The design procedure is illustrated in the following two examples.

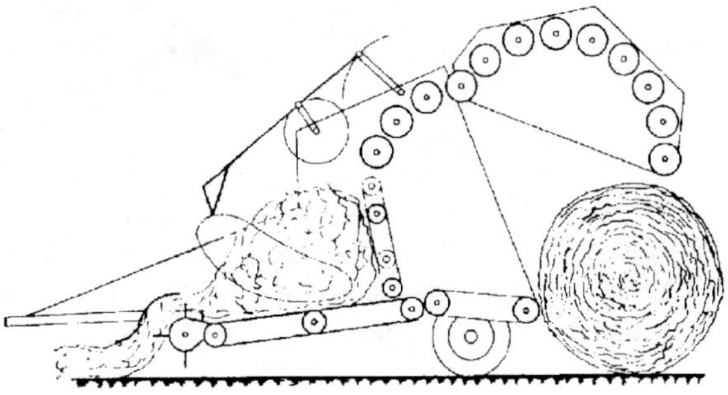

FIGURE 6.59 Coupler point used in packing mechanism in round baler.[11]

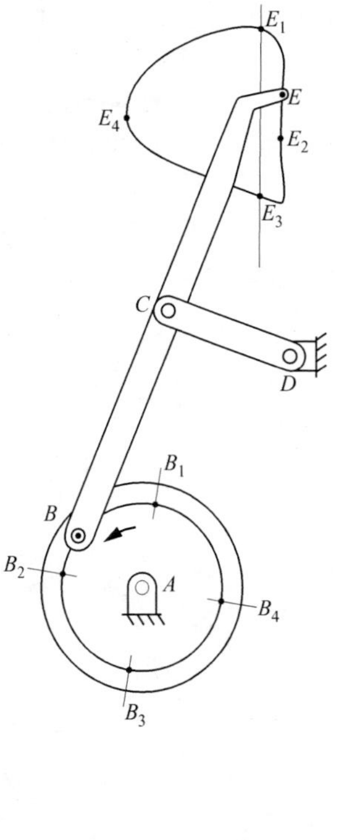

FIGURE 6.60 Coupler point used in film feed mechanism.[18]

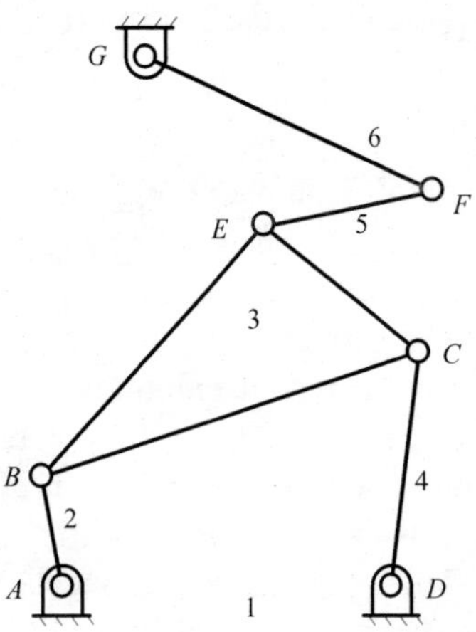

FIGURE 6.61 Six-link mechanism that can be designed using coupler curves.

EXAMPLE 6.7
Design of a Six-Link Dwell Mechanism Using a Coupler Curve

A mechanism of the type shown in Fig. 6.61 is to be designed such that link 6 is an oscillating lever and link 2 rotates a full 360°. The output link is to oscillate through a range of 30° during the first 120° of crank rotation. Link 6 is then to dwell for 90° of crank rotation and return during the remaining 150° of crank rotation.

Solution

To solve this problem, it is necessary to have access to an atlas of coupler curves or to use a program that can generate the coupler curves. Regardless of the procedure used, we must be able to determine the geometry of the curve and the travel distance along the curve as a function of input rotation. In the Hrones and Nelson atlas and in the programs *hr_crankrocker.m* and *hr_slidercrank.m* provided on the disk with this book, a dashed line is used for each 5° of crank rotation. We will use the four-bar program *hr_crankrocker.m* to generate candidate coupler curves. The first step is to visualize the shape of coupler curve that can be used to drive links 5 and 6. Several different geometries might be used, but the simplest is a curve of roughly elliptical shape. The coupler curves used are displayed in Figs. 6.62 and 6.63, and the design procedure is shown in Fig. 6.64. The procedure is described in the following.

1. Test different coupler curves to determine whether a portion of the curve in the vicinity of the minor axis is roughly circular in shape for the desired dwell period (90° or 18 dashes). Fig. 6.62 gives a set of curves generated with the program *hr_crankrocker.m* when $r_1 = 4$, $r_2 = 1$, $r_3 = 3$, and $r_4 = 4$. From the curves displayed, we will select the curve shown in Fig. 6.63.

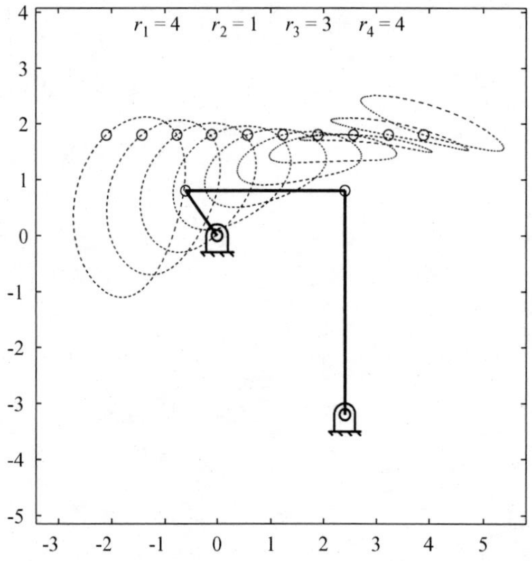

FIGURE 6.62 Coupler curves for Example 6.7. Note that each dash corresponds to 5° of crank rotation.

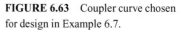

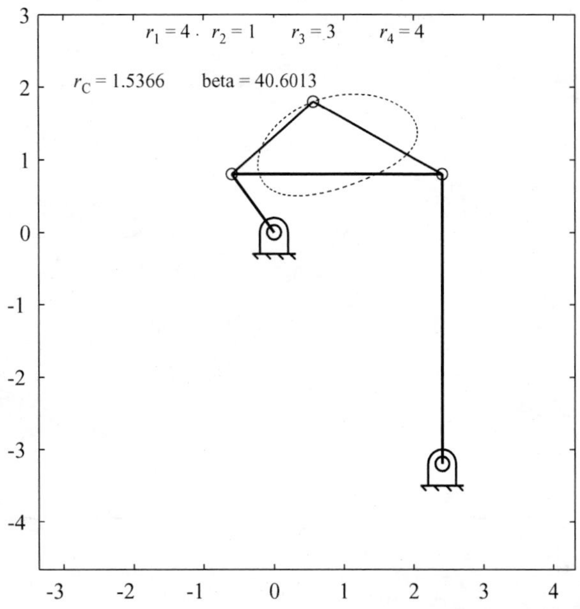

FIGURE 6.63 Coupler curve chosen for design in Example 6.7.

2. After a coupler curve is identified, find the center of the circle that best fits the circular region identified in step 1. The radius of the circle will be the length of link 5. Identify explicitly the beginning and end of the circular portion of the curve. The center of the circle arc will be one extreme position for point *F*. This is shown in Fig. 6.64, where the mechanism has been redrawn so that the frame link (r_1) is horizontal.
3. Point *F*′ corresponds to the second extreme position of *F*. To locate *F*′, identify the point on the coupler curve corresponding to 120° (24 dashes) of crank rotation beyond the dwell. Locate a perpendicular line to the coupler point at this point, and locate *F*′ on this line. Note that when link 5 is in an extreme position, it will be perpendicular to the coupler curve.
4. The pivot *G* must be located on the perpendicular bisector of the line *FF*′. Locate *G* such that the angle *FGF*′ is 30°. The parameters corresponding to the solution are as follows:

$$r_1 = 4, \quad r_5 = 1.682, \quad BE = 1.537$$
$$r_2 = 1, \quad r_6 = 2.694, \quad \beta = 40.6^\circ$$
$$r_3 = 3, \quad G_x = 0.697, \quad \theta_1 = 0$$
$$r_4 = 4, \quad G_y = 3.740$$

5. Compute and plot the motion of link 6 relative to link 2 to evaluate the design. The resulting mechanism is simply a four-bar linkage with the addition of two more links (Watt's six-bar mechanism). The two additional links are called a dyad and can be easily analyzed using the procedures given previously. A MATLAB routine (*sixbar.m*) for a six-bar linkage analysis based on the four-bar and dyad routines is provided on the disk with this book. Part of the analysis from this program is given in Fig. 6.65. The results are close to the design specifications, and the basic design is acceptable. Note in Fig. 6.65 that the angular velocity of link 6 is approximately zero during the dwell. The input (crank) velocity was 1 rad/s.

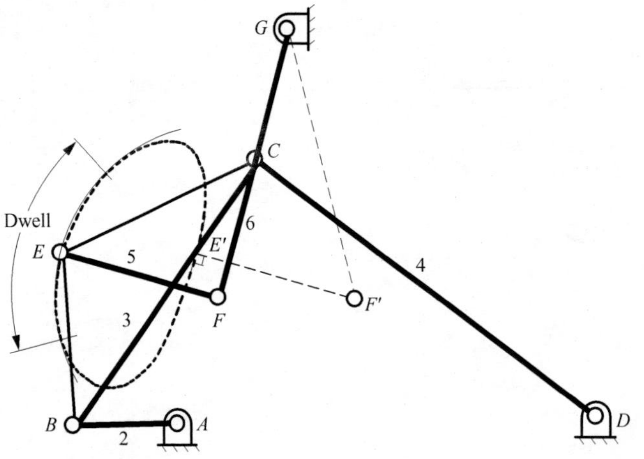

FIGURE 6.64 Design procedure for mechanism in Example 6.7.

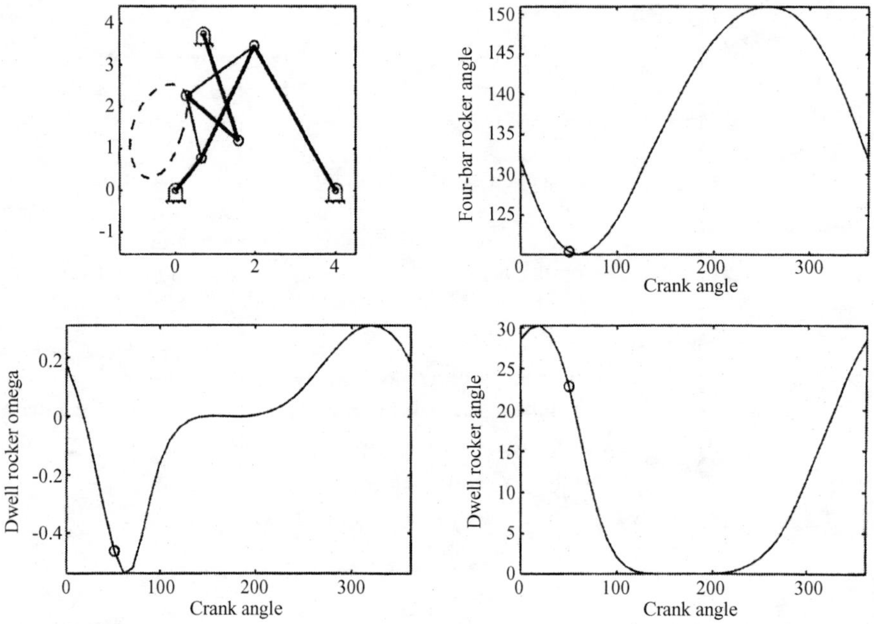

FIGURE 6.65 Analysis of linkage designed in Example 6.7. The velocity plot is based on a crank velocity of 1 rad/s.

This design procedure can yield a large number of candidate designs. The best design can be chosen by using an appropriate evaluation criterion. Typical criteria are linkage size, force transmission characteristics, and acceleration characteristics.

EXAMPLE 6.8
Design of a Six-Link Mechanism for a Double Oscillation

A mechanism of the type shown in Fig. 6.61 is to be designed such that link 6 will make two complete 30° oscillations for each revolution of the driving link.

Solution

For this problem, no timing information is required. Therefore, we need only to ensure that the output link makes two complete oscillations for one oscillation of the input crank. Again, we will use the four-bar program *hr_crankrocker.m* to generate candidate coupler curves. The first step is to visualize the shape of a coupler curve that can be used to drive links 5 and 6. One curve that will work for this type of problem is a figure-eight curve. The design procedure is shown in Fig. 6.66 and described in the following:

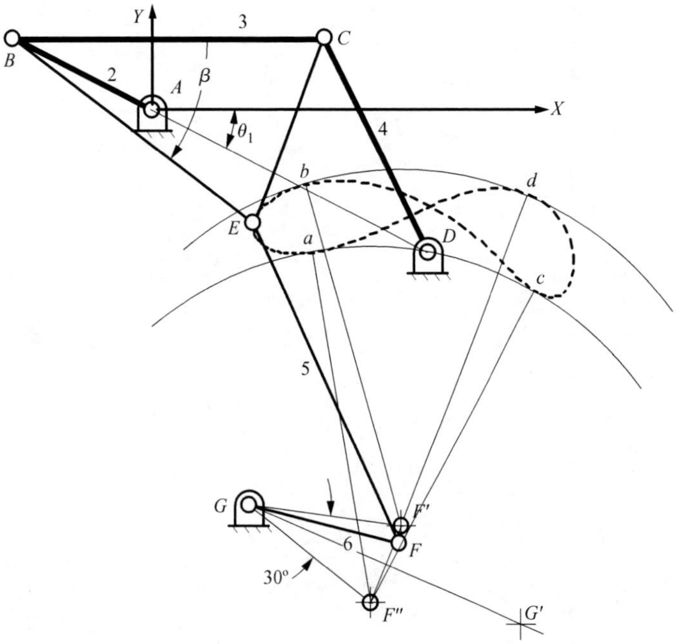

FIGURE 6.66 Procedure for designing linkage for Example 6.8.

1. Select a coupler curve that is a figure-eight curve with roughly equal lobes. The coupler curve selected is displayed in Fig. 6.67.
2. After the coupler curve is identified, select the length of link 5 and draw a circle or circle arc with a radius equal to the length of link 5 and tangent to the coupler curve at the two points *b* and *d*. The center, F', of this circle is one extreme position of point *F*. Draw another circle or circle arc of the same radius tangent to the coupler curve at points *a* and *c*. The center, F'', of this circle is the second extreme position of *F*.
3. The pivot point, *G*, must be located on the perpendicular bisector of the line $F'F''$. Locate *G* such that the angle $F'GF''$ is 30°. Link 6 is the link from F' to *G* (or from F'' to *G*). Note that there are two possible locations for point *G*. The location *G* is chosen in this example over G' because it will result in better transmission characteristics. If point G' is chosen, the linkage will lock up before it traverses its entire range of motion because the distance $G'b$ is slightly larger than $(EF + FG)$. The parameters corresponding to the solution are as follows:

$$
\begin{array}{lll}
r_1 = 2, & r_5 = 2.212, & BE = 1.927 \\
r_2 = 1, & r_6 = 1.000, & \beta = -36.44^\circ \\
r_3 = 2, & G_x = 0.625, & \theta_1 = -26.57^\circ \\
r_4 = 1.5, & G_y = -2.468 &
\end{array}
$$

4. Compute and plot the motion of link 6 relative to link 2 to evaluate the design. This is done in Fig. 6.68 based on the program (*sixbar.m*) provided on the disk with this book. Again, the input (crank) velocity was chosen as 1 rad/s.

The results given in Fig. 6.68 are very close to the design specifications. If more accurate results are desired, the location of *G* or the lengths of r_5 or r_6 could be adjusted slightly. This can be done

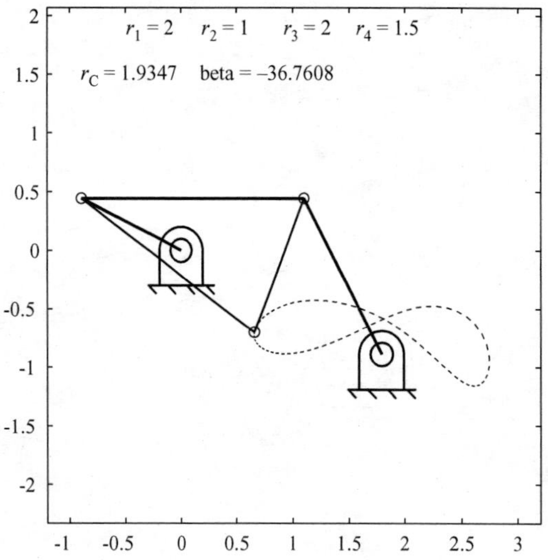

FIGURE 6.67 Curve that can be used for Example 6.8.

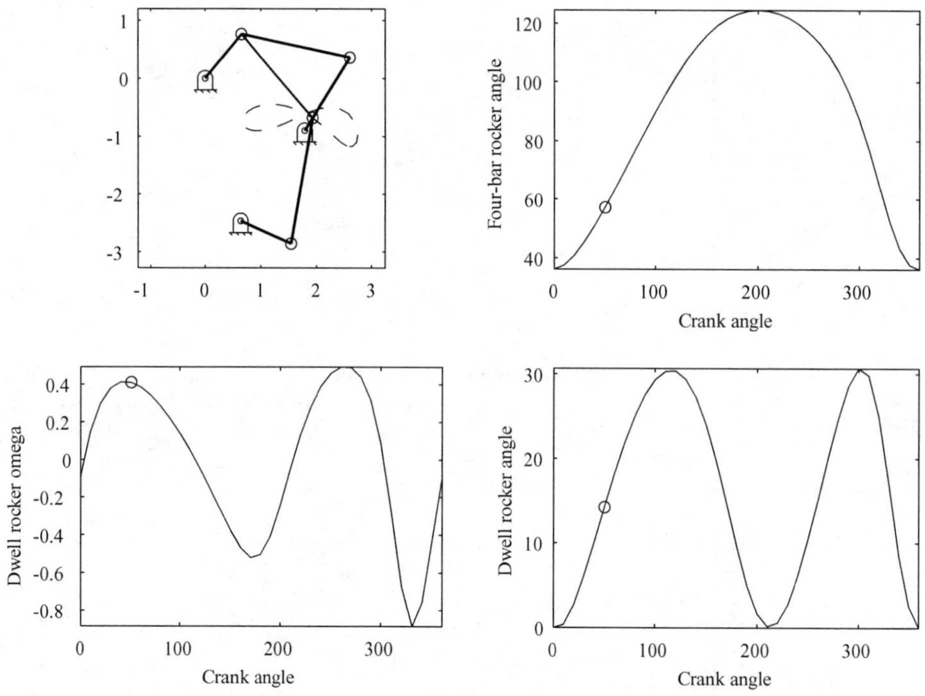

FIGURE 6.68 Analysis of mechanism designed for Example 6.8.

manually or by using an optimization program that minimizes the error created by the linkage. However, even if an optimization program is used, the graphical procedure, which is very simple and quick to apply, is a good means of generating an initial estimate of the optimum solution.

6.6.2 Motion Generation for Parallel Motion Using Coupler Curves

In industrial applications, it is sometimes necessary to move a rigid body along a curved path in such a way that the angular orientation of the rigid body does not change. This situation, shown in Fig. 6.69, is a special case of rigid-body guidance when all of the positions are parallel. If we attempt to use a four-bar linkage for this problem, only a parallelogram linkage can guide a linkage through more than two parallel positions in general,[14] and the design constraints for parallelogram linkages are severely restricted. Therefore, guiding a linkage in parallel motion along a complex path generally requires more than four links.

A relatively simple solution to parallel motion synthesis is to use a four-bar linkage and two parallelogram linkages in parallel to form an eight-link mechanism. The four-bar linkage defines a coupler path along which one point of the rigid body is guided, and the parallelogram linkages maintain the orientation of the rigid body relative to the ground. This configuration is shown in Fig. 6.70.

To design the eight-link mechanism, we need only find a four-bar linkage coupler curve that will approximate the curve that the output member must follow. This defines linkage *ABCDE* in Fig. 6.70. Next the parallelogram linkages are added to maintain the orientation of the rigid body. Referring to Fig. 6.70, we see that link *FG* is equal in length to *CB*, and link *GH* is equal in length to *AB*. Lengths *HA*, *BG*, and *CF* are equal, but the actual length is arbitrary from the standpoint of kinematics. Note that the parallelograms could also have been used with lengths *CD* and *DE*. The side of the linkage used depends on the design constraints.

In practical situations, the parallelograms may not work for the full range of motion of the four-bar linkage either because of a need to change branch or because of a mechanical interference among the links. If a full range of motion is required, the parallelogram linkages can be replaced by two cable, belt, or chain drives. This is shown in Fig. 6.71. The motion of link 2 relative to link 4 is equivalent in both cases if the two pulley or sprocket diameters are equal. Any kind of belt, chain, or cable drive can be used as long as there is no slipping at the pulleys.

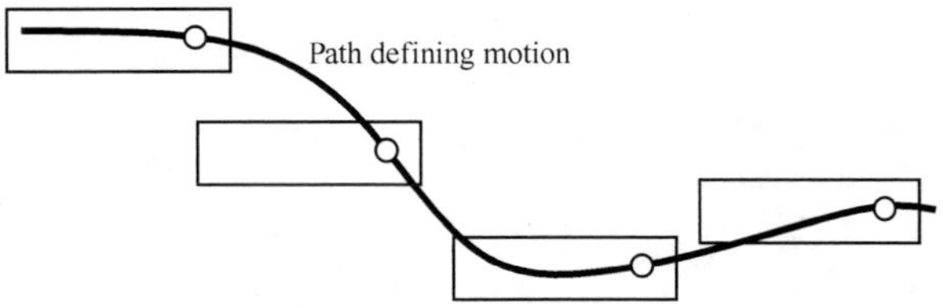

FIGURE 6.69 General parallel motion along a curved path.

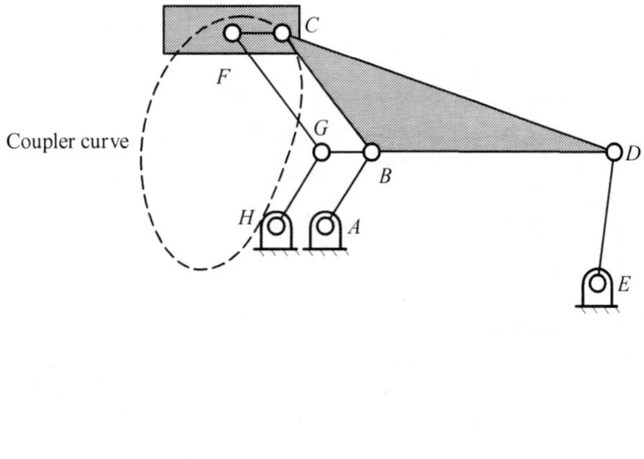

FIGURE 6.70 Eight-link mechanism to guide parallel motion along a curved path.

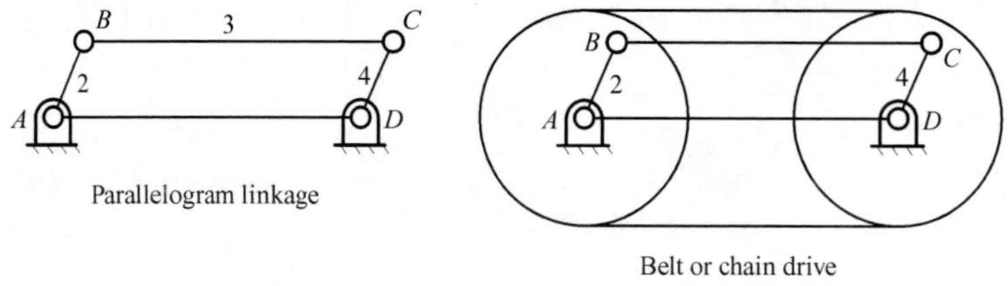

FIGURE 6.71 The motion of a parallelogram linkage can be duplicated by a belt or chain drive if the pulleys are of equal diameter.

The equivalent system corresponding to Fig. 6.70 is shown in Fig. 6.72. Different pulley diameters are used for the two equivalent parallelogram-linkage drives to illustrate that the two drives are separate. However, the two pulleys pivoting about point B must be fixed together.

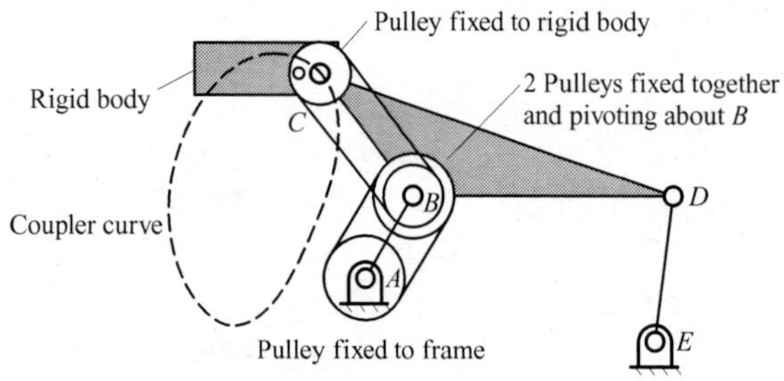

FIGURE 6.72 Replacement of the parallelogram linkages in Fig. 6.70 by belt drives.

EXAMPLE 6.9 *Design of an Eight-Link Mechanism for Parallel Motion Generation*

A test fixture must be removed from a hot hydraulic fluid bath. The fixture must be lifted vertically 6 in and then carried horizontally approximately 24 in along the approximate path shown in Fig. 6.73. The test fixture must remain parallel at all times. Design a linkage system that will move the fixture.

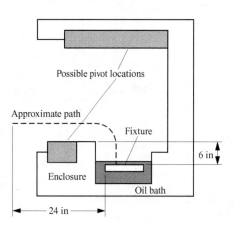

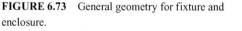

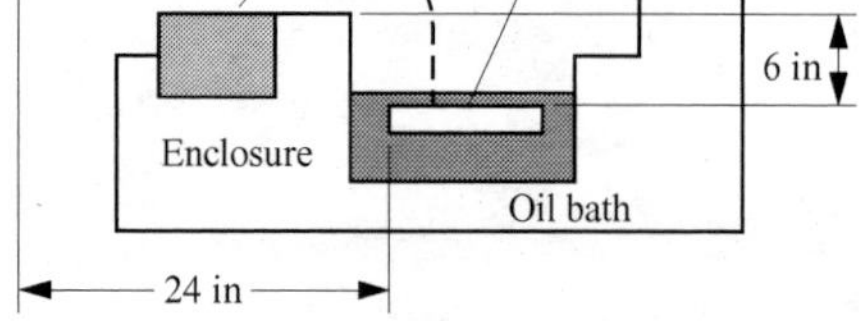

FIGURE 6.73 General geometry for fixture and enclosure.

Solution

To solve the problem, it is necessary to identify a four-bar linkage coupler curve that will match approximately the curve represented in Fig. 6.73. The important features of the linkage are the pivot locations, the 6-in rise in the coupler curve, and the lateral motion of approximately 24 in.

Two programs (*FourBarDesign* and *HRCrankRockerDesign*) for generating four-bar linkage coupler curves are available on the disk with this Book. The first program will generate coupler curves for both Grashof type I and type II linkages whereas the second program is limited to crank-rocker mechanisms. For this problem, a crank-rocker linkage is not necessary so the first program was used. The linkage was designed by trial and error, and the result is shown in Fig. 6.74.

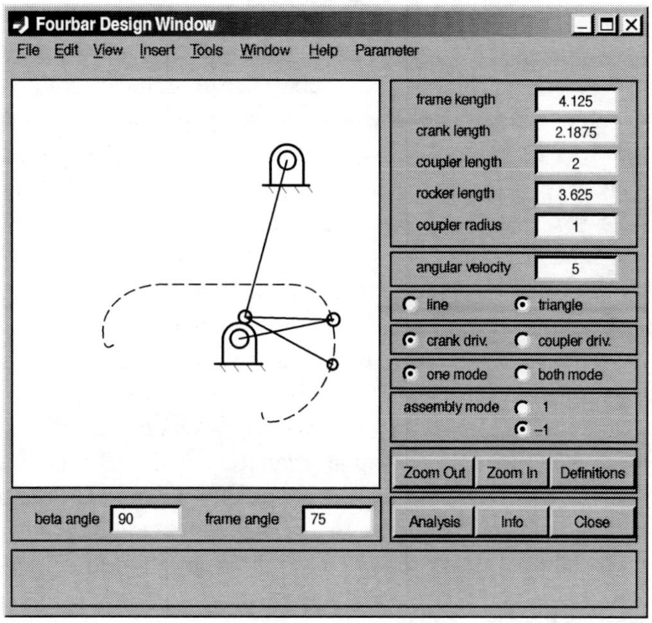

FIGURE 6.74 Screen capture from *FourBarDesign* program showing solution coupler curve.

The linkage is shown with the fixture in Fig. 6.75. Because of the range of motion required for the linkage, cable-driven pulleys are suggested for the final design rather than parallelogram linkages.

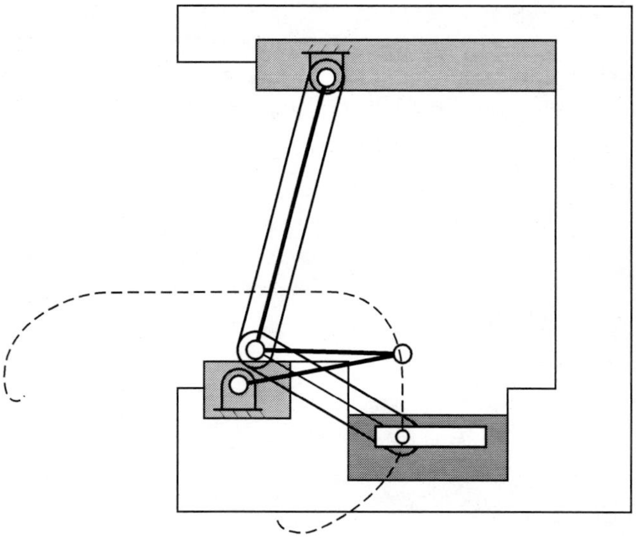

FIGURE 6.75 The mechanism located in the chamber.

6.6.3 Four-Bar Cognate Linkages

A given four-bar linkage with coupler point C will generate a unique coupler curve. It is interesting to note that there are two other four-bar linkages that will generate exactly the same coupler curve. The three four-bar linkages that will generate the same coupler curve are called cognates. From a design standpoint, one of the linkages may have more desirable motion characteristics than the others. Therefore, to select the best one, it is useful to identify all three linkages once the coupler curve is defined. The existence of the three cognate linkages was originally discovered by Roberts.[4, 7] A general discussion of cognate linkages and a proof for Roberts's theorem that identifies the geometric relationships among cognates are given in Chapter 7. In this chapter, we will limit our discussion to a procedure for finding cognates.

The geometry of the cognate linkages can be determined by considering extreme versions of the three linkages. The resulting diagram shown in Fig. 6.76 is called Roberts's linkage.[4] The mechanisms in this diagram will not move; however, the diagram shows the relationships that must exist among the three cognate linkages. These relationships are maintained when triangle MQO is shrunk while maintaining similarity, thereby permitting the linkages to move. In particular, triangles MQO, ABC, GCF, and CDE are similar. Also, figures $MACG$, $BQDC$, and $FCEO$ are parallelograms. The coupler point is C, and two cognate linkages share each of the pivots. Also, the couplers of each of the cognates are geometrically similar to each other and to the triangle formed by the pivots. If we identify the pivots as M, Q, and O, we can identify the three four-bar linkages by their pivots. That is, one four-bar linkage is the MQ four-bar, one is the MO four-bar linkage, and the third is the QO four-bar linkage.

The geometric relationships among three general cognate linkages are shown in Fig. 6.77. When determining the cognate linkages, it is assumed that the MQ linkage is known along with the coupler point C. The cognate linkages can be identified with the aid of Roberts's linkage, which reveals the geometric relationships among the three linkages. Given the positions of M and Q and the lengths r_2, r_3, r_4, r_5, r_6, and r_7, the equations for the location of pivot O and the corresponding angles and lengths of the other cognate linkages are shown in Table 6.1. Note that the cognates will all be of the same Grashof type but may be different subtypes. When the location of the coupler point is specified, the coordinates of A, B, and C must be given, or alternatively, the coordinates of A and B can be given along with the angle β and length r_5.

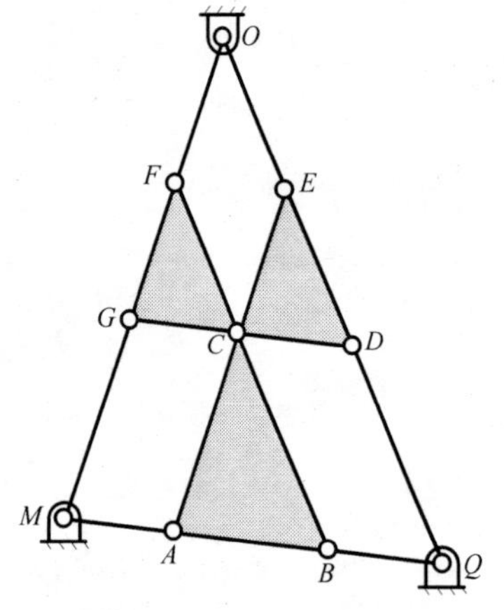

FIGURE 6.76 Roberts's linkage.

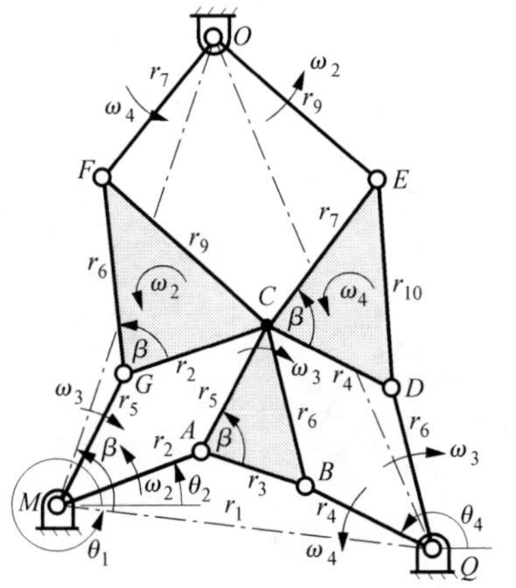

FIGURE 6.77 Three cognate linkages will generate the same coupler curve.

TABLE 6.1 Angle and Link Relationships Permitting the Cognate Linkages to Be Determined. The Variables Refer to the Diagram in Fig. 6.77. The Coordinates (x_A, y_A), (x_B, y_B), and (x_C, y_C) Are Assumed to Be Known from the Analysis of the MQ Linkage. Alternatively, β, ϕ, and λ Can Be Given Separately

$$r_6 = r_2 \frac{r_5}{r_3} \qquad r_7 = r_4 \frac{r_5}{r_3} \qquad r_8 = r_1 \frac{r_5}{r_3}$$

$$\beta = \tan^{-1}\left[\frac{y_C - y_A}{x_C - x_A}\right] - \tan^{-1}\left[\frac{y_B - y_A}{x_B - x_A}\right]$$

$$x_O = x_M + r_8 \cos(\theta_1 + \beta) \qquad y_O = y_M + r_8 \sin(\theta_1 + \beta)$$

$$x_G = x_M + (x_C - x_A) \qquad y_G = y_M + (y_C - y_A)$$

$$x_D = x_Q + (x_C - x_B) \qquad y_D = y_Q + (y_C - y_B)$$

$$\phi = \tan^{-1}\left[\frac{y_D - y_C}{x_D - x_C}\right] \qquad \lambda = \tan^{-1}\left[\frac{y_C - y_G}{x_C - x_G}\right]$$

$$x_E = x_D + r_1 \cos(\beta + \phi) \qquad y_E = y_D + r_7 \sin(\beta + \phi)$$

$$x_F = x_G + r_6 \cos(\lambda + \beta) \qquad y_F = y_G + r_6 \sin(\lambda + \beta)$$

$$r_9 = \sqrt{(x_E - x_O)^2 + (x_E - x_O)^2} \qquad r_{10} = \sqrt{(x_E - x_D)^2 + (x_E - x_D)^2}$$

The equations in Table 6.1 can be easily programmed to determine the geometry of the cognate linkages, and this is done in a program (*cognates.m*) given on the disk with this book. Figure 6.78 shows the cognate linkages for the mechanism shown in Fig. 6.77.

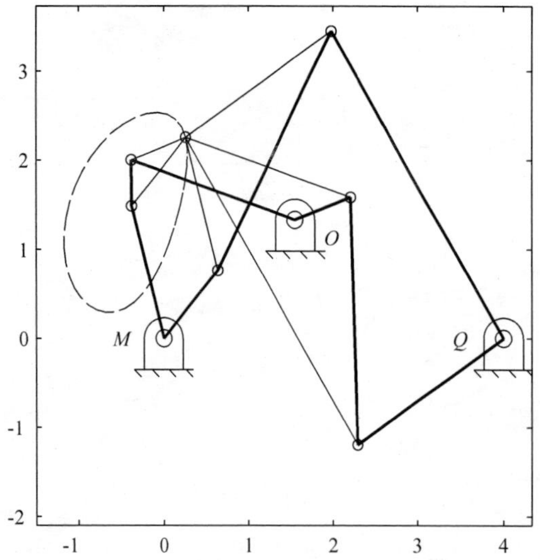

FIGURE 6.78 Three cognate linkages for the coupler curve in Fig. 6.63.

6.7 REFERENCES

[1]Kaufman, R. E, "Mechanism Design by Computer," *Machine Design*, Vol. 50, pp. 94–100 (1978).

[2]Waldron, K. J., "Improved Solutions of the Branch and Order Problems of Burmester Linkage Synthesis," *Journal of Mechanism and Machine Theory*, Vol. 13, pp. 199–207 (1978).

[3]Erdman, A. G., and D. Riley, "Computer-Aided Linkage Design Using the LINCAGES Package," ASME Paper No. 81-DET-121 (1981).

[4]Hall, A. S., *Kinematics and Linkage Design.* Balt Publishers, West Lafayette, IN (1961).

[5]Soni, A. H., *Mechanism Synthesis and Analysis,* McGraw–Hill Book Co., New York (1974).

[6]Arora, J. S., *Introduction to Optimal Design,* McGraw–Hill Book Co., New York (1989).

[7]Sandor, G. N., and A. G. Erdman, *Advanced Mechanism Design: Analysis and Synthesis,* Prentice–Hall, Inc., Englewood Cliffs, NJ (1984).

[8]Suh, C. H., and C. W. Radcliffe, *Kinematics and Mechanisms Design*, John Wiley & Sons, Inc., New York (1978).

[9]Waldron, K. J., "The Order Problem of Burmester Linkage Synthesis," *ASME Journal of Engineering for Industry*, Vol. 97, pp. 1405–1406 (1975).

[10]Hrones, J. A., and G. L. Nelson, *Analysis of the Four-Bar linkage*, The Technology Press of M.I.T., Cambridge, MA, and John Wiley & Sons, New York (1951).

[11]Tooten, K., "Entwicklung und Konstruktion einer neuen Rundballenpresse," *Konstruktion*, Vol. 39, pp. 285–290 (1987).

[12]Hartenberg, R. S., and J. Denavit, *Kinematic Synthesis of Linkages*, McGraw–Hill Book Co., New York (1964).

[13]Freudenstein, F., "Approximate Synthesis of Four-Bar Linkages," *Transactions of ASME*, Vol. 77, pp. 853–861, (August 1959).

[14]Song, S. M., *Theoretical and Numerical Improvements to Computer-Aided Linkage Design*, Ph.D. dissertation, The Ohio State University (1981).

PROBLEMS

DOUBLE-ROCKER EXERCISE PROBLEMS

6.1 Design a double-rocker, four-bar linkage so that the base link is 2-in long and the output rocker is 1-in long. The input link turns CCW 60° when the output link turns CW through 90°. The initial angle for the input link is 30° CCW from the horizontal, and the initial angle for the output link is –45°. The geometry is indicated in the figure.

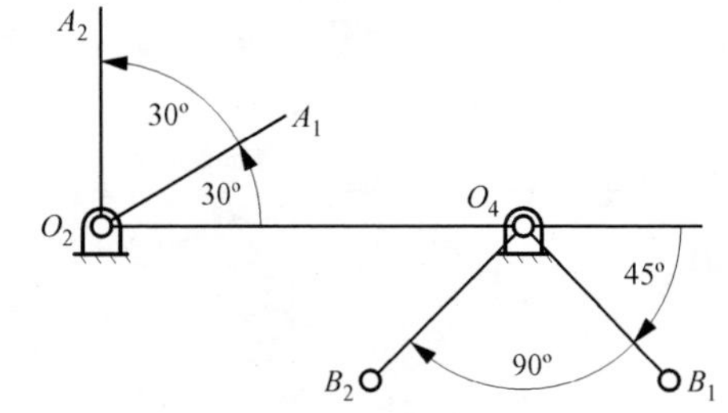

6.2 Design a double rocker, four-bar linkage so that the base link is 4-in long and the output rocker is 2-in long. The input link turns CCW 40° when the output link turns CCW through 80°. The initial angle for the input link is 20° CCW from the horizontal, and the initial angle for the output link is 25°. The geometry is indicated in the figure.

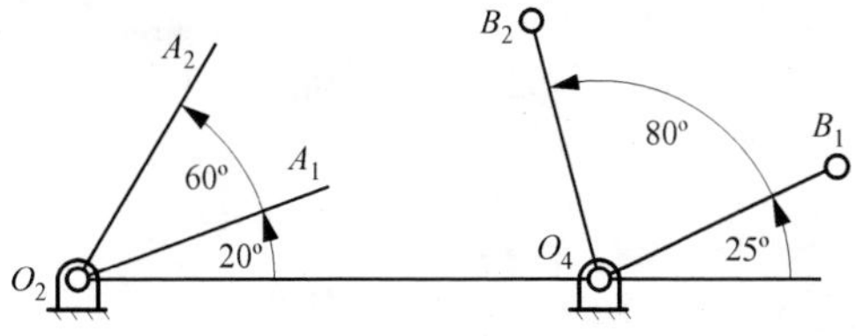

6.3 In a back hoe, a four-bar linkage is added at the bucket in part to amplify the motion that can be achieved by the hydraulic cylinder attached to the link that rotates the bucket as shown in the figure. Design the link attached to the bucket and the coupler if the frame link is 13-in long and the input link is 12-in long. The input link driven by the hydraulic cylinder rotates through an angle of 80°, and the output link rotates through an angle of 120°. From the figure, determine reasonable angles for the starting angles (θ_0 and ϕ_0) for both of the rockers.

RIGID-BODY GUIDANCE EXERCISE PROBLEMS

6.4 In the drawing, $AB = 1.25$ cm. Use A and B as circle points, and design a four-bar linkage to move its coupler through the three positions shown. Use Grashof's equation to identify the type of four-bar linkage designed.

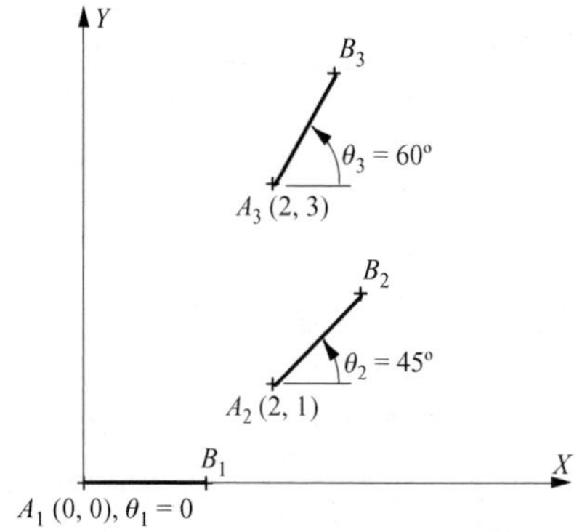

6.5 Using points A and B as circle points, design a four-bar linkage that will position the body defined by AB in the three positions shown. Draw the linkage in position 1, and use Grashof's equation to identify the type of four-bar linkage designed. Position A_1B_1 is horizontal, and position A_2B_2 is vertical. $AB = 1.25$ in.

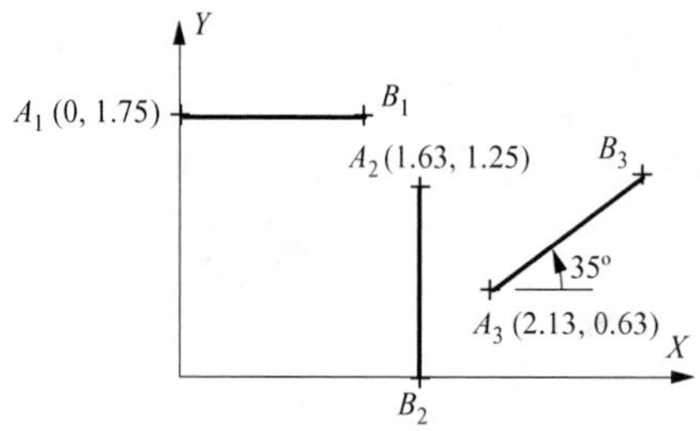

6.6 Design a four-bar linkage to move its coupler through the three positions shown using points A and B as moving pivots. $AB = 4$ cm. What is the Grashof type of the linkage generated?

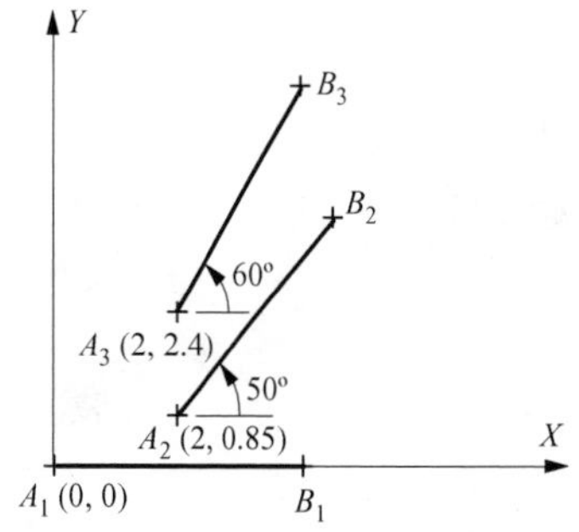

6.7 A four-bar linkage is to be designed to move its coupler plane through the three positions shown. The moving pivot (circle point) of one crank is at A and the fixed pivot (center point) of the other crank is at C^*. Draw the linkage in position 1 and use Grashof's equation to identify the type of four-bar linkage designed. Also determine whether the linkage changes branch in traversing the design positions. Positions A_1B_1 and A_2B_2 are horizontal, and position A_3B_3 is vertical. $AB = 3$ in.

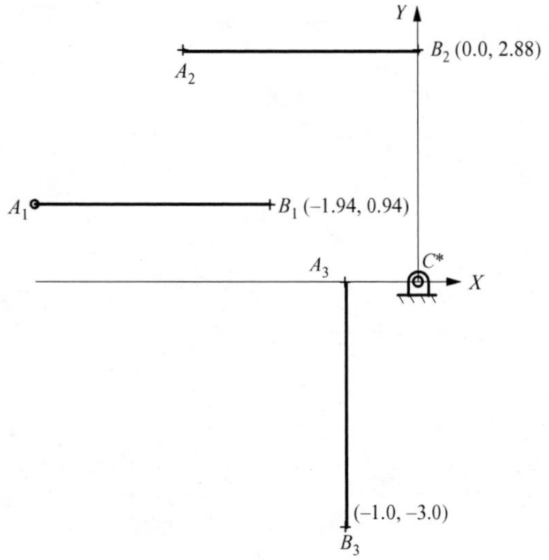

6.8 Design a four-bar linkage to move a coupler containing the line AB through the three positions shown. The moving pivot (circle point) of one crank is at A, and the fixed pivot (center point) of the other crank is at C^*. Draw the linkage in position 1, and use Grashof's equation to identify the type of four-bar linkage designed. Position A_1B_1 is horizontal, and positions A_2B_2 and A_3B_3 are vertical. $AB = 4$ in.

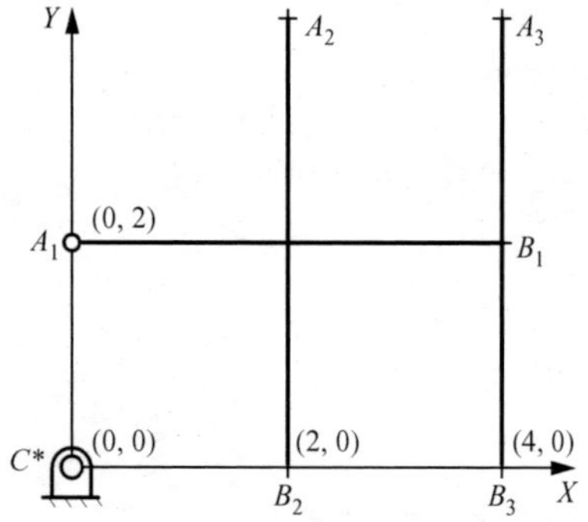

6.9 A mechanism must be designed to move a computer terminal from under a desk to its top. The system will be guided by a linkage, and the use of a four-bar linkage will be tried first. As a first attempt at the design, do the following:

(a) Use C^* as a center point and find the corresponding circle point C in position 1.

(b) Use A as a circle point and find the corresponding center point A^*.

(c) Draw the linkage in position 1.

(d) Determine the type of linkage (crank-rocker, double-rocker, etc.) resulting.

(e) Evaluate the linkage to determine whether you would recommend that it be manufactured.

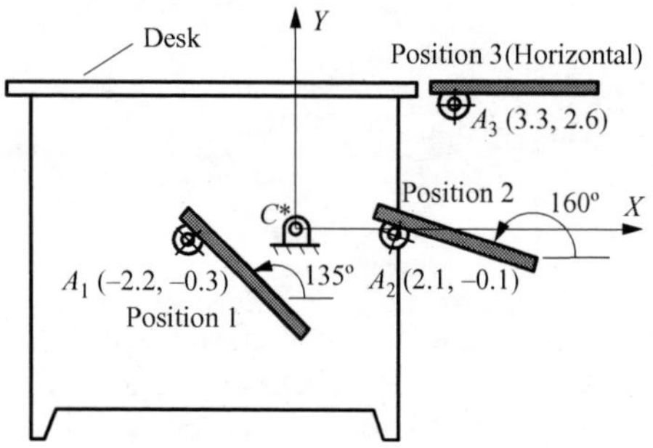

6.10 Design a four-bar linkage to move the coupler containing line segment AB through the three positions shown. The moving pivot for one crank is to be at A, and the fixed pivot for the other crank is to be at C^*. Draw the linkage in position 1 and determine the classification of the resulting linkage (e.g., crank-rocker, double-crank). Positions A_2B_2 and A_3B_3 are horizontal, and position A_1B_1 is vertical. $AB = 3.5$ in.

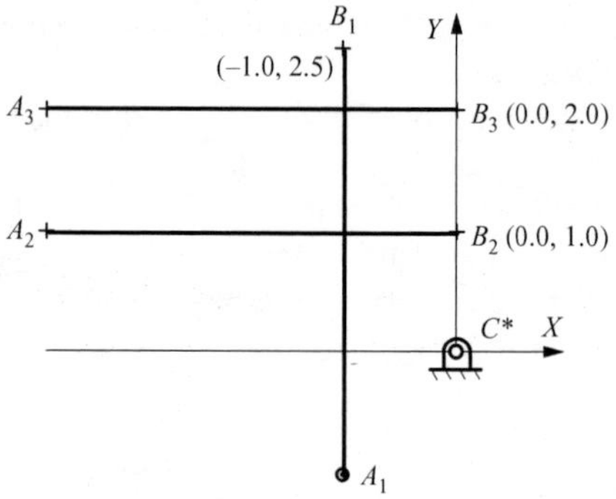

6.11 Design a four-bar linkage to move a coupler containing the line AB through the three positions shown. The moving pivot (circle point) of one crank is at A and the fixed pivot (center point) of the other crank is at C^*. Draw the linkage in position 1, and use Grashof's equation to identify the type of four-bar linkage designed. Position A_1B_1 is horizontal, and positions A_2B_2 and A_3B_3 are vertical. $AB = 6$ cm.

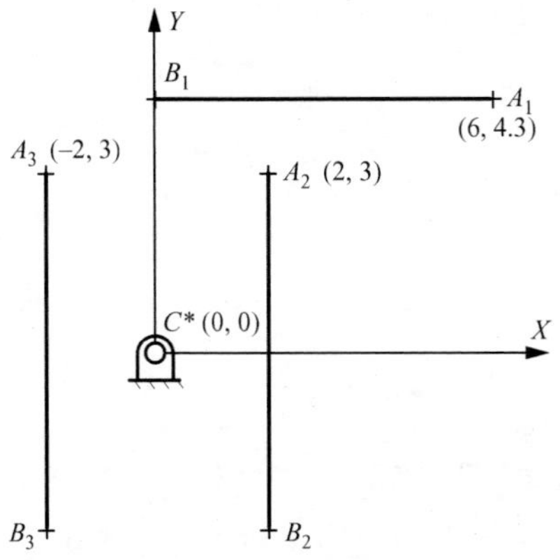

6.12 Design a four-bar linkage to move the coupler containing line segment AB through the three positions shown. The moving pivot for one crank is to be at A, and the fixed pivot for the other crank is to be at C^*. Draw the linkage in position 1 and determine the classification of the resulting linkage (e.g., crank-rocker, double-crank). Also check to determine whether the linkage will change branch as it moves from one position to another. Position A_1B_1 is horizontal, and position A_3B_3 is vertical. $AB = 5.1$ cm.

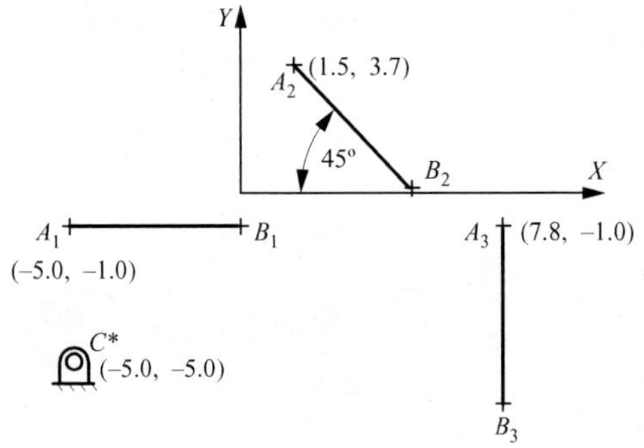

6.13 Synthesize a four-bar mechanism in *position 2* that moves its coupler through the three positions shown if points C^* and D^* are center points. Position A_1B_1 and position A_3B_3 are horizontal. $AB = 4$ cm.

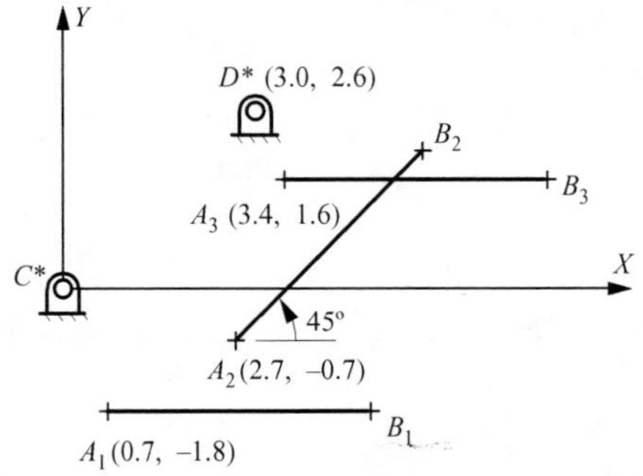

6.14 Synthesize a four-bar mechanism in *position 2* that moves its coupler through the three positions shown. Point A is a circle point, and point C^* is a center point. Position A_1B_1 and position A_3B_3 are horizontal. $AB = 4$ cm.

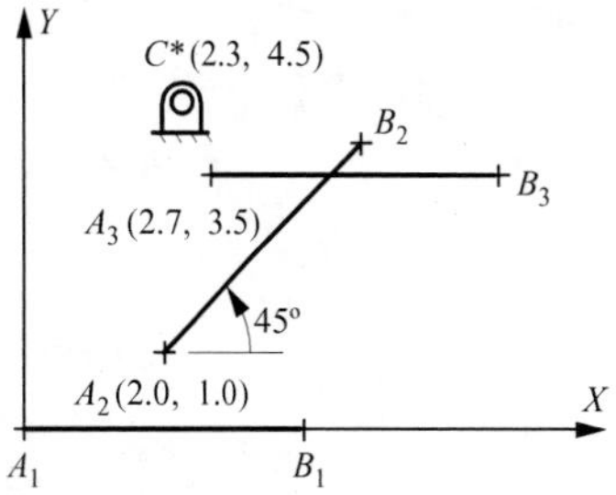

6.15 A hardware designer wants to use a four-bar linkage to guide a door through the three positions shown. Position 1 is horizontal, and position 3 is vertical. As a tentative design, she selects point B^* as a center point and A as a circle point. For the three positions shown, determine the location of the circle point B corresponding to the center point B^* and the center point A^* corresponding to the circle point A. Draw the linkage in position 1 and determine the Grashof type for the linkage. Indicate whether you think that this linkage should be put into production.

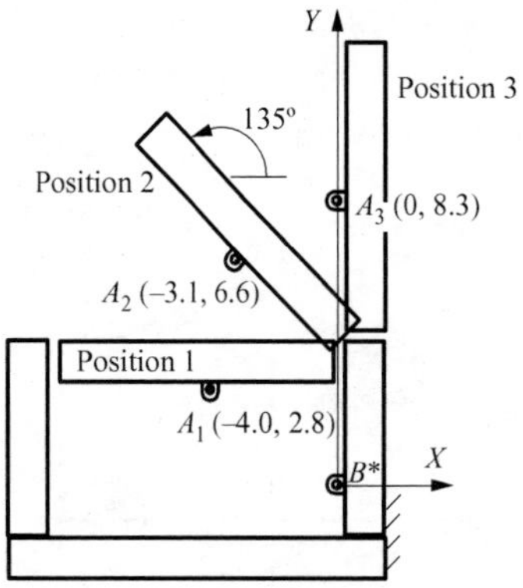

6.16 Design a *slider-crank mechanism* to move the coupler containing line segment AB through the three positions shown. The moving pivot for the crank is to be at A. Determine the slider point, and draw the linkage in position 1. Also check to determine whether the linkage can be moved from one position to another without being disassembled. Position A_1B_1 is horizontal, and position A_3B_3 is vertical. $AB = 2.0$ in.

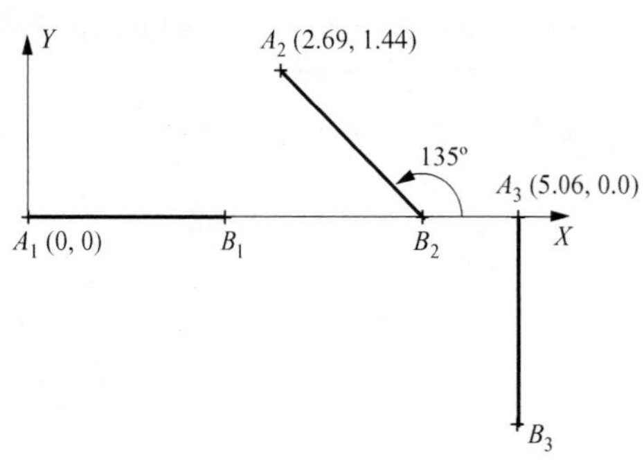

6.17 Design a *slider-crank mechanism* to move a coupler containing the line AB through the three positions shown. The line AB is 1.25 in long. The moving pivot (circle point) of the crank is at A. The approximate locations of the three poles (P_{12}, P_{13}, P_{23}) are shown, but these should be determined accurately after the positions are redrawn. Find A*, the slider point that lies above B_1 on a vertical line through B_1, and draw the linkage in position 1.

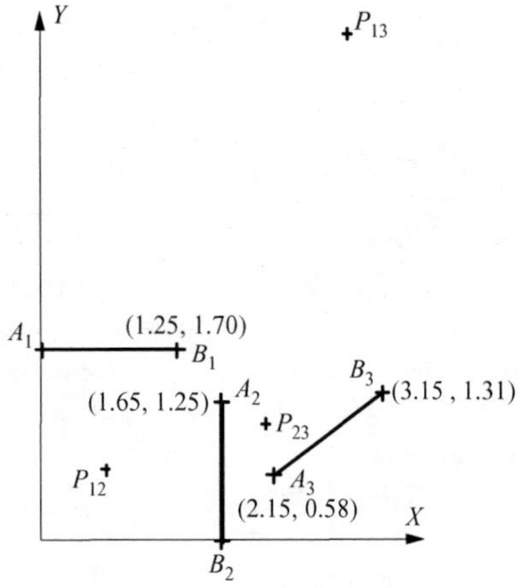

6.18 Design a *slider-crank linkage* to move a coupler containing the line AB through the three positions shown. The fixed pivot (center point) of the crank is at C*. Draw the linkage (including the slider line) in position 1. Position A_1B_1 is horizontal, and positions A_2B_2 and A_3B_3 are vertical. $AB = 4$ in.

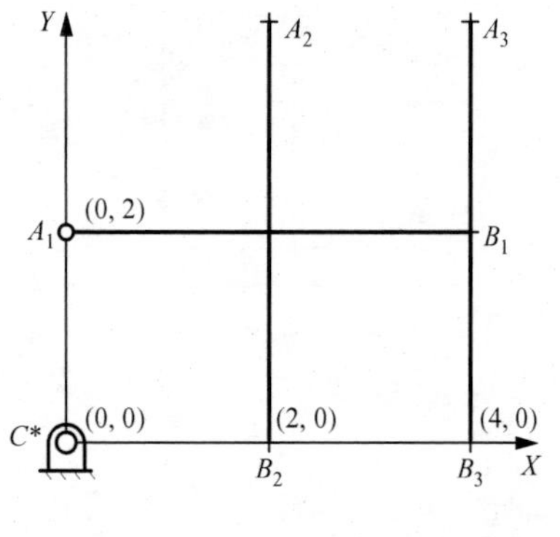

6.19 Design a *slider-crank mechanism* to move a coupler containing the line with A through the three positions shown. The moving pivot (circle point) of the crank is at A. Find the slider point that lies on line BC and draw the linkage (including the slider line) in position 1. Note that line BC is *not* the line on which the slider moves.

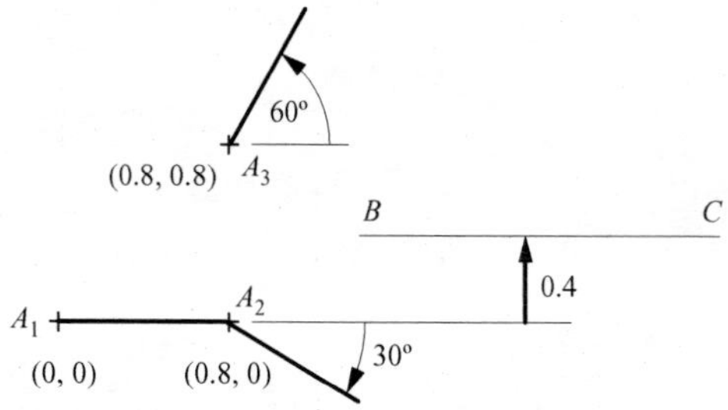

FUNCTION-GENERATION EXERCISE PROBLEMS

6.20 A device characterized by the input–output relationship $\phi = a_1 + a_2 \cos \theta$ is to be used to generate (approximately) the function $\phi = \theta^2$ (with θ and ϕ both in radians) over the range $0 '' \ \theta '' \ \pi/4$.

(a) Determine the number of precision points required to compute a_1 and a_2.

(b) Choose the best precision point values for θ from among 0, 0.17, 0.35, and 0.52, and determine the values of a_1 and a_2 that will allow the device to approximate the function.

(c) Find the error when $\theta = \pi/8$.

6.21 A mechanical device characterized by the input–output relationship $\phi = 2a_1 + 3a_2 \sin \theta + a_3^2$ is to be used to generate (approximately) the function $\phi = 2\theta^2$ (with θ and ϕ both in radians) over the range $0 '' \ \theta '' \ \pi/4$. Exterior constraints on the design require that the parameter $a_3 = 1$.

(a) Determine the number of precision points required to complete the design of the system.

(b) Use Chebyshev spacing, and determine the values for the unknown design variables that will allow the device to approximate the function.

(c) Find the error when $\theta = \pi/6$.

6.22 A mechanical device characterized by the input–output relationship $\phi = 2a_1 + a_2 \tan \theta + a_3$ is to be used to generate (approximately) the function $\phi = 3\theta^3$ (with θ and ϕ both in radians) over the range $0 '' \ \theta '' \ \pi/3$. Exterior constraints on the design require that the parameter $a_3 = 1$.

(a) Determine the number of precision points required to complete the design of the system.

(b) Use Chebyshev spacing, and determine the values for the unknown design variables that will allow the device to approximate the function.

(c) Find the error when $\theta = \pi/6$.

6.23 A mechanical device characterized by the input–output relationship $\phi = 2a_1 + a_2 \sin \theta$ is to be used to generate (approximately) the function $y = 2x^2$ over the range $0 '' \ x '' \ \pi/2$, where x, y, ϕ, and θ are all in radians. Assume that the use of the device will be such that the starting point and range for x can be the same as those for θ, and the range and starting point for y can be the same as those for ϕ.

(a) Determine the number of precision points required to complete the design of the system.

(b) Use Chebyshev spacing, and determine the values for the unknown design variables that will allow the device to approximate the function.

(c) Compute the error generated by the device for $x = \pi/4$.

6.24 Determine the link lengths and draw a four-bar linkage that will generate the function $\phi = \theta^2$ (with θ and ϕ both in radians) for values of θ between 0.5 and 1.0 radians. Use Chebyshev spacing with three precision points. The base length of the linkage must be 2 cm. Use the following angle information:

$$\theta_0 = 20°,\ \Delta\theta = 60°$$

$$\phi_0 = 45°,\ \Delta\phi = 50°$$

6.25 Determine the link lengths and draw a four-bar linkage that will generate the function $\phi = \sin\theta$ for values of θ between 0° and 90°. Use Chebyshev spacing with three precision points. The base length of the linkage must be 2 cm. Use the following angle information:

$$\theta_0 = 30°,\ \Delta\theta = 90°$$

$$\phi_0 = 30°,\ \Delta\phi = 60°$$

6.26 Design a four-bar linkage that generates the function $y = (\sqrt{x} - x + 3)$ for values of x between 1 and 4. Use the Chebyshev spacing for three precision points. The base length of the linkage must be 2 in. Use the following angle information:

$$\theta_0 = 45°,\ \Delta\theta = 50°$$

$$\phi_0 = 30°,\ \Delta\phi = 70°$$

Compute the error at $x = 2$.

6.27 Design a four-bar linkage to generate the function $y = x^2 - 1$ for values of x between 1 and 5. Use Chebyshev spacing with three precision points. The base length of the linkage must be 2 cm. Use the following angle information:

$$\theta_0 = 30°,\ \Delta\theta = 60°$$

$$\phi_0 = 45°,\ \Delta\phi = 90°$$

Compute the error at $x = 3$.

CRANK-ROCKER EXERCISE PROBLEMS

6.28 The output arm of a lawn sprinkler is to rotate through an angle of 90°, and the ratio of the times for the forward and reverse rotations is to be 1 to 1. Design the crank-rocker mechanism for the sprinkler. If the crank is to be 1 in long, give the lengths of the other links.

6.29 Design a crank-rocker mechanism such that with the crank turning at constant speed, the oscillating lever will have a time ratio of advance to return of 3:2. The lever is to oscillate through an angle of 80°, and the length of the base link is to be 2 in.

6.30 A packing mechanism requires that the crank (r_2) rotate at a constant velocity. The advance part of the cycle is to take twice as long as the return to give a quick-return mechanism. The distance between fixed pivots must be 0.5 m. Determine the lengths for r_2, r_3, and r_4.

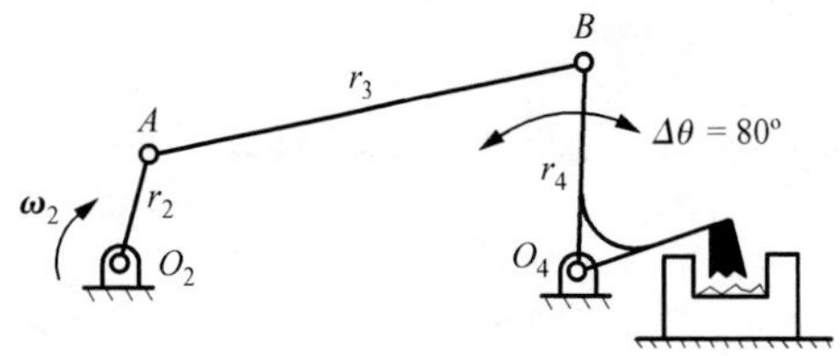

6.31 The rocker O_4B of a crank-rocker linkage swings symmetrically about the vertical through a total angle of 70°. The return motion should take 0.75 times the time that the forward motion takes. Assuming that the two pivots are 2.5 in apart, find the length of each of the links.

6.32 A crank-rocker is to be designed such that with the crank turning at a constant speed CCW, the rocker will have a time ratio of advance to return of 1.25. The rocking angle is to be 40°, and it rocks symmetrically about a vertical line through O_4. Assume that the two pivots are on the same horizontal line, 3 in apart.

6.33 Design a crank-rocker mechanism that has a base length of 2.0, a time ratio of 1.3, and a rocker oscillation angle of 100°. The oscillation is to be symmetric about a vertical line through O_4. Specify the length of each of the links.

6.34 A crank-rocker mechanism with a time ratio of $2\frac{1}{3}$ and a rocker oscillation angle of 72° is to be designed. The oscillation is to be symmetric about a vertical line through O_4. Draw the mechanism in any position. If the length of the base link is 2 in, give the lengths of the other three links. Also show the transmission angle in the position in which the linkage is drawn.

6.35 The mechanism shown is used to drive an oscillating sanding drum. The drum is rotated by a splined shaft that is cycled vertically. The vertical motion is driven by a four-bar linkage through a rack-and-pinion gear set (modeled as a rolling contact joint). The total vertical travel for the sander drum is 3 in, and the pinion has a 2-in radius. The sander mechanism requires that the crank (r_2) rotate at a constant velocity, and the advance part of the cycle is to take the same amount of time as the return part. The distance between fixed pivots must be 4 in. Determine the lengths for r_2, r_3, and r_4.

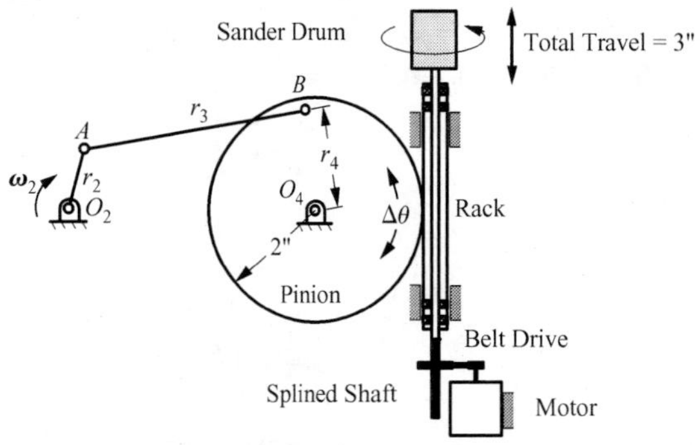

6.36 The mechanism shown is proposed for a rock crusher. The crusher hammer rotates through an angle of 20°, and the gear ratio R_G/R_P is 4:1, that is, the radius r_G is four times the radius r_P. Contact between the two gears can be treated as rolling contact. The crusher mechanism requires that the crank (r_2) rotate at a constant velocity, and the advance part of the cycle is to take 1.5 times as long as the return part. The distance between fixed pivots O_2 and O_4 must be 4 ft. Determine the lengths for r_2, r_3, and r_4.

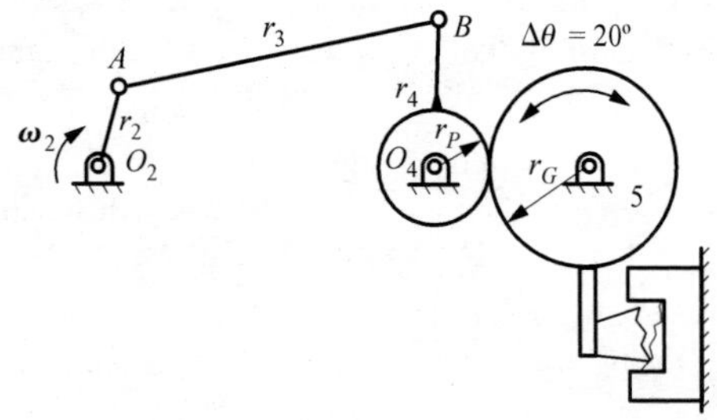

6.37 The mechanism shown is proposed for a shaper mechanism. The shaper cutter moves back and forth such that the forward (cutting) stroke takes twice as much time as the return stroke. The crank (r_2) rotates at a constant velocity. The follower link (r_4) is to be 4 in and to oscillate through an angle of 80°. Determine the lengths for r_1, r_2, and r_3.

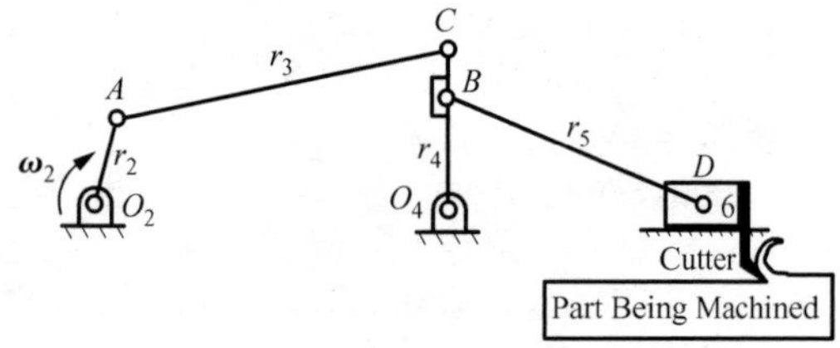

6.38 A crank-rocker is to be used in a door-closing mechanism. The door must open 100°. The crank motor is controlled by a timer mechanism such that it pauses when the door is fully open. Because of this, the mechanism can open and close the door in the same amount of time. If the crank (r_2) of the mechanism is to be 10-cm long, determine the lengths of the other links (r_1, r_3, and r_4). Sketch the mechanism to scale.

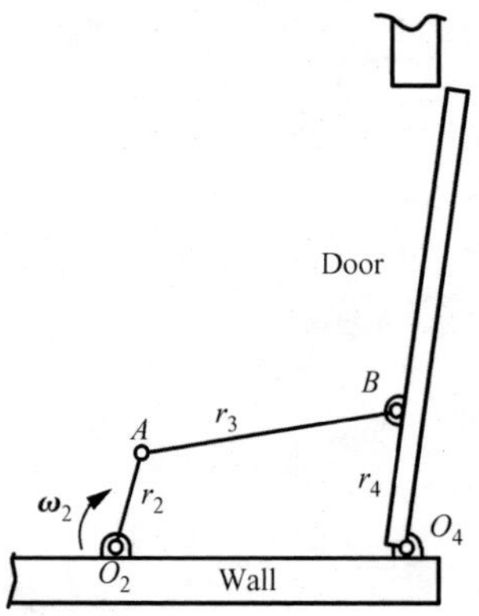

6.39 A crank-rocker is to be used for the rock crusher mechanism shown. The oscillation angle for the rocker is to be 80°, and the time for the working (crushing) stroke for the rocker is to be 1.1 times the return stroke. If the frame link (r_1) of the mechanism is to be 10-ft long, determine the lengths of the other links (r_2, r_3, and r_4). Sketch the mechanism to scale.

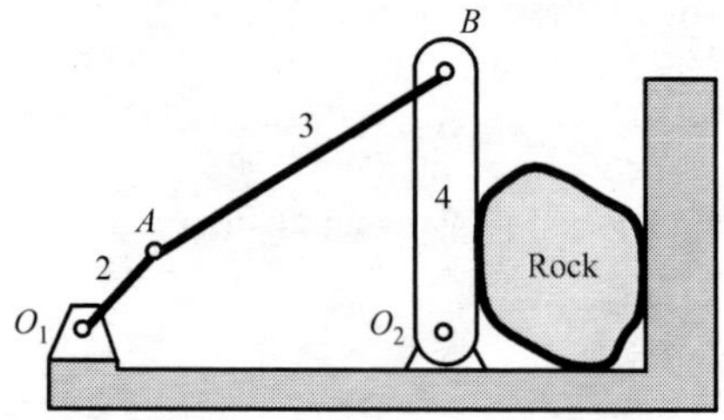

6.40 A crank-rocker is to be used in a windshield-wiping mechanism. The wiper must oscillate 80°. The times for the forward and return strokes for the wiper are the same. If the base link (r_1) of the mechanism is to be 10-cm long, determine the lengths of the other links (r_2, r_3, and r_4). Sketch the mechanism to scale.

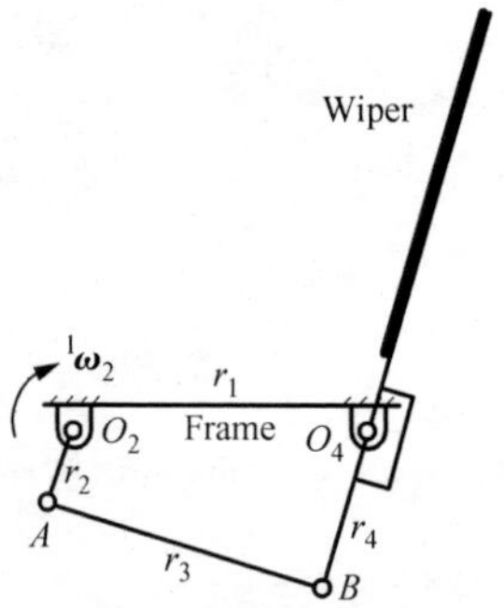

PATH-GENERATION EXERCISE PROBLEMS

6.41 Design a six-bar linkage like that shown in Fig. 6.61 such that the output link will do the following for one complete revolution of the input crank:

(a) Rotate CW by 30° for a CW rotation of 210° of the input crank.

(b) Rotate CCW by 30° for a CW rotation of 150° of the input crank.

6.42 Design a six-bar linkage like that shown in Fig. 6.61 such that the output link will make two complete 35° oscillations for each revolution of the driving link. (Hint: Select a coupler curve that is shaped like a figure eight.)

6.43 Design a six-bar linkage like that shown in Fig. 6.61 such that the output link will do the following for one complete revolution of the input crank:

(a) Rotate CW by 40°.

(b) Rotate CCW by 35°.

(c) Rotate CW by 30°.

(d) Rotate CCW by 35°.

(Hint: Select a figure-eight– or kidney-bean–shaped coupler curve.)

6.44 Design a six-bar linkage like that shown in Fig. 6.61 such that the displacement of the output link (link 6) is the given function of the input link rotation. The output displacement reaches maximum values of 30° and 60° at input rotations of 60° and 240°, respectively. The rotation of the output link is zero when the input rotation angle is 0°, 120°, and 360°.

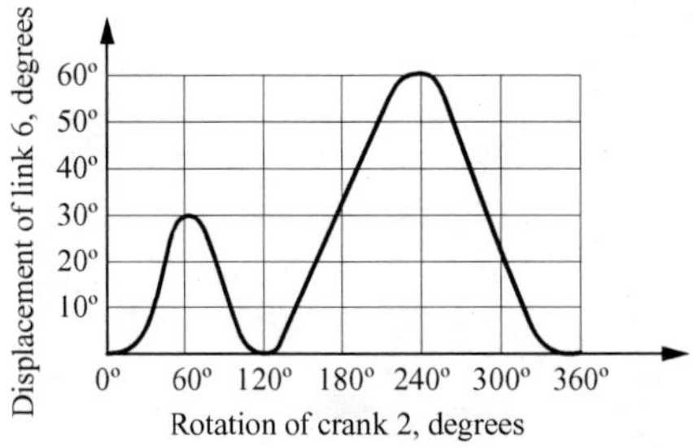

6.45 Design a six-bar linkage like that shown in Fig. 6.61 such that the displacement of the output link (link 6) is the given function of the input link rotation. The output link dwells for 90° of input rotation starting at 0° and 180°. The maximum rotation angle for link 6 is 15°.

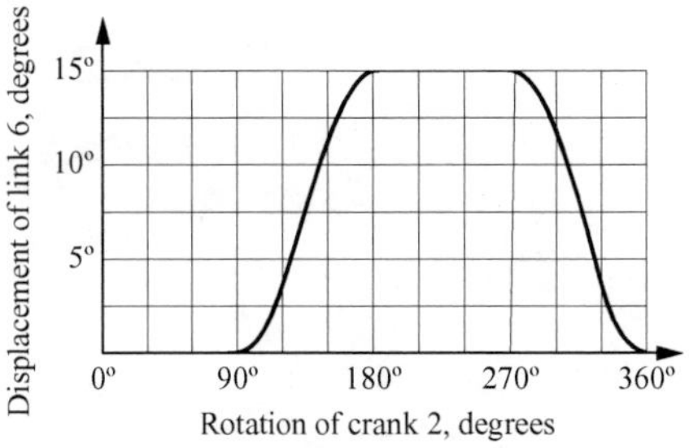

6.46 Design an eight-bar linkage like that shown in Fig. 6.70 such that the coupler remains horizontal while the specified point on the coupler moves approximately along the path given.

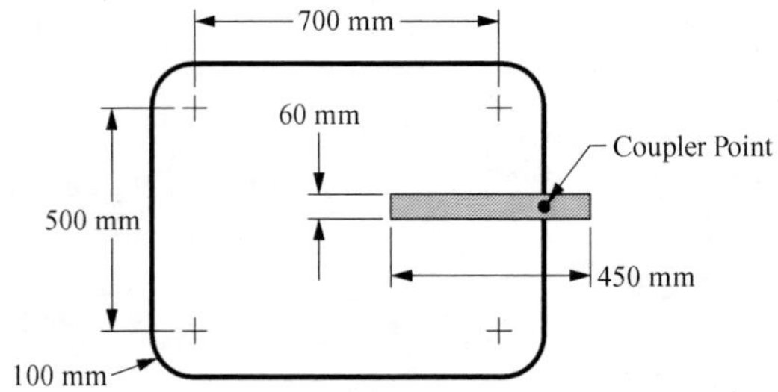

6.47 Re-solve Problem 6.46 if the coupler is inclined at an angle of 45°.

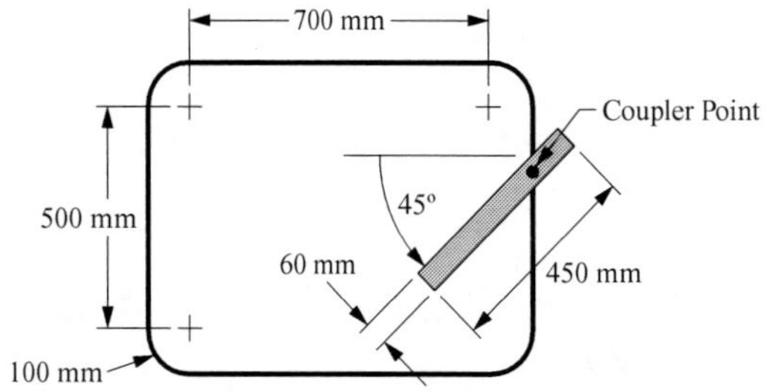

6.48 Design an eight-bar linkage like that shown in Fig. 6.70 such that the coupler remains horizontal while the given point on the coupler moves approximately along the path from A to B to C. The coupler can return either by retracing the path from C to B to A or by going directly from C to A. This means that the basic four-bar linkage need not be a crank-rocker.

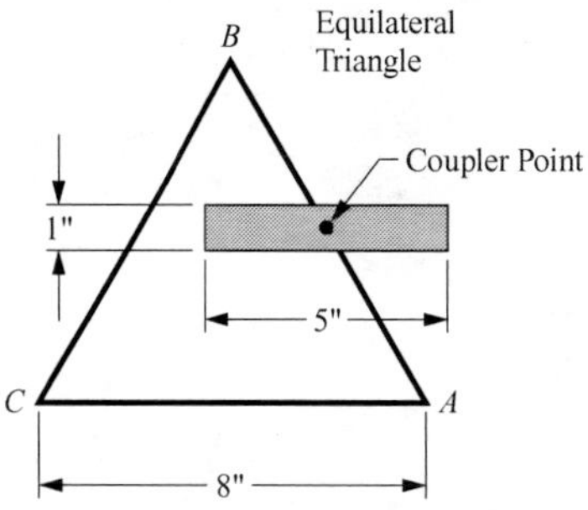

COGNATE LINKAGE EXERCISE PROBLEMS

6.49 Determine the two four-bar linkages cognate to the one shown. The dimensions are $MA = 10$ cm, $AB = 16$ cm, $AC = 32$ cm, $QB = 21$ cm, and $MQ = 24$ cm. Draw the cognates in the position for $\theta = 90°$.

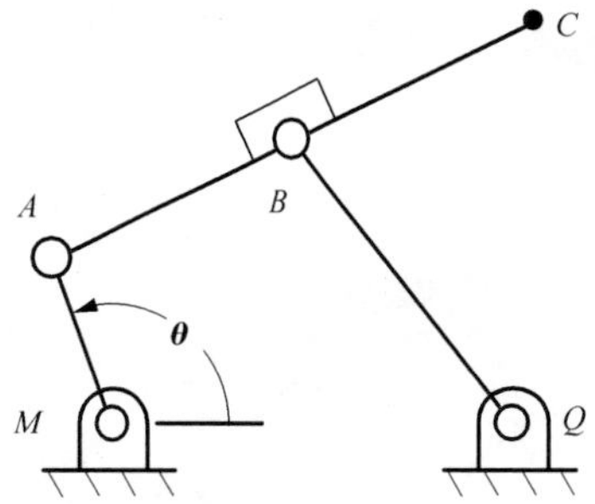

6.50 Determine the two four-bar linkages cognate to the one shown. The dimensions are $MQ = 1.5$ in, $AB = BC = BQ = AC = 1$ in, and $AM = 0.5$ in. Draw the cognates in the position for $\theta = 90°$.

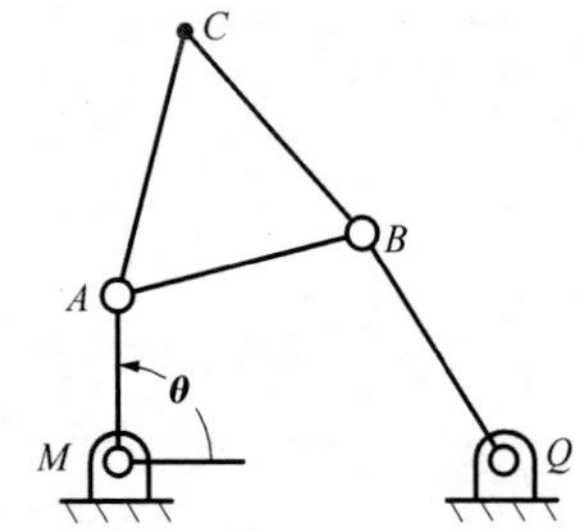

6.51 Determine the two four-bar linkages cognate to the one shown. The dimensions are $MQ = 2$ in, $AB = BC = BQ = 1$ in, and $AM = 1.5$ in. $AC = 0.75$ in. Draw the cognates in the position for $\theta = 45°$.

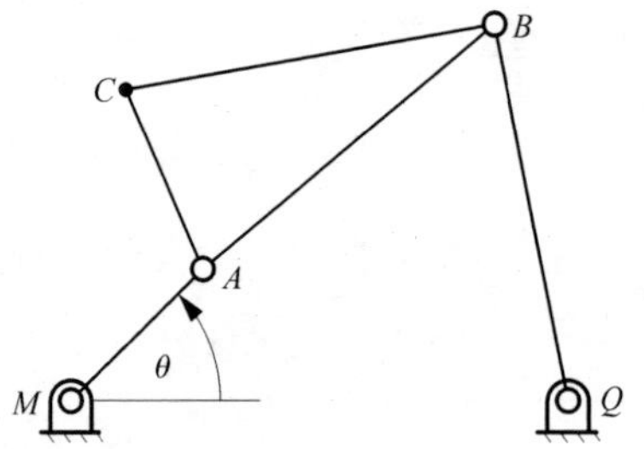

6.52 Determine the two four-bar linkages cognate for the drag-link mechanism shown. The dimensions are $MQ = 1$ m, $AM = BQ = 4$ m, and $AB = 2$ m, and angles CAB and CBA both equal 45°. Notice that the cognates will also be drag-link mechanisms. Draw the cognates in the position in which $\theta = 180°$.

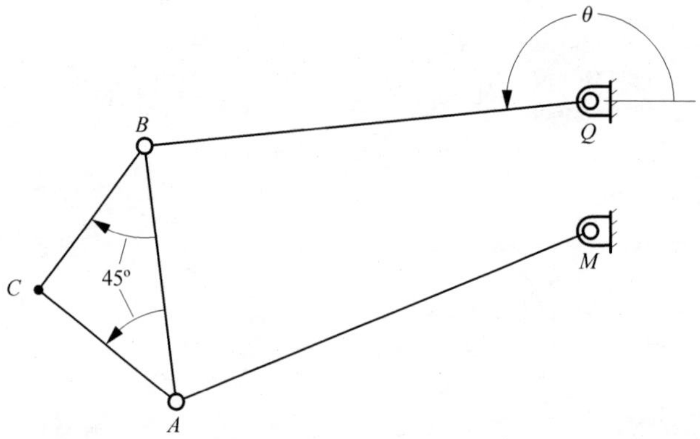

CHAPTER 7

SPECIAL MECHANISMS

7.1 SPECIAL PLANAR MECHANISMS

7.1.1 Introduction

Some mechanisms are unusual enough to require special attention. The classes of mechanisms discussed here meet a variety of common needs in mechanical engineering practice. For this reason they are important, but none requires such extensive treatment as to justify a chapter to themselves, as is the case with cam and gear mechanisms.

Generation of a straight line by a simple linkage mechanism is a recurring theme. Slides or roller ways are not always acceptable for implementation in real mechanism designs, and there continues to be a place for simple, four-bar linkages that can approximate a straight-line coupler point path with a high degree of accuracy. Likewise, linkages that can reproduce a path traced by one point at another tracing point with a change in scale find many uses ranging from machine tools for milling nonrotationally symmetric surfaces to remote actuation of robotic mechanisms.

Another recurring theme in mechanical engineering practice is the transfer of torque and motion between shafts that are not coaxial, particularly when the relative alignment of the shafts must change. Very common examples occur in the drive shafts of automobiles that must accommodate movements resulting in changes of shaft alignment caused by suspension movements and/or steering movements. There are also numerous examples of this situation in construction and manufacturing machinery.

Automotive steering and suspension mechanisms are among the most common linkage mechanisms in practical use. They are usually designed as decoupled, fundamentally planar linkages. However, misalignments are deliberately introduced to produce desirable effects such as a tendency for the steering to center itself. Thus, they become spatial linkages with complex interactions.

Yet another recurring need in practical linkage design is for indexing: intermittent, timed advancement of a drive in a constant direction. This technology had very numerous and visible applications in the days of mechanical punched-card readers and similar business machines. The problem is of continuing practical importance with many applications in manufacturing and packaging machinery.

7.1.2 Approximate Straight-Line Mechanisms

Approximate straight-line mechanisms occupy a very special place in the history of kinematics. These have been used in many practical devices from steam engines to stripchart recorders. The geometry of several linkages exhibiting approximate straight-line motions is discussed in the following.

Watt's Straight-Line Mechanism Toward the end of the 18th century, when James Watt and his contemporaries were developing the practical steam engines that powered the industrial revolution, there were no available means of machining long ways to a high degree of straightness or of achieving low-friction linear motion. This was needed both to guide the crosshead of the piston rod and for the valve gear that opened the valves in coordination with the piston motion. The solution used by Watt and his contemporaries was to devise a four-bar mechanism with an acceptably long coupler-point trajectory that approximated a straight line to an acceptable degree of accuracy.

Watt's straight-line mechanism continues to be of considerable practical importance.[1] The linkage is simple, and the configuration is very flexible, allowing great freedom to the designer. For example, the ratio of the lengths a and b shown in Fig. 7.1 is not very critical. The linkage will produce reasonably straight motion over a wide range of dimensional ratios b/a. It is not even essential that the two cranks have the same length. The essential feature is that the dimensions be such that the linkage is capable of assuming a position like that shown in Fig. 7.1 with the two cranks being parallel and opposed, with the coupler normal to both. If the cranks are of equal length the tracing point is the midpoint of the coupler, and the line of the coupler in the position shown is the straight line that is approximated.

Because of its simplicity and ability to provide low friction, approximately linear guidance, Watt's straight-line mechanism is useful anywhere exact conformance to linear motion is not essential. For example, it has been used in rear automotive suspensions of the live axle type to restrain lateral motion of the axle by constraining the center point of the axle to move along an approximate vertical straight line relative to the body.

The tracing point for the coupler curve shown in Fig. 7.1 is the midpoint of the coupler. The proportions of a and b are variable. In the case drawn, $a = 3$ and $b = 5$. The form of the coupler curve is known as a lemniscate. As can be seen, the central limbs of the lemniscate are good approximations to straight lines over a considerable length.

Chebyshev's Straight-Line Mechanism The Chebyshev approximate straight-line mechanism is also a linkage that is both of historical importance and of continuing practical importance.[1] Like the Watt mechanism, it is simple. Its advantages are that it provides a very long segment of the path of the coupler midpoint that is approximately linear and that both fixed pivots are on the same side of the linear path, as compared with the Watt mechanism, in which they are on opposite sides. However, the dimensions are more critical in this case. Referring to Fig. 7.2, we see that the required proportions are $a = 1$, $b = 2.5$, and $c = 2$. As already noted, the tracing point is the midpoint of the coupler. As can be seen, it approximates a straight line for a considerable distance. It might be noted that these proportions require that the linkage be a type 1 double-rocker. Since it is normally used for linear guidance of the tracing point, it is used in a coupler-driven mode.

Roberts's Straight-Line Mechanism Robert's approximate straight-line mechanism is also a symmetrical four-bar linkage, as shown in Fig. 7.3.[1] The coupler point indi-

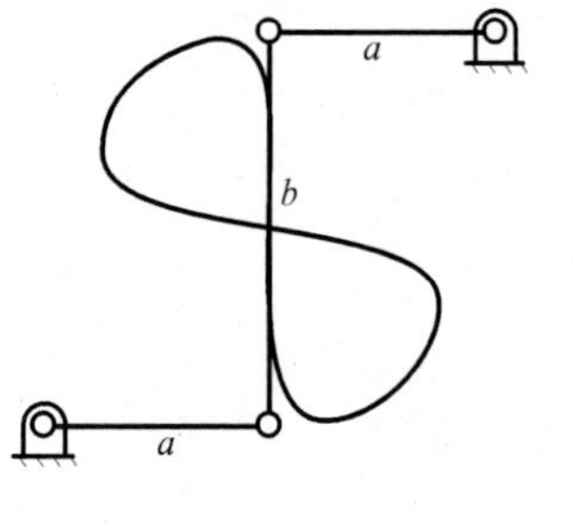

FIGURE 7.1 Watt's straight-line mechanism.

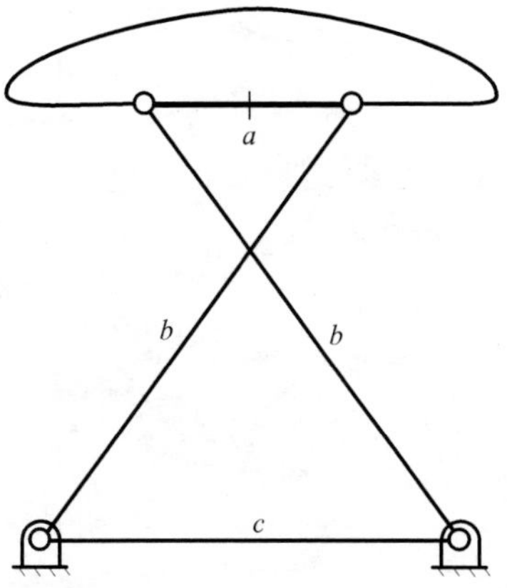

FIGURE 7.2 Chebyshev's approximate straight-line mechanism.

cated generates an approximate straight line for the motion between the fixed pivots. Referring to Fig. 7.3, we see that the required proportions are $a = 1$, $b = 1.2$, $c = 2$, and $d = 1.09$. These dimensions make the mechanism a type 2 double-rocker. It is normally used for linear guidance of the tracing point so that it is normally used in the coupler-driven mode.

Other Approximate Straight-Line Mechanisms There are many other four-bar linkage configurations that yield reasonable approximations to linear motion of a tracing point. Those used in level-luffing cranes and similar devices need to have the tracing point outside the interval between the coupler pivots. A good example is the level-luffing crane (Fig. 7.4) used on many docks to load and unload cargo. Here it is desirable that the path of the crane hook that carries the load be a horizontal straight line. This means that the load moves approximately in a horizontal plane when only turret and jib movements are used. Vertical motion is accomplished by the crane's winch hauling or lowering the cable. Horizontal motion of the load has two very significant advantages. First, little energy is used for turret or jib motions if the cranks are counterweighted to eliminate work done against gravity in moving the mechanism itself. The drives for those motions do not need to have large capacity. Second, it is relatively easy for the crane operator to visualize a horizontal trajectory of the load and determine whether that trajectory will interfere with fixed obstacles such as the side of the ship.

The jib of a typical level-luffing crane is arranged as a four-bar mechanism with a coupler point that approximately describes a horizontal straight line. The pulley at the end of the jib is placed at this point to produce the desired level-luffing action.

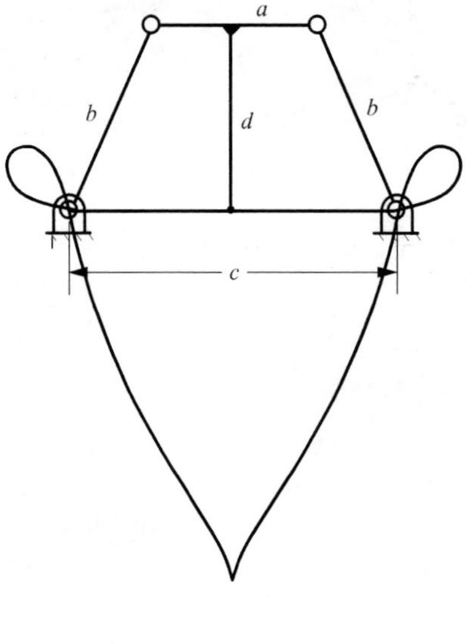

FIGURE 7.3 Roberts's approximate straight-line mechanism.

FIGURE 7.4 A level-luffing crane. The jib of the crane is configured as a four-bar mechanism that generates an approximate horizontal straight line at the axis of the sheave over which the cable passes at the end of the jib. This means that the load moves approximately in a horizontal plane when only turret and jib movements are used.

7.1.3 Exact Straight-Line Mechanisms

It is also possible, in principle, to generate a perfectly straight line with a linkage mechanism, but generally only at the cost of a relatively complex mechanism if large motions are desired. The first such mechanism to be invented was that of Peaucellier.[2] Hart[2] devised a simpler mechanism that also generates an exact straight line, and several mechanisms based on the slider-crank mechanism will generate a straight line for limited motion.[3] There are several other known exact straight-line generating linkages with revolute joints, but all are much more complex than the four-bar approximate straight-line generators discussed here.

A Peaucellier linkage is shown in Fig. 7.5. The linkage has a rhombic loop, *ABCD*, that forms a kite shape with the equal-length links *PB* and *PD*. The link *OA* is also equal in length to the base *OP*. Point *C* generates a true straight line normal to the base *OP*.

As may be seen, this is a much more complex linkage than the four-bar loops used previously to generate approximate straight lines. It has eight members and six joints, four of which are ternary joints.

If a slider is introduced, it is possible to generate an exact straight line using the slider-crank mechanism in Fig. 7.6. The range of motion is limited and a slider is required, but the basic mechanism is quite simple. Based on the geometry of the linkage, the output motion will be a simple sine function of the drive link (simple harmonic motion). As indicated in Fig. 7.6, the mechanism is made up of isosceles triangles.

7.1.4 Pantographs

A plagiograph is a mechanism that exactly reproduces the path of a tracing point at a second tracer point, usually with a change of scale. The most common class of plagiographs is the family of pantograph mechanisms.

Pantographs have found many applications beyond that of plagiographs. These range from carrying contacts to overhead cables on electric trains and streetcars to legs of walking machines. As will be seen, pantographs are also of theoretical importance in that they lead to the theory of *cognate* linkages (Section 6.6.3). Cognate mechanisms, in turn, are of great usefulness in practical machine design.

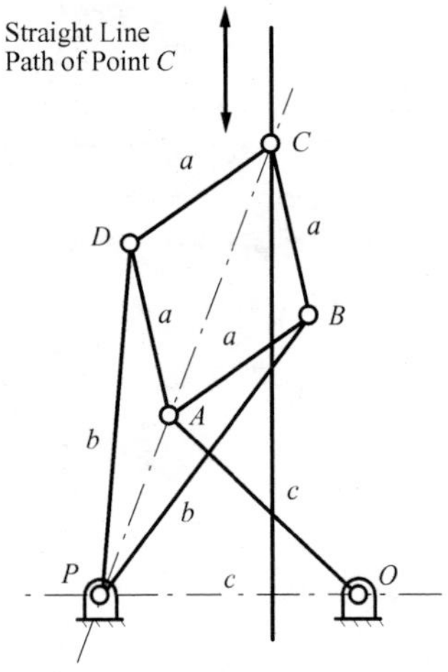

FIGURE 7.5 Peaucellier's exact straight-line mechanism. This was the first and most famous exact straight-line mechanism to be discovered. A number of others have since been discovered, including some that are a little simpler. *ABCD* is a rhombus, and links *PB* and *PD* have equal length. Link *OA* has the same length as the base *OP*. The path of point *C* is a true straight line normal to *OP*.

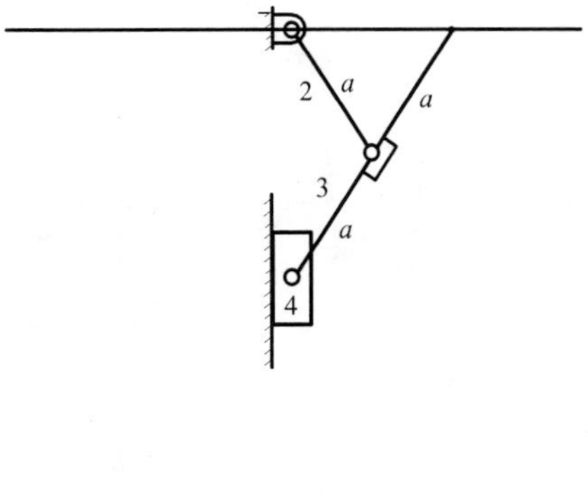

FIGURE 7.6 Straight-line mechanism based on isosceles slider-crank mechanism. The entire range of the straight line can be reached if the mechanism is driven by the coupler.

The Planar Collinear Pantograph The special properties of the pantograph linkage have been used in a variety of applications. They also have important theoretical implications leading to the theory of cognate linkages, which will be discussed briefly later in this chapter.

A simple form of planar pantograph linkage is shown in Fig. 7.7. In Fig. 7.7, link *AB* has the length *CD*. Likewise, link *AD* has the length *BC*. Consequently, *ABCD* is a parallelogram, regardless of the position of the linkage. Further, the lengths *OB* and *OC* are in the ratio 1:4, as are the lengths *CD* and *CE*. It follows that triangle *OBA* is similar to triangle *OCE*, because *OB/OC* is equal to *BA/CE* and angle *OBA* is equal to angle *OCE*. Consequently, the ratio of the lengths *OA* and *OE* is always 1:4. If point *A* traces any path in the plane of the linkage, point *E* will trace a geometrically similar path that is magnified by a factor of 4 compared with the path of point *A*. This is best understood by considering the path of point *A* to be a curve described in polar coordinates with origin at *O*. The position of the corresponding point on the path of point *E* is also described in polar coordinates centered on *O*. The angular coordinate of that point is the same as that of the corresponding point on the path of point *A*. Its radial coordinate is four times that of the corresponding point on the path of point *A*. Hence the curve is the same. It is simply scaled up by a factor of 4.

Because of the tracing property, pantograph mechanisms have been used a great deal to copy and rescale text and other geometric figures. The magnification factor can be set to any desired value by varying the proportions of the links. In the form of the linkage that is shown in Fig. 7.7, it is always equal to the ratio of length *OC* to *OB*, which must also be equal to the ratio of *CE* to *CD*.

An example of the use of the pantograph mechanism to copy plane curves is a copying mill used to produce plate cams. The reader will find an in-depth discussion of cam geometry in Chapter 8. Most plate cams are bounded by mathematically complicated curves. To produce cams using a copy mill, a master cam is produced at an enlarged scale by hand. The profile of the master is traced by a roller with its central axis located at point *E* of Fig. 7.7. The axis of the milling cutter is at point *A*. The ratio of the roller diameter to the cutter diameter is the pantograph ratio. Consequently, the mill produces a cam that is geometrically similar to the master but is reduced in size by the pantograph ratio. The use of point *E*, rather than point *A*, to trace the master provides improved accuracy, because errors in the master profile are reduced by the pantograph ratio. The large size of the master also facilitates its accurate manufacture.

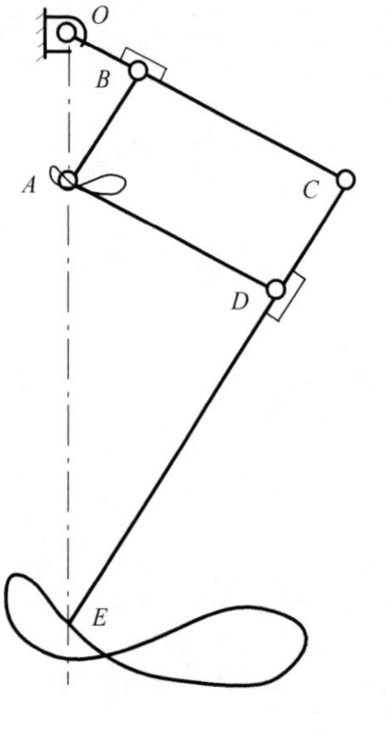

FIGURE 7.7 A simple form of a planar pantograph linkage. Any path traced by point *A* is reproduced by point *E* at a magnification of 4:1. *ABCD* is a parallelogram. The ratios of lengths *CD* to *CE* and *OB* to *OC* are both 1:4. Link *OC* is connected to the base by a fixed revolute joint at *O*.

The application just described is an example of inversion of the linkage by interchanging the tracing points A and E. The pantograph can also be inverted by hinging it to the base with a fixed revolute coincident with A, rather than at point O. This is shown in Fig. 7.8. The path of point O is now copied by a geometrically similar path of point E. However, the magnification ratio is now 3:1 rather than 4:1. This is because, with these dimensions, the ratio of length AE to AO is 3:1.

There are other variations on the same theme. Figure 7.9 shows the pantograph linkage used in the legs of the Adaptive Suspension Vehicle that was shown in Fig. 1.1. Here there is no fixed pivot. Rather, point O is on a vertical slide and point A is on a horizontal

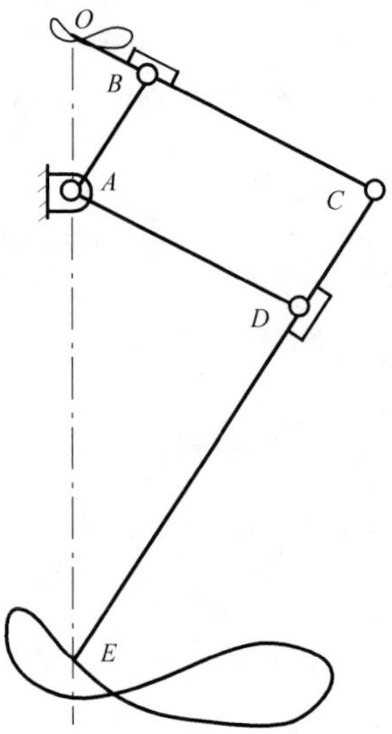

FIGURE 7.8 The pantograph of Fig. 7.7 inverted by mounting with a fixed revolute at point A. The paths of points O and E are geometrically similar. The magnification factor is now 3:1.

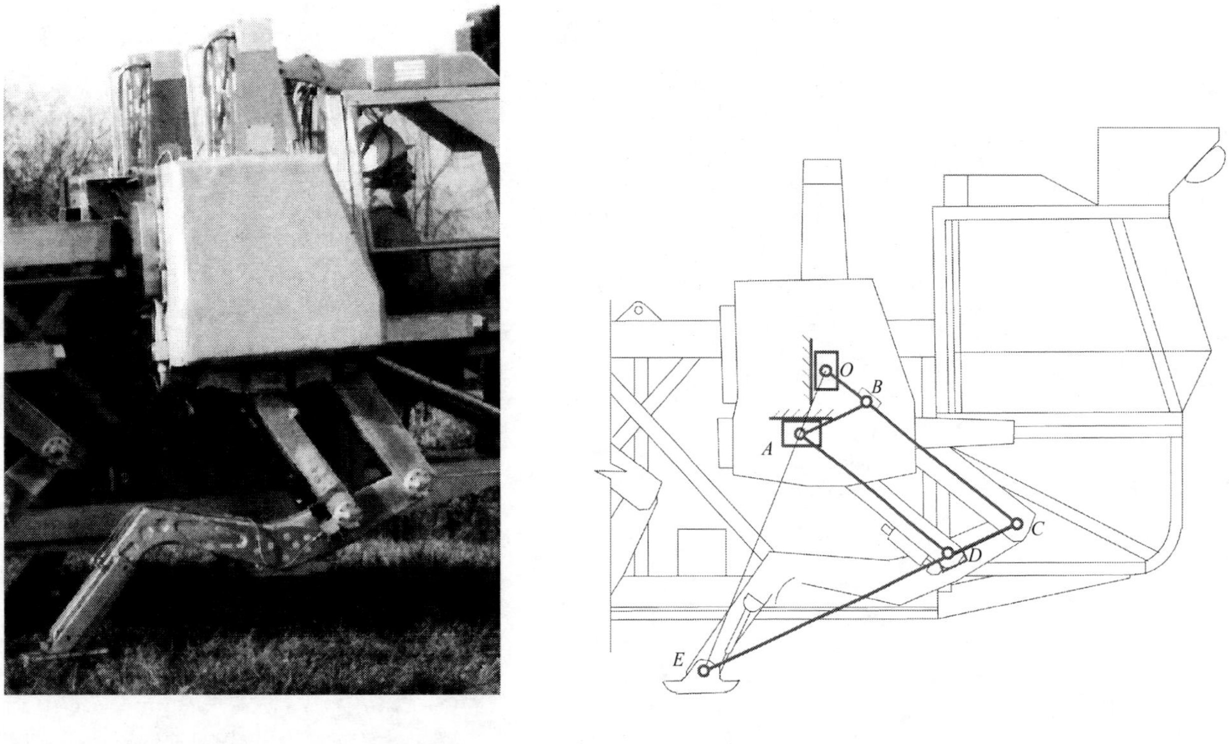

FIGURE 7.9 The leg mechanism of the Adaptive Suspension Vehicle. Point O moves on a slide that is vertical relative to the leg mounting structure to produce a corresponding vertical motion of the ankle point E. Point A moves on a slide that is horizontal relative to the vehicle body to drive point E along a horizontal path.

slide. Motion of point A alone, produced by a hydraulic cylinder, causes a horizontal rectilinear motion of the ankle point, E. Motion of point O alone, also produced by a hydraulic cylinder, causes a vertical rectilinear motion of point E. Simultaneous motion of points A and O results in motion of point E along a plane curve. This is what happens when the foot is picked up and the leg is swung back to its forward position. The magnification factor in this mechanism is 5:1 for the drive motion (point A) and 4:1 for the lift motion (point B).

Skew Pantographs A more general form of pantograph is the skew pantograph shown in Fig. 7.10. $OLMN$ is a parallelogram, and triangle NMQ is similar to triangle LPM. As shown in the following, triangle OPQ is always similar to triangle LPM. Consequently, the path traced by point Q is similar to that traced by point P, is rotated through angle a from the path of P about O, and is magnified by the ratio LM/LP.

These properties are proved as follows. Note that since $OLMN$ is a parallelogram, $\angle MLO = \angle ONM = \phi$. Likewise, $\angle LON = \angle NML = \pi - \phi$.

Triangles PLO and ONQ are similar for the following reasons:

$$\angle PLO = \angle ONQ = \phi + \alpha.$$

Also

$$\frac{NQ}{NM} = \frac{ML}{PL}$$

because triangles NMQ and LPM are similar and these are corresponding pairs of sides. Now $NM = OL$, and $ML = NO$ because $OLMN$ is a parallelogram. Making these substitutions, we get

$$\frac{NQ}{OL} = \frac{NO}{PL} \quad \text{or} \quad \frac{NQ}{NO} = \frac{OL}{PL}$$

which establishes that triangles PLO and ONQ are similar since NQ and NO, and OL and PL, are corresponding side pairs and the equal angles $\angle PLO$ and $\angle ONQ$ are the included angles.

Also, triangle QMP is similar to PLO and ONQ for the following reasons:

$$\angle QMP = 2\pi - \beta - \gamma - (\pi - \phi) = \pi + \phi - \beta - \gamma$$

Also, because α, β, and γ are the vertex angles of triangle LPM,

$$\alpha + \beta + \gamma = \pi$$

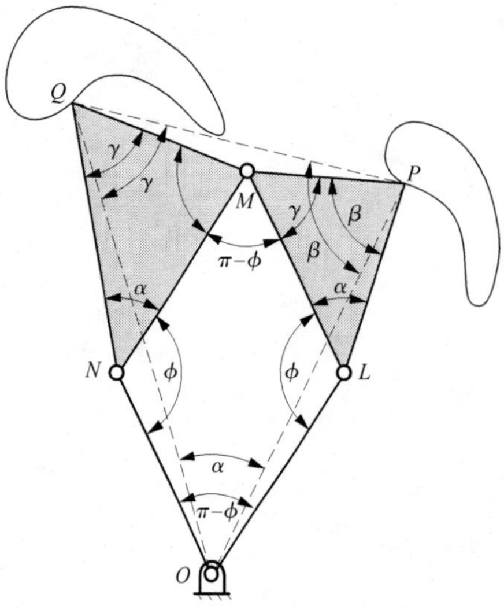

FIGURE 7.10 A skew pantograph. $OLMN$ is a parallelogram and triangles LPM and NMQ are similar. The triangle OPQ is always similar to triangles LPM and NMQ. Consequently, the path traced by point Q is similar to that traced by point P. The path traced by Q is rotated relative to that traced by P through angle α and it is magnified by the ratio $OQ/OP = LM/LP$.

so

$$\angle QMP = \pi + \phi - (\pi - \alpha) = \phi + \alpha = \angle ONQ$$

Because triangles *NMQ* and *LPM* are similar

$$\frac{MQ}{NQ} = \frac{PM}{LM}$$

or

$$\frac{PM}{MQ} = \frac{LM}{NQ} = \frac{ON}{NQ}$$

noting that $LM = ON$.

Therefore triangles *QMP* and *ONQ* are similar because the corresponding sides *PM* and *MQ*, and *ON* and *NQ*, are in the same ratio and the included angles *QMP* and *ONQ* are equal. Triangles *QMP* and *PLO* are similar because both are similar to *ONQ*.

It follows that

$$\angle NQO = \angle MQP$$

and so

$$\angle OQP = \angle NQM = \gamma$$

Likewise

$$\angle QPM = \angle OPL$$

and so

$$\angle QPO = \angle MPL = \beta$$

Consequently,

$$\angle POQ = \alpha$$

and triangle *OPQ* is similar to triangles *LPM* and *NMQ*.

The geometric similarity of the paths of points *P* and *Q* can be inferred from an argument similar to that employed in the case of the collinear pantograph. If the path of point *P* is considered to be a curve described in polar coordinates centered on *O*, the radial coordinate is *OP*. The path of *Q* is also described in polar coordinates centered on *O*. The radial coordinate is *LM/LP* times that of point *P*, and the angle reference is rotated through angle from that used for the path of point *P*.

Roberts's Theorem If the path of point *P* of the skew pantograph of the preceding section is a circle, then that of point *Q* will also be a circle, as shown in Fig. 7.11. Thus, if *P* is constrained to move on a circle by a crank rotating about fixed pivot, O_P, then a crank can also be connected to point *Q* from a fixed pivot at the center of its path, O_Q. Because the path of *Q* is similar to that of *P* and triangle *OPQ* is always similar to triangle *LPM*, it follows that triangle OO_PO_Q is also similar to triangle *LPM*. This creates two planar four-bar linkages, $OLPO_P$ and O_QQNO, for each of which *M* is a coupler point. Thus the path generated by point *M* as a coupler point of $OLPO_P$ is identical to the path traced by *M* as a coupler point of O_QQNO. Thus we have generated two completely different four-bar mechanisms that generate identical coupler curves. Linkages that have this property are called *cognates*.[4] These are the same cognates that were briefly discussed in section 6.6.3.

We can go further. If points *R* and *S* are located by constructing the parallelograms O_PPMR and O_QQMS, it can be shown that triangle *MRS* is similar to triangle *LPM* and hence that the four-bar linkage O_PRSO_Q is also cognate to $OLPO_P$ and O_QQNO, again with *M* as the tracing point. The assemblage shown in Fig. 7.12 is known as Roberts's mechanism.

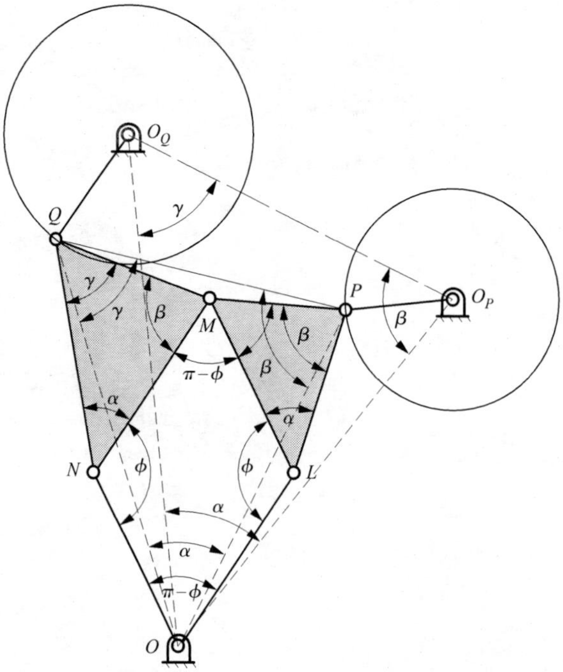

FIGURE 7.11 A pair of cognate linkages. The path of point P in the skew pantograph of Fig. 7.10 is a circle centered on O_P. Therefore the path of point Q is also a circle, with center O_Q, where triangle OO_PO_Q is similar to triangle LPM. Therefore cranks O_PP and O_QQ can be added, and the assemblage will be mobile. M is the common coupler point.

Roberts's theorem states that if a planar four-bar mechanism is constructed, a coupler point is selected, and the corresponding coupler curve is traced, then there are two other four-bar linkages that will generate the identical coupler curve. That is, there are two four-bar linkages that are cognate to the original four-bar. They may be obtained by constructing the Roberts's mechanism based on the original four-bar. In the case of Fig. 7.12, if we view $OLPO_P$ as the original four-bar linkage, with M being the selected coupler point, then the

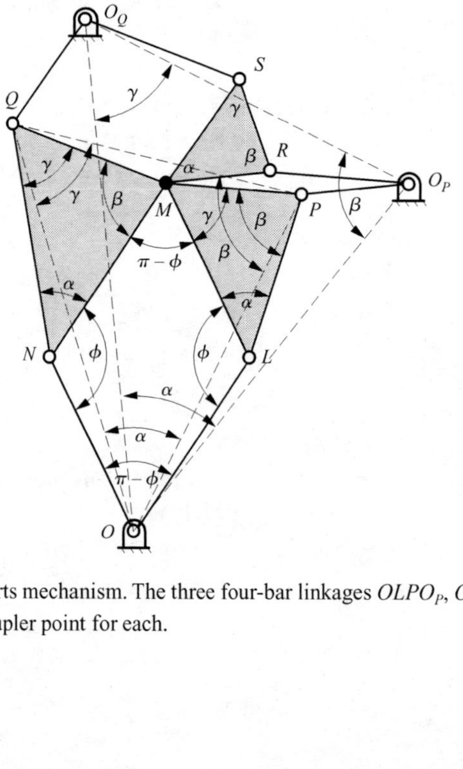

FIGURE 7.12 A general Roberts mechanism. The three four-bar linkages $OLPO_P$, O_PRSO_Q, and O_QQNO are all cognates with M as the coupler point for each.

cognates are O_QQNO and O_PRSO_Q with M being the coupler point in both cases. Starting with points O, L, P, O_P, and M, we can construct the remainder of the figure by first completing the parallelograms $OLMN$ and O_PRMP to locate points N and R. Triangles OO_PO_Q, NMQ, and MRS may then be constructed similar to triangle LPM to complete the figure.

If the original four-bar linkage is of Grashof type 1, then the cognates will also be type 1. Likewise, if the original four-bar is type 2, then the cognates are also type 2. Further, if the original four-bar is type 1 and is a crank-rocker linkage, then one of the cognates will also be a crank-rocker linkage. The other will be a type 1 double-rocker. The cognates of a drag-link linkage are both also drag links. The cognates of a type 1 double-rocker are both crank-rockers.

As indicated in Chapter 6, cognate linkages can be very useful when a linkage has been found that generates a desired path but that solution linkage has undesirable properties such as interference with other components. Often one of the cognates will produce the desired path without the problems of the original linkage.

EXAMPLE 7.1 Using Roberts's Theorem to Generate Cognates of Chebyshev Mechanism

The Chebyshev linkage of Fig. 7.2 is a type 1 double-rocker. As was discussed in Section 1.18, it is difficult to transfer motion from the tracing point of this linkage owing to interference with the cranks since the coupler tumbles between the cranks. As just discussed, the cognates of a type 1 double-rocker are both crank-rockers and should be free of this problem. Construct the cognates and, hence, produce a crank-rocker linkage with the same approximate straight-line coupler curve segment as the Chebyshev linkage.

Solution

Examination of Fig. 7.2 indicates that the coupler point is the midpoint of the line between the coupler pivots. That is, the triangle LPM of Fig. 7.12 has collapsed into a line. Therefore triangle OO_PO_Q will also be collapsed to a line. Since O corresponds to L, O_P corresponds to P, and O_Q corresponds to M in these triangles (corresponding vertices have the same vertical angles), it follows that O_Q will be midway between O and O_P, as shown in Fig. 7.13. Similarly, triangles RMS and MNQ will collapse to line segments.

Parallelograms $OLMN$ and O_PPMR are constructed as shown in Fig. 7.13 to locate points N and R. The line MQN is drawn. Note that in Fig. 7.12, N corresponds to L, M corresponds to P, and Q corresponds to M in the two similar triangles LPM and NMQ. Therefore Q will be at the midpoint of NM in

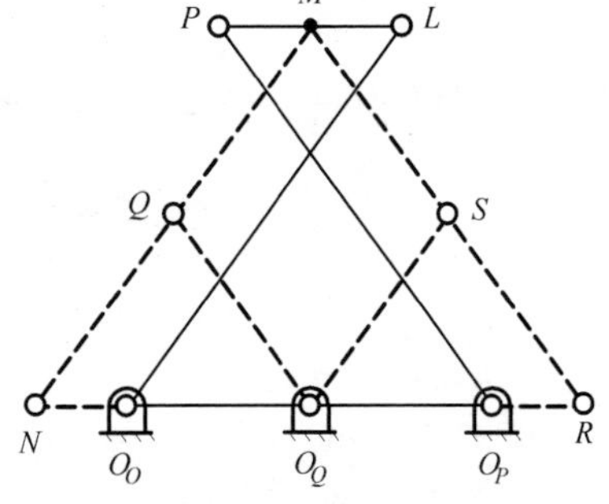

FIGURE 7.13 Construction of the cognates of the Chebyshev linkage shown in Fig. 7.2. $OLPO_P$ is the original Chebyshev four-bar mechanism, and M is the coupler point. The cognates are $ONQO_Q$ and O_PRSO_Q. Their symmetry with one another is a result of the bilateral symmetry of the original linkage.

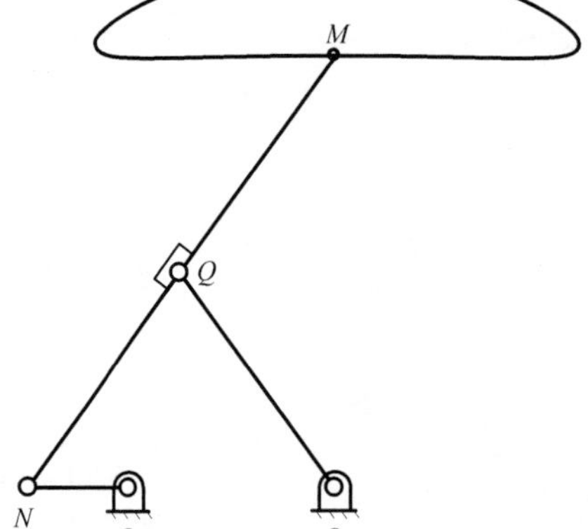

FIGURE 7.14 The cognate $ONQO_Q$ from Fig. 7.12 with its coupler curve plotted.

Fig. 7.13. Similarly, the line *RSM* is drawn to represent the coupler of the second cognate. The cranks $O_Q Q$ and $O_Q S$ are drawn to complete the two cognates shown by the dashed lines in Fig. 7.13.

The cognate $ONQO_Q$ is drawn on its own in Fig. 7.14 with the path of point *M* plotted. Not only is it much easier to transfer motion from this linkage than from the original Chebyshev linkage, but the linkage can be driven by continuous rotation of the crank *ON*, if desired.

7.2 SPHERICAL LINKAGES

Although spatial linkages, in general, will be discussed in Chapter 9, there are other classes of mechanisms that are not general spatial linkages in the sense of satisfying the spatial Kutzbach criterion [Eq. (1.3)] and are certainly not planar mechanisms. One of the most extensive and practically important such groups is the class of spherical mechanisms, which includes not only linkages but also spherical cam mechanisms and gears, namely bevel gears, and rolling contact bearings, namely tapered roller bearings.

Although it is beyond the scope of this book, spherical mechanism theory is an important component of spatial mechanism theory. This is because the rotational equations defined for spatial mechanisms in Chapter 9 are identical for spherical mechanisms. However, the translation equations, also discussed in Chapter 9, are absent in the case of spherical mechanisms. This allows inferences to be made on the basis of a spherical analog, and these can be applied to spatial mechanisms. There is also a way of generating valid translation equations directly from the rotational equations.

7.2.1 Introduction

Spherical linkages form a family much like planar linkages. However, whereas in a planar linkage all the revolute joint axes are parallel, in a spherical linkage they all intersect at a common point, called the concurrency point. Actually, planar linkages can be thought of as spherical linkages for which the concurrency point is at infinity.

There are many similarities in the properties of spherical and planar linkages. For example, spherical linkages obey the same form of the Kutzbach criterion that planar linkages do (Section 1.7):

$$M = 3(m - j - 1) + \sum_{i=1}^{j} f_i \tag{1.1}$$

Consequently, the simplest nontrivial spherical linkage is a four-bar linkage, just as in the planar case.

Also, there is a form of the Grashof inequality governing rotatability of joints that works for spherical linkages:

$$\alpha_\ell + \alpha_s < \alpha_p + \alpha_q$$

Here, instead of dealing with the lengths of the links, as in the case of a planar linkage, we work with the angles between successive joint axes. α_s is the smallest angle between two successive joints, α_ℓ is the largest such angle, and α_p and α_q are the other two angles.

As in the planar case, the inequality governs the presence of joints in a four-bar linkage that can be completely rotated. If the inequality is satisfied, there are two completely rotatable joints. They are the joints whose axes bound the angle α_s. Depending on which link is chosen as the base, the linkage will have characteristics similar to those of a crank-rocker planar four-bar, or a drag-link, or a type 1 double-rocker. If the inequality is not satisfied, there is no completely rotatable joint, and the linkage behaves like a type 2 planar linkage.

There is one variation from the planar analog. Whereas there is no limit on the length of a link in a planar linkage—beyond the fact that it must be less than the sum of the lengths of the other three links for it to be possible to assemble the loop—no side angle of a spherical linkage can be greater than 90°. This is because there are, in fact, always two angles between two lines that are supplements of one another. Either the angle or its supplement can be viewed as the angle between two axes in a spherical four-bar linkage. If the angle is greater than 90°, its supplement is less than 90°, so side angles in a spherical linkage can be said to have an upper limit of 90°.

The closure equations for a spherical four-bar linkage, such as that shown schematically in Fig. 7.15, may, in principle, be developed using a procedure analogous to that used to derive the closure equations for a planar four-bar linkage in Chapter 5. However, this becomes very complex because the entities being dealt with are angles rather than lengths. A more convenient procedure is to use the loop matrix transformations defined in Chapter 9. Using either method, the relationship between angle ϕ_1, considered to be the input angle, and ϕ_2, considered to be the output angle, of the linkage of Fig. 7.15 can be expressed as follows:

$$\sin\phi_1 \sin\phi_2 \sin\alpha_2 \sin\alpha_4 - \cos\phi_1 \cos\phi_2 \cos\alpha_1 \sin\alpha_2 \sin\alpha_4 + \cos\phi_1 \sin\alpha_1 \cos\alpha_2 \sin\alpha_4 + \cos\phi_2 \sin\alpha_1 \sin\alpha_2 \cos\alpha_4 + \cos\alpha_1 \cos\alpha_2 \cos\alpha_4 - \cos\alpha_3 = 0 \tag{7.1}$$

where $\phi_1, \phi_2, \phi_3,$ and ϕ_4 are the joint angles and $\alpha_1, \alpha_2, \alpha_3,$ and α_4 are the angles between the joint axes of the spherical four-bar loop as shown in Fig. 7.15.

If ϕ_1 is regarded as having a known value, this rather intimidating-looking equation has the form

$$P\cos\phi_2 + Q\sin\phi_2 + R = 0 \tag{7.2}$$

for which a solution was developed in Chapter 5. Here

$$\begin{aligned} P &= -\cos\phi_1 \cos\alpha_1 \sin\alpha_2 \sin\alpha_4 + \sin\alpha_1 \sin\alpha_2 \cos\alpha_4 \\ Q &= \sin\phi_1 \sin\alpha_2 \sin\alpha_4 \\ R &= \cos\phi_1 \sin\alpha_1 \cos\alpha_2 \sin\alpha_4 + \cos\alpha_1 \cos\alpha_2 \cos\alpha_4 - \cos\alpha_3 \end{aligned} \tag{7.3}$$

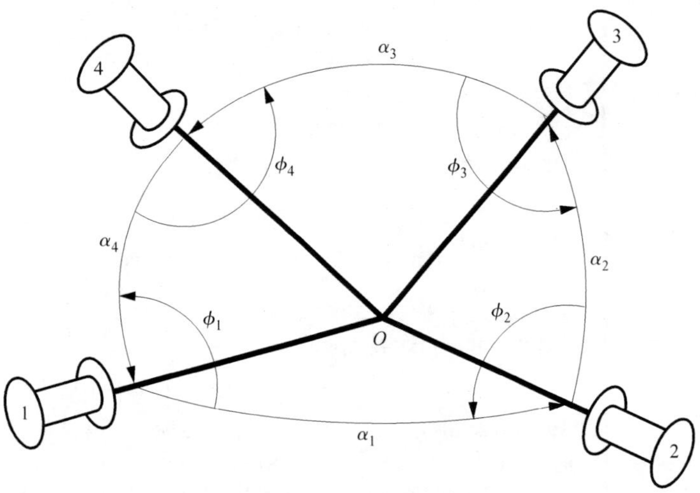

FIGURE 7.15 A schematic representation of a spherical four-bar mechanism. The heavy lines represent the joint axes with concurrency point O. $\alpha_1, \alpha_2, \alpha_3,$ and α_4 are the angles between the successive axes. ϕ_1, ϕ_2, ϕ_3, and ϕ_4 are the joint angles.

Hence referring to Table 5.1, we can obtain values for ϕ_2, given ϕ_1 from

$$t = \frac{-Q + \sigma\sqrt{P^2 + Q^2 - R^2}}{R - P} \tag{7.4}$$

where $\sigma = \pm 1$ is a sign variable, and

$$\phi_2 = 2\tan^{-1}(t). \tag{7.5}$$

We can also develop relationships between the angular velocities and accelerations about joints 1 and 2 by differentiation of Eq. (7.1). Differentiation of Eq. (7.1) with respect to time gives, after rearrangement,

$$\dot{\phi}_2 = -\dot{\phi}_1 \frac{\sin\alpha_4(\cos\phi_1 \sin\phi_2 \sin\alpha_2 + \sin\phi_1 \cos\phi_2 \cos\alpha_1 \sin\alpha_2 - \sin\phi_1 \cos\alpha_1 \cos\alpha_2)}{\sin\alpha_2(\sin\phi_1 \cos\phi_2 \sin\alpha_4 + \cos\phi_1 \sin\phi_2 \cos\alpha_1 \sin\alpha_4 - \sin\phi_2 \sin\alpha_1 \sin\alpha_4)} \tag{7.6}$$

Further differentiation gives

$$\ddot{\phi}_2 = \frac{\ddot{\phi}_1\dot{\phi}_2}{\dot{\phi}_1} + \frac{B}{A}\dot{\phi}_1\dot{\phi}_2 + \frac{C}{A}\dot{\phi}_1^2 + \frac{D}{A}\dot{\phi}_2^2 \tag{7.7}$$

where

$$\begin{aligned}
A &= \sin\alpha_2(\sin\phi_1 \cos\phi_2 \sin\alpha_4 + \cos\phi_1 \sin\phi_2 \cos\alpha_1 \sin\alpha_4 - \sin\phi_2 \sin\alpha_1 \cos\alpha_4)\\
B &= 2\sin\alpha_2 \sin\alpha_4(\sin\phi_1 \sin\phi_2 \cos\alpha_1 - \cos\phi_1 \cos\phi_2)\\
C &= \sin\alpha_4(\sin\phi_1 \sin\phi_2 \sin\alpha_2 - \cos\phi_1 \cos\phi_2 \cos\alpha_1 \sin\alpha_2 + \cos\phi_1 \sin\alpha_1 \cos\alpha_2)\\
D &= \sin\alpha_2(\sin\phi_1 \sin\phi_2 \sin\alpha_4 - \cos\phi_1 \cos\phi_2 \cos\alpha_1 \sin\alpha_4 + \cos\phi_2 \sin\alpha_1 \cos\alpha_4)
\end{aligned} \tag{7.8}$$

EXAMPLE 7.2
Analysis of a Spherical Four-Bar Mechanism

A spherical four-bar linkage is constructed with the angle between the axes of joints 1 and 2 (α_1) being 120°, the angle between axes 2 and 3 (α_2) 90°, that between axes 3 and 4 (α_3) 75°, and that between axes 1 and 4 (α_4) 30°. Member 1 is the base and the mechanism is a spherical crank-rocker linkage. Find the output angle, ϕ_2, when the driving joint angle, ϕ_1, is 90°.

If the input crank is driven at a constant angular velocity of 10 rad/s, find the angular velocity, $\dot{\phi}_2$, of the driven crank, and its angular acceleration, $\ddot{\phi}_2$, in the same position.

Solution

Substitution of the values

$$\alpha_1 = 120°,\ \alpha_2 = 90°,\ \alpha_3 = 75°,\ \alpha_4 = 30°,\ \phi_1 = 90°$$

into Eq. (7.3) gives

$$P = 0.75,\ Q = 0.5,\ R = -0.2588$$

Substitution of these values into Eq. (7.4) gives

$$t = -0.3603, \text{ or } t = 1.3515$$

Application of Eq. (7.5) gives

$$\phi_2 = -39.63°, \text{ or } \phi_2 = 107.00°$$

The two solutions correspond to the two solutions obtained in the solution of the position problem of a planar four-bar and have the same source in the reflection of the driven-crank and coupler about the plane of the moving joint axis of the driving crank and the fixed joint axis of the driven crank.

Substitution of these values plus $\dot{\phi}_1 = 10$ rad/s into Eq. (7.6) gives the values $\dot{\phi}_2 = 2.2302$ rad/s and $\dot{\phi}_2 = 0.8467$ rad/s, respectively corresponding to the two solutions for ϕ_2 given here. Further substitution into Eq. (7.8) gives the following sets of values:

for $\phi_2 = -39.63^\circ$, $A = 0.8634$, $B = 0.3189$, $C = -0.3189$, $D = 0.2588$
for $\phi_2 = 107.00^\circ$, $A = -0.8634$, $B = -0.4781$, $C = 0.4781$, $D = 0.2588$

When substituted into Eq. (7.7) with $\ddot{\phi}_1 = 0$ and the preceding values for $\dot{\phi}_1$ and $\dot{\phi}_2$, we get the following two values for the acceleration of the driven crank: $\ddot{\phi} = -27.20$ rad/s^2 and $\ddot{\phi}$ – 50.90 rad/s^2, respectively. Once again, these correspond to the two possible solutions of the position problem.

7.2.2 Gimbals

A set of gimbals is a spherical serial chain that allows an axis through the concurrency point to be placed in any possible direction. Gimbals are often used in the mounts of directional instruments such as theodolites or telescopes. They are also used in gyroscopes to allow the rotor axis freedom to assume any direction relative to the base of the instrument.

7.2.3 Universal Joints

The simplest means of transferring motion between noncoaxial shafts is by means of one or two universal joints. For this reason this very simple spherical mechanism appears in an enormous variety of applications. They may be found as components of the Stewart platform and 3-2-1 platform parallel mechanisms discussed in Chapter 9 and in many other situations. (Universal joints are also known as Cardan joints in Europe and Hooke joints in Britain.)

Properties of the Universal Joint A common need in machinery is to transfer rotation between two shafts that are not parallel to one another and that may be free to move relative to one another. A universal joint is a simple spherical four-bar mechanism that transfers rotary motion between two shafts whose axes pass through the concurrency point. The joint itself consists of two revolute joints whose axes are orthogonal to one another. They are often configured in a cross-shaped member as shown in Fig. 7.16. One of these joints is arranged with its axis at 90° to that of the driving shaft, and the other has its axis at 90° to that of the driven shaft. In practice, the ends of the shafts are often configured as clevises to mate with the cruciform shafts of the intermediate member. Together with the bearings in which the two shafts turn, the universal joint forms a spherical four-bar linkage with three sides being 90° angles. The fourth side is, in general, not 90°. This may be better seen in Fig. 7.17, in which only one side of each of the crossed intermediate shafts is shown.

In general, the angular motion is not uniformly transferred from the driving shaft to the driven shaft. The relationship between the angles of the driving shaft, θ_1, and the driven shaft, θ_2, is

$$\cos\gamma = \tan\theta_1 \tan\theta_2 \tag{7.9}$$

where γ is the angular misalignment of the shafts. This relationship can be quickly derived from Eq. (7.1). As is indicated in Fig. 7.17, $\alpha_2 = \alpha_3 = \alpha_4 = 90^\circ$. Also, $\alpha_1 = \gamma$ and $\phi_1 = \theta_1$,

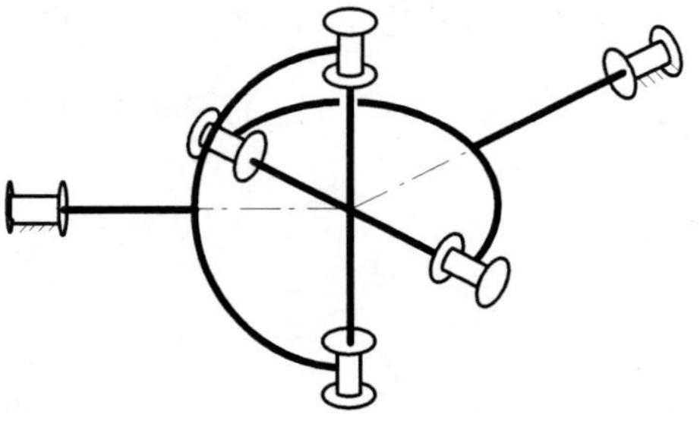

FIGURE 7.16 Universal, Cardan, or Hooke joint.

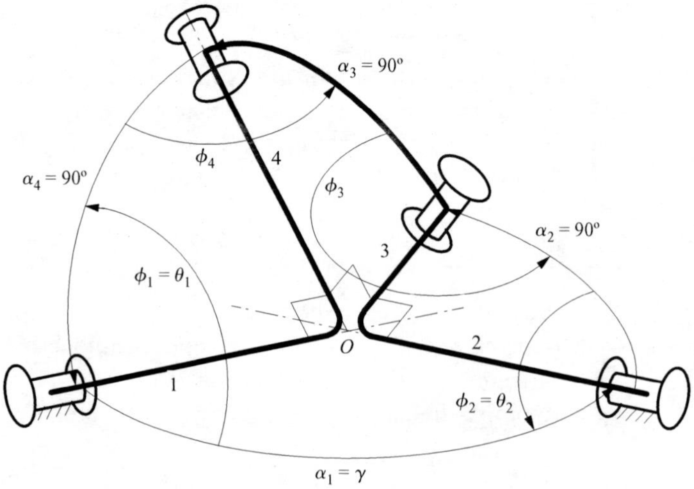

FIGURE 7.17 Universal joint geometry: γ is the angular misalignment of the shafts; θ_1 is the angle of the input shaft; θ_2 is the angle of the output shaft.

$\phi_2 = \theta_2$ where α_i and ϕ_i ($i = 1, 2, 3, 4$) are consistent with Eq. (7.1). Substituting these values into Eq. (7.1) reduces it to

$$\sin\theta_1 \sin\theta_2 - \cos\theta_1 \cos\theta_2 \cos\gamma = 0$$

which can be rearranged into Eq. (7.9).

If the driving shaft turns with a uniform angular velocity, the rotation of the driven shaft is not uniform but fluctuates. That is, a single universal joint is not a constant-velocity coupling like those that will be discussed in the next section. However, if the angle between the shaft axes is small, the fluctuation will also be small and is acceptable in many applications.

The angular velocity relationship can be obtained by differentiating Eq. (7.9) written in the form

$$\tan\theta_2 = \cos\gamma \cot\theta_1$$

Differentiation with respect to time gives

$$\dot{\theta}_2 \sec^2\theta_2 = -\dot{\theta}_1 \csc^2\theta_1 \cos\gamma$$

Hence the ratio of the magnitudes of the shaft velocities is

$$\frac{\omega_2}{\omega_1} = \frac{\dot{\theta}_2}{\dot{\theta}_1} = \frac{\cos^2\theta_2 \cos\gamma}{\sin^2\theta_1}$$

It is helpful to work in terms of the input angle, θ_1, alone. First use $\cos^2\theta = 1/(1 + \tan^2\theta)$ and then use the angle equation to eliminate $\tan^2\theta_2$:

$$\frac{\omega_2}{\omega_1} = \frac{\cos\gamma}{\sin^2\theta_1\left(1 + \tan^2\theta_2\right)} = \frac{\cos\gamma}{\sin^2\theta_1\left(1 + \cos^2\gamma \cot^2\theta_1\right)} = \frac{\cos\gamma}{\sin^2\theta_1 + \cos^2\gamma \cos^2\theta_1}$$

This expression can be further simplified by replacing $\sin^2\theta_1$ by $1 - \cos^2\theta_1$ as follows:

$$\frac{\omega_4}{\omega_2} = \frac{\cos\gamma}{1 - \cos^2\theta_1 + \cos^2\gamma \cos^2\theta_1} = \frac{\cos\gamma}{1 - \sin^2\gamma \cos^2\theta_1} \tag{7.10}$$

It may be seen that the velocity ratio is a function of θ_1 so that for constant input velocity the output velocity will fluctuate. The velocity ratio varies from $1/\cos\gamma$ to $\cos\gamma$ during the motion cycle. This relationship is plotted in Fig. 7.18.

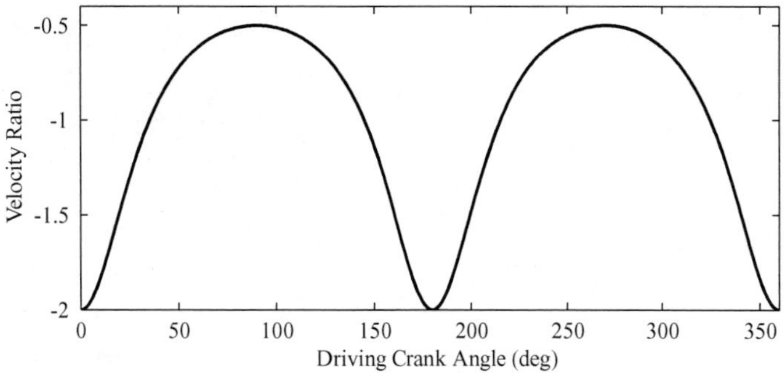

FIGURE 7.18 Velocity ratio fluctuation for a universal joint with $\gamma = 120°$. The negative values of the velocity ratio are an artifact of the way these angles are defined in Fig. 7.17. Examination of that figure indicates that θ_2 decreases when θ_1 increases. Looking from the driving shaft toward the driven shaft, we see that both shafts are rotating in the same direction.

EXAMPLE 7.3 ***Analysis of a Universal Joint for a Front-Wheel-Driven Car***

A simple automotive vehicle is driven via the front wheels. Universal joints are used in the shafts connecting the differential to the front wheels, as a low-cost alternative to the constant-velocity joints that are normally used to allow rotation of the front wheels about vertical axes for steering. At full steering lock, the inside front wheel is rotated 30° from the straight-ahead position. Calculate the percentage fluctuation in wheel velocity in this position.

Solution

If shaft 1 in Fig. 7.17 is viewed as the shaft from the engine and shaft 2 is viewed as the half-shaft driving the wheel, in the full lock position the angle between the axis of shaft 1 and the axis of shaft 2 will be 30°. That is, $\gamma = 180° - 30° = 150°$. Applying Eq. (7.10) we get

$$\frac{\omega_4}{\omega_2} = \frac{-0.8660}{1 - 0.25\cos^2\theta_1}$$

Thus, the maximum magnitude of the velocity ratio is 0.8660/0.75 = 1.155, and the minimum magnitude is 0.8660/1.25 = 0.693. Thus the maximum is 115% of the mean value of 1.0, and the minimum is 69% of the mean. The maximum percentage fluctuation is 31%.

Dual Universal Joints By using two universal joints in a symmetric combination, it is possible to have the second joint cancel out the fluctuation generated by the first. This combination then produces a constant-velocity action.[5] If the joints are aligned so that axis 3 of the first coupling is parallel to axis 2 of the second, as shown in Fig. 7.19, then $\theta_1' = \theta_2$ where the prime (′) is used to designate the angles of the second linkage. Hence, using Eq. (7.9), we have

$$\begin{aligned}\cos\gamma &= \tan\theta_1 \tan\theta_2 \\ \cos\gamma &= \tan\theta_1' \tan\theta_2'\end{aligned} \tag{7.11}$$

and

$$\tan\theta_2' = \frac{\cos\gamma}{\tan\theta_1'} = \frac{\cos\gamma}{\tan\theta_2} = \frac{\cos\gamma\tan\theta_1}{\cos\gamma} = \tan\theta_1 \tag{7.12}$$

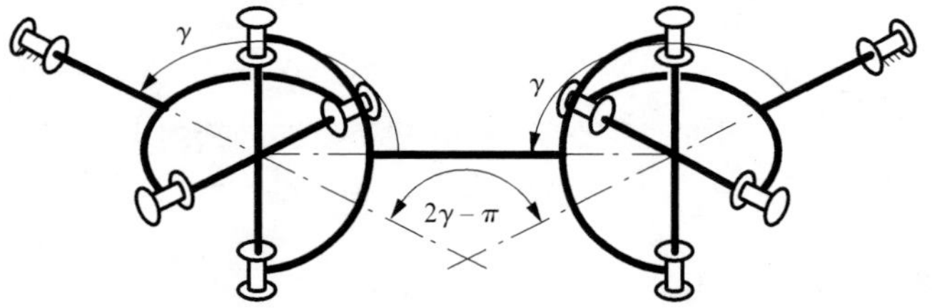

FIGURE 7.19 Dual universal joints arranged symmetrically. The combination provides a true constant-velocity coupling, as described in the text.

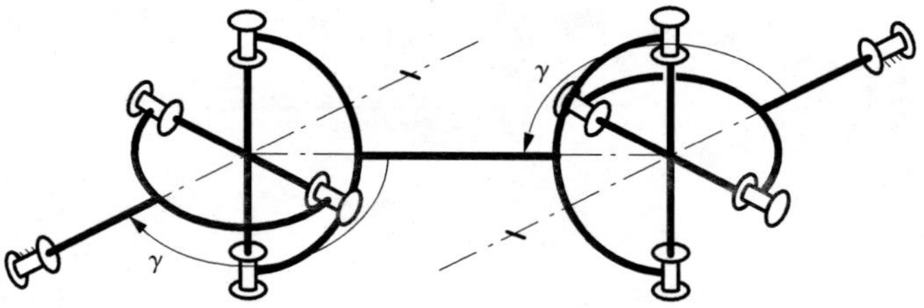

FIGURE 7.20 Dual universal joints on parallel, offset shafts. This arrangement also gives motion transfer between the input and output shafts at a constant velocity ratio.

Hence the output angle of the combined joint, θ_2', is always equal to the input angle θ_1. The same relationship is true if the shafts are not angulated, as in Fig. 7.19, but are parallel and offset, as in Fig. 7.20. This is also a configuration of considerable practical importance. In fact, the drive shafts of almost all front-engine, rear-wheel-driven automobiles feature this arrangement.

EXAMPLE 7.4 Analysis of a Universal Joint of a Rear-Wheel-Driven Car

A front-engine, rear-wheel-driven automobile employs a drive shaft with two universal joints in the alignment of Fig. 7.20 to transmit torque from the output shaft of the gearbox to the differential. The differential is mounted on the rear axle, and the suspension is of the live axle type (solid rear axle). The universal joints accommodate movement of the rear axle permitted by the suspension. The differential shaft is nominally parallel to the gearbox shaft. However, the suspension setup maintains this relationship only to a good approximation. Also, some fore–aft rocking of the differential housing occurs because of elastic deflection and backlash in suspension components. The angle γ, as defined in Fig. 7.20, varies from 175° to 160° between the suspension stops. The error in γ at the rear universal joint is estimated to be ±0.5°. Estimate the maximum percentage fluctuation in the velocity ratio between the gearbox shaft and the differential shaft.

Solution

Because the error in γ is small, we should be able to use a small-angle approximation with acceptable accuracy.

Equations (7.11) become

$$\cos\gamma = \tan\theta_1 \tan\theta_2$$

and

$$\cos(\gamma + \delta\gamma) = \tan\theta_1' \tan\theta_2'$$

or

$$\cos\gamma - \delta\gamma \sin\gamma = \tan\theta_1' \tan\theta_2'$$

Noting that

$$\tan\theta_1' = \tan\theta_2 = \frac{\cos\gamma}{\tan\theta_1}$$

$$\cos\gamma - \delta\gamma\sin\gamma = \frac{\cos\gamma\tan\theta_2'}{\tan\theta_1}$$

or

$$\tan\theta_2' = \tan\theta_1(1 - \delta\gamma\tan\gamma)$$

Differentiation of this expression with respect to time gives

$$\dot{\theta}_2' \sec^2\theta_2' = \dot{\theta}_1 \sec^2\theta_1(1 - \delta\gamma\tan\gamma)$$

Using

$$\sec^2\theta_2' = 1 + \tan^2\theta_2' = 1 + \tan^2\theta_1(1 - \delta\gamma\tan\gamma)^2$$

gives the velocity ratio

$$\frac{\theta_2'}{\theta_1} = \frac{1 - \delta\gamma \tan\gamma}{\cos^2\theta_1\left\{1 + \tan^2\theta_1\left(1 - \delta\gamma \tan\gamma\right)^2\right\}} = \frac{1 - \delta\gamma \tan\gamma}{1 - 2\delta\gamma \tan\gamma \sin^2\theta_1}$$

Here the small-angle approximation has been used by dropping the $\delta\gamma^2$ term in the expansion of the denominator. This expression may be further simplified by multiplying top and bottom by the factor $1 + 2\delta\gamma \tan\gamma \sin^2\theta_1$ and again applying the small-angle approximation. Then

$$\frac{\dot{\theta}_2'}{\dot{\theta}_1} = \left(1 + 2\delta\gamma \tan\gamma \sin^2\theta_1\right)\left(1 - \delta\gamma \tan\gamma\right) = 1 - \delta\gamma \tan\gamma + 2\delta\gamma \tan\gamma \sin^2\theta_1$$

or

$$\frac{\dot{\theta}_2'}{\dot{\theta}_1} = 1 - \delta\gamma \tan\gamma \cos 2\theta_1$$

It is clear from this expression that the maximum magnitude of the velocity ratio, R, is $1 + \delta\gamma \tan\gamma$ and the minimum value is $1 - \delta\gamma \tan\gamma$. Applying the values given in this particular problem, we find that $\tan\gamma$ will be at a maximum when $\gamma = 160°$ and $\delta\gamma = 15°$. Then

$$\delta\gamma = 0.5 \times \pi/180 = 0.00873 \text{ rad}$$

$$\tan\gamma = -0.364$$

so

$$R_{max} = 1.0032 \text{ and } R_{min} = 0.9968$$

The maximum percentage fluctuation of the velocity ratio is thus 0.32%.

7.3 CONSTANT-VELOCITY COUPLINGS

As can be seen in the preceding subsections, universal joints are not constant-velocity joints. Although paired universal joints can function as constant-velocity joints, the arrangement must satisfy special geometric conditions. There is a need for single joints that can provide true constant-velocity action and that can accommodate other changes of alignment such as plunging (movement in the direction of the shaft axis) of one shaft relative to the other.

7.3.1 Geometric Requirements of Constant-Velocity Couplings

An essential requirement for constant-velocity transfer of rotation between nonaligned shafts is that the coupling mechanism be symmetric relative to the plane that bisects the spatial angle between the shaft axes. Examination of Fig. 7.19 indicates that this condition is satisfied by the double universal joint. However, in many situations, such as the drive trains of front-wheel-driven automobiles, a more compact joint is needed.

7.3.2 Practical Constant-Velocity Couplings

A common commercial constant-velocity coupling uses bearing balls moving in shaped races between inner and outer journals to transmit torque. The races are shaped so that the centers of the balls are always in the plane of symmetry. The arrangement is shown in Fig. 7.21.

Figure 7.21 shows a ball-type constant-velocity coupling with six balls, and Fig. 7.22 shows a photograph of the coupling. The inner journal has a spherical outer surface with six equally spaced races with semicircular cross sections cut into it. The centerline of each race

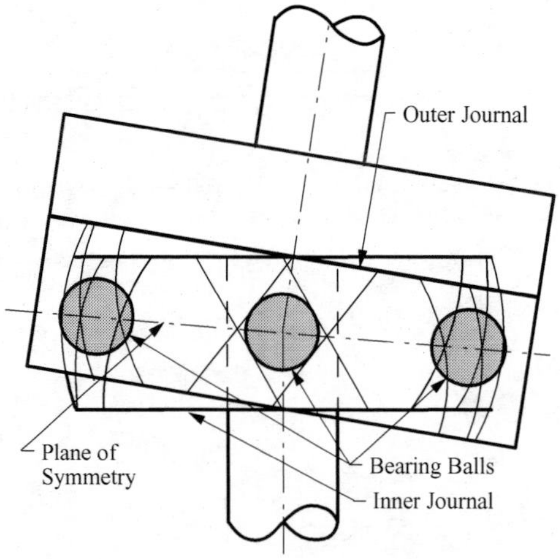

FIGURE 7.21 Ball-type constant-velocity coupling. The balls, six in the configuration shown, roll in races cut in the inner and outer journals. The centerlines of the races are great circles with their planes inclined to the journal axes at the same angle. Alternate races are cut with opposing angles. The angles of the races in the inner and outer races are also opposite. In this way the center of each ball is always at the intersection of the centerlines of the races in the inner and outer journals, which lies in the plane of symmetry of the angulated joint. Because the ball centers always lie in a common plane of symmetry, the condition for constant-velocity action is satisfied.

is a great circle of a neutral sphere that is slightly larger than the surface of the journal. The planes of the great circles are inclined at equal angles to the journal axis, and alternate races are cut at opposing angles. The outer journal has a spherical inner surface slightly larger than the neutral sphere. Races are also cut into it with their centerlines being great circles in the neutral sphere.

They are cut at the same angle to the journal axis as the races in the inner journal, and successive races are again cut at opposing angles. The joint is assembled with each ball rolling in inner and outer races that are at opposing angles. Therefore, the ball center is always at the intersection of the race centerlines. This ensures that all ball centers lie in a common plane at all times. This plane bisects the angle between the two journal axes and is, therefore, a plane

FIGURE 7.22 Ball-type constant-velocity coupling used in front-wheel-driven automobile.

of symmetry. Since the ball centers all lie in a common plane of symmetry at all times, the symmetry condition is satisfied and the joint transmits motion with constant velocity.

This type of joint can be made relatively compact and is commonly used in automotive drive shafts to allow smooth torque transmission despite the movements of the wheels permitted by the suspension.

7.4 AUTOMOTIVE STEERING AND SUSPENSION MECHANISMS

7.4.1 Introduction

Automotive steering and suspension mechanisms are primarily designed as separate, planar mechanisms acting in different planes. However, they are interconnected because they have common links. Also, both have modifications that make them spatial linkages. For example, the axis about which the wheel turns in response to movements of the steering linkage is not vertical. The inclination of the axis, called camber, creates a tendency for the steering to center itself at low speed, since it results in the vehicle body being raised slightly whenever the wheels are turned away from the straight-ahead position. Camber is not effective in providing centering at high speed. However, another modification, called caster, provides this action. The wheel steering axis is moved forward relative to the wheel a little way. The distance the wheel rotation axis trails the steering axis is the caster.

The interconnection, together with modifications such as camber that create a truly spatial character, can lead to undesirable dynamic interactions. It is very undesirable for suspension movements to be felt through the steering, or for the position of the steering linkage to influence suspension performance.

7.4.2 Steering Mechanisms

From a purely kinematic viewpoint, the essential geometry of an automotive steering linkage is that the axes of the front wheels should, at all times, be concurrent at the axis of the rear wheels. It is possible to synthesize a four-bar linkage that will constrain the front wheel axes to approximate this condition very closely. This is the basis of the Ackermann steering gear. As can be seen from Fig. 7.23, it is necessary that the front wheels be "toed out" to an increasing extent as the radius of curvature of the vehicle path is reduced.

However, a close approximation to Ackermann geometry is often not used on modern automobiles, particularly on high-performance vehicles and race cars. This is because, at high speed, steering becomes a dynamic problem. To change direction, it is necessary to develop lateral forces at the tire contacts with the road. The production of lateral force requires some slip between the wheel and the road. By using less toe-out than would be required by the Ackermann geometry, more lateral slip is generated at the outside front wheel, which also carries a greater share of the vehicle weight owing to dynamic load transfer and is, therefore, able to generate more lateral force. Some race car steering setups go so far as to reverse the kinematically ideal relationship by actually toeing the front wheels in by a small amount during turns. This very aggressive geometry produces very strong cornering action at the expense of tire wear, which is not, of course, such a concern in a race over a limited distance as it is in general automotive use.

Ackermann action, or any other desired relationship between the steering angles of the wheels, can be adequately approximated by an eight-bar steering linkage such as that shown in Fig. 7.24. Because the wheels move vertically with suspension travel, the joints at

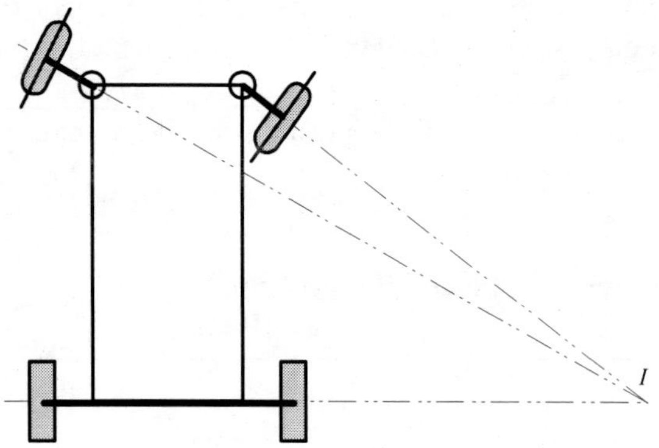

FIGURE 7.23 The Ackermann steering condition. Since the axes of all four wheels meet at a common instantaneous center, the wheels can roll without any lateral scuffing action. This is the ideal steering geometry at low speeds.

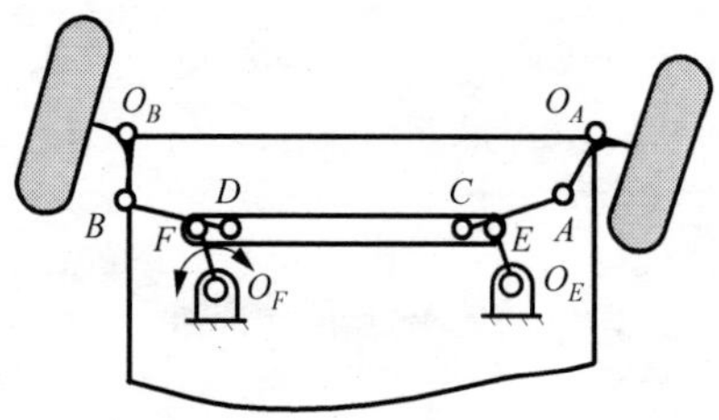

FIGURE 7.24 A typical steering gear arrangement. The Pitman arm, O_FF, is turned by the steering column. The four-bar loop O_FEFO_F is a parallelogram. O_EE is the idler arm, and EF is the relay rod. AC and BD are the tie rods, and O_AA and O_BB, which are fixed to the structures that carry the stub axles, are called the steering arms. The steering arms turn about the steering knuckles O_A and O_B. Note that the linkage is bilaterally symmetric about the centerline of the vehicle.

the ends of the tie rods must be spherical joints. Thus, the linkage becomes spatial, although still approximating the designed planar behavior.

In modern cars, it is more common to use a linear input to the steering linkage. This is typically produced by a rack-and-pinion type of steering box. This linear input is applied directly to the relay rod. This arrangement may be thought of as the limiting case of the mechanism in Fig. 7.24 as the arms O_EE and O_FF become infinitely long, producing the configuration of Fig. 7.25. It has the advantages of being simpler (using six members versus eight), more compact, and potentially lighter.

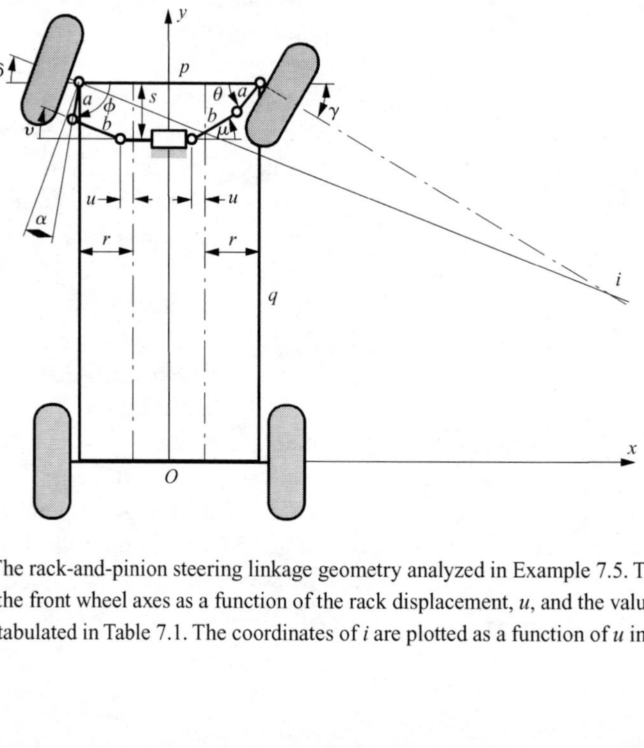

FIGURE 7.25 The rack-and-pinion steering linkage geometry analyzed in Example 7.5. The position of the intersection of the front wheel axes as a function of the rack displacement, u, and the values of the wheel angles γ and δ are tabulated in Table 7.1. The coordinates of i are plotted as a function of u in Fig. 7.26.

EXAMPLE 7.5
Analysis of a Rack-and-Pinion Type Steering Linkage

A steering linkage for an automobile is shown in Fig. 7.25. The wheel base of the automobile (distance between front and rear wheel axes) is $q = 100$ in. The distance between the steering knuckles is $p = 50$ in. The length of the steering arm is $a = 3$ in, and it is inclined at angle $\alpha = 9°$ to the plane of the wheel. The length of the tie rods is $b = 10$ in. When the wheels are in the straight-ahead position shown in Fig. 7.25, the inner ends of the tie rods are a distance $r = 10.08$ in from the steering knuckles in the lateral direction, and $s = 7.72$ in in the longitudinal direction.

Plot the x and y coordinates of the intersection of the front wheel axes for increments of 0.1 in of the rack displacement, u, in the range $0 < u''$ 1.5 in, where the reference frame has its origin at the middle of the rear axle, as shown. The x coordinate can be interpreted as the radius of curvature of the path followed by the vehicle, and the y coordinate is the error from perfect Ackermann geometry. As indicated in Fig. 7.23, if the Ackermann condition were exactly met, y would be zero at all times. Also calculate the angles of the inner and outer front wheels relative to the straight-ahead position throughout this range.

Solution

The linkage can be analyzed as two slider-crank linkages acting in parallel with a common input, u, applied to the sliders. Resolving components in the x and y directions respectively, we have for the right side

$$a\cos\theta + b\cos\mu = r + u \tag{7.13}$$

$$a\sin\theta + b\sin\mu = s \tag{7.14}$$

where μ is the tie rod angle as shown in Fig. 7.25.

Similarly, for the left side, we have

$$a\cos\phi + b\cos v = r - u \tag{7.15}$$

$$a\sin\phi + b\sin v = s \tag{7.16}$$

The angle μ may be eliminated from Eqs. (7.13) and (7.14) by segregating the μ terms on one side of each equation, squaring both sides of both equations, and adding to give

$$b^2 = \left(r + u - a\cos\theta\right)^2 + \left(s - a\sin\theta\right)^2$$

or

$$b^2 = r^2 + s^2 + a^2 + u^2 + 2ru - 2au\cos\theta - 2ar\cos\theta - 2as\sin\theta \tag{7.17}$$

This equation has the form

$$P\cos\theta + Q\sin\theta + R = 0 \tag{7.18}$$

where

$$\begin{aligned} P &= 2a\left(u + r\right) \\ Q &= 2as \\ R &= b^2 - a^2 - r^2 - s^2 - u^2 - 2ru \end{aligned} \tag{7.19}$$

Hence the standard solution of Table 5.1 may be applied to obtain values of θ corresponding to given values of u. Two values of θ are obtained for each value of u, one positive and one negative. Only the negative value is consistent with the configuration shown in Fig. 7.25, so the positive value is discarded.

Similarly, elimination of ν from Eqs. (7.15) and (7.16) gives

$$b^2 = \left(r - u - a\cos\phi\right)^2 + \left(s - a\sin\phi\right)^2$$

or

$$b^2 = r^2 + s^2 + a^2 + u^2 - 2ru + 2au\cos\phi - 2ar\cos\phi - 2as\sin\phi \tag{7.20}$$

This equation has the form

$$P'\cos\phi + Q'\sin\phi + R' = 0 \tag{7.21}$$

where

$$P' = 2a(r - u)$$
$$Q' = 2as$$
$$R' = b^2 - a^2 - r^2 - s^2 - u^2 + 2ru \tag{7.22}$$

for which the solution is also given by Table 5.1. Values of ϕ for incremental values of u throughout the specified range can be calculated. As was the case for θ, two values of are obtained for each value of u, one positive and one negative. Only the negative solution is consistent with the configuration drawn in Fig. 7.25, so the positive solution is discarded.

Now $\gamma = \pi/2 - \theta - \alpha$, and $\delta = \phi + \alpha - \pi/2$, where γ and δ are the steering angles of the inner and outer front wheels, as shown in Fig. 7.25, and values of γ and δ may now be calculated. The resulting values of γ and δ throughout the range of values of u are listed in Table 7.1. Also, γ and δ determine the location of the intersection, I, of the axes of the wheels:

$$\tan\gamma = \frac{q - y}{x - p/2}, \quad \tan\delta = \frac{q - y}{x + p/2} \tag{7.23}$$

Hence,

$$(x - p/2)\tan\gamma = (x + p/2)\tan\delta$$

which, when solved for x, gives

$$x = \frac{p}{2}\left(\frac{\tan\gamma + \tan\delta}{\tan\gamma - \tan\delta}\right) \tag{7.24}$$

Substitution for x into either of Eqs. (7.23) allows a solution for y to be obtained:

$$y = q - p\left(\frac{\tan\gamma\tan\delta}{\tan\gamma - \tan\delta}\right)$$

The results are tabulated in Table 7.1 and are plotted in Fig. 7.26. It may be seen that the linkage gives a reasonable approximation to the Ackermann condition, except at very large wheel angles.

TABLE 7.1 Numerical Values Obtained by Solution of Example 7.5

u	γ	δ	x	y
0.2	4.13	3.99	1475.17	−4.65
0.3	6.25	5.94	973.19	−3.91
0.4	8.43	7.87	718.74	−2.86
0.5	10.67	9.79	563.51	−1.50
0.6	12.99	11.68	457.89	0.17
0.7	15.38	13.56	380.59	2.18
0.8	17.88	15.43	320.98	4.52
0.9	20.50	17.29	273.11	7.23
1.0	23.28	19.13	233.42	10.34
1.1	26.25	20.98	199.57	13.90
1.2	29.50	22.81	169.98	17.99
1.3	33.13	24.65	143.39	22.74
1.4	37.38	26.48	118.66	28.44
1.5	42.87	28.31	94.09	35.86

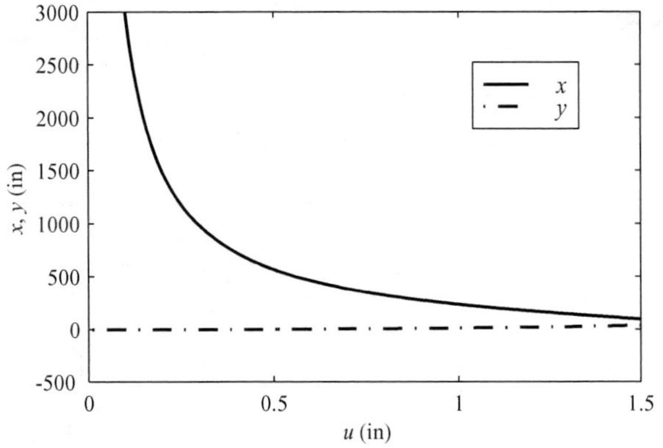

FIGURE 7.26 The coordinates of the intersection of the front wheel axes, *i*, plotted against the rack displacement, u. x approximates the radius of curvature of the vehicle's path, and y is the error in location of the intersection relative to the rear axle axis. That is, y is the deviation from the Ackermann condition. When $u = 0$, $x = \infty$ and $y = 0$. The values used in the plot are included in Table 7.1.

7.4.3 Suspension Mechanisms

An automotive suspension performs the function of a vibration filter, reducing the amplitudes of vibrations excited by geometric variations in the road surface. This is the function of the spring damper arrangements that are integral components of the suspension. Analysis of this vibration filtering action is normally covered in texts on mechanical vibrations and is beyond the scope of this book. Here we confine ourselves to the kinematic requirements of suspension mechanisms.

Automotive suspension mechanisms must allow controlled, single-degree-of-freedom motion of the wheel axis relative to the body of the vehicle. The travel allowed needs to be as close as possible to normal to the plane of the ground at the wheel contact. Also, it is necessary for the suspension mechanism to maintain the plane of the wheel as perpendicular as possible to the ground at all times. This is because automobile tires are designed to develop maximum lateral force when they are in the upright position, as opposed to motorcycle tires, which must function in inclined positions during hard cornering. Since the center of mass of an automotive vehicle is almost always higher than the wheel axes, there is a tendency for the body to roll toward the outside of a turn. Another objective of suspension design is to attempt to control this tendency to roll.

Automotive steering and suspension mechanisms are truly spatial mechanisms. However, their initial design generally rests on planar principles.

When viewed from the front, the instantaneous center of motion of the body of the vehicle relative to the ground is called the roll center. The location of the roll center for a typical independent suspension geometry is shown in Fig. 7.27. The center is located by using the Kennedy–Aronholdt theorem as described in Chapter 4.

Of course, the roll center moves as the position of the vehicle body moves. Whereas the roll center will be on the vehicle centerline for a road vehicle at rest on a level surface, it will shift off that line in the asymmetric positions that result from cornering. There is also a roll center for the rear suspension, so one can think of a roll axis, which is the line that passes through both roll centers.

The location of the roll center relative to the center of mass of the vehicle governs the effect of inertial forces caused by cornering on the system. Obviously, if the vertical distance between the roll center and the center of mass is large, the moment produced by lateral acceleration will be large. A suspension geometry that brings the roll center

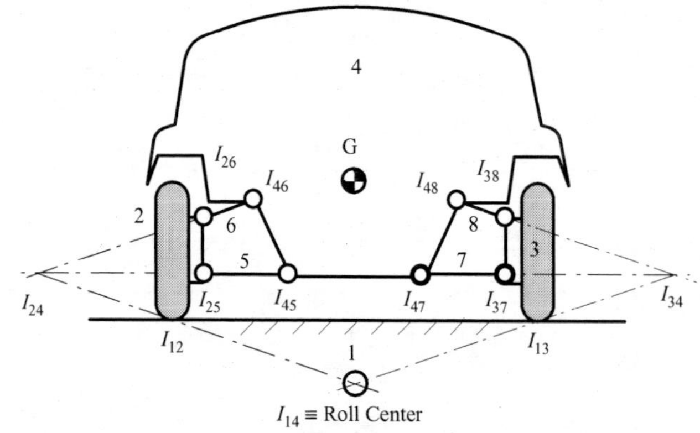

FIGURE 7.27 Roll center geometry for an automotive independent suspension system. The roll center is the instantaneous center of relative motion of the vehicle body and the ground.

progressively closer to the center of mass with increasing body roll might be attractive, because if the action of the suspension springs were linear, it would lead to increasing roll stiffness with increasing roll angle.

Suspension designers think of the roll center as the point of transfer of the inertial force between the sprung and unsprung masses of the vehicle. The unsprung mass comprises the wheels and suspension members directly attached to them whose position is directly determined by the road surface. The sprung mass is everything that moves when the springs are deflected.

7.5 INDEXING MECHANISMS

Indexing mechanisms are intermittent motion mechanisms that hold position alternately with a timed, unidirectional motion of the output member. This is distinct from other types of intermittent motion mechanisms such as dwell cams, which alternate forward and return motion with holding position. The output member of an indexing mechanism always advances in the same direction. Indexing mechanisms are of practical importance in applications such as weaving looms, advancing workpieces in repetitive manufacturing operations, and many instrument mechanisms.

7.5.1 Geneva Mechanisms

The most common type of indexing mechanism is a Geneva mechanism. Geneva mechanisms come in many varieties, both planar and spherical. When advancing, a Geneva mechanism is kinematically similar to an inverted slider-crank. When holding position, it functions as a simple journal bearing.

The name Geneva mechanism originated because these mechanisms were used in mechanical watch and clock movements in the days when mechanical movements were dominant, and Switzerland was the world center of the industry.

A simple example of a Geneva mechanism is shown in Fig. 7.28. The pin, P, on the driving wheel engages the slots in the star-shaped driven wheel to advance the driven wheel one-quarter turn for every rotation of the driving wheel. In between the advance movements, the eccentric cylindrical journal surfaces cut into the star wheel engage with the journal surface on the driving wheel to lock the star wheel in position, although the driving

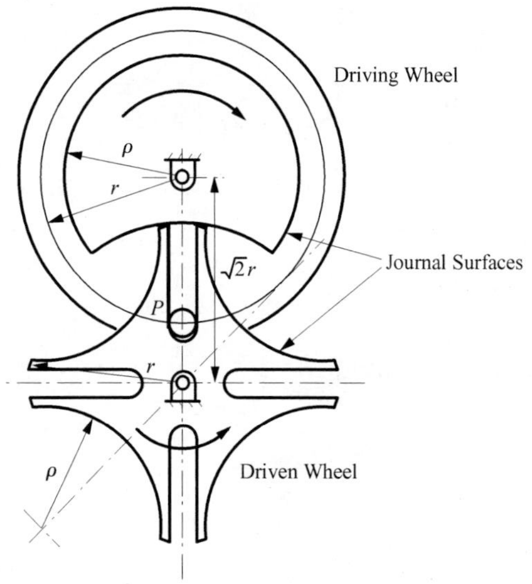

FIGURE 7.28 A four-station Geneva mechanism. The output member is the star wheel. The star wheel is advanced by the pin in the input wheel. The star wheel is advanced one-quarter revolution counterclockwise for every revolution of the input wheel. The advance movement occurs during one-quarter of a cycle with the star wheel being locked by the journal surface on the input wheel for the other three-quarters of the cycle.

wheel continues to rotate. The centerline of the slot must be tangent to the circle, with radius r, described by the center of the pin at the position in which the pin enters or leaves the slot. If this condition is not satisfied, there will be infinite acceleration at the beginning of advancement and infinite deceleration at the end. This condition dictates that the center distance of the two wheels should be $\sqrt{2}r$. It also requires that the outer radius of the star wheel be r. The radius of the journal surfaces is flexible. The centers of the cylindrical cutouts on the star wheel lie on a circle with radius $\sqrt{2}r$.

During the advancing phase of the cycle, the mechanism is kinematically equivalent to an inverted slider-crank. One of its attractions is that it smoothly accelerates and then decelerates the star wheel.

The motion of the star wheel may be analyzed by reference to Fig. 7.29. Resolving the sides of the triangle whose vertices are the two shaft axes and the pin axis in the vertical and horizontal directions, we get

$$r\sin\theta = x\sin\phi$$

$$r\cos\theta + x\cos\phi = \sqrt{2}r \tag{7.25}$$

Elimination of x by substitution from the first of these equations into the second gives

$$\cos\theta + \frac{\sin\theta}{\tan\phi} = \sqrt{2}$$

after canceling the common factor r. Rearrangement of this expression gives

$$\tan\phi = \frac{\sin\theta}{\sqrt{2} - \cos\theta} \tag{7.26}$$

or

$$\phi = \tan^{-1}\left(\frac{\sin\theta}{\sqrt{2} - \cos\theta}\right) \tag{7.27}$$

Differentiation of Eq. (7.26) with respect to time followed by simplification gives

$$\dot{\phi}\left(1 + \tan^2\phi\right) = \dot{\theta}\frac{\left(\sqrt{2}\cos\theta - 1\right)}{\left(\sqrt{2} - \cos\theta\right)^2}$$

Substitution for tan ϕ from Eq. (7.26) gives, after rearrangement and simplification,

$$\dot{\phi} = \dot{\theta}\left(\frac{\sqrt{2}\cos\theta - 1}{3 - 2\sqrt{2}\cos\theta}\right) \tag{7.28}$$

Differentiation again with respect to time gives, after simplification,

$$\ddot{\phi} = \ddot{\theta}\left(\frac{\sqrt{2}\cos\theta - 1}{3 - 2\sqrt{2}\cos\theta}\right) - \dot{\theta}^2 \frac{\sqrt{2}\sin\theta}{\left(3 - 2\sqrt{2}\cos\theta\right)^2}$$

In the usual case in which the driving wheel is driven at constant angular velocity, the first term disappears and

$$\ddot{\phi} = -\dot{\theta}^2 \frac{\sqrt{2}\sin\theta}{\left(3 - 2\sqrt{2}\cos\theta\right)^2} \tag{7.29}$$

Equations (7.27), (7.28), and (7.29) are plotted versus θ (in degrees) in Fig. 7.30. ϕ is plotted in radians. Of course, ϕ varies from – 45° to 45° during the advancement. The angular velocity curve is actually $\dot{\phi}/\dot{\theta}$, and the angular acceleration curve is $\ddot{\phi}/\dot{\theta}^2$.

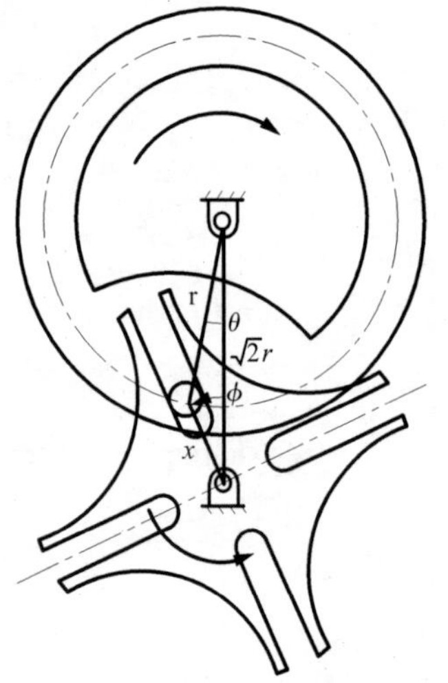

FIGURE 7.29 Kinematic modeling of the Geneva mechanism of Fig. 7.28. θ is the angle of rotation of the driving wheel, measured from the line of centers. ϕ is the angle of rotation of the star wheel.

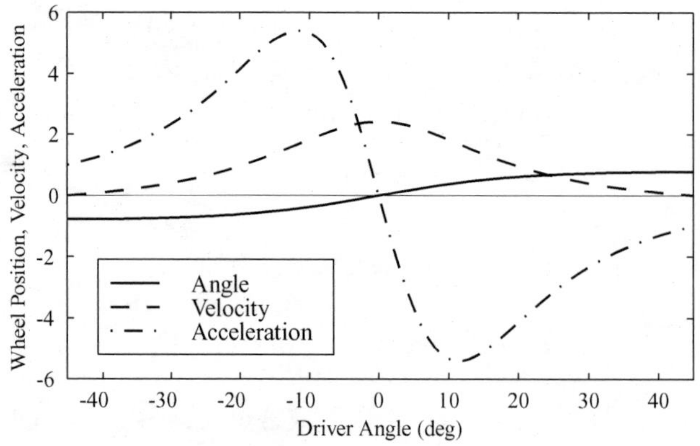

FIGURE 7.30 Position, velocity, and acceleration of the driven wheel of the Geneva mechanism shown in Figs. 7.28 and 7.29 during the advancement phase of the motion cycle. The angular position of the star wheel is in radians. The angular velocity and acceleration curves are respectively normalized to the driver angular velocity and driver angular velocity squared.

As can be seen from Fig. 7.30, the velocity and acceleration curves are smooth and well behaved, but the derivative of the acceleration (jerk) is infinite at the beginning and end of the advancement because the acceleration is discontinuous there. So far, we have considered only the simplest version of the Geneva mechanism: the four-station planar variety. The number of stations is the number of slots in the star wheel and may, in principle, be any number, although the geometric lower limit is three. There is also a practical upper limit at which the journal surfaces on the star wheel become too short to effectively lock the output between advancements. The number of pins on the driving wheel is usually one, but drivers with two or more are possible.

The essential geometry for relating the number of stations to the duration of the advancement is shown in Fig. 7.31. Here α is the angle between the slot centerline and the line of centers of the two wheels at the moment of engagement or disengagement of the pin. That is, α is half the angle between successive slots, or $360^\circ/(2N)$, where N is the number of stations. As already noted, the slot axis must be tangent to the circle traversed by the pin center at these positions to avoid infinite accelerations. This determines the relationship between N and the duration of the advancement, which is $\pi - 2\alpha$ by inspection of the figure. Consequently, the duration of the advancement increases with the number of stations, approaching a limit of 180° as the number of stations becomes very large. This has the advantage of making the advancement motion more gentle but the possible disadvantage of decreasing the duration of the period for which the output is stationary. The trade-off between these effects and the desirability of avoiding gearing downstream of the indexing mechanism determine the choice of the number of stations. Gearing downstream of an indexing mechanism should be avoided because of the inaccuracy and uncertainty in position introduced by necessary backlash in the gear train. Gear backlash is not usually a problem if the gears are in uniform motion. However, the discontinuous motion output from an indexing mechanism and consequent reversals of acceleration result in slapping across the backlash interval. Hence, any speed reduction should be done upstream of the indexing mechanism.

The number of stations also determines the ratio of the center distance of the wheel axes to the pin radius and the outside diameter of the star wheel. By inspection of Fig. 7.31, the former ratio is $1/\sin\alpha$ and the latter is $1/\tan\alpha$.

If we note that $\alpha = \pi/N$, Eqs. (7.27–7.29), respectively, become for this more general case

$$\phi = \tan^{-1}\left(\frac{\sin\alpha\sin\theta}{1-\sin\alpha\cos\theta}\right) \tag{7.30}$$

$$\dot{\phi} = \dot{\theta}\sin\alpha\left(\frac{\cos\theta-\sin\alpha}{1+\sin^2\alpha-2\sin\alpha\cos\theta}\right) \tag{7.31}$$

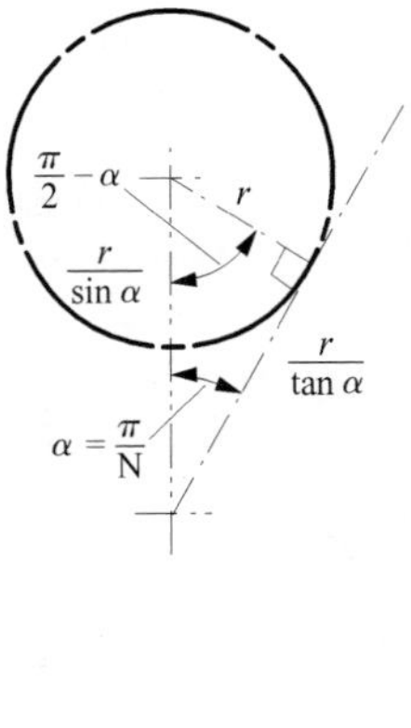

FIGURE 7.31 Critical geometry for a Geneva mechanism with N stations. α is the angle between the slot centerline and the line of centers at the moment of engagement of the pin; α is half the angle between successive slots on the star wheel.

$$\ddot{\phi} = -\dot{\theta}^2 \frac{\sin\alpha \cos^2\alpha \sin\theta}{\left(1 + \sin^2\alpha - 2\sin\alpha\cos\theta\right)^2} \tag{7.32}$$

Spherical Geneva mechanisms allow indexed motion transfer between angulated shafts. More importantly, a large number of stations can be accommodated without losing positive locking action between advances.

EXAMPLE 7.6
Analysis of a Geneva Wheel

An indexing drive is to be driven by a synchronous electric motor turning at 360 rpm. (The speed of a synchronous motor is locked to the alternating-current cycle frequency and so is essentially constant.) The single pin driver is to turn a six-station Geneva wheel. Compute the following:

a. the number of advances per second,

b. the angle through which the Geneva wheel advances during every revolution of the driving wheel,

c. the duration in seconds of the dwell in the output motion,

d. the peak angular velocity of the output shaft, and

e. the peak angular acceleration of the output shaft.

Solution

a. The number of advances per second is the number of revolutions of the driver per second, which is 360/60 = 6.

b. The angle advanced is $2\alpha = 360°/N = 60°$, with N, the number of stations, being 6 in this case. Hence $\alpha = 30°$.

c. The fraction of the cycle during which the output is locked (dwelling) is

$$\lambda = \frac{180 - 2\alpha}{360}$$

with α in degrees, giving $\lambda = 1/3$. The duration of the complete cycle is $T = 1/6$ s from part **a**. Hence the duration of the dwell is

$$\tau = \lambda T = 1/18 = 0.0555 \text{ s}$$

d. Referring to Eq. (7.32), we see that $\dot{\phi}$ is at its maximum value when $\theta = 0$. Also, for $N = 6$,

$$\sin\alpha = 0.5$$

so, substituting this value and $\theta = 0$ in Eq. (7.31) gives

$$\dot{\phi}_{max} = \dot{\theta}$$

$\dot{\theta}$ is the angular velocity of the drive wheel, so

$$\dot{\theta} = 2\pi \times 6 = 37.70 \text{ rad/s}$$

Therefore,

$$\dot{\phi}_{max} = 37.70 \text{ rad/s}$$

Note that ϕ is positive in the CCW direction and θ is positive in the CW direction (see Fig. 7.29). Therefore the positive values for both ϕ and θ indicate that the star wheel rotates in the opposite direction to the driver.

e. It is necessary to determine the value of θ that maximizes $\ddot{\phi}$. A straightforward way to do this would be to plot Eq. (7.32) in the same way as in Fig. 7.30, but with $\alpha = 30°$. $\ddot{\phi}$ and the angle θ at which it occurs could then be read directly from the plot.

Alternatively, we can differentiate Eq. (7.32) to identify the extrema of $\ddot{\phi}$. Noting that $\dot{\theta}$ is constant, we have

$$\frac{d\ddot{\phi}}{dt} = \frac{-\dot{\theta}^3 \sin\alpha \cos^2\alpha}{\left(1+\sin^2\alpha - 2\sin\alpha\cos\theta\right)^3}\left[\left(1+\sin^2\alpha - 2\sin\alpha\cos\theta\right)\cos\theta - 4\sin\alpha\sin^2\theta\right]$$

and so

$$\frac{d\ddot{\phi}}{dt} = 0$$

when

$$\left(1+\sin^2\alpha\right)\cos\theta - 2\sin\alpha\cos^2\theta - 4\sin\alpha\sin^2\theta = 0$$

Replacement of $\sin^2\theta$ by $1 - \cos^2\theta$ and rearrangement of the equation give

$$\cos^2\theta + \gamma\cos\theta - 2 = 0$$

where

$$\gamma = \frac{1+\sin^2\alpha}{2\sin\alpha} \tag{7.33}$$

The preceding equation can be treated as a quadratic equation in the variable $\cos\theta$. Solving for $\cos\theta$, we get

$$\cos\theta = \frac{-\gamma \pm \sqrt{\gamma^2+8}}{2}$$

It is possible to show that only the positive value of the square root gives a value of $\cos\theta$ with magnitude between 0 and 1 in the allowable range of $0 < \alpha < 60°$, so only that solution is valid. Hence, $\ddot{\phi}$ is at a maximum when

$$\theta = \pm\cos^{-1}\left(\frac{-\gamma + \sqrt{\gamma^2+8}}{2}\right) \tag{7.34}$$

where the ± sign now comes from inversion of the cosine, not from the quadratic solution. Equations (7.33) and (7.34) are of general validity for locating the maximal values of $\ddot{\phi}$. In the present case, substituting $\sin\alpha = 0.5$ in Eq. (7.33) gives

$$\gamma = 1.25$$

Hence Eq. (7.34) gives

$$\theta = \pm 22.90°$$

Substitution of these values into Eq. (7.32) gives

$$\frac{\ddot{\phi}}{\dot{\theta}^2} = \pm 1.372$$

Hence, since $\dot{\theta} = 6 \times 2\pi = 37.70$ rad/s, the peak angular acceleration is 1950 rad/s^2.

REFERENCES

[1]Hain, K., *Applied Kinematics,* McGraw-Hill Book Co., New York (1967).

[2]Dijksman, E. A., *Motion Geometry of Mechanisms,* Cambridge University Press (1976).

[3]Chironis, N. P., *Mechanisms, Linkages and Mechanical Controls*, McGraw-Hill Book Co., New York (1965).

[4]Bottema, O. and Roth, B., *Theoretical Kinematics,* North-Holland Press, New York (1979).

[5]Hunt, K. H., *Kinematic Geometry of Mechanisms,* Clarendon Press, Oxford (1978).

PROBLEMS

Exercise Problems Involving Cognate Linkages

7.1 A coupler curve has the approximate straight-line section shown in the figure. Design a four-bar linkage that will generate the portion of the curve shown. Describe the linkage in sufficient detail that it can be manufactured.

$$x_A = 6$$
$$y_A = 3$$
$$x_B = 18$$
$$y_B = 12$$

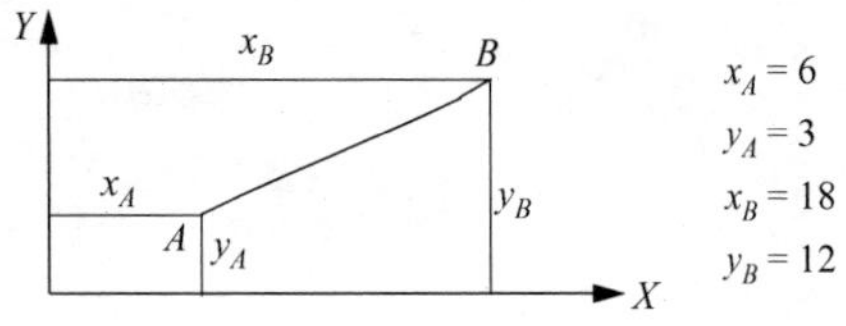

7.2 Re-solve Problem 7.1 if $x_A = 3$, $y_A = 3$, $s_B = 20$, and $y_B = 25$.

7.3 Determine the cognate linkages that will trace the same coupler curve as that traced by point C in the figure shown.

$$AB = 1.5"$$
$$BC = 1.25"$$
$$BD = 2.0"$$
$$BC = 3.0"$$
$$DE = 1.25"$$

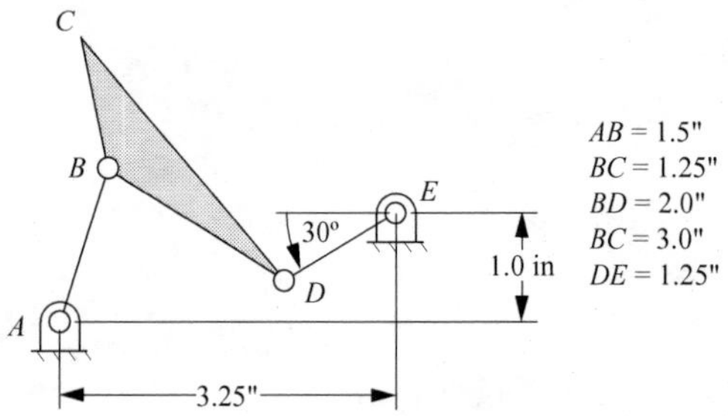

7.4 Determine the cognate linkages that will trace the same coupler curve as that traced by point C in the figure shown.

$$DE = 1.125"$$
$$BD = 2.25"$$
$$BC = 1.0"$$

Exercise Problems Involving Spherical Four-Bar Linkages

7.5 A spherical four-bar linkage is shown in the figure. If the angular velocity of link 2 is 100 rad/s (constant), find the angular velocity and angular acceleration of link 4 as a function of the rotation of link 2. Plot the angular velocity and angular acceleration of link 4 for a full rotation of link 2. Make the calculations for the assembly mode shown in the figure.

$$\alpha_1 = 110°$$
$$\alpha_2 = 90°$$
$$\alpha_3 = 90°$$
$$\alpha_4 = 90°$$

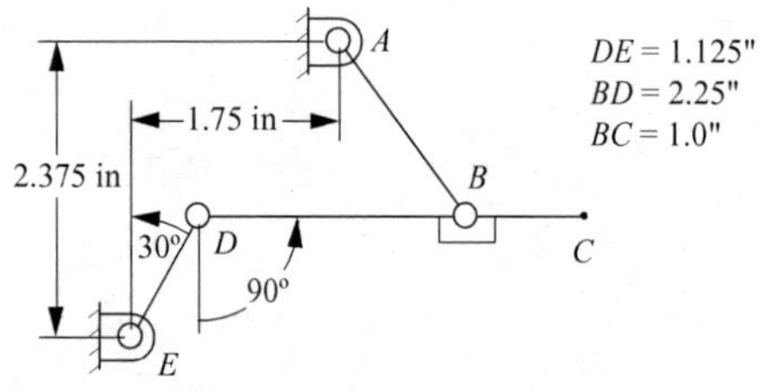

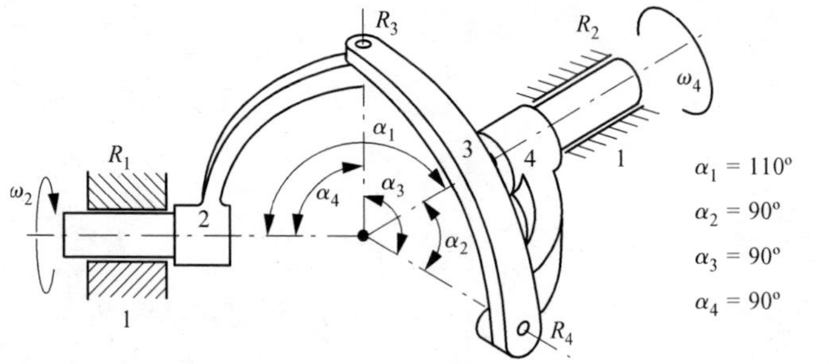

7.6 Re-solve Problem 7.5 if $\alpha_1 = 150°$ but all other data remain the same.

Exercise Problems Involving Steering Linkages

7.7 The mechanism shown is used for a steering linkage for an automobile. The wheel base is 110 in, and link $O_F F$ is driven by the steering column. The toe-in angle (α) is 9°. If the link dimensions are given as shown, determine the y error in the Ackermann steering condition (see Figs. 7.23 and 7.26) for a 10° CCW rotation of $O_F F$. Recall that the linkage $O_E EFO_F$ is a parallelogram.

$$O_B O_A = 50 \text{ in}$$
$$O_B B = O_A A = 3 \text{ in}$$
$$O_F F = O_E E = 3 \text{ in}$$
$$BD = AC = 12 \text{ in}$$
$$DC = 26 \text{ in}$$
$$O_F O_E = 28 \text{ in}$$
$$h = 8 \text{ in}$$

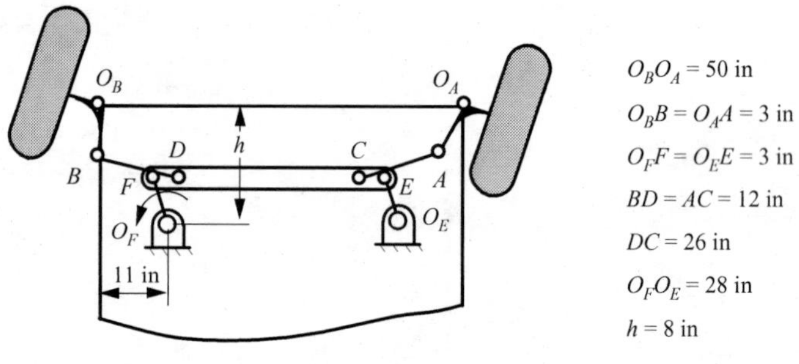

7.8 Write a computer program to analyze the steering linkage shown in Problem 7.7. If only h can change, determine the optimum value for h that will give the least error in y for the Ackermann steering condition for a ±15° rotation of $O_F F$.

7.9 In the rack-and-pinion mechanism shown in Fig. 7.25, the wheel base is 125 in. If the link dimensions are

$$p = 55 \text{ in}, \quad b = 12 \text{ in}$$
$$a = 3.5 \text{ in}, \quad r = 11 \text{ in}$$
$$\alpha = 10°, \quad s = 6.0 \text{ in}$$

plot the y error in the Ackermann steering condition as a function of the displacement u (see Fig. 7.26) for a ±1.5-in displacement of u.

7.10 A new subcompact automobile is being designed for rack-and-pinion steering. Assume that the wheel base is 90 in. Determine the other dimensions such that the error in the Ackermann steering condition is as small as possible for a ±1.5-in displacement of the rack.

Exercise Problems Involving Geneva Mechanisms

7.11 The center distance between the driver and follower of a Geneva mechanism is to be 3 in. The driver is to rotate five revolutions for each rotation of the follower. The driving pin is to enter the slot tangentially so that there will be no impact load. Do the following:

(a) Design the Geneva mechanism and draw it.

(b) Determine the angular velocity and acceleration of the Geneva wheel for one fifth of a revolution if the angular velocity of the driver is 100 rpm CCW. Plot the results.

7.12 Re-solve Problem 7.11 if the input link rotates three revolutions for each rotation of the follower. Conduct the velocity and acceleration analysis for one third of a rotation.

CHAPTER 8

PROFILE CAM DESIGN

8.1 INTRODUCTION

Cams are used for essentially the same purpose as linkages, that is, generation of irregular motion. Cams have an advantage over linkages because cams can be designed for much tighter motion specifications. In fact, in principle, any desired motion program can be exactly reproduced by a cam. Cam design is also, at least in principle, simpler than linkage design, although, in practice, it can be very laborious. Automation of cam design using interactive computing has not, at present, reached the same level of sophistication as that of linkage design.

The disadvantages of cams are manufacturing expense, poor wear resistance, and relatively poor high-speed capability. Although numerical control (NC) machining does cut the cost of cam manufacture in small lots, costs are still quite high in comparison with linkages. In large lots, molding or casting techniques cut cam costs, but not to the extent that stamping and so forth, can cut linkage costs for similar lot sizes.

Unless roller followers are used, cams wear quickly. However, roller followers are bulky and require larger cams, creating size and dynamic problems. In addition, the bearings in roller followers create their own reliability problems.

The worst problems with cams are, however, noise and follower bounce at high speeds. As a result, there is a preoccupation with dynamic optimization in cam design.

Cam design usually requires two steps (from a geometric point of view):

1. synthesis of the motion program for the follower and
2. generation of the cam profile.

If the motion program is fully specified throughout the motion cycle, as is the case, for example, with the stitch pattern cams in sewing machines, the first step is not needed. More usually, the motion program is specified only for portions of the cycle, allowing the synthesis of the remaining portions for optimal dynamic performance. An example is the cam controlling the valve opening in an automotive engine. Here the specification is that the valve should be fully closed for a specified interval and more or less fully open for another specified interval. For the portions of the cycle between those specified, a suitable program must be synthesized. This can be done, with varying levels of sophistication, to make the operation of the cam as smooth as possible. In general, the higher the level of dynamic performance required, the more difficult the synthesis process.

The second stage of the process, profile generation, is achieved by kinematic inversion. The cam is taken as the fixed link and a number of positions of the follower relative to the cam is constructed. A curve tangent to the various follower positions is drawn and becomes the cam profile. If the process is performed analytically, any level of accuracy can be achieved.

8.2 CAM–FOLLOWER SYSTEMS

A general cam–follower system consists of three elements as shown in Fig. 8.1. The first two are the cam and follower, and the third is a spring or other means of ensuring that the follower remains in contact with the cam. The function of the spring can be replaced by gravity or by constraining the follower between the two surfaces on the cam or constraining the cam between two surfaces on the follower. Both of these approaches are usually more expensive than using a spring and therefore are not commonly used.

A follower is characterized by its motion relative to the ground link and by the geometry of its face that contacts the cam. The cam–follower motion may be either rotational or translational, and translating followers may be either radial or offset. Examples of these are shown in Fig. 8.2. The follower surfaces may be either knife edged, flat, spherical (or cylindrical), or roller as shown in Fig. 8.3.

Actually, these geometries are all of the same class depending on the radius of curvature of the follower face. That is, the knife edge has a radius of curvature that is zero, the flat face has a radius of curvature that is infinite, and the general roller and cylindrical followers have a finite (but nonzero) radius of curvature. In this discussion, only planar cams will be considered, so no distinction between spherical and cylindrical follower faces will be made. Also, if only geometric information is of interest, no distinction needs to be made

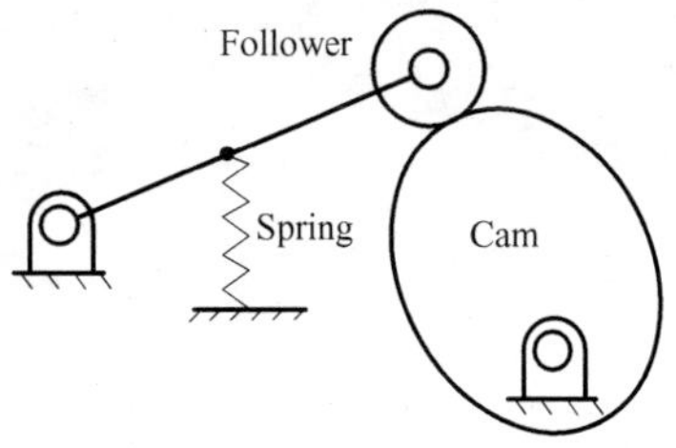

FIGURE 8.1 Elements of a cam–follower system.

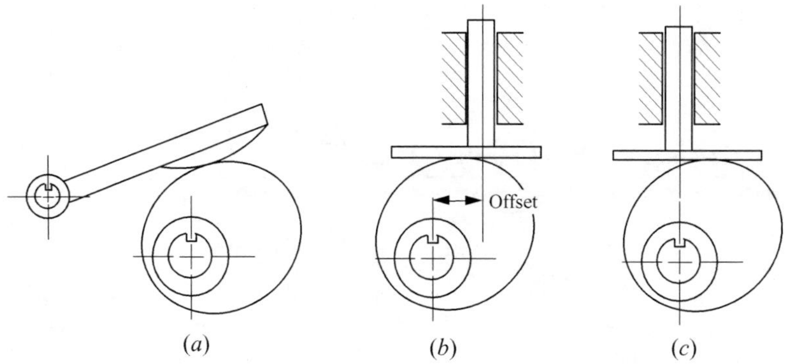

FIGURE 8.2 (a) Cylindrical-faced, oscillating follower. (b) Offset, flat-faced, translating follower. (c) Radial, flat-faced, translating follower.

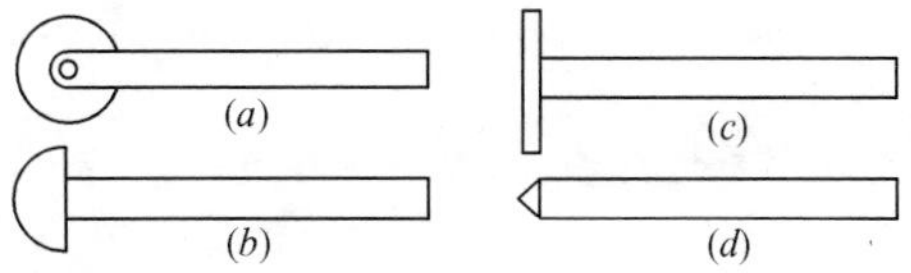

FIGURE 8.3 (a) Roller follower. (b) Cylindrical-faced follower. (c) Flat-faced follower. (d) Knife-edged follower.

between roller and rigid cylindrical-faced followers. Obviously, there is a significant difference from an overall design standpoint, however.

Although here we will consider only planar, rotating cams, in practice a large number of different cam geometries are found. Some of the different types of cams and follower systems are shown in Fig. 8.4.

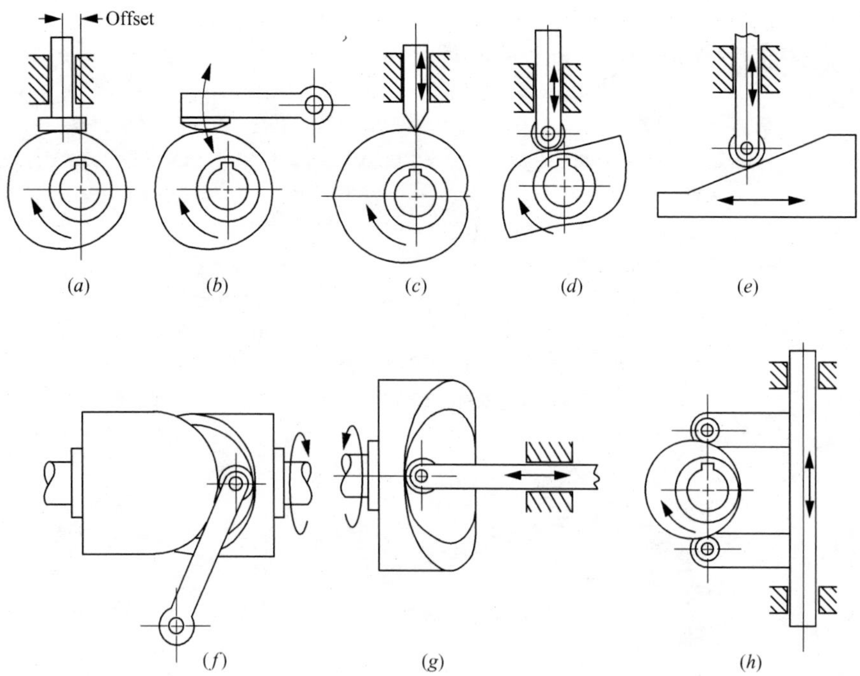

FIGURE 8.4 Some types of cams. (a) Radial cam and flat-faced, offset translating follower. (b) Radial cam and spherical-faced, oscillating follower (c) Radial (heart) cam and translating, knife-edged follower. (d) Radial two-lobe frog cam and translating, offset, roller follower. (e) Wedge cam and translating roller follower. (f) Cylindrical cam and oscillating roller follower. (g) End or face cam and translating roller follower. (h) Yoke cam and translating roller follower.

8.3 SYNTHESIS OF MOTION PROGRAMS

The problem of motion-program synthesis is the problem of filling in, in an optimal way, the portions of the motion cycle that are not completely specified. The characteristics of the problem may be demonstrated by consideration of a cam that is required to drive a follower that dwells at 0 for a cam rotation of 60°, dwells at 1.0 in for a cam rotation of 110° to 150°, and is required to move with constant velocity from a displacement of 0.8 to 0.2 in for 200° to 300° of cam rotation. The specified portions of the motion program are displayed in Fig. 8.5.

A simple solution to the problem of filling the gaps is simply to move the cam at constant velocity between the specified segments, giving a follower displacement diagram as shown in Fig. 8.6.

Notice, however, that if this is done, the velocity is discontinuous at cam angles 60°, 110°, 150°, 200°, 300°, and 360°, causing the acceleration to become infinite at these locations. Since the follower cannot follow an infinite acceleration, this leads to loss of contact and/or excessive local stresses and resultant noise and wear problems.

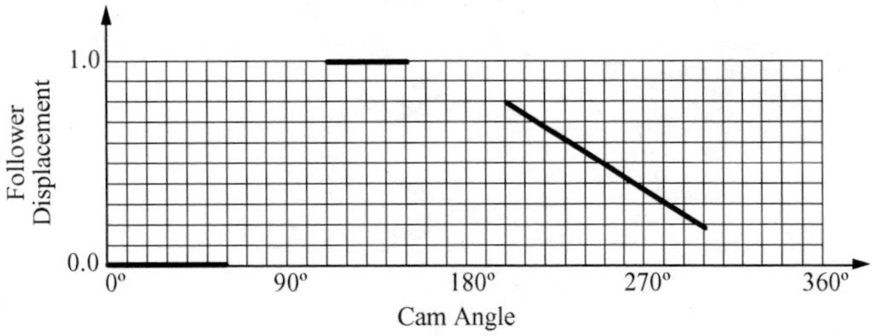

FIGURE 8.5 The statement of the required displacements of a cam design problem in graphical form.

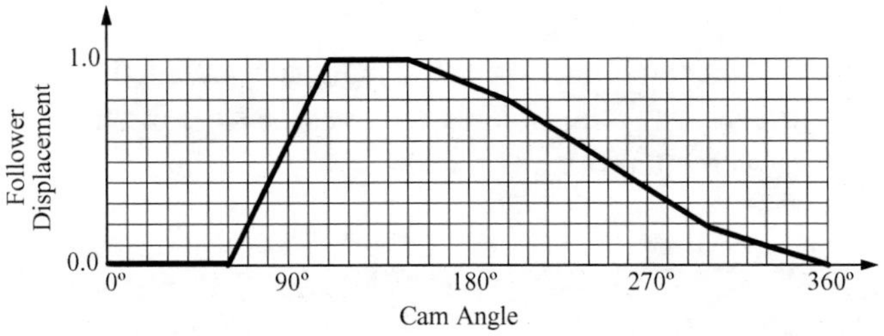

FIGURE 8.6 A cam angle–follower displacement program that satisfies the displacement requirements specified in Fig. 8.5.

The preceding motion program matches only the *displacements* at the ends of the segments. The infinite acceleration problem can be removed by matching both displacement and velocity at the ends of segments of the program. One way to do this is to subdivide the synthesized segments into two parts with a constant acceleration on the first and constant deceleration on the second. On such a subsegment, if the acceleration is a, the velocity is given by

$$v = v_0 + at$$

where v_0 is the velocity at the beginning of the segment. The displacement is given by

$$y = s_0 + v_0 t + \frac{a}{2} t^2$$

where s_0 is the displacement at the beginning of the segment. Now, if the cam is driven at constant velocity,

$$\theta = \theta_0 + \omega t$$

where θ is the cam angle, θ_0 is the cam angle at the beginning of the segment, and ω is the angular velocity. Hence

$$t = \frac{(\theta - \theta_0)}{\omega}$$

$$v = v_0 + a\frac{(\theta - \theta_0)}{\omega}$$

$$y = s_0 + v_0 \frac{(\theta - \theta_0)}{\omega} + a\frac{(\theta - \theta_0)^2}{2\omega^2}$$

Therefore, the relationship between s and θ, as plotted on the follower-displacement diagram, is parabolic (see Fig. 8.7). Cam–follower displacement programs that use this type of transition are called parabolic. The cam profiles developed from them are also called

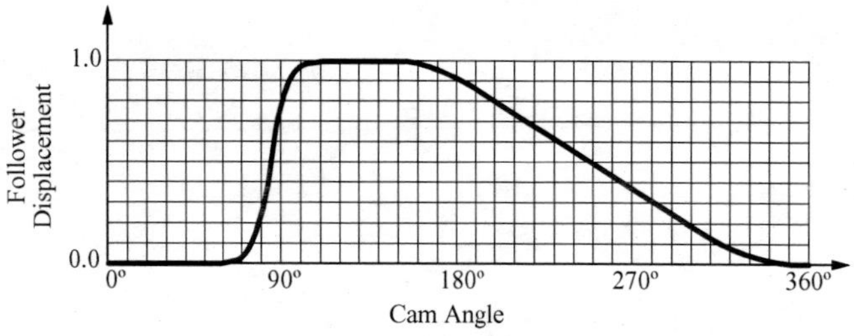

FIGURE 8.7 A follower displacement program that satisfies the displacement requirements of Fig. 8.5 using parabolic transitions. This is called a *parabolic* follower-displacement program.

"parabolic." It is important to understand that a so-called parabolic cam *does not* have a parabolic curve in its profile. Rather, the parabolas are in the transition curves used in the follower-displacement program.

8.4 ANALYSIS OF DIFFERENT TYPES OF FOLLOWER DISPLACEMENT FUNCTIONS

Several different standard functions can be used to connect the parts of the displacement diagram where a specific type of motion is required. These displacement profiles ultimately determine the shape of the cam. Many different types of motions have been used in practice, and some have been extensively studied. These include the following:

1. uniform motion,
2. parabolic motion,
3. simple harmonic motion,
4. cycloidal motion, and
5. general polynomial motion.

low speeds

The first two types of program have already been introduced. The first four types of program can be generated graphically as well as analytically, but the fifth type is generated only analytically. Both graphical and analytical development will be considered here, where possible. Both methods assume that the angular velocity, ω, of the cam is constant. If this is the case, then

$$y = y(\theta)$$

and

$$\theta = \theta_0 + \omega t$$

Here, y is used as a generic output variable. It may correspond to either a linear or angular displacement of the follower. Note that if the cam motion is given as a function of time, the motion can easily be represented as a function of the cam rotation in degrees using the preceding expressions.

The higher derivatives are given by

$$\dot{y} = \frac{dy(\theta)}{dt} = \frac{dy}{d\theta}\frac{d\theta}{dt} = y'\omega$$

and

$$\ddot{y} = \frac{d^2 y(\theta)}{dt^2} = \frac{d}{dt}\left(\frac{dy}{d\theta}\frac{d\theta}{dt}\right) = \frac{d^2 y}{d\theta^2}\left(\frac{d\theta}{dt}\right)^2 + \frac{dy}{d\theta}\frac{d^2\theta}{dt^2} = \frac{d^2 y}{d\theta^2}\omega^2 + \frac{dy}{d\theta}\alpha$$

But because ω is constant, $\alpha = 0$ and

$$\ddot{y} = y''\omega^2$$

Therefore, $\dot{y}$ is a simple constant times y', and $\ddot{y}$ is also a constant times y''. Consequently, even though we ultimately want to know the response to the time derivatives ($\dot{y}$ and $\ddot{y}$), we may work directly with the derivatives (y' and y'') with respect to the cam displacement. If the cam velocity is not a constant, then the cam profile can be designed for only one operating situation if higher derivatives are important. In the following, a constant-velocity cam is assumed, and y is again used to represent either an angular or linear displacement of the follower. Similarly, θ is used for the displacement of the cam, and it may be either an angular or a linear displacement.

The follower curves can be studied in terms of the simple diagram shown in Fig. 8.8. A general displacement diagram will be made up of three or more parts:

1. rises (1 or more),
2. returns (1 or more), and
3. dwells (0 or more).

Both the rise and return parts will contain one or more inflection points. These are points where a maximum slope is reached, and they correspond to points on the cam surface with maximum steepness. These points are identified by the locations where the curvature of the diagram changes sign. At the inflection points, the radius of curvature of the curve is infinite.

In each of the standard curve cases, we will look at mainly the rise part of the follower profile. The return part can be determined using the mirror images of the curves considered.

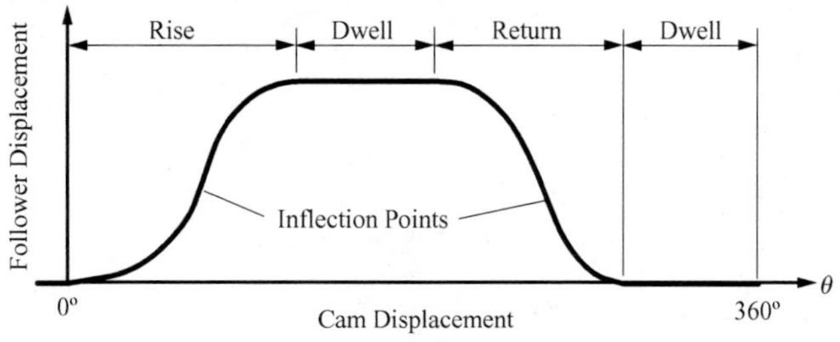

FIGURE 8.8 Terminology used when discussing follower-displacement programs.

8.5 UNIFORM MOTION

Uniform motion is represented in Fig. 8.9. To derive the equations for the follower displacement, a general form for the mathematical expression corresponding to the type of motion is assumed. The general equation will have undetermined constants in it, and these constants can be determined by matching boundary conditions at the two ends of the curve. For uniform motion, the general form of the curve used is

$$y = C\theta$$

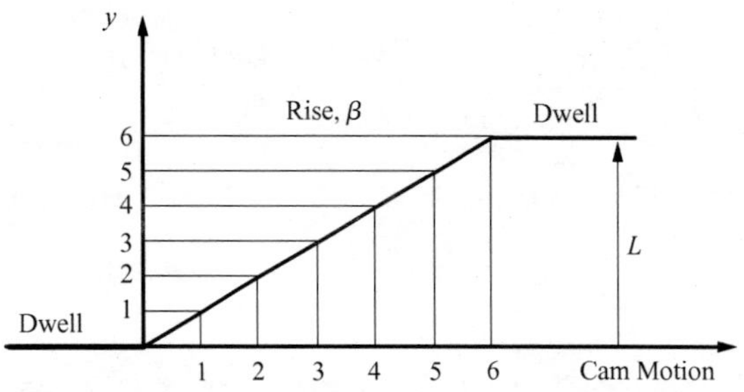

FIGURE 8.9 Uniform motion.

If L is the amount of the rise, and β is the cam rotation required for the rise, then the constant C must be L/β and y becomes

$$y = \frac{L}{\beta}\theta$$

During the rise, the velocity and acceleration are

$$\dot{y} = \frac{L}{\beta}\omega$$

and

$$\ddot{y} = 0$$

The displacement, velocity, and acceleration are plotted in Fig. 8.10. As noted earlier, the acceleration is infinite at the points where the uniform motion meets the dwells. Therefore, even for low speeds and elastic members, the forces transmitted will be very large. For *very* low speeds, however, this type of displacement diagram might be acceptable.

Graphically, the uniform motion–displacement diagram is characterized by a uniform change in y for a uniform change in the cam motion. This condition is shown in Fig. 8.9.

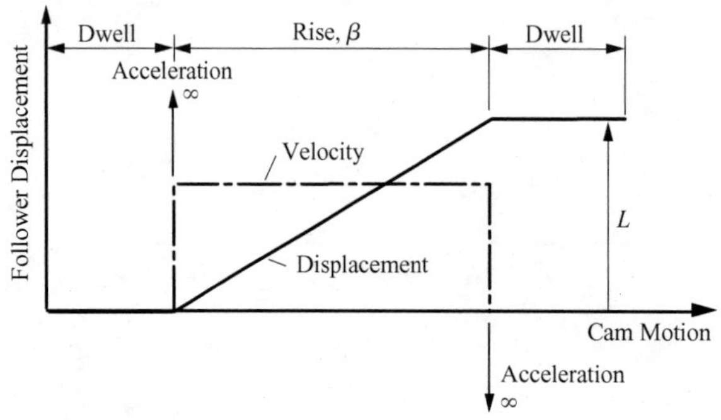

FIGURE 8.10 Displacement, velocity, and acceleration relations for uniform motion.

8.6 PARABOLIC MOTION

The equations for parabolic motion can be derived using the same procedure as described in Section 8.3. However, two parabolas must be used for each transition. The two parabolas meet at the point midway between the ends of the two dwell regions. The general form for both parabolas is

$$y = C_0 + C_1\theta + C_2\theta^2 \tag{8.1}$$

and

$$y' = C_1 + 2C_2\theta$$
$$y'' = 2C_2 \tag{8.2}$$

If the cam displacement is taken as 0 at the beginning of the rise, then at $\theta = 0$, $y = y' = 0$. Then, $C_0 = C_1 = 0$. Also, at $\theta = \beta/2$, $y = L/2$. Therefore, the displacement and first and second derivatives with respect to θ are

$$y = 2L\left(\frac{\theta}{\beta}\right)^2$$
$$y' = 4\frac{L}{\beta^2}\theta$$
$$y'' = 4\frac{L}{\beta^2} \tag{8.3}$$

and the velocity and acceleration are

$$\dot{y} = 4\frac{L\omega}{\beta^2}\theta$$
$$\ddot{y} = 4\frac{L\omega^2}{\beta^2}$$

At the point at which the curve meets the first dwell, the velocity and acceleration are continuous, but the third derivative, or jerk, is infinite. This derivative is proportional to the change in force and for high-speed cams is an important aspect of the motion. Although not so serious as having an infinite acceleration pulse, an infinite jerk can excite vibratory behavior in the system.

For the second half of the rise, the conditions to match are at $\theta = \beta/2$, $y = L/2$, and at $\theta = \beta$, $y = L$, and $y' = 0$. Then from Eqs. (8.61) and (8.62), we get

$$\frac{L}{2} = C_0 + C_1\frac{\beta}{2} + C_2\left(\frac{\beta}{2}\right)^2$$
$$L = C_0 + C_1\beta + C_2\beta^2$$
$$0 = C_1 + 2C_2\beta$$

The solution to this linear set of equations yields

$$C_0 = -L$$
$$C_1 = \frac{4L}{\beta}$$
$$C_2 = -\frac{2L}{\beta^2}$$

so that

$$y = L\left[1 - 2\left(1 - \frac{\theta}{\beta}\right)^2\right] \tag{8.4}$$

and

$$y' = \frac{4L}{\beta}\left(1 - \frac{\theta}{\beta}\right)$$

$$y'' = -\frac{4L}{\beta^2}$$

Finally, the velocity, acceleration, and jerk are given by

$$\dot{y} = \frac{4L\omega}{\beta}\left(1 - \frac{\theta}{\beta}\right)$$

$$\ddot{y} = -\frac{4L\omega^2}{\beta^2}$$

These equations apply to the segment of the program to the right of the inflection point shown in Fig. 8.11.

Graphically, the part of the curve up to the inflection point can be generated using the construction shown in Fig. 8.12. For the construction, the horizontal axis is divided into uniform increments, and the maximum rise is evenly divided into the same number of equal increments. The point at the origin is then connected to each of the points on the line of the maximum rise. Points on the displacement curve are given by the intersection of the diagonal lines with the corresponding vertical lines.

A cam return using parabolic motion is shown in Fig. 8.13. To determine the equations for the return from $y = L$ to 0 during the angular displacement β, we can use Eq. (8.1) again but with different boundary conditions. To simplify the equations, we will shift the origin of the coordinate system to the end of the dwell at the beginning of the return. For the first part of the return, $y = L$ and $y' = 0$ at $\theta = 0$ and $y = L/2$ at $\theta = \beta/2$. For these condition, $C_0 = L$, $C_1 = 0$, and $C_2 = \frac{-2L}{\beta^2}$

The displacement equation is

$$y = L\left[1 - 2\left(\frac{\theta}{\beta}\right)^2\right] \tag{8.5}$$

For the second half of the return, the conditions to match are at $\theta = \beta/2$, $y = L/2$, and at $\theta = \beta$, $y = 0$, and $y' = 0$. For these conditions,

$$y = 2L\left(1 - \frac{\theta}{\beta}\right)^2 \tag{8.6}$$

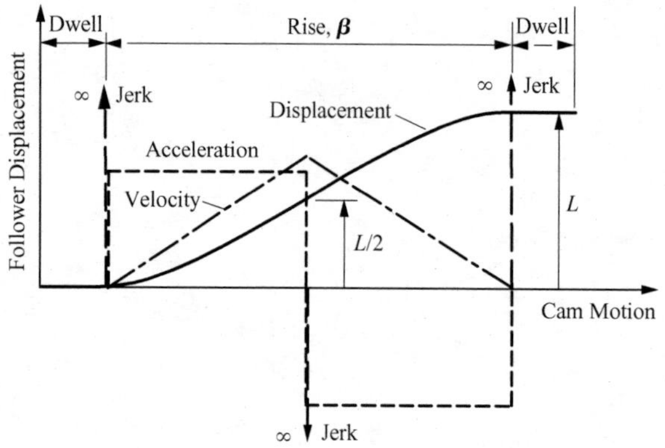

FIGURE 8.11 Displacement, velocity, acceleration, and jerk relations for parabolic motion during rise.

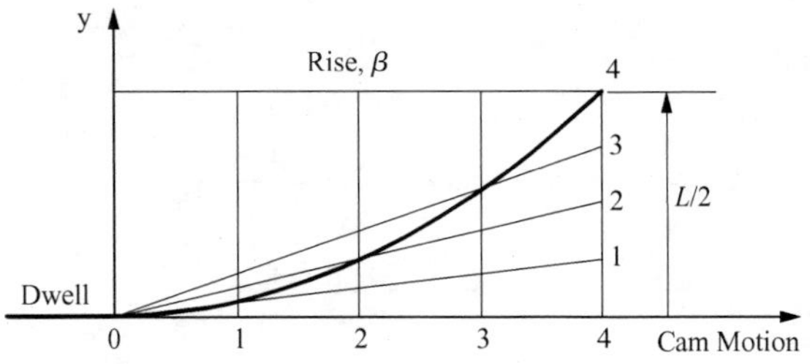

FIGURE 8.12 Construction of parabolic segment of follower-displacement program.

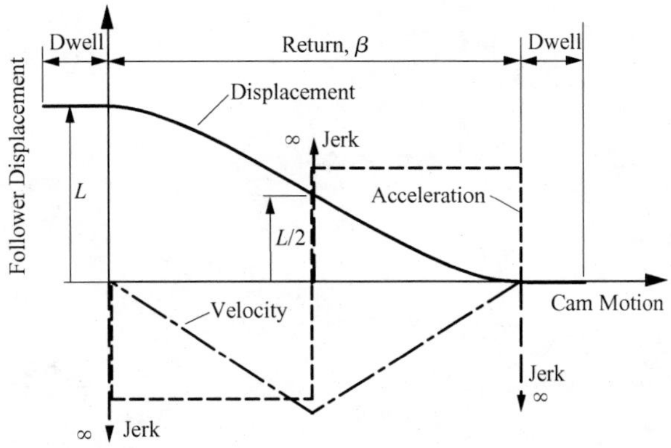

FIGURE 8.13 Displacement, velocity, acceleration, and jerk relations for parabolic motion during return.

In general, the rise and return will not always start at $\theta = 0$. However, in these cases, a simple coordinate transformation can be used. If the rise or return actually starts at $\theta = \gamma$, substitute $(\theta - \gamma)$ wherever θ appears in Eqs. (8.3)–(8.6).

EXAMPLE 8.1 *Design for Parabolic Motion*

Design a parabolic cam–follower displacement program to provide a dwell at zero lift for the first 120° of the motion cycle and to dwell at 0.8 in lift for cam angles from 180° to 210°. The cam profile will be laid out using 10° plotting intervals. Assume that the cam rotates with constant angular velocity.

Solution

The motion specification is as shown in Fig. 8.14. For the first part of the rise ending at $\phi = 150°$ in the interval 120° to 180°, Eq. (8.3) applies if we use $\theta = (\phi - 120°)$ and $0.8 = L$. The resulting expression for the first part of the rise is

$$y = 2L\left(\frac{\theta}{\beta}\right)^2 = 1.6\left(\frac{\phi - 120°}{60°}\right)^2 \tag{8.7}$$

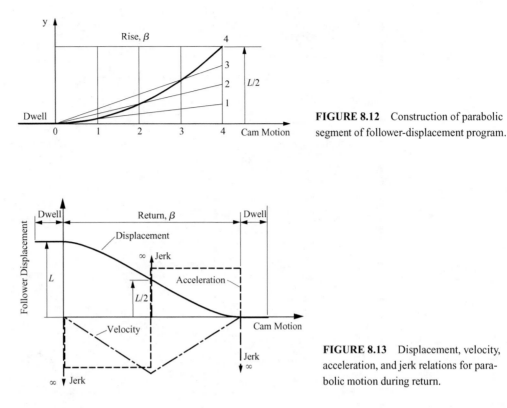

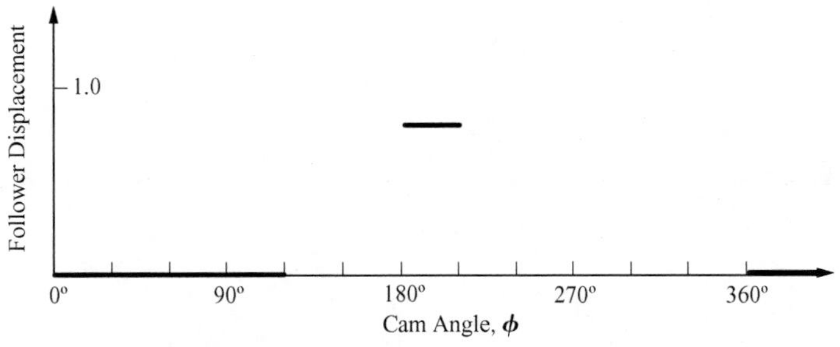

FIGURE 8.14 The motion specification for Example 8.1.

For the second part of the rise starting at $\theta = 150°$, Eq. (8.4) applies if we use $\theta = (\phi - 120°)$ and $0.8 = L$. The resulting expression is

$$y = L\left[1 - 2\left(1 - \frac{\theta}{\beta}\right)^2\right] = 0.8\left[1 - 2\left(1 - \frac{(\phi - 120°)}{60°}\right)^2\right] \tag{8.8}$$

Using Eqs. (8.7) and (8.8) produces the successive lifts given in Table 8.1. For the first part of the return ending at $\theta = 285°$ in the interval 210° to 360°, Eq. (8.5) applies if we use $\theta = (\phi - 210°)$ and $0.8 = L$. The resulting expression for the first part of the return is

$$y = L\left[1 - 2\left(\frac{\theta}{\beta}\right)^2\right] = 0.8\left[1 - 2\left(\frac{(\phi - 210°)}{150°}\right)^2\right] \tag{8.9}$$

For the second part of the return starting at $\theta = 285°$, Eq. (8.6) applies if we use $\theta = (\phi - 210°)$ and $0.8 = L$. The resulting expression is

$$y = 2L\left(1 - \frac{\theta}{\beta}\right)^2 = 1.6\left(1 - \frac{\phi - 210°}{150°}\right)^2 \tag{8.10}$$

Using Eqs. (8.9) and (8.10) produces points on the return curve given in Table 8.2. The resulting transition curves are plotted in Fig. 8.15. Notice that the lift values are tabulated to four decimal places. Cam and follower systems normally use very rigid components and even small profile variations are important. For this reason, we normally work with at least four decimal places when doing cam calculations. Gears are another type of profile mechanism in which the components are very rigid and, consequently, even tiny profile variations can be important.

TABLE 8.1 Cam–Follower Data for Rise in Example 8.1

θ	120°	130°	140°	150°	160°	170°	180°
y	0.0000	0.0444	0.1778	0.4000	0.6222	0.7556	0.8000

TABLE 8.2 Cam–Follower Data for Return in Example 8.1

θ	210°	220°	230°	240°	250°	260°	270°	280°
y	0.8000	0.7929	0.7716	0.7360	0.6862	0.6222	0.5440	0.4516
θ	290°	300°	310°	320°	330°	340°	350°	360°
y	0.3484	0.2560	0.1778	0.1138	0.0640	0.0284	0.0071	0.0000

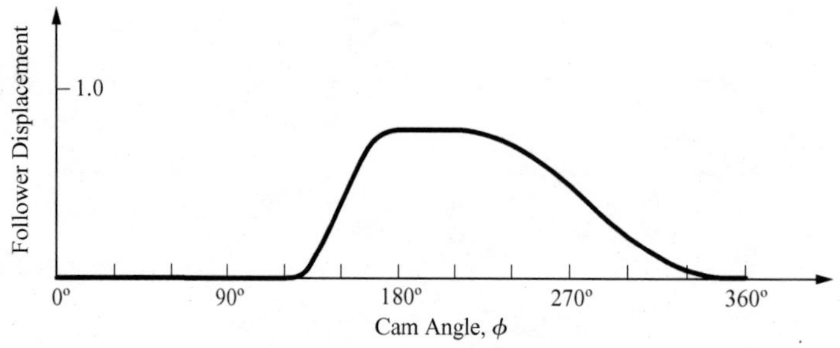

FIGURE 8.15 The parabolic follower-displacement program generated in Example 8.1.

8.7 HARMONIC FOLLOWER-DISPLACEMENT PROGRAMS

Simple harmonic motion can be generated by an offset (eccentric) circular cam with a radial follower and is therefore a common form to use for a displacement diagram. Cams with this type of transition curve are commonly referred to as "harmonic cams." The equations for simple harmonic motion are formed from the basic equation

$$y = C_0 + C_1 \cos C_2\theta = C_0\left(1 + \frac{C_1}{C_0}\cos C_2\theta\right)$$

The displacement, velocity, acceleration, and jerk diagrams are shown in Fig. 8.16. Simple harmonic motion produces a sine velocity curve and a cosine acceleration curve. There is no discontinuity at the transition point, so that θ is defined for all angles between zero and β. The equations for a rise starting from $\theta = 0$ and ending at $\theta = \beta$ and $y = L$ are

$$\begin{aligned}
y &= \frac{L}{2}\left(1 - \cos\frac{\pi\theta}{\beta}\right)\\
y' &= \frac{\pi L}{2\beta}\sin\frac{\pi\theta}{\beta}, \quad \dot{y} = \frac{\pi L\omega}{2\beta}\sin\frac{\pi\theta}{\beta}\\
y'' &= \frac{L}{2}\left(\frac{\pi}{\beta}\right)^2\cos\frac{\pi\theta}{\beta}, \quad \ddot{y} = \frac{L}{2}\left(\frac{\pi\omega}{\beta}\right)^2\cos\frac{\pi\theta}{\beta}\\
y''' &= -\frac{L}{2}\left(\frac{\pi}{\beta}\right)^3\sin\frac{\pi\theta}{\beta}, \quad \dddot{y} = -\frac{L}{2}\left(\frac{\pi\omega}{\beta}\right)^3\sin\frac{\pi\theta}{\beta}
\end{aligned} \tag{8.11}$$

The equations for the return from $\theta = 0$, $y = L$ to $\theta = \beta$, $y = 0$ are

$$\begin{aligned}
y &= \frac{L}{2}\left(1 + \cos\frac{\pi\theta}{\beta}\right)\\
y' &= -\frac{\pi L}{2\beta}\sin\frac{\pi\theta}{\beta}, \quad \dot{y} = -\frac{\pi L\omega}{2\beta}\sin\frac{\pi\theta}{\beta}
\end{aligned} \tag{8.12}$$

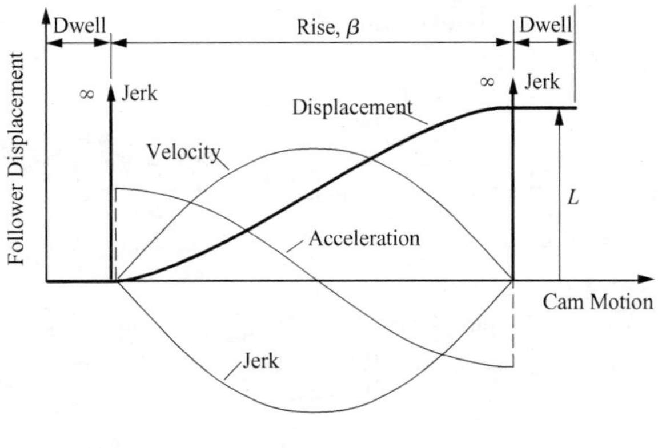

FIGURE 8.16 Shape of the displacement, velocity, acceleration, and jerk curves for simple harmonic motion.

$$y'' = -\frac{L}{2}\left(\frac{\pi}{\beta}\right)^2 \cos\frac{\pi\theta}{\beta}, \quad \ddot{y} = -\frac{L}{2}\left(\frac{\pi\omega}{\beta}\right)^2 \cos\frac{\pi\theta}{\beta}$$

$$y''' = \frac{L}{2}\left(\frac{\pi}{\beta}\right)^3 \sin\frac{\pi\theta}{\beta}, \quad \dddot{y} = \frac{L}{2}\left(\frac{\pi\omega}{\beta}\right)^3 \sin\frac{\pi\theta}{\beta}$$

A simple harmonic displacement diagram can be generated graphically by drawing a semicircle on the vertical axis and dividing it into an even number of segments. The cam motion axis is then divided into the same number of even increments, and horizontal lines are drawn from the points on the semicircle axis. The intersections of the horizontal lines with the corresponding vertical lines give the location of points on the simple harmonic curve. This construction is shown in Fig. 8.17. For the construction, note that

$$\frac{\Delta\alpha}{\Delta\theta} = \frac{180}{\beta}$$

where β is the cam rotation for the follower to move from lift 0 to L. With the advent of computers, the graphical procedure is typically used only for schematic representations of simple harmonic motion.

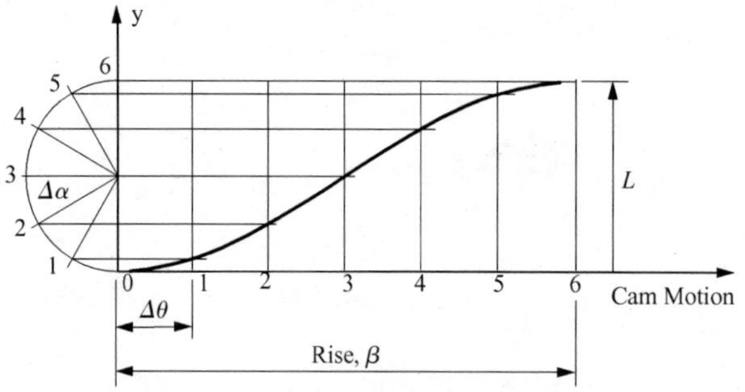

FIGURE 8.17 Graphical construction of displacement diagram for a simple harmonic rise.

EXAMPLE 8.2 ***Design for Harmonic Motion***

Design a harmonic cam to satisfy the same motion specifications as for Example 8.1. That is, the motion program is to provide a dwell at zero lift for the first 120° of the motion cycle and to dwell at 0.8 in lift for cam angles from 180° to 210°. The cam profile will be laid out using 10° plotting intervals.

Solution

The motion specification is as shown in Fig. 8.14 where ϕ is the cam rotation angle.

The rise in the interval 120° to 180° can be computed using Eq. (8.11) if we use $\theta = (\phi - 120°)$ and $0.8 = L$. The resulting expression for the rise is

$$y = \frac{L}{2}\left(1 - \cos\frac{\pi\theta}{\beta}\right) = 0.4\left(1 - \cos\frac{\pi(\phi - 120°)}{60°}\right) \tag{8.13}$$

The results are given in Table 8.3.

For the return in the interval 210° to 360°, Eq. (8.12) applies if we use $\theta = (\phi - 210°)$ and $0.8 = L$. The resulting expression for the return is

$$y = \frac{L}{2}\left(1 + \cos\frac{\pi\theta}{\beta}\right) = 0.4\left(1 + \cos\frac{\pi(\phi - 210°)}{150°}\right) \tag{8.14}$$

Using this equation produces the successive values for y given in Table 8.4.

TABLE 8.3 Cam–Follower Data for Rise Using Simple Harmonic Motion in Example 8.2

θ	120°	130°	140°	150°	160°	170°	180°
y	0.0000	0.0536	0.2000	0.4000	0.6000	0.7464	0.8000

TABLE 8.4 Cam–follower Data for Return in Example 8.2

θ	210°	220°	230°	240°	250°	260°	270°	280°
y	0.8000	0.7913	0.7654	0.7236	0.6677	0.6000	0.5236	0.4418
θ	290°	300°	310°	320°	330°	340°	350°	360°
y	0.3582	0.2764	0.2000	0.1323	0.0764	0.0346	0.0087	0.0000

The tabulated lift values may be compared with those of Example 8.1 to observe the differences between comparable parabolic and harmonic transition curves. If plotted, the follower-displacement program would be difficult to distinguish from Fig. 8.15. However, there will be important differences in the values for the derivatives.

8.8 CYCLOIDAL FOLLOWER-DISPLACEMENT PROGRAMS

All of the motions given so far have nonzero values of acceleration (and therefore infinite jerk) at the beginnings and ends of the motion and therefore are limited to relatively low speeds. Cycloidal motion has zero acceleration at the beginning and end of the motion and so is useful for relatively high speeds.

A cycloidal transition produces a sinusoidal acceleration curve. The equations for the rise are

$$y = L\left(\frac{\theta}{\beta} - \frac{1}{2\pi}\sin\frac{2\pi\theta}{\beta}\right)$$

$$y' = \frac{L}{\beta}\left(1 - \cos\frac{2\pi\theta}{\beta}\right), \quad \dot{y} = \frac{L\omega}{\beta}\left(1 - \cos\frac{2\pi\theta}{\beta}\right)$$

$$y'' = \frac{2L\pi}{\beta^2}\sin\frac{2\pi\theta}{\beta}, \quad \ddot{y} = 2L\pi\left(\frac{\omega}{\beta}\right)^2 \sin\frac{2\pi\theta}{\beta}$$

$$y''' = \frac{4L\pi^2}{\beta^3}\cos\frac{2\pi\theta}{\beta}, \quad \dddot{y} = 4L\pi^2\left(\frac{\omega}{\beta}\right)^3 \cos\frac{2\pi\theta}{\beta}$$

These curves are plotted in Fig. 8.18. There is no discontinuity at the inflection point, and therefore the equations are valid for values of θ from zero to β. The curve is symmetric, and the return is given by $\bar{y} = L - y$. Therefore, $\bar{y}' = -y'$, $\bar{y}'' = -y''$, and $\bar{y}''' = -y'''$.

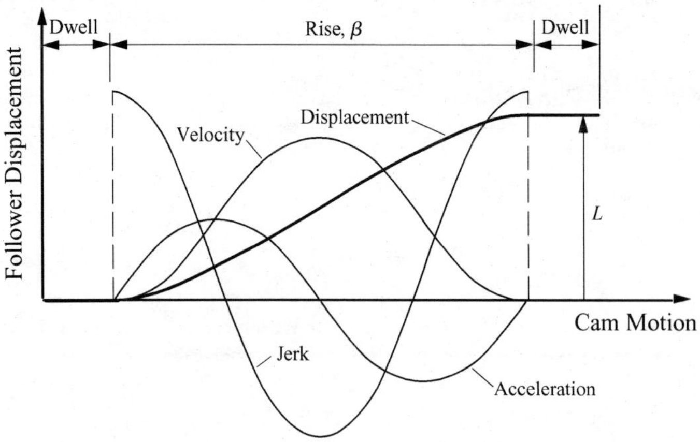

FIGURE 8.18 Shape of the displacement, velocity, acceleration, and jerk relations for cycloidal motion.

Cycloidal motion may be obtained by rolling a circle of radius $L/2\pi$, where L is the total rise, on the displacement axis as shown in Fig. 8.19. However, to construct the curve graphically, a more convenient, alternative way is shown in Fig. 8.19. First, a circle with diameter L/π and center at (β, L) is divided into an even number of increments, and the resulting points are projected onto the displacement axis. The cam motion axis is divided into the same number of increments. A series of lines parallel to the line from the origin to the point (β, L) is then drawn from the projected points on the circle diameter. The intersections of these lines with the corresponding vertical lines from the cam-motion axis give points on the cycloidal curve.

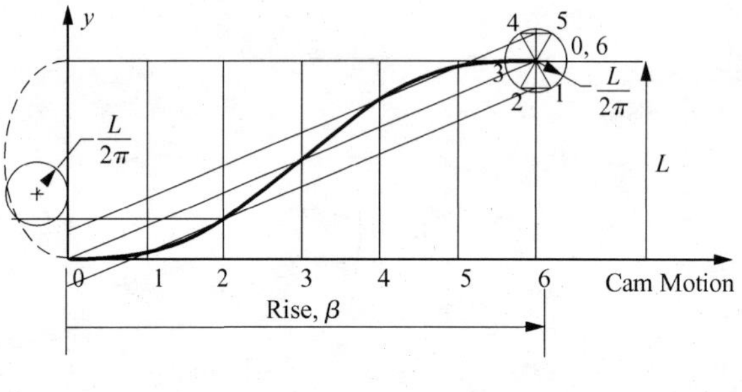

FIGURE 8.19 Graphical construction of displacement diagram for cycloidal motion.

8.9 GENERAL POLYNOMIAL FOLLOWER-DISPLACEMENT PROGRAMS

For high-speed machines, it is common to specify a general polynomial profile for a cam. Depending on the order of the polynomial chosen, it is theoretically possible to match almost any conditions posed by the designer. A polynomial curve is fitted to the rise or return. Only odd-order polynomials are appropriate for rises or returns between dwells if the same conditions are to be matched at both ends of the polynomial. A first-order polynomial gives constant velocity and infinite acceleration at the beginning and end of the transition. This is the uniform motion profile discussed previously. A third-order polynomial gives a parabolic velocity variation, linear acceleration, and infinite jerk at the beginning and end of the transition. A fifth-order polynomial gives finite acceleration and jerk. The derivative of jerk is infinite at the ends of the transition. A fifth-order fit is the practical maximum unless great care is taken during manufacturing. Dynamic effects resulting from manufacturing errors tend to become more important than those from curve fitting at this stage.

For a general polynomial follower displacement, the displacement function is given by

$$y = f(\theta) = \sum_{i=0}^{n} A_i \theta^i$$

where θ is the cam angle, and the A's must be determined from the conditions to be matched. The equation permits us to match the same number of conditions as there are A's, that is, $n + 1$ conditions. When n is large and the angles are measured in degrees, the terms in the summation can vary greatly in size. For example, if θ is 100° and n is 10, the coefficients of θ^i in the equation can vary hugely, and round-off error will make it difficult to obtain an accurate solution. Therefore, it is convenient to rewrite the displacement equation in terms of the cam rotation angle β, which gives the range over which the equation is to be used. The resulting equation is

$$y = f(\theta) = \sum_{i=0}^{n} C_i \left(\frac{\theta}{\beta}\right)^i$$

Now the coefficients of the constants are always numbers between 0 and 1, and round-off error problems have been greatly reduced. The constants in the two equations are related by the simple expression

$$A_i = \frac{C_i}{\beta^i}$$

The conditions to be matched will typically involve at least the velocity and acceleration of the follower, and the required equations for these conditions can be written as

$$\dot{y} = \dot{f}(\theta) = \frac{1}{\beta}\frac{d\theta}{dt}\sum_{i=1}^{n} iC_i \left(\frac{\theta}{\beta}\right)^{(i-1)}$$

and

$$\ddot{y} = \ddot{f}(\theta) = \frac{1}{\beta}\frac{d^2\theta}{dt^2}\sum_{i=1}^{n} iC_i \left(\frac{\theta}{\beta}\right)^{(i-1)} + \frac{1}{\beta^2}\left(\frac{d\theta}{dt}\right)^2 \sum_{i=2}^{n} i(i-1)C_i \left(\frac{\theta}{\beta}\right)^{(i-2)}$$

Notice that the summation on the velocity term starts at 1 because C_0 does not appear in the equation, and the summation on the acceleration term starts at 2 because neither C_0 nor C_1 appears in the acceleration equation.

Now if a constant-velocity cam is used,

$$\frac{d\theta}{dt} = \omega$$

and

$$\frac{d^2\theta}{dt^2} = 0$$

where ω is the angular velocity of the cam. The follower equations may then be written as the following:

$$y = f(\theta) = \sum_{i=1}^{n} C_i \left(\frac{\theta}{\beta}\right)^i$$

$$\dot{y} = \dot{f}(\theta) = \frac{\omega}{\beta} \sum_{i=1}^{n} iC_i \left(\frac{\theta}{\beta}\right)^{(i-1)}$$

$$\ddot{y} = \ddot{f}(\theta) = \left(\frac{\omega}{\beta}\right)^2 \sum_{i=2}^{n} i(i-1)C_i \left(\frac{\theta}{\beta}\right)^{(i-2)}$$

$$\dddot{y} = \dddot{f}(\theta) = \left(\frac{\omega}{\beta}\right)^3 \sum_{i=3}^{n} i(i-1)(i-2)C_i \left(\frac{\theta}{\beta}\right)^{(i-3)}$$

As an example of the use of the polynomial profile, assume that we begin and end the follower displacement with a dwell as shown in Fig. 8.20 and assume that we want to match the position, velocity, and acceleration at both the beginning and end of the period being considered.

For points A and B in Fig. 8.20, the following conditions apply:

$$\theta = 0 \Rightarrow y = \dot{y} = \ddot{y} = 0$$

$$\theta = \beta \Rightarrow y = L$$
$$\dot{y} = \ddot{y} = 0$$

There are six conditions, so the position equation must have six constants. The resulting equations for position, velocity, and acceleration are

$$y = C_0 + C_1\left(\frac{\theta}{\beta}\right) + C_2\left(\frac{\theta}{\beta}\right)^2 + C_3\left(\frac{\theta}{\beta}\right)^3 + C_4\left(\frac{\theta}{\beta}\right)^4 + C_5\left(\frac{\theta}{\beta}\right)^5$$

$$\dot{y} = \frac{\omega}{\beta}\left[C_1 + 2C_2\left(\frac{\theta}{\beta}\right) + 3C_3\left(\frac{\theta}{\beta}\right)^2 + 4C_4\left(\frac{\theta}{\beta}\right)^3 + 5C_5\left(\frac{\theta}{\beta}\right)^4\right]$$

$$\ddot{y} = \left(\frac{\omega}{\beta}\right)^2\left[2C_2 + 6C_3\left(\frac{\theta}{\beta}\right) + 12C_4\left(\frac{\theta}{\beta}\right)^2 + 20C_5\left(\frac{\theta}{\beta}\right)^3\right]$$

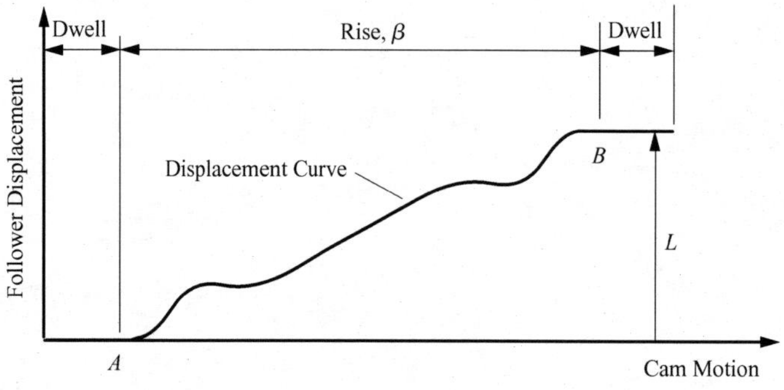

FIGURE 8.20 Initial information for polynomial profile example.

Evaluation of these equations at the beginning and end of the rise period gives the following six equations that must be solved:

$$0 = C_0$$

$$0 = \frac{\omega}{\beta} C_1$$

$$0 = \left(\frac{\omega}{\beta}\right)^2 2C_2$$

$$L = C_0 + C_1 + C_2 + C_3 + C_4 + C_5$$

$$0 = \frac{\omega}{\beta}\left[C_1 + 2C_2 + 3C_3 + 4C_4 + 5C_5\right]$$

$$0 = \left(\frac{\omega}{\beta}\right)^2 \left[2C_2 + 6C_3 + 12C_4 + 20C_5\right]$$

Solution for the unknown constants C_0 through C_6 gives

$$C_0 = C_1 = C_2 = 0$$
$$C_3 = 10L, \quad C_4 = -15L, \quad C_5 = 6L$$

The displacement equation can then be written in the form

$$y = 10L\left(\frac{\theta}{\beta}\right)^3 - 15L\left(\frac{\theta}{\beta}\right)^4 + 6L\left(\frac{\theta}{\beta}\right)^5$$

This is called the 3-4-5 polynomial transition because of the powers of the terms that remain in the expression. The first three derivatives and the velocity, acceleration, and jerk are given by

$$y' = \frac{30L}{\beta}\left[\left(\frac{\theta}{\beta}\right)^2 - 2\left(\frac{\theta}{\beta}\right)^3 + \left(\frac{\theta}{\beta}\right)^4\right], \quad \dot{y} = \frac{30\omega L}{\beta}\left[\left(\frac{\theta}{\beta}\right)^2 - 2\left(\frac{\theta}{\beta}\right)^3 + \left(\frac{\theta}{\beta}\right)^4\right]$$

$$y'' = \frac{60L}{\beta^2}\left[\left(\frac{\theta}{\beta}\right) - 3\left(\frac{\theta}{\beta}\right)^2 + 2\left(\frac{\theta}{\beta}\right)^3\right], \quad \ddot{y} = 60L\left(\frac{\omega}{\beta}\right)^2\left[\left(\frac{\theta}{\beta}\right) - 3\left(\frac{\theta}{\beta}\right)^2 + 2\left(\frac{\theta}{\beta}\right)^3\right]$$

$$y''' = \frac{60L}{\beta^3}\left[1 - 6\left(\frac{\theta}{\beta}\right) + 6\left(\frac{\theta}{\beta}\right)^2\right], \quad \dddot{y} = 60L\left(\frac{\omega}{\beta}\right)^3\left[1 - 6\left(\frac{\theta}{\beta}\right) + 6\left(\frac{\theta}{\beta}\right)^2\right]$$

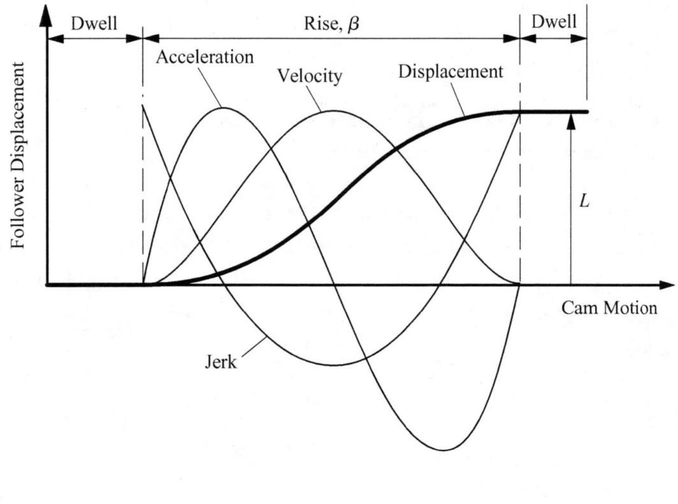

FIGURE 8.21 Shape of the displacement, velocity, acceleration, and jerk relations for the 3-4-5 polynomial motion.

These general relationships are plotted in Fig. 8.21. The displacement results are visually similar to the cycloidal curve, but the velocity, acceleration, and jerk are somewhat different. In general, this type of cam will begin and end its motion more slowly than the other types, and to produce such a cam, extreme machining accuracy is required, especially at the beginning and end of the motion. The machining is commonly done on a computer numerically controlled (CNC) milling machine.

TABLE 8.5 Comparison of the Different Types of Cam–Follower Motion for $\beta = L = 1$

θ	y (linear)	y (parabolic)	y (harmonic)	y (cycloidal)	y (polynomial)
0.00	0.0000	0.0000	0.0000	0.0000	0.0000
0.05	0.0500	0.0050	0.0062	0.0008	0.0012
0.10	0.1000	0.0200	0.0245	0.0065	0.0086
0.15	0.1500	0.0450	0.0545	0.0212	0.0266
0.20	0.2000	0.0800	0.0955	0.0486	0.0579
0.25	0.2500	0.1250	0.1464	0.0908	0.1035
0.30	0.3000	0.1800	0.2061	0.1486	0.1631
0.35	0.3500	0.2450	0.2730	0.2212	0.2352
0.40	0.4000	0.3200	0.3455	0.3065	0.3174
0.45	0.4500	0.4050	0.4218	0.4008	0.4069
0.50	0.5000	0.5000	0.5000	0.5000	0.5000
0.55	0.5500	0.5950	0.5782	0.5992	0.5931
0.60	0.6000	0.6800	0.6545	0.6935	0.6826
0.65	0.6500	0.7550	0.7270	0.7788	0.7648
0.70	0.7000	0.8200	0.7939	0.8514	0.8369
0.75	0.7500	0.8750	0.8536	0.9092	0.8965
0.80	0.8000	0.9200	0.9045	0.9514	0.9421
0.85	0.8500	0.9550	0.9455	0.9788	0.9734
0.90	0.9000	0.9800	0.9755	0.9935	0.9914
0.95	0.9500	0.9950	0.9938	0.9992	0.9988
1.00	1.0000	1.0000	1.0000	1.0000	1.0000

To compare the profiles generated by the different follower-displacement programs, let $\beta = L = 1$, and vary θ from 0 to β. We can then compute y as a function of θ in increments of 0.05. The results are shown in Table 8.5. Notice that the variation among the different profiles is very small in most cases. This emphasizes that extreme accuracy must be achieved if the benefits of using the different follower-displacement programs are to be realized.

8.10 DETERMINING THE CAM PROFILE

Once the follower motion is determined as a function of the cam displacement, the cam surface can be found either graphically or analytically. For extremely accurate cams, the geometry must be determined analytically and the machining must be done using CNC milling machines. For low-speed cams, however, a graphical layout and manual machining are adequate.

In both the graphical and analytical approaches to determining the cam geometry, the cam mechanism must be inverted. That is, the cam is taken as the reference system, and the frame and follower are considered to move relative to the cam. To maintain the correct relative motion, the follower will move relative to the cam in a direction opposite to the motion of the cam relative to the follower.

If we restrict our discussions to planar, rotating cams, four general types of followers are possible: (a) a translating cylindrical-faced follower, (b) a translating flat-faced follower, (c) a rotating cylindrical-faced follower, and (d) a rotating flat-faced follower (Fig. 8.22).

Notice that the cam geometry is independent of the type of joint between the cylindrical-faced follower and the cam. The kinematic design procedure is exactly the same when a roller follower or a solid cylindrical-faced follower is involved. We will consider both graphical and analytical approaches to the design of the cam for each type of follower shown in Fig. 8.22.

8.10.1 Graphical Cam Profile Layout

As already indicated, cam profiles are laid out graphically using inversion. That is, the cam is viewed as stationary, and the successive positions of the follower are located relative to it. This results in a polar plot of successive follower positions. The cam profile is then filled in as the envelope curve of the follower positions.

The first step in laying out the cam profile is to select a base circle radius. The base circle represents the position of the follower at zero lift. Successive lift values are plotted radially outward from the base circle.

Choosing a large base circle radius results in a large cam. However, if the base circle is too small the cam profile may have hollows of smaller radius than the follower. Since the follower will bridge across such a hollow, it will not follow the desired lift program. Obviously, this situation must be avoided, and it is therefore necessary to have a means of computing the radius of curvature of the cam at different locations.

The pressure angle of a cam is the angle between the contact normal and the velocity of the point on the follower at the contact location. Reducing the pressure angle reduces the contact loads and promotes smoother operation with less wear. Increasing the base circle radius decreases the maximum value of pressure angle. Thus, it is good practice to use the largest base circle that the design constraints will allow. As a general rule of thumb, the base circle radius should be two to three times the maximum lift value.

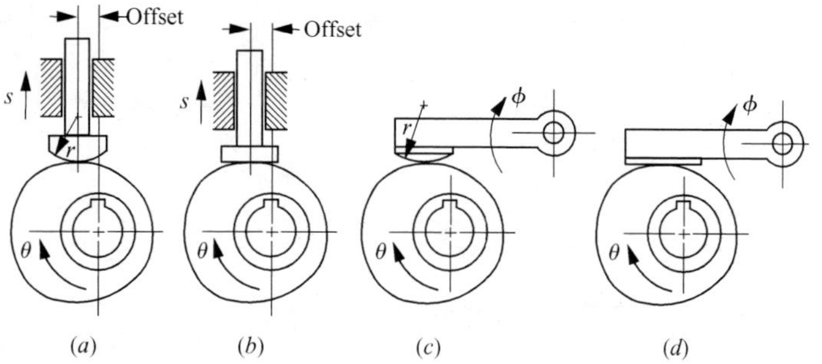

FIGURE 8.22 Common follower configurations for planar, rotating cams. (a) Translating cylindrical-faced follower; (b) translating flat-faced follower; (c) rotating cylindrical-faced follower; (d) rotating flat-faced follower.

EXAMPLE 8.3
Layout of a Cam Profile for a Radial Roller Follower

Lay out a cam profile using the harmonic follower displacement profile of Example 8.2. That is, the follower is to dwell at zero lift for the first 120° of the motion cycle and to dwell at 0.8 in lift for cam angles from 180° to 210°. The cam is to have a translating, roller follower with a 1-in roller diameter. The cam will rotate clockwise. Lay out the cam profile using 10° plotting intervals.

Solution The basic motion specification is as shown in Fig. 8.15. Using the results of Example 8.2 produces the lift values to be plotted given in Table 8.6. Notice that the dwells correspond to locations on the cam where the radius is constant.

TABLE 8.6 Follower Displacements for Example 8.3

θ	0, 360°	10°	20°	30°	40°	50°	60°	70°	80°
y	0.0000	0.0000	0.0000	0.0000	0.0000	0.0000	0.0000	0.0000	0.0000
θ	90°	100°	110°	120°	130°	140°	150°	160°	170°
y	0.0000	0.0000	0.0000	0.0000	0.0536	0.2000	0.4000	0.6000	0.7464
θ	180°	190°	200°	210°	220°	230°	240°	250°	260°
y	0.8000	0.8000	0.8000	0.8000	0.7913	0.7654	0.7236	0.6677	0.6000
θ	270°	280°	290°	300°	310°	320°	330°	340°	350°
y	0.5236	0.4418	0.3582	0.2764	0.2000	0.1323	0.0764	0.0346	0.0087

The layout of the cam is accomplished by drawing radial lines at 10° increments. Because the cam rotates clockwise, the radial lines are laid off and labeled in the counterclockwise direction, as shown in Fig. 8.23. Next, the base circle and the prime circle are drawn. The *base circle* is chosen to have a 1.5-in radius, and it is the largest circle that can be drawn inside the cam profile and be tangent to the cam profile. The radius of the *prime circle* is equal to $r_b + r_0$ where r_b is the base circle radius and r_0 is the radius of the roller follower. In this problem, the prime-circle radius is 2.0 in. The cam profile is initially laid off from the prime circle to give the pitch curve. The *pitch curve* is the curve traced by the center of the roller follower. Notice that the pitch curve will be the cam profile if r_0 is zero. This corresponds to the case of a knife-edged follower.

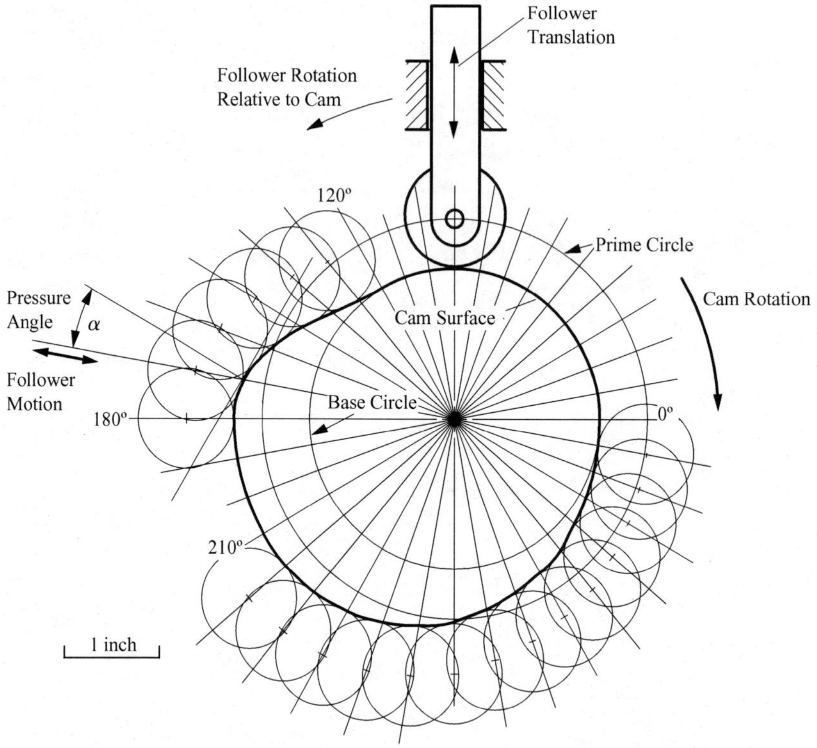

FIGURE 8.23 Layout of the cam profile for Example 8.3. The process of laying out a cam profile is one of inversion. That is, the cam is viewed as being stationary, and successive positions of the follower are plotted relative to it. In this case, a prime circle of 2.0-in radius was chosen. This represents the location of the follower center at zero lift. Positive lift values are plotted outward from the base circle. The successive positions of the follower are then drawn using the plotted points as centers. Finally, the profile is plotted as an envelope curve of the successive follower positions. Because of the inversion, if the cam is to rotate clockwise, the positions of the follower must be plotted in the opposite direction, that is, counterclockwise.

Once the radial lines and prime circle are established, the displacements can be laid off from the prime circle as shown in Fig. 8.23. The radius of the follower is drawn with its center located on the pitch curve at a series of locations. The cam can be defined by drawing a curve tangent to roller locations as shown in Fig. 8.23.

As indicated before, an important parameter for cam motion is the pressure angle. In the case of the translating, roller follower, this is the angle between the direction of the follower travel and the normal to the curve. For a given force on the follower roller, the force in the direction of travel of the follower will be proportional to the cosine of the pressure angle. The force normal to the travel of the follower is proportional to the sine of the pressure angle. Wear on the follower stem will increase with the normal force. Therefore, from design considerations, we want the pressure angle (α) to be as small as possible.

The maximum pressure angle will occur at the *pitch points*. These correspond to the inflection points on the follower displacement curves (see Fig. 8.8). If the torque on the cam is more or less constant, the pressure angles at the pitch points will correspond to the parts of the cycle where the maximum normal force occurs and hence the times when the follower stem wear will be greatest. It will also correspond to the parts of the cycle where the follower will tend to bind in the stem bearing. Because of problems with wear and binding, the pressure angle is usually limited to angles on the order of $\pm 30°$. If the pressure angle becomes excessive, the base circle should be increased or the follower-displacement profile should be changed.

The problem statement indicated that a roller follower was to be designed. However, the construction would be *exactly* the same if a solid cylindrical-faced follower were involved. From the standpoint of the cam geometry, the important issues are the radius of the cylindrical face and the direction of translation relative to the cam.

EXAMPLE 8.4
Layout of a Cam Profile for a Radial Flat-Faced Follower

Again, lay out a cam profile using the harmonic displacement profile of Examples 8.2 and 8.3. The cam is to have a translating flat-faced follower that is offset by 0.2 in. The cam will rotate clockwise. Lay out the cam profile using 10° plotting intervals.

Solution

The basic motion specification is the same as in Example 8.3 (Table 8.6). The layout of the cam is again accomplished by drawing radial lines at 10° increments. Because the cam rotates clockwise, the radial lines are laid off and labeled in the counterclockwise direction as was done in Fig. 8.23. Next the base circle is drawn. Because a flat-faced follower is being designed, there is no prime circle. However, selection of the base circle requires careful consideration.

A major restriction on the cam profile driving a flat-faced follower is that the profile must form a convex surface. This means that the vectors from every point on the cam to the corresponding center of curvature must point toward the interior of the cam. An alternative way to approach the convexity problem is to imagine an arbitrary line drawn across the face of the cam. If it is possible to select an arbitrary line that intersects the cam at more than two points, the cam profile is not convex. If the cam is not convex, the flat-faced follower cannot contact the cam at all points, and the desired motion will not be generated. This condition will be illustrated mathematically when an analytical approach to cam synthesis is discussed. Clearly, the cam generated in Fig. 8.23 does not satisfy the convexity condition; however, this is not necessarily an issue with roller followers. When the resulting cam is not convex for flat-faced followers, we must increase the size of the base circle or change the follower-displacement function. The effect of changing the base circle can be easily investigated by running one of the cam design programs supplied on the disk with this book.

To begin the construction, we can select a base circle somewhat arbitrarily. However, if the radius of curvature at some location on the resulting cam is too small, the base circle diameter must be increased.

The follower is offset, but this does not affect the geometry of the cam. All points on the follower have the same velocity because its motion is pure translation. Therefore, from a kinematic standpoint, the actual location of the follower stem is not important. From a machine design standpoint it is important, however, because the larger the offset, the higher the moment on the follower stem.

We can lay off the displacements in Table 8.6 from the base circle and along the radial lines. At each of these locations on the radial lines, draw a line perpendicular to each radial line. These perpendicular lines correspond to the face of the follower. This is illustrated in Fig. 8.24. The lines for different positions of the follower will form an envelope that defines the geometry of the cam surface. We construct the outline of the cam by drawing a curve that contacts the lines corresponding to the different positions of the follower face at the tangent points.

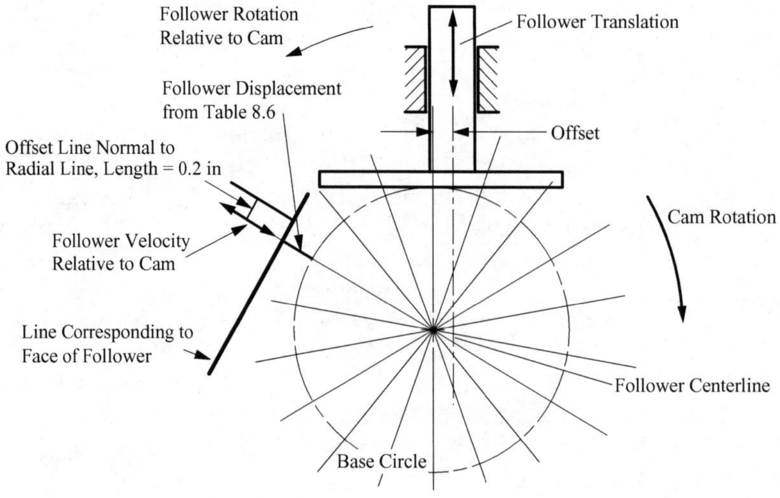

FIGURE 8.24 Basic construction lines for determining the cam profile for a flat-faced follower.

As the lines corresponding to the different positions of the follower face are drawn, successive lines will intersect. For the geometry to be valid, the angle increment for successive intersections must be positive. If an intersection requires a negative angle increment, it will not be possible to generate the cam, and a larger base circle must be used. This situation is illustrated in the current problem in Fig. 8.25 for the positions corresponding to rotation angles of 150°, 160°, 170°, and 180°. In Fig. 8.25, a base circle radius of 1.5 in was chosen. The angle increment for the intersection corresponding to 160° and 170° is positive, but the increment corresponding to 170° and 180° is negative. This situation makes the cam nonconvex and indicates that the base circle is too small and must be increased.

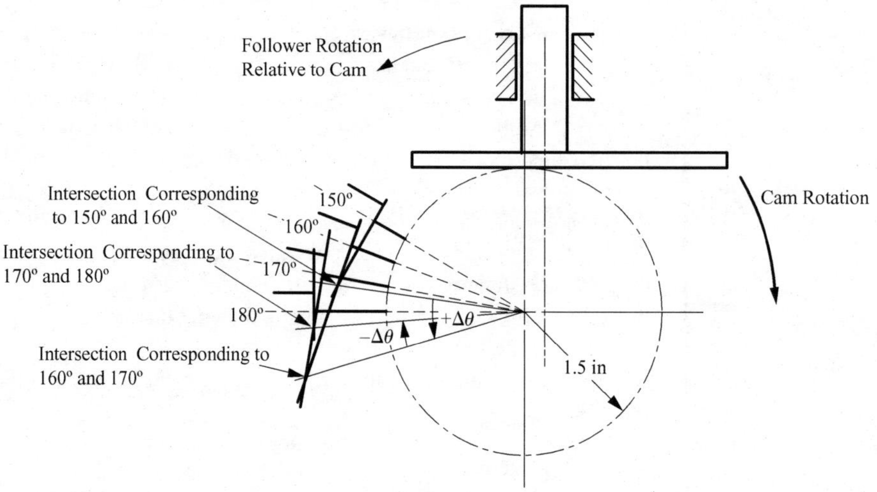

FIGURE 8.25 Condition when the base circle is too small to generate an acceptable cam for a flat-faced follower.

The smallest base circle is the one for which the angle increment corresponding to 170° and 180° is no longer negative, that is, when it is zero. This occurs when the follower-face lines corresponding to 160°, 170°, and 180° intersect. This occurs for a base circle radius of approximately 5.5 in. For this base circle, the cam will have a point or cusp corresponding to the location where the face lines intersect. The envelope of the face lines and the resulting cam is shown in Fig. 8.26. The cam designed for the roller follower and for the same displacement profile is also shown in Fig. 8.26 for comparison. Based on the size of the cam required, a flat-faced follower would not be a good choice for this type of displacement profile.

After the follower-face locations are found, the stem locations can be shown by drawing parallel lines to the radial lines. These are also shown in Fig. 8.26.

As indicated before, an important parameter for cam motion is the pressure angle. When a flat-faced follower is used, the normal to the follower profile is always in the direction of the follower travel if the follower face is perpendicular to the stem. This makes the pressure angle always zero; however, there can be significant lateral loads on the follower bearings caused by the frictional force

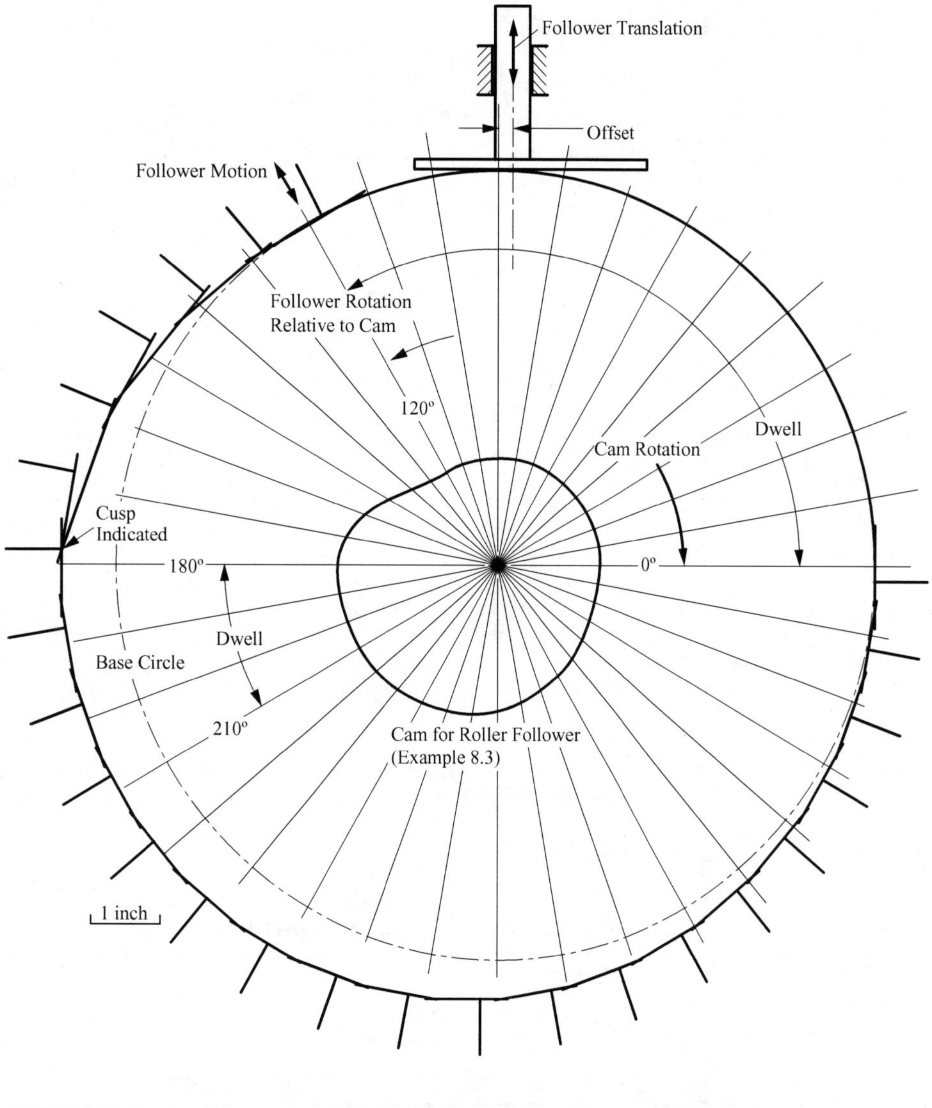

FIGURE 8.26 Envelope generated by drawing lines corresponding to the follower face for Example 8.4. The base circle is the minimum possible for the flat-faced follower to generate the profile indicated in Table 8.6. The cam generated for the roller follower in Example 8.3 is included for comparison.

at the cam–follower interface and by the moment generated by the normal force at the cam–follower interface and the offset line of action. The friction force can be reduced by lubrication but never completely eliminated, and the bearing couple that opposes the moment from the normal force must be addressed in the design of the cam and follower system. Depending on the lubrication and design, the lateral forces can be as high as or higher than the corresponding lateral force with a roller follower. Also, the cam may be so large that, to avoid the convexity condition, the roller follower would be preferred from size considerations.

Another important parameter that must be determined for the design of a cam for a flat-faced follower is the size (length) of the follower face. It is essential that the face be long enough on both sides to maintain contact with the cam on a tangent line. The minimum length of the follower face can be established by direct measurement. The actual length would be equal to the minimum length plus a small increment.

EXAMPLE 8.5 *Layout of a Cam Profile for an Oscillating Cylindrical Follower*

Lay out a cam profile assuming that the follower starts from a dwell for 0° to 120° of cam rotation, and the cam rotates clockwise. The rise occurs during the cam rotation from 120° to 200°. The follower then dwells for 40° of cam rotation, and the return occurs for the cam rotation from 240° to 360°. The amplitude of the follower rotation is 30°, and the follower radius is 0.75 in. Lay out the cam profile using 20° plotting intervals. (This plotting interval is too coarse for the development of an accurate cam; however, it will be used to simplify the resulting drawing.)

Solution

The basic motion specification is visually similar to that shown in Fig. 8.15; however, the follower motion is a rotation instead of a translation. To begin the design, we must determine the follower rotation, ϕ, as a function of the cam rotation, θ. Assume parabolic motion for the follower. From section 8.6, the equations for each part of the motion are

$$0 < \theta \le 120°: \quad \phi = 0$$

$$120° \le \theta \le 160°: \quad \phi = 2L\left(\frac{\Delta\theta}{\beta}\right)^2 = 60\left(\frac{\theta - 120°}{80°}\right)^2$$

$$160° \le \theta \le 200°: \quad \phi = L\left[1 - 2\left(1 - \frac{\Delta\theta}{\beta}\right)^2\right] = 30\left[1 - 2\left(1 - \frac{\theta - 120°}{80°}\right)^2\right]$$

$$200° \le \theta \le 240°: \quad \phi = 30°$$

$$240° \le \theta \le 300°: \quad \phi = L\left[1 - 2\left(\frac{\Delta\theta}{\beta}\right)^2\right] = 30\left[1 - 2\left(\frac{\theta - 240°}{120°}\right)^2\right]$$

$$300° \le \theta \le 360°: \quad \phi = 2L\left(1 - \frac{\Delta\theta}{\beta}\right)^2 = 60\left(1 - \frac{\theta - 240°}{120°}\right)^2$$

Here, L is treated as the generic amplitude of the follower motion. In this case, L is given as 30°.

Using these equations provides the lift values to be plotted given in Table 8.7. Notice that the dwells correspond to locations on the cam where the radius is constant.

TABLE 8.7 Follower Displacements for Example 8.5

θ	0, 360°	20°	40°	60°	80°	100°	120°	140°	160°
y	0.0000	0.0000	0.0000	0.0000	0.0000	0.0000	0.0000	3.7500°	15.0000°
θ	180°	200°	220°	240°	260°	280°	300°	320°	340°
y	26.2500°	30.0000°	30.0000°	30.0000°	28.3333°	23.3333°	15.0000°	6.6666°	1.6666°

The cam–follower system is similar to that shown in Fig. 8.27, and the points shown in Fig. 8.27 will be used to describe the layout of the cam. In particular, A is the location of the axis of rotation of the cam, B is the center of curvature of the follower, and C is the rotation axis of the follower.

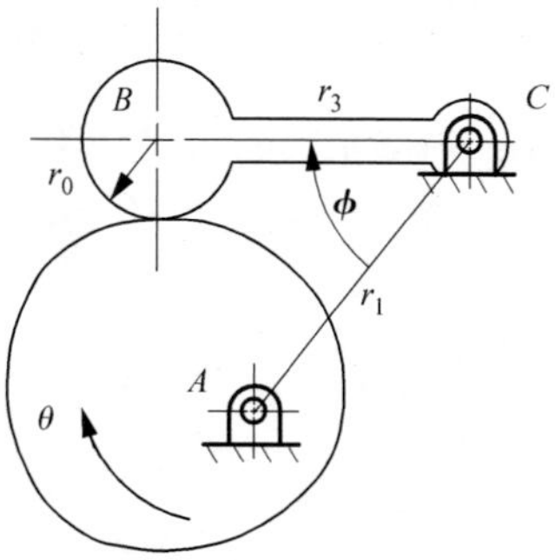

FIGURE 8.27 Cam–follower system to be designed in Example 8.5.

The first step in the cam layout is to draw the base circle and prime circle. The *base circle* is chosen to have a 1.25-in radius, and the radius of the *prime circle* is equal to $r_b + r_0 = 1.25 + 0.75 = 2.0$ in. The base circle radius is the radius of the cam during the dwell for the first 120° of cam rotation.

The second step is to select the distance from the cam rotation axis to the pivot of the follower (AC). The larger the value chosen, the smaller will be the pressure angle; however, this distance also directly affects the size of the cam–follower system. We will choose the distance between pivots to be 4 in. When we invert the motion, the follower pivot will appear to rotate around the cam. Therefore, we must draw a circle with a radius of 4 in about the cam for the follower pivot circle. The pivot circle is shown in Fig. 8.28.

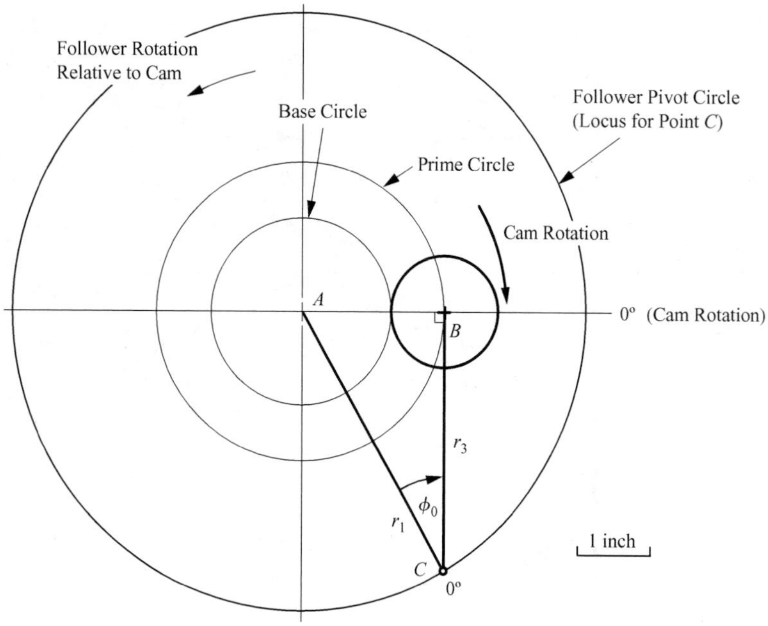

FIGURE 8.28 Location of the follower in the initial position. This determines the reference angle ϕ_0.

The third step is to determine the length of the follower ($BC = r_3$) and the reference angle ϕ_0 for ϕ. We will locate the follower in the initial dwell position in such a way that the pressure angle is zero. This is done by drawing a line tangent to the prime circle through the ray corresponding to $\theta = 0$. The intersection of this tangent line with the follower pivot circle will give the location of the follower pivot for the initial position of the cam. Two intersections will be given. One will correspond to a CW rotation of the follower, and the second will correspond to a CCW rotation. Based on the problem statement, we will choose the intersection corresponding to the CW rotation as shown in Fig. 8.28. Because a right triangle is involved, the follower length is given by

$$r_3 = \sqrt{r_1^2 - (r_b + r_0)^2} = \sqrt{4^2 - 2^2} = 3.464$$

We also need to determine the base angle, ϕ_0, because all subsequent displacements of the follower will be measured relative to this angle. If we let the distance between the cam and follower pivots be r_1, the angle ϕ_0 is given directly by

$$\phi_0 = \tan^{-1}\left(\frac{r_b + r_0}{r_3}\right) = \tan^{-1}\left(\frac{2}{3.464}\right) = 30.000^\circ$$

The location of pivot C for the follower when the cam angle is 0° gives the first position of the follower pivot. Subsequent positions of the pivot will be at angle increments of 20°. Therefore, the fourth step in the cam layout is to draw radial lines at 20° increments from the cam rotation axis to the follower pivot circle starting from the initial position of AC corresponding to the cam rotation angle of 0°. Label the radial lines corresponding to the beginning and end of dwells. These radial lines are shown in Fig. 8.29.

The fifth step is to draw a line tangent to the prime circle from the intersection of the radial lines and the follower pivot circle, as shown in Fig. 8.29. These lines give the position of the follower relative to the cam, if the cam is a simple cylinder. These lines will give the base lines from which to measure the ϕ angles given in Table 8.7. Next lay off lines 3.464-in long at the angles indicated in Table 8.7 from the corresponding base lines. The ends of these lines will be the centers of the cylindrical cam follower in the different positions. Draw circles corresponding to the follower, and construct the cam surface tangent to the follower positions. The final cam is shown in Fig. 8.29.

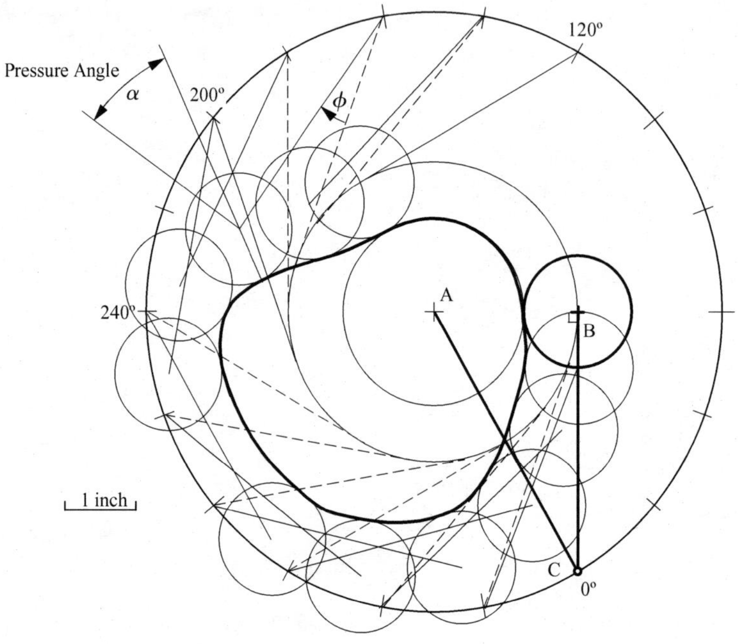

FIGURE 8.29 Final layout of the cam profile for Example 8.5.

As in the case of an axial roller follower, an important parameter for cam motion is the pressure angle. For the oscillating cylindrical follower, this is the angle between the velocity of the contact point on the follower (vector normal to line from contact point and point C) and the normal to the cam at the contact point. To reduce wear on the follower pivot, we want the pressure angle to be as small as possible. In the design shown in Fig. 8.29, the pressure angle will become fairly high ($\alpha > 30°$) in the rise region. To improve the design, the diameter of the base circle should be increased.

The problem statement indicated that a cylindrical follower was to be designed. However, the construction would be *exactly* the same if a roller follower were involved. From the standpoint of the cam geometry, the important issues are the radius of the cylindrical face and the direction of motion relative to the cam.

EXAMPLE 8.6 *Layout of the Cam Profile for an Oscillating, Flat-Faced Follower*

Lay out the rise portion of the cam profile for the follower motion indicated in Table 8.7. The cam will rotate *counterclockwise*. Assume that the follower face angle is 170°, and lay out the cam profile using 20° plotting intervals. Again, this plotting interval is too coarse for an accurate cam; however, it will be used to illustrate the procedure.

Solution

The cam–follower system is similar to that shown in Fig. 8.30, and the points shown in that figure will be used to describe the layout of the cam. Point A is the location of the axis of rotation of the cam, C is the rotation axis of the follower, and β is the follower face angle. Point B is the location of the intersection of the centerline of the follower stem with the face of the follower.

The first step in the cam layout is to select and draw the base circle. The base circle is chosen to be 2.0 in.

The second step is to select the distance from the cam rotation axis to the pivot of the follower (AC). The value chosen will affect the size of the cam, and typically the smallest value possible is chosen. The pivot distance must be large enough that the cam does not contact the follower pivot. Also, the force between the cam and follower will increase as the distance decreases. Therefore, it may be necessary to increase the pivot distance from machine design considerations. We will choose the distance between pivots to be 4 in. When we invert the motion, the follower pivot will appear to rotate around the cam. Therefore, we must draw a circle with a radius of 4 in about the cam for the follower pivot circle, as shown in Fig. 8.31.

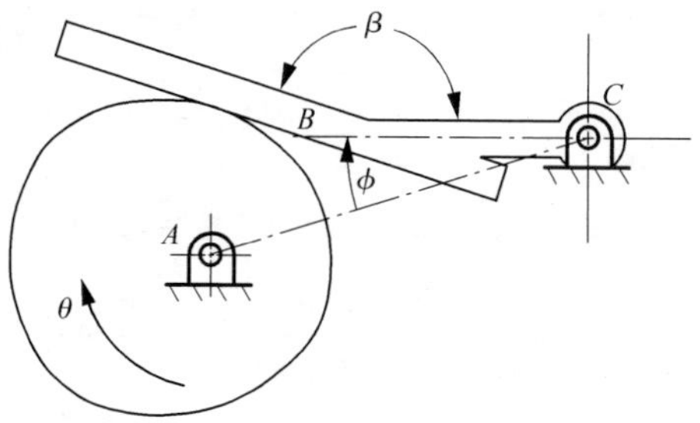

FIGURE 8.30 Cam–follower system to be designed in Example 8.6.

The third step is to determine the reference angle ϕ_0 for ϕ. The location of the follower to determine ϕ_0 will affect the length of the follower and therefore the cost of the system. For simplicity, we will locate the follower in the initial dwell position (cam angle $\theta = 0$) in such a way that point B contacts the cam in that position. This is done by drawing a line tangent to the base circle at B. Then construct a line at an angle of 170° to the tangent line at B. The intersection of this line with the follower pivot circle will locate C in the initial position. This is shown in Fig. 8.31. The length BC can then be computed using the law of cosines. That is,

$$BC^2 + AB^2 = AC^2 + 2(BC)(AB)\cos 100°$$

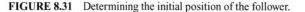

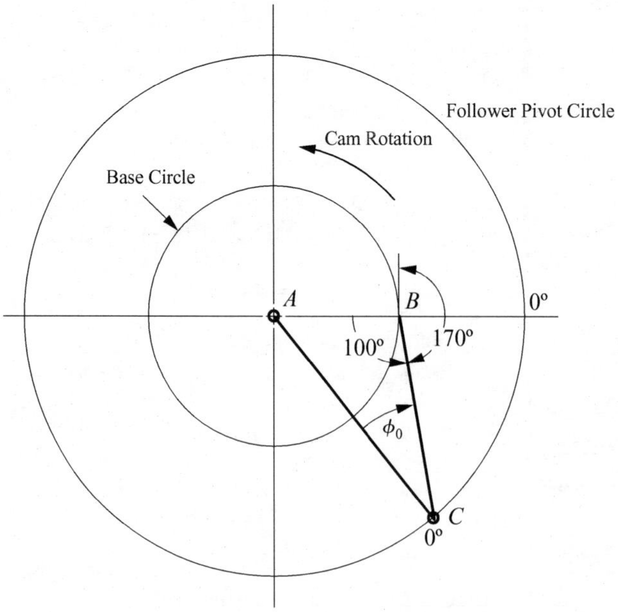

FIGURE 8.31 Determining the initial position of the follower.

or

$$BC^2 - 2(BC)(AB)\cos 100° + (AB^2 - AC^2) = 0$$

and

$$BC = \frac{2(AB)\cos 100° + \sqrt{[2(AB)\cos 100°]^2 - 4(AB^2 - AC^2)}}{2} = \frac{-0.694 + \sqrt{48.482}}{2} = 3.134$$

The base angle, ϕ_0, can be computed using the law of sines. That is,

$$\phi_0 = \sin^{-1}\left[\frac{AB}{AC}\sin 100°\right] = \sin^{-1}\left[\frac{2}{4}\sin 100°\right] = 29.499°$$

This angle is important because all subsequent displacements of the follower will be measured relative to this angle.

The location of pivot C for the follower when the cam angle is zero gives the first position of the follower pivot. Subsequent positions of the pivot will be at increments of 20° in the clockwise direction (opposite the cam rotation). Therefore, the fourth step in the cam layout is to draw radial lines at 20° increments from the cam rotation axis to the follower pivot circle starting from the initial position of AC corresponding to the cam rotation angle of 0°. These will be the positions of AC for each 20° rotation of the cam. Label the radial lines corresponding to the beginning and end of the first dwell and the second dwell. In the dwell regions, the cam will have a circular contour. These radial lines are shown in Fig. 8.32.

The fifth step is to draw the line CB relative to each position of AC, where the angle between CB and AC is $(\phi_0 + \phi)$ measured in the clockwise direction about C. This will locate the successive positions of B. Next, draw a line through each position of B at an angle of 170° to BC. This will locate the successive positions of the face of the cam follower. Construct the cam surface tangent to the follower positions. The rise portion of the final cam is shown in Fig. 8.32.

Because of the follower face angle β, the pressure angle will not be constant as in the case of the axial flat-faced follower. The pressure angle will depend on the contact point as shown in Fig. 8.32

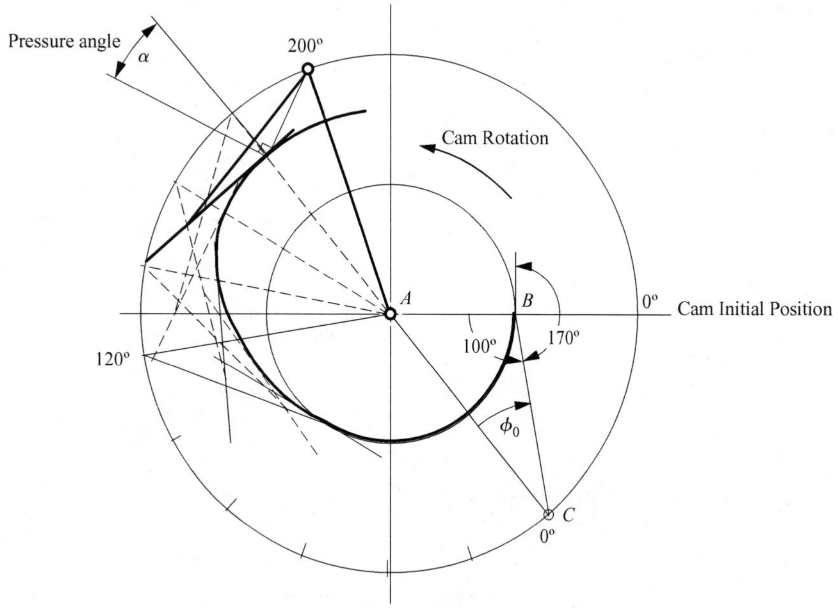

FIGURE 8.32 Final layout of the rise portion of the cam profile for Example 8.6.

and will be equal to 10° ± ζ, where ζ is the angle between a line from the contact point to C and the line BC. If the follower face angle is 180°, the pressure angle will be a constant, that is, 0°. Because of this, the angle β would be 180° unless specific design conditions dictated otherwise.

8.10.2 Analytical Determination of Cam Profile

Although the graphical approach works well for low-speed cams, for high speeds greater accuracy is required, making analytical techniques necessary. The analytical approach to determining the cam profiles also uses inversion. The general procedure is to establish a coordinate system on both the cam and the frame. To determine the location of the follower relative to the cam, it is necessary only to determine the location of the follower relative to the cam coordinate system. Successive positions of the follower will generate an envelope that will define the geometry of the cam profile.

The approach to the design of each of the four different follower systems considered is slightly different, and in each case the analytical approach will follow much the same procedure as was illustrated in the graphical approach.

Analytical Determination of Cam Profile for an Offset, Radial Roller Follower Prior to determining the geometry of the cam, it is assumed that the basic motion specification for the follower is known in the form $y = f(\theta)$, where y is the displacement of the follower and θ is the cam rotation angle. The base circle radius (r_b), the follower radius (r_0), and the offset δ are also assumed to be known. The positive direction for $\boldsymbol{\delta}$ is defined by rotating R 90° in the counterclockwise direction. The procedure is the same for both a roller follower and a cylindrical-faced follower. We will first locate successive positions of the roller center and then determine the envelope formed by the rollers.

Two positions of the follower relative to the cam are shown in Fig. 8.33. In the figure, it is assumed that the cam rotates clockwise, which means that the follower moves relative to the cam in the counterclockwise direction. The radial position of the center of the follower from the origin of the coordinate system located at the center of the cam is given by

$$R = r_0 + r_b + f(\theta) \tag{8.15}$$

where $f(\theta)$ is the function defining the follower displacement as a function of the cam rotation angle, θ. Referring to Fig. 8.33, we have

$$x = R\cos\theta - \delta\sin\theta = \left[r_0 + r_b + f(\theta)\right]\cos\theta - \delta\sin\theta \tag{8.16}$$

and

$$y = R\sin\theta + \delta\cos\theta = \left[r_0 + r_b + f(\theta)\right]\sin\theta - \delta\cos\theta \tag{8.17}$$

Given the follower displacement, the center of the roller can be easily computed as a function of the cam rotation angle θ. These equations will also define the cam profile if a knife-edged follower is involved. Also, if the cutter radius is the same as the roller radius, the coordinates can be used to generate the cam profile directly. However, for other cases, we must determine the cam profile indirectly.

As the cam angle θ is incremented, the roller follower can be represented in a series of positions as shown in Fig. 8.34. In any given position, the coordinates of all points on the roller follower can be defined relative to the cam. The cam surface is tangent to the successive positions of the rollers. Therefore, to determine the cam profile, we must locate points on a curve that is tangent to the series of circles.

The series of circles will form an envelope that will define the cam profile. Using envelope theory,[1,2] it is possible to define the profile exactly; however, envelope theory is somewhat complex except in the case of translating followers. Fortunately, if fine enough increments (less than 1°) are used, the cam profile can be determined very accurately using numerical techniques, and this is the approach that we will use here. The numerical techniques are much simpler than envelope theory, and once the path of the center of the follower is known, the cam profile can be determined without knowledge of whether an oscillating or translating follower was used.

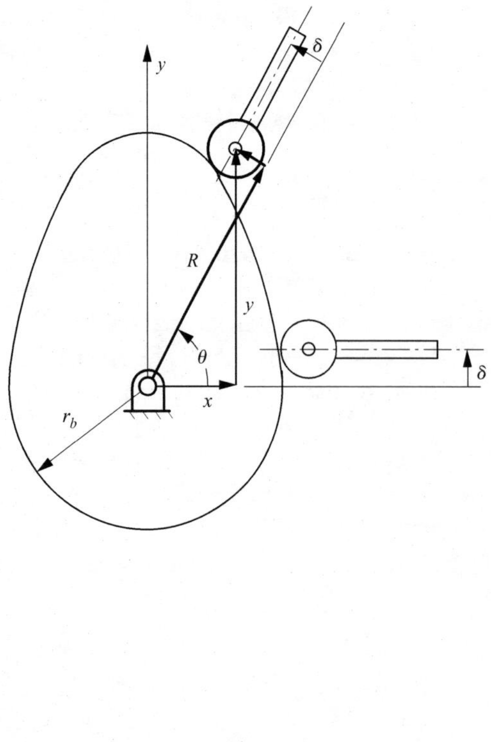

FIGURE 8.33 Two positions of the roller follower relative to the cam.

Referring to Fig. 8.34, we can approximate the cam profile by a series of points defined in a variety of ways. Some of these are as follows:

1. intersections of roller circles (A),
2. average tangent location formed by successive tangent lines (B),
3. intersections of successive tangent lines (C), and
4. tangent points formed by a circle tangent to three successive positions of the roller (D).

Other schemes based on fitting other curves to the circles could also be developed. However, it is apparent that each of the procedures will converge to the true tangent points defining the cam profile if the successive positions of the follower are close enough together.

Of the approximate methods available, procedures 2 and 4 will be the most accurate, and the simpler of these is procedure 4. It is also the procedure that is the more accurate of the two. Therefore, this is the procedure that will be developed here. This procedure is especially simple to program, and it can be made as accurate as desired by using increasingly smaller increments of the cam rotation angle. To begin the procedure, we will first determine an approximate location for the center of curvature of the cam as a function of θ.

Cam Radius of Curvature The radius of curvature for a cam is important for several reasons. These include the following:

- If the cam is concave in a given area, the radius of curvature determines the minimum diameter of the cutter that can be used to machine the cam. The radius of curvature of the cam cannot be smaller than the cutter radius if the cam is concave in the area being machined.
- If the cam is concave in a given area, the radius of curvature defines the minimum diameter of the follower that can be used with the cam.

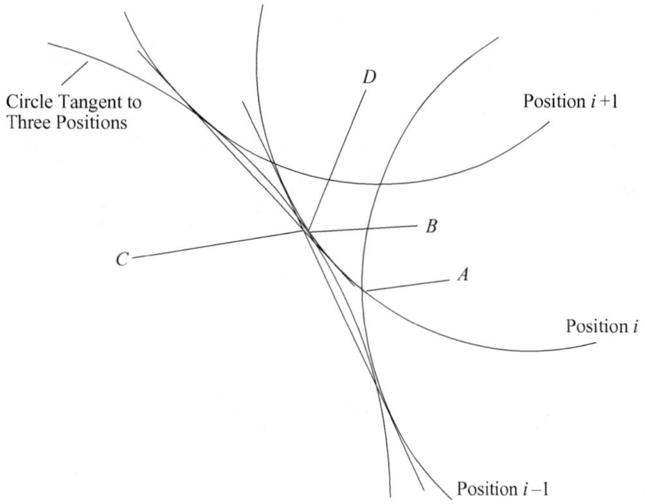

FIGURE 8.34 Approximate procedures for locating a point on the cam profile given three successive positions of the roller follower. Point A is found by the simple intersection of two successive positions, point B is the average tangent location in position i, point C is the intersection of two successive tangents, and point D is the tangent location in position i of a circle tangent to positions $i-1$, i, and $i+1$.

- The contact stresses between the cam and the follower are a function of the cam radius of curvature.

If we have a parametric expression for the cam geometry in terms of $x(\theta)$ and $y(\theta)$, an expression for the radius of curvature, ρ, in the x–y plane is given from calculus as

$$\rho = \frac{\sqrt{\left[(dx/d\theta)^2 + (dy/d\theta)^2\right]^3}}{(dx/d\theta)(d^2y/d\theta^2) - (dy/d\theta)(d^2x/d\theta^2)} \tag{8.18}$$

To determine ρ, we need only differentiate the given expressions for $x(\theta)$ and $y(\theta)$, and substitute the resulting expressions into Eq. (8.18).

The radius of curvature given in Eq. (8.18) will have a magnitude and direction, and both are important. When the cam profile is convex, the radius of curvature is positive, and when the cam is concave, the radius of curvature is negative. The radius can also be zero, which corresponds to a cusp. Technically, the cusp can be concave or convex, but from a practical standpoint, cusps are of interest only for convex surfaces. The transition between concave and convex areas of the cam results in the radius of curvature becoming infinite. The physical interpretations of the various signs of ρ are shown in Fig. 8.35.

Equation (8.18) applies to any cam profile regardless of the type of follower. However, to apply it directly, an analytical expression for $x(\theta)$ and $y(\theta)$ must be available. Except in the case of a translating flat-faced follower, simple expressions for $x(\theta)$ and $y(\theta)$ generally will not be available. Because of this, the purely analytical approach to determining the radius of curvature will not be addressed here except for this special case. Alternatively, a simpler numerical approach will be used.

If the points defining the cam profile are relatively close together, the radius of curvature can be determined numerically. This can be done by evaluating the derivatives in Eq. (8.18) numerically or by fitting circles to the points of the cam profile. Often an approximate value for the radius of curvature is sufficient because in most cases we do not wish to design cams that are close to the operating limits defined by the radii of curvature.

To determine the center of curvature of the cam profile, we will assume that for a given angle θ, the center of curvature of the cam is the same as the center of curvature of the prime curve defined by the locations of the center of the cylindrical follower. We can approximate the center of curvature of the prime by fitting a circle through three successive positions of the center of the cylindrical follower. Designate these positions as $p_{i-1} = (x_{i-1}, y_{i-1})$, $p_i = (x_i, y_i)$, and $p_{i+1} = (x_{i+1}, y_{i+1})$. Also, let the approximate location for the center of curvature be designated as $p_c = (x_c, y_c)$. We can now use Eq. (6.16) in Section 6.3

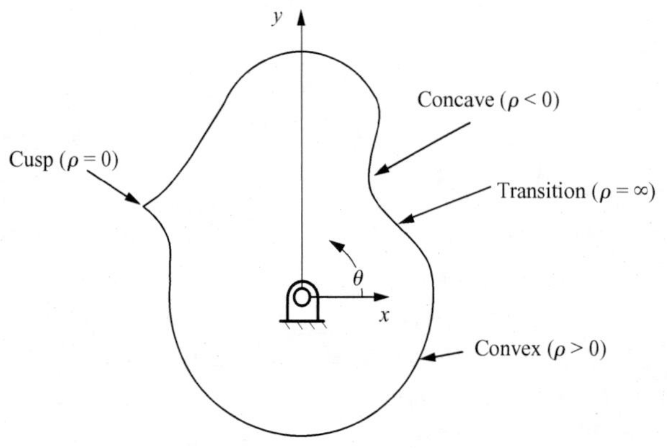

FIGURE 8.35 Interpretation of the sign of ρ.

to find the location of p_c because the procedure for finding p_c is the same as that required to find a pole or centerpoint. The result is

$$\begin{bmatrix} 2(x_{i+1}-x_i) & 2(y_{i+1}-y_i) \\ 2(x_{i-1}-x_i) & 2(y_{i-1}-y_i) \end{bmatrix} \begin{Bmatrix} x_c \\ y_c \end{Bmatrix} = \begin{Bmatrix} (x_{i+1}^2 - x_i^2) + (y_{i+1}^2 - y_i^2) \\ (x_{i-1}^2 - x_i^2) + (y_{i-1}^2 - y_i^2) \end{Bmatrix} \tag{8.19}$$

This linear matrix equation can be solved easily for (x_c, y_c). The magnitude of the radius of curvature of the prime curve is given by

$$\rho = \left| \boldsymbol{r}_{p_i/p_c} \right| = \sqrt{(x_i - x_c)^2 + (y_i - y_c)^2} \tag{8.20}$$

Once the center of curvature is known, the sign of the radius of curvature can be found by taking the cross product of the vector $r_{p_i/p_{i-1}}$ with the vector r_{p_{i+1}/p_i}. The vectors are shown in Fig. 8.36, and the cross product is given by

$$\boldsymbol{r}_{p_i/p_{i-1}} \times \boldsymbol{r}_{p_{i+1}/p_i} = \left[(x_i - x_{i-1})(y_{i+1} - y_i) - (x_{i+1} - x_i)(y_i - y_{i-1}) \right] \boldsymbol{k} \tag{8.21}$$

If the cross product is in the positive $\boldsymbol{k}$ direction, the radius of curvature is positive, and the cam is convex at (x_i, y_i). If the cross product is in the negative $\boldsymbol{k}$ direction, the cam is concave. If the determinant of the coefficient matrix in Eq. (8.19) is zero, then (x_c, y_c) is at infinity, $\boldsymbol{r}_{p_i/p_c}$ is infinite, and an inflection point is indicated. If $(x_c, y_c) = (x_i, y_i)$, the radius of curvature is zero and a cusp is indicated.

Profile Approximation Using Center of Curvature To locate points on the cam profile, we will approximate the center of curvature of three successive positions of the follower as shown in Fig. 8.37. From Eq. (8.19), the center of curvature is approximated as the intersection of lines through the midpoints of the line segments connecting successive follower centers and normal to these line segments as shown in Fig. 8.37.

The corresponding point on the cam profile lies on a line through this center of curvature and the center of the second roller circle. The location of this point (X_i, Y_i) is at the point where this line and the second roller circle intersect. Because there are two such points of intersection, care must be taken to find the right point. For the inner profile the desired point lies on the same side of the follower curve as the cam center.

To locate the line formed by the center of curvature and the second follower center, first calculate the slope orientation angle for the line using

$$\psi_i = \tan^{-1}\left(\frac{y_i - y_c}{x_i - x_c} \right) \tag{8.22}$$

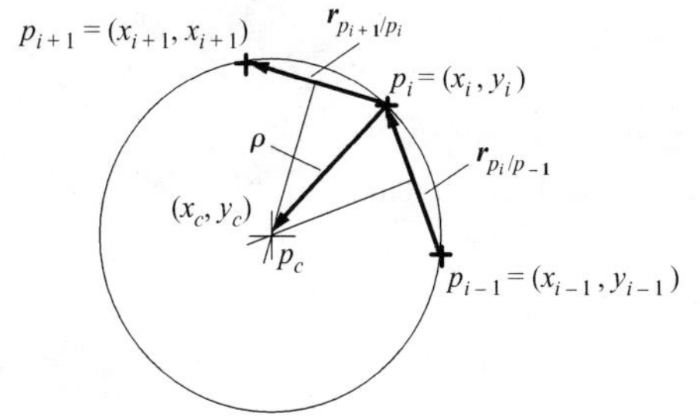

FIGURE 8.36 Use of vectors to determine the sign of ρ.

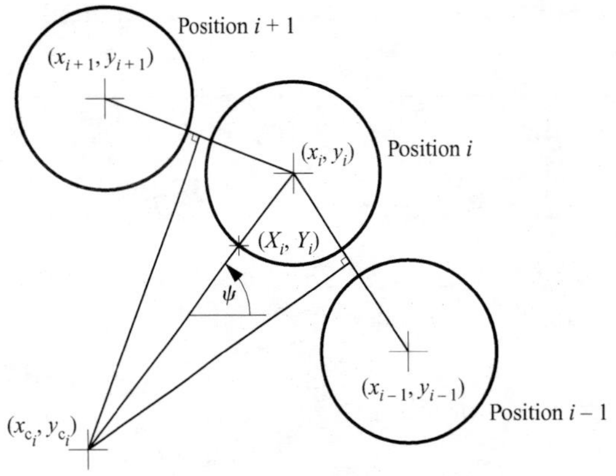

FIGURE 8.37 Approximate center of curvature of roller positions.

This angle is measured from the horizontal axis to the line from the center of curvature of the cam to the contact point. Note that the center of curvature, the contact point, and the center of the cam follower are all collinear. Equation (8.22) can be used directly when the cam is convex. Then the contact point will be located between the center of curvature and the center of the cylindrical follower. However, if the cam surface is concave, the follower center will be located between the center of curvature and the contact point.

The profile can be tested for concavity by solving Eq. (8.21). If the result is positive, the profile is convex and the coordinates on the cam profile are given by

$$\begin{aligned} X_i &= x_i - r_0 \cos\psi_i \\ Y_i &= y_i - r_0 \sin\psi_i \end{aligned} \tag{8.23}$$

If the result is negative, the profile is concave and the coordinates on the cam profile are given by

$$\begin{aligned} X_i &= x_i + r_o \cos\psi_i \\ Y_i &= y_i + r_o \sin\psi_i \end{aligned} \tag{8.24}$$

Calculation of the Pressure Angle As indicated previously, the pressure angle is the angle between the outward normal to the cam at the contact point and the direction of the velocity of the follower. The pressure angle is nominally the angle $\phi_i = \psi_i - \theta$, although to use this expression it is necessary to be careful with plus and minus angles. Another way to compute the pressure angle is to locate the center of curvature of the cam relative to the frame coordinate system and draw a line from the center of curvature to the center of the cylindrical follower. Because the cam is assumed to move horizontally, the inclination angle for the line connecting the cam center of curvature with the center of the cylindrical follower will be the pressure angle.

The equations necessary to determine points on the cam profile are summarized in Table 8.8. These can be easily programmed to determine the (X_i, Y_i) coordinates of points on the cam profile, and a MATLAB program for doing this is included on the disk with this book. Given the (X_i, Y_i) coordinates, the cam can be machined on a CNC milling machine. The accuracy of the profile will be determined in part by the angle increment chosen for the cam rotation angle θ.

TABLE 8.8 Summary of Equations for Determining the Cam Profile Coordinates and Pressure Angle for a Translating Cylindrical-Faced or Roller Follower. The Follower Displacement Is Assumed to Be Given by *f(θ)*, the Radius of the Follower Is r_0, and the Base Circle Radius Is r_b. There Are Assumed to Be *n* Points on the Cam Profile. δ is the Follower Offset.

Radius of curvature

$$\begin{Bmatrix} x_c \\ y_c \end{Bmatrix} = \begin{bmatrix} 2(X_{i+1}-X_i) & 2(Y_{i+1}-Y_i) \\ 2(X_{i-1}-X_i) & 2(Y_{i-1}-Y_i) \end{bmatrix}^{-1} \begin{Bmatrix} (X_{i+1}^2 - X_i^2) + (Y_{i+1}^2 - Y_i^2) \\ (X_{i-1}^2 - X_i^2) + (Y_{i-1}^2 - Y_i^2) \end{Bmatrix}$$

$$\rho = \frac{\left[(X_i - X_{i-1})(Y_{i+1} - Y_i) - (X_{i+1} - X_i)(Y_i - Y_{i-1})\right]}{\left|(X_i - X_{i-1})(Y_{i+1} - Y_i) - (X_{i+1} - X_i)(Y_i - Y_{i-1})\right|} \sqrt{(X_i - x_c)^2 + (Y_i - y_c)^2}$$

Cam coordinates

$$x_i = \left[r_0 + r_b + f(\theta_i)\right]\cos\theta_i - \delta\sin\theta_i$$

$$y_i = \left[r_0 + r_b + f(\theta_i)\right]\sin\theta_i + \delta\cos\theta_i$$

$$\psi_i = \tan^{-1}\left(\frac{y_i - y_c}{x_i - x_c}\right) \qquad (i = 1,\ 2,\ 3,\ \ldots,\ n)$$

$$\begin{aligned} X_i &= x_i - r_0\cos\psi_i \\ Y_i &= y_i - r_0\sin\psi_i \end{aligned} \quad \text{(convex)}$$

$$\begin{aligned} X_i &= x_i + r_0\cos\psi_i \\ Y_i &= y_i + r_0\sin\psi_i \end{aligned} \quad \text{(concave)}$$

Pressure angle

$$\phi_i = \psi_i - \theta$$

EXAMPLE 8.7
Cam Profile Coordinates for a Radial Roller Follower

Determine the cam profile assuming that the follower starts from a dwell from 0° to 90° and rotates CW. The rise occurs with cycloidal motion during the cam rotation from 90° to 180°. The follower then dwells for 60° of cam rotation, and the return occurs with simple harmonic motion for the cam rotation from 240° to 360°. The amplitude of the follower translation is 2 cm, and the follower radius is 1 cm. The base circle radius is 4 cm, and the offset is 0.5 cm.

Solution

To solve the problem, we must identify the equations for the follower motion as a function of the cam rotation angle θ, and then select an increment for θ. From Sections 8.7 and 8.8, the equations (expressed in terms of radians) for each part of the motion are

$$0 \le \theta \le \pi/2: \qquad y = 0$$

$$\pi/2 \le \theta \le \pi: \qquad f(\theta) = \frac{2L}{\pi}\left(\left(\theta - \frac{\pi}{2}\right) - \frac{1}{4}\sin 4\left(\theta - \frac{\pi}{2}\right)\right)$$

$$\pi \le \theta \le 4\pi/3: \qquad f(\theta) = 2, \quad f'(\theta) = f''(\theta) = 0$$

$$4\pi/3 \le \theta \le 2\pi: \qquad f(\theta) = \frac{L}{2}\left(1 + \cos\frac{3}{2}\left(\theta - \frac{4\pi}{3}\right)\right)$$

These equations correspond to $f(\theta)$ in Table 8.8, and using the equations in Table 8.8 we can compute the coordinates of the cam as accurately as we wish. For this problem, an angle increment of 0.1° was used. The problem was solved using the program included on the disk with this book. With this program, it is possible to evaluate quickly the cam profile for areas where the follower roller is too large. The cam, displacement diagram, radius of curvature, and pressure angle plots are shown in Fig. 8.38.

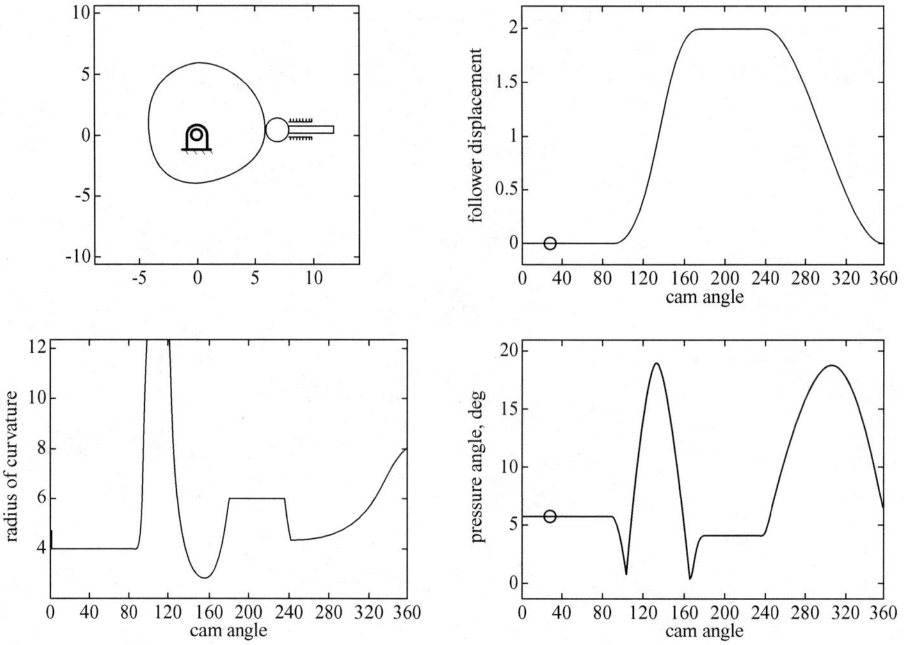

FIGURE 8.38 Cam profile, follower displacement, radius of curvature, and pressure angle for Example 8.7.

Analytical Determination of the Cam Profile for a Radial Flat-Faced Follower The development of the equations for a radial flat-faced follower can be accomplished using a procedure similar to that for a roller follower. Again, we must invert the mechanism so that the follower appears to rotate about the cam.

The radial displacement of the follower relative to the origin of the coordinate system located at the center of the cam is given by

$$R = r_b + f(\theta) \tag{8.25}$$

where $f(\theta)$ is the function defining the follower displacement as a function of the cam rotation angle θ. Referring to Fig. 8.39, we can write Eq. (8.25) as

$$R = y\sin\theta + x\cos\theta$$

If t is the distance from the follower axis to the point of contact,

$$t = y\cos\theta - x\sin\theta = \frac{dR}{d\theta} = f'(\theta)$$

The maximum and minimum values for t will give the minimum limits for the length of the follower face. Note that x and y are defined relative to the coordinate system fixed to the cam. Solving for x and y gives

$$x = R\cos\theta - t\sin\theta$$
$$y = R\sin\theta + t\cos\theta$$

and in terms of $f(\theta)$,

$$x = \left[r_b + f(\theta)\right]\cos\theta - f'(\theta)\sin\theta$$
$$y = \left[r_b + f(\theta)\right]\sin\theta + f'(\theta)\cos\theta \tag{8.26}$$

In general, we want to use the smallest base circle that will satisfy the geometric constraints. Normally, the base circle is determined in part by the pressure angle; however, for a radial, flat-faced follower, *the pressure angle is always zero*. Therefore, we must select another criterion for determining the base circle radius. The minimum base circle radius will be the one that avoids cusps in the cam profile.

For a given displacement profile, the cam becomes sharper and sharper as the base circle radius decreases. This is shown in Fig. 8.40. Eventually, the cam surface will generate a sharp point or cusp. This condition gives the limiting radius for the base circle.

To establish an equation for the base circle, we can use Eq. (8.18) directly because we have analytical expressions for $x(\theta)$ and $y(\theta)$. For Eq. (8.18), we need the first and second derivatives of $x(\theta)$ and $y(\theta)$. These are given in the following:

$$\frac{\partial x}{\partial\theta} = f'(\theta)\cos\theta - \left[r_b + f(\theta)\right]\sin\theta - f''(\theta)\sin\theta - f'(\theta)\cos\theta = -\left[r_b + f(\theta) + f''(\theta)\right]\sin\theta$$

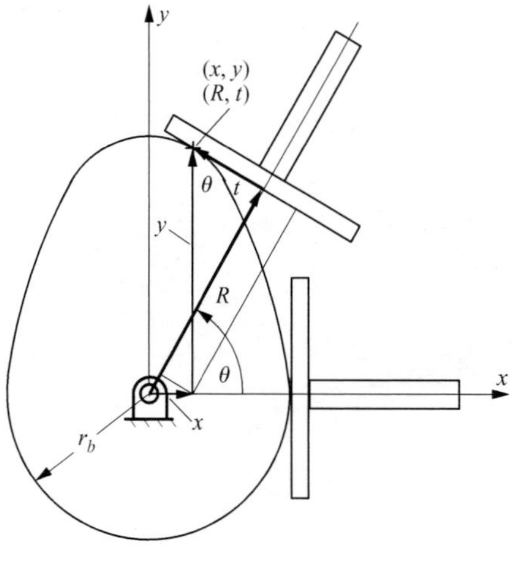

FIGURE 8.39 Radial, flat-faced follower.

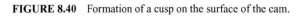

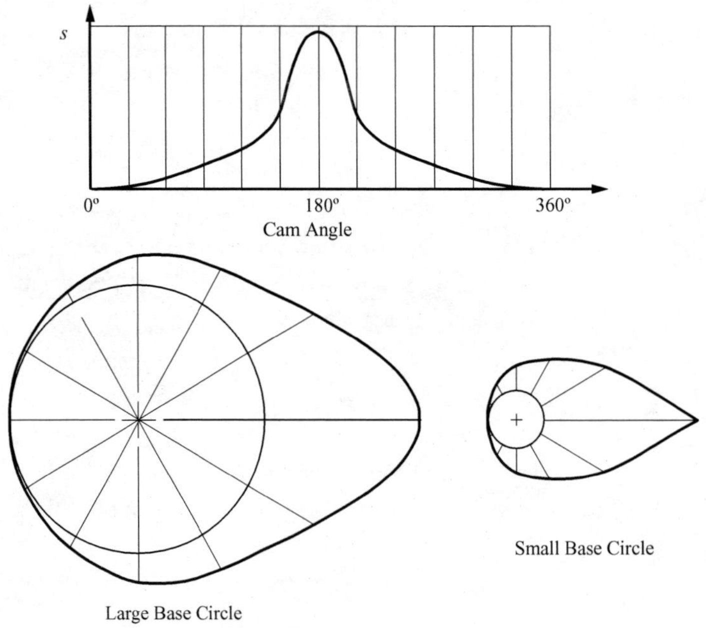

FIGURE 8.40 Formation of a cusp on the surface of the cam.

and

$$\frac{\partial^2 x}{\partial \theta^2} = -\left[f'(\theta) + f'''(\theta)\right]\sin\theta - \left[r_b + f'(\theta) + f'''(\theta)\right]\cos\theta$$

Also

$$\frac{\partial y}{\partial \theta} = f'(\theta)\sin\theta + \left[r_b + f(\theta)\right]\cos\theta + f''(\theta)\cos\theta - f'(\theta)\sin\theta = \left[r_b + f(\theta) + f''(\theta)\right]\cos\theta$$

and

$$\frac{\partial^2 y}{\partial \theta^2} = \left[f'(\theta) + f'''(\theta)\right]\cos\theta - \left[r_b + f(\theta) + f''(\theta)\right]\sin\theta$$

Substitution into Eq. (8.18) gives

$$\rho = \frac{\sqrt{\left[(dx/d\theta)^2 + (dy/d\theta)^2\right]^3}}{(dx/d\theta)(d^2y/d\theta^2) - (dy/d\theta)(d^2x/d\theta^2)} = \left[r_b + f(\theta) + f''(\theta)\right]$$

For there to be no cusp (and for the cam to be convex) at all locations

$$\rho \geq 0$$

or

$$\left[r_b + f(\theta) + f''(\theta)\right] \geq 0 \qquad (8.27)$$

for all θ. Both $f(\theta)$ and $f''(\theta)$ will be determined by the follower-displacement schedule. Therefore, only r_b can be externally controlled in Eq. (8.27); that is,

$$r_b \geq -f(\theta) - f''(\theta)$$

If $-f(\theta) - f''(\theta)$ is negative, then any positive or zero value of the base circle radius will be acceptable from a cusp standpoint.

If the cam rotates counterclockwise, the equations developed must be modified slightly. In general, we will treat the follower displacement as a function of the angular displacement rather than the absolute angle. That is, the follower is assumed to translate a given distance regardless of the direction of rotation of the cam. The equations of Sections 8.3–8.9 were derived assuming that the cam angles were positive. When the cam rotates in the counterclockwise direction relative to the frame, the follower will rotate clockwise relative to the cam. This results in negative values for θ. However, the expressions for $f(\theta)$ must use the absolute values of θ. The effect of this is that the correct sign of the derivative $f'(\theta)$ is not preserved for counterclockwise rotation of the cam. The problem is re-solved by changing the sign of the derivative term in Eq. (8.26). That is, when a counterclockwise rotation of the cam is involved, the cam coordinates are given by

$$x = \left[r_b + f(\theta)\right]\cos\theta + f'(\theta)\sin\theta$$
$$y = \left[r_b + f(\theta)\right]\sin\theta - f'(\theta)\cos\theta$$

The equations necessary to determine points on the cam profile and to determine the length of the follower face are summarized in Table 8.9. These can be programmed easily to determine the (x_i, y_i) coordinates of points on the cam profile relative to the cam coordinate system, and a MATLAB program for doing this is included on the disk with this book. Given the (x_i, y_i) coordinates, the cam can be machined on a CNC milling machine. The accuracy of the profile will be determined in part by the angle increment chosen for the cam rotation angle θ.

TABLE 8.9 Summary of Equations for Determining the Cam Profile Coordinates, Minimum Face Length, and Minimum Base Circle Radius for a Radial Flat-Faced Follower. The Follower Displacement Is Assumed to Be Given by *f(θ)*, and the Base Circle Radius Is r_b

Cam coordinates—clockwise rotation of cam

$$x_i = \left[r_b + f(\theta_i)\right]\cos\theta_i - f'(\theta_i)\sin\theta_i$$
$$y_i = \left[r_b + f(\theta_i)\right]\sin\theta + f'(\theta_i)\cos\theta_i$$

Cam coordinates—counterclockwise rotation of cam

$$x = \left[r_b + f(\theta)\right]\cos\theta + f'(\theta)\sin\theta$$
$$y = \left[r_b + f(\theta)\right]\sin\theta - f'(\theta)\cos\theta$$

(continued)

TABLE 8.9 continued

Minimum face length
$$t_{\max,\min} = f'(\theta_i)\Big|_{\max,\min}$$
Radius of curvature
$$\rho = \left[r_b + f(\theta) + f''(\theta)\right]$$

EXAMPLE 8.8
Cam Profile Coordinates for Radial Flat-Faced Follower

Determine the cam profile for the follower motion given in Example 8.7. First find the minimum base circle radius based on avoiding cusps, and use that base circle to design the cam.

Solution

To solve the problem, we must determine the derivatives of the functions for the follower displacement. Because derivatives are involved, the angles in the displacement functions will be converted to radians. For the different intervals, the functions and derivatives are summarized in the following:

$$0 \le \theta \le \pi/2: \; f(\theta) = f'(\theta) = f''(\theta) = 0$$

$$\pi/2 \le \theta \le \pi: \; f(\theta) = \frac{2L}{\pi}\left(\left(\theta - \frac{\pi}{2}\right) - \frac{1}{4}\sin 4\left(\theta - \frac{\pi}{2}\right)\right), \; f'(\theta) = \frac{2L}{\pi}\left(1 - \cos 4\left(\theta - \frac{\pi}{2}\right)\right),$$

$$f''(\theta) = \frac{8L}{\pi}\left(\sin 4\left(\theta - \frac{\pi}{2}\right)\right)$$

$$\pi \le \theta \le 4\pi/3: \; f(\theta) = 2, \; f'(\theta) = f''(\theta) = 0$$

$$4\pi/3 \le \theta \le 2\pi: \; f(\theta) = \frac{L}{2}\left(1 + \cos\frac{3}{2}\left(\theta - \frac{4\pi}{3}\right)\right), \; f'(\theta) = -\frac{3L}{4}\sin\frac{3}{2}\left(\theta - \frac{4\pi}{3}\right),$$

$$f''(\theta) = -\frac{9L}{8}\cos\frac{3}{2}\left(\theta - \frac{4\pi}{3}\right)$$

Given the equations for the follower displacement, we now need only to increment θ and to evaluate the expressions in Table 8.9 to determine the minimum base circle radius and limiting values for the face length. We can then determine the cam coordinates. The values are computed for 10° increments of θ in Table 8.10. From that table, it is clear that the base circle radius must be at least 3.147 cm and the follower face needs to be at least 2.47 cm above the centerline and 1.5 cm below it. Note that a negative value for t implies a distance below the stem centerline, and a positive value implies a distance above the centerline.

The cam will be designed with a base circle radius of 3.2 cm, and the follower face will be 2.6 cm above the stem centerline and 1.6 cm below it. The results obtained from the MATLAB program included on the disk with this book are shown in Fig. 8.41. To illustrate the effect of choosing a base circle radius less than the critical value, the program was rerun with the base circle radius of 1 cm. The results are shown in Fig. 8.42. The result is clearly a cam that cannot be manufactured.

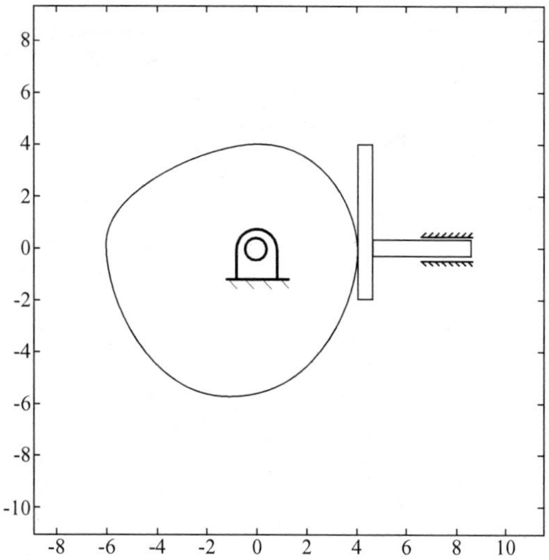

FIGURE 8.41 Cam designed for Example 8.8.

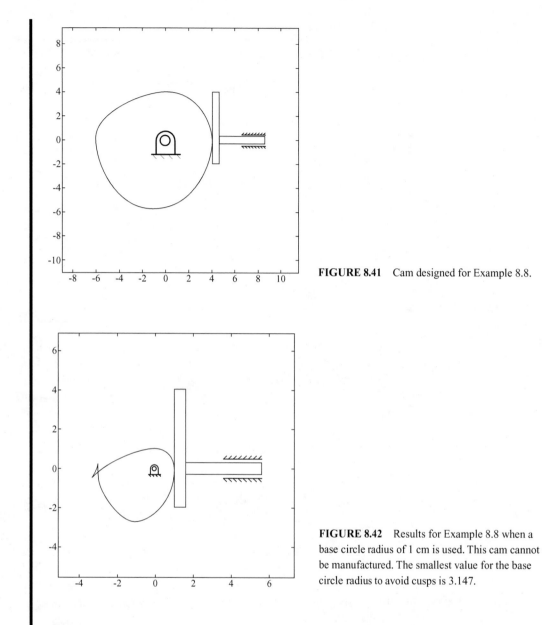

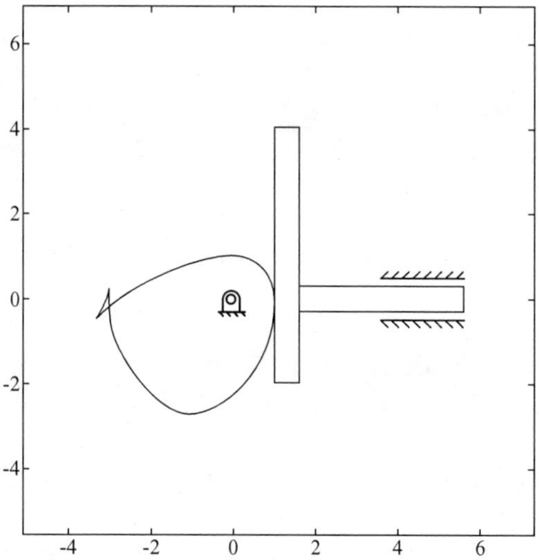

FIGURE 8.42 Results for Example 8.8 when a base circle radius of 1 cm is used. This cam cannot be manufactured. The smallest value for the base circle radius to avoid cusps is 3.147.

TABLE 8.10 Values for *f(θ)* and Its Derivatives for Follower Displacement Specified for Example 8.8

θ	$f(\theta)$ (cm)	$f'(\theta)$ (cm)	$f''(\theta)$ (cm)	r_{bmin} (cm)	t (cm)
0°	0.000	0.000	0.000	0.000	0.000
			—dwell—		
90°	0.000	0.000	0.000	0.000	0.000
100°	0.018	0.298	3.274	−3.291	0.298
110°	0.131	1.052	5.016	−5.147	1.052
120°	0.391	1.910	4.411	−4.802	1.910
130°	0.780	2.470	1.742	−2.522	2.470
140°	1.220	2.470	−1.742	0.522	2.470
150°	1.609	1.910	−4.411	2.802	1.910

(continued)

TABLE 8.10 continued

160°	1.869	1.052	− 5.016	3.147	1.052
170°	1.982	0.298	− 3.274	1.291	0.298
180°	2.000	0.000	0.000	− 2.000	0.000
			—dwell—		
240°	2.000	− 0.000	− 2.250	0.250	− 0.000
250°	1.966	− 0.388	− 2.173	0.207	− 0.388
260°	1.866	− 0.750	− 1.949	0.083	− 0.750
270°	1.707	− 1.061	− 1.591	− 0.116	− 1.061
280°	1.500	− 1.299	− 1.125	− 0.375	− 1.299
290°	1.259	− 1.449	− 0.582	− 0.676	− 1.449
300°	1.000	− 1.500	0.000	− 1.000	− 1.500
310°	0.741	− 1.449	0.582	− 1.324	− 1.449
320°	0.500	− 1.299	1.125	− 1.625	− 1.299
330°	0.293	− 1.061	1.591	− 1.884	− 1.061
340°	0.134	− 0.750	1.949	− 2.083	− 0.750
350°	0.034	− 0.388	2.173	− 2.207	− 0.388

Analytical Determination of a Cam Profile for an Oscillating, Cylindrical Follower The equations for an oscillating, cylindrical follower can be derived on the basis of the graphical procedure. Again, we must invert the mechanism so that the follower appears to rotate about the cam. To begin the procedure, we will assume that the cam base-circle radius r_b, the radius r_0 of the cylindrical follower, the pivot distance r_1, and the distance r_3 from the follower pivot to the center of the cylindrical contour are known.

In the procedure, the prime curve will be located first. This is the path traced by the center of curvature of the cylindrical follower. The cam profile can then be determined using the procedure developed in the first subsection of Section 8.10.2. The follower is assumed to begin in its lowest position when the follower contacts the base circle on the cam, as shown in Fig. 8.43. For this position, we need to determine the initial angles, θ_0 and ϕ_0, where θ_0 gives the initial angle for the cam and ϕ_0 gives the initial angle for the follower. The motion of the cam and follower will be measured relative to these initial angles, respectively. From Fig. 8.43a, these angles can be computed using the law of cosines. That is,

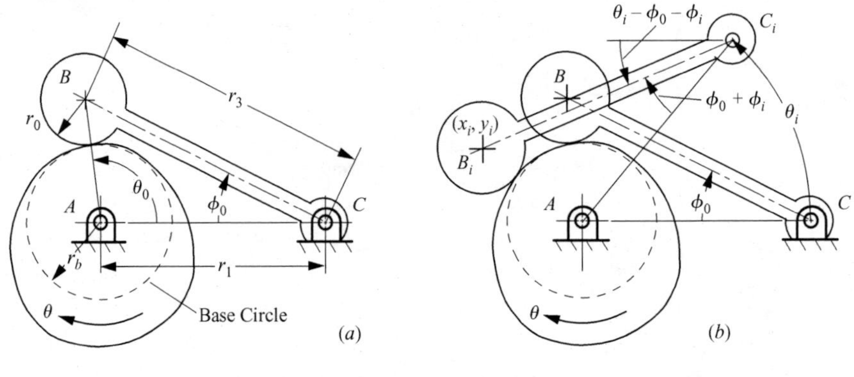

FIGURE 8.43 Oscillating, roller-faced follower. (a) Initial geometry. (b) Displaced geometry.

$$\phi_0 = \cos^{-1}\left[\frac{r_1^2 + r_3^2 - (r_b + r_0)^2}{2r_1 r_3}\right] \tag{8.28}$$

and

$$\theta_0 = \cos^{-1}\left[\frac{r_1^2 + (r_b + r_0)^2 - r_3^2}{2r_1(r_b + r_0)}\right] \tag{8.29}$$

To compute the coordinates of the center of the follower (B) relative to a coordinate system at point A on the cam, we will assume that the cam rotates clockwise so that the follower rotates *counterclockwise* relative to the cam.

Referring to Fig. 8.43b, for a given cam rotation angle θ_i, we have that the coordinates of point B_i are given by

$$x_i = r_1 \cos\theta_i + r_3 \cos[\pi + \theta_i - \phi_i - \phi_0] \tag{8.30}$$

and

$$y_i = r_1 \sin\theta_i + r_3 \sin[\pi + \theta_i - \phi_i - \phi_0] \tag{8.31}$$

Given the coordinates of B_i for a series of cam rotation angles (θ_i), we can compute the coordinates of the corresponding contact points (X_i, Y_i) on the cam face using the procedure in Section 8.10.2.

To compute the pressure angle at any given position, we must find the angle between a vector in the direction of the follower travel and a vector that is normal to the follower roller at each location, as shown in Fig. 8.44. The direction of travel of the follower pivot (point C) relative to the cam is simply θ the cam rotation angle (see Fig. 8.44); therefore, a vector in the direction of travel of point B relative to the cam is

$$\boldsymbol{a} = 1\angle\gamma_i$$

where

$$\gamma_i = \theta_i - \phi_i - \phi_0 + \pi/2$$

A vector in the direction normal to the roller is the line from (X_i, Y_i) to (x_i, y_i); therefore, the resulting vector is

$$\boldsymbol{b} = 1\angle\lambda_i$$

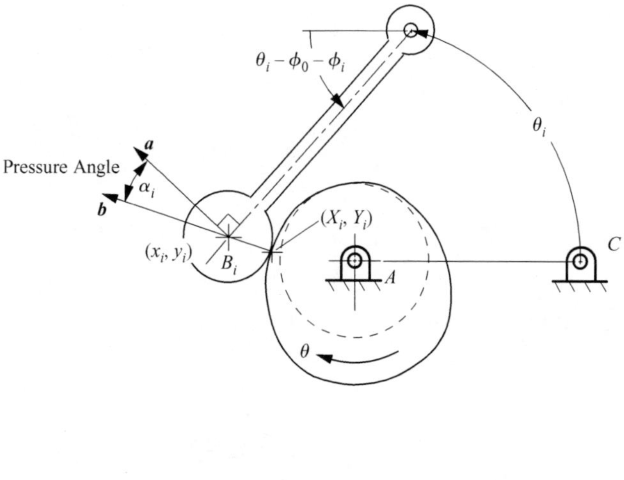

FIGURE 8.44 Pressure angle for oscillating, roller-faced follower.

where

$$\lambda_i = \tan^{-1}\left[\frac{y_i - Y_i}{x_i - X_i}\right]$$

The resulting pressure angle is simply the angle between the vectors ***a*** and ***b***. That is,

$$\alpha_i = \cos^{-1}\left[\frac{\mathbf{a}\cdot\mathbf{b}}{|\mathbf{a}||\mathbf{b}|}\right] = \cos^{-1}\left[\cos\gamma_i\cos\lambda_i + \sin\gamma_i\sin\lambda_i\right] \tag{8.32}$$

The equations to determine points on the cam profile are summarized in Table 8.11. In Table 8.11, the equations for computing (X_i, Y_i) and for the radius of curvature of the cam are taken from Table 8.8. These can be programmed easily to determine the (X_i, Y_i) coordinates of points on the cam profile, and a MATLAB program for doing this is included on the disk with this book. Given the (X_i, Y_i) coordinates, the cam can be machined on a CNC milling machine. The accuracy of the profile will be determined in part by the increment chosen for the cam rotation angle θ.

TABLE 8.11 Summary of Equations for Determining the Cam Profile Coordinates and Pressure Angle for an Oscillating Cylindrical-Faced or Roller Follower. The Follower Oscillation ϕ Is Assumed to Be Given by $f(\theta)$, the Radius of the Follower Is r_0, the Base Circle Radius is r_b, the Distance Between the Cam and Follower Pivots Is r_1, and the Length of the Follower Is r_3. There Are Assumed to Be n Points on the Cam Profile

Radius of curvature

$$\begin{Bmatrix} x_c \\ y_c \end{Bmatrix} = \begin{bmatrix} 2(X_{i+1} - X_i) & 2(Y_{i+1} - Y_i) \\ 2(X_{i-1} - X_i) & 2(Y_{i-1} - Y_i) \end{bmatrix}^{-1} \begin{Bmatrix} (X_{i+1}^2 - X_i^2) + (Y_{i+1}^2 - Y_i^2) \\ (X_{i-1}^2 - X_i^2) + (Y_{i-1}^2 - Y_i^2) \end{Bmatrix}$$

$$\rho = \frac{\left[(X_i - X_{i-1})(Y_{i+1} - Y_i) - (X_{i+1} - X_i)(Y_i - Y_{i-1})\right]}{\left|(X_i - X_{i-1})(Y_{i+1} - Y_i) - (X_{i+1} - X_i)(Y_i - Y_{i-1})\right|}\sqrt{(X_i - x_c)^2 + (Y_i - y_c)^2}$$

Cam coordinates

$$\phi_0 = \cos^{-1}\left[\frac{r_1^2 + r_3^2 - (r_b + r_0)^2}{2r_1r_3}\right]$$

$$x_i = r_1\cos\theta_i + r_3\cos\left[\pi + \theta_i - \phi_i - \phi_0\right];\quad y_i = r_1\sin\theta_i + r_3\sin\left[\pi + \theta_i - \phi_i - \phi_0\right]$$

$$\psi_i = \tan^{-1}\left(\frac{y_i - y_c}{x_i - x_c}\right) \qquad (i = 1, 2, 3, \ldots, n)$$

(continued)

TABLE 8.11 continued

$$\begin{aligned} X_i &= x_i - r_0 \cos\psi_i \\ Y_i &= y_i - r_0 \sin\psi_i \end{aligned} \quad \text{(convex)}$$

$$\begin{aligned} X_i &= x_i + r_0 \cos\psi_i \\ Y_i &= y_i + r_0 \sin\psi_i \end{aligned} \quad \text{(concave)}$$

Pressure angle

$$\gamma_i = \theta_i - \phi_i - \phi_0 + \pi/2$$

$$\lambda_i = \tan^{-1}\left(\frac{y_i - Y_i}{x_i - X_i}\right)$$

$$\alpha_i = \cos^{-1}\left[\cos\gamma_i \cos\lambda_i + \sin\gamma_i \sin\lambda_i\right]$$

EXAMPLE 8.9 *Cam Profile Coordinates for a Roller Follower That Oscillates*

Determine the cam profile assuming that the follower dwells while the cam rotates *counterclockwise* from 0° to 90°. The rise occurs with 3-4-5 polynomial motion during the cam rotation from 90° to 180°. The follower then dwells for 90° of cam rotation, and the return occurs with simple harmonic motion for the cam rotation from 270° to 360°. The amplitude of the follower oscillation is 30°, and the follower radius is 1 in. The base circle radius is 2 in and the distance between pivots is 6 in. The length of the follower is to be determined such that the pressure angle starts out at zero.

Solution

To solve the problem, we must identify the equations for the follower motion as a function of the cam rotation angle θ and then select an increment for θ. Because the cam is rotating counterclockwise, the follower rotates clockwise relative to the cam. Mathematically, this is accomplished by using negative angles for the displacements starting from 0. However, the equations developed for the follower displacements give the follower position as a function of the cam position and do not depend on the direction of cam rotation. For a given angular displacement, the rise will be the same whether the cam is to be designed for clockwise or counterclockwise rotation. Therefore, we must use the magnitude of the cam angle from the start of the interval over which the function is defined. In the equations, we will let $\bar{\theta}$ be the magnitude of θ. Then from Sections 8.9 and 8.7, the equations (expressed in terms of radians) for each part of the motion become

$$0 < \bar{\theta} \le \pi/2: \ \phi = 0$$

$$\begin{aligned} \pi/2 \le \bar{\theta} \le \pi \ (\beta = \pi/2;\ L = \pi/6):\ \phi &= 10L\left(\frac{\bar{\theta} - \pi/2}{\beta}\right)^3 - 15L\left(\frac{\bar{\theta} - \pi/2}{\beta}\right)^4 + 6L\left(\frac{\bar{\theta} - \pi/2}{\beta}\right)^5 \\ &= \left(\frac{5\pi}{3}\right)\left(\frac{\bar{\theta} - \pi/2}{\pi/2}\right)^3 - \left(\frac{5\pi}{2}\right)\left(\frac{\bar{\theta} - \pi/2}{\pi/2}\right)^4 + \pi\left(\frac{\bar{\theta} - \pi/2}{\pi/2}\right)^5 \end{aligned}$$

$$\pi \le \bar{\theta} \le 3\pi/2: \ \phi = \frac{\pi}{6}$$

$$3\pi/2 \le \bar{\theta} \le 2\pi \quad (\beta = \pi/2;\ L = \pi/6):\ \phi = \frac{L}{2}\left(1 + \cos\frac{\pi}{\beta}\left(\bar{\theta} - \frac{3\pi}{2}\right)\right) = \frac{\pi}{12}\left(1 + \cos 2\left(\bar{\theta} - \frac{3\pi}{2}\right)\right)$$

To determine the length, r_3, of the follower that will give zero pressure angle in the initial position, refer to Fig. 8.44. From that figure, the angle between the (r_0+r_b) and r_3 must be 90° for the pressure angle to be zero during a dwell. Therefore,

$$r_3 = \sqrt{r_1^2 - (r_b + r_0)^2} = \sqrt{6^2 - (2+1)^2} = 5.196 \text{ in}$$

The equations for ϕ and r_3 can be used to determine ϕ_0 in Table 8.11, and using the equations in Table 8.11 we can compute the coordinates of the cam as accurately as we wish by using a small increment for the cam rotation angle θ.

For the calculations, the angle θ is incremented in the negative direction (the follower rotates CW relative to the cam). Therefore, the points corresponding to the center of the roller (prime curve points) will be generated and labeled initially in the CW direction. However, the equations in Table 8.11 were derived assuming that the points are ordered in the CCW direction. Therefore, after all of the prime points are generated, they must be reordered in the CCW direction. After the prime points are reordered in this way, the corresponding points on the cam surface can be computed directly as was done in Example 8.7.

For plotting purposes, we have used the program on the disk included with this book with an angle increment of 1°, which is adequate for visual purposes. If we want to machine the cam with high accuracy, a finer increment for θ would be used. It should be noted, however, that when very fine increments are used, the errors of the computations using MATLAB can be significant. The cam, displacement diagram, radius of curvature, and pressure angle plots are shown in Fig. 8.45.

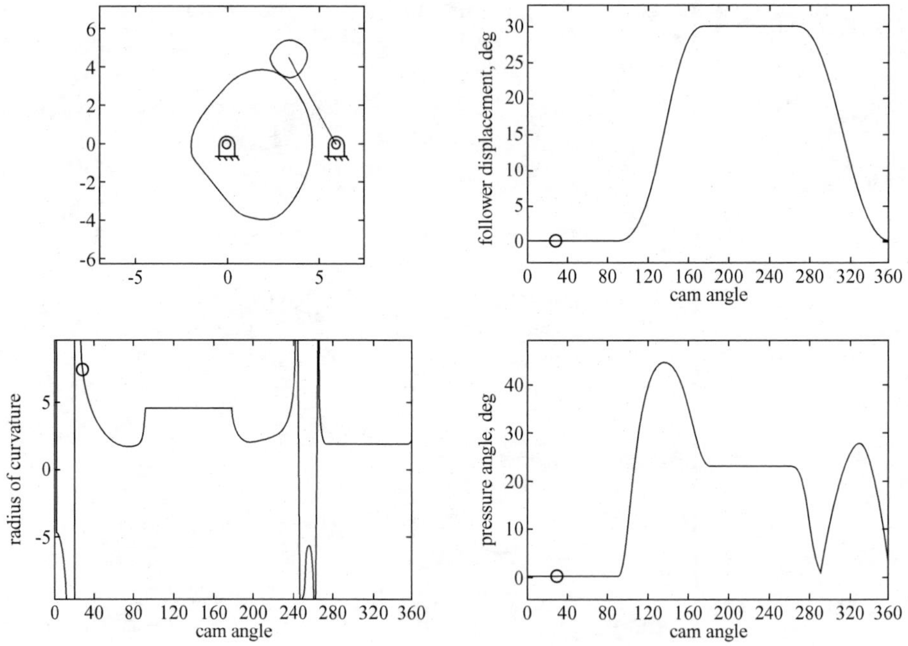

FIGURE 8.45 Cam profile, follower displacement, radius of curvature, and pressure angle for Example 8.9.

Analytical Determination of a Cam Profile for a Flat-Faced Follower That Oscillates The cam–follower system is shown in Fig. 8.46, and the points shown in that figure will be used to describe the design of the cam. Point A is the location of the axis of rotation of the cam, C is the axis of rotation of the follower, and d is the follower offset. Point B is the location of the tangent point between the face of the follower and the cam surface, and D is located at the intersection of the follower face and a line from C perpendicular to the follower face. The distance R is the perpendicular distance from the follower face to the center of rotation of the cam.

The development of the equations for an oscillating flat-faced follower is similar to the graphical procedure in Example 8.6. As in the other cases, we must invert the mechanism so that the follower appears to rotate about the cam. To begin the procedure, we will assume that the cam base radius r_b, the pivot distance r_1, and the follower angle β are known.

In the procedure, we will locate the line representing the face of the cam first. We will then locate the points on the cam by locating successive circles that are tangent to three lines.

The first step is to determine the reference angle ϕ_0 that gives the orientation of the follower in the initial position. As shown in Fig. 8.46, in this position,

$$R = r_b = AB$$

From the geometry in Fig. 8.47, we have

$$AE = \frac{r_1}{1 + d/R} = \frac{r_1}{1 + d/r_b}$$

Then

$$BE = \sqrt{AE^2 - r_b^2}$$

and

$$\phi_0 = \tan^{-1}\frac{r_b}{BE}$$

For each position of the cam given by θ, we will know $\phi(\theta)$ from the follower-displacement equations. The orientation of the follower face relative to the cam is then given by the angle $\phi + \phi_0$.

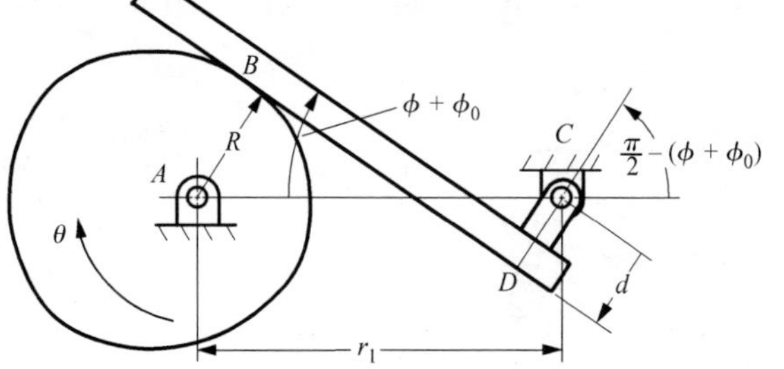

FIGURE 8.46 Geometry for oscillating, flat-faced follower.

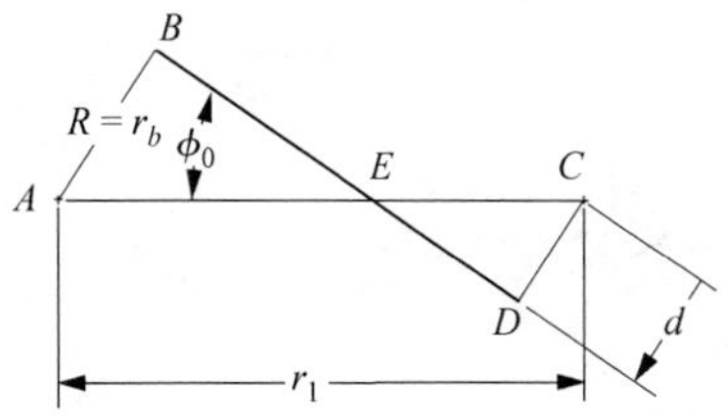

FIGURE 8.47 Geometry for finding ϕ_0.

To locate the follower relative to the cam as the cam rotates, we can invert the motion relative to the cam. For simplicity, we will again assume that the cam rotates CW relative to the frame, which means that the frame rotates CCW relative to the cam. A typical position is shown in Fig. 8.48.

For a given rotation of the cam, the coordinates of point C relative to the cam are

$$x_C = r_1 \cos\theta$$

and

$$y_C = r_1 \sin\theta$$

Similarly, the coordinates of point D are

$$x_D = x_C + d\cos\left(\frac{3\pi}{2} - \phi - \phi_0 + \theta\right)$$

and

$$y_D = y_C + d\sin\left(\frac{3\pi}{2} - \phi - \phi_0 + \theta\right)$$

To locate the line defining the follower face, we need to locate a line oriented at an angle of $\theta_i - \phi_i - \phi_0$ and passing through D_i. The equation of the line defining the follower face can be defined parametrically in terms of the distance τ from D_i as shown in Fig. 8.49. The parametric equations are

$$x_f = x_D + \tau\cos\zeta \tag{8.33}$$

and

$$y_f = y_D + \tau\sin\zeta \tag{8.34}$$

where

$$\zeta = \theta - \phi - \phi_0$$

Using Eqs. (8.33) and (8.34), we can define a line corresponding to the follower face for each position chosen for the cam. To define the cam profile, we must locate a series of points that are tangent to the follower face in each position. The coordinates of the tangent points can be approximated using the geometry shown in Fig. 8.50. Assume that we have

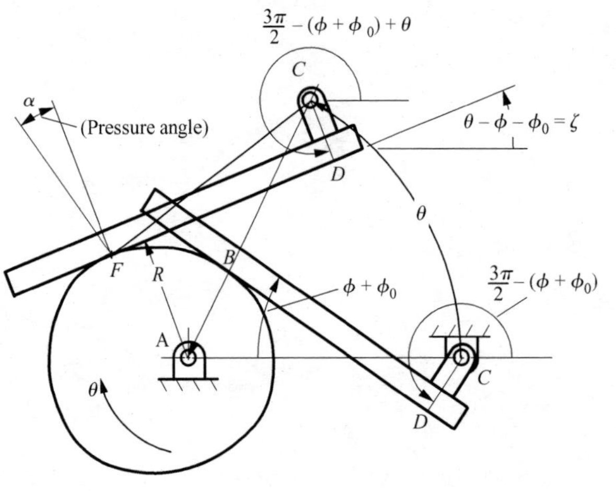

FIGURE 8.48 Motion of an oscillating, flat-faced follower relative to a cam.

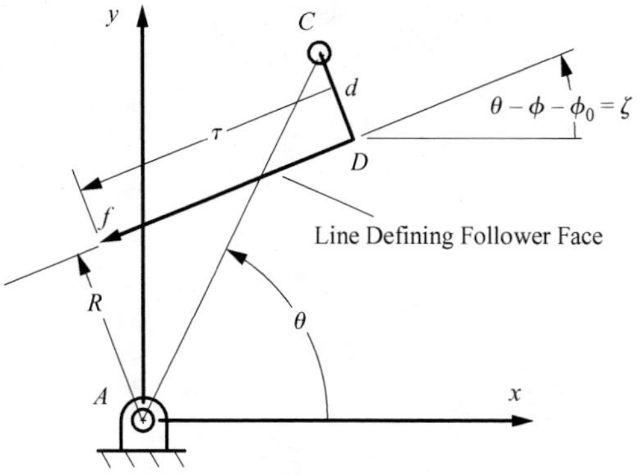

FIGURE 8.49 Parametric line defining a follower face. Here, τ would be negative.

three positions ($i-1$, i, and $i+1$) of the follower relative to the cam. Each follower face line can be defined in terms of the coordinates of D and τ and ζ. To determine the location of the cam contact point on the centerline, approximate the cam by a circle that is tangent to each of the lines simultaneously. Referring to Fig. 8.50, we see that this can be done as follows:

1. Find the successive intersections (G_i and G_{i+1}) of the face lines. To find G_i, use Eqs. (8.33) and (8.34), set $x_{f_i} = x_{f_i-1}$ and $y_{f_i} = y_{f_i-1}$, and solve the resulting set of linear equations for τ_{i-1} and τ_i:

$$\begin{Bmatrix} x_{D_i} - x_{D_{i-1}} \\ y_{D_i} - y_{D_{i-1}} \end{Bmatrix} = \begin{bmatrix} -\cos\zeta_i & \cos\zeta_{i-1} \\ -\sin\zeta_i & \sin\zeta_{i-1} \end{bmatrix} \begin{Bmatrix} \tau_i \\ \tau_{i-1} \end{Bmatrix}$$

The location of G_i is then given by

$$x_{G_i} = x_{D_i} + \tau_i \cos\zeta_i$$

and

$$y_{G_i} = y_{D_i} + \tau_i \sin\zeta_i$$

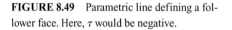

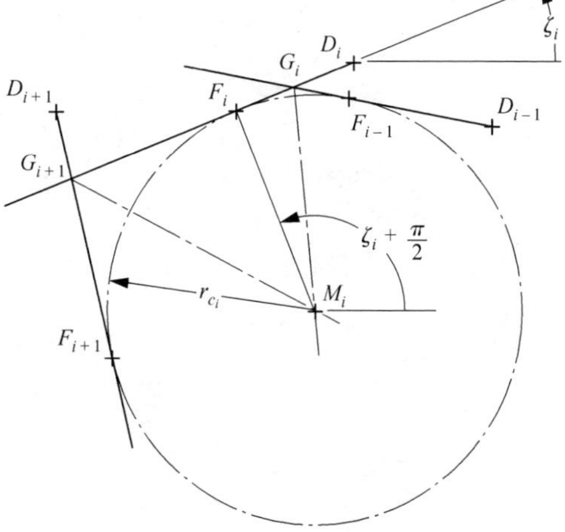

FIGURE 8.50 Locating a circle that is tangent to three successive positions of the follower face relative to the cam.

2. Find the equation of the line that bisects the angle between positions i and $i-1$ of the face line. This line passes through point G_i and is oriented at an angle of

$$\gamma_i = \frac{\zeta_i + \zeta_{i-1}}{2} + \frac{3\pi}{2}$$

The parametric equation of the line is then given by

$$x_{m_i} = x_{G_i} + v_i \cos\gamma_i$$

and

$$y_{m_i} = y_{G_i} + v_i \sin\gamma_i$$

where v_i is the distance from G_i in the positive γ_i direction.

3. Find the intersection of the lines bisecting the angles at G_i and G_{i+1}. For this, set $x_{m_i} = x_{m_i+1}$ and $y_{m_i} = y_{m_i+1}$ and solve the resulting set of linear equations for v_i and v_{i+1}.

$$\begin{Bmatrix} x_{G_i} - x_{G_{i+1}} \\ y_{G_i} - y_{G_{i+1}} \end{Bmatrix} = \begin{bmatrix} -\cos\gamma_i & \cos\gamma_{i+1} \\ -\sin\gamma_i & \sin\gamma_{i+1} \end{bmatrix} \begin{Bmatrix} v_i \\ v_{i+1} \end{Bmatrix}$$

The coordinates of the center of the circle tangent to the three positions of the face line are then given by

$$x_{M_i} = x_{G_i} + v_i \cos\gamma_i$$

and

$$y_{M_i} = y_{G_i} + v_i \sin\gamma_i$$

4. Find the radius of the tangent circle and coordinates of the tangent points. These are obtained by locating a line through M_i and perpendicular to each face line. The coordinates of the point F_i are given by

$$x_{F_i} = x_{M_i} + r_{c_i} \cos\left(\zeta_i + \frac{\pi}{2}\right) = x_{G_i} + \eta_i \cos\zeta_i$$

and

$$y_{F_i} = y_{M_i} + r_{c_i} \sin\left(\zeta_i + \frac{\pi}{2}\right) = y_{G_i} + \eta_i \sin\zeta_i$$

where η_i is the distance from G_i to the tangency point. Both r_{c_i} and η_i can be found by solving the resulting set of simultaneous linear equations:

$$\begin{Bmatrix} x_{M_i} - x_{G_i} \\ y_{M_i} - y_{G_i} \end{Bmatrix} = \begin{bmatrix} -\cos\left(\zeta_i + \frac{\pi}{2}\right) & \cos\zeta_i \\ -\sin\left(\zeta_i + \frac{\pi}{2}\right) & \sin\zeta_i \end{bmatrix} \begin{Bmatrix} r_{c_i} \\ \eta_i \end{Bmatrix} \tag{8.35}$$

The location of the tangent point is then given by

$$x_{F_i} = x_{G_i} + \eta_i \cos \zeta_i \tag{8.36}$$

and

$$y_{F_i} = y_{G_i} + \eta_i \sin \zeta_i \tag{8.37}$$

To find the tangency points on the other faces, substitute $i-1$ for i and then $i+1$ for i in Eqs. (8.36) and (8.37).

5. The cam coordinates can be approximated by the points F_i computed in step 4. To determine the minimum face length, we can compute the distance from F_i to D_i for each position of the cam.

To compute the pressure angle at any given position, we must find the angle between a vector in the direction of the follower travel and a vector that is normal to the follower face at each location as shown in Fig. 8.48. The direction of travel of the follower is given by a unit vector $\boldsymbol{a}$ perpendicular to line F_iC_i. This vector is given by

$$\boldsymbol{a} = 1\angle\psi_i$$

where

$$\psi_i = \tan^{-1}\left[\frac{y_{F_i} - y_{C_i}}{x_{F_i} - x_{C_i}}\right] - \frac{\pi}{2}$$

We can approximate the direction that is perpendicular to the follower face by a unit vector $\boldsymbol{b}$ from M_i to F_i or

$$\boldsymbol{b} = 1\angle\lambda_i$$

where

$$\lambda_i = \tan^{-1}\left[\frac{y_{F_i} - y_{M_i}}{x_{F_i} - x_{M_i}}\right] = \zeta_i + \frac{\pi}{2}$$

The resulting pressure angle is simply the angle between the vectors $\boldsymbol{a}$ and $\boldsymbol{b}$. That is,

$$\alpha_i = \cos^{-1}\left[\frac{\boldsymbol{a}\cdot\boldsymbol{b}}{|\boldsymbol{a}||\boldsymbol{b}|}\right] = \cos^{-1}\left[\cos\psi_i \cos\lambda_i + \sin\psi_i \sin\lambda_i\right] \tag{8.38}$$

The equations necessary to determine points on the cam profile are summarized in Table 8.12, and the equations for the pressure angle and radius of curvature of the cam are summarized in Table 8.13. The equations for the radius of curvature are taken from Table 8.8. The equations in Table 8.12 can be easily programmed to determine the coordinates of points on the cam profile, and a MATLAB program for doing so is included on the disk with this book. Given the coordinates of a set of sequential points on the profile, the cam can be machined on a CNC milling machine. The accuracy of the profile will be determined in part by the increment chosen for the cam rotation angle θ.

TABLE 8.12 Summary of Equations for Determining the Cam Profile Coordinates for an Oscillating Flat-Faced Follower. The Follower Oscillation ϕ Is Assumed to Be Given By $f(\theta)$, the Follower Offset Is d, the Base Circle Radius Is r_b, and the Distance between the Cam and Follower Pivots Is r_1. There Are Assumed to Be n Points on the Cam Profile

Cam coordinates

$$AE = \frac{r_1}{1 + d/r_b}, \qquad BE = \sqrt{AE^2 - r_b^2}$$

$$\phi_0 = \tan^{-1}\frac{r_b}{BE}$$

$$x_{C_i} = r_1 \cos\theta_i, \qquad y_{C_i} = r_1 \sin\theta_i$$

$$x_{D_i} = x_{C_i} + d\cos\left(\frac{3\pi}{2} - \phi_i - \phi_0 + \theta_i\right), \qquad y_{D_i} = y_{C_i} + d\sin\left(\frac{3\pi}{2} - \phi_i - \phi_0 + \theta_i\right)$$

$$\zeta_i = \theta_i - \phi_i - \phi_0$$

$$\begin{Bmatrix} x_{D_i} - x_{D_{i-1}} \\ y_{D_i} - y_{D_{i-1}} \end{Bmatrix} = \begin{bmatrix} -\cos\zeta_i & \cos\zeta_{i-1} \\ -\sin\zeta_i & \sin\zeta_{i-1} \end{bmatrix} \begin{Bmatrix} \tau_i \\ \tau_{i-1} \end{Bmatrix} \quad (i = 2, 3, \ldots, n)$$

$$\begin{Bmatrix} x_{D_1} - x_{D_n} \\ y_{D_1} - y_{D_n} \end{Bmatrix} = \begin{bmatrix} -\cos\zeta_1 & \cos\zeta_n \\ -\sin\zeta_1 & \sin\zeta_n \end{bmatrix} \begin{Bmatrix} \tau_i \\ \tau_n \end{Bmatrix}$$

$$x_{G_i} = x_{D_i} + \tau_i \cos\zeta_i, \qquad y_{G_i} = y_{D_i} + \tau_i \sin\zeta_i$$

$$\gamma_i = \frac{\zeta_i + \zeta_{i-1}}{2} + \frac{3\pi}{2}$$

$$\begin{Bmatrix} x_{G_i} - x_{G_{i+1}} \\ y_{G_i} - y_{G_{i+1}} \end{Bmatrix} = \begin{bmatrix} -\cos\gamma_i & \cos\gamma_{i+1} \\ -\sin\gamma_i & \sin\gamma_{i+1} \end{bmatrix} \begin{Bmatrix} v_i \\ V_{i+1} \end{Bmatrix} \quad (i = 1, 2, \ldots, n-1)$$

$$\begin{Bmatrix} x_{G_n} - x_{G_1} \\ y_{G_n} - y_{G_1} \end{Bmatrix} = \begin{bmatrix} -\cos\gamma_n & \cos\gamma_1 \\ -\sin\gamma_n & \sin\gamma_1 \end{bmatrix} \begin{Bmatrix} v_n \\ v_1 \end{Bmatrix}$$

$$x_{M_i} = x_{G_i} + v_i \cos\gamma_i, \qquad y_{M_i} = y_{G_i} + v_i \sin\gamma_i$$

$$\begin{Bmatrix} x_{M_i} - x_{G_i} \\ y_{M_i} - y_{G_i} \end{Bmatrix} = \begin{bmatrix} -\cos(\zeta_i + \pi/2) & \cos\zeta_i \\ -\sin(\zeta_i + \pi/2) & \sin\zeta_i \end{bmatrix} \begin{Bmatrix} r_{c_i} \\ \eta_i \end{Bmatrix}$$

$$x_{F_i} = x_{G_i} + \eta_i \cos\zeta_i, \qquad y_{F_i} = y_{G_i} + \eta_i \sin\zeta_i$$

TABLE 8.13 Summary of Equations for Determining the Pressure Angle and Radius of Curvature for an Oscillating Flat-Faced Follower

Pressure angle
$$\psi_i = \tan^{-1}\left[\frac{y_{F_i} - y_{C_i}}{x_{F_i} - x_{C_i}}\right] - \frac{\pi}{2}$$ $$\lambda_i = \tan^{-1}\left[\frac{y_{F_i} - y_{M_i}}{x_{F_i} - x_{M_i}}\right]$$ $$\alpha_i = \cos^{-1}\left[\cos\psi_i \cos\lambda_i + \sin\psi_i \sin\lambda_i\right]$$
Radius of curvature
$$\begin{Bmatrix} x_c \\ y_c \end{Bmatrix} = \begin{bmatrix} 2(X_{i+1} - X_i) & 2(Y_{i+1} - Y_i) \\ 2(X_{i-1} - X_i) & 2(Y_{i-1} - Y_i) \end{bmatrix}^{-1} \begin{Bmatrix} (X_{i+1}^2 - X_i^2) + (Y_{i+1}^2 - Y_i^2) \\ (X_{i-1}^2 - X_i^2) + (Y_{i-1}^2 - Y_i^2) \end{Bmatrix}$$ $$\rho = \frac{\left[(X_i - X_{i-1})(Y_{i+1} - Y_i) - (X_{i+1} - X_i)(Y_i - Y_{i-1})\right]}{\left|(X_i - X_{i-1})(Y_{i+1} - Y_i) - (X_{i+1} - X_i)(Y_i - Y_{i-1})\right|}\sqrt{(X_i - x_c)^2 + (Y_i - y_c)^2}$$

EXAMPLE 8.10 ***Cam Profile Coordinates for a Flat-Faced Follower That Oscillates***

Assume that the follower starts from a dwell from 0° to 45° and rotates CW. The rise occurs with simple harmonic motion during the cam rotation from 45° to 180°. The follower then dwells for 90° of cam rotation, and the return occurs with simple harmonic motion for the cam rotation from 270° to 360°. The amplitude of the follower oscillation is 20°, and the follower offset is 0.5 in. The base circle radius is 2 in, and the distance between pivots is 6 in.

Solution

To solve the problem, we must specify the length of the follower face, identify the equations for the follower motion as a function of the cam rotation angle θ, and then select an increment for θ. The length of the follower face is somewhat arbitrary as long as it is large enough to maintain contact with the cam. The minimum value can be calculated by computing the distance F_i to D_i for each position of the follower relative to the cam. However, in this example, we will select the length to be 9 in, which is large enough to ensure that the follower will maintain contact with the cam.

The second part of the displacement schedule is similar to that used in Example 8.9, and the equation for the rise portion can be obtained from Section 8.7. The resulting equations (expressed in terms of radians) are as follows:

$$0 \le \theta \le \pi/2: \ \phi = 0$$

$$\pi/4 \le \theta \le \pi \ (\beta = 3\pi/4;\ L = \pi/9):\ \phi = \frac{L}{2}\left(1 - \cos\frac{\pi}{\beta}\left(\theta - \frac{\pi}{4}\right)\right) = \frac{\pi}{18}\left(1 - \cos\frac{4}{3}\left(\theta - \frac{\pi}{4}\right)\right)$$

$$\pi \le \theta \le 3\pi/2: \ \phi = \frac{\pi}{6}$$

$$3\pi/2 \le \theta \le 2\pi \ \left(\beta = \pi/2;\ L = \pi/9\right): \ \phi = \frac{L}{2}\left(1 + \cos\frac{\pi}{\beta}\left(\theta - \frac{3\pi}{2}\right)\right) = \frac{\pi}{18}\left(1 + \cos 2\left(\theta - \frac{3\pi}{2}\right)\right)$$

Given the equations for the follower displacement, we now need only increment θ and evaluate the expressions in Table 8.12 and 8.13 to determine the cam coordinates and pressure angle. The values were computed for 2° increments of θ, and the results obtained from the MATLAB program included on the disk with this book are shown in Fig. 8.51.

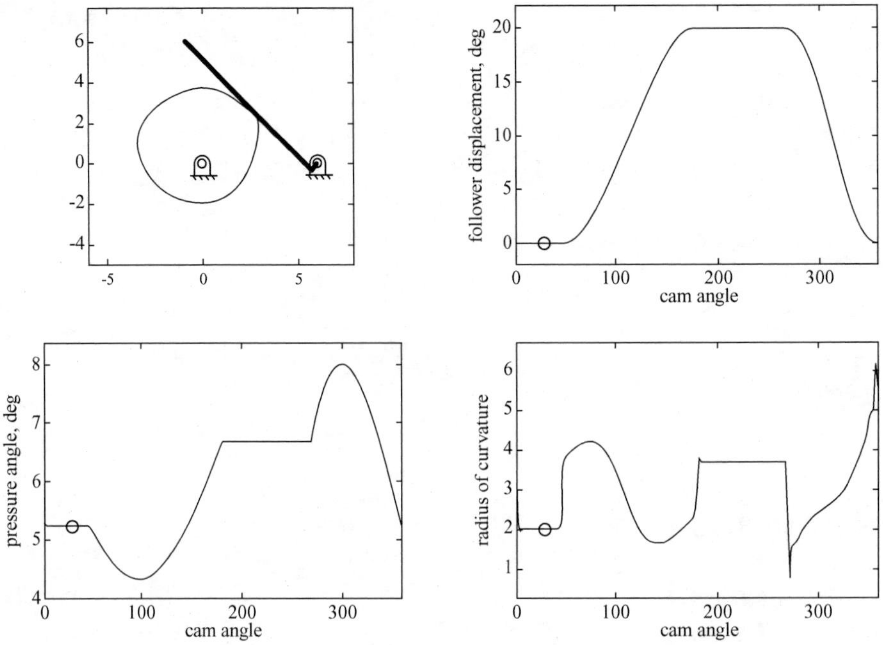

FIGURE 8.51 Cam profile, follower displacement, radius of curvature, and pressure angle for Example 8.10.

It is much more difficult to design a cam for an oscillating flat-faced follower than for the other types of followers. For example, if the amplitude of oscillation in Example 8.10 is changed to 30°, a cam will be developed that has a discontinuity and therefore cannot be manufactured. Changing the base circle radius may not always improve the situation, and the extent to which the base circle can be changed is limited by the distance between pivots. The problem can be improved by reducing the amplitude of oscillation, by changing the functions chosen for the rise and return, or by increasing the ranges chosen for the rise and return. However, in some cases, it may be necessary to choose another type of follower.

REFERENCES

[1]Chen, F. Y., *Mechanics and Design of Cam Mechanisms*, Pergamon Press, New York (1982).

[2] Wilson, C. E., and Sadler, J. P. *Kinematics and Dynamics of Machinery*, Harper Collins, New York (1993).

PROBLEMS

EXERCISE PROBLEMS ON FOLLOWER-DISPLACEMENT SCHEDULES

8.1 A cam that is designed for cycloidal motion drives a flat-faced follower. During the rise, the follower displaces 1 in for 180° of cam rotation. If the cam angular velocity is constant at 100 rpm, determine the displacement, velocity, and acceleration of the follower at a cam angle of 60°.

8.2 A constant-velocity cam is designed for simple harmonic motion. If the flat-faced follower displaces 2 in for 180° of cam rotation and the cam angular velocity is 100 rpm, determine the displacement, velocity, and acceleration when the cam angle is 45°.

8.3 A cam drives a radial, knife-edged follower through a 1.5-in rise in 180° of cycloidal motion. Give the displacement at 60° and 100°. If this cam is rotating at 200 rpm, what are the velocity (ds/dt) and the acceleration (d^2s/dt^2) at $\theta = 60°$?

8.4 Draw the displacement schedule for a follower that rises through a total displacement of 1.5 in with constant acceleration for 1/4 revolution, constant velocity for 1/8 revolution, and constant deceleration for 1/4 revolution of the cam. The cam then dwells for 1/8 revolution, and returns with simple harmonic motion in 1/4 revolution of the cam.

8.5 Draw the displacement schedule for a follower that rises through a total displacement of 20 mm with constant acceleration for 1/8 revolution, constant velocity for 1/4 revolution, and constant deceleration for 1/8 revolution of the cam. The cam then dwells for 1/4 revolution and returns with simple harmonic motion in 1/4 revolution of the cam.

8.6 Draw the displacement schedule for a follower that rises through a total displacement of 30 mm with constant acceleration for 90° of rotation and constant deceleration for 45° of cam rotation. The follower returns 15 mm with simple harmonic motion in 90° of cam rotation and dwells for 45° of cam rotation. It then returns the remaining 15 mm with simple harmonic motion during the remaining 90° of cam rotation.

8.7 Draw the displacement schedule for a follower that rises through a total displacement of 3 in with cycloidal motion in 120° of cam rotation. The follower then dwells for 90° and returns to 0° with simple harmonic motion in 90° of cam rotation. The follower then dwells for 60° before repeating the cycle.

8.8 A cam returns from a full lift of 1.2 in during its initial 60° rotation. The first 0.4 in of the return is half-cycloidal. This is followed by a half-harmonic return. Determine β_1 and β_2 so that the motion has continuous first and second derivatives. Draw a freehand sketch of y', y'', and y''' indicating any possible mismatch in the third derivative.

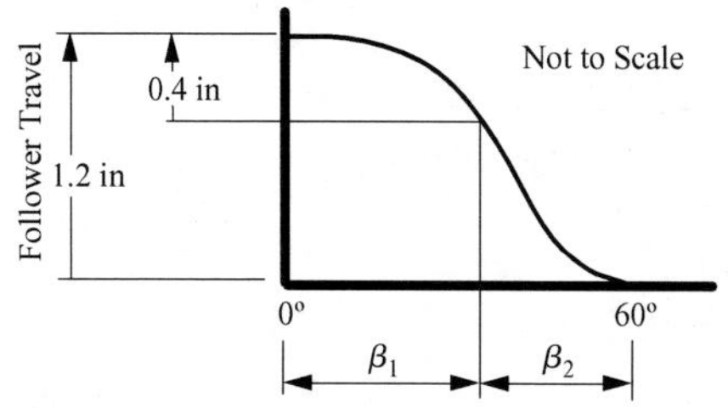

8.9 Assume that s is the cam–follower displacement and θ is the cam rotation. The rise is 1.0 cm after 1.0 rad of rotation, and the rise begins and ends at a dwell. The displacement equation for the follower during the rise period is

$$s = h\sum_{i=0}^{n} C_i \left(\frac{\theta}{\beta}\right)^i$$

If the position, velocity, and acceleration are continuous at $\theta = 0$, and the position and velocity are continuous at $\theta = 1.0$ rad, determine the value of n required in the equation, and find the coefficients C_i if $\dot{\theta} = 2$ rad/s. Note: Use the minimum possible number of terms.

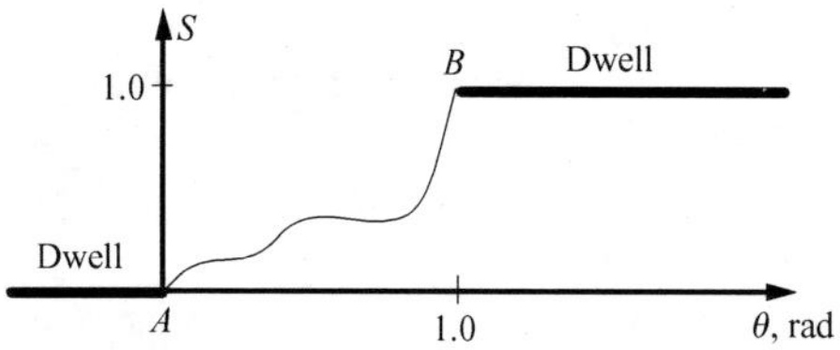

8.10 Re-solve Problem 8.9 if $\theta = 0.8$ rad and $\dot{\theta} = 200$ rad/s.

8.11 For the cam-displacement schedule given, h is the rise, β is the angle through which the rise takes place, and s is the displacement at any given angle θ. The displacement equation for the follower during the rise period is

$$s = h\sum_{i=0}^{5} a_i \left(\frac{\theta}{\beta}\right)^i$$

Determine the required values for $a_0, \ldots, a_5$ such that the displacement, velocity, and acceleration functions are continuous at the end points of the rise portion.

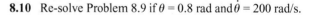

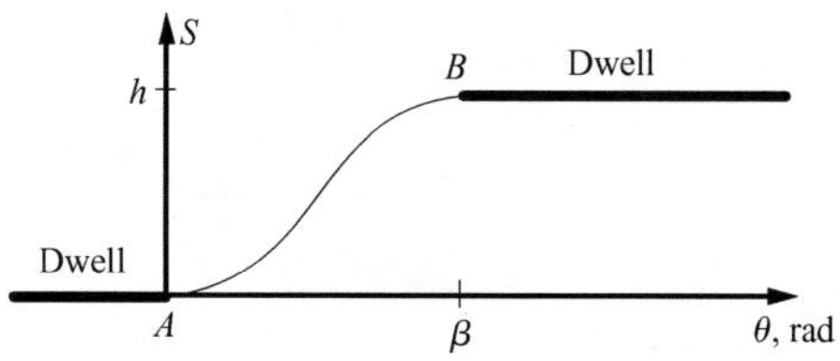

8.12 Re-solve Problem 8.11 if $h = 20$ mm and $\beta = 120°$.

8.13 Re-solve Problem 8.11 if $h = 2$ in and $\beta = 90°$.

8.14 Assume that s is the cam–follower displacement and θ is the cam rotation. The rise is h after β degrees of rotation, and the rise begins at a dwell and ends with a constant velocity segment. The displacement equation for the follower during the rise period is

$$s = h\sum_{i=0}^{n} C_i\left(\frac{\theta}{\beta}\right)^i$$

If the position, velocity, and acceleration are continuous at $\theta = 0$ and the position and velocity are continuous at $\theta = \beta$, determine the n required in the equation, and find the coefficients C_i that will satisfy the requirements if $s = h = 1.0$.

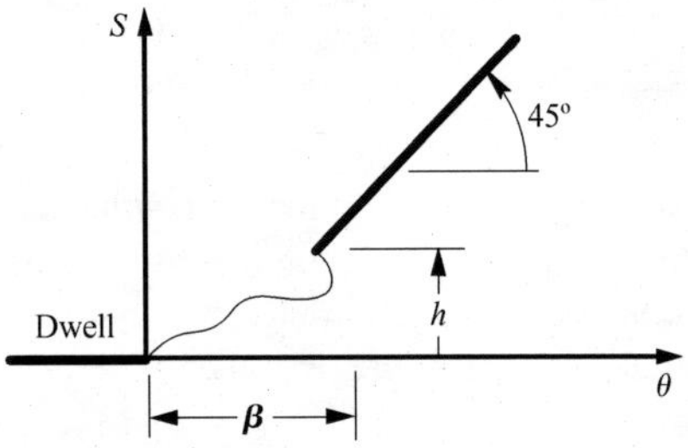

8.15 A follower moves with simple harmonic motion a distance of 20 mm in 45° of cam rotation. The follower then moves 20 mm more with cycloidal motion to complete its rise. The follower then dwells and returns 25 mm with cycloidal motion and then moves the remaining 15 mm with harmonic motion in 45°. Find the intervals of cam rotation for the cycloidal motions and dwell by matching velocities and accelerations, then determine the equations for the displacement (S) as a function of θ for the entire motion cycle.

EXERCISE PROBLEMS ON GRAPHICAL CAM DESIGN

8.16 Construct the part of the profile of a disk cam that follows the displacement diagram shown. The cam has a 5-cm-diameter pitch circle and is rotating counterclockwise. The follower is a knife-edged, radial, translating follower. Use 10° increments for the construction.

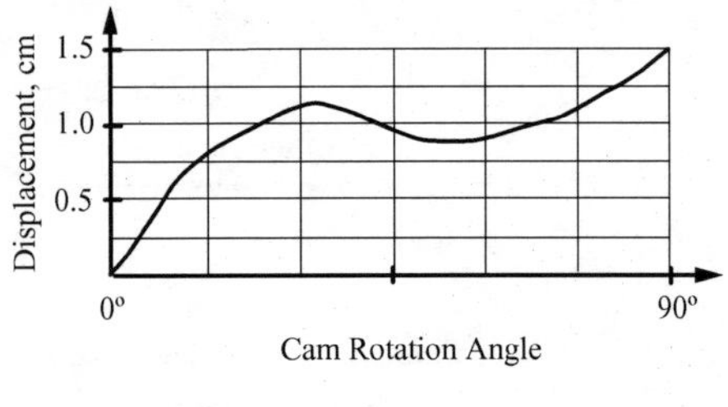

8.17 Construct the profile of a disk cam that follows the displacement diagram shown. The follower is a radial roller and has a diameter of 10 mm. The base circle diameter of the cam is to be 40 mm and the cam rotates clockwise.

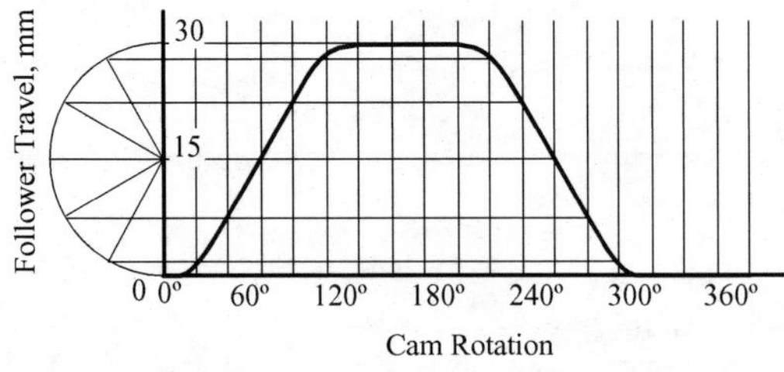

8.18 Accurately sketch one-half of the cam profile (stations 0–6) for the cam follower, base circle, and displacement diagram given. The base circle diameter is 1.2 in.

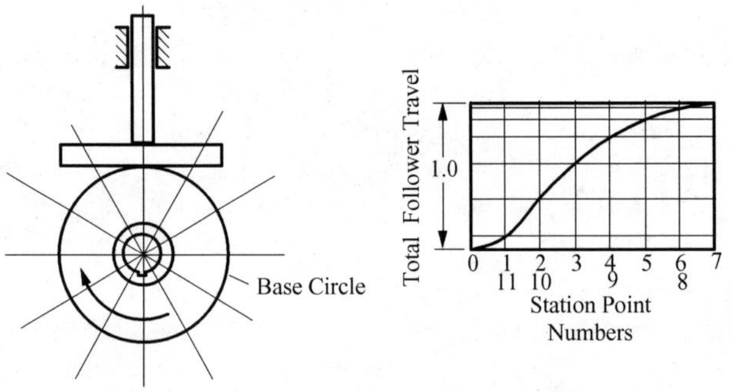

8.19 Lay out a cam profile using a harmonic follower displacement (both rise and return). Assume that the cam is to dwell at zero lift for the first 100° of the motion cycle and to dwell at a 1 in lift for cam angles from 160° to 210°. The cam is to have a translating, radial, roller follower with a 1 in roller diameter, and the base circle radius is to be 1.5 in. The cam will rotate clockwise. Lay out the cam profile using 20° plotting intervals.

8.20 Lay out a cam profile using a cycloidal follower displacement (both rise and return) if the cam is to dwell at zero lift for the first 80° of the motion cycle and to dwell at 2 in lift for cam angles from 120° to 190°. The cam is to have a translating, radial, roller follower with a roller diameter of 0.8 in. The cam will rotate counterclockwise, and the base circle diameter is 2 in. Lay out the cam profile using 20° plotting intervals.

8.21 Lay out a cam profile assuming that an oscillating roller follower starts from a dwell for 0° to 140° of cam rotation, and the cam rotates clockwise. The rise occurs with parabolic motion during the cam rotation from 140° to 220°. The follower then dwells for 40° of cam rotation, and the return occurs with parabolic motion for the cam rotation from 260° to 360°. The amplitude of the follower rotation is 35°, and the follower radius is 1 in. The base circle radius is 2 in, and the distance between the cam axis and follower rotation axis is 4 in. Lay out the cam profile using 20° plotting intervals such that the pressure angle is 0° when the follower is in the bottom dwell position.

8.22 Lay out the rise portion of the cam profile if a flat-faced, translating, radial follower's motion is uniform. The total rise is 1.5 in, and the rise occurs over 100° of cam rotation. The follower dwells for 90° of cam rotation prior to the beginning of the rise and dwells for 80° of cam rotation at the end of the rise. The cam will rotate counterclockwise, and the base circle radius is 3 in.

EXERCISE PROBLEMS ON ANALYTICAL CAM DESIGN

8.23 In the sketch shown, the disk cam is used to position the radial, flat-faced follower in a computing mechanism. The cam profile is to be designed to give a follower displacement S for a CCW cam rotation θ according to the function $S = k\theta^2$ starting from dwell. For 60° of cam rotation from the starting position, the lift of the follower is 1.0 cm. By analytical methods, determine the distances R and L when the cam has been turned 45° from the starting position. Also calculate whether cusps in the cam profile would occur in the total rotation of 60°.

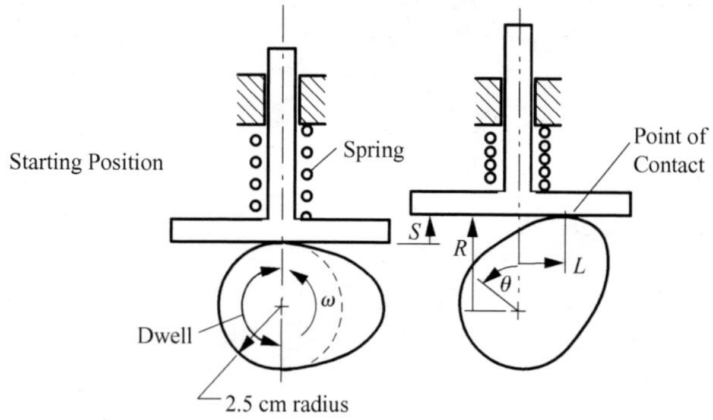

8.24 Determine the cam profile assuming that the translating cylindrical-faced follower starts from a dwell from 0° to 80°, and the cam rotates clockwise. The rise occurs with cycloidal motion during the cam rotation from 80° to 180°. The follower then dwells for 60° of cam rotation, and the return occurs with simple harmonic motion for the cam rotation from 240° to 360°. The amplitude of the follower translation is 3 cm, and the follower radius is 0.75 cm. The base circle radius is 5 cm, and the offset is 0.5 cm.

8.25 Re-solve Problem 8.24 if the amplitude of the follower translation is 4 cm, the follower radius is 1 cm, the base circle radius is 5 cm, and the offset is 1 cm.

8.26 Re-solve Problem 8.24 if the cam rotates counterclockwise.

8.27 Determine the cam profile assuming that the translating flat-faced follower starts from a dwell from 0° to 80° and rotates clockwise. The rise occurs with parabolic motion during the cam rotation from 80° to 180°. The follower then dwells for 60° of cam rotation, and the return occurs with simple harmonic motion for the cam rotation from 240° to 360°. The amplitude of the follower translation is 3 cm. First find the minimum base circle radius based on avoiding cusps, and use that base circle to design the cam.

8.28 Re-solve Problem 8.27 if the cam rotates counterclockwise.

8.29 Determine the cam profile assuming that an oscillating cylindrical-faced follower dwells while the cam rotates counterclockwise from 0° to 100°. The rise occurs with 3-4-5 polynomial motion during the cam rotation from 100° to 190°. The follower then dwells for 80° of cam rotation, and the return occurs with simple harmonic motion for the cam rotation from 270° to 360°. The amplitude of the follower oscillation is 25°, and the follower radius is 0.75 in. The base circle radius is 2 in, and the distance between pivots is 6 in. The length of the follower is to be determined such that the pressure angle starts out at zero.

8.30 Re-solve Problem 8.29 if the cam rotates clockwise.

8.31 Design a cam and oscillating roller follower assuming that the follower starts from a dwell for 0° to 80° of cam rotation and the cam rotates clockwise. The rise occurs with cycloidal motion during the cam rotation from 80° to 200°. The follower then dwells for 40° of cam rotation, and the return occurs with cycloidal motion for the cam rotation from 240° to 360°. The amplitude of the follower rotation is 45°. Determine the cam base circle radius, distance between cam and follower pivots, the length of the follower, and the radius of the follower for acceptable performance.

8.32 Determine the cam profile assuming that an oscillating flat-faced follower starts from a dwell from 0° to 45° and rotates counterclockwise. The rise occurs with simple harmonic motion during the cam rotation from 45° to 180°. The follower then dwells for 90° of cam rotation, and the return occurs with simple harmonic motion for the cam rotation from 270° to 360°. The amplitude of the follower oscillation is 20°, and the follower offset is 0.5 in. The base circle radius is 5 in, and the distance between pivots is 8 in.

8.33 Re-solve Problem 8.32 if the cam rotates clockwise.

8.34 Design a cam system assuming that an oscillating flat-faced follower starts from a dwell for 0° to 100° of cam rotation and the cam rotates counterclockwise. The rise occurs with uniform motion during the cam rotation from 100° to 200°. The follower then dwells for 40° of cam rotation, and the return occurs with parabolic motion for the cam rotation from 240° to 360°. The oscillation angle is 20°.

8.35 Design a cam system assuming that an oscillating flat-faced follower starts from a dwell for 0° to 50° of cam rotation and the cam rotates clockwise. The rise occurs with cycloidal motion during the cam rotation from 50° to 200°. The follower then dwells for 90° of cam rotation, and the return occurs with harmonic motion for the cam rotation from 290° to 360°. The oscillation angle is 25°.

8.36 Determine the cam profile assuming that the translating knife-edged follower starts from a dwell from 0° to 80° and rotates clockwise. The rise occurs with cycloidal motion during the cam rotation from 80° to 180°. The follower then dwells for 60° of cam rotation, and the return occurs with simple harmonic motion for the cam rotation from 240° to 360°. The amplitude of the follower translation is 4 cm. The base circle radius is 5 cm, and the offset is 0.5 cm.

8.37 A radial flat-faced follower is to move through a total displacement of 20 mm with harmonic motion while the cam rotates through 30°. Find the minimum radius of the base circle that is necessary to avoid cusps.

8.38 A radial flat-faced follower is to move through a total displacement of 3 in with cycloidal motion while the cam rotates through 90°. Find the minimum radius of the base circle that is necessary to avoid cusps.

8.39 A radial roller follower is to move through a total displacement of $L = 19$ mm with harmonic motion while the cam rotates 60°. The roller radius is 5 mm. Use the program supplied with the book and find the minimum radius necessary to avoid cusps during the interval indicated.

8.40 A radial roller follower is to move through a total displacement of $L = 45$ mm with cycloidal motion. The roller radius is 5 mm, and the cam rotates 90° during the rise. Use the program supplied with the book and find the minimum radius necessary to avoid cusps during the interval.

8.41 Assume that a flat-faced translating follower is used with the displacement schedule in Problem 8.10. Determine if a cusp is present at $\theta = 60°$.

8.42 Assume that a flat-faced translating follower is used with the displacement schedule in Problem 8.12. Determine if a cusp is present at $\theta = 90°$.

INDEX

INDEX

Italicized page numbers reflect pages on which photographs appear.

A

Acceleration, 2, 3
chain rule for, 102
Coriolis component of, *see* Coriolis term
of coupler point, 186–187
in elliptic trammel mechanism, 224–228
equivalent linkages, 124–128
in four-bar linkages, 180–182
general coincident points, analysis using, 130–136
graphical analysis of, 31, 65–67, 79–84, 89–95, 96–144
higher pairs, mechanisms with, 244–248
in Oldham mechanism, 229–233
in planar linkage analysis, 174–175
points *P* and *Q* fixed to *B*, 104–105
quick-return mechanism, 107–111
of rigid body, 184–187
rolling contacts, 111–120
in RPRP mechanism, 216–218
in RRPP mechanism, 219–223
in slider-crank mechanism, 195–200, 207–211
in spatial mechanisms, 422–423, 426–428
special-case equations for, 104–106
Acceleration image theorem, 79–84, 94–95
Ackermann geometry, 349–350
Actuation, 32–37, 48–53
Actuators, 2
commutated motors, 50–51
controlled/servomotors, 52
definition, 48
electrical, 49–52
hydraulic, 53
noncommutated motors, 51–52
operational stability, 48–49
pneumatic, 53
solenoids, 52
speed control, 52
Adaptive Suspension Vehicle, *1*, *335*
Addendum, 464–466
Addendum circle, 464–465
AGMA, 520, 524
Air motors, 53
Analysis techniques, 2
Angular acceleration
chain rule for, 103–104
quick-return mechanism, 107–111
rigid body, 185
rolling contacts, 116–120
velocity image theorem, 77
Angular bevel gears, 521, 524, *524*
Angular velocity, 2, 61, 64
chain rule for, 102–103
friction drives, 459
general equations for, 99–100
and instant centers of velocity, 145, 163
inversion analysis of, 86–88
quick-return mechanism, 107–108
reference frames, 97
rigid body, 185
rolling contacts, 112, 118–120
slider-crank inversion, 209
velocity image theorem, 76–77
Animation, 10
Annular gears, 474–475
Approximate straight-line mechanisms, 329–331, *332*
Chebyshev straight-line mechanisms, 330, 331
Roberts straight-line mechanism, 330–331
Watt straight-line mechanism, 330
Armature, 49
Aronholdt. *See* Kennedy-Aronholdt theorem
Assembly configurations, 270–271
Automotive applications
acceleration/braking, dynamic force analysis of, 610–613
balancing of eight-cylinder V engine, 655–657
steering mechanisms, 349–353, 360–361
suspension mechanisms, 329, 349, 353–354
universal joints, 345–347
Axial joints, 432–435. *See also* Cylindrical joints; Prismatic joints; Revolute joints
Axial pitch, *497*, 499, 504–505, 510, 514–516, 528–529
Axodes, 151

B

Backhoe, *200*
Balancing, 629–661
exercises, 657–661
and expressions for inertial forces, 646–648
of multicylinder machines, 649–657
multiplane (dynamic), 633–639
of reciprocating masses, 639–648, 659–661
single-plane (static), 630–633
Base pitch, 464–465
Bearings
ball bushings, 47
hydrodynamic, 44
hydrostatic, 44–45
lubrication of, 47
rolling-element bearings, *7*, 45
solid contact bearings, 45
Bennett mechanism, 26–28
Bernoulli, Johann, 145
Bevel gears, 111, 517–527, *518*
angular, 521, 524, *524*
crown, 521–522, *522*
exercises, 529
face gears, 522, *523*
formulas for, 525
hypoid gears, 526–527, *527*
loads with, 602–603
miter gears, 521, *523*
nomenclature, 520–521
planetary gear trains with, 549–550
spiral, 525–526, *526*
Tredgold's approximation for, 519–520
Zerol, 524
Binary links, 7–9
Blank fabrication, 475–476
Braking, dynamic force analysis of, 610–613
Branch, change of, 270–272
Brushes, motor, 50
Brushless direct current (DC) motor, 50
Bucket support linkages, 28–29

C

Cams, 9
contacts, *see* Cam contacts
design, *see* Cam design
graphical force analysis of, 571–573
harmonic, 373–375
linkages *vs.*, 47–48, 362
lubrication of cam and follower pairs, 47
radius of curvature for, 393–395, 397
Cam contacts
analysis of mechanism with, 244–246
friction in, 579
graphical analysis of, 96, 111, 118–128, 141–142
instant centers of velocity of general cam-pair contact, 149–150
Cam design, 362–420
cam-follower systems, 363–364
exercises, 417–420
follower-displacement functions, 366–380, 417–418
profile, *see* Profile cam design
synthesis of motion programs, use of, 364–366
and types of motion, 366
Cardan joints. *See* Universal joints
Center of mass, 608
Centrodes, 150–152, *152*

Chain rule, 101–104
Chebyshev approximate straight-line mechanism, 330, 331
Chebyshev linkage, 339–340
Chebyshev polynomial, use for precision points of, 288–289
Circle method, to find instant center, 155–156
Circular pitch, 464–465
Closed chains, 8
Closed circuits, 8
Closed-loop linkages
  planar linkage analysis, 175–184
  spatial linkage analysis, 445–448
Closures, constraint, 19–21, 29
CNC milling machines, 475, 487
Cognate linkages, 318–320
  of Chebyshev mechanism, 339–340
  exercises, 327–328, 360
  and pantographs, 333, 337–340
Coincident points, general. *See* General coincident points
Commutated motors, 50–51
Complex number notation, 171, 248–251
Compound gear trains, *534,* 534–540
  concentric gear trains, 537–540, *538*
  exercises, 554–556
  velocity ratio for, 534–536
Compound joints, 5–6
Compound mechanisms
  closure/loop equation approach for, 233–243
  lubrication, 47
  rotating-radius method to find velocity, 158–159
Compound wound motor, 51
Computer-aided design, 2, 10–11, 171, 258–259. *See also* MATLAB
Concentric gear trains, 537–540, *538*
Connecting rods, balancing and, 639–641, 649
Connectivity, 5–6, 11, 13, 23–24
Conservation of energy, 590–597, 604–606, 615–618
Conservation of momentum, 615–618
Constant-velocity couplings, 347–349, *348*
Constant velocity ratio (spur gears), 458–461
Constraint analysis, 11–23
  and idle degrees of freedom, 23–25
  and overconstrained linkages, 25–29
  of spatial linkages, 18–23
Contacts
  cam, *see* Cam contacts
  rolling, *see* Rolling contacts
Contact ratio
  parallel-shaft helical gears, 505–506
  spur gears, 467–471
Coordinate transformation operators, 171
Coordination, problem of robotic, 428
Coriolis term, 122
  acceleration, component of, 96, 107, 109
  position, function of, 131
  velocities, function of, 101, 105, 127, 131, 132
Couple
  force and, 561
  moment of, 560–561
Coupler (definition), 32
Coupler curves, 85
  design of six-bar linkages using, 309–314
  Hrones and Nelson coupler-curve atlas, 308
  motion generation for parallel motion, 315–317
Coupler-driven linkages, 37, 42–44
Coupler point, velocity/acceleration analysis of, 186–187
Cranks, 31–34. *See also* Slider-crank mechanisms
  design, given circle or center points, 282
  inversion, solution by, 84–85
  synthesis of, with chosen fixed pivots, 266–268
Crank-rocker linkages
  actuation, 34, 36
  centrodes associated with instant center, 151
  change of branch, 271
  motion limits, 40
  synthesis of, 294–308, 325–326
  topological interference, 41–42
Crossed helical gears, *498,* 509–512
Crown bevel gears, 521–522, *522*
Curvature
  center of, 112–113, 114, 118, 122–125, 128–134, 136, 141–144, 148, 243–244, 246–248, 383, 387, 393–396, 404
  radius of, 112, 116, 133, 148, 349, 351, 353, 363, 367, 381, 383, 393–395, 397–398, 402, 406, 408, 413, 415–416
Cycloidal follower-displacement programs, 375–376
Cycloidal tooth geometries, 461–462
Cylindrical joints, 4, 5, 432

D

D'Alembert's principle, 559, 619
Dedendum, 464–466
Dedendum circle, 464–465
Degrees of freedom. *See also* Connectivity; Mobility
  idle, 23–25
  number of, 3, 5–6, 11, 13–15
Design. *See also* Cam design; Planar linkage design; Profile cam design
  analysis and synthesis, 2–3
  historic perspective, 1–2
  practical design considerations, 44–53
Diametral pitch, 464–467
Different mechanism, 17
Differential gear train, 543, *543*
Digital control, actuator, 48
Diophantine equation, 15, 18
Direction of rotation (gear trains), 530–531
Direct kinematics (serial chains), 428–438
Double-cranks. *See* Drag-link mechanisms
Double rocker linkages, 259–262, 321
  analytical solution procedure, 261–262
  drive failure, 271
  graphical solution procedure, 260–261
  type 1, 34, 37, 42–43, 330
  type 2, 34, 36, 44, 331
Drag-link mechanisms, 34, 37, 41–44
  centrodes associated with instant center, 151–152
  change of branch, 271
Drilling-mud pump, force analysis of, 576–578, 592–594
Dual universal joints, 345–347
Dynamic balancing, 633–639
Dynamic equilibrium, 619–624
Dynamic equilibrium equations, 609
Dynamic force analysis, 559, 608–628
  conservation of energy, 590–597, 615–618
  conservation of momentum, 615–618
  exercises, 626–628
  flywheels, 624–626
  particle kinetics, 610–618
  rigid bodies, 619–624

E

EDM (electron-discharge machining), 475
Eight-cylinder V engine, 655–657
Eight-link mechanism for parallel motion generation, 315–317
Einstein, Albert, 31
Electrical actuators, 49–52
Electron-discharge machining (EDM), 475
Elliptic trammels, 257–258
  analytical equations for, 223–228
  design of, 268–270
End effector. *See* Hand, robot
Energy, conservation of, 590–597, 604–606, 615–618
Engineering *vs.* science, 2–3
Engines
  internal combustion, 187, *188,* 639, 649–657
  multicylinder, 649–657
  single cylinder, 641–643
Equations of motion, 609
Equilibrium
  dynamic, 619–624
  static, 562
Equivalence, kinematic, 5
Equivalent linkages, analysis of cam contact using, 124–128
Euler's equation, 608–609
Exact straight-line mechanisms, 332–333
Externally applied forces, 629

F

Face gears, 522, *523*
Ferguson's paradox, 553–554
Five-bar linkage, example of geared, 116
Fixed links (frame), 8, 31, 32
Fluctuating forces. *See* Shaking forces

Flyball governor, dynamic force analysis of, 613–615
Flywheels, 624–626
Followers, cam. *See* Cams
Foot-pump mechanism, *209,* 209–211
Force analysis. *See* Dynamic force analysis; Static force analysis
Forces (definition), 560–561
Formed cutters, gear, 475, *476*
Fouling, gear, 475
Four-bar linkages, 257
 acceleration analysis of, 71–74, 180–182, 184
 analytical closure equations for, 171, 175–184
 analytical force analysis of, 573–575
 cognate linkages, *see* cognate linkages
 conservation of power, analysis using, 594–595
 equivalent linkages, 124
 function generation using, 285–287, 289–293, 324–325
 graphical analysis of, 67–74, 569–571
 Grashof's rules, 32–37, 58–59
 instant center, 151, 154–155
 mobility analysis of, 14, 16–18
 motion generation, 258, 263–266, 270, 272–274
 position analysis of, 67–69, 176–179, 182–184
 position synthesis of, 272–274
 spherical, 342–343, 360
 topological and physical limitations of, 40–41
 transmission angle in, 575–576
 velocity analysis of, 69–71, 176, 179–180, 182, 184
Four-link mechanisms, 257. *See also* Elliptic trammels; Four-bar linkages; Oldham mechanism; Rapson Slide mechanism; Scotch Yoke mechanism; Slider-crank mechanisms
Frames
 definition, 8, 32
 reference, *see* Reference frames
Free-body diagrams, 562–565, 604
Friction, 578–586
 in cam contact, 579
 and lubrication, 47, 128
 in revolute joints, 581–582
 in slider-crank mechanism, 583–586
 in slider joints, 579–581
Friction drives, 458–459
Front-end loader, *28,* 28–29
Function generation (planar linkages), 283–294

G

Gears
 bevel, *see* Bevel gears
 conjugacy, 459
 helical, *see* Helical gears
 internal, 474–475
 lubrication of, 47
 manufacture of, 475–479, *476, 477, 479,* 501, *501, 502*
 spur, *see* Spur gears
 standards for, 465–467
 terminology, 464–465, 497–500
 worm, *see* Worm gears
Gear loads, 597–603
 bevel gears, 602–603
 exercises, 607
 helical gears, 599–601
 spur gears, 597–599
 worm gears, 601–602
Gear trains, 530–558
 compound, *see* Compound gear trains
 and direction of rotation, 530–531
 exercises, 554–558
 instant centers of velocity for, 163–164
 planetary, *see* Planetary gear trains
 simple, 531–533
General coincident points, 105–106, 128–136
 acceleration analysis involving, 130–136
 exercises, 142–144
 momentarily coincident, 105
 velocity analysis involving, 130
Geneva mechanisms, 354–359, 361
Gimbals, 343
Graphical analysis, 60–61
 of acceleration, *see* Acceleration
 of cam contact, *see* Cam contacts
 chain rule in, 101–104
 of crank-rocker linkages, 295–300
 exercises, 89–95, 136–144, 165–170
 force analysis, static, 565–573
 of four-bar linkages, *see* Four-bar linkages
 function generation, 293–300
 of general coincident points, 105–106, 128–136
 of instant centers of velocity, 145–170
 inversion, solution by, 84–88
 of pin-in-slot joint mechanism, 128, 132–136
 of position, 61
 of quick-return mechanism, 107–111
 and reference frames, 96–98
 rolling contact, linkages with, 96, 105–106, 111–120, 139–141
 rotating sliding joints, linkages with, 106–111, 136–139
 of six-bar linkages, 78–79, 81–83
 of slider-crank mechanisms, 74–76
 special case equations, 104–106
 of velocity, *see* Velocity
Grashof linkages
 exercises, 58–59
 neutral, 37
 type 1 and type 2, 33–34, 37, 178, 339
Grashof's rules, 32–37, 39–40, 58–59

H

Hall effect sensors, 50
Hand, robot, 428–429
Harmonic follower-displacement programs, 373–375
Helical gears, 111, *496,* 496–512, *498*
 crossed, *498,* 509–512
 exercises, 528–529
 formulas for, 509–510, 512
 loads with, 599–601
 manufacture of, 501, *501, 502*
 minimum tooth number with, 501–503
 with parallel shafts, *see* Parallel-shaft helical gears
 replacement of spur gears with, 507–509
 terminology, 497–500
Herringbone gears, 496, *497*
Hertzian contact stresses, 459
Higher pair joints, 3–6, 9, 47
Higher pair mechanisms. *See also* Cam contacts; Gear trains; Pin-in-slot joints; Rolling contacts; Sliding joints/sliders
 closure equations for, 243–248
 degrees of freedom for, 15
 and instant centers of velocity, 145
Hobbing, 478–479, *479, 501*
Hooke joints. *See* Universal joints
Hrones and Nelson coupler-curve atlas, 308
Hydraulic actuators, 53
Hydraulic impactor, dynamic force analysis of, 615–618
Hydraulic shaft puller, *189*
Hydrodynamic bearings, 44
Hydrodynamic lubrication, 44
Hydrostatic bearings, 44–45
Hypoid gears, 526–527, *527*

I

Idle degrees of freedom, 23–25
Indexing mechanisms, 329, 354–359, 361
Induction motors, 51–52, 52
Inertia forces, 629, 633, 640–644, 646–648, 650
Inertia matrix, 609
Inertial reference frames, 31
Informal synthesis techniques, 3
In-plane forces, 586
Instantaneous screw axis (ISA), 151
Instant centers of velocity, 145–170
 andcentrodes, 150–152, 151, *152*
 circle diagram as strategy for finding, 155–156
 of curved slider, 148
 definition, 145–146
 drafting programs, finding using, 164
 exercises, 165–170
 of gear mechanism, 163–164
 of general cam-pair contact, 149–150
 instantaneous, 146
 and Kennedy-Aronholdt theorem, 153–155
 location of, 147–148, 155–156, 164

permanent, 146
of prismatic joint, 148–149
proof of existence of, 146–147
for quick-return mechanisms, 160–163
at revolute joint, 148
of rolling contact pair, 149
rotating-radius method to find velocities, 156–159
of Stephenson-II six-bar linkage, 159–160
Interference
with spur gears, 479–482
topological, 40–44
Interference point, 479
Internal combustion engine, 187, *188,* 639, 649–657
Inverse position kinematics (serial chains), 428, 438
Inverse velocity kinematics (serial chains), 438, 444–445
Inversion, 17, 30, 260, 293
analytical equation for slider-crank, 200–211
of RRPP mechanism, 228–233
solution by, 84–88
Inverters, 52
Involute function, 471–474
Involutes
bevel gears, *see* Bevel gears
helical gears, 496
spur gears, 461–463, 471–474, 487–493
worms, meshing of, 513
Involutometry, 471–474

J

Joints, 1, 3, *7,* 8, 96
Cardan, *see* Universal joints
constant velocity, 347–349, *348*
compound, 5–6, 47
definition, 44
higher pair, 3–6, 9, 47
Hooke, *see* Universal joints
lower pair, 3–7, 448–452, *see also* Revolute joints
lubrication, 128
pin-in-slot, *see* Pin-in-slot joints
prismatic, *see* Prismatic joints
revolute, *see* Revolute joints
rolling contact, *see* Rolling contacts
sliding, *see* Sliding joints/sliders
solid contact, 45
spherical, 7
universal, *see* Universal joints

K

Kennedy-Aronholdt theorem, 153–155
Kinematics (definition), 2
Kinematic equivalence, 5
Kinematic joints. *See* Joints
Kinetics, 3, 31, 608
KINSYN, 259
Kutzbach criterion, 18

L

LEGOS Technics, *12*
Lemniscate, 330
Leonardo da Vinci, 1
Level-luffing crane, 331, *332*
Limits, motion, 31–32
LINCAGES, 259
Line of action, 465
Linkages
cams *vs.,* 47–48, 362
coupler-driven, 37
definition, 8–9
drag-link, *see* Drag-link mechanisms
equivalent, 124–128
exercises, 54
transition, 37
Linkage analysis. *See* Planar linkage analysis; Spatial linkage analysis
Lower pair joints, 3–7, 448–452. *See also* Revolute joints
Lubrication of joints, 44–45, 47, 128

M

Machine dynamics problems, 609
Magnets, permanent, 50, 51
Manipulators
acceleration analysis of, 426–428
direct rate kinematics of three-axis, 441–443
parallel, 452–454
velocity analysis of, 423–426
MATLAB
analytical linkage analysis, 178, 180, 181, 185, 194, 195, 207, 208, 212, 216
centrodes, 151
inertial forces, expressions for, 646
planar linkage design, 279, 281, 283, 291, 308, 311
profile cam design, 396, 406
Mechanisms
definition, 1, 8–9
design of, 1–3
idealized, 3
Meshing spur gears, *460*
Miter gears, 523, *523*
Mobility
computation of, 13–16
definition, 11, 13
examples, 14–16
in spatial mechanism (example), 19–22
Mobility equation
connectivity, determining, 23–24
uses of, 29
Module, 465
Moments, 560–561
Momentum, conservation of, 615–618
Motion
equations of, 609
types of, 366
Motion generation (cams), 364–376
follower-displacement programs, 366–380, 417–418
parabolic motion, 368–372
synthesis of motion programs, 364–366
and types of motion, 366
uniform motion, 367–368
Motion generation (planar linkages), 259
change of branch, 270–272
crank with chosen fixed pivots, 266–268
elliptic trammels, 268–270
and order problem, 270–272
for parallel motion using coupler curves, 315–317
rigid body guidance, 276–283, 321–324
slider cranks, 268–270, 274–275
three positions with selected moving pivots, 266, 272–274
two positions, 263–266
Motion limits, 31–32, 38–40
Motion platforms, 452–454
mechanisms actuated in parallel, 452
Stewart platform, 452–454
3–2–1 platform, 454
Motors. *See* Actuators
Multicylinder machines
balancing, 649–657
eight-cylinder V engine, 655–657
three-cylinder in-line engine, 653–655
Multiplane balancing, 633–639

N

Newton-Euler equations, 608
Newton's laws of motion, 31, 559, 562, 608
No-load speed, actuator, 49
Nonstandard gearing, 482–487
Normal pitch, 497–498, 503, 509, 528–529
Numerical control (NC) machining, 362

O

Oldham mechanism, 17. *See also* Elliptic trammels
analytical equations for, 228–233
use of, 257
Osculating circles, 113–114, 118, 124, 130, 148
Out-of-plane forces, 586–590, 606–607
Overconstraint, 25–29

P

Pantographs, 333–340
planar collinear, 334–336
and Roberts' theorem, 337–339
skew, 336–338
Parabolic motion (cams), 368–372
Parallel-shaft helical gears, 503–510
axial force, designing for, 509
center distance of, 504
contact ratio for, 505–506
minimum width for, 504
velocity ratio for, 504

Particle kinetics, 610–618
conservation of energy, 615–618
conservation of momentum, 615–618
with flyball governor, 613–615
with hydraulic impactor, 615–618
with vehicle acceleration/braking, 610–613
Path synthesis (planar linkage), 308–320, 326–327
four-bar cognate linkages, 318–320, 327–328
six-bar linkages, 309–314
Peaucellier linkage, 332–333
Ping-pong table linkage, *189*
Pin-in-slot joints, 5, 200, *201*
graphical analysis of, 106, 128, 132–136
instant centers used to analyze, 163–164
inversions, 30
kinematic analysis of mechanism with, 246–247
Pinion
interference, 479–481
internal gear, 474–475
and rack, *see* Rack and pinion
Piston mass, reciprocating, 639, 644–646
Pitch circles, 464–465
Pitch cylinder, 460
Pitch diameter, 464–465
Pitch point, 464
Plagiographs, 333–340
Planar collinear pantographs, 334–336
Planar linkages, 7–9
exercises, 54–57
overconstrained, 27
visualization of, 9–10
Planar linkage analysis, 171–254
acceleration representation for, 174–175
for compound mechanisms, 233–243
for elliptic trammel, 223–228
exercises, 251–256
four-bar linkages, 175–184
graphical approach to, *see* Graphical analysis
for higher pair mechanisms, 243–248
for Oldham mechanism, 228–233
position representation for, 172
for rigid body, 184–187
for RPRP mechanisms, 211–218, 229–230
for RRPP mechanisms, 218–223
for slider-crank inversion, 200–211
for slider-crank mechanism, 187–200
special mechanisms, *see* Special mechanisms
vector *vs.* complex-number notations for, 171, 248–251
velocity equations/analysis, 97–98, 172–173, 179–180, 182, 194, 205–207, 209–211, 216–218
Planar linkage design, 257–328
crank-rocker linkages, 294–308, 325–326
double rockers, 259–262, 321
exercises, 321–328
function generation, 283–300, 324–325
motion generation, 259, 263–283
path synthesis, 308–320, 326–327
Planetary gear trains, 540–554, *541, 543*
with bevel gears, 549–550
equation method for analysis of, 544–550
exercises, 556–558
nomenclature for, 542–543
in series, 547–548
tabular method for analysis of, 550–554
Plate cam with roller follower, graphical analysis of, 118–120
Pneumatic actuators, 53
Poles (rigid body guidance), 279–281
Polynomial follower-displacement programs, 376–380
Position
chain rule for, 102
describing, 2
Position analysis/equations, 219
for compound mechanisms, 237–243
for elliptic trammel mechanism, 224–228
for four-bar linkage, 176–179, 182–184
graphical analysis, 61
for Oldham mechanism, 228–232
planar linkage analysis, 172
for rigid body, 184–186
for RPRP mechanisms, 212–216
for RRPP mechanism, 219–221
serial chains, position kinematics for, 428–438
for slider-crank inversion, 202–206, 209
for slider-crank mechanism, 190–194, 196–199
Power, conservation of, 590–597, 604–606
Prime mover, 2, 48
Principal axes of inertia, 609
Prismatic joints, 4, 5, 7, 8, 432, 434
analytical linkage analysis, 211, 218
constraint analysis, 21
degrees of freedom for, 16–17
free-body diagrams, 562
instant centers of velocity of, 148–149
position analysis, 61
practical design considerations, 46–47
Profile cam design, 380–416
analytical determination, 391–416
graphical layout, 381–391
Punch press, dynamic force analysis of, 625–626
Pure rolling contact, 4–5

Q

Quatenary links, 8
Quick-return mechanisms
graphical analysis, 107–111
instant centers of velocity for, 160–163

R

Rack, 460
Cartesian coordinates of involute tooth generated with, 487–493
undercutting, 480–481
Rack and pinion, 480–481
helical gear, *497*
spur gear, 460, *460*
steering, 351–352
Radius of curvature (cam), 393–395, 397
Rapson slide, 258
Rational synthesis techniques, 2
Reciprocating masses, balancing, 639–643, 659–661
RECSYN, 259
Reference frames
fixed links and, 31, 32
multiple, 31, 96–98
principal, principal axes of inertia as, 609
Reuleaux, Franz, 3, 13
Reversing mechanisms (gear trains), 533
Revolute joints, 4, 5, 7, 40, 432, 434
actuators, connecting to base of, 32
analytical linkage analysis, 175, 200, 211, 218
constraint analysis, 21
degrees of freedom for, 16–17
equivalent linkages, 124
free-body diagrams, 562, 565
friction in, 581–582
instant centers of velocity at, 148
lubrication, 44–45, 47
position analysis, 61
practical design considerations, 44–45
spherical linkages, 27
Rigid bodies, 276–283
acceleration image theorem, 79–84, 94–95
analytical equations for, 184–187
center of circle, finding, 281
coordinate transformations, 276–278
and crank design, 282
dynamic equilibrium of systems of, 619–624
exercises, 321–324
image pole, 281
poles, finding, 279–281
and slider design, 282–283
velocity image theorem, 76–79, 94–95
Robert's approximate straight-line mechanism, 330–331
Robert's theorem, 318, 337–339
Robotic mechanisms, 21–23, 428–429, 586–590
Rockers, 32–34, 36, 41–43
Rolling contacts, 5, 6, 45, 47
basic relationships, 112–118
closure equations for, 243, 247–248
example, 116–118
free-body diagrams, 563–564

graphical analysis of, 96, 105–106, 111–120, 139–141
instant centers of velocity of, 149
plate cam with roller follower, 118–120, 247–248
pure, 4–5, 47, 149
Rotating-radius method, 156–159
Rotating sliding joints, graphical analysis of linkages with, 106–111, 136–139
Rotor, 49, 50
RPRP mechanisms, analytical equations for, 211–218
acceleration equations, 216–218
velocity equations, 216–218
when θ_2 is known, 212–213
when r_3 is known, 215–216
when r_4 is known, 213–215
RRPP mechanisms
analytical equations for, 218–223
inversion of, 17, *see also* Elliptic trammels; Oldham mechanism
Run away (actuator), 49, 51

S

SCARA robot, 586–590
Science *vs.* engineering, 2–3
Scotch yoke mechanism, 17–18, 222–223, 257
Serial chains, 421
direct position kinematics for, 428–438
direct velocity kinematics for, 438–444
inverse position kinematics for, 428, 438
inverse velocity kinematics for, 438, 444–445
Series wound motor, 51
Servomotors, 52
Shaking forces, 629, 633, 639, 644, 646–657. *See also* Balancing
calculation, 641–643
exercises, 658–659
Shaping, gear, 477, *477,* 479–480, *502*
Shunt wound motor, 50
Simple gear trains, 531–533
Single-plane balancing, 630–633
Six-bar linkages
centrodes, 152, *152*
design of, using coupler curves, 309–314
graphical analysis of, 78–79, 81–83, 116
inversion, solution by, 84
Stephenson, 16, 84, 159–160
Watt, 16, 39
Skew pantographs, 336–338
Sliders. *See* Sliding joints/sliders
Slider-crank mechanisms, 257–258
analytical equations for, 187–200
balancing, 640–641, 643–648
conservation of power, analysis using, 592–594
with crank input, 196, 198–199
degrees of freedom for, 16
design of, 46, 268–270, 274–275
friction in, 583–586
graphical analysis of, 74–76
instant centers, circle method to find, 155–156
inversion, analytical equations for, 200–211
inversion example, 17, 30
motion limits for, 38–40
position synthesis of, 274–275
with slider input, 197, 199–200
Sliding joints/sliders
analytical linkage analysis, 175, 200, 211
degrees of freedom for, 16
design of, 46–47, 282–283
equivalent linkages, 125–126
friction in, 579–581
graphical analysis of linkages with rotating, 96, 106–111, 128, 136–139
instant centers of velocity of curved, 148
jamming in, 46–47
Sliding velocity (cam mechanism), 128
Solenoids, 52
Solution branches, 270–271
Spatial linkages
exercises, 57–58
overconstrained, 26–27
visualization of, 10–11
Spatial linkage analysis, 421–457
acceleration relationships, 422–423, 426–428
closed-loop linkages, 445–448
constraint analysis, 18–23
exercises, 455–457
lower pair joints, 448–452
motion platforms, 452–454
robotic mechanisms, 428–429
serial chains, 428–445
velocity relationships, 422–426
Special mechanisms, 329–361. *See also* Special planar mechanisms
automotive steering/suspension mechanisms, 329, 349–354, 360–361
constant-velocity couplings, 347–349, *348*
exercises, 360–361
four-bar linkages, 342–343, 360
gimbals, 343
indexing mechanisms, 329, 354–359
spherical linkages, 340–347
universal joints, 343–347
Special planar mechanisms, 329–340
approximate straight-line mechanisms, 329–331, *332*
exact straight-line mechanisms, 332–333
pantographs, 333–340
Spherical joints, 7
Spherical linkages, 340–347
four-bar linkages, 342–343, 360
gimbals, 343
overconstrained, 27–28
universal joints, 343–347
Spiral bevel gears, 525–526, *526*
Spur gears, 111, 458–495
constant velocity ratio for, 459–461
contact ratio for, 467–471
exercises, 494–495, 528
formulas for, 485–486
helical gear replacement of, 507–509
interference/undercutting with, 479–483
internal gears, 474–475
involute tooth geometry, 461–463, 471–474, 487–493
loads with, 597–599
manufacture of, 475–480, *476, 477, 479*
meshing, *460*
nonstandard, 482–487
standards for, 465–467
terminology, 464–465
Stall/stall torque (actuator), 49, 51
Static balancing, 630–633
Static equilibrium, 562
Static force analysis, 559–607
analytical approach to, 573–578
characteristics of forces, 560–561
and conservation of energy/power, 590–597, 604–606
constraint criterion, 20–21
couples, 560–561
equilibrium, static, 562
exercises, 604–607
free-body diagrams, use of, 562–565, 604
friction considerations in, 579–586
with gear loads, 597–603, 607
graphical approach to, 565–573
and in-plane/out-of-plane force systems, 586–590, 606–607
moments, 560–561
virtual work, 595–597
Static machines, 559
Stator, 49, 50
Steering mechanisms, 329, 349–353, 360–361
Stephenson six-bar linkages, 16, 84, 159–160
Stepping motors, 52
Stewart platform, 24–25, 452–454
Straight-line mechanisms
approximate, 329–331
exact, 332–333
Suspension, automotive, 329, 349, 353–354
Synchronous motors, 50, 52
Synthesis techniques, 2–3

T

Ternary links, 7–8
Three-axis manipulator, direct rate kinematics of, 441–443
Three-cylinder in-line engine, 653–655
3–2–1 platform, 454
Topological interference, 40–44
Topology, 8
Torque motors, 51
Transition linkages, 37
Transverse pitch, 497, 499, 508–509, 528
Tredgold's approximation, 519–520
Turning links, 32, 41

U

Unbalance, 629–634
Undercutting
  with helical gears, 501–503
  with spur gears, 479–483
Uniform motion
  cams, 367–368
  gears, 458
Universal joints, 6, 343–347
  dual, 345–347
  input-output relationship of, 446–448
  properties of, 343–345

V

Vector notation, 171, 248–251
Velocity
  angular, *see* Angular velocity
  chain rule for, 102–103
  of coupler point, 186–187
  in elliptic trammel mechanism, 224–228
  equivalent linkages, 124–128
  in four-bar linkages, 179–180, 182, 184
  friction drives, 459
  general coincident points, analysis using, 130
  general equations for, 98–100
  graphical analysis of, 62–65, 76–79, 89–95, 98–144
  higher pairs, mechanisms with, 244–248
  instant centers of, *see* Instant centers of velocity
  inversion analysis of, 86–88
  in Oldham mechanism, 229–233
  in planar linkage analysis, 172–173
  quick-return mechanism, 107–111
  and reference frame, 31
  of rigid body, 184–186
  rolling contacts, 111–120
  in RPRP mechanism, 216–218
  in RRPP mechanism, 219–223
  serial chains, direct and inverse velocity problems, 438–445
  in slider-crank inversion, 205–207, 209–211
  in slider-crank mechanism, 194, 196–200, 198–200
  sliding, in cam mechanism, 128
  in spatial mechanisms, 422–426
  special case equations for, 104–106
  of two points fixed in a lamina, 104–105
Velocity image theorem, 76–79
Velocity polygons, planar, 62–65, 97–98
Velocity ratio (compound gear trains), 534–536
Vibration, 633, 639. *See also* Shaking forces
Vice-grip pliers
  free-body diagram, 564–565
  graphical force analysis of, 567–569
  virtual work, analysis using, 596–597
Virtual link, 112, 114, 118–120, 124–126, 130–131
Virtual work, 595–597
Visualization, 9–11

W

Walking toy, *201*
Watt, James, 2, 330
Watt six-bar linkages, 16, 39
Watt straight-line mechanism, 330
Whole depth, 465–466
Work, virtual, 595–597
Worm gears, *513*, 513–517
  exercises, 529
  formulas for, 516
  geometry, 517
  loads with, 601–602
  nomenclature, 514–516
  types of, 513–514

Z

Zerol gears, 524